MARK B

Frequency-Response Methods in Control Systems

OTHER IEEE PRESS BOOKS

Programs for Digital Signal Processing, *Edited by the Digital Signal Processing Committee*
Automatic Speech & Speaker Recognition, *Edited by N. R. Dixon and T. B. Martin*
Speech Analysis, *Edited by R. W. Schafer and J. D. Markel*
The Engineer in Transition to Management, *I. Gray*
Multidimensional Systems: Theory & Applications, *Edited by N. K. Bose*
Analog Integrated Circuits, *Edited by A. B. Grebene*
Integrated-Circuit Operational Amplifiers, *Edited by R. G. Meyer*
Modern Spectrum Analysis, *Edited by D. G. Childers*
Digital Image Processing for Remote Sensing, *Edited by R. Bernstein*
Reflector Antennas, *Edited by A. W. Love*
Phase-Locked Loops & Their Application, *Edited by W. C. Lindsey and M. K. Simon*
Digital Signal Computers and Processors, *Edited by A. C. Salazar*
Systems Engineering: Methodology and Applications, *Edited by A. P. Sage*
Modern Crystal and Mechanical Filters, *Edited by D. F. Sheahan and R. A. Johnson*
Electrical Noise: Fundamentals and Sources, *Edited by M. S. Gupta*
Computer Methods in Image Analysis, *Edited by J. K. Aggarwal, R. O. Duda, and A. Rosenfeld*
Microprocessors: Fundamentals and Applications, *Edited by W. C. Lin*
Machine Recognition of Patterns, *Edited by A. K. Agrawala*
Turning Points in American Electrical History, *Edited by J. E. Brittain*
Charge-Coupled Devices: Technology and Applications, *Edited by R. Melen and D. Buss*
Spread Spectrum Techniques, *Edited by R. C. Dixon*
Electronic Switching: Central Office Systems of the World, *Edited by A. E. Joel, Jr.*
Electromagnetic Horn Antennas, *Edited by A. W. Love*
Waveform Quantization and Coding, *Edited by N. S. Jayant*
Communication Satellite Systems: An Overview of the Technology, *Edited by R. G. Gould and Y. F. Lum*
Literature Survey of Communication Satellite Systems and Technology, *Edited by J. H. W. Unger*
Solar Cells, *Edited by C. E. Backus*
Computer Networking, *Edited by R. P. Blanc and I. W. Cotton*
Communications Channels: Characterization and Behavior, *Edited by B. Goldberg*
Large-Scale Networks: Theory and Design, *Edited by F. T. Boesch*
Optical Fiber Technology, *Edited by D. Gloge*
Selected Papers in Digital Signal Processing, II, *Edited by the Digital Signal Processing Committee*
A Guide for Better Technical Presentations, *Edited by R. M. Woelfle*
Career Management: A Guide to Combating Obsolescence, *Edited by H. G. Kaufman*
Energy and Man: Technical and Social Aspects of Energy, *Edited by M. G. Morgan*
Magnetic Bubble Technology: Integrated-Circuit Magnetics for Digital Storage and Processing, *Edited by H. Chang*
Frequency Synthesis: Techniques and Applications, *Edited by J. Gorski-Popiel*
Literature in Digital Processing: Author and Permuted Title Index (Revised and Expanded Edition), *Edited by H. D. Helms, J. F. Kaiser, and L. R. Rabiner*
Data Communications via Fading Channels, *Edited by K. Brayer*
Nonlinear Networks: Theory and Analysis, *Edited by A. N. Willson, Jr.*
Computer Communications, *Edited by P. E. Green, Jr. and R. W. Lucky*
Stability of Large Electric Power Systems, *Edited by R. T. Byerly and E. W. Kimbark*
Automatic Test Equipment: Hardware, Software, and Management, *Edited by F. Liguori*
Key Papers in the Development of Coding Theory, *Edited by E. R. Berkekamp*
Technology and Social Institutions, *Edited by K. Chen*
Key Papers in the Development of Information Theory, *Edited by D. Slepian*
Computer-Aided Filter Design, *Edited by G. Szentirmai*
Laser Devices and Applications, *Edited by I. P. Kaminow and A. E. Siegman*
Integrated Optics, *Edited by D. Marcuse*
Laser Theory, *Edited by F. S. Barnes*
Digital Signal Processing, *Edited by L. R. Rabiner and C. M. Rader*
Minicomputers: Hardware, Software, and Applications, *Edited by J. D. Schoeffler and R. H. Temple*
Semiconductor Memories, *Edited by D. A. Hodges*
Power Semiconductor Applications, Volume II: Equipment and Systems, *Edited by J. D. Harnden, Jr. and F. B. Golden*
Power Semiconductor Applications, Volume I: General Considerations, *Edited by J. D. Harnden, Jr. and F. B. Golden*
A Practical Guide to Minicomputer Applications, *Edited by F. F. Coury*
Active Inductorless Filters, *Edited by S. K. Mitra*

Frequency-Response Methods in Control Systems

Edited by
Alistair G.J. MacFarlane
Professor of Control Engineering
University of Cambridge

A volume in the IEEE PRESS Selected Reprint Series,
prepared under the sponsorship of the
IEEE Control Systems Society.

IEEE PRESS

The Institute of Electrical and Electronics Engineers, Inc. New York

PRINTED IN THE UNITED STATES OF AMERICA

IEEE International Standard Book Numbers: Clothbound: 0-87942-125-8
Paperbound: 0-87942-126-6

Library of Congress Catalog Card Number 79-90572

Sole Worldwide Distributor (Exclusive of IEEE):

JOHN WILEY & SONS, INC.
605 Third Ave.
New York, NY 10016

Wiley Order Numbers: Clothbound: 0-471-06486-6
Paperbound: 0-471-06426-2

Contents

Preface

The aim of this book is to present a wide-ranging survey of the frequency-response methods used in automatic control. It was conceived by the Information Dissemination Committee of the IEEE Control Systems Society as a memorial volume to commemorate the life and work of H. Nyquist.

The material presented consists of selected reprints, plus extensive editorial surveys and a bibliography. Part I gives a survey of the development of frequency-response methods in automatic control; in order to give a proper perspective it is essentially a brief history of the whole subject. Its preparation was a surprisingly arduous job in which I was greatly helped by the book by Rörentrop (1971). Part II is concerned with the genesis and development of classical frequency-response ideas, and Part III with their extension to nonlinear, time-varying, and stochastic systems. Systems having many input and output variables are considered in Part IV, and Part V deals briefly with some ideas in the theory of multidimensional systems which are emerging from work on image processing in several spatial dimensions. Finally, an extensive Bibliography of frequency-response methods in control with some coverage of related topics is given. For ease of access, the references in the Bibliography are organized into the same sections as are used in the main body of the text, and are further subdivided for quick access to a specific field.

In undertaking this task I have been greatly encouraged and helped by many friends and colleagues. I am particularly grateful to Prof. Eli Jury who painstakingly read the entire manuscript of the editorial material several times, and made a large number of corrections and improvements; to Profs. Stephen Kahne, Lucien Polak, Charlie Desoer, and Len Silverman who advised, encouraged, and assisted in bringing a vague idea to a finished reality; to Prof. Howard Rosenbrock, Dr. Basil Kouvaritakis, Dr. David Owens, Dr. Ian Postlethwaite, Dr. Nick Karcanias, and Dr. John Edmunds for their comments on Part IV; to Dr. Alistair Mees for his careful checking of Part III; to Dr. Tom Fuller for reading the draft editorial manuscript and checking the historical material in Part I; to Prof. Ya. Z. Tsypkin for useful advice on Parts I-III; to Prof. Murray Wonham for reading the draft manuscript and suggesting several useful improvements; and to Prof. Brian Anderson for some helpful suggestions. Their efforts have undoubtedly prevented omissions and removed many blemishes; for those which remain I beg the reader's indulgence. Prof. Stephen Kahne was most helpful in securing a translation of Professor Ya. Z. Tsypkin's 1946 paper; this translation was speedily and expertly provided by Dr. Ljubomir Jocić. I am particularly conscious of the fact that a number of important papers do not appear here as selected reprints; to keep the finished volume down to a practicable size it was inevitable that many of those initially selected could not be retained. It is hoped, however, that the combination of editorial survey and bibliography which has been given will enable the reader to quickly locate most papers relevant to the topics treated here.

In preparing this volume I have been repeatedly impressed by the power, practical utility, and generality of the concepts and techniques which have developed from Nyquist's seminal paper of 1932. His ideas are still flourishing at the frontiers of current research and will surely continue to be a source of vigorous development in the future. I am glad to have been associated with this enterprise, which I hope will be a worthy memorial to his work in the field of feedback theory.

A. G. J. MacFarlane
Cambridge
November 1978

In Memoriam Harry Nyquist

1889–1976

Obituary Statement: Harry Nyquist

HENDRIK W. BODE

HARRY Nyquist died April 4, 1976 in Harlingen, Texas. He was 87 years old and had been ill for some time. His passing is a landmark event for engineers in many fields to which he made major contributions.

To control theorists, Nyquist is no doubt best known as the inventor of the Nyquist diagram, defining the conditions for stability of negative feedback systems. This has become a foundation stone for control theory the world over, applicable in a much wider range of situations than that for which it was originally enunciated.

The so-called Nyquist interval, or Nyquist signaling rate, plays a similar fundamental role for modern communications engineering. Nyquist's calculation of the thermal noise level in a transmission band of given width is another fundamental for communication engineers, as is a variety of more specific inventions such as the vestigial sideband system now used universally in television transmission.

Nyquist was born in Nilsby, Sweden, on February 7, 1889, and emigrated to this country in 1907 at the age of 18. He spent the next ten years completing his education, supporting himself in the mean time through teaching and summer jobs. (There is a strong Horatio Alger flavor in all of this.)

Nyquist finished his formal education with a Ph.D. degree in physics from Yale University in 1917. He was immediately employed by the A.T.&T. Company, and spent essentially the rest of his life with the Bell System, either with the A.T.&T. Company's so-called D&R Department, or with Bell Laboratories. He retired formally in 1954, but continued as a part-time consultant for the Bell System or for various federal agencies for several years thereafter. All told, his working lifetime covered more than half a century.

Much of Nyquist's most important research stemmed originally from the practical needs of the telephone system. For several years after joining the Bell System, he was concerned with high-speed telegraphy, including systems based on metallic return paths and the then-new carrier technology. This led in due course to his fundamental work on the relation between signaling speed, pulse shape, and the probability of intersymbol interference, subjects of importance for data systems and the like even today.

The high point of Nyquist's creative activities probably took place in the decade or so straddling the end of the 1920's and the beginning of the 1930's. This is the period when he made his principal studies of television transmission and other phase-related systems, including the basic invention of vestigial sideband transmission for television circuits. This is also the period when Nyquist made his fundamental studies of thermal noise in communication circuits, giving communication systems engineers a fundamental point of departure in planning new systems.

Nyquist's most conspicuous contribution in these years, however, was probably the enunciation of his stability criterion for feedback systems. This was indeed a theoretical contribution which came just in time. Both the communication and control fields badly needed the improvement in performance promised by whole-hearted exploitation of the negative feedback principle, but before Nyquist's formulation, the design task of actually realizing such improvements in performance in a stable system had often been unmanageably difficult. Nyquist's formulation brought the whole subject within the scope of rational design practice.

In his later years, Nyquist's attention turned increasingly to digitalized systems, including, in particular, digital coding and some secrecy and switching problems. This was an easy step for Nyquist to take, since so much of the digital universe is spiritual kin to the idealized telegraph

The author is with Harvard University, Cambridge, MA.

Reprinted from *IEEE Trans. Automat. Contr.*, vol. AC-22, pp. 897–898, Dec. 1977.

systems on which he had worked earlier. It has had the happy result, however, that it made available the vast storehouse of design techniques, including many of Nyquist's own contributions, which has accumulated from earlier epochs. There has been no need for communication engineers to develop brand new answers for every new problem in the digital era.

Any recital of Nyquist's theoretical contributions must include the fact that he was also an exceptionally prolific inventor. During his Bell System career, he was granted 138 American patents, not counting a substantial number of foreign filings. The subject matter of these many patents covers a wide range. Many of the patents, of course, are individually important and interesting as adroit solutions of isolated technical problems. A considerable number, however, are of special interest because they are all related to the general problem of measuring and correcting for distortion which may be exhibited by transmission media of various sorts, whether one is concerned with speech, TV, data, or whatnot. The distortion problem is, of course, a fundamental one which one must expect to encounter in one way or another in any transmission system. The rich collection of inventive devices represented by Nyquist's patents amounts, in the aggregate, to a developed design theory for approaching such problems, whatever the particular situation.

Nyquist received many honors in recognition of his many contributions in the communication and control fields. These include, among others, the NAE Founders' Medal of Honor (1969), the Ballantine Medal of the Franklin Institute (1960), the IEEE's Medal of Honor (1960), and the ASME Oldenburger Medal (1975). Personally, he was quiet and reserved, but a very good associate for intimate friends and colleagues.

Frequency-Response Methods in Control Systems

Part I

The Development of Frequency-Response Methods in Automatic Control

ALISTAIR G. J. MacFARLANE, SENIOR MEMBER, IEEE

Editor's Note: As readers of this journal will recall, in 1976 the Control Systems Society named three distinguished control systems specialists as Consulting Editors. One of the charges to these men was to submit an invited paper on a topic of their choice for publication without the usual IDC review procedures. At the same time Professor A. G. J. MacFarlane, Professor of Control Engineering at Cambridge University, was invited by the IDC to prepare an IEEE Press reprint book of important papers on frequency-domain methods in control and systems engineering. The coincidence of these two decisions has led to the following paper. "The Development of Frequency-Response Methods in Automatic Control" is one part of the IEEE Press book, *Frequency-Response Methods in Control Systems*, edited by A. G. J. MacFarlane and sponsored by the Control Systems Society. The book will appear in mid-1979. The paper has been selected by Consulting Editor Nathaniel Nichols and should be of substantial interest to TRANSACTIONS readers. It also conveys some of the spirit and content of the book which may be purchased from IEEE Press when available.

S. KAHNE

CONTRARY to popular belief, most good engineering theory arises from work on an important practical problem; this was certainly the case with Nyquist's famous stability criterion [169]. His attack on the problem of feedback amplifier stability produced a tool of such flexibility and power that its use rapidly spread to the wider field of automatic control. This fusion of the dynamical interests of the control and communication engineer has been immensely fruitful. In order to appreciate fully the far-reaching implications of Nyquist's 1932 paper, one must first consider the developments in automatic control and telecommunications which led up to it.

Early Developments in Automatic Control

Although automatic control devices of various sorts had been in use since the beginnings of technology [152], Watt's use of the flyball governor can be taken as the starting point for the development of automatic control as a science [153], [154]. The early Watt governors worked satisfactorily, no doubt largely due to the considerable amounts of friction present in their mechanism, and the device was therefore widely adopted. In fact, it has been estimated that by 1868 there were some 75 000 Watt governors working in England alone [75]. However, during the middle of the 19th century, as engine designs changed and manufacturing techniques improved, an increasing tendency for such systems to hunt became apparent; that is, for the engine speed to vary cyclically with time. This phenomenon had also appeared in governed clockwork drives used to regulate the speed of astronomical telescopes and had been investigated by Airy (when he was Astronomer Royal) [1]–[3], [75]. Airy had, not unnaturally, attacked this problem with the tools of his own trade: the theory of celestial mechanics. He carried out his investigations with great skill and insight, and essentially got to the root of the mathematical problems involved. Unfortunately, his work was rather intricate and difficult to follow; it therefore did not become widely known, and the subject remained shrouded in mystery to engineers grappling with the problem of fluctuating engine speeds. This problem of the hunting of governed engines became a very serious one (75 000 engines, large numbers of them hunting!) and so attracted the attention of a number of outstandingly able engineers and physicists [153], [154], [76]. It was solved by classic investigations made by Maxwell [150], who founded the theory of automatic control systems with his paper "On Governors," and by the Russian engineer Vyschnegradsky [226], [227], who published his results in terms of a design rule, relating the engineering parameters of the system to its stability. Vyschnegradsky's analysis showed that the engine design changes which had been taking place since Watt's time—a decrease in friction due to improved manufacturing techniques, a decreased moment of inertia arising from the use of smaller flywheels, and an increased mass of

Manuscript received August 30, 1978.
The author is with the Control and Management Systems Division, Department of Engineering, Cambridge University, Cambridge, England.

Reprinted from *IEEE Trans. Automat. Contr.*, vol. AC-24, pp. 250–265, Apr. 1979.

flyball weights to cope with larger steam valves—were all destabilizing, and their cumulative effect had inevitably led to the ubiquitous phenomenon of hunting speed. Maxwell's fundamentally important contribution lay in recognizing that the behavior of an automatic feedback control system in the vicinity of an equilibrium condition could be approximated by a linear differential equation, and hence that the stability of the control system could be discussed in terms of the location of the roots of an associated algebraic equation.

Following the presentation of his work on governors, Maxwell posed the general problem of investigating the stability of a dynamical system in terms of the location of the roots of its characteristic equation. At that time Hermite's work on this problem (which had been published some years before) was not widely known [94]. A solution was put forward by Routh in his Adams Prize Essay of 1877 [74]; this work is of great interest in the context of the Nyquist stability criterion since hindsight shows that it contains the seeds of an appropriate use of complex variable mappings for the investigation of stability. In 1895 an alternative necessary and sufficient criterion for all the roots of an algebraic equation to have negative real parts was given by Hurwitz in terms of a set of determinants [99]. Andronov [5] has given an interesting description of Vyschnegradsky's work and its effect on the subsequent development of automatic control. Andronov also discusses the important investigations made by Stodola and his collaboration with Hurwitz. Jury [106] describes the background to Routh's work and its subsequent development.

Several important advances in automatic control technology were made in the latter half of the 19th century. A key modification to the flyball governor was the introduction of a simple means of setting the desired running speed of the engine being controlled by balancing the centrifugal force of the flyballs against a spring, and using the preset spring tension to set the running speed of the engine. This brought the idea of a variable set-point of operation into automatic control. Lincke [133] proposed the use of hydraulic power amplifiers to reduce the load on the flyball mechanism, whose primary function is that of speed measurement. This enabled an integral control action to be introduced into the governor system in a simple and efficient way, and hence greatly reduced the steady-state error in governed engine speed. The idea of integral control action had previously been discussed in various ways by Preuss [186], Siemens [208], [209], and by Maxwell [150] in his 1868 paper. In his work on torpedos Whitehead made considerable use of feedback mechanisms for depth control; in some of these devices a practical form of derivative feedback action was present and used to increase the overall damping of the closed-loop system [93], [191], [84], [26]. Thus by the 1870's the use of proportional, integral, and derivative feedback action in closed-loop control systems was well established. The use of feedback for the position control of massive objects was proposed by Farcot between 1868 and 1873 for naval applications; he called such devices servomechanisms [65].

When power-amplifying devices were introduced into automatic control systems, as by Lincke, the individual functions of the various parts of the overall control system became more clearly apparent. It was appreciated that various forms of the control device had certain common features; Marié specifically drew attention to the common features of certain means of controlling speed, pressure, and temperature [149]. Lincke went even further and commented on the similarities to biological regulating systems. The growing practical importance of automatic control was marked by the award of the Nobel Prize for Physics in 1912 to the Swedish inventor Dalen "for his invention of automatic regulators to be used in conjunction with gas accumulators for lighting beacons and light buoys" [91].

The Development of the Feedback Amplifier and the Genesis of Frequency-Response Techniques

The use of ordinary differential equations, together with algebraic tests to determine the location of the roots of the associated characteristic equations, remained virtually the sole analytical tools of the automatic control engineer until well into the present century. Just as these first developments arose out of struggles with the practical problem of engine governing, so the next theoretical advances came from the work on another important technical problem: long-distance audio telephony. A revolution in the technology of communication and information processing began with L. de Forest's addition of an extra electrode to Fleming's thermionic valve to create the triode amplifying valve in 1906. This invention removed the chief obstacle to the development of long-distance telephony, namely the attenuation in cable transmission. While the mechanical engineers concerned with the problems of servomechanisms were naturally using differential equations as their basic theoretical tool, electrical engineers and communications engineers had evolved their own distinctive approaches to dynamical phenomena. The development of ac electrical power systems had led to an acute need for appropriate means of handling the "arithmetic" of ac network studies, and Steinmetz [212] developed the use of complex numbers for the representation of sinusoidal voltages and currents. Schenkel [206] discussed the representation of impedance functions by simple loci (straight lines and circles) in the complex plane. Such forms of impedance diagram were also considered by Campbell [43] and Bloch [29]. Two distinctive approaches to dynamical systems now began to develop which were associated with different ways of thinking about such systems and which, in view of their historical evolution, can be conveniently called the "mechanical engineers' viewpoint" and the "communication engineers' viewpoint," respectively. A mechanical engineer using a differential equations approach modeled his system in terms of some real or abstract "mechanism" and wrote his system-describing equations down from a detailed study of the relevant physical mechanism. The communication engineer's viewpoint, however, was quite different. It was natural for him to regard his various bits of apparatus in terms of "boxes" into which certain signals were injected and out of which emerged appropriate responses. Thus it was a natural next step for a communications engineer, in considering his system's behavior, to replace the actual boxes in which distinct pieces of physical apparatus were housed by abstract boxes which represented their effect on the signals passing through them. A combination of this "operator" viewpoint with the electrical engineer's flexible use of complex-variable representations of sinusoidal waveforms made the use of Fourier analysis-based techniques for studying dynamical phenomena in communication systems virtually inevitable. Following the pioneering work of Heaviside [92] on operational methods for solving differential equations, integral transform methods and their application to practical problems were put on a secure foundation by the work of Bromwich [37], Wagner [229], Carson [46], [47], Campbell and Foster [44], Doetsch [59], and others; thus by the late 1920's and early 1930's the integral-transform approach to the analysis of dynamical phenomena in communication systems was available for the study of feedback devices, given someone with the initiative and skill to use it.

The role of positive feedback in the deliberate generation of oscillations for high-frequency modulated-carrier radio telegraphy emerged shortly after the development of the triode amplifying valve; a patent on the use of inductive feedback to produce a high-frequency alternating current using an amplifying valve was granted to Strauss in Austria in 1912; similar developments were credited to Meissner in Germany in 1913, to Franklin and Round in England, and to Armstrong and Langmuir in the U.S.A. [191]. Armstrong, in 1914, developed the use of positive feedback in his "regenerative receiver" [28]. The central role of the feedback concept in steam engine control systems had been considered by Barkhausen [9], and Barkhausen's ideas were discussed by Möller [164] in his treatment of feedback effects in electrical circuits. Further development of the idea of a feedback loop of dependence in an oscillator circuit led Barkhausen [10] to give a "formula for self-excitation":

$$KF(j\omega)=1$$

where K is an amplifier gain factor and $F(j\omega)$ is the frequency-dependent gain of an associated feedback loop in the oscillator circuit. The *Barkhausen criterion* which developed from this formula was orginally intended for the determination of the self-excitation frequency of ac generators for use in radio transmitters. Prior to the appearance of Nyquist's 1932 paper, however, the phenomenon of conditional stability was not understood and hence it was widely believed that, for a given frequency-dependent gain function $F(j\omega)$, there was only a single value of the scalar gain parameter K which separated stable and unstable regions of behavior. Thus, particularly in the German literature, Barkhausen's equation came to be used as the basis of a stability criterion for positive and negative feedback amplifiers [135], [97]. An important early contribution to the development of frequency-response methods for the analysis of linear dynamical systems was made in 1928 by Küpfmüller. In this paper [124] he gave a comprehensive discussion of the relationships between frequency transmission characteristics and transient response behavior. In another paper published in the same year, Küpfmüller [125] dealt with the problem of closed-loop stability. Here, however, he did not use a fully-developed frequency-domain approach. Küpfmüller represented the system's dynamical behavior in terms of an integral equation, and hence developed an approximate criterion for closed-loop stability in terms of time-response quantities measured and calculated from the system's transient response. Küpfmüller's technique of approximately determining closed-loop stability from such time-response measurements seems to have remained relatively unknown outside Germany. In his history of automatic control, Rörentrop [191] refers to further work done in Germany in the 1930's on frequency-response criteria for feedback system stability, and in particular he refers to the development by Strecker of a frequency-domain stability criterion of what we would now call Nyquist type. This work appears to have remained virtually unknown and was only described in the scientific literature available after the end of the Second World War [213]–[216]. In his book Strecker [215] refers to having presented a frequency-response stability criterion at a colloquium at the Central Laboratory of Siemens and Halske in 1930, and to having presented his results to a wider audience at a seminar held by the Society of German Electrical Engineers in 1938. Rörentrop [191] says that the manuscript of this lecture is still available and that in it Strecker considered the case of open-loop unstable systems.

The truly epoch-making event in the development of frequency-response methods was undoubtedly the appearance of Nyquist's classic paper [169] on feedback amplifier stability, which arose directly from work on the problems of long-distance telephony. In 1915 the Bell System completed an experimental telephone link between New York and San Francisco which showed that reliable voice communication over transcontinental distances was a practicable proposition. This link used heavy copper open-wire circuits (weighing half a ton/mi) and was inductively loaded to have a cut-off frequency of 1000 Hz. The attenuation over a 3000 mi distance was 60 dB and, with a net gain of 42 dB provided by six repeating amplifiers, this was reduced to a tolerable net attenuation figure of 18 dB overall. The use of carrier systems on open-wire circuits was soon well advanced and had resulted in a substantial economy in conductor costs with multiplex operation in a frequency range well above the audible.

A change to cable operations, however, posed a number of severe technical problems. In particular, because the conductors were small, the attenuation was large and this required the use of many repeating amplifiers. Thus a crucial technical problem had to be overcome, that of repeatedly passing signals through amplifiers, each of which contained unavoidable and significant nonlinearities, while keeping the total distortion over transcontinental distances within acceptable limits. It required an effective amplifier linearity to within better than several parts in a thousand in order to maintain intelligibility of the transmitted audio signals. Such an acute difficulty could only be overcome by a major invention, and this was provided by H. Black of the Bell Telephone Laboratory when he put forward the idea of a feedback amplifier. Black's important discovery was that high gain in a nonlinear and variable amplifying device could be traded for a reduction in nonlinear distortion, and that an accurate, stable, and highly linear overall gain could be achieved by the suitable use of a precision linear passive component in conjunction with a high-gain nonlinear amplifer. By 1932 Black and his colleagues could build feedback amplifers which performed remarkably well. They had, however, a tendency to "sing," the telephone engineer's expressive term for instability in amplifers handling audio signals. Some "sang" when the loop gain of the feedback amplifier was increased (which was not unexpected), but others "sang" when the loop gain was reduced (which was quite unexpected). The situation was not unlike that associated with the hunting governors of around 1868—an important practical device was exhibiting mysterious behavior. Moreover, it was behavior whose explanation was not easily within the compass of existing theoretical tools, since a feedback amplifier might well have of the order of 50 independent energy-storing elements within it (such as inductors, capacitors, etc.). Its description in terms of a set of differential equations, as in the classical analyses of mechanical automatic control systems, was thus hardly feasible in view of the rudimentary facilities available at that time for the computer solution of such equations. Nyquist's famous paper solved this mystery; it opened up wholly new perspectives in the theory of feedback mechanisms and hence started a new era in automatic control. Prior to 1932 the differential-equation-based approach had been the major tool of the control theorist; within the decade following Nyquist's paper these techniques were almost completely superseded by methods based on complex-variable theory which were the direct offspring of his new approach. The background to his invention and its subsequent development have been described in a fascinating article by Black [28]. It is clear from this that Black used a stability argument of frequency-response type, saying there that "...consequently, I knew that in order to avoid self-oscillation in a feedback amplifier it would be sufficient that at no frequency from zero to infinity should $\mu\beta$ be real, positive, and greater than unity." The prototype Black feedback amplifier was tested in December 1927 and development of a carrier system for transcontinental cable telephony, its first application, started in 1928. Field trials of a system using a 25-mi section of cable with 2 terminal and 68 repeater amplifiers were held at Morristown, NJ in 1930, and successfully completed in 1931. Black [27] described his amplifier in a paper which makes interesting references to the stability problem. In particular he mentions the phenomenon of conditional stability in the following words: "However, one noticeable feature about the field of $\mu\beta$ is that it implies that even though the phase shift is zero and the absolute value of $\mu\beta$ exceeds unity, self-oscillations or singing will not result. This may or may not be true. When the author first thought about this matter he suspected that owing to practical nonlinearity, singing would result whenever the gain around the closed loop equalled or exceeded the loss and simultaneously the phase shift was zero, i.e., $\mu\beta=|\mu\beta|+j0\geqslant 1$. Results of experiments, however, seemed to indicate something more was involved and these matters were described to Mr. H. Nyquist, who developed a more general criterion for freedom from instability applicable to an amplifier having linear positive constants." Nyquist himself has also briefly described the events which led to his writing the 1932 paper [170].

Nyquist's open-loop gain frequency-response form of solution of the feedback stability problem was of immense practical value because it was formulated in terms of a quantity (gain) which was directly measurable on a piece of equipment. This direct link with experimental measurements was a completely new and vitally important development in applied dynamical work. The application of Nyquist's stability criterion did *not* depend on the availability of a system model in the form of a differential equation or characteristic polynomial. Furthermore, the form of the Nyquist locus gave an immediate and vivid indication of how an unstable, or poorly damped, system's feedback performance could be improved by modifying its open-loop gain versus frequency behavior in an appropriate way.

It seems clear that when Nyquist set out to write his 1932 paper he was aware that the fundamental phenomenon which he had to explain was that of conditional stability. The successful theoretical explanation of this counter-intuitive effect is given due prominence in the paper. It is also clear that Nyquist was fully aware of the great generality and practical usefulness of his stability criterion. He, therefore, attempted to prove its validity for a wide class of systems, including those involving a pure time-delay effect, and he took the primary system description to be a directly-measurable frequency response characteristic.

The importance of the feedback amplifier to the Bell Laboratories' development of long-distance telephony led to a careful experimental study of feedback amplifier stability by Peterson *et al.* [178]. These experiments fully supported Nyquist's theoretical predictions and thus completely vindicated his analysis. It is altogether too easy, with hindsight and our exposure to current knowledge, to underestimate the magnitude of Black's invention and Nyquist's theoretical achievement. Things looked very different in their time. The granting of a patent to Black for his amplifier took more than nine years (the final patent, No. 2,102,671, was issued on December 21, 1937). The

U.S. Patent Office cited technical papers claiming that the output could not be connected back to the input of an amplifier, while remaining stable, unless the loop gain were less than one; and the British Patent Office, in Black's words, treated the application "in the same manner as one for a perpetual-motion machine."

Nyquist's work had shown the great power of complex-variable theory for the analysis of feedback system behavior, and it was inevitable that a tool of such promise would be further developed for design purposes. It was a natural inference from the developments presented in his paper that the closeness of approach of the Nyquist locus to the critical point in the complex plane gave a measure of closed-loop damping. This was investigated by Ludwig [135] who gave a neat formula for estimating the real part of a pair of complex conjugate roots associated with the dominant mode in the case where the Nyquist locus passes near the critical point. Thus, it soon became clear that the key to making an unstable (or otherwise unsatisfactory) feedback system stable (or better damped) lay in an appropriate modification of the amplitude and phase characteristics of the open-loop gain function for the feedback loop involved. Extensive and fruitless experimental studies were made, particularly by F. B. Anderson in the Bell Telephone Laboratories, in attempts to build feedback amplifiers having loops which combined a fast cutoff in gain with a small associated phase shift. It therefore became important to analyze the way in which the amplitude and phase frequency functions of a loop gain transfer function are related. In another of the classic papers which lie at the foundation of feedback theory Bode [30] carried out such an analysis, extending previous work by Lee and Wiener [128]. This paper, written in a beautifully clear and engaging manner, showed how there is associated with any given amplitude/gain frequency function an appropriate minimum-phase frequency function. Bode was thus able to give rules for the optimum shaping of the loop-gain frequency function for a feedback amplifier. He introduced logarithmic units of amplitude gain and logarithmic scales of frequency, and hence the logarithmic gain and linear phase versus logarithmic frequency diagrams which bear his name. The critical point in the gain plane was put at its now standard and familiar location of $(-1+j0)$, and the concepts of gain and phase margin were introduced. Bode's classic work appeared in an extended form in his book *Network Analysis and Feedback Amplifier Design* [31].

Nyquist's criterion is not easy to prove rigorously for the class of systems which he far-sightedly attempted to deal with in his classic paper and the need for a rigorous approach to a simpler class of systems soon became apparent. For the case when the open-loop gain is an analytic rational function, Nyquist himself had given a simple complex variable argument in an Appendix to his 1932 paper. This approach was soon realized to provide a simple route to a satisfactory proof for the restricted class of system functions which could be specified as rational functions of a complex frequency variable. MacColl [140] gave such a proof using the Principle of the Argument, and this became the standard form of exposition appearing in influential books by Bode [31], James *et al.* [101], and many others. Such simplified presentations did scant justice to the far-reaching nature of Nyquist's classic paper, but they soon made the stability criterion a cornerstone of frequency-response methods based on complex function theory.

The treatment given in Nyquist's 1932 paper had specifically excluded systems having poles in the closed right-half plane. A pure integration effect, however, often occurs in the open-loop transmission of servomechanisms incorporating an electric or hydraulic motor, and the appropriate extension to the Nyquist criterion to handle transfer function poles at the origin of the complex frequency plane was described in various wartime reports such as MacColl's [139] and in a paper by Hall [86]. Using the complex-variable approach based on the Principle of the Argument which had by then become the standard one, Frey [73] extended the Nyquist stability criterion to deal with the case where the feedback system may be open-loop unstable, and this simple first version of the Nyquist criterion finally assumed the form which became familiar in a multitude of textbooks.

The Spread of the Frequency-Response Approach

By the beginning of the twentieth century the basic concepts of automatic control and their analytical discussion in terms of ordinary differential equations and their related characteristic algebraic equations were well established. These techniques were consolidated in review papers by Hort [98] and Von Mises [228], and in early textbooks on automatic control by Tolle [219] and Trinks [220]. The further development of automatic control devices received great impetus from important studies carried out by Minorsky [161] on the automatic steering of ships, and by Hazen [90] on shaft-positioning servomechanisms. Minorsky proposed the use of a proportional-plus-derivative-plus-integral control action for the steering control. His work was of particular significance in being practically tested in a famous series of trials on the automatic steering of the USS New Mexico in 1922–23 [162]. Both Minorsky's and Hazen's work was explained in terms of ordinary differential equations, and their success with practical devices led to the widespread use of this approach to the analysis of automatic control systems.

In the chemical process industries the introduction of feedback control tended at first to develop in isolation from the developments in mechanical and electrical engineering. One very important difference in the process industries was (and still, to a large extent, is) that the time-scale of controlled-variable behavior was sufficiently slow on many process plants to make manual feedback control action a feasible proposition. In the chemical industry the first step along the road to automatic feedback control was the introduction of indicating instruments to monitor plant operation, followed by the attachment of pen recorders to these indicators to secure a record of plant behavior. The natural development was then to go one step further and use the movement of the pen on the recorder to effect feedback action on control valves in the plant through the use of pneumatic transducers, amplifiers, and transmission lines. During the 1930's these pneumatic controllers were steadily developed, and the idea of using an integral action term, long standard in mechanical governing, transferred to this field of control. Here, however, it was called "reset action" since the behavior of the pneumatic controller with the integral control term added was analogous to that which would have been obtained if the reference input had been slowly adjusted (or reset) to the appropriate new value required to cancel out a steady-state disturbance. In the late 1930's and early 1940's, derivative action (usually called pre-act in this context) was introduced for these pneumatic controllers to give the full "3-term" controller or "PID" (Proportional, Integral, and Derivative) controller. A theoretical basis for applied process control was laid by papers by Ivanoff [100] on temperature control, and by Callander *et al.* [42] on the effect of time-lags in control systems. It is interesting to note that this paper by Callendar *et al.* probably contains the first published description of the application of an analog computer to an automatic control problem. Ziegler and Nichols [244] made an important study which led to formulas from which proportional, reset (integral) and pre-act (derivative) controller settings could be determined from the experimentally measured values of the lag and "reaction rate" of a process which was to be controlled.

By the late 1930's there were thus two separate but well-developed methods of attacking the analysis of feedback system behavior.

1) The "time-response approach" which involved ordinary differential equations and their associated characteristic algebraic equations, and which was much used in mechanical, naval, aeronautical, and chemical engineering studies of automatic control systems; and

2) the "frequency-response approach" which involved Nyquist and Bode plots, transfer functions, etc., and which was used for studies of feedback amplifiers.

The frequency-response approach had the appealing advantage of dealing with pieces of apparatus in terms of abstract "boxes" or "blocks" which represented their effect on the signals passing through them. This proved to be a very flexible and general way of representing systems, and it was found that when such "block" diagrams were drawn for different kinds of control systems the ubiquitous loop of feedback dependence, which is the hallmark of a feedback mechanism in a representation of this sort, sprang into sudden prominence. The power and flexibility of the tools developed by Nyquist and Bode were such that their spread to other fields in which feedback principles were used was inevitable. Some early work on using the techniques of the feedback amplifier designer for the analysis of more general systems was done by Taplin at MIT in 1937 [101]. A crucial step in the transference of the telephone engineer's viewpoint to the analysis of other kinds of system was taken by Harris, also of MIT, who made the fundamentally important contribution of introducing the use of transfer functions into the analysis of general feedback systems [87]. Harris's idea enabled a mechanical servomechanism or a chemical process control system to be represented in block diagram terms, and thus analyzed using the powerful tools available to the feedback amplifier designer.

In 1938 Mikhailov gave a frequency response criterion for systems described by a known nth order constant coefficient linear differential equation and thus having an explicitly known characteristic polynomial $p(s)$ [159]. It was stated in terms of the locus of $p(j\omega)$ in a complex p-plane and so bore a superficial resemblance to the Nyquist criterion. It is, however, an essentially different thing in that it requires that the governing differential equation of the system being investigated must be known, whereas the essential virtue of the Nyquist criterion is that the Nyquist locus is something which can be directly measured for a plant whose behavior in terms of a differential equation description may well not be available. A criterion of this form was also formulated by Cremer [51] and Leonhard [131], independently of each other and of Mikhailov. In the German literature the criterion is accordingly known as the Cremer–Leonhard criterion; in the French literature it is usually called the Leonhard criterion. In the Russian technical literature the Nyquist stability criterion is often called the Mikhailov–Nyquist criterion. Work on generalizing the Nyquist criterion to deal with neutrally stable and unstable open-loop systems was done by Mikhailov [160] and Tsypkin [221].

The 1939–45 world war created an urgent need for high-performance servomechanisms and led to great advances in ways of designing and building feedback control systems. From the point of view of the development of automatic control design techniques, the chief result of the immense pooling of effort and experience involved was to spread rapidly the use of frequency-response ideas into the mechanical, aeronautical, naval and later the chemical fields, and to produce a unified and coherent theory for single-loop feedback systems. Important reports written by Brown and Hall [101] were circulated among defense scientists and engineers and soon, accelerated by the end of the war, a number of classic publications and textbooks became available which resulted in the widespread dissemination and adoption of frequency-response ideas. Herwald [95] discussed the use of block diagrams and operational calculus for the study of the transient behavior of automatic control systems, including the use of compensating networks. Ferrel [69] laid particular stress on the parallels between electromechanical control system design and electrical network design. He suggested the use of the now-familiar asymptotic Bode diagrams. Graham [83] made notable use of these diagrams and discussed dynamic errors, the effects of noise, and the use of tachometric feedback compensation. Brown and Hall [39] gave a classic treatment of the analysis and design of servomechanisms and Harris [88] gave a wide-ranging and thorough treatment of analysis and design in the frequency domain. The work done at the MIT Radiation Lab was summarized in a notable book by James *et al.* [101]; the first use of inverse Nyquist diagrams is discussed in their book and credited to Marcy [148]. Gardner and Barnes [77] gave a widely used treatment of the mathematical background to these developments.

British contributions were summarized in papers by Whiteley [231], [232]. The historical background to British work by Daniel, Tustin, Porter, Williams, Whiteley, and others has been described by Porter [183] and Westcott [230]. Several of the wartime and post-war historical developments in Britain and America have been discussed by Bennett [24]. German work during and after the war has been summarized by Rörentrop [191]. Applications of the Nyquist criterion to feedback control loops were treated in the German literature in papers by Feiss [66]–[68] and an important textbook was produced by Oldenbourg and Sartorious [171]. Leonhard [130] discussed frequency-response design techniques and extended the Mikhailov criterion approach [131]. Tsypkin [221], [222] discussed the effect of a pure delay in the feedback loop. Among the many textbooks used by designers, the two-volume work of Chestnut and Meyer [49] had a notable impact.

Since the rotating aerial of a radar system only illuminates its target intermittently, many of the fire-control systems developed during the Second World War had to be designed to deal with data available in a pulsed or sampled form. The basis for an effective treatment of sampled-data automatic control systems was laid by Hurewicz whose work is described in [101]. In particular, in his contribution to this book, Hurewicz developed an appropriate extension of the Nyquist stability criterion to sampled-data systems. The development of digital computing techniques soon led to further work on such discrete-time systems. Digital control systems operating on continuous-time plants require analysis techniques which enable both discrete-time and continuous-time systems, and their interconnection through suitable interfaces, to be looked at from a unified standpoint. Linvill [134] discussed this problem from the transform point of view, including a consideration of the Nyquist approach to closed-loop stability. Frequency-response methods of analyzing sampled-data systems were studied by Tsypkin [223]. A "z-transform" theory for systems described by difference equations emerged to match the "s-transform" theory for systems described by differential equations [188] and was treated in textbooks by Ragazzini and Franklin [188], Jury [104], [105], Freeman [72], and others. The "equivalence" between continuous-time and discrete-time system analysis methods has been discussed by Steiglitz [211].

The unique feature of the Nyquist–Bode diagram approach to closed-loop system stability and behavior is that it can make a direct use of experimentally-measurable gain characteristics. Using such data one can make inferential deductions about the behavior of the closed-loop system's characteristic frequencies. Nevertheless, there are many situations in which one does have a direct knowledge of the form of the plant transfer function and it then becomes a natural question to ask: what direct deductions can be made from this of the way in which the closed-loop characteristic frequencies vary with a gain parameter? This question was answered in 1948 by Evans who brought the complex-variable-based approach to linear feedback systems to its fully developed state by the introduction of his root-locus method [62]–[64].

The effect of random disturbances on automatic control systems was also studied during the Second World War [101]. In 1920 the autocorrelation function had been introduced by G. I. Taylor in his work on turbulent flow in fluids [217]; N. Wiener realized that this function was the link between the time and frequency-response descriptions of a stochastic process, and based his classic studies of random process analysis [233] and their relationships to communication and control theory [235] on the generalized Fourier transform of this function. Wiener became deeply interested in the relationships between control and communication problems and in the similarities between such problems in engineering and physiology. In addition to his important wartime report on time-series analysis he wrote a seminal book on cybernetics [234]. His books had the important effect of propagating feedback-control ideas in gèneral, and frequency-response methods in particular, into the fields of stochastic system theory and physiology.

The "harmonic balance" methods developed in studies of nonlinear mechanics by Krylov and Bogoliubov [122] led to attempts to extend frequency-response methods to nonlinear feedback control problems. From these efforts emerged the describing function method which extended the use of Nyquist diagrams to the study of nonlinear feedback system stability. This was developed independently in a number of countries: by Goldfarb [80] in Russia, by Daniel and Tustin in England [225], by Oppelt [173] in Germany, by Dutilh [60] in France, and by Kochenburger [120] in the United States. Although at first resting on rather shaky theoretical foundations, this technique proved of great use in many practical studies and its introduction marked an important consolidation in the use of frequency-response methods. Investigations by Bass [18] Sandberg [204], Bergen and Franks [25], Kudrewicz [123], and Mees [156], [157] have subsequently placed the method on a sounder basis.

Aizerman [4] greatly stimulated the study of nonlinear feedback problems by putting forward his famous conjecture on the stability of systems incorporating a "sector-bounded" nonlinearity. This led to work on what is known in the Russian literature as the "problem of absolute stability." Despite the fact that Pliss [179] demonstrated by means of a counterexample that the Aizerman conjecture is not generally true, it became manifestly important to discover for what classes of system the conjecture did hold. Such a class of systems was found by Popov [182] in a classic study which led to his famous stability criterion. Popov's work led to a resurgence of interest in frequency-response treatments of nonlinear problems out of which emerged the various forms of "circle criteria" for stability [205], [243], [166]. Some important early work on the application of frequency-response methods to nonlinear systems was done by Tsypkin [224] and Naumov and Tsypkin [167].

The Development of Optimal and Multivariable Control

By the early 1950's frequency-response methods reigned virtually supreme over the applied control field; they were the routinely-used tools for the analysis and design of feedback mechanisms and automatic control systems. A good impression of the classical frequency-response approach at this period can be obtained from the collection of papers edited by Oldenburger [172]. Block diagrams, with their associated transfer functions, had become widely familiar to engineers handling many different kinds of linear dynamical models of physical systems, and were being used with great flexibility and insight. In many ways frequency-response concepts had developed into a vital medium of communication, giving a unified means of approaching and analysing a wide range of feedback phenomena from a common point of view. The Nyquist diagram and Bode diagram, with their direct relationship to physically-measurable plant responses, had become an indispensable means of assessing closed-loop stability for a wide range of practical control systems, and the describing function technique had emerged as a useful, though somewhat heuristic, means of handling many common types of nonlinearity. Evans' root-locus method had provided a further powerful tool for the design of linear feedback systems of fairly high order, and the representation of stochastic disturbances and their effects was well established in frequency-response terms. The position had changed completely from that of the late 1920's, when the time-response methods were unchallenged. However, the pendulum of fashion was about to swing back rapidly.

The emergence of the stored-program digital computer as a reliable and widely available engineering device by the late 1950's was a necessary prerequisite for the next developments in automatic control systems analysis and design. It was now reasonable to attempt much deeper and more comprehensive studies in automatic control theory, since the computing power and versatility of the big scientific machines made the lengthy and intricate calculations involved a practicable proposition. At the same time, the development of small and reliable special-purpose digital computers offered the possibility of implementing more ambitious control schemes via information-processing devices of unprecedented computing speed and flexibility. It was a natural step, therefore, to consider the simultaneous control of a number of interacting variables, and to consider different types of controller objective, such as the minimization of fuel consumption, for which the now-classical frequency-response theory was quite inappropriate.

As with the previous major developments in automatic control theory, these next advances arose out of an important technical problem, in this case the launching, maneuvering, guidance, and tracking of space vehicles. Both in the USA and the USSR, an enormous research and development effort was expended on these problems, and from this came rapid progress. The nature of these next developments in automatic control theory was profoundly influenced by two things.

1) The fact that the objects being controlled and tracked were essentially ballistic in nature meant that accurate mechanical models of the devices being controlled were normally available. Moreover, the systems involved could be fitted with measuring devices of great precision.

2) Many of the performance criteria which the final control schemes had to satisfy were of an "economic" nature. For example, a satellite position-control scheme might have to operate in such a way that a desired maneuver was executed for the minimum expenditure of fuel. A natural result of these aspects of the related control problems was to refocus attention on an approach to control via sets of ordinary differential equations. For dynamical systems having an overall performance specification given in terms of making some functional of the behavior (performance index) achieve an extremum value there was an obvious and strong analogy with the classical variational formulations of analytical mechanics given by Lagrange and Hamilton [127]. In the USSR, Pontryagin laid the foundations of what came to be called optimal control theory by an elegant generalization of the Hamiltonian approach to geometrical optics in the form of his famous maximum principle [35], [181].

An important aspect of this treatment of multivariable control problems in terms of sets of differential equations was the systematic use of sets of first-order equations. Moigno [163] had shown that any nth-order ordinary differential equation may be reduced to an equivalent set of first-order equations by means of a set of simple substitutions, and Cauchy [48] had previously studied the conditions under which such a system of equations had a unique solution. Poincaré saw the deep significance of formulating general dynamical theories in terms of sets of first-order differential equations, and introduced the now familiar idea of considering the relevant set of dynamical system variables in terms of the trajectory of a point in an n-dimensional space. He established this approach as a standard one by building the whole of his famous treatise on celestial mechanics around it [180]. One of the first major applications of the Poincaré formulation of dynamical theory was Lyapunov's celebrated study of stability [132]. Poincaré's approach to dynamics rapidly became the standard one for control engineers working on aerospace problems with these revitalized time-domain techniques, which collectively became known as the state-space approach. The concept of state now dominates the whole of applied dynamical theory. What is fundamental about dynamical systems is that their present behavior is influenced by their past history; dynamical system behavior cannot, therefore, be specified simply in terms of "instantaneous" relationships between a set of input and a set of output variables. An extra set of variables is required whose purpose is to take into account the past history of the system; these variables are the state variables of the system. The use of state-space treatments of dynamical and feedback systems immediately led to a deeper study of the scientific and mathematical problems of automatic control than had ever before been attempted, and their introduction can be said to mark the emergence of control studies as a mature scientific discipline. Even the most cursory study of the literature of the subject will show what a profound change occurred between the mid 1950's and the late 1960's.

Pontryagin's maximum principle proved invaluable in dealing with situations where there were constraints on system inputs reflecting limitations of resources, and gave a dramatic demonstration of the power and potential of this new differential-equation-based approach. Bellman's work on dynamic programming was also concerned with the problem of dynamic optimization under constraint [19]–[22]. Bellman made clear the great usefulness of the concept of state for the formulation and solution of many problems in decision and control. It was inevitable that the linear multivariable feedback control problem would now be thoroughly examined from this point of view, and Kalman gave a definitive treatment of the linear optimal control problem with a quadratic form of performance index [108], [111]. This work had one particular feature which distinguished it from most previous studies of the feedback design problem—it gave a synthesis procedure by means of which the feedback system design was obtained directly from the problem specification [115]. This, at first sight at any rate, eliminated the trial and error procedures normally associated with feedback system design. Previous attempts had been made to treat feedback system design within an analytical framework [168] but never before had the multivariable problem been so treated. Although it can be argued that such a synthesis procedure simply shifts the burden of design decision on to the choice of performance index, there is no doubt that the emergence of this elegant and powerful synthesis solution to a multivariable feedback problem marked a new high point in the development of feedback system design procedures.

The rapidly growing importance of state-space methods led to an investigation of the relationships between state-space models and transfer function representations by Gilbert [79] and Kalman [113], and algorithms were developed for obtaining minimal-order state-space dynamical models from given transfer function matrices. Such studies led to the introduction of the fundamental structural concepts of controllability and observability [109], [79]. Certain classical dynamical ideas such as those associated with the characteristic modes of vibration of a linear dynamical system were now seen to be useful in the state-space formulation and their relevance to control ideas and problems was examined. Rosenbrock put forward the idea of modal control [192] in which the action of a feedback controller was envisaged in terms of a shift of characteristic (modal) frequency. This important and physically appealing concept eventually led to a huge literature on the problem of "pole-shifting" and its use for design purposes [82], [61], [238], [96], [210], [53], [54], [184]. Wonham [238] proved that a sufficient condition for all the closed-loop characteristic frequencies of a controllable system to be arbitrarily allocatable under feedback (within mild constraints imposed by physical considerations) is that all the states of the system are accessible. This key result further underlined and reinforced the importance of the concept of state.

The use of these revitalized time-response methods had a profound effect on control work, and made crucially important contributions to solving the guidance problems of the space program. In the research literature of automatic control frequency-response methods went into a steep decline. Even worse, from the frequency-response protagonist's point of view, was to follow. Filtering theory, at one time a seemingly impregnable bastion of frequency-response ideas, was also undergoing the state-space-method revolution. Kalman and Bucy had realized that the problem of signal recovery from corrupted measurements which, following Wiener's work, had been almost invariably attacked along a frequency-response route, was also amenable to the multivariable time-response approach [110], [41]. Because of the ease with which it handled the nonstationary case, their work led to an immediate advance in filtering technique. From the point of view of the development of general feedback theory, however, it had an especial significance, since it clearly demonstrated the basic role of feedback in filtering theory. The form of multivariable filter which emerged from their studies, the Kalman–Bucy filter, essentially consisted of a dynamical model of the message-generating signal process with multivariable feedback connected around it. This work showed that a deep and exact duality existed between the problems of multivariable feedback control and multivariable feedback filtering [109].

It was now a natural next step to put together the optimal control treatment of a deterministic linear plant, whose performance is specified in terms of a quadratic cost function, with the Kalman–Bucy filtering method of extracting state estimates from observations corrupted by Gaussian noise processes. Thus emerged the standard treatment of the "LQG" (linear-quadratic-Gaussian) optimal control problem [7] which became the linch-pin of the state-space treatment of multivariable control, and which was treated in many standard textbooks [6], [129], [40], [116], [201]. The key ideas of the LQG problem and its background, and an excellent survey of the relevant literature up to 1970, are given in [245] which was devoted to this topic.

The Development of a Frequency-Response Approach to Multivariable Problems

Optimal feedback control and optimal feedback filtering theory had such a great success when applied to aerospace problems that this naturally led to attempts to apply these techniques to a wide range of earth-bound industrial processes. It soon became clear that they were less than immediately applicable in many such cases, principally because the plant models available were not sufficiently accurate, and the performance indices required to stipulate the desired controlled plant behavior were much less obvious in form than in the aerospace context. Moreover, the controller which resulted from a direct application of optimal control and optimal filtering synthesis techniques was in general a complicated one; in fact, if it incorporated a full Kalman–Bucy filter, it would have a dynamical complexity equal to that of the plant it was controlling, since the filter essentially consisted of a plant model with feedback around it. What was needed for many process control problems was a relatively simple controller which would stabilize a plant, for which only a very approximate model might be available, about an operating point and which would have some integral action in order to mitigate the effect of low-frequency disturbances. The sophisticated optimal control methods proved difficult to use by industrial engineers brought up on frequency-response ideas who essentially needed to use a mixture of physical insight and straightforward techniques, such as the use of integral and derivative action, to solve their problems. For these reasons an interest in frequency-response methods slowly began to revive. It was obvious that a huge gap in techniques existed between the classical single-loop frequency-response methods, which were still in use for many industrial applications, and the elegant and powerful multivariable time-response methods developed for aerospace applications.

An important first step towards closing the yawning gap between an optimal control approach and the classical frequency-response approach was taken by Kalman [112] who studied the frequency-domain characterization of optimality. A systematic attack on the whole problem of developing a frequency-response analysis and design theory for multivariable feedback systems was begun in a pioneering paper by Rosenbrock [193] which ushered in a decade of increasing interest in a rejuvenated frequency-response approach. Prior to this new point-of-departure, some fairly straightforward work had been done on the multivariable control problem. Boksenbom and Hood [34] put forward the idea of a noninteracting controller. Their procedure consisted simply of choosing a cascaded compensator of such type that the overall transfer function matrix of the compensated system had a diagonal form. If such a compensator could be found then the controller design could be finished off using standard single-loop design techniques. The required compensating matrix usually arising from such a procedure is necessarily a complicated one, and the most succinct objection to this approach is simply that it is not necessary to go to such drastic lengths merely to reduce interaction. A natural further step in this initial approach to multivariable control was to see what could be achieved by way of standard matrix calculations using rational matrices; papers studying the problem in this way were produced by Golomb and Usdin [81], Raymond [190], Kavanagh [117]–[119], and Freeman [70], [71]. Rosenbrock, however, opened up a completely new line of development by seeking to reduce a multivariable problem to one amenable to classical techniques in a more sophisticated way. In his inverse Nyquist array design method [194] the aim was to *reduce* interaction to an amount which would then enable single-loop techniques to be employed, rather than to eliminate it completely. The Rosenbrock approach was based upon a careful use of a specific criterion of partial interaction, the diagonal dominance concept. The success of his inverse Nyquist array method led other investigators to develop ways of reducing the multivariable design problem to an eventual succession of single-loop problems [151].

In the noninteracting, or partially noninteracting, approach to multivariable control the motivation was the eventual deployment of classical single-loop frequency-response techniques during the final stages of a design study. An alternative approach, however, is to investigate the transfer-function matrix representation as a single object in its own right and to ask: how can the key basic concepts of the classical single-loop approach be suitably extended? What are the relevant generalizations to the multivariable case of the specific concepts of pole, zero, Nyquist diagram, and root-locus diagram and, further, what essentially new frequency-domain ideas can be developed in the multivariable context? It soon emerged that there was no single line of attack suitable for finding the answer to such very deep and far-reaching questions. The various aspects of the main research lines which developed can be conveniently labeled as the algebraic, geometric, and complex-variable approaches.

The algebraic approach developed from further studies of the relationships between state-space and frequency-response representations and of the problem of generalizing the concepts of pole and zero to the multivariable case. In his study of the minimal realization problem, Kalman [113] had made use of McMillan's canonical form [155] for a rational transfer-function matrix. The so-called Smith–McMillan form was used by Rosenbrock in his treatment of multivariable zeros [195], [196], [198]. Rosenbrock gave a particularly comprehensive treatment of the multivariable zero problem as a part of his important and pioneering work on an algebraic theory of linear dynamical systems. In this work he made a systematic use of a particular polynomial matrix representation which he called the system matrix [195]. These studies by Kalman and Rosenbrock showed the great power and relevance of algebraic theories for fundamental studies of the linear multivariable control problem, and they were soon followed by a strong and sustained research effort on the algebraic approach. Surveys of work on algebraic systems theory have been given by Barnett [12] and Sain [203]. Kalman's work has shown the importance of using module theory in the algebraic approach to dynamical systems; from the mathematical point of view this leads to a particularly "clean" treatment [114], [116].

The central role of a system's state in discussing its feedback control had been established by its part in optimal control theory and by Wonham's pole-shifting theorem. Kalman and Bucy had shown how to estimate unknown states from noise-corrupted system outputs. It was thus natural to seek ways of using system model information to recover inaccessible system states from the uncorrupted outputs of deterministic dynamical systems, and Luenberger [136]–[138] introduced the use of observers for this purpose. The idea had been emerging of separating a feedback problem into the two steps of 1) working out what to do if a system's state was completely accessible, and 2) devising a means of estimating the system's inaccessible states from the information contained in its accessible outputs. In the stochastic linear optimization problem a certainty-equivalence principle had been established [102], [239], [236], [13] which had shown that the stochastic optimal control problem could indeed be solved in this way. A similar sort of "separation principle" was established for the problem of pole-shifting using an observer: the same closed-loop poles are obtained using an observer (constructed with perfect plant model information) as would have been obtained if all the system's states had been available for feedback purposes [52]. These results and ideas led naturally to a deeper study of the problems of dynamic compensation [36], [237] which further closed the gap between the classical frequency-response methods and those of what was (unfortunately) becoming known as "modern" control theory.

A linear vector space approach to control problems obviously has geometrical as well as algebraic aspects. Wonham and Morse [240] carried out a definitive and far-ranging study of the geometrical treatment of multivariable control problems, which culminated in Wonham's elegant and important book on this topic [241]. This definitive text opened up a whole new prospect for control studies. In this work the dynamical significance of certain classes of subspaces of the state space plays a key role, and investigations of such topics as decoupling is carried out in a crisp and intuitively appealing way. Independent studies of a geometrical approach were carried out by Basile and Marro [14]–[17]. It seems clear that the geometrical theory has a key role to play in bringing together state-space and frequency-response approaches to the multivariable case [147].

Yet another line of approach to the multivariable feedback problem arises from the observation that the classical Nyquist–Bode–Evans formulation of the single-loop case is based on complex-variable theory. Surely, it was thought, complex-variable ideas must have a role to play in the multivariable context, particularly when the algebraic studies had shown how to extend to the multivariable case such basic complex-variable concepts as poles and zeros. An early attempt to extend Nyquist diagram ideas to the multivariable problem was made by Bohn [32], [33]. In a series of papers MacFarlane and his collaborators demonstrated that algebraic functions could be used to deploy complex variable theory in the multivariable feedback context [141]–[146]. It was shown that the poles and zeros associated with transfer-function matrices by algebraic means, via the Smith–McMillan form for a matrix of rational transfer functions, were related to the poles and zeros of an appropriate function of a complex variable. This line of investigation in turn led to a generalization of the classical Nyquist stability criterion to the multivariable case [141]. Following earlier heuristic treatments of this generalization, complex-variable proofs were provided by Barman and Katzenelson [11] and MacFarlane and Postlethwaite [142]. The generalization of the Nyquist stability criterion to the multivariable situation was soon followed by complementary generalizations of the root locus technique [121], [142], [143], [185], [145].

Together with these counter-revolutionary developments of the classical frequency-response approaches came an increasing interest in the existence of links between state-space models and methods and the various algebraic, geometric, and complex-variable techniques and results. It was discovered that deep and important links existed between the poles, zeros, and root-locus asymptotes of the complex-variable characterizations and the basic operators of a state-space description [145]. These findings emphasized the deep significance for control studies of the algebraic and geometric approaches which were being so rapidly developed.

Since much of the motivation for work on frequency-response methods arose from the need to develop robust design methods for plants described in terms of models derived from sketchy experimental data, a number of different design approaches in the frequency domain began to emerge. Many of these techniques were conceived in terms of interactive graphical working, where the designer interacts with a computer-driven display [198]. As such, they placed great stress on the insight and intuition which could be deployed by an experienced designer; this was in great contrast to the specification-and-synthesis approach which had been the hallmark of the optimal control solution.

Many of these approaches naturally sought to capitalize on the experience and insight existing for single-loop frequency-response designs. The most straightforward way to do this is to somehow reduce a multivariable design problem to a set of separate single-loop design problems. In Rosenbrock's inverse Nyquist array method [194], [198], [165] this was done by using a compensator to first make the system diagonally-dominant. A careful use of this specific form of criterion of partial noninteraction enabled the stability and performance of the closed-loop system to be inferred from its diagonal transmittances alone, and hence enabled a multivariable design to be completed using single-loop techniques. Mayne's sequential return difference method [151] took a different line of approach to the deployment of single-loop techniques. It was built around a series of formulas for the transmittance seen between an input and output of a feedback system, having one particular feedback loop opened, when all the other feedback loop gains were made large. Providing that one could find a suitable place to start, this enabled the designer to proceed to design one loop at a time, and give it a suitably high value of loop gain before proceeding to the next one.

Other investigators were less concerned with the direct deployment of single-loop techniques and looked for ways of using the generalized Nyquist and root-locus results as the basis of design methods. MacFarlane and Kouvaritakis [144] developed a design approach based on a manipulation of the frequency-dependent eigenvalues and eigenvectors of a transfer function matrix. This line of attack was later extended to handle the general case of a plant having a differing number of inputs and outputs by incorporating a state-space-based root-locus approach as an integral part of the overall procedure [145].

The interest and importance of the multivariable control problem generated a wide range of other investigations. Owens [174]–[176] studied ways of expanding transfer function matrices as sums of dyads and developed a design approach on this basis. Wolovich developed multivariable frequency-response approaches to compensation, decoupling, and pole placement [237]. Sain investigated design methods based on transfer-function matrix factorization and polynomial matrix manipulation [202], [78], [177]. Bengtsson used geometrical ideas in the spirit of Wonham's work to devise a multivariable design approach [23]. Davison made extensive investigations of the multivariable control problem and developed an approach which, although state-space based, was in the same engineering spirit as the more frequency-biased work. His studies emphasized the importance of robustness to parameter variation [55]–[58]. Youla and Bongiorno extended the analytical feedback design technique developed by Newton [168] to the multivariable case [242].

As the broad outlines of the frequency-response theory of linear multivariable control systems began to emerge, interest rose in the appropriate extensions of nonlinear criteria such as the describing function and circle criterion, and work to this end was started by several workers [224], [157], [197], [50], [8], [189], [158].

Multidimensional Filtering

The need to enhance the quality of pictures transmitted back to earth from exploring satellites and space probes resulted in work on the "multidimensional" filtering of video signals, that is on their simultaneous processing in more than one spatial dimension. This further generalization of the problem of dynamic filtering led to a study of the stability of multidimensional feedback filters, and this in turn led to an appropriate extension of frequency-domain techniques, including that of determining closed-loop stability via Nyquist-type criteria. Jury [107] has given a very comprehensive survey of work in this area.

Epilogue

From our present vantage point we can attempt to put frequency-response methods into perspective. Nyquist started a completely new line of development in automatic control when he analyzed the problem of closed-loop stability from the signal-transmission viewpoint rather than the mechanistic viewpoint. In so doing he showed the engineers designing and developing feedback devices and automatic control systems how to use the powerful tools which can be forged from the theory of functions of a complex variable. His famous stability criterion had an immediate and lasting success because it related to quantities which could be directly measured and because it was expressed in terms of variables which could be immediately understood and interpreted in terms of appropriate actions to be taken to improve a feedback system's performance. The frequency-response concepts, and the immensely popular and useful design techniques based upon them, satisfied a criterion of great importance in engineering work—they enabled engineers to quickly and fluently communicate to each other the essential features of a feedback control situation. Complex-variable methods are of such power and potential that their continued use and development is surely not in doubt. Even at the height of the "state-space revolution" the classical Nyquist–Bode–Evans techniques were the workhorses of many designers for their single-loop work.

The real significance of the introduction of state-space methods is that it marked the beginning of a new, more general, more rigorous, deeper, and more far-reaching approach to automatic control. We are now beginning to see that automatic control is a vast subject, still in the early stages of development, and requiring a great breadth of approach in setting up adequate theoretical foundations. Its scope is such that no single approach, via the "time domain" or the "frequency domain" alone, is going to be sufficient for the development of adequate analysis and design techniques. What it is hoped will emerge clearly from the contents of this book is that Nyquist's ideas, and the frequency-response approach developed from them, are alive at the frontiers of current research, and that they will continue to play an indispensable role in whatever grand theoretical edifice emerges in time. Nyquist made truly outstanding contributions to engineering. He carried on a great tradition in the applied sciences going back to Fourier whose epochal work first appeared in 1811 [45], and in doing so transformed the arts of telegraph transmission and feedback systems development into exact sciences. May his spirit live on in the work collected here, and in the future developments of feedback and control.

References

[1] G. B. Airy "On the regulator of the clockwork for effecting uniform movement of equatoreals," *Mem. Roy. Astron. Soc.*, vol. 11, pp. 249–267, 1840.

[2] ——, "Supplement to a paper on the regulation of the clockwork for effecting uniform movement of equatoreals," *Mem. Roy. Astron. Soc.*, vol. 20, pp. 115–119, 1851.

[3] ——, "On a method of regulating the clockwork for equatoreals," *Monthly Notices Roy. Astron. Soc.*, vol. 11, pp. 17–18, 1851.

[4] M. A. Aizermann, "On a problem concerning the stability in the large of dynamic systems," *Usp. Mat. Nauk.*, vol. 4, pp. 187–188, 1949.

[5] A. A. Andronov, and I. N. Vosnesenskii, *The Work of J. C. Maxwell, I. A. Vyschnegradsky and A. Stodola in the Theory of Machine Control* (in Russian), A. A. Andronov. Moscow: Sobranie Trudov, Izdat ANSSSR, 1956, pp. 473–521.

[6] M. Athans and P. L. Falb, *Optimal Control.* New York: McGraw-Hill, 1966.

[7] M. Athans, "The role and use of the stochastic linear-quadratic-Gaussian problem in control system design," *IEEE Trans. Automat. Contr.*, vol. AC-16, pp. 529–551, 1971.

[8] D. P. Atherton, *Nonlinear Control Engineering.* London, England: Van Nostrand Reinhold, 1975.

[9] H. Barkhausen, *Das Problem der Schwingungserzeugung.* Leipzig, 1907.

[10] ——, *Lehrbuch der Elektronenrohren.* Leipzig: Hirzel, 1921.

[11] J. F. Barman and J. Katzenelson, "A generalized Nyquist-type stability criterion for multivariable feedback systems," *Int. J. Contr.*, vol. 20, pp. 593–622, 1974.

[12] S. Barnett, "Some topics in algebraic systems theory: A survey," *Int. J. Contr.*, vol. 19, pp. 669–688, 1974.

[13] Y. Bar-Shalom and E. Tse, "Dual effect, certainty equivalence, and separation in stochastic control," *IEEE Trans. Automat. Contr.*, vol. AC-19, pp. 494–500, 1974.

[14] G. Basile and G. Marro, "Luoghi caratteristici delo spazio degli stati relativi al controllo dei sistemi lineari," *L'Ettrotechnica*, vol. 55, no. 12, pp. 1–7, 1968.

[15] ——, "Controlled and conditioned invariant subspaces in linear system theory," *J. Opt. Theory Appl.*, vol. 3, no. 5, pp. 306–315, 1969.

[16] ——, "On the observability of linear time-invariant systems with unknown inputs," *J. Opt. Theory Appl.*, vol. 3, no. 6, pp. 410–415, 1969.

[17] ——, "A state space approach to non-interacting controls," *Ricerche di Automatica*, vol. 1, pp. 68–77, 1970.

[18] R. W. Bass, "Equivalent linearization, nonlinear circuit synthesis and the stabilization and optimization of control systems," in *Proc. Symp. Nonlinear Circuit Anal.*, Polytech. Inst. of Brooklyn, M.R.I. ser., New York, 1956, pp. 163–198. ——, "Mathematical legitimacy of equivalent linearization for describing function," in *Proc. 1st IFAC Congr.*, Moscow, Butterworths, London, vol. 2, 1961, pp. 895–905.

[19] R. Bellman, "The theory of dynamic programming," *Bull. Amer. Math. Soc.*, vol. 60, pp. 503–516, 1954.

[20] ——, "On the application of the theory of dynamic programming to the study of control processes," in *Proceedings of the Symposium on Nonlinear Circuit Analysis.* New York: Polytechnic Inst. of Brooklyn Press, 1956, pp. 199–213.

[21] ——, *Dynamic Programming.* Princeton, NJ: Princeton Univ. Press, 1957.

[22] ——, *Adaptive Control Processes: A Guided Tour.* Princeton, NJ: Princeton Univ. Press, 1961.

[23] G. Bengtsson, "A theory for control of linear multivariable systems," Division of Automat. Contr., Lund Inst. Tech., Rep. 7341, 1973.

[24] S. Bennett, "The emergence of a discipline: Automatic control 1940–1960," *Automatica*, vol. 12, pp. 113–121, 1976.

[25] A. R. Bergen and R. L. Franks, "Justification of the describing function method," *SIAM J. Contr.*, vol. 9, no. 4, pp. 568–589, 1971.

[26] P. Bethell, "The development of the torpedo," *Engineering*, vol. 160, pp. 4–5, 1946.

[27] H. S. Black, "Stabilized feedback amplifiers," *Bell Syst. Tech. J.*, vol. 13, pp. 1–18, 1934.

[28] ——, "Inventing the negative feedback amplifier," *IEEE Spectrum*, vol. 14, pp. 54–60, 1977.

[29] O. Bloch, "Die Ortskurven der graphischen Elektrotechnik, nach einheitlicher Methode behandelt," dissertation, ETH, Zürich, 1917.

[30] H. W. Bode, "Relations between attenuation and phase in feedback amplifier design," *Bell Syst. Tech. J.*, vol. 19, pp. 421–454, 1940.

[31] ——, *Network Analysis and Feedback Amplifier Design.* Princeton, NJ: Van Nostrand, 1945.

[32] E. V. Bohn, "Design and synthesis methods for a class of multivariable feedback control systems based on single variable methods," *AIEE Trans.*, vol. 81, part II, pp. 109–115, 1962.

[33] E. V. Bohn and T. Kasvand, "Use of matrix transformations and system eigenvalues in the design of linear multivariable control systems," *Proc. IEE*, vol. 110, pp. 989–997, 1963.

[34] A. S. Boksenbom and R. Hood, "General algebraic method applied to control analysis of complex engine types," Nat. Advisory Committee for Aeronautics, Washington, DC, Rep. NCA-TR-980, 1949.

[35] V. Boltyanskii, R. Gamkrelidze, and L. S. Pontryagin, "On the theory of optimal processes," *Rep. Acad. Sci. USSR*, vol. 110, no. 1, pp. 7–10. Trans. in *Selected Papers on Mathematical Trends in Control Theory*, R. Bellman and K. Kalaba, Eds. New York: Dover, 1964.

[36] F. M. Brasch and J. B. Pearson, "Pole placement using dynamic compensators," *IEEE Trans. Automat. Contr.* vol. AC-15, part 1, pp. 34–43, 1970.

[37] T. J. Bromwich, "Normal co-ordinates in dynamical systems," *Proc. London Math. Soc.*, vol. 15, pp. 401–448, 1916.

[38] G. S. Brown, "Behaviour and design of servomechanisms," report privately printed under the auspices of the Fire Contr. Committee (Sec. D-2) of the Nat. Defence Res. Committee.

[39] G. S. Brown and A. C. Hall, "Dynamic behaviour and design of servomechanisms," *Trans. ASME*, vol. 68, pp. 503–524, 1946.

[40] A. E. Bryson and Y. C. Ho, *Applied Optimal Control.* Waltham, MA: Blaisdell, 1969.

[41] R. S. Bucy and P. Joseph, *Filtering for Stochastic Processes with Applications to Guidance.* New York: Wiley-Interscience, 1968.

[42] A. Callendar, D. R. Hartree, and A. Porter, "Time lag in a control system," *Phil. Trans. Roy. Soc. London*, vol. 235A, pp. 415–444, 1936.

[43] G. A. Campbell, *AIEE Trans.*, vol. 38, pp. 873, 1911.

[44] G. A. Campbell and R. M. Foster, "Fourier integrals for practical applications," Bell Telephone Syst. monograph B-584, NY, 1931.

[45] H. S. Carslaw, *Fourier's Series and Integrals*, 3rd ed. London, 1930.

[46] J. R. Carson, "The Heaviside operational calculus," *Bell Syst. Tech. J.*, vol. 1, p. 43, 1922.

[47] ——, *Electrical Circuit Theory and the Operational Calculus.* New York: McGraw-Hill, 1926.

[48] A. Cauchy, Comptes rendus acad. science, Paris, 14, 1020 and 15, 14, 1842.

[49] H. Chestnut and R. Meyer, *Servomechanisms and Regulating System Design*, vol. I, II. New York: Wiley, 1951, 1955.

[50] P. A. Cook, *Modified Multivariable Circle Theorems in Recent Mathematical Developments in Control*, D. J. Bell, Ed. London: Academic, 1973.

[51] L. Cremer, "Ein neues Verfahren zur Beurteilung der Stabilität linearer Regelungs-systeme," *Z. Angew. Math. Mech.*, vol. 25–27, 5/6, (quoted by Gille *et al.*, p. 175).

[52] J. B. Cruz, *Feedback Systems.* New York: McGraw-Hill, 1972.

[53] E. J. Davison, "On pole assignment in multivariable linear systems," *IEEE Trans. Automat. Contr.*, vol. AC-13, pp. 747–748, 1968.

[54] E. J. Davison and H. W. Smith, "Pole assignment in linear time-invariant multivariable systems with constant disturbances," *Automatica*, vol. 7, pp. 489–498, 1971.

[55] E. J. Davison and A. Goldenberg, "Robust control of a general servomechanism problem: The servocompensator," *Automatica*, vol. 11, no. 5, pp. 461–472, 1975.

[56] E. J. Davison, "Multivariable tuning regulators: The feedforward and robust control of a general servomechanism problem," *IEEE Trans. Automat. Contr.*, vol. AC-21, pp. 35–47, 1976.

[57] ——, "The robust decentralized control of a general servomechanism problem," *IEEE Trans. Automat. Contr.*, vol. AC-21, pp. 14–24, 1976.

[58] ——, "Steady-state invertibility and feedforward control of linear time-invariant systems," *IEEE Trans. Automat. Contr.*, vol. AC-21, pp. 529–534, 1976.

[59] G. Doetsch, *Theorie und Anwendung der Laplace-Transformation.* Berlin: Springer, 1937.

[60] J. Dutilh, "Theorie des servomechanisms a relais," *Onde Elec.*, pp. 438–445, 1950.

[61] J. K. Ellis and G. W. T. White, "An introduction to modal analysis and control," *Control*, vol. 9, no. 82, pp. 193–197; no. 83, pp. 252–266; no. 84, pp. 317–321, 1965.

[62] W. R. Evans, "Graphical analysis of control systems," *AIEE Trans.*, vol. 67, pp. 547–551, 1948.

[63] ——, "Control system synthesis by root locus method," *AIEE Trans.*, vol. 69, pp. 1–4, 1950.

[64] ——, *Control System Dynamics.* New York: McGraw-Hill, 1953.

[65] J. Farcot, *Le Servo-Moteur on Moteur Asservi.* Paris: Baudrey, 1873.

[66] R. Feiss, "Untersuchung der Stabilität von Regulierungen anhand des Vektorbildes," dissertation, ETH Zurich, 1939.
[67] ——, "Regenerations theorie und Stabilität von Regulierungen," *Schweiz. Bauzeitung*, vol. 115, pp. 97–99, 1940.
[68] ——, "Eine neue Methode zur Bestimmung der Stabilitat von Regulierungen," *Schweiz. Beuzeitung*, vol. 118, pp. 61–65, 1941.
[69] E. B. Ferrell, "The servo problem as a transmission problem," *Proc. IRE*, vol. 33, pp. 763–767, 1945.
[70] H. Freeman, "A synthesis method for multipole control systems," *AIEE Trans.*, vol. 76, pp. 28–31, 1957.
[71] ——, "Stability and physical realizability considerations in the synthesis of multipole control systems," *AIEE Trans.*, part 2, vol. 77, pp. 1–15, 1958.
[72] ——, *Discrete-Time Systems*. New York: Wiley, 1965.
[73] W. Frey, "A generalization of the Nyquist and Leonhard stability criteria," *Brown Boveri Rev.*, vol. 33, pp. 59–65, 1946.
[74] A. T. Fuller, Ed., *Stability of Motion*. London: Taylor and Francis, 1975.
[75] A. T. Fuller, "The early development of control theory," *Trans. ASME, J. Dynamic Syst., Meas. Contr.*, vol. 98, pp. 109–118, 1976.
[76] ——, "The early development of control theory II," *Trans. ASME, J. Dynamic Syst., Meas. Contr.*, vol. 98, pp. 224–235, 1976.
[77] M. F. Gardner and J. L. Barnes, *Transients in Linear Systems*, vol. I. New York: Wiley, 1942.
[78] R. R. Gejji and M. K. Sain, "Application of polynomial techniques to multivariable control of jet engines," Preprints of Fourth IFAC Symp. Multivariable Technol. Syst., Fredericton, N.B., 1977.
[79] E. G. Gilbert, "Controllability and observability in multivariable control systems," *J. Siam Contr.*, ser. A, vol. 1, no. 2, pp. 128–151, 1963.
[80] L. C. Goldfarb, "On some nonlinear phenomena in regulatory system," *Avtomat. Telemech.* pp. 349–383, Trans. in *Frequency Response*, R. Oldenburger, Ed. New York: Macmillan, 1956.
[81] M. Golomb and E. Usdin, "A theory of multidimensional servo systems," *J. Franklin Inst.*, vol. 253, no. 1, pp. 28–57, 1952.
[82] M. R. Gordon-Clark, "A novel approach to the control of dynamically unfavorable processes," *IEEE Trans. Automat. Contr.*, vol. AC-9, pp. 411–419, 1964.
[83] R. E. Graham, "Linear servo theory," *Bell Syst. Tech. J.*, vol. 25, pp. 616–651, 1946.
[84] E. Gray, *The Devil's Device: The Story of Robert Whitehead, Inventor of the Torpedo*. London: Seeley, 1975.
[85] A. C. Hall, *The Analysis and Synthesis of Linear Servomechanisms*. Cambridge, MA: MIT Tech. Press, 1943.
[86] ——, "Application of circuit theory to the design of servomechanisms," *J. Franklin Inst.*, vol. 242, pp. 279–307, 1946.
[87] H. Harris, "The analysis and design of servomechanisms," OSRD Rep. No. 454, 1942.
[88] H. Harris, Jr. "The frequency response of automatic control systems," *AIEE Trans.*, vol. 65, pp. 539–546, 1946.
[89] D. R. Hartree, A. Porter, A. Callendar, and A. B. Stephenson, "Time lag in a controll system—II," *Proc. Roy. Soc. London*, vol. 161 A, pp. 460–476, 1937.
[90] H. L. Hazen, "Theory of servomechanisms," *J. Franklin Inst.*, vol. 218, pp. 279–331, 1934.
[91] N. Heathcote, *Nobel Prize Winners in Physics* 1901–1950. New York: Schuman, 1953.
[92] O. Heaviside, *Electromagnetic Theory*. London, 1899.
[93] J. B. Henderson, "On the application of hydraulic machinery to the loading, discharging, steering and working of steamships," *Trans. Inst. Nav. Arch.*, pp. 153ff, 1884.
[94] C. Hermite, "Sur le nombre des racines d'une equation algebrique comprise entre des limites donees," *J. Reine Angew. Math.*, vol. 52, pp. 39–51, 1854.
[95] S. W. Herwald, "Considerations in servomechanisms design," *AIEE Trans.*, vol. 63, pp. 871–876, 1944.
[96] M. Heymann, "Pole assignment in multi-input linear systems," *IEEE Trans. Automat. Contr.*, vol. AC-13, no. 6, pp. 748–749, 1968.
[97] P. M. Honnell, "The generalized transmission matrix stability criterion," *AIEE Trans.*, vol. 70, pp. 292–298, 1951.
[98] W. Hort, "Die Entwicklung des Problems der stetigen Kraftmaschinen—Regelung nebst einem Versuch der Theorie unstetiger Regelungsvorgänge," *Zeitschrift Math. Phys.*, vol. 50, pp. 233–279, 1904.
[99] A. Hurwitz, "Uber die Bedingungen, unter welchen eine Gleichung nur Wurzelm mit negativen reelen Teilen besitzt," *Math. Annalen*, pp. 273–284, 1895.
[100] A. Ivanoff, "Theoretical foundations of the automatic regulation of temperature," *J. Inst. Fuel*, vol. 7, pp. 117–138, 1934.
[101] H. M. James, N. B. Nicholls, and R. S. Phillips, *Theory of Servomechanisms*. New York: McGraw-Hill, 1947.
[102] P. D. Joseph and J. Tou, "On linear control theory," *AIEE Trans.*, vol. 80, pp. 193–196, 1961.
[103] E. I. Jury, "Analysis and synthesis of sampled-data control systems," *AIEE Trans.*, vol. 73, pp. 332–346, 1954.
[104] ——, *Sampled-Data Control Systems*. New York: Wiley, 1958.
[105] ——, *Theory and Application of the z-Transform Method*. New York: Wiley, 1964.
[106] ——, "Stability tests for one-, two- and multidimensional linear systems," *Proc. IEE*, vol. 124, pp. 1237–1240, 1977.
[107] ——, "Stability of multidimensional scalar and matrix polynomials," *Proc. IEEE*, vol. 66, no. 9, pp. 1018–1048, 1978.
[108] R. E. Kalman, "Contributions to the theory of optimal control," *Bol. Soc. Math. Mexicana*, vol. 5, pp. 102–119, 1960.
[109] ——, "On the general theory of control systems," in *Proceedings of the First IFAC Congress in Moscow*, vol. 1. London: Butterworth, pp. 481–492, 1960.
[110] R. E. Kalman and R. S. Bucy, "New results in linear filtering and prediction theory," *Trans. ASME J. Basic Eng.*, vol. 83, ser. D, pp. 95–108, 1961.
[111] R. E. Kalman, "The theory of optimal control and the calculus of variations," in *Mathematical Optimization Techniques*, R. Bellman, Ed. Berkeley, CA: Univ. of California Press, 1963.
[112] ——, "When is a linear control system optimal?" *J. Basic Eng.*, ser. D., vol. 86, pp. 51–60, 1964.
[113] ——, "Irreducible realizations and the degree of a rational matrix," *J. SIAM Contr.*, vol. 13, pp. 520–544, 1965.
[114] ——, "Algebraic structure of linear dynamical systems—I: The Module of Σ," *Proc. Nat. Acad. Sci. U.S.*, vol. 54, pp. 1503–1508, 1965.
[115] R. E. Kalman and T. Englar, "ASP—The automatic synthesis program (program C)," NASA Contractor Rep. CR-475, 1966.
[116] R. E. Kalman, P. L. Falb, and M. A. Arbib, *Topics in Mathematical Systems Theory*. New York: McGraw-Hill, 1969.
[117] R. J. Kavanagh, "Noninteraction in linear multivariable systems," *AIEE Trans.* vol. 76, pp. 95–100, 1957.
[118] ——, "The application of matrix methods to multivariable control systems," *J. Franklin Inst.*, vol. 262, pp. 349–367, 1957.
[119] ——, "Multivariable control system synthesis," *AIEE Trans.*, part 2, vol. 77, pp. 425–429, 1958.
[120] R. J. Kochenburger, "A frequency response method for analysing and synthesising contactor servomechanisms," *AIEE Trans.*, vol. 69, pp. 270–283, 1950.
[121] B. Kouvaritakis and U. Shaked, "Asymptotic behaviour of root loci of linear multivariable systems," *Int. J. Contr.*, vol. 23, pp. 297–340, 1976.
[122] N. Krylov and N. Bogoliubov, *Introduction to Nonlinear Mechanics*. Princeton, NJ: Princeton Univ. Press, 1943.
[123] J. Kudrewicz, "Theorems on the existence of periodic vibrations," in *Proc. Fourth IFAC Congr.*, Warsaw, Sect. 4.1, pp. 46–60, 1969.
[124] K. Küpfmüller, "Uber Beziehungen zwischen Frequenzcharakteristiken und Ausgleichsvorgangen in linearen Systemen," *Elekt. Nachrichten tech*, vol. 5, pp. 18–32, 1928.
[125] ——, "Die Dynamik der selbsttätigen Verstarkungsregler," *Elekt. Nachrichtentech.*, vol. 5, p. 459, 1928.
[126] ——, *Theoretische Elecktrotechnik*. Berlin, 1941.
[127] C. Lanczos, *The Variational Principles of Mechanics*. Toronto, Canada: Univ. of Toronto Press, 1960.
[128] Y. W. Lee, "Synthesis of electrical networks by means of Fourier transforms of Laguerre's functions," *J. Math. Phys.*, vol. 11, pp. 83–113, 1932.
[129] E. B. Lee and L. Markus, *Foundations of Optimal Control Theory*. New York: Wiley, 1967.
[130] A. Leonhard, *Die selbsttätige Regelung in der Elektrotechnik*. Berlin: Springer, 1940.
[131] ——, "Neues Verfahren zur Stabilitatsuntersuchung," *Arch. Elektrotech.* vol. 38, pp. 17–28, 1944.
[132] A. M. Liapunov, "Probleme generale de la stabilite du mouvement," *Annales de la Faculte des Sciences de Toulouse*, 1907, reprinted as *Annals of Mathematics Study No.* 17. Princeton, NJ: Princeton Univ. Press, 1947.
[133] M. Lincke, "Das mechanische Relais," *VDI-Zeitschrift*, 1879.
[134] W. K. Linvill, "Sampled-data control systems studied through comparison of sampling with amplitude modulation," *AIEE Trans.*, vol. 70, part II, pp. 1779–1788, 1951.
[135] E. H. Ludwig, "Die Stabilisierung von Regelanordnungen mit Röhrenverstärkern durch Dämpfung oder elastische Rückführung," *Arch. Elektrotech.*, vol. 34, 269ff, 1940.
[136] D. G. Luenberger, "Observing the state of a linear system," *IEEE Trans. Mil. Electron.*, vol. MIL-8, pp. 74–80, 1964.
[137] ——, "Observers for multivariable systems," *IEEE Trans. Automat. Contr.*, vol. AC-11, pp. 190–197, 1966.
[138] ——, "An introduction to observers," *IEEE Trans. Automat. Contr.*, vol. AC-16, pp. 596–602, 1971.
[139] L. A. MacColl, "The analysis and synthesis of linear servomechanisms," NRDC Rep., Sec. D-2 Fire Control.

[140] ——, *Fundamental Theory of Servomechanisms*. New York: Van Nostrand, 1945.

[141] A. G. J. MacFarlane, "The return-difference and return-ratio matrices and their use in the analysis and design of multivariable feedback control systems," *Proc. Inst. Elec. Eng.*, vol. 117, pp. 2037–2049, 1970.

[142] A. G. J. MacFarlane and I. Postlethwaite, "The generalized Nyquist stability criterion and multivariable root loci," *Int. J. Contr.*, vol. 25, pp. 81–127, 1977.

[143] ——, "Characteristic frequency functions and characteristic gain functions," *Int. J. Contr.* vol. 26, pp. 265–278, 1977.

[144] A. G. J. MacFarlane and B. Kouvaritakis, "A design technique for linear multivariable feedback systems," *Int. J. Contr.*, vol. 25, pp. 837–874, 1977.

[145] A. G. J. MacFarlane, B. Kouvaritakis, and J. M. Edmunds, "Complex variable methods for multivariable feedback systems analysis and design," in *Proc. Alternatives for Linear Multivariable Contr.*, Nat. Eng. Consortium, Chicago, IL, 1977, pp. 189–228.

[146] A. G. J. MacFarlane and I. Postlethwaite, "Extended principle of the argument," *Int. J. Contr.*, vol. 27, pp. 49–55, 1978.

[147] A. G. J. MacFarlane and N. Karcanias, "Relationships between state-space and frequency-response concepts," *Proc. Seventh IFAC World Congr.*, Preprints, vol. 3, 1978, pp. 1771–1779.

[148] H. T. Marcy, Parallel circuits in servomechanisms, *AIEE Trans.*, vol. 65, p. 521, 1946.

[149] G. Marie, "Etude comparee des regulateurs de vitesse, de pression, de temperature," *Annls. Mines*, 7th ser., vol. 14, pp. 450–548, 1878.

[150] J. C. Maxwell, "On governors," *Proc. Roy. Soc. London*, vol. 16, pp. 270–283, 1868.

[151] D. Q. Mayne, "The design of linear multivariable systems," *Automatica*, vol. 9, pp. 201–207, 1973.

[152] O. Mayr, *The Origins of Feedback Control*. Cambridge, MA: MIT Press, 1970.

[153] ——, "Victorian physicists and speed regulation: An encounter between science and technology," *Notes and Rec. Roy. Soc. London*, vol. 26, pp. 205–228, 1971.

[154] ——, "Maxwell and the origins of cybernetics," *Isis*, vol. 62, pp. 424–444, 1971.

[155] B. McMillan, "Introduction to formal realizability theory," *Bell Syst. Tech. J.*, vol. 31, pp. 217–279, 541–600, 1952.

[156] A. I. Mees, "The describing function matrix," *J. Inst. Math. Appl.*, vol. 10, pp. 49–67, 1972.

[157] ——, "Describing functions, circle criteria and multiple-loop feedback systems," *Proc. Inst. Elec. Eng.*, vol. 120, pp. 126–130, 1973.

[158] A. I. Mees and P. E. Rapp, "Stability criteria for multiple-loop nonlinear feedback systems," *Proc. Fourth IFAC Symp. Multivariable Tech. Syst.*, Fredericton, N.B., 1977.

[159] A. V. Mikhailov, "Methods for harmonic analysis in the automatic control system theory" (in Russian), *Avtomat. Telemekh.*, vol. 3, p. 27, 1938.

[160] ——, "Stability theory of linear feedback circuit with lumped parameters" (in Russian), *J. Tech. Phys.*, vol. 1, pp. 20–31, 1939.

[161] N. Minorsky, "Directional stability of automatically steered bodies, *J. Amer. Soc. Naval Eng.*, vol. 42, pp. 280–309, 1922.

[162] ——, "Automatic steering tests," *J. Amer. Soc. Naval Eng.*, vol. 42, pp. 285–310, 1930.

[163] F. L. N. M. Moigno, *Lecons de Calcul d'apres Cauchy*. Paris, 1844.

[164] H. G. Moller, *Die Elektronenröhren und ihre Technischen Anwendungen*. Braunschweig: Vieweg, 1920.

[165] N. Munro, "Design of controllers for open-loop unstable multivariable system using inverse Nyquist array," *Proc. Inst. Elec. Eng.*, vol. 119, pp. 1377–1382, 1972.

[166] K. S. Narendra and J. H. Taylor, *Frequency Domain Criteria for Absolute Stability*. New York: Academic, 1973.

[167] B. N. Naumov and Y. Z. Tsypkin, "Frequency criterion for process absolute stability in nonlinear automatic control system" (in Russian), *Avtomat. Telemekh.*, vol. 25, no. 6, pp. 852–866, 1964.

[168] G. C. Newton, Jr., L. A. Gould, and J. Kaiser, *Analytical Design of Linear Feedback Controls*. New York: Wiley, 1957.

[169] H. Nyquist, "Regeneration theory," *Bell Syst. Tech. J.*, vol. 11, pp. 126–147, 1932.

[170] ——, in *Frequency Response*, R. Oldenburger, Ed. New York: MacMillan, 1956.

[171] R. C. Oldenbourg and H. Sartorius, *Dynamik Selbsttätiger Regelungen*. Munich: Oldenbourg, 1944.

[172] R. Oldenburger, *Frequency Response*. New York: MacMillan, 1956.

[173] W. Oppelt, "Locus curve method for regulators with friction," *Z. Deut. Ingr. Berlin*, vol. 90, pp. 179–183, 1948, trans. as Rep. 1691, Nat. Bureau Standards, Washington, DC, 1952.

[174] D. H. Owens, "Dyadic approximation method for multivariable-control systems analysis with a nuclear reactor application," *Proc. Inst. Elec. Eng.*, vol. 120, pp. 801–809, 1973.

[175] ——, "Dyadic expansion for the analysis of linear multivariable systems," *Proc. Inst. Elec. Eng.*, vol. 121, pp. 713–716, 1974.

[176] ——, "Dyadic expansion, characteristic loci and multivariable-control systems design," *Proc. Inst. Elec. Eng.*, vol. 122, pp. 315–320. 1975.

[177] J. L. Peczkowski and M. K. Sain, "Linear multivariable synthesis with transfer functions," in *Proc. NEC Inter. Forum on Alternatives for Multivariable Control*, Chicago, IL, 1977.

[178] E. Peterson, J. G. Kreer, and L. A. Ware, "Regeneration theory and experiment," *Bell Syst. Tech. J.*, vol. 13, pp. 680–700, 1934.

[179] V. A. Pliss, "On the Aizerman problem for a system of three differential equations," *Dokl. Akad. Nauk SSSR*, vol. 121, p. 3, 1958.

[180] H. Poincaré, *Methodes Nouvelles de la Mecanique Celeste*. Paris: Gautier Villars, 1892.

[181] L. S. Pontryagin, V. G. Boltyanskii, R. V. Gamkrelidze, and Y. F. Mischensko, *The Mathematical Theory of Optimal Processes*. New York: Interscience, 1963.

[182] V. M. Popov, "On the absolute stability of nonlinear control systems," *Avtomat. Telemekh.*, vol. 22, p. 8, 1961.

[183] A. Porter, "The servo panel—A unique contribution to control-systems engineering," *Electron. Power*, vol. 11, pp. 330–333, 1965.

[184] B. Porter and T. R. Crossley, *Modal Control*. London: Taylor and Francis, 1972.

[185] I. Postlethwaite, "The asymptotic behaviour, the angles of departure, and the angles of approach of the characteristic frequency loci," *Int. J. Contr.*, vol. 25, pp. 677–695, 1977.

[186] J. Preuss, "On a new steam-engine governor," *Phil. Mag.*, vol. 62, pp. 297–299, 1823.

[187] J. R. Ragazzini and L. A. Zadeh, "The analysis of sampled-data systems," *AIEE Trans.*, vol. 71, part II, pp. 225–234, 1952.

[188] J. R. Ragazzini, and G. Franklin, *Sampled-Data Control Systems*. New York: McGraw-Hill, 1958.

[189] N. Ramani and D. P. Atherton, "Stability of nonlinear multivariable systems," in *Proc. Third IFAC Symp. Multivariable Tech. Syst.*, Manchester, 1974, Paper S-10.

[190] F. H. Raymond, "Introduction a l'etude des asservissements multiples simultanes," *Bull. Soc. Fr. Mecan.*, vol. 7, pp. 18–25, 1953.

[191] K. Rörentrop, *Entwicklung der Modernen Regelungstechnik*. Munich: Oldenbourg, 1971.

[192] H. H. Rosenbrock, "Distinctive problems of process control," *Chem. Eng. Prog.*, vol. 58, pp. 43–50, 1962.

[193] ——, "On the design of linear multivariable control systems," in *Proc. Third IFAC Cong.*, London, 1966, vol. 1, pp. 1–16.

[194] ——, "Design of multivariable control systems using the inverse Nyquist array," *Proc. Inst. Elec. Eng.*, vol. 116, pp. 1929–1936, 1969.

[195] ——, *State Space and Multivariable Theory*. London: Nelson, 1970.

[196] ——, "The zeros of a system," *Int. J. Contr.*, vol. 18, pp. 297–299, 1973.

[197] ——, "Multivariable circle theorems," in *Recent Mathematical Developments in Control*, D. J. Bell, Ed. London: Academic, 1973.

[198] ——, *Computer-Aided Control System Design*. London: Academic, 1974.

[199] E. N. Rozenvasser, "On the construction of a Liapunov function for a class of nonlinear systems," *Izv. Akad. Nauk SSSR*, vol. 2, 1960.

[200] ——, "Remarks on a method for constructing a Liapunov function," *Prikl. Mat. Mekh.*, vol. 24, p. 4, 1960.

[201] A. P. Sage and C. C. White, *Optimum Systems Control*. Englewood Cliffs, NJ: Prentice-Hall, 1977.

[202] M. K. Sain, "A free-modular algorithm for minimal design of linear multivariable systems," in *Proc. Sixth IFAC Cong.*, part 1B, pp. 9.1.1–9.1.7, 1975.

[203] ——, "The growing algebraic presence in systems engineering: An introduction," *Proc. IEEE*, vol. 64, no. 1, pp. 96–111, 1976.

[204] I. W. Sandberg, "On the response of nonlinear control systems to periodic input signals," *Bell Syst. Tech. J.*, vol. 43, pp. 911–926, 1964.

[205] ——, "A frequency domain condition for the stability of systems containing a single time-varying nonlinear element," *Bell Syst. Tech. J.*, vol. 43, pp. 1601–1608, 1964.

[206] Schenkel, "Geometrische Orter an Wechselstromdiagrammen," *Elektrotechn. Zeit.*, p. 1043, 1901.

[207] U. Shaked, "The angles of departure and approach of the root loci in linear multivariable systems," *Int. J. Contr.*, vol. 23, pp. 445–457, 1976.

[208] C. W. Siemens, "On an improved governor for steam engines," in *Proc. Inst. Mech. Eng.*, pp. 75–87, 1853.

[209] ——, "On uniform rotation," *Phil. Trans. Roy. Soc. London*, vol. 156, pp. 657–670, 1866.
[210] J. D. Simon and S. K. Mitter, "A theory of modal control," *Inform. Contr.*, vol. 13, pp. 316–353, 1968.
[211] K. Steiglitz, "The equivalence of digital and analog signal processing," *Inform. Contr.*, vol. 8, pp. 455–467, 1965.
[212] C. P. Steinmetz, *Theory and Calculation of Alternating Current Phenomena*, 1897.
[213] F. Strecker, *Die Elektrische Selbsterregung, mit einer Theorie der Aktiven Netzwerke*. Stuttgart: Hirzel, 1947.
[214] ——, "Aktive Netzwerke und das allgemeine Ortskriterium für Stabilität," *Frequenz.*, vol. 3, pp. 78–84, 1949.
[215] ——, *Praktische Stabilitätsprüfung Mittels Ortskurven und Numerischer Verfahren*. Berlin: Springer, 1950.
[216] ——, "Stabilitätsprufung durch geschlossene und offene Ortskunen," *Arch. Elek. Ubertragung*, vol. 4, p. 199, 1950.
[217] G. I. Taylor, "Diffusion by continuous movements," *Proc. London Math. Soc.*, vol. 20, pp. 196–212, 1920.
[218] M. Tolle, *Beiträge zur Beurteilung der Zentrifugalregulatoren*, VDI-Zeitschrift, 1895 and 1896.
[219] ——, *Die Regelung der Kraftmaschinen*. Berlin: Springer, 1905.
[220] W. Trinks, *Governors and the Governing of Prime Movers*. New York: Van Nostrand, 1919.
[221] Ya. Z. Tsypkin, "Stability of system with time delay feedback" (in Russian), *Avtomat. Telemek.*, vol. 7, pp. 107–129, 1946.
[222] ——, "Stability of feedback systems" (in Russian), *Radiotechnika*, vol. 5, pp. 33–44, 1946.
[223] ——, "Frequency method of analysing intermittent regulating systems," in *Frequency Response*, R. Oldenburger, Ed. New York: Macmillan, 1956.
[224] ——, *Theorie der Relaissysteme der Automatishen Regelung*, R. Oldenbourg, Ed. Berlin: Verlag Technik, 1958.
[225] A. Tustin, "The effects of backlash and of speed dependent friction on the stability of closed cycle control systems," *J. Inst. Elec. Eng.*, part II, vol. 94, pp. 143–151, 1947.
[226] J. A. Vyschnegradsky, "Sur la theorie generale des regulateurs," *Comptes Rendus*, vol. 83, pp. 318–321, 1876.
[227] ——, "Uber direkt wirkende Regulatoren," *Civilingenieur*, vol. 23, pp. 95–131, 1877.
[228] R. Von Mises, "Regulierung des Maschinenganges," *Encyk. Math. Wissenschaften*, vol. 4, part 2, article 10, pp. 254–296, 1911.
[229] K. W. Wagner, "On a formula of Heaviside's for the solution of transients" (in German), *Archiv. Elecktrotech.*, vol. 4, pp. 159–193, 1916.
[230] J. H. Westcott, "Twenty years after: A review of postwar developments," *Electron. Power*, vol. 11, pp. 334–340, 1965.
[231] A. L. Whiteley, "Theory of servo systems with particular reference to stabilization," *J. Inst. Elec. Eng.*, vol. 93, part II, pp. 353–372, 1946.
[232] ——, "Fundamental principles of automatic regulators and servo mechanisms," *J. Inst. Elec. Eng.*, vol. 94, part IIA, pp. 5–22, 1947.
[233] N. Wiener, "Generalized harmonic analysis," *Acta Math.*, vol. 55, pp. 117–258, 1930.
[234] ——, *Cybernetics or Control and Communication in the Animal and the Machine*. Cambridge, MA: MIT Press, 1948.
[235] ——, *Extrapolation, Interpolation and Smoothing of Stationary Time Series*. Cambridge, MA: MIT Press, 1949.
[236] H. S. Witsenhausen, "Separation of estimation and control," *Proc. IEEE*, vol. 59, pp. 1557–1566, 1971.
[237] W. A. Wolovich, *Linear Multivariable Systems*. New York: Springer, 1974.
[238] W. M. Wonham, "On pole assignment in multi-input controllable linear systems," *IEEE Trans. Automat. Contr.*, vol. AC-12, pp. 660–665, 1967.
[239] ——, "On the separation theorem of stochastic control," *SIAM J. Contr.*, vol. 6, pp. 312–326, 1968.
[240] W. M. Wonham and A. S. Morse, "Decoupling and pole assignment in linear multivariable systems: A geometric approach," *SIAM J. Contr.*, vol. 8, pp. 1–18, 1970.
[241] W. M. Wonham, *Linear multivariable control: A Geometric Approach*. Berlin: Springer, 1974.
[242] D. C. Youla, H. A. Jabr, and J. J. Bongiorno, Jr., "Modern Wiener–Hopf design of optimal controllers—Part II: The multivariable case," *IEEE Trans. Automat. Contr.*, vol. AC-21, pp. 319–338, 1976.
[243] G. Zames, "On the input-output stability of time-varying nonlinear feedback systems," *IEEE Trans. Automat. Contr.*, vol. AC-11, pp. 228–238, 465–476, 1966.
[244] J. G. Ziegler, and N. B. Nichols, "Optimum settings for automatic controllers," *Trans. ASME*, vol. 64, pp. 759–768, 1942.
[245] IEEE, Special Issue, *IEEE Trans. Automat. Contr.*, vol. AC-16, Dec. 1971.

Part II
The Classical Frequency-Response Techniques

The great importance of Nyquist's stability criterion stems from its direct relationship to physically measurable quantities. In writing his classic paper [44], Nyquist therefore sought to deal with as wide a class of dynamical systems as possible, and thus did not confine himself to those which could be specified in terms of a simple rational transfer function. The arrangement he considered is shown in Fig. 1. The network is specified in terms of its impulse response $G(t)$ which is such that:

1) $G(t)$ has bounded variation for $-\infty < t < \infty$,
2) $G(t) = 0$, for $-\infty < t < 0$,
3) $\int_{-\infty}^{+\infty} |G(t)|\, dt < \infty$.

These conditions specifically exclude open-loop unstable networks. An associated frequency-response is defined by

$$J(j\omega) = \int_{-\infty}^{+\infty} G(t)\, e^{-j\omega t}\, dt,$$

and it is explicitly stated that $J(j\omega)$ may be obtained directly by means of computations or measurements, in which latter case $J(-j\omega)$ is to be taken as the complex conjugate of $J(j\omega)$. An auxiliary function

$$w(z) = \frac{1}{2\pi j} \int_I \frac{AJ(j\omega)}{(j\omega - z)}\, d(j\omega)$$

where

$$\int_I [\cdot]\, dz = \lim_{M\to\infty} \int_{-jM}^{+jM} [\cdot]\, dz$$

is introduced; this Cauchy representation extends the frequency-response characteristic to a function analytic in the open right-half complex plane. The quantity A is a scalar gain factor.

A disturbance $f_0(t)$ is applied anywhere in the feedback path and thought of in terms of a response repeatedly traversing the feedback loop. After n trips round the loop, this response signal is represented by Nyquist in the form

$$f_n(t) = \frac{1}{2\pi j} \int_{S+} F(z)\, w^n(z)\, e^{zt}\, dz$$

where

$$f_0(t) = \frac{1}{2\pi j} \int_{S+} F(z) e^{zt}\, dz$$

and $S+$ is a large semicircular arc in the right-half plane joining the points $-jM$ and $+jM$. Since $F(z)$ is analytic in the open right-half complex plane, these contour integrals can be taken

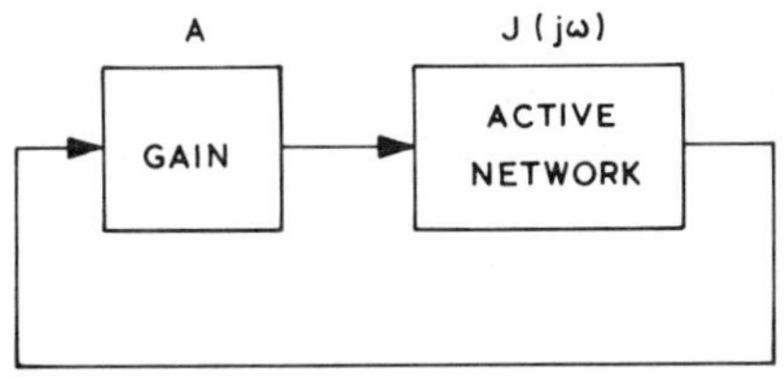

Fig. 1.

along any stipulated path joining their end points. They are the familiar Bromwich-Wagner forms of integral used in the standard treatment of Laplace transform integrals, and the large semicircular arc $S+$ is simply chosen for convenience in handling the investigation of contour integral properties. Nyquist thus proceeds to consider the sum

$$s_n(t) = \sum_{k=0}^{n} f_k(t) = \frac{1}{2\pi j} \int_{S+} F(z)\,[1 + w(z) + \cdots + w^n(z)]$$

and the limit

$$s(t) = \sum_{k=0}^{\infty} f_k(t) = \lim_{n\to\infty} \frac{1}{2\pi j} \int_{S+} s_n(z)\, e^{zt}\, dz$$

where

$$s_n = F + Fw + \cdots + Fw^n = \frac{F(1 - w^{n+1})}{(1 - w)}.$$

He then poses the question: what properties of $w(z)$ and hence of $AJ(j\omega)$ will determine whether $s(t)$ converges to zero or diverges as $t \to \infty$? In answering it Nyquist first shows that

$$s(t) = \frac{1}{2\pi j} \int_{S+} \frac{F(z)}{[1 - w(z)]}\, e^{zt}\, dz,$$

which simply says that the result of the applied disturbance is to produce a response whose transform is the disturbance transform divided by the loop return difference evaluated at the point where the disturbance enters. His next step is crucial: the question of closed-loop stability (in terms of $s(t)$ converging to zero) is tackled by finding out whether or not the transform of $s(t)$ has any singularities in the closed right-half plane. The resulting condition for closed-loop stability is finally given in his famous Nyquist diagram rule: "plot plus and minus the imaginary part of $AJ(j\omega)$ against the real part for all frequencies from 0 to ∞. If the point $1 + j0$ lies completely outside this curve the system is stable; if not it is unstable."

Nyquist's line of argument, though deeply interesting to follow, is unfortunately not rigorous for the class of systems which he considered. This lack of rigor, however, should in no way be regarded as detracting from his great achievement; more than thirty years were to pass before a rigorous proof was supplied by Desoer [12]. The necessity that the return-difference function $[1 - w(z)]$ should not vanish in the closed-right-half plane obviously holds, but the proof that this is also sufficient for closed-loop stability is what is hard to show for the general class of systems considered by Nyquist. The snags involved arise from the facts that:

1) when dealing with fairly general classes of system it is imperative to give a careful statement of what is meant by stability;
2) there are known examples of functions which are analytic in the right-half plane yet do not satisfy the conditions which are regarded as defining a "stable" response.

The informal definition of stability used by Nyquist is essentially that which is now called "input-output stability" (Willems [55], Desoer and Vidyasagar [14]). In a careful formulation of this approach the system is regarded in terms of a mapping between normed spaces, and the basic requirement for stability is taken to be the boundedness of this map. One method of attack is to take the input and output spaces to be function spaces of a stipulated type (L^1-spaces, L^2-spaces, $\cdots$, L^p-spaces, for example) and then to attempt to show that an input of admissible type (let us say in the space L^1) always produces an output of admissible type (also in the space L^1). To see how difficulties then arise in tying such an approach in with a characterization in terms of right-half-plane analyticity can best be done by considering examples of the sort given by Cook [10]. Let $h(t)$ be the impulse response of a single-input single-output system whose response to an input $r(t)$ is given by the convolution integral

$$y(t) = \int_{-\infty}^{t} h(t - \tau)\, r(\tau)\, d\tau$$

and let $g(s)$ be the Laplace transform of $h(t)$. Then a necessary and sufficient condition for bounded-input bounded-output stability is that

$$\int_0^\infty |h(t)|\, dt < \infty$$

which implies that $g(s)$ is holomorphic and bounded in the open right-half plane. However, and this is where the technical difficulties referred to really come from, the convergence of the integral is *not* implied by $g(s)$ being analytic for $\mathrm{Re}(s) > 0$. Counter examples are

$$h(t) = \sin \frac{\sqrt{t}}{t}$$

for which

$$g(s) = \pi \,\mathrm{erf}\left[\frac{1}{2\sqrt{s}}\right]$$

and

$$h(t) = \frac{\sin t^2}{t}$$

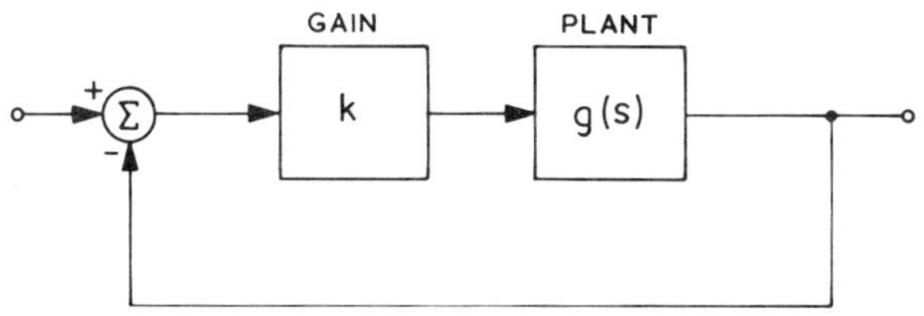

Fig. 2.

for which the transform, expressed in terms of the error function erf, and given by

$$g(s) = \frac{\pi}{4}\left[1 - \mathrm{erf}\,\frac{(1+j)s}{2\sqrt{2}}\right]\left[1 - \mathrm{erf}\,\frac{(1-j)s}{2\sqrt{2}}\right]$$

is entire (that is, analytic in the whole finite complex plane). Hence, in the case when a plant transfer function is not rational, the proof of the Nyquist stability criterion contains real technical difficulties and cannot be based on simply showing that the closed-loop transfer function has no singularities in the closed right-half complex plane.

In the simple case where the plant can be described by a rational transfer function, a sound proof can be based on the Principle of the Argument, since in this case it is sufficient for closed-loop stability that the closed-loop transfer function be analytic in the closed right-half plane. The essence of such an approach was given by Nyquist himself in an appendix to his classic paper. Following the work of MacColl [39] and Bode [5], this soon became the standard form and was extended by Frey [15] to handle the open-loop unstable case. Thus, for the system shown in Fig. 2, where

$$g(s) = \frac{n(s)}{d(s)},$$

$n(s)$ and $d(s)$ are polynomials in the complex frequency variable s with no common factor and k is a scalar gain parameter, one has the following classic result.

Nyquist Stability Criterion (I): The feedback system shown in Fig. 2 is closed-loop stable if and only if the Nyquist diagram of $g(s)$ encircles the critical point $(-1/k + j0)$ p_0 times in an anticlockwise direction, where p_0 is the number of right-half plane poles of the open-loop transfer function $g(s)$. Note that the number of encirclements here (and subsequently) is taken to be that made by the "complete" Nyquist diagram, that is, by the appropriate map of the entire imaginary axis of the frequency plane (s-plane) plus a suitable closure when imaginary axis singularities of $g(s)$ are present.

The first rigorous proof of the Nyquist Stability Criterion for a more general class of systems was given by Desoer [12]. He assumed that the plant was linear time-invariant and non-anticipative (causal) and that it satisfied the following conditions.

1) The output y, the zero-input response z, and the input u are related by

$$y(t) = z(t) + \int_0^t g(t - \tau)\, u(\tau)\, d\tau, \qquad \text{for all } t \geqslant 0$$

where g is the response to a unit impulse.

2) For all initial states, the zero-input response is bounded on $[0, \infty)$ and $z(t) \to z_\infty$ as $t \to \infty$ where z_∞ is a finite number which depends on the initial state.

3) The unit impulse response g is given by

$$g(t) = 1(t)\,[r + g_1(t)]$$

where the constant r is nonnegative; $1(t)$ is the unit step function; g_1 is bounded on $[0, \infty)$, is an element of $L^1(0, \infty)$, and $g_1 \to 0$ as $t \to \infty$.

Under these conditions he established the following version of the Nyquist Stability Criterion.

Nyquist Stability Criterion (II): If the Nyquist diagram of $\hat{g}(s)$, where $\hat{g}(s)$ is the Laplace transform of $g(t)$ does not encircle or go through the critical point

$$(-1/k, 0), \quad \text{then}$$

a) The impulse response of the closed-loop system is bounded, tends to zero as $t \to \infty$, and is an element of $L^1(0, \infty)$.

b) For any initial state, the zero-input response of the closed-loop system is bounded and goes to zero as $t \to \infty$.

c) For any initial state and for any bounded input, the response of the closed-loop system is bounded.

d) Let r be positive; then for any input which tends to a constant u_∞ as $t \to \infty$, and for any initial state, the output y tends to u_∞ as $t \to \infty$. Let r be zero and $u \to 0$ as $t \to \infty$; then for any initial state, the output $y \to 0$. Furthermore, if the Nyquist diagram of $\hat{g}(s)$ encircles the critical point $(-1/k, 0)$ a finite number of times, then the impulse response of the closed-loop system grows exponentially as $t \to \infty$.

The closed-loop system transfer function is given by

$$H(s) = \frac{k\hat{g}(s)}{1 + k\hat{g}(s)}, \qquad \operatorname{Re} s > k g_M$$

where

$$g_M = \sup_{t \geqslant 0} |g(t)|.$$

Since it follows from the Principle of the Argument that the return-difference $[1 + k\hat{g}(s)]$ is $\neq 0$ for all $\operatorname{Re} s \geqslant 0$ if and only if the Nyquist diagram of $\hat{g}(s)$ does not encircle or go through the critical point $(-1/k, 0)$, it follows that Desoer's careful proof shows that the nonvanishing of the return-difference in the closed right-half plane is indeed both necessary and sufficient for closed-loop stability, interpreted in terms of conditions a)–d) inclusive above.

The class of plants to which the Nyquist criterion could be legitimately applied was further extended by Desoer and Wu [13] to the case where the impulse response is of the form

$$g(t) = r + g_a(t) + \sum_{i=0}^{\infty} g_i \delta(t - t_i)$$

where r is a nonnegative constant, g_a is integrable on $[0, \infty)$, and $\sum_{i=0}^{\infty} |g_i| < \infty$. For a plant of this sort, whose impulse response may have an infinite sequence of impulses (as may for example occur in systems incorporating lossless transmission lines), they showed that

$$\inf_{\operatorname{Re} s \geqslant 0} |1 + k\hat{g}(s)| > 0,$$

is a sufficient condition for closed-loop stability. This condition can be checked (for this class of plants) by drawing a Nyquist diagram for $\hat{g}(s)$ in the usual manner, since it is equivalent to the requirement that the map of the closed right-half s-plane into the $\hat{g}$-plane be bounded away from the critical point $(-1/k, 0)$. Desoer and Wu showed that the closed-loop stability resulting from a satisfaction of the Nyquist criterion has the desirable features that one would hope for: a bounded input produces a bounded output, an input with finite energy (ie one in the function space L^2) produces an output with finite energy, and a continuous input produces a continuous output.

The class of admissible plants was further extended by Callier and Desoer [8] to include ones with a finite number of right-half plane poles.

They showed that

$$\inf_{\operatorname{Re} s \geqslant 0} |1 + k\hat{g}(s)| > 0 \tag{2.1}$$

is necessary and sufficient for the closed-loop transfer function to be the Laplace transform of the derivative of a function of bounded variation on $[0, \infty)$, which in turn implies that the closed-loop system is L^p-stable for all p, $1 \leqslant p \leqslant \infty$. Callier and Desoer also gave an appropriate graphical test for condition (2.1) to be satisfied. Unfortunately, the price paid for this degree of generality is that the graphical test does not simply consist of drawing a Nyquist diagram. A simplified form of this graphical test was later given by Callier and Desoer [9]. A comprehensive discussion of the input-output treatment of feedback system stability is given in the book by Desoer and Vidyasagar [14].

I. Mikhailov Criterion

Mikhailov's criterion applies to systems described by a known nth-order constant coefficient linear differential equation and thus having an explicitly known characteristic polynomial $p(s)$ (Mikhailov [41]). It is stated in terms of the locus of $p(j\omega)$ in a complex p plane and so bears a superficial resemblance to the Nyquist criterion. It is, however, an essentially different result in that it requires that the governing differential equation of the system being investigated must be known, whereas the essential virtue of the Nyquist criterion is that the Nyquist locus is something which can be directly measured for a plant whose behavior in terms of a differential equation description may well not be available. A criterion of this form was also formulated in Germany by Leonhard [35] and Cremer [11].

The Mikhailov criterion is obtained by a simple application of the Principle of the Argument. Let $p(s)$ be the characteristic equation of a linear dynamical system, let C be a closed Jordan contour in the s-plane, and let Γ be the image of C, under the mapping $p(s)$, in the p-plane. Let $p(s)$ have P zeros inside C. Then the net phase change associated with one traverse of Γ as s traverses C once in the anticlockwise direction is $2\pi P$. Hence on obtains the following.

Mikhailov Stability Criterion: If $p(j\omega)$ is plotted for ω increasing continuously from 0 to ∞ (the Mikhailov locus) then the dynamical system with nth-order characteristic polynomial $p(s)$ will be stable if and only if the phase of $p(j\omega)$ increases continuously from 0 to $n\pi/2$. Further developments of this criterion have been made by Leonhard [36].

II. Bode's Work and the Further Development of Nyquist-Diagram-Based Techniques

The approach to feedback system stability based on Nyquist diagrams had a further striking advantage in addition to its direct relationship to experimentally measurable quantities: it gave an indication of what should be done to an open-loop frequency response in order to improve closed-loop behavior. As pointed out by Ludwig [38] and realized by Bode and others, the closeness of approach of the Nyquist locus to the critical point gave a measure of closed-loop damping. Hence the key to an improved closed-loop response was seen to lie in a suitable shaping of the open-loop frequency-response characteristic. Considerations of this sort led to Bode's classic studies on the relationship between gain and phase characteristics (Bode [4], [5]) during which the critical point in the gain plane was put in its now-standard place at $(-1+j0)$, and the gain and phase margin measures of relative closed-loop stability were introduced. By the end of the Second World War the Nyquist–Bode approach to the analysis and design of feedback control systems had been firmly established by the work of Harris [24], Brown and Hall [7], Leonhard [35], Cremer [11], Strecker [49], Oldenbourg and Sartorius [45], and others (see Part I). A good example of its state of development at that time is given by Hall [23]; this first appeared in a wartime report. The Nyquist–Bode approach to feedback system design was further developed in an important book by Horowitz [26] on the synthesis of feedback systems. In this book Horowitz considered the effects of large plant parameter variations on the design problem, and further studied this problem in a series of papers (Horowitz and Sidi [27], Horowitz [28], Horowitz and Sidi [29]). The effect of time delays on the closed-loop stability of feedback systems was considered by Tsypkin [50].

An extension of frequency-response methods to sampled-data systems was developed by Hurewicz in the early 1940's and is described in the book by James, Nichols and Phillips [30]. Hurewicz developed the appropriate extension of the Nyquist stability criterion to sampled-data systems. The increasing importance of digital devices in the 1950's led to a renewed interest in the use of frequency-response techniques in this area, and Linvill [37] and Tsypkin [51] gave suitable extensions of the Laplace transform approach for handling interconnections of digital and analog devices. An alternative approach of developing a "z-transform" for discrete-time signals to complement the "s-transform" for continuous-time signals was developed by Ragazzini and Zadeh [47], Jury [31], [32] and others (Barker [1], [2]; Bergen and Ragazzini [3]; Helm [25]; Kuo [34]; Tsypkin [52]; and Freeman [22]).

The striking success of the state-space approach to multivariable systems in the late 1950's and early 1960's sharply reduced the interest in frequency-response methods of the great majority of theoreticians working on automatic control. Nevertheless the basic frequency-response approach remained the workhorse of very many designers of industrial control systems. It therefore became a matter of great interest to explore links between the new state-space-based approaches and the classical frequency-response methods, and a notable step in this direction was taken by Kalman [33] which established certain frequency-response properties of an optimal single-loop feedback control system.

III. The Evans' Root-Locus Method

The closed-loop characteristic frequencies and the gain parameter of the feedback system of Fig. 2 are related by

$$1 + kg(s) = 0$$

If

$$g(s) = \frac{\alpha \prod_{j=1}^{m} (s - z_j)}{\prod_{i=1}^{n} (s - p_i)},$$

then this characteristic equation can be rewritten in the form

$$\frac{\alpha \prod_{j=1}^{m} (s - z_j)}{\prod_{i=1}^{n} (s - p_i)} = -\frac{1}{k},$$

and the closed-loop frequencies for a particular value of gain parameter k' must be such that the expression

$$\frac{\prod_{j=1}^{m} (s - z_j)}{\prod_{i=1}^{n} (s - p_i)}$$

has a phase of 180° and a modulus of $1/k'\alpha$. Evans [19]–[21] showed how the set of possible locations of closed-loop frequencies in the s-plane could be determined by simple graphical constructions given the locations in the s-plane of the poles and zeros of $g(s)$. After the graphical construction of this set of "root loci," he further showed how they can be calibrated in the gain parameter k, again by the use of simple graphical constructions based on a knowledge of the pole and zero locations.

Evans' brilliantly simple idea enabled design engineers to rapidly sketch the variation of closed-loop characteristic frequencies with gain for quite complicated transfer functions, and the method rapidly developed into one of the key tools of the control engineer.

IV. Algebraic Functions, Encirclements, and Topological Considerations

It is instructive at this point to look briefly at the root locus method from the point of view of algebraic function theory which was later used (see Part IV) to extend Nyquist and root locus techniques to the multivariable case. If

$$g(s) = \frac{n(s)}{d(s)}$$

where $n(s)$ and $d(s)$ are polynomials in s, then the equation

$$1 + k\,g(s) = 0$$

can be written in the form

$$d(s) + kn(s) = 0.$$

This takes the form

$$d(s)\gamma - n(s) = 0 \qquad (2.2)$$

on making the substitution

$$\gamma = -1/k.$$

Now consider (2.2). It gives both open-loop gain as a function of frequency s and, for the feedback system of Fig. 2, closed-loop frequency as a function of the gain parameter γ. If we plug a specific value of $s = \bar{s}$ in (2.2) and solve for γ we obtain

$$\gamma = \frac{n(\bar{s})}{d(\bar{s})} = g(\bar{s}),$$

and if we plug in a specific value of $\gamma = \bar{\gamma}$ and solve for s we obtain the n values of closed-loop characteristic frequency $\{s_i : i = 1, 2, \cdots, n\}$ which correspond to this value of the gain parameter. Equation (2.2) thus defines two algebraic functions: a gain function $\gamma(s)$ giving open-loop gain as a function of frequency, and a frequency function $s(\gamma)$ giving closed-loop frequency as a function of gain. In this case (a single-input single-output plant), the gain function is a single-valued function of s, and the frequency function is an n-valued function of γ. The frequency function is thus defined on an n-sheeted Riemann surface; it is of considerable interest to note that Nyquist's classic paper involved a discussion of this surface. There are two important aspects of the fact that an open-loop gain function and a closed-loop frequency function are related via a single defining equation. Firstly, this provides a natural point of view for a generalization of these ideas to multivariable systems. Secondly, it shows that, from the complex-variable analytic-function point of view, the two classical approaches to studying the behavior of a feedback system, namely in terms of open-loop gain as a function of frequency (Nyquist-Bode), or in terms of closed-loop frequency as a function of gain (Evans' root locus), are simply different ways of looking at the same physical situation.

The implications of the fact that the Nyquist diagram "lives on" a Riemann surface have been investigated by MacFarlane and Postlethwaite [40], and by De Carlo and Saeks [18] who have thus been led to consider the Nyquist stability criterion from the viewpoint of algebraic topology. These studies shed an interesting light on the role played in Nyquist stability theory by encirclements of a critical point (Saeks [48]). The relationship between encirclements and stability for a fairly general class of operators has also been considered by Davis [17].

V. The Frequency-Response Approach to Optimization and the Wiener-Hopf Design Technique

Following Wiener's classical frequency-response studies of stochastic processes and of the problem of filtering stochastic signals from stochastic disturbances (Wiener [53], [54]; Paley and Wiener [46]) the frequency-response analysis of control systems behavior was extended to handle stochastic inputs (James, Nichols, and Phillips [30]; Davenport and Root [16]). Bode and Shannon [6] gave a simple treatment of Wiener's spectral factorization solution of an optimal filtering problem. This general approach to stochastic problems is often called the Wiener-Hopf approach since Wiener based his solution on the so-called Wiener-Hopf integral equation. Since Parseval's theorem can be used to turn quadratic performance-index integrals with respect to time into equivalent integrals with respect to a frequency variable, it was realized that Wiener-Hopf techniques of solving optimal filtering problems could be used to attack optimal control problems. In particular Newton used this approach to study an analytical formulation of the problem of designing feedback control systems under various forms of constraint (Newton, Gould, and Kaiser [43]). This gave another line of attack for the frequency-response design of feedback systems which was further extended by Youla, Bongiorno, and Jabr [56].

References

[1] R. H. Barker, "The theory of pulse monitored servomechanisms and their use for prediction," Rep. 1046, Signals Research and Development Establishment, Christchurch, England, 1950.

[2] —, "The pulse transfer function and its application to sampling servomechanisms," *Proc. IEE*, 99(4), 302-317, 1952.

[3] A. R. Bergen and J. R. Ragazzini, "Sampled-data processing techniques for feedback control systems," *Trans. AIEE*, 73(2), 236-247, 1954.

[4] H. W. Bode, "Relations between attenuation and phase in feedback amplifier design," *Bell Syst. Tech. J.*, 19, 421-454, 1940.

[5] —, *Network Analysis and Feedback Amplifier Design*. Princeton, NJ: Van Nostrand, 1945.

[6] H. W. Bode and C. E. Shannon, "A simplified derivation of linear least square smoothing and prediction theory," *Proc. IRE*, 38, 417-425, 1950.

[7] G. S. Brown and A. C. Hall, "Dynamic-behaviour and design of servomechanisms," *Trans. ASME*, 68, 503-524, 1946.

[8] F. M. Callier and C. A. Desoer, "A graphical test for checking the stability of a linear time-invariant feedback system, *IEEE Trans. Automat. Control*, AC-17, 773-780, 1972.

[9] —, "On simplifying a graphical stability criterion for linear distributed feedback systems," *IEEE Trans. Automat. Control*, AC-21, 128-129, 1976.

[10] P. Cook, "Stability of linear constant multivariable systems," *Proc. IEE*, 120, 1557, 1973.

[11] L. Cremer, "Ein neues Verfahren zur Beurteilung der Stabilitat linearer Regelungs-systeme," *Z. fur angew. Mathematik und Mechanik*, 25-27, 5/6, 1947.

[12] C. A. Desoer, "A general formulation of the Nyquist criterion," *IEEE Trans. Circuit Theory*, CT-12, 230-234, 1965.

[13] C. A. Desoer and M. Y. Wu, "Stability of linear time-invariant systems," *IEEE Trans. Circuit Theory*, CT-15, 245-250, 1968.

[14] C. A. Desoer and M. Vidyasagar, *Feedback Systems: Input-Output Properties*. New York: Academic Press, 1975.

[15] W. Frey, "A generalization of the Nyquist and Leonhard stability criteria," *Brown Boveri Review*, 33, 59-65, 1946.

[16] W. B. Davenport and W. L. Root, *An Introduction to the Theory of Random Signals and Noise*. New York: McGraw-Hill, 1958.

[17] J. H. Davis, "Fredholm operators, encirclements, and stability criteria," *SIAM J. Control*, 10, 608-622, 1972.

[18] R. De Carlo and R. Saeks, "The encirclement criterion: An approach using algebraic topology," *Int. J. Control*, 26, 279-287, 1977.

[19] W. R. Evans, "Graphical analysis of control systems," *Trans. AIEE*, 67, 547-551, 1948.

[20] —, "Control system synthesis by root locus method," *Trans. AIEE*, 69, 1-4, 1950.

[21] —, *Control System Dynamics*. New York: McGraw-Hill, 1953.

[22] H. Freeman, *Discrete-Time Systems*. New York: Wiley, 1965.

[23] A. C. Hall, "Application of circuit theory to the design of servomechanisms," *J. Franklin Inst.*, 242, 279-307, 1946.

[24] H. Harris, Jr., "The frequency response of automatic control systems," *Trans. AIEE*, 65, 539-546, 1946.

[25] H. A. Helm, "The Z-transformation," *Bell Syst. Tech. J.*, 38(1), 177-196, 1959.

[26] I. Horowitz, *Synthesis of Feedback Systems*. New York: Academic Press, 1963.

[27] I. Horowitz, and M. Sidi, "Synthesis of feedback systems with

large plant ignorance for prescribed time-domain tolerances," *Int. J. Control*, 16, 287-309, 1972.
[28] I. Horowitz, "A synthesis theory for linear time-varying feedback systems with plant uncertainty," *IEEE Trans. Automat. Control*, AC-20, 454-464, 1975.
[29] I. Horowitz and M. Sidi, "Optimum synthesis of nonminimum phase feedback systems with plant uncertainty," *Int. J. Control*, 27, 361-386, 1978.
[30] H. M. James, N. B. Nichols, and R. S. Phillips, *Theory of Servomechanisms*. New York: McGraw-Hill, 1947.
[31] E. I. Jury, "Analysis and synthesis of sampled-data control systems," *Trans. AIEE*, 73(1), 332-346, 1954.
[32] —, *Sampled-Data Control Systems*. New York: Wiley, 1958.
[33] R. E. Kalman, "When is a linear control system optimal?," *J. Basic Eng.*, Ser. D., 86, 51-60, 1964.
[34] B. Kuo, *Analysis and Synthesis of Sampled-Data Control Systems*. Englewood Cliffs, NJ: Prentice-Hall, 1963.
[35] A. Leonhard, "Neues Verfahren zur Stabilitatsuntersuchung," *Arch. der Elektrotechnik*, 38, 17-28, 1944.
[36] —, *Die Selbsttatige Regelung*. Berlin: Springer, 1957.
[37] W. K. Linvill, "Sampled-data control systems studied through comparison of sampling with amplitude modulation," *Trans. AIEE*, 70, Part II, 1779-1788, 1951.
[38] E. H. Ludwig, "Die Stabilisierung von Regelanordunugen mit Rohrenverstarkern durch Dampfung oder elastische Ruckfuhrung," *Arch. Elektrotechnik*, 34, 269ff, 1940.
[39] L. A. MacColl, *Fundamental Theory of Servomechanisms*. New York: Van Nostrand, 1945.
[40] A. G. J. MacFarlane and I. Postlethwaite, "The generalized Nyquist stability criterion and multivariable root loci," *Int. J. Control*, 25, 81-127, 1977.
[41] A. V. Mikhailov, "Methods for harmonic analysis in the automatic control system theory," (in Russian) *Avtomatika i Telemekhanika*, 3, 27, 1938.
[42] —, "Stability theory of linear feedback circuit with lumped parameters," (in Russian) *J. Technical Physics*, 1, 20-31, 1939.
[43] G. C. Newton, Jr., L. A. Gould, and J. Kaiser, *Analytical Design of Linear Feedback Controls*. New York: Wiley, 1957.
[44] H. Nyquist, "Regeneration theory," *Bell Syst. Tech. J.*, 11, 126-147, 1932.
[45] R. C. Oldenbourg and H. Sartorius, *Dynamik Selbsttatiger Regelungen*. Munich: Oldenbourg, 1944.
[46] R. E. A. C. Paley and N. Wiener, "Fourier transforms in the complex domain," *American Mathematical Society Colloquium Publication No. 19*, Providence, RI, 1934.
[47] J. R. Ragazzini and L. A. Zadeh, "The analysis of sampled-data systems," *Trans. AIEE*, 71(2), 225-232, 1952.
[48] R. Saeks, "On the encirclement condition and its generalization," *IEEE Trans. Circuits and Syst.*, CAS-22, 780-785, 1975.
[49] F. Strecker, *Praktische Stabilitatsprufung mittels Ortskurven und numerischer Verfahren*. Berlin: Springer, 1950.
[50] Ya. Z. Tsypkin, "Stability of system with time delay feedback (in Russian) *Avtomatika i Telemekhanika*, 7, 107-129, 1946.
[51] —, "Frequency method of analyzing intermittent regulating systems," in *Frequency Response*, edited by R. Oldenburger. New York: Macmillan, 1956.
[52] —, *Sampled Systems Theory and Its Applications*, Vols. 1 and 2. Oxford: Pergamon Press, 1964.
[53] N. Wiener, "Generalized harmonic analysis," *Acta. Math.*, 55, 117-258, 1930.
[54] —, *Extrapolation, Interpolation and Smoothing of Stationary Time Series*. Cambridge, MA: M.I.T. Press, 1949.
[55] J. C. Willems, *The Analysis of Feedback Systems*. Cambridge, MA: M.I.T. Press, 1971.
[56] D. C. Youla, J. J. Bongiorno, Jr., and H. A. Jabr, "Modern Wiener-Hopf design of optimal controllers Part 1: The single-input-output case, *IEEE Trans. Automat. Control*, AC-21, 3-13, 1976.

Regeneration Theory

By H. NYQUIST

Regeneration or feed-back is of considerable importance in many applications of vacuum tubes. The most obvious example is that of vacuum tube oscillators, where the feed-back is carried beyond the singing point. Another application is the 21-circuit test of balance, in which the current due to the unbalance between two impedances is fed back, the gain being increased until singing occurs. Still other applications are cases where portions of the output current of amplifiers are fed back to the input either unintentionally or by design. For the purpose of investigating the stability of such devices they may be looked on as amplifiers whose output is connected to the input through a transducer. This paper deals with the theory of stability of such systems.

Preliminary Discussion

WHEN the output of an amplifier is connected to the input through a transducer the resulting combination may be either stable or unstable. The circuit will be said to be stable when an impressed small disturbance, which itself dies out, results in a response which dies out. It will be said to be unstable when such a disturbance results in a response which goes on indefinitely, either staying at a relatively small value or increasing until it is limited by the non-linearity of the amplifier. When thus limited, the disturbance does not grow further. The net gain of the round trip circuit is then zero. Otherwise stated, the more the response increases the more does the non-linearity decrease the gain until at the point of operation the gain of the amplifier is just equal to the loss in the feed-back admittance. An oscillator under these conditions would ordinarily be called stable but it will simplify the present paper to use the definitions above and call it unstable. Now, this fact as to equality of gain and loss appears to be an accident connected with the non-linearity of the circuit and far from throwing light on the conditions for stability actually diverts attention from the essential facts. In the present discussion this difficulty will be avoided by the use of a strictly linear amplifier, which implies an amplifier of unlimited power carrying capacity. The attention will then be centered on whether an initial impulse dies out or results in a runaway condition. If a runaway condition takes place in such an amplifier, it follows that a non-linear amplifier having the same gain for small current and decreasing gain with increasing current will be unstable as well.

Steady-State Theories and Experience

First, a discussion will be made of certain steady-state theories; and reasons why they are unsatisfactory will be pointed out. The most obvious method may be referred to as the series treatment. Let the complex quantity $AJ(i\omega)$ represent the ratio by which the amplifier and feed-back circuit modify the current in one round trip, that is, let the magnitude of AJ represent the ratio numerically and let the angle of AJ represent the phase shift. It will be convenient to refer to AJ as an admittance, although it does not have the dimensions of the quantity usually so called. Let the current

$$I_0 = \cos \omega t = \text{real part of } e^{i\omega t} \tag{a}$$

be impressed on the circuit. The first round trip is then represented by

$$I_1 = \text{real part of } AJe^{i\omega t} \tag{b}$$

and the nth by

$$I_m = \text{real part of } A^nJ^ne^{i\omega t}. \tag{c}$$

The total current of the original impressed current and the first n round trips is

$$I_n = \text{real part of } (1 + AJ + A^2J^2 + \cdots A^nJ^n)e^{i\omega t}. \tag{d}$$

If the expression in parentheses converges as n increases indefinitely, the conclusion is that the total current equals the limit of (d) as n increases indefinitely. Now

$$1 + AJ + \cdots A^nJ^n = \frac{1 - A^{n+1}J^{n+1}}{1 - AJ}. \tag{e}$$

If $|AJ| < 1$ this converges to $1/(1 - AJ)$ which leads to an answer which accords with experiment. When $|AJ| > 1$ an examination of the numerator in (e) shows that the expression does not converge but can be made as great as desired by taking n sufficiently large. The most obvious conclusion is that when $|AJ| > 1$ for some frequency there is a runaway condition. This disagrees with experiment, for instance, in the case where AJ is a negative quantity numerically greater than one. The next suggestion is to assume that somehow the expression $1/(1 - AJ)$ may be used instead of the limit of (e). This, however, in addition to being arbitrary, disagrees with experimental results in the case where AJ is positive and greater than 1, where the expression $1/(1 - AJ)$ leads to a finite current but where experiment indicates an unstable condition.

The fundamental difficulty with this method can be made apparent by considering the nature of the current expressed by (a) above. Does the expression $\cos \omega t$ indicate a current which has been going on for all time or was the current zero up to a certain time and $\cos \omega t$ thereafter? In the former case we introduce infinities into our expressions and make the equations invalid; in the latter case there will be transients or building-up processes whose importance may increase as n increases but which are tacitly neglected in equations (b) – (e). Briefly then, the difficulty with this method is that it neglects the building-up processes.

Another method is as follows: Let the voltage (or current) at any point be made up of two components

$$V = V_1 + V_2, \qquad (f)$$

where V is the total voltage, V_1 is the part due directly to the impressed voltage, that is to say, without the feed-back, and V_2 is the component due to feed-back alone. We have

$$V_2 = AJV. \qquad (g)$$

Eliminating V_2 between (f) and (g)

$$V = V_1/(1 - AJ). \qquad (h)$$

This result agrees with experiment when $|AJ| < 1$ but does not generally agree when AJ is positive and greater than unity. The difficulty with this method is that it does not investigate whether or not a steady state exists. It simply assumes tacitly that a steady state exists and if so it gives the correct value. When a steady state does not exist this method yields no information, nor does it give any information as to whether or not a steady state exists, which is the important point.

The experimental facts do not appear to have been formulated precisely but appear to be well known to those working with these circuits. They may be stated loosely as follows: There is an unstable condition whenever there is at least one frequency for which AJ is positive and greater than unity. On the other hand, when AJ is negative it may be very much greater than unity and the condition is nevertheless stable. There are instances of $|AJ|$ being about 100 without the conditions being unstable. This, as will appear, accords closely with the rule deduced below.

Notation and Restrictions

The following notation will be used in connection with integrals:

$$\int_I \phi(z)dz = \lim_{M\to\infty} \int_{-iM}^{+iM} \phi(z)dz, \tag{1}$$

the path of integration being along the imaginary axis (see equation 9), i.e., the straight line joining $-iM$ and $+iM$;

$$\int_{s+} \phi(z)dz = \lim_{M\to\infty} \int_{-iM}^{iM} \phi(z)dz, \tag{2}$$

the path of integration being along a semicircle [1] having the origin for center and passing through the points $-iM$, M, iM;

$$\int_C \phi(z)dz = \lim_{M\to\infty} \int_{-iM}^{-iM} \phi(z)dz, \tag{3}$$

the path of integration being first along the semicircle referred to and then along a straight line from iM to $-iM$. Referring to Fig. 1 it

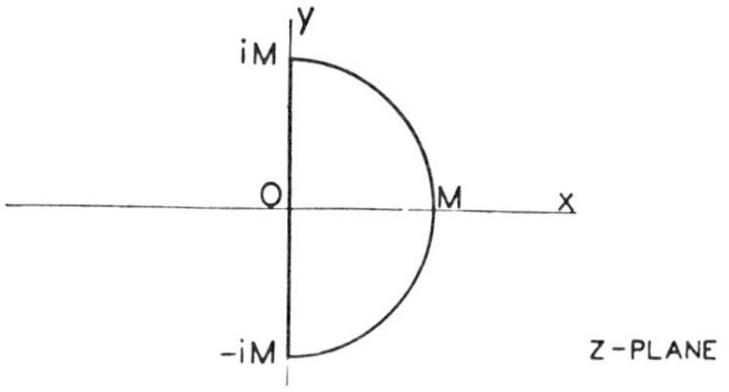

Fig. 1—Paths of integration in the z-plane.

will be seen that

$$\int_{s+} - \int_I = \int_C. \tag{4}$$

The total feed-back circuit is made up of an amplifier in tandem with a network. The amplifier is characterized by the amplifying ratio A which is independent of frequency. The network is characterized by the ratio $J(i\omega)$ which is a function of frequency but does not depend on the gain. The total effect of the amplifier and the network is to multiply the wave by the ratio $AJ(i\omega)$. An alternative way of characterizing the amplifier and network is to say that the amplifier is

[1] For physical interpretation of paths of integration for which $x > 0$ reference is made to a paper by J. R. Carson, "Notes on the Heaviside Operational Calculus," *B. S. T. J.*, Jan. 1930. For purposes of the present discussion the semicircle is preferable to the path there discussed.

characterized by the amplifying factor A which is independent of time, and the network by the real function $G(t)$ which is the response caused by a unit impulse applied at time $t = 0$. The combined effect of the amplifier and network is to convert a unit impulse to the function $AG(t)$. Both these characterizations will be used.

The restrictions which are imposed on the functions in order that the subsequent reasoning may be valid will now be stated. There is no restriction on A other than that it should be real and independent of time and frequency. In stating the restrictions on the network it is convenient to begin with the expression G. They are

$$G(t) \text{ has bounded variation}, \quad -\infty < t < \infty. \tag{AI}$$

$$G(t) = 0, \quad -\infty < t < 0. \tag{AII}$$

$$\int_{-\infty}^{\infty} |G(t)|\, dt \text{ exists.} \tag{AIII}$$

It may be shown [2] that under these conditions $G(t)$ may be expressed by the equation

$$G(t) = \frac{1}{2\pi i}\int_I J(i\omega)e^{i\omega t}d(i\omega), \tag{5}$$

where

$$J(i\omega) = \int_{-\infty}^{\infty} G(t)e^{-i\omega t}dt. \tag{6}$$

These expressions may be taken to define J. The function may, however, be obtained directly from computations or measurements; in the latter case the function is not defined for negative values of ω. It must be defined as follows to be consistent with the definition in (6):

$$J(-i\omega) = \text{complex conjugate of } J(i\omega). \tag{7}$$

While the final results will be expressed in terms of $AJ(i\omega)$ it will be convenient for the purpose of the intervening mathematics to define an auxiliary and closely related function

$$w(z) = \frac{1}{2\pi i}\int_I \frac{AJ(i\omega)}{i\omega - z}d(i\omega), \quad 0 < x < \infty, \tag{8}$$

where

$$z = x + iy \tag{9}$$

and where x and y are real. Further, we shall define

$$w(iy) = \lim_{x\to 0} w(z). \tag{10}$$

[2] See Appendix II for fuller discussion.

The function will not be defined for $x < 0$ nor for $|z| = \infty$. As defined it is analytic[3] for $0 < x < \infty$ and at least continuous for $x = 0$.

The following restrictions on the network may be deduced:

$$\lim_{y \to \infty} y|J(iy)| \text{ exists.} \tag{BI}$$

$$J(iy) \text{ is continuous.} \tag{BII}$$

$$w(iy) = AJ(iy). \tag{BIII}$$

Equation (5) may now be written

$$AG(t) = \frac{1}{2\pi i}\int_I w(z)e^{zt}dz = \frac{1}{2\pi i}\int_{I+} w(z)e^{zt}dz. \tag{11}$$

From a physical standpoint these restrictions are not of consequence. Any network made up of positive resistances, conductances, inductances, and capacitances meets them. Restriction (AII) says that the response must not precede the cause and is obviously fulfilled physically. Restriction (AIII) is fulfilled if the response dies out at least exponentially, which is also assured. Restriction (AI) says that the transmission must fall off with frequency. Physically there are always enough distributed constants present to insure this. This effect will be illustrated in example 8 below. Every physical network falls off in transmission sooner or later and it is ample for our purposes if it begins to fall off, say, at optical frequencies. We may say then that the reasoning applies to all linear networks which occur in nature. It also applies to other linear networks which are not physically producible but which may be specified mathematically. See example 7 below.

A temporary wave $f_0(t)$ is to be introduced into the system and an investigation will be made of whether the resultant disturbance in the system dies out. It has associated with it a function $F(z)$ defined by

$$f_0(t) = \frac{1}{2\pi i}\int_I F(z)e^{zt}dz = \frac{1}{2\pi i}\int_{I+} F(z)e^{zt}dz. \tag{12}$$

$F(z)$ and $f_0(t)$ are to be made subject to the same restrictions as $w(z)$ and $G(t)$ respectively.

Derivation of a Series for the Total Current

Let the amplifier be linear and of infinite power-carrying capacity. Let the output be connected to the input in such a way that the

[3] W. F. Osgood, "Lehrbuch der Funktionentheorie," 5th ed., Kap. 7, § 1, Hauptsatz. For definition of "analytic" see Kap. 6, § 5.

amplification ratio for one round trip is equal to the complex quantity AJ, where A is a function of the gain only and J is a function of ω only, being defined for all values of frequency from 0 to ∞.

Let the disturbing wave $f_0(t)$ be applied anywhere in the circuit. We have

$$f_0(t) = \frac{1}{2\pi}\int_{-\infty}^{+\infty} F(i\omega)e^{i\omega t}d\omega \tag{13}$$

or

$$f_0(t) = \frac{1}{2\pi i}\int_{s+} F(z)e^{zt}dz. \tag{13'}$$

The wave traverses the circuit and on completing the first trip it becomes

$$f_1(t) = \frac{1}{2\pi}\int_{-\infty}^{\infty} w(i\omega)F(i\omega)e^{i\omega t}d\omega \tag{14}$$

$$= \frac{1}{2\pi i}\int_{s+} w(z)F(z)e^{zt}dz. \tag{14'}$$

After traversing the circuit a second time it becomes

$$f_2(t) = \frac{1}{2\pi i}\int_{s+} Fw^2e^{zt}dz, \tag{15}$$

and after traversing the circuit n times

$$f_n(t) = \frac{1}{2\pi i}\int_{s+} Fw^ne^{zt}dz. \tag{16}$$

Adding the voltage of the original impulse and the first n round trips we have a total of

$$s_n(t) = \sum_{k=0}^{n} f_k(t) = \frac{1}{2\pi i}\int_{s+} F(1 + w + \cdots w^n)e^{zt}dz. \tag{17}$$

The total voltage at the point in question at the time t is given by the limiting value which (17) approaches as n is increased indefinitely [4]

$$s(t) = \sum_{k=0}^{\infty} f_k(t) = \lim_{n\to\infty}\frac{1}{2\pi i}\int_{s+} S_n(z)e^{zt}dz, \tag{18}$$

where

$$S_n = F + Fw + Fw^2 + \cdots Fw^n = \frac{F(1 - w^{n+1})}{1 - w}. \tag{19}$$

[4] Mr. Carson has called my attention to the fact that this series can also be derived from Theorem IX, p. 49, of his Electric Circuit Theory. Whereas the present derivation is analogous to the theory expressed in equations (a)–(e) above, the alternative derivation would be analogous to that in equations (f)–(h).

Convergence of Series

We shall next prove that the limit $s(t)$ exists for all finite values of t. It may be stated as of incidental interest that the limit

$$\int_{s+} S_\infty(z) e^{izt} dz \tag{20}$$

does not necessarily exist although the limit $s(t)$ does. Choose M_0 and N such that

$$|f_0(\lambda)| \leq M_0. \qquad 0 \leq \lambda \leq t. \tag{21}$$

$$|G(t-\lambda)| \leq N. \quad 0 \leq \lambda \leq t. \tag{22}$$

We may write [5]

$$f_1(t) = \int_{-\infty}^{\infty} G(t-\lambda) f_0(\lambda) d\lambda. \tag{23}$$

$$|f_1(t)| \leq \int_0^t M_0 N d\lambda = M_0 N t. \tag{24}$$

$$f_2(t) = \int_{-\infty}^{\infty} G(t-\lambda) f_1(\lambda) d\lambda. \tag{25}$$

$$|f_2(t)| \leq \int_0^t M_0 N^2 t dt = M_0 N^2 t^2/2! \tag{26}$$

Similarly

$$|f_n(t)| \leq M_0 N^n t^n/n! \tag{27}$$

$$|s_n(t)| \leq M_0(1 + Nt + \cdots N^n t^n/n!). \tag{28}$$

It is shown in almost any text [6] dealing with the convergence of series that the series in parentheses converges to e^{Nt} as n increases indefinitely. Consequently, $s_n(t)$ converges absolutely as n increases indefinitely.

Relation Between $s(t)$ and w

Next consider what happens to $s(t)$ as t increases. As t increases indefinitely $s(t)$ may converge to zero, indicating a condition of stability, or it may go beyond any value however large, indicating a runaway condition. The question which presents itself is: *Referring to (18) and (19), what properties of $w(z)$ and further what properties of $AJ(i\omega)$ determine whether $s(t)$ converges to zero or diverges as t increases*

[5] G. A. Campbell, "Fourier Integral," *B. S. T. J.*, Oct. 1928, Pair 202.
[6] E.g., Whittaker and Watson, "Modern Analysis," 2d ed., p. 531.

indefinitely? From (18) and (19)

$$s(t) = \lim_{n\to\infty} \frac{1}{2\pi i} \int_{s+} F\left(\frac{1}{1-w} - \frac{w^{n+1}}{1-w}\right) e^{zt}dz. \quad (29)$$

We may write

$$s(t) = \frac{1}{2\pi i}\int_{s+} [F/(1-w)]e^{zt}dz - \lim_{n\to\infty} \frac{1}{2\pi i}\int_{s+} [Fw^{n+1}/(1-w)]e^{zt}dz \quad (30)$$

provided these functions exist. Let them be called $q_0(t)$ and $\lim_{n\to\infty} q_n(t)$ respectively. Then

$$q_n(t) = \int_{-\infty}^{\infty} q_0(t-\lambda)\phi(\lambda)d\lambda. \quad (31)$$

where

$$\phi(\lambda) = \frac{1}{2\pi i}\int_{s+} w^{n+1}e^{z\lambda}dz. \quad (32)$$

By the methods used under the discussion of convergence above it can then be shown that this expression exists and approaches zero as n increases indefinitely provided $q_0(t)$ exists and is equal to zero for $t < 0$. Equation (29) may therefore be written, subject to these conditions

$$s(t) = \frac{1}{2\pi i}\int_{s+} [F/(1-w)]e^{zt}dz. \quad (33)$$

In the first place the integral is zero for negative values of t because the integrand approaches zero faster than the path of integration increases. Moreover,

$$\int_I [F/(1-w)]e^{zt}dz \quad (34)$$

exists for all values of t and approaches zero for large values of t if $1 - w$ does not equal zero on the imaginary axis. Moreover, the integral

$$\int_C [F/(1-w)]e^{zt}dz \quad (35)$$

exists because

1. Since F and w are both analytic within the curve the integrand does not have any essential singularity there,
2. The poles, if any, lie within a finite distance of the origin because $w \to 0$ as $|z|$ increases, and
3. These two statements insure that the total number of poles is finite.

We shall next evaluate the integral for a very large value of t. It will suffice to take the C integral since the I integral approaches zero. Assume originally that $1 - w$ does not have a root on the imaginary axis and that $F(z)$ has the special value $w'(z)$. The integral may be written

$$\frac{1}{2\pi i}\int_C [w'/(1 - w)]e^{zt}dz. \tag{36}$$

Changing variables it becomes

$$\frac{1}{2\pi i}\int_D [1/(1 - w)]e^{zt}dw, \tag{37}$$

where z is a function of w and D is the curve in the w plane which corresponds to the curve C in the z plane. More specifically the imaginary axis becomes the locus $x = 0$ and the semicircle becomes a small curve which spirals around the origin. See Fig. 2. The function

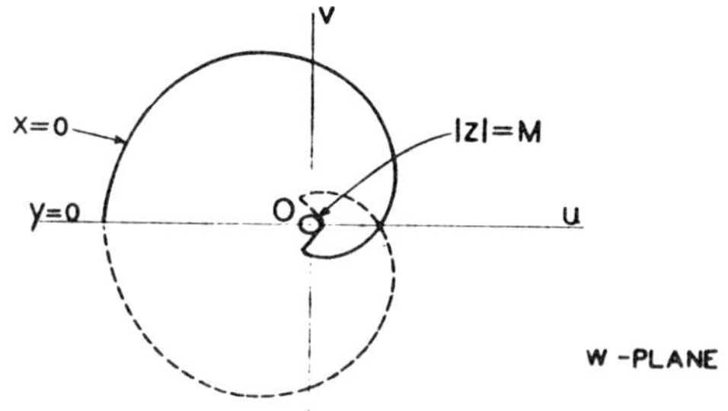

Fig. 2—Representative paths of integration in the w-plane corresponding to paths in Fig. 1.

z and, therefore, the integrand is, in general, multivalued and the curve of integration must be considered as carried out over the appropriate Riemann surface.[7]

Now let the path of integration shrink, taking care that it does not shrink across the pole at $w = 1$ and initially that it does not shrink across such branch points as interfere with its passage, if any. This shrinking does not alter the integral[8] because the integrand is analytic at all other points. At branch points which interfere with the passage of the path the branches stopped may be severed, transposed and connected in such a way that the shrinking may be continued past the branch point. This can be done without altering the value of the integral. Thus the curve can be shrunk until it becomes one or more very small circles surrounding the pole. The value of the total integral

[7] Osgood, loc. cit., Kap. 8.
[8] Osgood, loc. cit., Kap. 7, § 3, Satz 1.

(for very large values of t) is by the method of residues [9]

$$\sum_{j=1}^{n} r_j e^{z_j t}, \tag{38}$$

where z_j ($j = 1, 2 \cdots n$) is a root of $1 - w = 0$ and r_j is its order. The real part of z_j is positive because the curve in Fig. 1 encloses points with $x > 0$ only. The system is therefore stable or unstable according to whether

$$\sum_{j=1}^{n} r_j$$

is equal to zero or not. But the latter expression is seen from the procedure just gone through to equal the number of times that the locus $x = 0$ encircles the point $w = 1$.

If F does not equal w' the calculation is somewhat longer but not essentially different. The integral then equals

$$\sum_{j=1}^{n} \frac{F(z_j)}{w(z_j)} e^{z_j t} \tag{39}$$

if all the roots of $1 - w = 0$ are distinct. If the roots are not distinct the expression becomes

$$\sum_{j=1}^{n} \sum_{k=1}^{r_j} A_{jk} t^{k-1} e^{z_j t}, \tag{40}$$

where A_{jr_j}, at least, is finite and different from zero for general values of F. It appears then that unless F is specially chosen the result is essentially the same as for $F = w'$. The circuit is stable if the point lies wholly outside the locus $x = 0$. It is unstable if the point is within the curve. It can also be shown that if the point is on the curve conditions are unstable. We may now enunciate the following

Rule: Plot plus and minus the imaginary part of $AJ(i\omega)$ against the real part for all frequencies from 0 to ∞. If the point $1 + i0$ lies completely outside this curve the system is stable; if not it is unstable.

In case of doubt as to whether a point is inside or outside the curve the following criterion may be used: Draw a line from the point ($u = 1$, $v = 0$) to the point $z = -i\infty$. Keep one end of the line fixed at ($u = 1$, $v = 0$) and let the other end describe the curve from $z = -i\infty$ to $z = i\infty$, these two points being the same in the w plane. If the net angle through which the line turns is zero the point ($u = 1$, $v = 0$) is on the outside, otherwise it is on the inside.

If AJ be written $|AJ|(\cos\theta + i\sin\theta)$ and if the angle always

[9] Osgood, loc. cit., Kap. 7, § 11, Satz 1.

changes in the same direction with increasing ω, where ω is real, the rule can be stated as follows: The system is stable or unstable according to whether or not a real frequency exists for which the feed-back ratio is real and equal to or greater than unity.

In case $d\theta/d\omega$ changes sign we may have the case illustrated in Figs. 3 and 4. In these cases there are frequencies for which w is real and

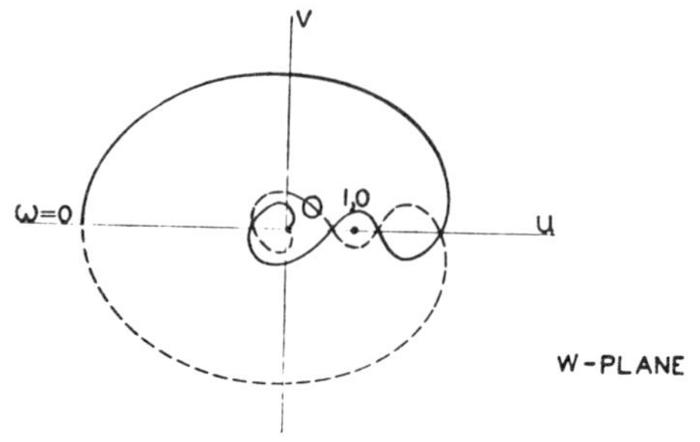

Fig. 3—Illustrating case where amplifying ratio is real and greater than unity for two frequencies, but where nevertheless the path of integration does not include the point 1, 0.

greater than 1. On the other hand, the point (1, 0) is outside of the locus $x = 0$ and, therefore, according to the rule there is a stable condition.

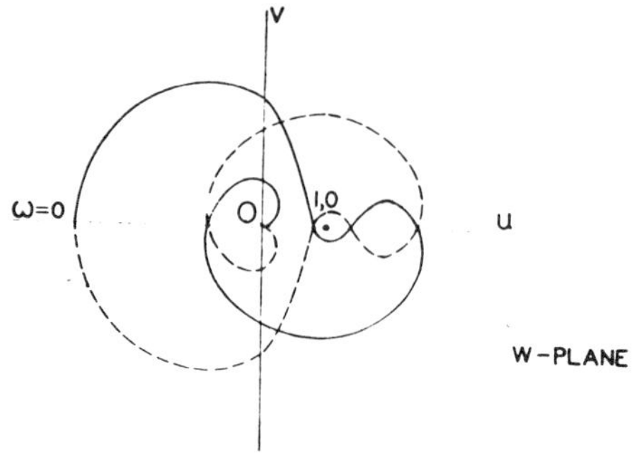

Fig. 4—Illustrating case where amplifying ratio is real and greater than unity for two frequencies, but where nevertheless the path of integration does not include the point 1, 0.

If networks of this type were used we should have the following interesting sequence of events: For low values of A the system is in a stable condition. Then as the gain is increased gradually, the system becomes unstable. Then as the gain is increased gradually still further, the system again becomes stable. As the gain is still further increased the system may again become unstable.

Examples

The following examples are intended to give a more detailed picture of certain rather simple special cases. They serve to illustrate the previous discussion. In all the cases F is taken equal to AJ so that f_0 is equal to AG. This simplifies the discussion but does not detract from the illustrative value.

1. Let the network be pure resistance except for the distortionless amplifier and a single bridged condenser, and let the amplifier be such that there is no reversal. We have

$$AJ(i\omega) = \frac{B}{\alpha + i\omega}, \tag{41}$$

where A and α are real positive constants. In (18) [10]

$$\begin{aligned} f_n &= \frac{1}{2\pi i}\int_I A^{n+1}J^{n+1}(i\omega)e^{i\omega t}di\omega \\ &= Be^{-\alpha t}(B^n t^n/n!). \end{aligned} \tag{42}$$

$$s(t) = Be^{-\alpha t}(1 + Bt + B^2t^2/2! + \cdots). \tag{43}$$

The successive terms f_0, f_1, etc., represent the impressed wave and the successive round trips. The whole series is the total current.

It is suggested that the reader should sketch the first few terms graphically for $B = \alpha$, and sketch the admittance diagrams for $B < \alpha$, and $B > \alpha$.

The expression in parentheses equals e^{Bt} and

$$s(t) = Be^{(B-\alpha)t}. \tag{44}$$

This expression will be seen to converge to 0 as t increases or fail to do so according to whether $B < \alpha$ or $B \geq \alpha$. This will be found to check the rule as applied to the admittance diagram.

2. Let the network be as in 1 except that the amplifier is so arranged that there is a reversal. Then

$$AJ(i\omega) = \frac{-B}{\alpha + i\omega}. \tag{45}$$

$$f_n = (-1)^{n+1}Be^{-\alpha t}(B^n t^n/n!). \tag{46}$$

The solution is the same as in 1 except that every other term in the series has its sign reversed:

$$\begin{aligned} s(t) &= -Be^{-\alpha t}(1 - Bt + B^2t^2/2! + \cdots) \\ &= -Be^{(-\alpha-B)t}. \end{aligned} \tag{47}$$

[10] Campbell, loc. cit. Pair 105.

This converges to 0 as t increases regardless of how great B may be taken. If the admittance diagram is drawn this is again found to check the rule.

3. Let the network be as in 1 except that there are two separated condensers bridged across resistance circuits. Then

$$AJ(i\omega) = \frac{B^2}{(\alpha + i\omega)^2}. \tag{48}$$

The solution for $s(t)$ is obtained most simply by taking every other term in the series obtained in 1.

$$\begin{aligned} s(t) &= Be^{-\alpha t}(Bt + B^3t^3/3! + \cdots) \\ &= Be^{-\alpha t} \sinh Bt. \end{aligned} \tag{49}$$

4. Let the network be as in 3 except that there is a reversal. Then

$$AJ(i\omega) = \frac{-B^2}{(\alpha + i\omega)^2}. \tag{50}$$

The solution is obtained most directly by reversing the sign of every other term in the series obtained in 3.

$$\begin{aligned} s(t) &= -Be^{-\alpha t}(Bt - B^3t^3/3! + \cdots) \\ &= -Be^{-\alpha t} \sin Bt. \end{aligned} \tag{51}$$

This is a most instructive example. An approximate diagram has been made in Fig. 5, which shows that as the gain is increased the

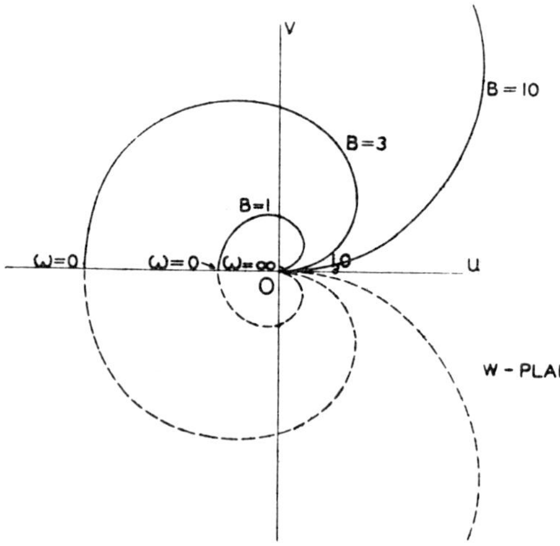

Fig. 5—Illustrating Example 4, with three values for B.

feed-back ratio may be made arbitrarily great and the angle arbitrarily small without the condition being unstable. This agrees with the expression just obtained, which shows that the only effect of increasing the gain is to increase the frequency of the resulting transient.

5. Let the conditions be as in 1 and 3 except for the fact that four separated condensers are used. Then

$$AJ(i\omega) = \frac{B^4}{(\alpha + i\omega)^4}. \tag{52}$$

The solution is most readily obtained by selecting every fourth term in the series obtained in 1.

$$\begin{aligned} s(t) &= Be^{-\alpha t}(B^3t^3/3! + B^7t^7/7! + \cdots) \\ &= \tfrac{1}{2}Be^{-\alpha t}(\sinh Bt - \sin Bt). \end{aligned} \tag{53}$$

This indicates a condition of instability when $B \geq \alpha$, agreeing with the result deducible from the admittance diagram.

6. Let the conditions be as in 5 except that there is a reversal. Then

$$Y = \frac{-B^4}{(\alpha + i\omega)^4}. \tag{54}$$

The solution is most readily obtained by changing the sign of every other term in the series obtained in 5.

$$s(t) = Be^{-\alpha t}(-B^3t^3/3! + B^7t^7/7! - \cdots). \tag{55}$$

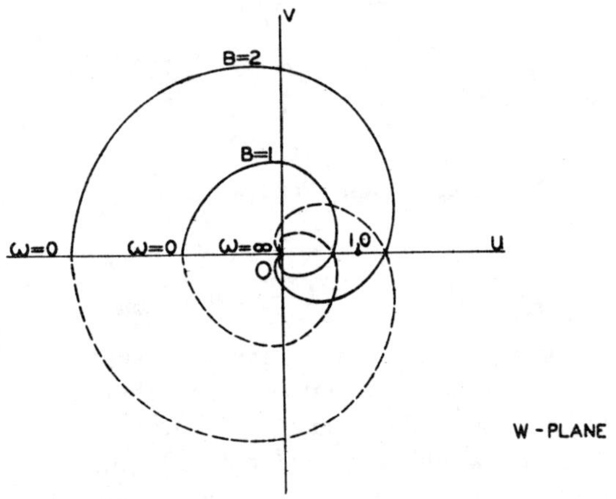

Fig. 6—Illustrating Example 6, with two values for B.

For large values of t this approaches

$$s(t) = -\tfrac{1}{2}Be^{(B/\sqrt{2}-\alpha)t}\sin(Bt/\sqrt{2} - \pi/4). \tag{56}$$

This example is interesting because it shows a case of instability although there is a reversal. Fig. 6 shows the admittance diagram for $B\sqrt{2} - \alpha < 0$ and for $B\sqrt{2} - \alpha > 0$.

7. Let

$$AG(t) = f_0(t) = A(1 - t), \qquad 0 \leq t \leq 1. \tag{57}$$

$$AG(t) = f_0(t) = 0, \qquad -\infty < t < 0, \qquad 1 < t < \infty. \tag{57'}$$

We have

$$AJ(i\omega) = A\int_0^1 (1 - t)e^{-i\omega t}dt$$
$$= A\left(\frac{1 - e^{-i\omega}}{\omega^2} + \frac{1}{i\omega}\right). \tag{58}$$

Fig. 7 is a plot of this case for $A = 1$.

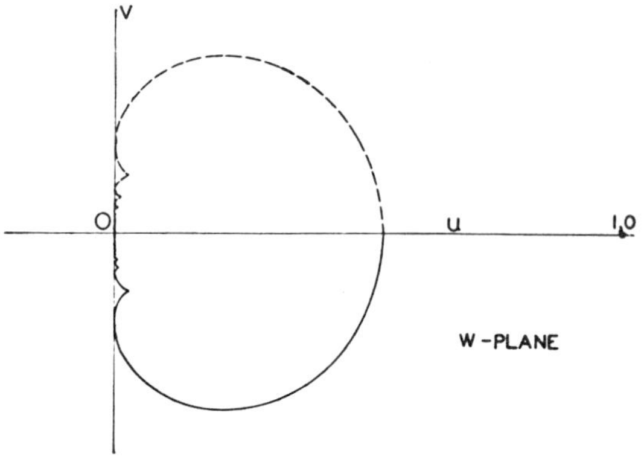

Fig. 7—Illustrating Example 7.

8. Let

$$AJ(i\omega) = \frac{A(1 + i\omega)}{(1 + i2\omega)}. \tag{59}$$

This is plotted on Fig. 8 for $A = 3$. It will be seen that the point 1 lies outside of the locus and for that reason we should expect that the system would be stable. We should expect from inspecting the diagram that the system would be stable for $A < 1$ and $A > 2$ and that it would be unstable for $1 \leq A \leq 2$. We have overlooked one fact, however; the expression for $AJ(i\omega)$ does not approach zero as ω

increases indefinitely. Therefore, it does not come within restriction (BI) and consequently the reasoning leading up to the rule does not apply.

The admittance in question can be made up by bridging a capacity in series with a resistance across a resistance line. This admittance

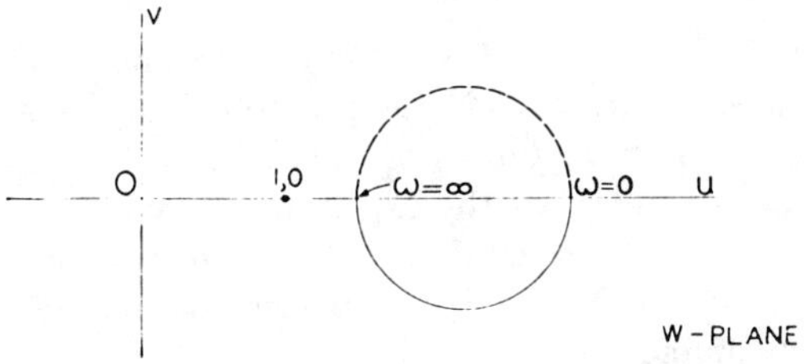

Fig. 8—Illustrating Example 8, without distributed constants.

obviously does not approach zero as the frequency increases. In any actual network there would, however, be a small amount of distributed capacity which, as the frequency is increased indefinitely, would cause the transmission through the network to approach zero. This is shown graphically in Fig. 9. The effect of the distributed capacity is

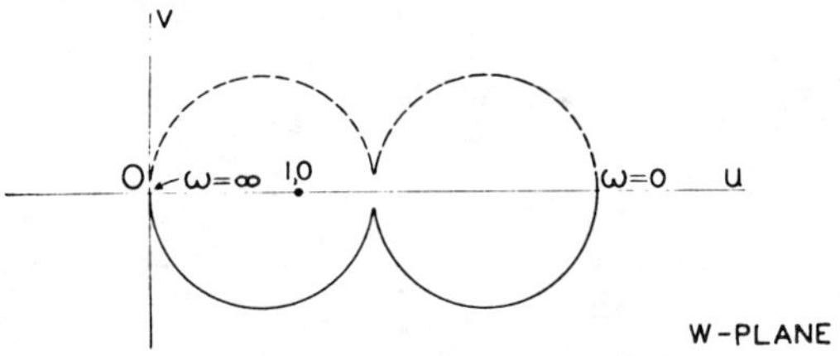

Fig. 9—Illustrating Example 8, with distributed constants.

essentially to cut a corridor from the circle in Fig. 8 to the origin, which insures that the point lies inside the locus.

Appendix I

Alternative Procedure

In some cases $AJ(i\omega)$ may be given as an analytic expression in $(i\omega)$. In that case the analytic expression may be used to define w for all values of z for which it exists. If the value for $AJ(i\omega)$ satisfies all the restrictions the value thus defined equals the w defined above for $0 \leq x < \infty$ only. For $-\infty < x < 0$ it equals the analytic continuation of the function w defined above. If there are no essential singularities anywhere including at ∞, the integral in (33) may be evaluated by the theory of residues by completing the path of integration so that all the poles of the integrand are included. We then have

$$s(t) = \sum_{j=1}^{j=n} \sum_{k=1}^{r_j} A_{jk} t^{k-1} e^{z_j t}. \tag{60}$$

If the network is made up of a finite number of lumped constants there is no essential singularity and the preceding expression converges because it has only a finite number of terms. In other cases there is an infinite number of terms, but the expression may still be expected to converge, at least, in the usual case. Then the system is stable if all the roots of $1 - w = 0$ have $x < 0$. If some of the roots have $x \geq 0$ the system is unstable.

The calculation then divides into three parts:

1. The recognition that the impedance function is $1 - w$.[11]
2. The determination of whether the impedance function has zeros for which $x \geq 0$.[12]

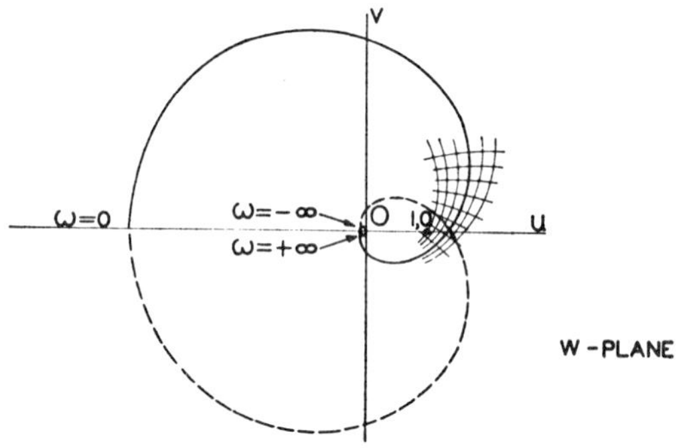

Fig. 10—Network of loci x = const., and y = const.

3. A deduction of a rule for determining whether there are roots for which $x \geq 0$. The actual solution of the equation is usually too laborious.

To proceed with the third step, plot the locus $x = 0$ in the w plane, i.e., plot the imaginary part of w against the real part for all the values of y, $-\infty < y < \infty$. See Fig. 10. Other loci representing

$$x = \text{const.} \tag{61}$$

and

$$y = \text{const.} \tag{62}$$

[11] Cf. H. W. Nichols, *Phys. Rev.*, vol. 10, pp. 171–193, 1917.
[12] Cf. Thompson and Tait, "Natural Philosophy," vol. I, § 344.

may be considered and are indicated by the network shown in the figure in fine lines. On one side of the curve x is positive and on the other it is negative. Consider the equation

$$w(z) - 1 = 0$$

and what happens to it as A increases from a very small to a very large value. At first the locus $x = 0$ lies wholly to the left of the point. For this case the roots must have $x < 0$. As A increases there may come a time when the curve or successive convolutions of it will sweep over the point $w = 1$. For every such crossing at least one of the roots changes the sign of its x. We conclude that if the point $w = 1$ lies inside the curve the system is unstable. It is now possible to enunciate the rule as given in the main part of the paper but there deduced with what appears to be a more general method.

Appendix II

Discussion of Restrictions

The purpose of this appendix is to discuss more fully the restrictions which are placed on the functions defining the network. A full discussion in the main text would have interrupted the main argument too much.

Define an additional function

$$n(z) = \frac{1}{2\pi i}\int_I \frac{AJ(i\lambda)}{i\lambda - z}\, d(i\lambda), \qquad -\infty < x < 0. \tag{63}$$

$$n(iy) = \lim_{x\to 0} n(z).$$

This definition is similar to that for $w(z)$ given previously. It is shown in the theorem [13] referred to that these functions are analytic for $x \neq 0$ if $AJ(i\omega)$ is continuous. We have not proved, as yet, that the restrictions placed on $G(t)$ necessarily imply that $J(i\omega)$ is continuous. For the time being we shall assume that $J(i\omega)$ may have finite discontinuities. The theorem need not be restricted to the case where $J(i\omega)$ is continuous. From an examination of the second proof it will be seen to be sufficient that $\int_I J(i\omega)d(i\omega)$ exist. Moreover, that proof can be slightly modified to include all cases where conditions (AI)–(AIII) are satisfied.

[13] Osgood, loc. cit.

For, from the equation at top of page 298 [13]

$$\left|\frac{w(z_0 - \Delta z) - w(z_0)}{\Delta z} - \frac{1}{2\pi i}\int_I \frac{AJ(i\lambda)}{(i\lambda - z_0)^2} d(i\lambda)\right|$$
$$\leq |\Delta z| \left|\frac{1}{2\pi i}\int_I \frac{AJ(i\lambda)d(i\lambda)}{(i\lambda - z_0 - \Delta z)(i\lambda - z_0)^2}\right|, \qquad x_0 > 0. \quad (64)$$

It is required to show that the integral exists. Now

$$\int_I \frac{AJ(i\lambda)d(i\lambda)}{(i\lambda - z_0 - \Delta z)(i\lambda - z_0)^2}$$
$$= \int_I \frac{AJ(i\lambda)d(i\lambda)}{(i\lambda - z_0)^3}\left(1 + \frac{\Delta z}{i\lambda - z_0} + \frac{\Delta z^2}{i\lambda - z_0} + \text{etc.}\right) \quad (65)$$

if Δz is taken small enough so the series converges. It will be sufficient to confine attention to the first term. Divide the path of integration into three parts,

$$-\infty < \lambda < -|z_0| - 1, \qquad -|z_0| - 1 < \lambda < |z_0| + 1, \qquad |z_0| + 1 < \lambda < \infty.$$

In the middle part the integral exists because both the integrand and the range of integration are finite. In the other ranges the integral exists if the integrand falls off sufficiently rapidly with increasing λ. It is sufficient for this purpose that condition (BI) be satisfied. The same proof applies to $n(z)$.

Next, consider $\lim_{x \to 0} w(z) = w(iy)$. If iy is a point where $J(iy)$ is continuous, a straightforward calculation yields

$$w(iy) = AJ(iy)/2 + P(iy). \quad (66a)$$

Likewise,

$$n(iy) = -AJ(iy)/2 + P(iy) \quad (66b)$$

where $P(iy)$ is the principal value [14] of the integral

$$\frac{1}{2\pi i}\int_I \frac{AJ(i\lambda)}{i\lambda - iy} d(i\lambda).$$

Subtracting

$$w(iy) - n(iy) = AJ(iy) \quad (67)$$

If (iy) is a point of discontinuity of $J(iy)$

$$|w| \text{ and } |n| \text{ increase indefinitely as } x \to 0. \quad (68)$$

Next, evaluate the integral

$$\frac{1}{2\pi i}\int_{z+I} w(z)e^{zt}dz,$$

[14] E. W. Hobson, "Functions of a Real Variable," vol. I, 3d edition, § 352.

where the path of integration is from $x - i\infty$ to $x + i\infty$ along the line $x =$ const. On account of the analytic nature of the integrand this integral is independent of x (for $x > 0$). It may be written then

$$\lim_{x\to 0}\frac{1}{2\pi i}\int_{x+I} w(z)e^{zt}dz = \lim_{x\to 0}\frac{1}{2\pi i}\int_{x+I}\frac{1}{2\pi i}\int_I \frac{AJ(i\lambda)}{i\lambda - z}e^{zt}d(i\lambda)dz$$

$$= \lim_{x\to 0}\frac{1}{2\pi i}\int_{x+I}\frac{1}{2\pi i}\lim_{M\to\infty}\left[\int_{-iM}^{iy-i\delta} + \int_{iy-i\delta}^{iy+i\delta} + \int_{iy+i\delta}^{iM}\right]\frac{AJ(i\lambda)}{i\lambda - z}e^{zt}d(i\lambda)dz$$

$$= \lim_{x\to 0}\left[\frac{1}{2\pi i}\int_{x+I}\frac{1}{2\pi i}\int_{iy-i\delta}^{iy+i\delta}\frac{AJ(i\lambda)}{i\lambda - z}e^{zt}d(i\lambda)dz + Q(t,\delta)\right], \quad x>0, \qquad (69)$$

where δ is real and positive. The function Q defined by this equation exists for all values of t and for all values of δ. Similarly,

$$\lim_{x\to 0}\frac{1}{2\pi i}\int_{x+I} n(z)e^{zt}dz$$

$$= \left[\lim_{x\to 0}\frac{1}{2\pi i}\int_{x+I}\frac{1}{2\pi i}\int_{iy+i\delta}^{iy+i\delta}\frac{AJ(i\lambda)}{i\lambda - z}e^{zt}d(i\lambda)dz + Q(t,\delta)\right], \quad x<0, \qquad (70)$$

Subtracting and dropping the limit designations

$$\frac{1}{2\pi i}\int_{x+I} w(z)e^{zt}dz - \frac{1}{2\pi i}\int_{x+I} n(z)e^{zt}dz = \frac{1}{2\pi i}\int_I AJ(i\lambda)e^{i\lambda t}d(i\lambda). \qquad (71)$$

The first integral is zero for $t < 0$ as can be seen by taking x sufficiently large. Likewise, the second is equal to zero for $t > 0$. Therefore,

$$\frac{1}{2\pi i}\int_{x+I} w(z)e^{zt}dz = \frac{1}{2\pi i}\int_I AJ(i\omega)e^{i\omega t}d(i\omega) = AG(t), \quad 0 < t < \infty \qquad (72)$$

$$-\frac{1}{2\pi i}\int_{x+I} n(z)e^{zt}dz$$

$$= \frac{1}{2\pi i}\int_I AJ(i\omega)e^{i\omega t}d(i\omega) = AG(t) \quad -\infty < t < 0. \qquad (73)$$

We may now conclude that

$$\int_I n(iy)e^{iyt}d(iy) = 0, \qquad -\infty < t < \infty \qquad (74)$$

provided

$$G(t) = 0, \qquad -\infty < t < 0. \qquad \text{(AII)}$$

But (74) is equivalent to

$$n(z) = 0, \qquad (74')$$

which taken with (67) gives

$$w(iy) = AJ(iy). \qquad \text{(BIII)}$$

(BIII) is, therefore, a necessary consequence of (AII). (74′) taken with (68) shows that

$$J(iy) \text{ is continuous.} \qquad \text{(BII)}$$

It may be shown [15] that (BI) is a consequence of (AI). Consequently all the B conditions are deducible from the A conditions.

Conversely, it may be inquired whether the A conditions are deducible from the B conditions. This is of interest if $AJ(i\omega)$ is given and is known to satisfy the B conditions, whereas nothing is known about G.

Condition AII is a consequence of BIII as may be seen from (67) and (74). On the other hand AI and AIII cannot be inferred from the B conditions. It can be shown by examining (5), however, that if the slightly more severe condition

$$\lim_{y \to \infty} y^{\gamma} J(iy) \text{ exists,} \qquad (\gamma > 1), \qquad \text{(BI}a\text{)}$$

is satisfied then

$$G(t) \text{ exists,} \qquad -\infty < t < \infty, \qquad \text{(AI}a\text{)}$$

which, together with AII, insures the validity of the reasoning.

It remains to show that the measured value of $J(i\omega)$ is equal to that defined by (6). The measurement consists essentially in applying a sinusoidal wave and determining the response after a long period. Let the impressed wave be

$$E = \text{real part of } e^{i\omega t}, \qquad t \geqq 0. \qquad (75)$$
$$E = 0, \qquad t < 0. \qquad (75')$$

The response is

$$\text{real part of} \int_0^t AG(\lambda) e^{i\omega(t-\lambda)} d\lambda$$
$$= \text{real part of } Ae^{i\omega t} \int_0^t G(\lambda) e^{-i\omega\lambda} d\lambda. \qquad (76)$$

For large values of t this approaches

$$\text{real part of } Ae^{i\omega t} J(i\omega). \qquad (77)$$

Consequently, the measurements yield the value $AJ(i\omega)$.

[15] See Hobson, loc. cit., vol. II, 2d edition, § 335. It will be apparent that K depends on the total variation but is independent of the limits of integration.

Stability of Systems with Delayed Feedback

YA. Z. TSYPKIN

Translation by L. Jocić and S. Kahne

Abstract–**Stability conditions are derived for systems with delayed feedback. Influence of the delay time and associated parameters is investigated for several simple control systems. A generalized criterion is given, which enlarges greatly the class of systems with delayed feedback under consideration. Finally, a comparison is made of the results, derived from the established criterion, with an approximation method often encountered in the literature.**

We refer to a system characterized by the property that the feedback variable at time t depends upon the system state at time $t - \tau$, τ-constant, as a system with delayed feedback. Such a system can be represented as having a delay element in its feedback loop (Fig. 1). The essential characteristic of the delay element is that the input variable is repeated exactly at the output after a time period τ, which will be called the delay time (Fig. 2). In fact, the delay element may be a part of the system itself (I), or located in the feedback loop (II).

Electrical power systems which have their feedbacks closed through tie-lines, systems with acoustic feedback, etc., are examples of systems with delayed feedback. Many other control systems belong to this class after a suitable approximation is made in their description.

The presence of a delay element introduces new qualitative characteristics into a system, which may cause undesired instability. For this reason, the analysis of such systems has considerable significance.

There exists a large number of papers dealing with this problem. Most of them, [1]–[11], have been applying an approximation method based upon the Hurwitz criterion for stability analysis. However, the method has not been derived precisely, and as we shall see later, it often leads to qualitatively wrong results. Other authors have used graphical approaches to treat delayed feedback systems [12], [13], or approximate graphical or numerical solutions of the characteristic equation [14]–[16]. Needless to say these numerically posed problems do not leave any space for general conclusions, and they appear cumbersome. Finally, the work reported in [10], [17] has raised a question regarding methods, which avoid the explicit solution of the characteristic equation. Nevertheless these methods are not generally applicable, and in some places these papers contain errors leading to questionable conclusions.

Therefore no previous work that we are aware of has established a sufficiently general and exact method for analysis of systems with delayed feedback. The paper presented here is dedicated to this goal. Stability criteria proposed below are

The author is with the Research Institute for Aircraft Equipment, Ministry of Aviation Industry, USSR.

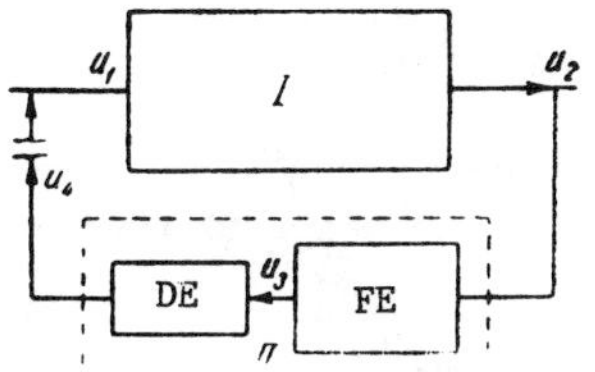

Fig. 1. Block diagram of a system with delayed feedback. I: Forward element. II: Feedback path. DE: Delay element. FE: Feedback element.

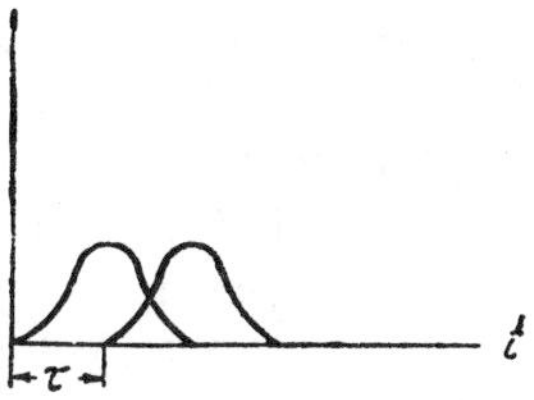

Fig. 2.

based upon considerations of frequency characteristics of the part of the system without time-delay. The criteria obtained simplify greatly the stability analysis of systems with delayed feedback.

I. Equations and Frequency Characteristics of Systems with Delayed Feedback

Let us form the equations describing systems with delayed feedback. In order to abbreviate further equations, we will use the time derivative operator

$$D^k = \frac{d^k}{dt^k}, \quad k = 1, 2, \cdots.$$

It is possible then to write the differential equation corresponding to system I (Fig. 1) as

$$Q_1(D)u_2 = P_1(D)u_1, \tag{1}$$

where $Q_1(D)$ and $P_1(D)$ are polynomials in D.

The feedback path II (Fig. 1) is composed of two elements: a feedback element and a delay element. The differential equation for the feedback element has a form similar to (1):

$$Q_2(D)u_3 = P_2(D)u_2, \tag{2}$$

and the delay element is described by

$$u_4 = u_3(t - \tau). \tag{3}$$

After expanding the right-hand part of the previous equation in a Taylor series, one can rewrite (3) as follows

$$u_4 = e^{-\tau D}u_3. \tag{4}$$

Reprinted with permission from *Avtomat. Telemekh.*, vol. 7, pp. 107–129, #2-3, 1946.

By eliminating u_2 and u_3 from (1), (2), and (4), we obtain the open-loop system equation (Fig. 3) as

$$Q(D)u_4 = P(D)e^{-\tau D}u_1, \tag{5}$$

where

$$Q(D) = Q_1(D)Q_2(D), \quad P(D) = P_1(D)P_2(D).$$

It is easy to see that the equation for the closed-loop system (Fig. 1) can be obtained from (5) by setting $u_4 = u_1$, to get

$$\{Q(D) - P(D)e^{-\tau D}\} u_1 = 0. \tag{6}$$

When $\tau = 0$, this equation transforms into an ordinary differential equation of the closed-loop system without the delay element

$$\{Q(D) - P(D)\} u_1 = 0. \tag{7}$$

The system described by (7) will be referred to as the *equivalent system*.

The equation of the system with delayed feedback (6) differs from the differential equation describing the equivalent system (7), in that it contains not only the function $u_1(t)$, but also $u_1(t - \tau)$. In the literature this type of equation is called a difference-differential equation [18], [19], or the histero-differential equation [20]. A general theory of such equations is undeveloped up to now. In order to obtain solutions of the histero-differential equations one has to solve transcendental characteristic equations, which is by itself a cumbersome operation, possible for numerically specified systems only. Another way of solving these equations is, for example, by employing the Laplace transformation [19], although in that case the form of the obtained solution precludes any further investigations.

Furthermore, for stability analysis it is not necessary to know exact solutions of system equations; it suffices to determine the character of roots of the characteristic equation. For this reason we will not be primarily concerned with the solutions of histero-differential equations, and we refer the interested reader to the literature [18]-[21].

An essential role in the following stability analysis will be played by the frequency characteristics of the open-loop system. We turn our attention now to the determination of these characteristics.

Suppose that the input of the open-loop system (Fig. 3) is sinusoidal:

$$u_1 = u_{1m}e^{j\omega t}, \qquad j = \sqrt{-1}.$$

The output variable u_4 will be also sinusoidal in the steady state, with different amplitude and phase.

It is well known [22] that u_4 can be found from (5) by replacing D with $j\omega$:

$$u_4 = \frac{P(j\omega)}{Q(j\omega)} e^{-j\tau\omega} u_1.$$

The ratio

$$W_\tau(j\omega) = \frac{u_4}{u_1} = \frac{P(j\omega)}{Q(j\omega)} e^{-j\tau\omega} \tag{8}$$

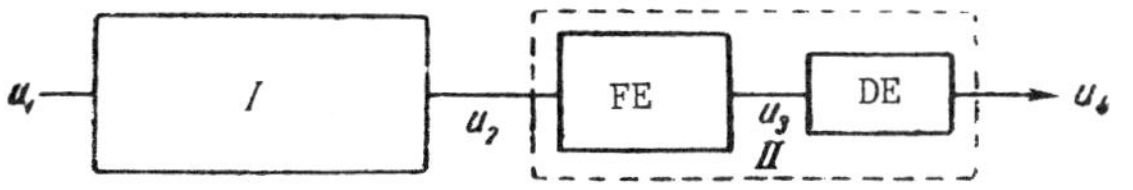

Fig. 3. System with open feedback path.

is the transfer function of the open-loop system. It is obvious that the ratio $W(j\omega) = P(j\omega)/Q(j\omega)$ is the transfer function of the equivalent system. By separating the real and imaginary part, $W(jw)$ can be represented as follows

$$W(j\omega) = \frac{P(j\omega)}{Q(j\omega)} = A(\omega) + jB(\omega) \tag{9}$$

or

$$W(j\omega) = W_0(\omega)e^{j\theta(\omega)}, \tag{10}$$

where

$$W_0(\omega) = \sqrt{A^2(\omega) + B^2(\omega)} \qquad \theta(\omega) = \arctan \frac{B(\omega)}{A(\omega)},$$

and therefore, according to (8), the open-loop transfer function of the system with time-delayed feedback can be represented as follows

$$W_\tau(j\omega) = W_0(j\omega)e^{j[\theta(\omega) - \tau\omega]}. \tag{11}$$

It is easy to see from (10) that the transfer function represents the relation between the amplitude and the phase at the output and the frequency of the input sinusoidal signal. Let us observe that in order to determine the transfer function it is not necessary to start with the time-domain system equations, as we did earlier. The transfer functions of nonelectrical systems can be obtained by means of analogies [23] with the well-known complex laws for electrical quantities.

II. Stability Conditions

Stability problems for linear systems can be reduced to the analysis of roots of the characteristic equations. A given system is said to be stable if all the roots of the characteristic equation have negative real part, and unstable if there exists at least one root with a positive real part.

The characteristic equation for a system with delayed feedback can be derived from (6) by replacing the operator D with z and by equating to zero the expression in parenthesis:

$$Q(z) - P(z)e^{-\tau z} = 0. \tag{12}$$

The necessary and sufficient conditions for stability are expressed, then, as follows:

$$\text{Re}\,[z_k] < 0,$$

where z_k are the roots of the characteristic equation (12).

In the case of $\tau = 0$, which corresponds to the equivalent system, the characteristic equation takes the form of this algebraic equation:

$$Q(z) - P(z) = 0. \tag{13}$$

Since the characteristic equation (12) of the system with time-delayed feedback is a transcendental rather than algebraic equation, it is not possible to apply directly the well-known Hurwitz stability criterion. Nevertheless, it will be shown that by using the open-loop transfer function of the equivalent system one can establish simple and straightforward stability criteria for systems with delayed feedback.

III. Stability Criteria for Systems with Delayed Feedback

Let us draw a graph of the transfer function (10) in polar coordinates (W_0, θ), for the different values of the frequency ω in the interval between 0 and ∞. Then, according to Nyquist [24], the equivalent system is stable if the point $(1, j0)$ is outside the graph (Fig. 4(a)), and unstable if the point $(1, j0)$ is inside it (Fig. 4(b)).[1]

It is easy to show that the relative position of the point $(1, j0)$ with respect to the polar plot of the transfer function determines the signs of the real parts of the roots of the characteristic equation:[2] in the case of Fig. 4(a) the real parts of all characteristic roots are negative, while in the case of Fig. 4(b) a certain number of roots have positive real parts.

If the polar plot passes through the point $(1, j0)$, then the characteristic equation will have two pure imaginary roots, and the remaining roots will have negative real parts. Therefore, crossing of the polar plot of $W(j\omega)$ through the point $(1, j0)$ corresponds to the sign change of real parts of characteristic roots.

Let us consider now a polar plot of the open-loop transfer function $W_\tau(j\omega)$ for the system with delayed feedback:

$$W_\tau(j\omega) = W_0(\omega)\, e^{j[\theta(\omega) - \tau\omega]}.$$

This graph differs from the one obtained for equivalent system transfer function

$$W(j\omega) = W_0(\omega)\, e^{j\theta(\omega)}$$

by the fact that the radius-vectors $W_\tau(j\omega)$ are shifted in clockwise direction by additional angles proportional to ω. The coefficient of proportionality is the delay time τ. It is absolutely clear that the presence of the delay element, which transforms the plots of $W(j\omega)$ as indicated above, may cause instability of the closed loop system.

Let us assume that the equivalent system is stable. This means that the curve $W(j\omega)$ does not encircle the point $(1, j0)$, and all roots of the characteristic equation (13) are located in the left half of the complex z-plane (Fig. 5(a)). By increasing τ monotonically from 0, the roots of the characteristic equation (12) will relocate in the z-plane; the polar plot of $W(j\omega)$ will change as indicated above. For a certain value $\tau = \tau_0$, the curve $W(j\omega)$ will pass through the point $(1, j0)$. In this case the characteristic equation (12) will have two conjugate roots on the imaginary axis of the z-plane (Fig. 4(b)), whose magnitudes are equal to the frequency $\omega = \omega_0$. $(1, j0)$ is the corresponding point on the $W_\tau(j\omega)$ plane.

Further increase in τ may cause the encirclement of the point $(1, j0)$ in which case the characteristic equation (12) would have two roots in the right half of the z-plane (Fig. 5(c)) and, consequently, the system would be unstable.

[1] The arrow indicates the direction of increased frequency.

[2] See Appendix, and also [25].

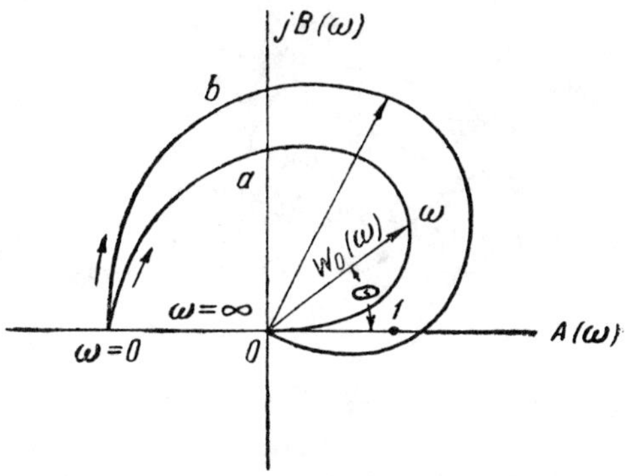

Fig. 4. Frequency characteristics of open-loop transfer function $W(j\omega)$ for equivalent system. a: Stable equivalent system. b: Unstable case.

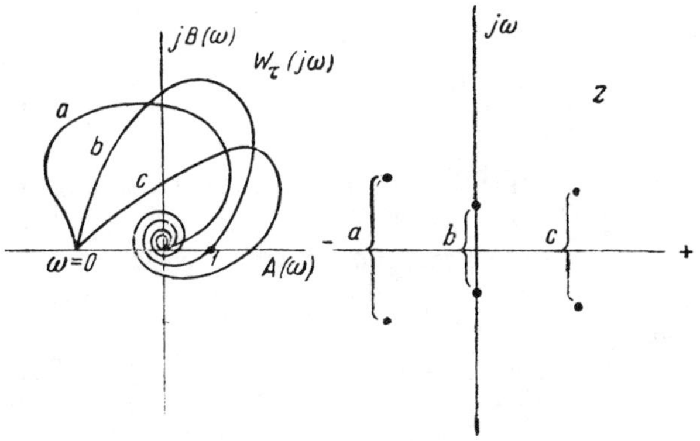

Fig. 5. Variations of the frequency characteristics ($W_\tau(j\omega)$-plane) and of the characteristics roots (z-plane) as τ increases. a: $\tau < \tau_0$. b: $\tau = \tau_0$. c: $\tau > \tau_0$.

Increase in τ could also cause the plot of $W(j\omega)$ to contain the point $(1, j0)$, now and then, and to encircle it, i.e., the roots of the characteristic equation (12) could be passing back and forth from the left half plane. As a consequence, the system may become stable and again unstable, and vice versa.

We will refer to τ_0 and ω_0 as the critical delay time and critical frequency, respectively. Critical delay time determines the transfer of a pair of characteristic roots through the imaginary axis $j\omega$ and therefore, system stability. It is obvious that the critical delay time and critical frequency are determined by the equation

$$W_\tau(j\omega) = 1 \tag{14}$$

or

$$W_0(\omega)\, e^{j[\theta(\omega) - \tau\omega]} = 1. \tag{15}$$

This equation is satisfied if the following conditions are met:

$$W_0(\omega) = 1 \tag{16}$$

and

$$\theta(\omega) - \tau\omega = -2\pi n, \tag{17}$$

where n is a positive integer

We solve (16) with respect to ω to get the critical frequencies ω_{0i}. By substituting ω_{0i} in (17) we find the critical delay

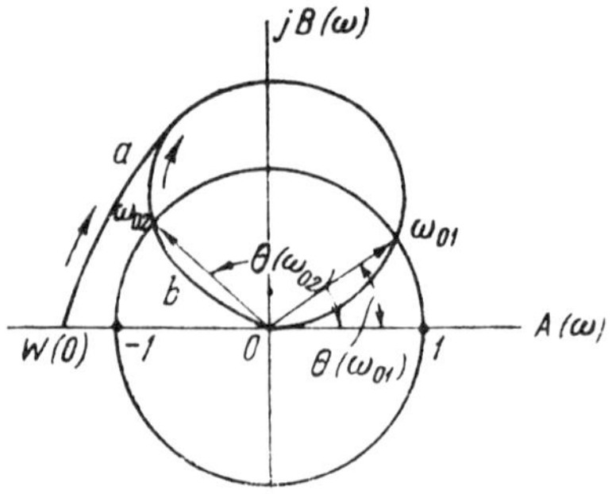

Fig. 6. Determination of critical frequencies ω_{0i}, and critical delay-times τ_{0i} from the graph of an open-loop equivalent system. a: There exists one critical frequency. b: Two critical frequencies are present.

times

$$\tau_{0i}(n) = \frac{\theta(\omega_{0i})}{\omega_{0i}} + \frac{2\pi n}{\omega_{0i}}. \tag{18}$$

Conditions (16) and (17) have a straightforward interpretation in the $W(j\omega)$ plane. Plot first a circle with center at the origin of the $W(j\omega)$ plane, and unit radius (Fig. 6). The intersection of the $W(j\omega)$ curve with this circle determines critical frequencies ω_{0i}, and by dividing the angles $\theta(\omega_{0i})$ by corresponding critical frequencies we get critical delay times τ_{0i}.

Stability boundaries are determined only by those critical delay times τ_{0i}, at which the $W_\tau(j\omega)$-curve contains the point $(1, j0)$, without encircling it. These points τ_{0i} are called *limiting* values. Therefore, in order to establish regions of stability and instability it suffices to find the boundary delay times.

As can be seen from (18), the boundary delay times are functions of system parameters. This offers an opportunity to analyze the influence of system parameters on system stability. Considering the arrangement of Fig. 6 one can draw several general conclusions regarding stability of systems with delayed feedback, and to formulate simple stability criteria.

1) Let

$$W_0(\omega) < 1$$

for all ω. Then, critical frequencies do not exist, and the system is stable for all τ. This case is not particularly interesting, and it will not be pursued any further.

2) Let

$$W_0(j0) < -1.$$

Then, there exists a single critical frequency ω_0 (Fig. 6(a)) which corresponds to a limiting value of the delay time τ_0. The system is stable for $\tau < \tau_0$, and unstable if $\tau < \tau_0$. The remaining $\tau_0(n)$ are greater than τ_0 for any positive $n > 1$, and their consideration is unnecessary.

3) Let

$$|W_0(j0)| < 1$$

(or in particular $W_0(0) = 0$). Then, there exist two critical frequencies ω_{01} and ω_{02} (Fig. 6(b)), with $\omega_{01} > \omega_{02}$. Hence, $\tau_{01} < \tau_{02}$, and τ_{01} is the limiting delay time. The system is stable for $\tau < \tau_{01}$, and unstable if $\tau_{02} > \tau > \tau_{01}$.

If $\tau_{02} < \tau_{01}$, further increase in τ causes an alternation of stable and unstable behavior. System is stable for $\tau_{02}(n-1) < \tau < \tau_{01}(n)$, and unstable for $\tau_{01}(n) < \tau < \tau_{02}(n)$. On the other hand, if $\tau_{02} > \tau_{01}(1)$ the system will be unstable for all $\tau > \tau_{01}$.

If a closed system with delayed feedback is unstable, then the growing oscillations have frequencies for which

$$W_0(\omega) > 1, \tag{19}$$

i.e., the frequencies determined by the parts of the plot outside the unit circle. The frequency of growing oscillations decreases as $\tau(\tau > \tau_{01})$ increases.

If the system is unstable for larger τ, i.e., if the alternation of stability and instability domains is missing, then resulting oscillations occur at several frequencies lower than ω_{01}. The number of these frequencies is always finite, and it increases with increasing τ. If, for example,

$$\tau_{01}(n-1) < \tau < \tau_{01}(n),$$

the number of frequencies will equal n.

In systems with delayed feedback (for example, in control systems) we try usually to keep the delay time τ low. For this reason, the most important is the smallest limiting delay time $\tau_{0\,\min}$. Consequently, for such systems one can formulate the following practical stability criterion: *A system with delayed feedback is stable, if its delay time τ is smaller than the minimum limiting delay time, i.e.,*

$$\tau < \tau_{0\,\min}.$$

From the above considerations, one can see that for stability analysis of systems with time-delayed feedback it suffices to know only the open-loop transfer function.

The relations established here determine the limiting values for delay time, and permits one to construct domains of stability and instability, thus giving a full picture of the influence of system parameters on stability.

IV. Stability Analysis of Certain Systems

Before we turn our attention to the stability analysis of certain typical systems with delayed feedback, let us make a few preliminary remarks.

It is often convenient to express the open-loop transfer function in terms of the dimensionless quantity x proportional to the frequency

$$x = \frac{\omega}{\omega_c}. \tag{20}$$

In this case, (16) and (17) which determine the critical frequencies and delay times become

$$W_0(x) = 1, \tag{21}$$

$$T_{0i}(n) = \omega_c . \tau_{0i}(n) = \frac{\theta(x_{0i})}{x_{0i}} + \frac{2\pi n}{x_{0i}}. \tag{22}$$

A. Let us consider now the simplest pressure control system [26]. By u_2 we denote the variation of pressure from its nominal value, and u_4 describes the behavior of the controlling mechanism. Then, we can write equations for the plant and the positional[3] control mechanism as follows

$$(T_aD + z_1)u_2 = u_1, \tag{23}$$

$$u_4 = -ae^{-\tau D}u_2, \quad u_4 = u_1, \tag{24}$$

where T_a is the plant time constant, z_1 is the load coefficient, and a is a positive coefficient.

It is obvious from (24) that we assume that the action of the controlling mechanism is delayed by a constant time τ, with respect to the response of the sensor measuring the controlled variable u_2. The controller equation for the equivalent system is given by

$$u_4 = -au_2. \tag{25}$$

Noting that

$$Q(D) = T_aD + z_1, P(D) = -a,$$

we obtain from (9) the following open-loop transfer function:

$$W(j\omega) = \frac{-a}{T_aj\omega + z_1}. \tag{26}$$

By using the following notation

$$x = \frac{\omega}{z_1}T_a \qquad \gamma = \frac{a}{z_1}, \tag{27}$$

we can represent the transfer function in the form

$$W(jx) = \frac{-\gamma}{jx + 1}, \tag{28}$$

or according to (9), we get finally

$$W(jx) = \frac{\gamma}{\sqrt{x^2 + 1}}e^{j[\pi - \arctan x]}. \tag{29}$$

The polar plot of the equivalent system transfer function, given by (29), is a semicircle (Fig. 7(a)). By constructing the unit circle we get x_0 and T_0. This system is stable if $T < T_0$, and unstable if $T > T_0$.

In order to investigate the influence of γ on stability we have to redraw the $W(jx)/\gamma$ on Fig. 7(b) and instead of the unit circle we draw a circle of radius $1/\gamma$. Changes in γ are reflected then by changes in circle radius.

If $\gamma \leqslant 1$, the x_0 does not exist and system is always stable. For $\gamma > 1$ the system is stable if $T < T_0$. Larger γ corresponds to a larger x_0 and smaller T_0. When $T = T_0$ the system starts to oscillate at the frequency

$$\omega = \frac{x_0 z_1}{T_a}. \tag{30}$$

The values x_0 and T_0 can be derived from (21) and (22) as

$$x_0 = \sqrt{\gamma^2 - 1}, \tag{31}$$

$$T_0 = \frac{\pi - \arctan\sqrt{\gamma^2 - 1}}{\sqrt{\gamma^2 - 1}}. \tag{32}$$

[3]According to the terminology used by Oppelt [26].

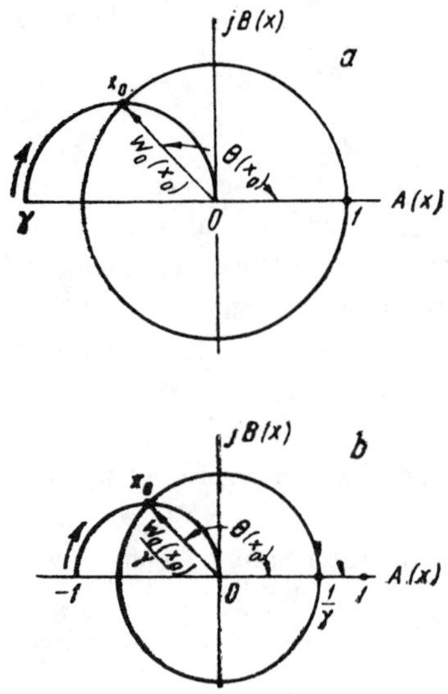

Fig. 7. a: Frequency characteristic of a simple pressure control system (system A). b: Normalized frequency diagram for system A.

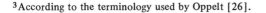

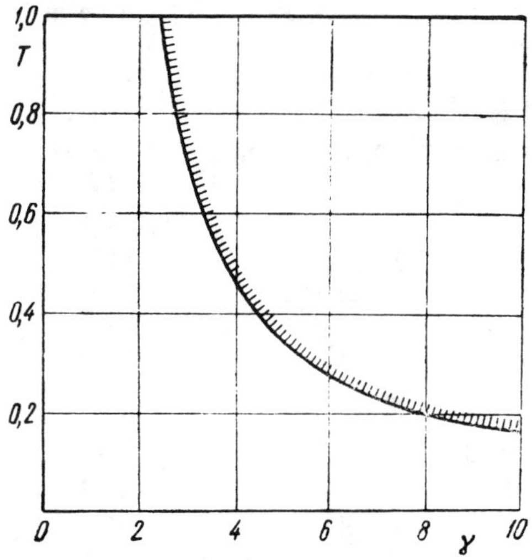

Fig. 8. Stability boundary $T_0 = f(\gamma)$ for system A. Unshaded side corresponds to the stability domain.

The stability limit, determined by (32), divides the plane (T, γ) in two parts (Fig. 8). The lower portion corresponds to a stable system, and the upper part to an unstable system.

We refer to a point with coordinates

$$T = \frac{z_1}{T_a}\tau \qquad \gamma = \frac{a}{z_1}, \tag{33}$$

as the *parameter point*. It is obvious that to each parameter point corresponds a system described by (23) and (24), and vice versa. A change in system parameters forces a coordinate change of the parameter point. The given system is stable if the parameter point is located within the stability region, and unstable otherwise. For $\gamma >> 1$ the stability limit equation can be simplified as follows

$$x_0 \approx \gamma \qquad \arctan\sqrt{\gamma^2 - 1} = \arctan\gamma \approx \frac{\pi}{2},$$

and hence,

$$T_0 = \frac{\pi}{2\gamma}. \tag{34}$$

By increasing γ (i.e., a) we decrease T_0, thus implying that as the regulator sensitivity increases the system becomes unstable for smaller τ, i.e., the presence of the delay always deteriorates the exactness of control. It is interesting also to notice that system stability is almost independent upon load changes.

B. Consider now the electrical system represented by Fig. 9. This system is the electrical analog of many control systems for regulation of temperature, voltage, etc. In particular it represents a system for pendulum control which was investigated in detail by Minorsky [17].

Equations describing this system may be written in the following form:

$$(LCD^2 + RCD + 1)u_2 = u_1, \tag{35}$$

$$MDi_a = -u_1. \tag{36}$$

By assuming that the anode current i_a is lagging behind the grid voltage, we get

$$i_a = Su_2(t - \tau), \tag{37}$$

where S denotes the slope of the tube's characteristics. Hence, (36) can be rewritten

$$MSDu_2 e^{-\tau D} = -u_1. \tag{38}$$

We open the loop in points 1 - 1, and obtain the following open-loop transfer function:

$$W(j\omega) = -\gamma \frac{j\omega}{\omega_{c.}^2 - \omega^2 + \delta j\omega},$$

where

$$\omega_{c.}^2 = \frac{1}{LC} \qquad \delta = \frac{R}{L} \qquad \gamma_1 = \frac{MS}{LC} = a\omega_c^2 \qquad a = MS. \tag{39}$$

Furthermore, we introduce the following dimensionless quantities

$$x = \frac{\omega}{\omega_{c.}} \qquad \beta = \frac{\delta}{\omega_{c.}}$$

and write the transfer function in the form (10), to get[4]

$$W(jx) = \gamma \frac{x}{\sqrt{(1 - x^2)^2 + \beta^2 x^2}} \exp j\left[\frac{3}{2}\pi - \arctan\frac{\beta x}{1 - x^2}\right], \tag{40}$$

where

$$\gamma = \frac{\gamma_1}{\omega_{c.}} = a\omega_{c.}.$$

A family of amplitude-phase characteristics for different values of β and $\gamma = 1$ is shown in Fig. 10. The arrows indicate the direction in which x increases. Let us construct a circle of radius $1/\gamma$ centered at the origin. For small values of β there exist two critical values of x: x_{01} and x_{02}. As β increases the $W(j\omega)$-plots gather around the origin. Therefore, starting with a certain value of β, the system becomes absolutely stable for all T. We reach a similar conclusion by considering the case of decreasing λ with β = const. The system is stable if $T < T_{01}$, and unstable for $T_{02} > T > T_{01}$. If $T_{01}(1) > T_{02}$, then a smooth increase in T will cause the regions of stability and instability to alternate.

[4]When the argument of arctg passes through infinity ($x = 1$) the system phase decreases by π.

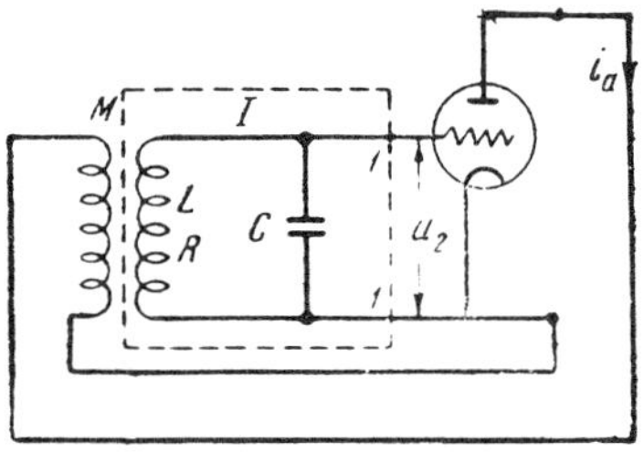

Fig. 9. Electrical system modeled in example B.

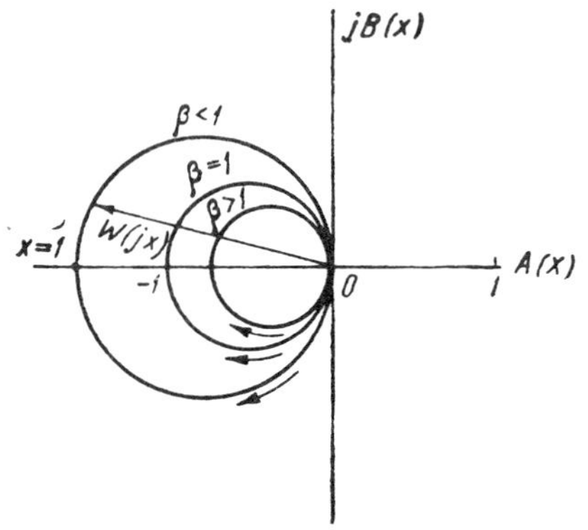

Fig. 10. Normalized polar plot of the transfer function $W(jx)$ representing system B for different values of β.

In order to establish stability regions we need to find x_{0i} and $T_{0i}(n)$. By equating the magnitude of the transfer function to one, we get after some elementary transformations,

$$x^4 - (2 - \beta^2 + \gamma^2)x^2 + 1 = 0,$$

and hence,

$$x_{01,02} = \sqrt{\frac{2 - \beta^2 + \gamma^2}{2} \pm \sqrt{\frac{(2 - \beta^2 + \gamma^2)^2}{4} - 1}}, \tag{41}$$

and according to (22),

$$T_{0i}(n) = \omega_{c.}\tau_{0i} = \frac{\frac{3}{2}\pi - \arctan\frac{\beta x_{0i}}{1 - x_{0i}^2}}{x_{0i}} + \frac{2\pi n}{x_{0i}}. \tag{42}$$

It is easy to see that the number of critical values x_{0i} is determined by the sign of the discriminant, i.e., for

$\gamma < \beta$ there is none;
$\gamma = \beta$ there is one: $x_0 = 1$;
$\gamma > \beta$ there are two critical values.

Therefore, in the first case the system is stable for all T, in the second case there will be oscillations with frequency $\omega =$

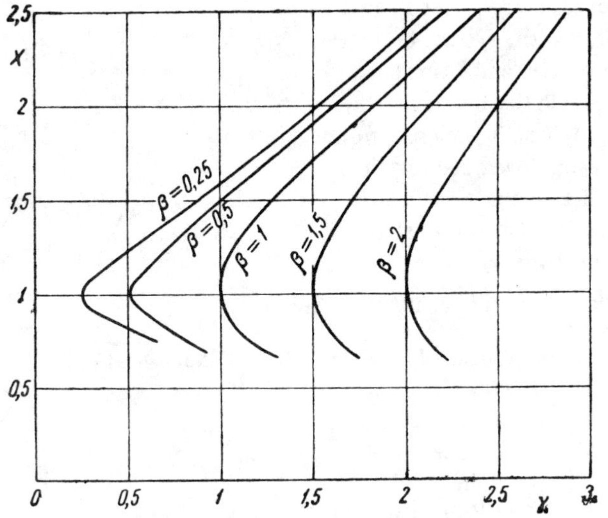

Fig. 11. Dependence of the normalized critical frequency upon γ for different values of β.

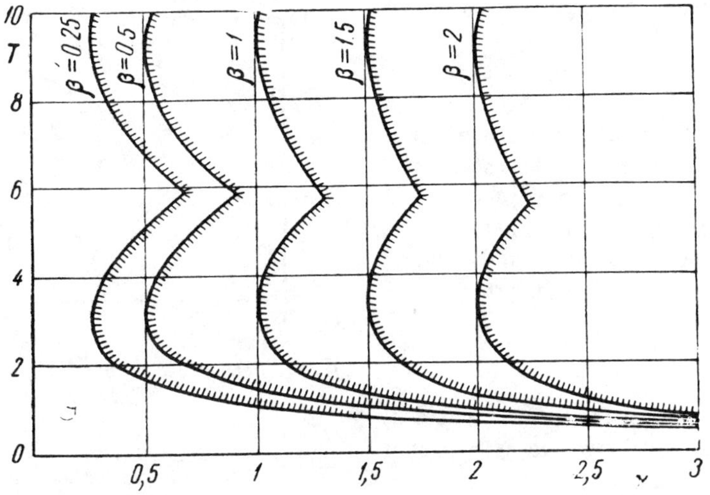

Fig. 12. Stability boundaries $T_0 = f(\gamma, \beta)$ for system B. Unshaded side corresponds to the stability domain.

ω_0 provided $T = T_0$, and finally, in the third case the system is stable whenever $T < T_{01}$.

Fig. 11 displays the dependence of x_0 in terms of γ.

Boundaries of the stability regions in the (T, γ)-plane are specified by (42), and they vary for different β (Fig. 12). The region on the shaded side of the boundary corresponds to unstable systems, the opposite to stable ones.

As it can be seen from Fig. 12, the alternation of stability and instability regions appears for γ greater than β, but close to it, as T increases continually. The stability region is wider for larger β. By increasing γ for constant β the region of stability gets smaller.

Fig. 12 represents by itself a cross section of the hyperplane $T_0 = f(\gamma, \beta)$ with $\beta = \text{const.}$, which separates stability and instability regions. The parameter point is specified by means of the three coordinates

$$T = \omega_c.\tau, \qquad \gamma = a\omega_c., \qquad \beta = \frac{\delta}{\omega_c}. \tag{43}$$

The analysis of the influence of parameters is either reduced to the determination of the trajectory of the parameter point in the (T, γ, β)-space, or to the question of finding a trajectory in the (T, γ)-plane, simultaneously taking into account the relocation of the stability boundary with different β. For example, by eliminating ω_c from the first two equations in (43) we get the equation of motion of the parameter point as follows:

$$T = \frac{\tau}{a}\gamma. \tag{44}$$

If t, a, δ are given, then the parameter point moves from the origin along a straight line, as ω_c increases. From the third equation in (44) we see that the stability boundary moves towards the origin as ω_c increases. For a certain $\omega_c = \overline{\omega}_c$ the parameter point belongs to the boundary corresponding to $\beta = \delta / \overline{\omega}_c$. Consequently, the system is stable if $\omega_c < \overline{\omega}_c$, and unstable if $\omega_c > \overline{\omega}_c$.

It is not difficult to see that smaller $\overline{\omega}_c$ corresponds to larger τ and a, and smaller γ. In other words, the system becomes unstable for smaller τ's if a and ω_c are larger and δ smaller.

The parameter point belongs to the stability boundary; then oscillations with frequency $\omega_0 = x_0\omega_c$ (x_0 is obtained from Fig. 11) will arise in the system. To the lower stability limit (Fig. 12) corresponds the upper branch of the curve x_0 (Fig. 11), where $x > 1$ and, hence, $\omega > \omega_c$; to the second stability limit corresponds the lower part of the curve x_0, where $x < 1$, thus $\omega < \omega_c$; the third limit is again determined by the upper branch of x-curve, etc.

If a parameter point belongs to the region of instability, then the frequency of the growing oscillations is determined by those values of x which are located between two branches of x_0, specified by a given β. When $\gamma \gg \beta$ the frequency of oscillations is higher than $\omega_c(x > 1)$. For $\gamma \simeq \beta$ the oscillations may have the frequency lower than $\omega_c(x < 1)$. In treating the problem, Minorsky [17] arrived at the conclusion that similar systems are able theoretically to sustain growing oscillations at infinitely many frequencies, though only the first frequency occurs in practice, and the remaining higher frequencies are not observed.

According to the analysis presented above, this conclusion is false. The error appears as a consequence of the fact that the condition (19) $W_0(\omega) > 1$, which determines frequencies of the self-sustained oscillations, was not taken into account.

C. As a final example, we consider the same system treated in B. under the condition that the feedback loop is closed directly through the network, rather than through the mutual inductance. In this case (38) should be replaced by the following equation

$$au_2 = -u_1,$$

where a is a constant depending upon the tube transconductance and the amount of feedback. The frequency characteristic of the open loop system is given by

$$W(j\omega) = \gamma \frac{1}{\sqrt{(1-x^2)^2 + \beta^2 x^2}} \exp j\left[\pi - \arctan\frac{\beta x}{1-x^2}\right] \tag{46}$$

where $\gamma = a$, and the remaining notation is the same as for the system in B. A family of curves for $\gamma = 1$ and different β is shown in Fig. 13. It is easy to see that for small β's it is possible to have two values for X_0, and thus, all conclusions made for system B hold again.

By equating the amplitude of the open-loop transfer function (46) with unity, we get

$$x^4 - (2-\beta^2)x^2 + 1 - \gamma^2 = 0,$$

so that

$$x_{01,02} = \sqrt{\frac{2-\beta^2}{2} \pm \sqrt{\frac{(2-\beta^2)^2}{4} - (1-\gamma^2)}}. \tag{47}$$

By exploring the discriminant we obtain for $\beta < \sqrt{2}$:

1) when $\gamma < \sqrt{1-(1-\beta^2/2)^2}$, then x_0 does not have any critical value, and the system is stable for all T;
2) when $\gamma = \sqrt{1-(\beta^2/2)^2}$ there exists a single critical value $x_{01} = \sqrt{2-\beta^2/2}$, hence, there will be oscillations in the system only if $T = T_0$;
3) for $1 > \gamma > \sqrt{1-(1-\beta^2/2)^2}$, there exist two critical values: x_{01} and x_{02}, and alternation of the stability and instability regions is possible;
4) if $\beta > \sqrt{2}$ and $\gamma > 1$, then there will be a single critical value X_{01}, and the system will be stable for $T < T_{01}$, and unstable for $T > T_{01}$.

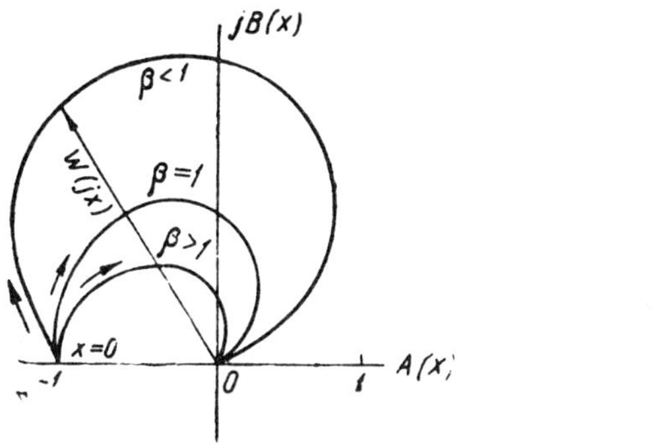

Fig. 13. Normalized polar plot $W(jx)$ for system C for different values of β.

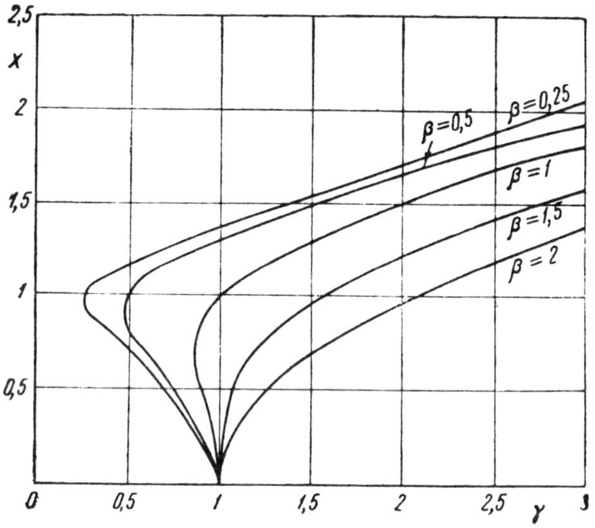

Fig. 14. Dependence of the normalized critical frequency upon γ for different values of β.

The dependence of x_0 upon γ, for different β's, determines the domain of frequencies which may occur, and it is represented in Fig. 14.

By combining (47) and (22) we get

$$T_{0i}(n) = \omega_0\tau_{0i}(n) = \frac{\pi - \arctan\dfrac{\beta x_0}{1-x_0}}{x_{0i}} + \frac{2\pi n}{x_{0i}}. \tag{48}$$

The regions of stability and instability constructed according to (48) are shown in Fig. 15.

The type of stability boundaries coincides with the nature of stability boundaries for system A when $\beta > \sqrt{2}$; otherwise with the ones corresponding to system B.

Influence of system parameters and delay time is determined as before. Trajectory of the parameter point in terms of ω_c is

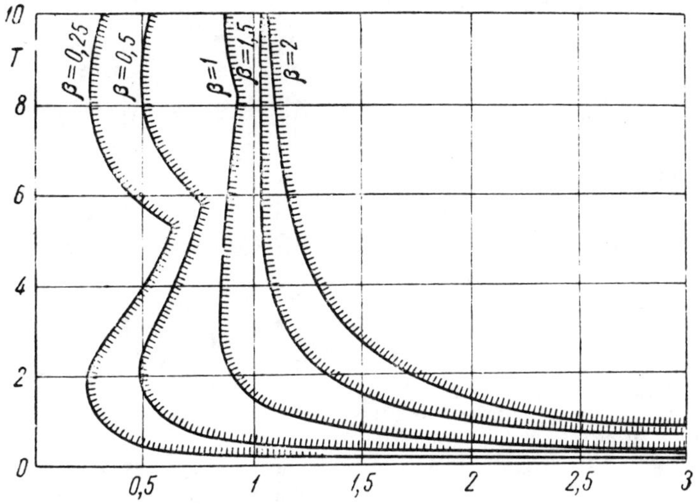

Fig. 15. Stability boundaries $T_0 = f(\gamma, \beta)$ for system C. Unshaded side corresponds to the stability domain.

the straight line parallel to the T - axis:

$$\gamma = a, \quad T = \omega_c . \tau. \tag{49}$$

We remark, however, that for $\gamma \gg 1$ and remaining conditions unchanged, the stability boundary T_0 is located below the boundary for system B. As before, the system becomes unstable for smaller values of τ, as a and ω_c increase.

These examples illustrate how simple it is to apply criteria for the stability of systems with delayed feedback derived in Section III. The formulas which determine stability boundaries and regions of stability and instability in the (T, γ)-plane permit us to analyze the influence of system parameters and the delay time on system stability, and at the same time they suggest ways to eliminate instability. Based on these examples, one can conclude that the presence of the time-delay requires lower values for ω_c and a, and therefore it decreases system efficiency.

V. Generalization of the Stability Criteria

In certain systems with delayed feedback the change of the delay time τ has a consequence that the input signal is repeated at the output without distortion after the time τ, but in a τ-dependent scale; in this case the equation describing a delay element has the following form:

$$u_4 = f(\tau)\, u_3(t - \tau), \tag{50}$$

where $f(\tau)$ is a continuous function of τ. Therefore, the modulus of the open-loop transfer function of the equivalent system is equal to $W_0(\omega) f(\tau)$.

According to (16) and (18), the conditions which determine critical values ω_{0i} and τ_{0i} are written as follows:

$$W_0(\omega) = \frac{1}{f(\tau)}, \tag{51}$$

$$\tau_0 = \frac{\theta(\omega)}{\omega}. \tag{52}$$

Critical frequencies are then found from

$$W_0(\omega) = \frac{1}{f\left[\frac{\theta(\omega)}{\omega}\right]}, \tag{53}$$

which is obtained from (51) by substituting τ from the relation (52).

After the critical frequencies are determined and substituted in (52), we find the following critical delay times:

$$\tau_{0i}(n) = \frac{\theta(\omega_{0i})}{\omega_{0i}} + \frac{2\pi n}{\omega_{0i}}. \tag{54}$$

The critical delay times may be determined as follows: For all ω's in the $W(j\omega)$-plane, plot vectors starting at the origin and having magnitude $W_0(j\omega)$ and phase $\Theta(\omega)$. The end points of these vectors form a curve which intersects the $W(j\omega)$ plot at points corresponding to the critical frequencies ω_{0i}. The critical delay times are determined by the ratio $\Theta(\omega_{0i})/\omega_{0i}$ at these intersection points.

In order to analyze stability for a given delay-time $\tau = \bar{\tau}$, one can use the previously derived criteria. It suffices to plot a circle or radii $1/f(\bar{\tau})$ centered at the origin of the $W(j\omega)$-plane, to find

$$\bar{\tau}_0 = \frac{\theta(\bar{\omega})}{\bar{\omega}}, \tag{55}$$

where $\bar{\omega}$ is a point where the circle intersects the $W(j\omega)$-curve. If $\bar{\tau} < \bar{\tau}_0$, the system will be stable; the system is unstable if $\bar{\tau} > \bar{\tau}_0$.

The previous reasoning was based upon the assumption that the equivalent system is stable. It is equally easy to establish stability criteria for systems with unstable equivalent systems. The polar plot of the unstable equivalent system transfer function will encircle the point $(1, j0)$, (Fig. 16). By constructing a unit circle, it is easy to see that the existence of a single critical frequency ω_{01} (Fig. 16(a)) implies system instability for any τ. When there exist two critical frequencies ω_{01} and ω_{02} (Fig. 16(b)), then the system will be stable only if $W(j0) < -1$ and $\tau_{01}(1) > \tau > \tau_{02}$.

The generalized stability criteria presented above enable us to enlarge considerably the class of systems which can be analyzed, and to apply them, for example, to derive the conditions for self-excitement of decimeter wave generators [27].

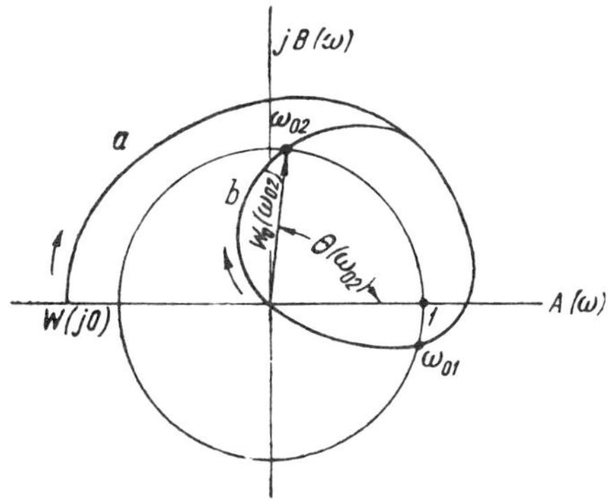

Fig. 16. Determination of critical frequencies ω_{0i} and critical delay-times τ_{0i} from the transfer function $W(j\omega)$ of the unstable equivalent system. a: There exists one critical frequency. b: Two critical frequencies are present.

VI. On an Approximation Method for Stability Analysis

The most popular technique for analysis of systems with delayed feedback is the approximation method. This can be explained by the fact that this method replaces a hystero-differential equation by an ordinary differential equation, and, therefore, it enables one to use the well-known Hurwitz criterion.

The essence of the approximation method can be summarized as follows. Instead of the characteristic equation

$$Q(z) - P(z)\,e^{-\tau z} = 0. \tag{56}$$

one considers the equation

$$Q(z) = P(z)\left(1 - \tau z + \frac{\tau^2}{2!}z^2 - \cdots + (\cdots 1)^n \frac{\tau^n}{n!}z^n\right) = 0, \tag{57}$$

obtained from (56) by replacing the term $e^{-\tau z}$ by an nth order polynomial, which is an $(n + 1)$ order truncation of the Taylor series for $e^{-\tau z}$. Equation (57) is an algebraic equation, to which it is possible to apply the Hurwitz criterion. This approximation, however, cannot be justified, and the method may lead to wrong conclusions.

Let us consider, for example, the characteristic equation corresponding to the pressure control system (A)

$$T_a z + z_1 + a e^{-\tau z} = 0. \tag{58}$$

by using the following notation

$$y = \frac{z}{z_1}T_a, \quad \gamma = \frac{a}{z_1}, \quad T = \frac{\tau}{T_a}z, \tag{59}$$

we get

$$y + 1 + \gamma e^{-Ty} = 0. \tag{60}$$

In the first approximation the term e^{-Ty} is often replaced by the first two terms of the series expansion to get

$$(1 - \gamma T)y + 1 + \gamma = 0,$$

and, hence,

$$y = -\frac{1 + \gamma}{1 - \gamma T}.$$

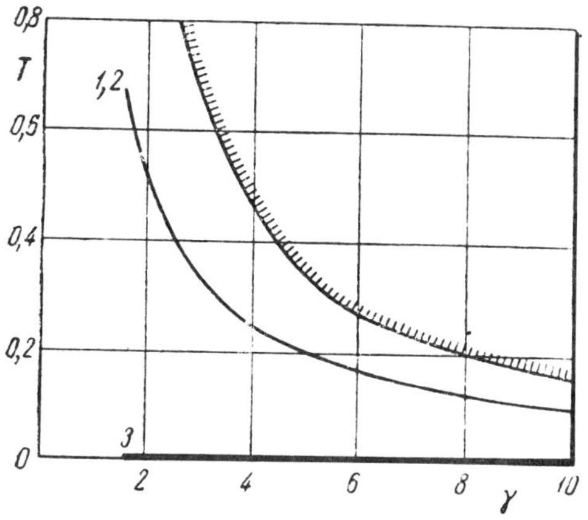

Fig. 17. Comparison of the stability boundary for system A, obtained by our method (shaded line), and by means of the first, second, and third approximations of the exponential term (1, 2, and 3, respectively).

Therefore, one concludes that the system is stable if $T < 1/\lambda$, $y < 0$, and *periodically* unstable when $T > 1/\gamma$ and $y > 0$. The stability boundary is given then by

$$T = \frac{1}{\gamma}.$$

Now, replace e^{-Ty} by the three-term expension (second approximation), to obtain

$$\frac{T^2}{2!}y^2 + (1 - \gamma T)y + 1 + \gamma = 0.$$

The stability boundary remains the same, except that for $T > 1/\gamma$, the system is oscillatory unstable. Finally, in the third approximation

$$-\frac{T^3}{3!}y^3 + \frac{T^2}{2!}y^2 + (1 - \gamma T)y + 1 + \gamma = 0,$$

which implies that the system is unstable for any arbitrarily small T.

Comparison of this results with the ones derived in Section IV is given in Fig. 17. We see that, the higher the order of approximation, the worse are the results obtained. Furthermore, for constant T the location of boundaries and type of instability depends upon the order of approximation, which, of course, cannot happen in reality. It is obvious that (60) does not have positive real roots, and hence, as established earlier, this system cannot be aperiodically unstable. Replacing e^{-Ty} by a polynomial, one essentially changes the structure of the equation, which implies the qualitatively wrong conclusion regarding this type of instability.

Similar results for system B (Section IV) are represented on Fig. 18. Besides the above-mentioned paradoxical conclusions, the approximation method precludes one from establishing facts regarding the alternation of stability and instability regions.

In the above examples the stability boundary obtained by using the approximation method is located below the exact boundary. It is possible to have examples in which the approximation boundary intersects with the exact one in several points. We are not going to treat them here, however.

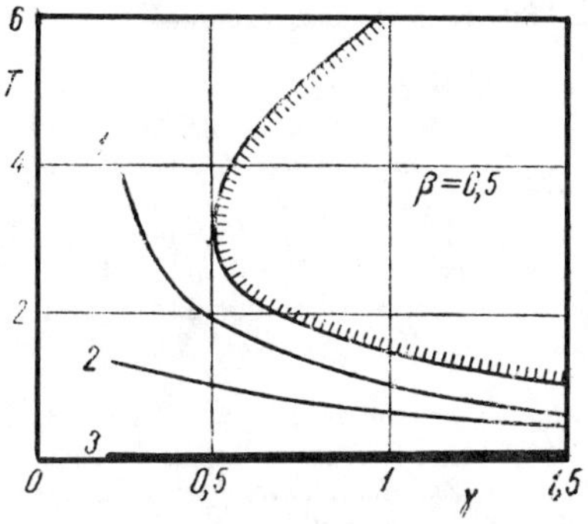

Fig. 18. Comparison of the stability boundary for system B, obtained by our method (shaded line), and by means of the first, second, and third approximation of the exponential term (1, 2, and 3, respectively).

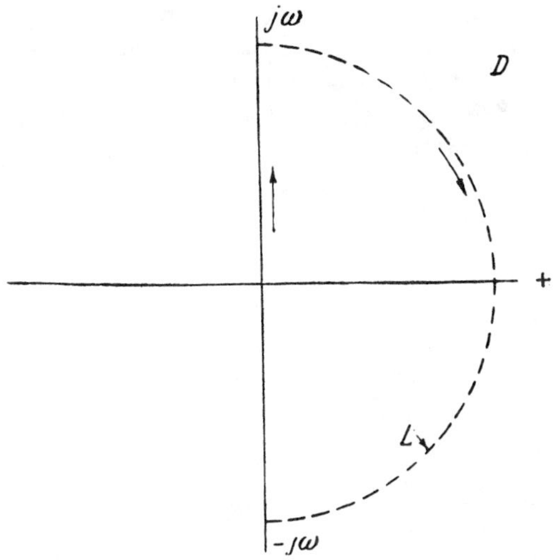

Fig. 19.

This comparison of results derived by the approximation method with the exact ones implies that the approximation method may lead to not only quantitatively, but also qualitatively wrong results, and hence its application for stability analysis is not appropriate.

Conclusion

In this paper we establish a criterion for stability of systems with time-delayed feedback. The criterion is based upon consideration of frequency characteristics of the open-loop transfer function for the equivalent system. This enabled us to simplify greatly the stability analysis of systems with delayed feedback.

The analysis of the influence of system parameters and the delay-time is reduced to the problem of finding the trajectory of the parameter point through stability and instability regions, constructed according to the derived equations.

Several concrete examples of the systems with delayed feedback are considered also. The indicated generalization of the stability criterion enabled us to greatly enlarge the class of systems which can be treated. Towards the end, we compare the results of the stability analysis based upon the method formulated in this paper, and the approximation method, which is widely accepted in the literature, to conclude that the latter can lead to wrong results.

Acknowledgment

The author considers as his most pleasant duty to express his profound indebtedness to Prof. K. F. Teodorchik for discussion regarding questions raised in this paper, and to Ing. Yu. I. Goldfain for his help in computing and drawing the graphs.

Appendix

In Section V we have assumed tacitly that the Nyquist criterion can be applied to systems with delayed feedback. Since this generalization of the Nyquist criterion is not encountered in the literature, we think that it may be useful to present it here.

Consider the function

$$f(D) = \frac{Q(D) - P(D)\, e^{-\tau D}}{Q(D)},$$

which represents the ratio of the characteristic polynomials corresponding to the system (12) with delayed feedback and the open-loop system without the delay element, or $f(D) = 1 - W(D)\, e^{-\tau D}$. We assume that the open-loop system is stable, and hence all the poles of $f(D)$ are in the left half of the D-plane.

Stability conditions require that all zeros belong also to the left-half of the D-plane. In order to establish a stability criterion we use the Principle of the Argument, and choose for integration the contour L consisting of the imaginary axis and a semicircle of arbitrarily large radius, which belongs to the right half of the D-plane[5] (Fig. 19).

According to the Principle of the Argument, the stability conditions can be rewritten in the following form [25]

$$\Delta L \arg f(D) = 0,$$

i.e., the change in argument of the complex function $f(D)$ along the contour L must be zero.

The change in argument when D takes values on the semicircle of the arbitrarily large radius in the right half of the D-plane, is equal to zero since in this case

$$D = \lim_{R\to\infty} R e^{j\varphi} = \lim_{R\to\infty} R(\cos\varphi + j\sin\varphi),$$

where ϕ varies from $-\pi/2$ to $+\pi/2$, and hence

$$\lim_{R\to\infty} j(Re^{j\varphi}) = \lim_{R\to\infty} (1 - W(Re^{j\omega})\, e^{-\tau R\cos\varphi}\, e^{-j\tau R\sin\varphi}).$$

Therefore, the stability conditions can be rewritten as

$$\Delta \arg j(j\omega) = \Delta \arg (1 - W(j\omega)\, e^{-j\tau\omega}) = 0$$

where ω varies between $-\infty$ and $+\infty$, or

$$\Delta \arg_{-\infty \leqslant \omega \leqslant +\infty} (W(j\omega)\, e^{-j\tau\omega} - 1) = 0.$$

By plotting the curve $W_\tau(j\omega) = W(j\omega)\, e^{-j\tau\omega}$ (Fig. 5) in the complex W-plane for all $\omega \geqslant 0$,[6] we see easily that $W_\tau(j\omega) - 1$

[5]It is easy to see that function $f(D)$ fulfills all the necessary conditions for application of the Principle of Argument (e.g., [25]).

[6]For $\omega \leqslant 0$, the curve $W_\tau(j\omega)$ is symmetric to the curve $W_\tau(j\omega)$, $\omega \geqslant 0$, with respect to the horizontal axis, and hence it is unnecessary to draw the part corresponding to $\omega \leqslant 0$ (e.g., [25]).

itself represents a vector starting at $(1, j0)$ and ending on the $W_T(j\omega)$-curve. Therefore, the argument variation of $W_T(j\omega) - 1$ will be equal to zero only in the case when the point $(1, j0)$ is not encircled by the curve $W_T(j\omega)$, which corresponds to the stability. If the point $(1, j0)$ is encircled by the curve $W_T(j\omega)$, then the change in argument of $W_T(j\omega) - 1$ is nonzero, and the system is unstable.

REFERENCES

[1] T. Stain, *Regelung und Ausgleich in Dampfanlagen*, Springer, 1925. Russian translation: *Adjustment and Control of Steam Power Plants*, GNTI, 1931, p. 188.

[2] M. Lang, "Theorie des Regelvorganges elecktrischer Industrieöfen," *Elecktrowärme*, 9, 201 (1934).

[3] W. Stablein, *Die Technik der Fernwerkanlagen*, München, 1934. Russian translation: *Techniques for Remote Control*, *GONTI*, 1939, p. 89.

[4] S. G. Gerasimov, "Physical foundations for dynamic control of thermal processes," *ONTI*, 1934, p. 71, (in Russian).

[5] D. A. Wicker, "Effect of delays in automatic control processes," *Avtomatika i Telemekhanika*, 6, 59 (1937).

[6] P. S. Koshchiev, "Towards theory of tracking systems," *Avtomatika i Telemekhanika*, 5, 81 (1940).

[7] N. I. Chistiakov, "On phase lag computation for an automatic frequency control amplifier," *Electrosviaz*, 7, 27, (1940).

[8] B. I. Rubin and Yu. E. Heiman, "Fundamentals of aircraft control," *LII GBF*, 27 (1940).

[9] V. A. Bogomolov, "Power control of a hydroplant by the rate of flow," *Avtomatika i Telemekhanika*, 4-5, 103 (1941).

[10] N. Minorsky, "Control problems," *J. Franklin Institute*, 232, 6, 524 (1941).

[11] M. Lang, "Physik and regeltechnik," *Phys. ZS.*, 9-12, 209, (1944).

[12] F. Reinhardt, "Selbsterregte Schwingungen beim Parallelbetrieb von Synchronmaschinen," *Siemens ZS.*, 10, 413 (1925).

[13] D. A. Wicker, "Dynamics of resistive voltage controllers," *Electrichestvo*, 9, 26 (1934).

[14] A. Callender, D. Hartree, and A. Porter, "Time-lag in a control system. I," *Phil. Trans. Roy. Soc. London*, 235, 756, 415 (1936).

[15] D. Hartree, A. Porter, A. Callender, and A. Stevenson, "Time-lag in a control system. II," *Proc. Roy. Soc. London*, 161, 907, 460 (1937).

[16] F. Reinhardt, "Der Parallelbetrieb von Synchrongeneratoren mit Kraftmaschinenreglen konstanter Verzögerungzeit," *Wiss. Veröffentlichungen aus den Siemens-Werken*, 18, 1, 24 (1939).

[17] N. Minorsky, "Self-excited oscillation in dynamical systems possessing retarded actions," *J. Appl. Mechanics*, 9, 2, (1942).

[18] A. Heins, "On the solution of linear difference-differential equations," *J. Math. Physics*, 19, 2, 153 (1940).

[19] R. Churchill, *Modern Mathematics in Engineering*. New York: McGraw-Hill, 1944, p. 23.

[20] L. Silberstein, "On a histero-differential equation arising in a probability problem," *Phil. Mag.*, 29, 192, 75 (1940).

[21] E. Kamke, *Differentialgleichungen. Losungsmethoden und Losungen*, Leipzig, 1942, p. 493.

[22] T. Fray, "Introduction to differential equations," *GNTI*, 1933.

[23] A. Harkevich, "Theory of electroacoustic apparatus," *Sviazizdat*, 1940.

[24] H. Nyquist, "Regeneration theory," *Bell Syst. Tech. J.*, 11, 1, 126 (1932).

[25] Ya. Z. Tsypkin, "Stability of feedback systems," *Radiotechnika*, 1, 5, 33 (1946).

[26] W. Oppelt, "Vergleichende Betrachtung verschiedener Regelaufgaben hinsichtlich der geeigneten Regelgesetzmässigkeit," *Luftfahrtforschung*, 16, 8, p. 448.

[27] Ya. Z. Tsypkin, "Towards a theory of klystrons," *Radiotechnika*, 1, 49, 1947.

Control System Synthesis by Root Locus Method

WALTER R. EVANS
MEMBER AIEE

Synopsis: The root locus method determines all of the roots of the differential equation of a control system by a graphical plot which readily permits synthesis for desired transient response or frequency response. The base points for this plot on the complex plane are the zeros and poles of the open loop transfer function, which are readily available. The locus of roots is a plot of the values of s which make this transfer function equal to -1 as loop gain is increased from zero to infinity. The plot can be established in approximate form by inspection and the significant parts of the locus calculated accurately and quickly by use of a simple device. For multiple loop systems, one solves the innermost loop first, which then permits the next loop to be solved by another root locus plot. The resultant plot gives a complete picture of the system, which is particularly valuable for unusual systems or those which have wide variations in parameters.

THE root locus method is the result of an effort to determine the roots of the differential equation of a control system by using the concepts now associated with frequency response methods.[1] The roots are desired, of course, because they describe the natural response of the system. The simplifying feature of the control system problem is that the open loop transfer function is known as a product of terms. Each term, such as $1/(1+Ts)$, can be easily treated in the same manner as an admittance such as $1/(R+jx)$. It is treated as a vector in the sense used by electrical engineers in solving a-c circuits. The phase shift and attenuation of a signal of the form e^{st} being transmitted is represented by $1/(1+Ts)$ in which s in general is a complex number. The key idea in the root locus method is that the values of s which make transfer function around the loop equal to -1 are roots of the differential equation of the system.

The opening section in this paper, Background Theory, outlines the over-all pattern of analysis. The following section on Root Locus Plot points out the great usefulness of knowing factors of the open loop transfer function in finding the roots.

The graphical nature of the method requires that specific examples be used to demonstrate the method itself under the topics: Single Loop Example, Multiple Loop System, and Corrective Networks. The topic Correlation with Other Methods suggests methods by which experience in frequency methods can be extended to this method. The topic Other Applications includes the classic problem of solving an nth degree polynomial. Finally, the section on Graphical Calculations describes the key features of a plastic device called a "Spirule", which permits calculations to be made from direct measurement on the plot.

Background Theory

The over-all pattern of analysis can be outlined before explaining the technique of sketching a root locus plot. Thus consider the general single loop system shown in Figure 1.

Note that each transfer function is of the form $KG(s)$ in which K is a static gain constant and $G(s)$ is a function of the complex number. In general, $G(s)$ has both numerator and denominator known in factored form. The values of s which make the function zero or infinite can therefore be seen by inspection and are called zeros and poles respectively. The closed loop transfer function can be expressed directly from Figure 1 as given in equation 1

$$\frac{\theta_0}{\theta_i}(s)=\frac{K_\mu G_\mu(s)}{1+K_\mu G_\mu(s)K_\beta G_\beta(s)} \tag{1}$$

The problem of finding the roots of the differential equation here appears in the form of finding values of s which make the denominator zero. After these values are determined by the root locus method, the denominator can be expressed in factored form. The zeros of the function θ_0/θ_i can be seen from equation 1 to be the zeros of $G_\mu(s)$ and the poles of $G_\beta(s)$. The function can now be expressed as shown in equation 2

$$\frac{\theta_0}{\theta_i}(s)=K_c s^\gamma\frac{(1-s/q_1)(1-s/q_2)\ldots}{(1-s/r_1)(1-s/r_2)\ldots.} \tag{2}$$

The constant K_c and the exponent γ depend upon the specific system but for control systems γ is often zero and K_c is often 1.

The full power of the Laplace Transform[2] or an equivalent method now can be used. The transient response of the output for a unit step input, for example, is given by equation 3

$$\theta_0(t)=1-\sum_{i=1}^{i=n}A_i e^{r_i t} \tag{3}$$

The amplitude A_i is given by equation 4

$$A_i=\left[\frac{\theta_0}{\theta_i}(s)(1-s/r_i)\right]_{s=r_i} \tag{4}$$

The closed loop frequency response, on the other hand, can be obtained by substituting $s=j\omega$ into equation 2. Fortunately, the calculation in finding A_i or $\theta_0/\theta_i(j\omega)$ involves the same problem of multiplying vectors that arises in making a root locus plot, and can be calculated quickly from the resultant root locus plot.

Paper 50-11, recommended by the AIEE Feedback-Control Systems Committee and approved by the AIEE Technical Program Committee for presentation at the AIEE Winter General Meeting, New York, N. Y., January 30–February 3, 1950. Manuscript submitted November 15, 1948; made available for printing November 22, 1949.

WALTER R. EVANS is with North American Aviation, Inc., Downey, Calif.

The author wishes to express his appreciation for the assistance given by his fellow workers, K. R. Jackson and R. M. Osborn, in the preparation of this paper. In particular, Mr. Osborn contributed the circuit analysis example.

Reprinted from *AIEE Trans.*, vol. 69, pp. 66–69, 1950.

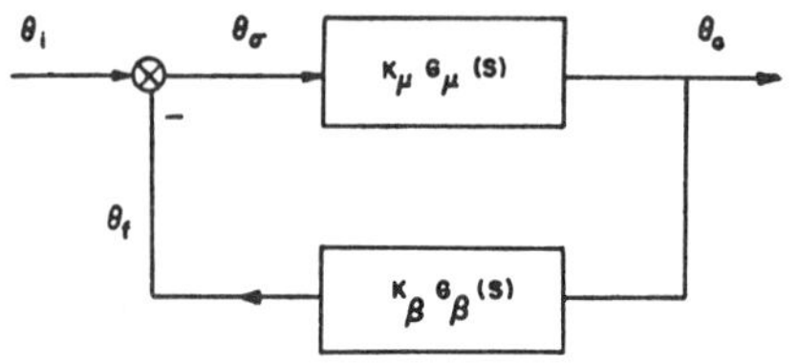

Figure 1 (left). General block diagram

Figure 3 (right). Single loop root locus

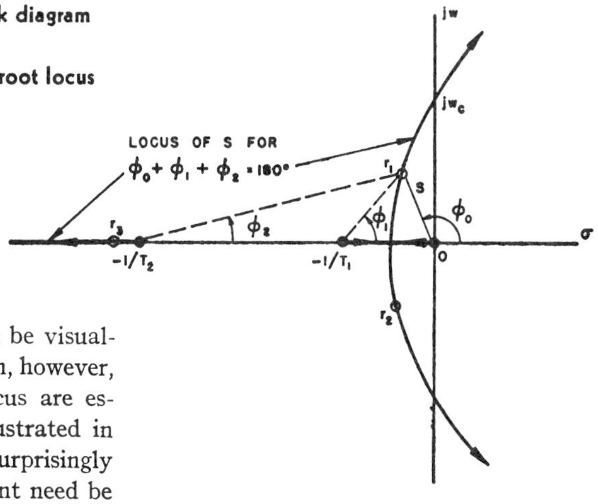

Root Locus Plot

The open loop transfer function is typically of the form given in equation 5.

$$K_\mu G_\mu(s)K_\beta G_\beta(s)=\frac{K(1+T_2 s)\,[\sigma_3{}^2+\omega_3{}^2]}{s(1+T_1 s)\,[(s+\sigma_3)^2+\omega_3{}^2]} \quad (5)$$

The parameters such as T_1 are constant for a given problem, whereas s assumes many values; therefore, it is convenient to convert equation 5 to the form of equation 6.

$$K_\mu G_\mu(s)K_\beta G_\beta(s)=\frac{K(1/T_2+s)\,T_2\,[\sigma_3{}^2+\omega_3{}^2]}{s(1/T_1+s)\,T_1\,[(s+\sigma_3+j\omega_3)(s+\sigma_3-j\omega_3)]} \quad (6)$$

The poles and zeros of the function are plotted and a general value of s is assumed as shown in Figure 2.

Note that poles are represented as dots, and zeros as crosses. All of the complex terms involved in equation 6 are represented by vectors with heads at the general point s and tails at the zeros or poles. The angle of each vector is measured with respect to a line parallel to the positive real axis. The magnitude of each vector is simply its length on the plot.

In seeking to find the values of s which make the open loop function equal to -1, the value -1 is considered as a vector whose angle is 180 degrees $\pm$ n 360 degrees, where n is an integer, and whose magnitude is unity. Then one can consider first the problem of finding the locus of values for which the angle condition alone is satisfied. In general, one pictures the exploratory s point at various positions on the plane, and imagines the lines from the poles and zeros to be constructed

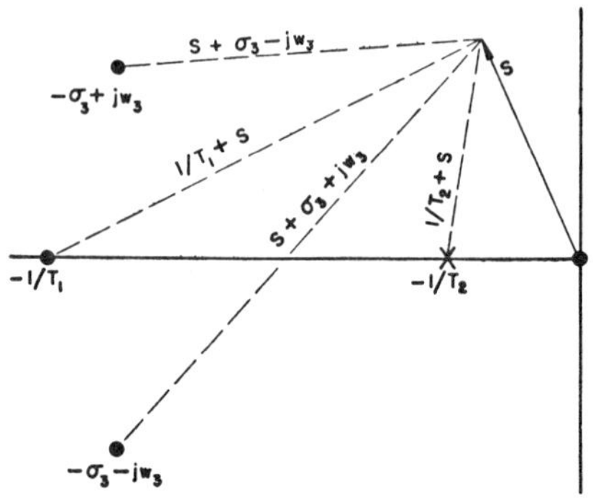

Figure 2. Root locus plot

so that the angles in turn can be visualized. For any specific problem, however, many special parts of the locus are established by inspection as illustrated in examples in later sections. Surprisingly few trial positions of the s point need be assumed to permit the complete locus to be sketched.

After the locus has been determined, one considers the second condition for a root, that is, that the magnitude of $K_\mu G_\mu(s)K_\beta G_\beta(s)$ be unity. In general, one selects a particular value of s along the locus, estimates the lengths of the vectors, and calculates the static gain $K_\mu K_\beta=1/G_\mu(s)G_\beta(s)$. After acquiring some experience, one usually can select the desired position of a dominant root to determine the allowable loop gain. The position of roots along other parts of the locus usually can be determined with less than two trials each.

An interesting fact to note from equation 6 is that for very low gain, the roots are very close to the poles in order that corresponding vectors be very small. For very high gain, the roots approach infinity or terminate on a zero.

Single Loop Example

Consider a single loop system such as shown in Figure 1 in which the transfer functions are given in equation 7.

$$K_\mu G_\mu(s)=\frac{K}{(1+T_1 s)(1+T_2 s)s};\,K_\beta G_\beta(s)=1 \quad (7)$$

The poles of the open loop function are at 0, $-1/T_1$ and $-1/T_2$ as represented by dots in Figure 3.

The locus along the real axis is determined by inspection because all of the angles are either 0 degrees or 180 degrees. An odd number of angles must therefore be 180 degrees as shown by the intervals between 0 and $-1/T_1$, and from $-1/T_2$ to $-\infty$. Along the $j\omega$ axis, ϕ_0 is 90 degrees so that ϕ_2 must be the complement of ϕ_1, as estimated at $s=j\omega_c$. For very large values of s, all angles are essentially equal so the locus for the complex roots finally approaches radial lines at ± 60 degrees.

The point where the locus breaks away from the real axis is found by considering a value of s just above the real axis. The decrease in ϕ_0 from 180 degrees can be made equal to the sum of ϕ_1 and ϕ_2 if the reciprocal of the length from the trial point to the origin is equal to the sum of the reciprocals of lengths from the trial point to $-1/T_1$ and $-1/T_2$. If a damping ratio of 0.5 for the complex roots is desired, the roots r_1 and r_2 are fixed by the intersection with the locus of radial lines at ± 60 degrees with respect to negative real axis.

In calculating K for $s=r_1$, it is convenient to consider a term $(1+T_1 s)$ as a ratio of lengths from the pole $-1/T_1$ to the s point and from s to the origin respectively. After making gain $K=1/\text{-}[G(s)]_{s=r_1}$ a good first trial for finding r_3 is to assume that it is near $-1/T_2$ and solve for $(1/T_2+s)$. After the roots are determined to the desired accuracy, the over-all transfer function can be expressed as given in equation 8.

$$\frac{\theta_0}{\theta_i}=\frac{1}{\left(1-\dfrac{s}{r_1}\right)\left(1-\dfrac{s}{r_2}\right)\left(1-\dfrac{s}{r_3}\right)} \quad (8)$$

The procedure in handling a multiple loop system now can be explained.

Multiple Loop System

Consider a multiple loop system in which the single loop system just solved is the forward path of another loop, as shown in Figure 4.

θ_o/θ_i is given in factored form by equation 8 so the roots of the inner loop now serve as base points for the new locus plot. For convenience, however, neglect the effect of the term $(1-s/r_3)$ so that the locus for the outer loop is shown in Figure 5.

The locus for the outer loop would be a circle about the $-1/T$ point as a center if the effect of θ_o/θ_i were completely neglected. Actually, the vectors from the points r_1 and r_2 introduce net angles so that the locus is modified as shown. The

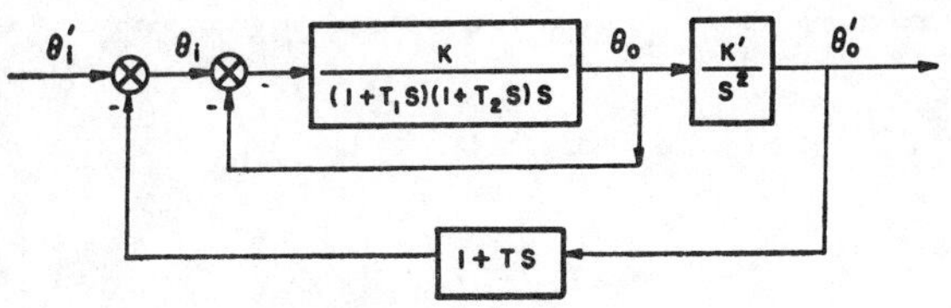

Figure 4 (above). Multiple loop block diagram

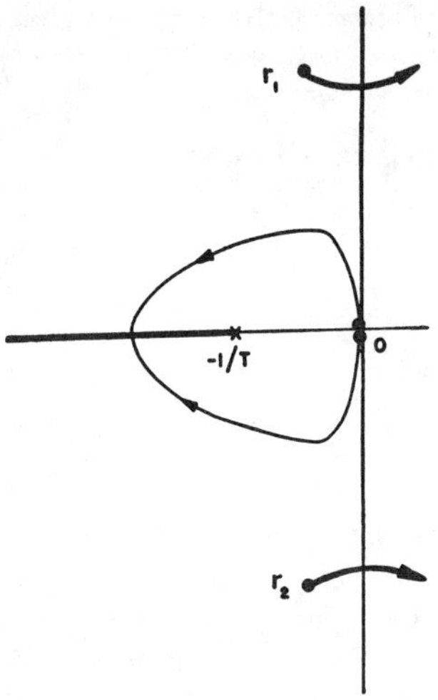

Figure 5 (right). Multiple loop root locus

angle at which the locus emerges from r_1 can be found by considering a value of s close to the point r_1, and solving for the angle of the vector $(s-r_1)$.

Assume that the static loop gain desired is higher than that allowed by the given system. The first modification suggested by the plot is to move the r_1 and r_2 points farther to the left by obtaining greater damping in the inner loop. If these points are moved far to the left, the loci from these points terminate in the negative real axis and the loci from the origin curve back and cross the $j\omega$ axis. Moving the $-1/T$ point closer to the origin would then be effective in permitting still higher loop gain. The next aspect of synthesis involves adding corrective networks.

Corrective Networks

Consider a somewhat unusual system which arises in instrument servos whose open loop transfer function is identified by the poles p_1 and p_2 in Figure 6(A). As loop gain is increased from zero, the roots which start from p_1 and p_2 move directly toward the unstable half plane. These roots could be made to move away from the $j\omega$ axis if 180 degrees phase shift were added. A simple network to add is three lag networks in series, each having a time constant T such that 60 degrees phase shift is introduced at p_1. The resultant locus plot is shown in Figure 6(B).

The gain now is limited only by the requirement that the new pair of roots do not cross the $j\omega$ axis. A value of gain is selected to obtain critical damping of these roots and the corresponding positions of all the roots are shown in Figures 6(A) and 6(B) as small circles.

Actually, greater damping could be achieved for roots which originate at p_1 and p_2 if a phase shifting bridge were used rather than the 3-lag networks. Its transfer function is $(3-Ts)/(1+Ts)$ and is of the "nonminimum phase" type of circuit.

Since these types of correction are somewhat unusual, it is perhaps well to point out that the analysis has been verified by actual test and application.

These examples serve to indicate the reasoning process in synthesizing a control system by root locus method. An engineer draws upon all of his experience, however, in seeking to improve a given system; therefore, it is well to indicate the correlation between this method and other methods.

Correlation with Other Methods

The valuable concepts of frequency response methods[1] are in a sense merely extended by the root locus system. Thus a transfer function with s having a complex value rather than just a pure imaginary value corresponds to a damped sinusoid being transmitted rather than an undamped one. The frequency and gain for which the Nyquist plot passes through the -1 point are exactly the same values for which the root locus crosses the $j\omega$ axis. Many other correlations appear in solving a single problem by both methods.

The results of root locus analysis can be easily converted to frequency response data. Thus one merely assumes values of s along the $j\omega$ axis, estimates the phase angles and vector lengths to the zeros and poles, and calculates the sum of the angles for total phase shift and the product of lengths for attenuation. The inverse problem of determining zeros and poles from experimental data is the more difficult one. Many techniques are already available, however, such as drawing asymptotes to the logarithmic attenuation curve. For unusual cases, particularly those in which resonant peaks are involved, the conformal mapping technique originated by Dr. Profos of Switzerland is recommended.[3]

The transient response is described by the poles of the transfer function. The inverse problem in this case is to locate the poles from an experimental transient response. One might use dead time, maximum build-up rate, overshoot, natural frequency of oscillation, and the damping rate as effective clues in solving this problem.

Other Applications

Many systems require a set of simultaneous equations to describe them and are said to be multicoupled. The corresponding block diagrams have several inputs to each loop so that the root locus method cannot be applied immediately. One should first lay out the diagram so that the main line of action of the signals forms the main loop with incidental coupling effects appearing as feedbacks and feed forwards. One then proceeds to isolate loops by replacing a signal which comes from within a loop by an equivalent signal at the output, replacing a signal entering a loop by an equivalent signal at the input. One can and should keep the physical picture of the equivalent system in mind as these manipulations are carried out.

The techniques of the root locus method can be used effectively in analyzing electric circuits. As a simple example, consider the lead-lag network of Figure 7(A).

It can be shown that the transfer function of this network is as given in equation 9

$$\frac{V_0}{V_i}=\frac{(1+R_1C_1s)(1+R_2C_2s)R_3}{(1+R_1C_1s)(1+R_2C_2s)R_3+R_1[1+(R_2+R_3)C_2s]} \quad (9)$$

The denominator can be factored algebraically by multiplying out and finding the zeros of the resulting quadratic. As an alternative, it will be noted that the zeros of the denominator must satisfy equation 10

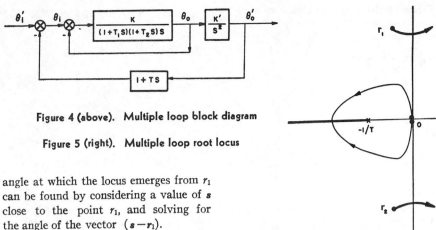

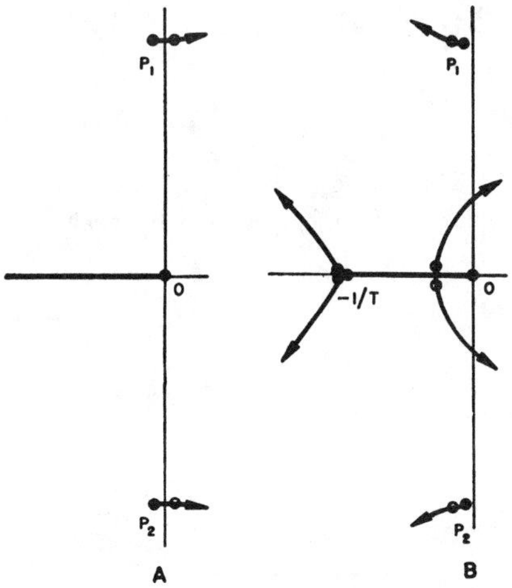

Figure 6. (A) Basic system. (B) Corrected system

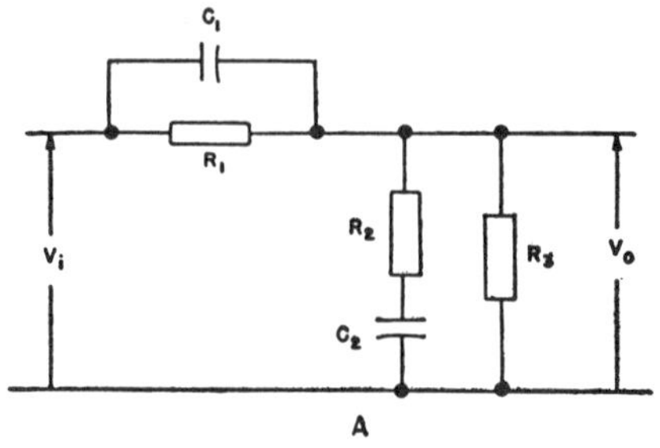

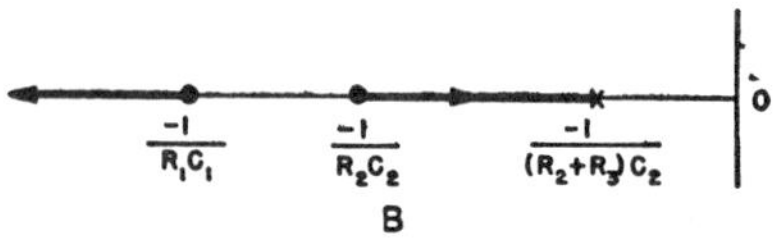

Figure 7 (left). (A) Circuit diagram. (B) Root locus

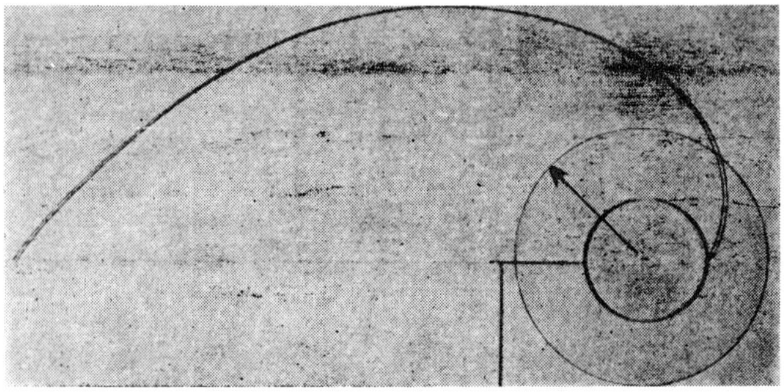

Figure 8 (right). Spirule

$$\frac{(1/R_1C_1+s)(1/R_2C_2+s)R_3(R_1C_1)(R_2C_2)}{[1/(R_2+R_3)C_2+s](R_2+R_3)C_2R_1} = -1 \quad (10)$$

The vectors in this expression are represented according to the root locus scheme in Figure 7(B). The two roots are thereby bounded as shown by the two dots and the cross. Their exact locations could be estimated or accurately determined by graphical methods.

The locus of roots now is simply intervals along the negative real axis between the open loop zeros and poles as shown in Figure 7 (B). The exact location of the roots along these intervals is determined in the usual way. Note that the constant in equation 10 is of the form $R'C_1$, in which R' is the effective value of R_2 and R_3 in parallel.

In more complicated networks, the advantages of the root locus concept over algebraic methods becomes greater; its particular advantage is in retaining at all times a clear picture of the relationships between the over-all network parameters and the parameters of individual circuit elements.

In the classical problem of finding roots, the differential equation is given in the form of a sum of terms of successively higher order. This can be converted to the form shown in equation 10

$$s^n+as^{n-1}+bs^{n-2}+\ldots+m = [(s+a)s+b]s+\ldots+m \quad (11)$$

This corresponds to a block diagram with another loop closed for each higher order term. Solve for the roots of the first loop which corresponds to the quantities in brackets above and proceed as before for the multiple loop system. If the roots close to the origin are of most interest, substitute $s=1/x$ first and solve for root values of x. Other combinations are, of course, possible because a single root locus basically determines the factors of the sum of two terms.

The root locus method is thus an analytical tool which can be applied to other problems than control system synthesis for which it was developed. But in attacking a new problem one would probably do well to try first to develop a method of analysis which is natural for that problem rather than seek to apply any existing methods.

Graphical Calculations

The root locus plot is first established in approximate form by inspection. Any significant point on the locus then can be checked by using the techniques indicated in this section. Note that only two calculations are involved, adding angles and multiplying lengths. Fortunately, all of these angles and lengths can be measured at the s point. Thus angles previously pictured at the zeros and poles also appear at the s point but between a horizontal line to the left and lines to the zeros and poles. A piece of transparent paper or plastic pivoted at the s point can be rotated successively through each of these angles to obtain their sum.

The reader can duplicate the "spirule" with two pieces of transparent paper, one for the disk and the other for the arm. Several procedures are possible, but the over-all purpose is to successively rotate the arm with respect to the disk through each of the angles of interest. Thus for adding phase angles, the disk is held fixed while the arm is rotated from a pole to the horizontal, whereas the two move together in getting aligned on the next pole. For multiplying lengths, the disk is held fixed while the arm is rotated from the position where a pole is on the straight line to the position where the pole is on the logarithmic curve. Rotations are made in the opposite directions for zeros than they are for poles.

Conclusions

The definite opinion of engineers using this method is that its prime advantage is the complete picture of a system which the root locus plot presents. Changing an open loop parameter merely shifts a point and modifies the locus. By means of the root locus method, all of the zeros and poles of the over-all function can be determined.

Any linear system is completely defined by this determination, and its response to any particular input function can be determined readily by standard mathematical or graphical methods.

References

1. PRINCIPLES OF SERVOMECHANISMS (book), **G. S. Brown, D. P. Campbell.** John Wiley and Sons, New York, N. Y., 1948.

2. TRANSIENTS IN LINEAR SYSTEMS (book), **M. F. Gardner, J. L. Barnes.** John Wiley and Sons, New York, N. Y., 1942.

3. GRAPHICAL ANALYSIS OF CONTROL SYSTEMS, **W. R. Evans.** *AIEE Transactions*, volume **67**, 1948, pages 547–51.

The Analysis of Sampled-Data Systems

J. R. RAGAZZINI
MEMBER AIEE

L. A. ZADEH
ASSOCIATE MEMBER AIEE

THERE is an important class of feedback control systems known as sampled-data systems or sampling servomechanisms in which the data at one or more points consist of trains of pulses or sequences of numbers. Such systems may have a variety of forms, a common example of which is shown in Figure 1. In the case illustrated, the sampling is performed on the control error by a so-called sampler which is indicated as a mechanical switch which closes momentarily every T seconds. The data at the output of such a switch consist of a train of equally spaced pulses of short duration whose envelope is the control error function. In some practical systems, the separation between successive pulses is controlled by some characteristic of the input signal and consequently is not constant. Such systems will not be considered in this paper.

In a typical sampled-data system such as that shown in Figure 1, the sampler is followed by a smoothing circuit, commonly referred to as hold or clamp circuit, whose function is to reproduce approximately the form of the original error function by an interpolation or extrapolation of the pulse train. Following the hold circuit, there are the usual components of the feedback loop, shown in Figure 1 as H and G, comprising amplifiers, shaping networks, and the controlled member.

It is apparent that the insertion of a sampler into an otherwise continuous control system in general should result in an inferior performance due to a loss of information in the control data. Yet, sampled-data systems have certain engineering advantages which make them preferable in some applications to continuous-data systems. The most important of these advantages is the fact that error sampling devices can be made extremely sensitive at the expense of bandwidth. An example of such a device is the electromechanical galvanometer and chopper bar. In this device a very sensitive though sluggish galvanometer is used to detect error and its position is sampled periodically by means of a chopper bar. The latter permits an auxiliary source of power to rotate a sizable potentiometer to a position determined by the clamped galvanometer needle. The process is carried out at uniform intervals and a sampled and clamped output is obtained for use in the continuous part of the control system. Bandwidth is lost through the sluggishness of the unloaded galvanometer, but the power gain is enormous. Similar devices for measurement of pressure errors, flow, or other phenomena can be devised along the same general lines.

In addition, there are some systems in which the data-collecting or transmission means are intermittent. Radars and multichannel time-division communication links are examples of this type of device. Such devices may be treated, in general, as sampled-data systems provided the duration of sampling is small by comparison with the settling time of the system.

Despite the increasing use of sampled-data devices in the fields of communication and control, the volume of published material on such devices is still rather limited.[1–10] The several different methods which have been developed for the analysis of sampled-data systems are closely related to the well-known mathematical techniques of solution of difference equations. It is the purpose of this paper to unify and extend the methods described in the literature and to investigate certain basic aspects of sampled-data systems.

Input-Output Relations

A central problem in the analysis of sampled-data systems is that of establishing a mathematical relation between the input and output of a specified system. This problem has received considerable attention in the literature of sampled-data systems, with the result that several different types of input-output relations have been developed, notably by Shannon,[1] Hurewicz,[2] and Linvill.[3] Shannon's relation involves the Fourier transforms of the sampled input and output; Hurewicz's relation is based on the use of so-called generating functions, which in this paper are referred to as z-transforms and which are, in fact, a disguised form of the Laplace transforms; while Linvill's relation involves directly the Laplace transforms of the input and output. The principal difference between Shannon's and Hurewicz's relations on the one hand, and that of Linvill on the other, is the fact that the former yield only the values of the output at the sampling instants, while the latter provides the expression for the output at all times, though at the cost of greater labor.

The analysis presented in this section has a dual objective: to achieve a unification of the approaches used by Shannon, Hurewicz, and Linvill; and to formulate the input-output relations for the basic types of sampled-data systems. In the next section, the problem of establishing a relation between the input and output will be approached from a significantly different point of view. Specifically, a sampled-data system will be treated as a time-variant system and its behavior will be characterized by a system function which involves both frequency and time.

The basic component of sampled-data systems is the sampler, whose output has the form of a train of narrow pulses occurring at the sampling instants 0, $\pm T$, $\pm 2T$, . . . , where T is the sampling interval; see Figure 2. The frequency $\omega_0 = 2\pi/T$ is called the sampling frequency.

For purposes of mathematical convenience, it is expedient to treat the output pulses as impulses whose areas are equal to the values of the sampled time function at the respective sampling instants. (This is permissible provided the pulse duration is small compared with the settling time of the system and the gain of the amplifier following the sampler is multiplied by a factor equal to the time duration of the sampling pulse.) Thus, if the input and output of the sampler are denoted by $r(t)$ and $r^*(t)$ respectively, the

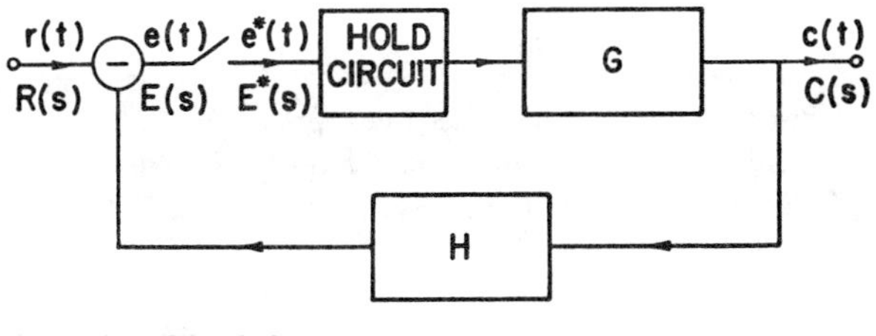

Figure 1. Typical sampled-data control system

Paper 52-161, recommended by the AIEE Feedback Control Systems Committee and approved by the AIEE Technical Program Committee for presentation at the AIEE Summer General Meeting, Minneapolis, Minn., June 23–27, 1952. Manuscript submitted March 21, 1952; made available for printing April 16, 1952.

J. R. RAGAZZINI and L. A. ZADEH are both with the Department of Electrical Engineering, Columbia University, New York, N. Y.

Reprinted from *AIEE Trans.*, vol. 71, pp. 225–234, 1952.

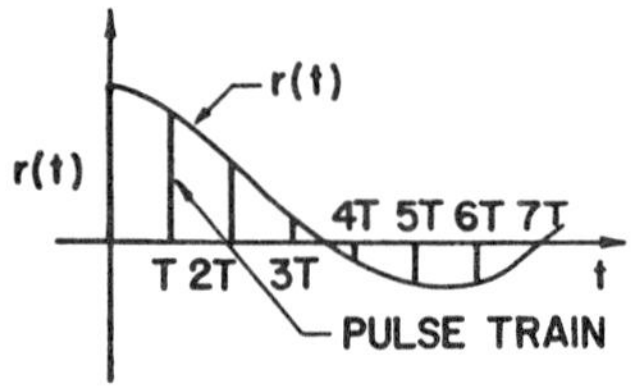

Figure 2. Pulse train at output of sampler

relation between them reads

$$r^*(t) = r(t)\delta_T(t) \tag{1}$$

where $\delta_T(t)$ represents a train of unit impulses (delta functions)

$$\delta_T(t) = \sum_{n=-\infty}^{\infty} \delta(t-nT) \tag{2}$$

Equation 1 may be written equivalently as

$$r^*(t) = \sum_{n=0}^{\infty} r(nT)\delta(t-nT) \tag{3}$$

where the negative values of n are absent by virtue of the assumption that $r(t)$ vanishes for negative values of t.

Equation 3 furnishes an explicit expression for the output of the sampler. It is more convenient, however, to deal with the Laplace transform of $r^*(t)$, which is denoted by $R^*(s)$

$$R^*(s) = \mathfrak{L}\{r(t)\delta_T(t)\} \tag{4}$$

One expression for $R^*(s)$ can be obtained at once by transforming both sides of equation 3; this yields

$$R^*(s) = \sum_{n=0}^{\infty} r(nT)\epsilon^{-nTs} \tag{5}$$

An alternative expression for $R^*(s)$ can be obtained by expressing $\delta_T(t)$ in the form of a complex Fourier series

$$\delta_T(t) = \frac{1}{T}\sum_{n=-\infty}^{\infty} \epsilon^{jn\omega_0 t} \tag{6}$$

and substituting this expression in equation 1. Then, transforming the resulting series term by term there results

$$R^*(s) = \frac{1}{T}\sum_{n=-\infty}^{\infty} R(s+jn\omega_0) \tag{7}$$

where $R(s)$ is the Laplace transform of $r(t)$. It is of interest to note that the equivalence between the two expressions for $R^*(s)$

$$\frac{1}{T}\sum_{n=-\infty}^{\infty} R(s+jn\omega_0) = \sum_{n=0}^{\infty} r(nT)\epsilon^{-nTs} \tag{8}$$

was discovered more than a century ago by Poisson, and that equation 8 is essentially equivalent to the Poisson summation rule.

An inspection of either of the alternative expressions for $R^*(s)$ indicates that when s in $R^*(s)$ is replaced by $s+jm\omega_0$, where m is any integer, the resulting expression is identical with $R^*(s)$. This implies that $R^*(s)$ is a periodic function of s with period $j\omega_0$; thus

$$R^*(s+jm\omega_0) = R^*(s) \tag{9}$$

where m = any integer.

The infinite series expression for $R^*(s)$ given by equation 5 readily can be put into closed form whenever $r(t)$ is a linear combination of products of polynomials and exponential functions. For instance, when $r(t) = \epsilon^{-at}$, the right-hand member of equation 5 is a geometric series which upon summation yields

$$R^*(s) = \frac{1}{1-\epsilon^{-at}\epsilon^{-Ts}} \tag{10}$$

When expressed in the form given by equation 5, the transform of the pulsed output, $R^*(s)$, is a function of ϵ^{sT}. This suggests that an auxiliary variable $z = \epsilon^{sT}$ be introduced and that $R^*(s)$ be written in terms of this variable. When this is done, the function $R^*(s)$, expressed as a function of z, is called the z-transform of $r(t)$. For notational convenience it is denoted by $R^*(z)$ although strictly speaking it should be written as $R^*(1/T \log z)$. With this convention, the transform given in equation 10, for example, reads

$$R^*(z) = \frac{1}{1-\epsilon^{-aT}z^{-1}} \tag{11}$$

In what follows, the symbols $R^*(s)$ and $R^*(z)$ will be used interchangeably since they represent the same quantity, namely the Laplace transform of $r(t)\delta_T(t)$. Needless to say, in cases where $r(t)$ has the form of a sequence of impulses (or numbers equal to the areas of respective impulses), the z-transform $R^*(s)$ is simply the Laplace transform of $r(t)$, and not of $r(t)\text{-}\delta_T(t)$.

It will be noted that the z-transform as defined is closely related to the generating function used by Hurewicz. However, the z-transform is a more natural concept since it stems directly from the Laplace transform of the sampled time function. It is of historical interest to note that generating functions, which, as pointed out, are essentially equivalent to z-transforms, were introduced by Laplace[11] and were extensively used by him in connection with the solution of difference equations.

In practice, $R^*(z)$ is generally a rational function of z, and its inversion, that is the determination of a function $r(t)$ of which $R^*(z)$ is the z-transform, is most rapidly carried out by using a table of z-transforms such as the one compiled in Table I. (More extensive tables of closely related types of transforms may be found in references 12 and 13.) One use of this table is in finding the z-transform corresponding to the Laplace transform of a given function. Despite its brevity, Table I is adequate for most practical purposes in view of the fact that both the Laplace transforms and the z-transforms can be expanded into partial fractions each term of which can be inverted individually.

It is important to note that the inverse of a z-transform is not unique. Thus, if $F^*(z)$ is an entry in the table and $f(t)$ is its correspondent, then any function of time which coincides with $f(t)$ at the sampling instants $0, T, 2T, 3T, \ldots$, has the same z-transform as $f(t)$. To put it another way, if $G^*(z)$ is the z-transform of some function $g(t)$, then the inverse of $G^*(z)$, as found from the table, is not, in general, identical with $g(t)$, although it coincides with $g(t)$ at the sampling instants. Thus, from the z-transform of a function one can find only the values of the function at the sampling instants. In this connection, it should be noted that the value of a time function at the nth sampling instant is equal to the coefficient of z^{-n} in the power series expansion of its z-transform (regarded as a function of z^{-1}). In cases requiring numerical computations, this property of z-transforms affords an alternative, and frequently convenient, means of calculating the values of corresponding time functions at the sampling instants.

It will be helpful to summarize at this

Table I. Abbreviated Table of Laplace and z-Transforms

	Laplace Transform $F(s)$	Time Function $f(t)$	z-Transform $F^*(z)$
(1)	1	$\delta(t)$	z^{-0}
(2)	ϵ^{-nTs}	$\delta(t-nT)$	z^{-n}
(3)	$\frac{1}{s}$	1	$\frac{1}{1-z^{-1}}$
(4)	$\frac{1}{s^2}$	t	$\frac{Tz^{-1}}{(1-z^{-1})^2}$
(5)	$\frac{1}{s+a}$	ϵ^{-at}	$\frac{1}{(1-\epsilon^{-aT}z^{-1})}$
(6)	$\frac{a}{s(s+a)}$	$(1-\epsilon^{-at})$	$\frac{z^{-1}(1-\epsilon^{-aT})}{(1-z^{-1})(1-\epsilon^{-aT}z^{-1})}$
(7)	$\frac{a}{s^2+a^2}$	$\sin at$	$\frac{\sin aTz^{-1}}{1-(2\cos aT)z^{-1}+z^{-2}}$
(8)	$F(s+a)$	$\epsilon^{-at}f(t)$	$F^*(\epsilon^{-aT}z)$
(9)	$\epsilon^{-sT}F(s)$	$f(t-T)$	$z^{-1}F^*(z)$
(10)	$\epsilon^{as}F(s)$	$f(t+a)$	$z^{a/T}F^*(z)$
(11)	$\frac{1}{s-\frac{1}{T}ln\, a}$	$a^{t/T}$	$\frac{z}{z-a}$
(12)	$\frac{s}{s^2+a^2}$	$\cos at$	$\frac{1-\cos aTz^{-1}}{1-(2\cos aT)z^{-1}+z^{-2}}$

stage the basic points of the foregoing discussion:

1. A sampler transforms a function $r(t)$ into a train of impulses, $r^*(t)=r(t)\delta_T(t)$, where $\delta_T(t)$ represents a train of unit impulses with period T.

2. The Laplace transform of $r^*(t)$, $R^*(s)$, is expressible in two different but equivalent forms given by equations 5 and 7.

3. $R^*(s)$ is a periodic function of s with period $j\omega_0$, where ω_0 is the sampling frequency.

4. The z-transform of $r(t)$, $R^*(z)$, is equal to $R^*(s)$ with ϵ^{sT} in $R^*(s)$ replaced by z; that is

$$R^*(z)=\mathfrak{L}\{r(t)\delta_T(t)\} \tag{12}$$

with ϵ^{sT} replaced by z.

As a preliminary to the consideration of sampled-data feedback systems, it will be helpful to establish one basic property of z-transforms. The property in question concerns the relation between the z-transforms of the output and input of the system illustrated in Figure 3. Denoting the input by $r(t)$, the output by $c(t)$, and the transfer function by $G(s)$, this relation reads

$$C^*(z)=G^*(z)R^*(z) \tag{13}$$

where $C^*(z)$ and $R^*(z)$ are the z-transforms of $c(t)$ and $r(t)$ respectively, and $G^*(z)$ is referred to as the starred transfer function. The importance of this relation derives from its similarity to the familiar relation $C(s)=G(s)R(s)$, which would obtain in the absence of samplers. This similarity makes it possible to treat z-transforms and starred transfer functions in much the same manner as the conventional Laplace transforms and transfer functions.

The proof of equation 13 is quite simple. From inspection of Figure 3, it is evident that the Laplace transform of $c(t)$ is given by

$$C(s)=G(s)R^*(s) \tag{14}$$

and correspondingly, by applying equation 7

$$C^*(s)=\frac{1}{T}\sum_{n=-\infty}^{\infty} G(s+jn\omega_0)R^*(s+jn\omega_0) \tag{15}$$

Because of the periodicity of $R^*(s)$, the following identity is noted

$$R^*(s+jn\omega_0)\equiv R^*(s) \tag{16}$$

Consequently equation 15 reduces to

$$C^*(s)=R^*(s)\left[\frac{1}{T}\sum_{n=-\infty}^{\infty} G(s+jn\omega_0)\right] \tag{17}$$

Denoting the bracketed term by $G^*(s)$

$$G^*(s)=\frac{1}{T}\sum_{n=-\infty}^{\infty} G(s+jn\omega_0) \tag{18}$$

equation 17 assumes the following form

$$C^*(s)=G^*(s)R^*(s) \tag{19}$$

which is equivalent to equation 13. It is seen that the starred transfer function $G^*(s)$, which is related to the transfer function $G(s)$ by equation 18, may be regarded as the ratio of the z-transforms of the output and input of the sampled-data system under consideration.

The mathematical essence of the foregoing discussion is the fact that a relation of the form $C(s)=G(s)R^*(s)$ implies $C^*(s)=G^*(s)R^*(s)$. This fact *per se* is very useful in the analysis of sampled-data systems involving one or more feedback loops. In the sequel, the process of passing from equation 14 to equation 19 will be referred to as the z-transformation of both sides of equation 14. The tacit understanding exists, of course, that the quantities actually subjected to the z-transformation are the time functions corresponding to the two members of equation 14.

Among the properties of the starred transfer function $G^*(s)$ there are two that are of particular importance. First, suppose that an input of the form $r(t)=\epsilon^{st}$ is applied to the system shown in Figure 3. This input is transformed by the sampler into an impulse train $r^*(t)$ which in view of equations 1 and 6 may be written as

$$r^*(t)=\frac{1}{T}\sum_{n=-\infty}^{\infty} \epsilon^{(s+jn\omega_0)t} \tag{20}$$

Operating on this expression with the transfer function $G(s)$ gives

$$c(t)=\frac{1}{T}\sum_{n=-\infty}^{\infty} G(s+jn\omega_0)\epsilon^{(s+jn\omega_0)t} \tag{21}$$

Sampling $c(t)$ and taking note of equation 18 yields after minor simplifications the expression for the sampled response of the system to $r(t)=\epsilon^{rt}$; that is

$$c^*(t)=[G^*(s)\epsilon^{st}]\delta_T(t) \tag{22}$$

where $\delta_T(t)$ denotes a train of unit impulses. It is seen that the response has the form of a train of impulses whose envelope is the bracketed term in equation 22. More specifically, this means that $G^*(s)\epsilon^{st}$ represents the envelope of the response of the system to an input of the form ϵ^{st}. Consequently, it may be concluded that the starred transfer function $G^*(s)$ relates the input $r(t)$ and the envelope of the sampled output $c^*(t)$ in the same manner as the transfer function $G(s)$ relates the input and output of N.

Another important property of $G^*(s)$ concerns the impulsive response of N which is denoted by $g(t)$. Since $G(s)$ is the Laplace transform of $g(t)$, it follows at once from equations 7 and 18 that $G^*(s)$ is the z-transform of $g(t)$, that is

$$G^*(s)=\mathfrak{L}\{g(t)\delta_T(t)\} \tag{23}$$

Consequently, $G^*(s)$ may be expressed in terms of the values of $g(t)$ at the sampling instants $t_n=nT$ or, alternatively, in terms of the system function $G(s)$ via equation 18. Needless to say, $G^*(s)$ may be obtained directly from either $g(t)$ or $G(s)$ by the use of a table of z-transforms such as Table I.

It frequently happens that the system N consists of a tandem combination of two or more systems. In particular, if N consists of two networks N_1 and N_2 with respective transfer functions $G_1(s)$ and $G_2(s)$, then the transfer function of N is given by the usual relation

$$G(s)=G_1(s)G_2(s) \tag{24}$$

and correspondingly the associated starred transfer function is given by

$$G^*(s)=\frac{1}{T}\sum_{n=-\infty}^{\infty} G_1(s+jn\omega_0)G_2(s+jn\omega_0) \tag{25}$$

which in abbreviated form will be written

$$G^*(s)=G_1G_2{}^*(s) \tag{26}$$

The important point noted here is that the starred transfer function $G^*(s)$ of two cascaded linear systems N_1 and N_2 which are not separated by a sampler is not the product of the respective starred transfer functions $G_1(s)$ and $G_2(s)$ but rather a new transfer function given by equation 25. On the other hand, if N_1 and N_2 are separated by a sampler, as shown in Figure 4, then from equation 19 it follows at once that the z-transform of the output of N_2 is $G_1{}^*(s)G_2{}^*(s)R^*(s)$. Hence, in this case the over-all starred transfer function is

$$G^*(s)=G_1{}^*(s)G_2{}^*(s) \tag{27}$$

Consequently, it may be concluded that the over-all starred transfer function of two or more networks cascaded through samplers is equal to the product of the starred transfer functions of the individual networks.

The expressions for the z-transforms of the output of more complex structures such as those encountered in feedback

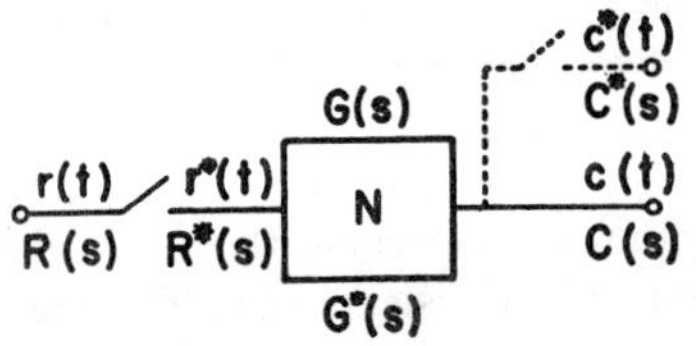

Figure 3. Pulsed linear system showing important variables and their transforms

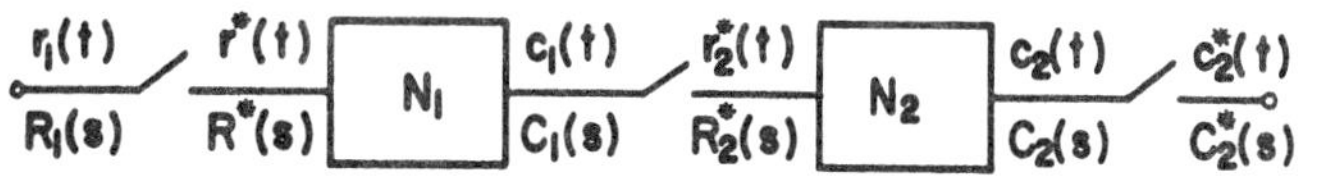

$$C_2^*(s) = R_1^*(s)\,G_1^*(s)\,G_2^*(s)$$

Figure 4. Cascaded linear systems separated by sampler

systems in general can be derived in a similar manner. Such expressions for several basic types of sampled-data systems are given in Table II. In this table, the first column gives the basic structure, the second gives the expression for the Laplace transform of the output, and the third gives the z-transform of the output.

It will suffice to go through the derivation of $C(s)$ and $C^*(s)$ for a typical system, say number 6 in the table. On inspection of the block diagram, it is seen that the expression for the Laplace transform of the error is

$$E(s)=R(s)-H(s)C^*(s) \tag{28}$$

where $C^*(s)$ is the Laplace transform of the input to the feedback circuit or, equivalently, the z-transform of the output of the system.

The Laplace transform of the output $C(s)$ is related to $E(s)$ by

$$C(s)=G(s)E(s) \tag{29}$$

Combining this relation with equation 28 gives

$$C(s)=G(s)R(s)-G(s)H(s)C^*(s) \tag{30}$$

Applying the z-transformation (see equation 19 and following) to both sides of this equation results in

$$C^*(s)=GR^*(s)-GH^*(s)C^*(s) \tag{31}$$

which upon solving for $C^*(s)$ yields the z-transform of the output

$$C^*(s)=\frac{GR^*(s)}{1+GH^*(s)} \tag{32}$$

as given in Table II. Finally, substituting this expression into equation 30 gives the Laplace transform of the output

$$C(s)=G(s)\left[R(s)-\frac{H(s)GR^*(s)}{1+GH^*(s)}\right] \tag{33}$$

which is the expression for $C(s)$ listed in the table.

As an illustration of the use of the expressions given in Table II, a typical problem involving the fourth structure shown in the table will be considered. Suppose that $H(s)=1$ and $G(s)=K/(s+a)$, where K and a are constants, and that it is desired to determine the values of the response of the system to a unit step input at the sampling instants. To this end, the z-transform of the output must be found. From Table II, this is

$$C^*(z)=\frac{G^*(z)R^*(z)}{1+GH^*(z)} \tag{34}$$

Referring to Table I, the z-transform of the unit step is

$$R^*(z)=\frac{1}{1-z^{-1}} \tag{35}$$

From the same table, the z-transform associated with $G(s)$ is

$$G^*(z)=\frac{K}{1-\epsilon^{-aT}z^{-1}} \tag{36}$$

Substituting these expressions in equation 34, there results after minor simplifications

$$C^*(z)=\frac{K}{(1-z^{-1})(1+K-\epsilon^{-aT}z^{-1})} \tag{37}$$

Expanding this into partial fractions

$$C^*(z)=\frac{K}{(1+K-\epsilon^{-aT})(1-z^{-1})}-\frac{K\epsilon^{-aT}}{(1+K-\epsilon^{-aT})(1+K-\epsilon^{-aT}z^{-1})} \tag{38}$$

finding the respective inverse transforms from Table I and combining the results yields

$$c(t)=\frac{K}{(1+K-\epsilon^{-aT})}\left\{1-\left(\frac{\epsilon^{-aT}}{1+K}\right)^{\frac{t+T}{T}}\right\} \tag{39}$$

This function coincides with the actual output at the sampling instants and hence at the nth instant, $t_n=nT$, the value of the response to a unit step is

$$c(nT)=\frac{K}{(1+K-\epsilon^{-aT})}\left\{1-\left(\frac{\epsilon^{-aT}}{1+K}\right)^{n+1}\right\} \tag{40}$$

Table II. Output Transforms for Basic Sampled-Data Systems

	System	Laplace Transform of Output $C(s)$	z-Transform of Output $C^*(z)$
(1)		$R^*(s)$	$R^*(z)$
(2)	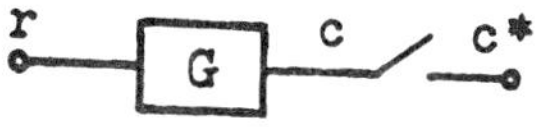	$GR^*(s)$	$GR^*(z)$
(3)	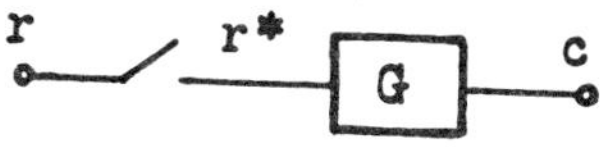	$G(s)R^*(s)$	$G^*(z)R^*(z)$
(4)	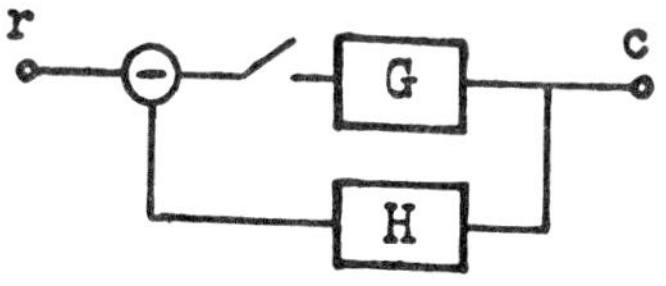	$\frac{G(s)R^*(s)}{1+HG^*(s)}$	$\frac{G^*(z)R^*(z)}{1+HG^*(z)}$
(5)	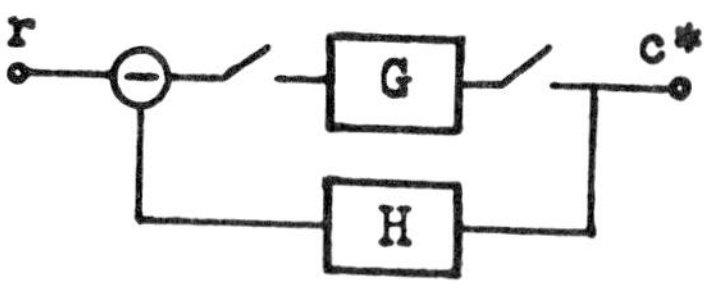	$\frac{G^*(s)R^*(s)}{1+H^*(s)G^*(s)}$	$\frac{G^*(z)R^*(z)}{1+H^*(z)G^*(z)}$
(6)	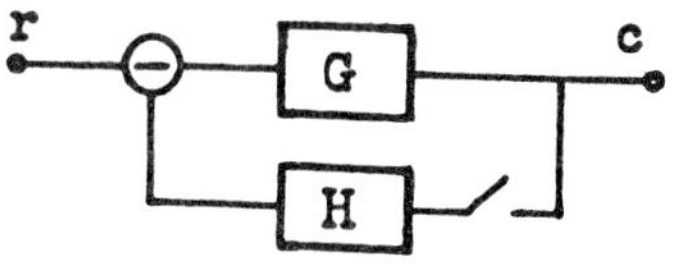	$G(s)\left[R(s)-\frac{H(s)RG^*(s)}{1+HG^*(s)}\right]$	$\frac{RG^*(z)}{1+HG^*(z)}$
(7)	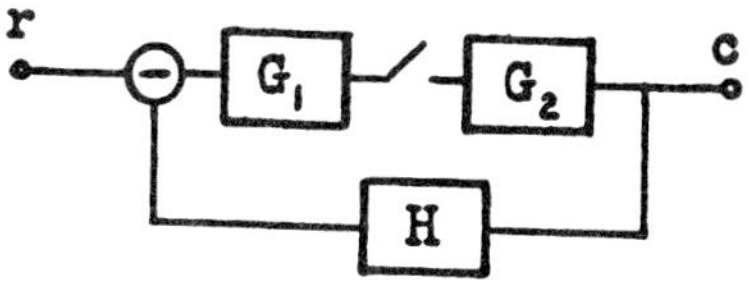	$\frac{G_2(s)RG_1^*(s)}{1+HG_1G_2^*(s)}$	$\frac{G_2^*(z)RG_1^*(z)}{1+HG_1G_2^*(z)}$

A sequence of ordinates obtained by evaluating $c(nT)$ for successive values of n yields a graph which can be used to assess the transient performance of the system. It will be noted that the system is stable for all K and a such that $\epsilon^{-aT}<1+K$. A brief discussion of the question of stability will be given in a subsequent section.

Variable Network Approach

By employing the techniques discussed in the preceding section one can obtain, in most practical cases, an explicit expression for the z-transform $C^*(s)$ and, if need be, the Laplace transform $C(s)$ of the output of a specified sampled-data system. The former can be used to find the values of the output at the sampling instants. The latter may be used, in principle, to determine the output at all times by calculating the inverse Laplace transform of $C(s)$. In practice, however, the inversion of $C(s)$ is difficult because $C(s)$ is a rational function in both s and ϵ^{sT} and no tables of inverse transforms for such functions are available.

An alternative approach which works quite well in those cases where an approximate expression for the continuous output—and not just its values at the sampling instants—is desired, is based on treating a sampling system as a periodically varying linear network. This approach is developed in the sequel, following a brief introductory discussion of the frequency analysis technique of handling time-variant systems.[14]

In using the frequency analysis technique, a linear time-variant system N is characterized by its system function $K(s;t)$, which is defined by the statement that $K(s;t)\epsilon^{st}$ represents the response of N to an exponential input ϵ^{st}. If the system function of N is known, then the response of N to an arbitrary input $r(t)$ can be obtained by superposition. More specifically, the output is given by

$$c(t)=\mathcal{L}^{-1}\{K(s;t)R(s)\} \qquad (41)$$

where $\mathcal{L}^{-1}$ represents the inverse Laplace transformation and $R(s)$ is the Laplace transform of $r(t)$. The variable t in $K(s;t)$ should be treated as if it were a parameter. This implies that in evaluating the inverse Laplace transform of $K(s;t)R(s)$, one may use a standard table of Laplace transforms and treat t in $K(s;t)$ as a constant.

When N varies in time with period T, its system function $K(s;t)$ is likewise a periodic function of time with period T. Consequently, $K(s;t)$ may be expanded into a Fourier series of the form

$$K(s;t)=\sum_{n=-\infty}^{\infty} K_n(s)\epsilon^{jn\omega_0 t} \qquad (42)$$

where $\omega_0=2\pi/T$ and the $K_n(s)$ represent the coefficients of the series. Thus, in the case of a periodically varying network, the problem of determination of $K(s;t)$ may be reduced to that of finding the coefficients of the Fourier series expansion of $K(s;t)$. In practice, a few terms in equation 42 usually provide an adequate approximation to $K(s;t)$, so that in many cases only two or at most three coefficients in the Fourier series expansion of $K(s;t)$ need be determined. (Note that $K_{-n}(s)$, is the conjugate of $K_n(s)$ since $K(s;t)$ is a real function of time.) Once $K(s;t)$—or, rather, an approximation to it—has been determined, the system function $K(s;t)$ can be used in the conventional manner for the purpose of obtaining the response of N to a specified input, for the investigation of the stability of N, for the calculation of the mean-square value of the response of N to a random input, for the determination of the ripple in the output, and many other purposes that are not pertinent to the present analysis.

The application of the general approach just outlined to the analysis of a sampled-data system is quite straightforward. For simplicity, the third system in Table II will be considered first. An input of the form ϵ^{st} is transformed by the sampler into a series of exponential terms which may be written as

$$\frac{1}{T}\sum_{n=-\infty}^{\infty} \epsilon^{(s+jn\omega_0)t} \qquad (43)$$

The response of the network N (following the sampler) to this input is

$$\frac{1}{T}\sum_{n=-\infty}^{\infty} G(s+jn\omega_0)\epsilon^{(s+jn\omega_0)t} \qquad (44)$$

where $G(s)$ is the system function (transfer function) of N. Consequently, from the definition of the system function $K(s;t)$ of the over-all system, it follows that

$$K(s;t)=\frac{1}{T}\sum_{n=-\infty}^{\infty} G(s+jn\omega_0)\epsilon^{jn\omega_0 t} \qquad (45)$$

which is in effect a complex Fourier series expansion of $K(s;t)$. It is seen that the coefficient $K_n(s)$ of $\epsilon^{jn\omega_0 t}$ is equal to $1/T\ G(s+jn\omega_0)$.

As a simple illustration of the use of this expression suppose that the input is a unit-step, that $G(s)=1/(s+a)$, and that ω_0 is such that $K(s;t)$ is adequately approximated by the first two terms in equation 45. In this case, $R(s)=1/s$ and

$$K(s;t)=\frac{1}{T}\left[\frac{1}{s+a}+\frac{\epsilon^{j\omega_0 t}}{s+a+j\omega_0}+\frac{\epsilon^{-j\omega_0 t}}{s+a-j\omega_0}\right] \qquad (46)$$

Substituting these expressions in equation 41 and performing the inverse Laplace transformation with the help of a standard table of Laplace transforms, with t treated as a constant, one readily obtains

$$c(t)=\frac{1}{Ta}(1-\epsilon^{-aT})+\frac{2}{T(a^2+\omega_0^2)}\times [a\cos\omega_0 t+\omega_0\sin\omega_0 t-a\epsilon^{-aT}] \qquad (47)$$

which is the desired expression for the output.

Turning to feedback systems, consider the fourth system in Table II. In this case, it is expedient to obtain first the expression for $e^*(t)$ corresponding to an exponential input $r(t)=\epsilon^{st}$. In view of equation 22, this is

$$e^*(t)=\frac{\epsilon^{st}}{1+GH^*(s)}\frac{1}{T}\sum_{n=-\infty}^{\infty}\epsilon^{jn\omega_0 t} \qquad (48)$$

where the second factor represents $\delta_T(t)$. To deduce $K(s;t)$ from this expression, it is sufficient to find the response of the forward circuit, characterized by $G(s)$, to $e^*(t)$ and divide the result by ϵ^{st}. This yields

$$K(s;t)=\frac{1}{T[1+GH^*(s)]}\sum_{n=-\infty}^{\infty} G(s+jn\omega_0)\epsilon^{jn\omega_0 t} \qquad (49)$$

which is in effect a complex Fourier series expansion of $K(s;t)$, with the coefficient of $\epsilon^{j\omega_0 t}$ being

$$K_n(s)=\frac{G(s+jn\omega_0)}{T[1+GH^*(s)]} \qquad (50)$$

It will be noted that, as should be expected, at the sampling instants $t_m=mT$, $K(s;t)$ reduces to

$$K(s;mT)=\frac{G^*(s)}{1+GH^*(s)} \qquad (51)$$

which will be recognized as the starred transfer function of the over-all system.

In the case under consideration, the determination of the response of the system to a given input is complicated somewhat by the fact that the denominator of $K_n(s)$ is a rational function in ϵ^{sT}, rather than in s. For purely numerical computations this is generally not objectionable. However, in analytical work it is usually necessary to approximate the term $GH^*(s)$ in equation 50 by a few terms in its expansion

$$GH^*(s)=\frac{1}{T}\sum_{n=-\infty}^{\infty} G(s+jn\omega_0)\times H(s+jn\omega_0) \qquad (52)$$

In this way, one obtains a rational function approximation to $K_n(s)$.

In the final analysis, the results obtainable by the method outlined in this section are also obtainable, although less conveniently, from the expression for the Laplace transform of the output $C(s)$. The chief advantage of the system function approach is that the function $K(s;t)$ is essentially a time-varying transfer function and as such provides a clear picture of the state of the system at each instant.

Response to a Random Input

The expression for the system function obtained in the preceding section has an immediate application in connection with the important problem of determining the statistical characteristics of the response of a sampled-data system to a random input. Since a general discussion of this problem is outside the scope of the present paper, the following analysis is limited to the case where the input is a stationary time series, and it is desired to obtain the expression for the mean-square value of the output at a specified instant of time. This particular problem has considerable bearing on the design of sampled-data systems that are optimum in the sense of the minimum rms error criterion.

A general expression for the mean-square value of the output of a time-variant system is given in reference 14; it reads

$$\sigma^2(t) = \int_0^\infty |K(j\omega;t)|^2 S(\omega)df,\ \omega = 2\pi f \quad (53)$$

where $S(\omega)$ is the power spectrum function of the input; $K(j\omega;t)$ is the system function with s replaced by $j\omega$; and $\sigma^2(t)$ is the mean-square value of the output at a specified instant t. To apply this equation to a sampled-data system it is only necessary to substitute the expressions for the system function of the system and the power spectrum of the input into equation 53 and carry out the necessary integration. In the majority of practical cases, the integration in question is most readily carried out by graphical means.

When the specified instant of time t coincides with a sampling instant, $t = nT$, the formula given above assumes a much simpler form. Thus, as was shown in the preceding section, for $t = nT$ the system function $K(s;t)$ becomes identical with the starred transfer function $K^*(s)$ of the over-all system. Consequently, equation 53 reduces to

$$\sigma^2 = \int_0^\infty |K^*(j\omega)|^2 S(\omega)df \quad (54)$$

where $K^*(j\omega)$ is the starred transfer function with s replaced by $j\omega$; and σ^2 is the mean-square value of the output at any sampling instant.

Sometimes it is more convenient to express σ^2 in terms of the autocorrelation function[2] of the input, rather than in terms of its power spectrum. It can be shown readily that, in terms of the autocorrelation function of the input, $\psi(\tau)$, σ^2 is given by the following expression

$$\sigma^2 = \sum_{n=0}^{\infty} \sum_{m=0}^{\infty} k(nT)k(mT)\psi[(n-m)T] \quad (55)$$

where $k(t)$ is the inverse z-transform of $K^*(z)$. This expression is useful chiefly in those cases where the autocorrelation function $\psi(\tau)$ drops off rapidly with increase in τ.

The Hold System

As stated previously, the function of the hold circuit is to reconstruct approximately the original time function from the impulse train generated by the sampler. It is evident that if it were possible to realize a perfect hold circuit, a sampled-data system incorporating such a circuit would be identical with a continuous-data system. However, in general, a perfect hold circuit is not realizable because of the random nature of the time function which has to be reconstructed. Furthermore, a very important consideration in the design of hold circuits is the fact that a close approximation of the original time function requires, in general, a long time delay, which is undesirable in view of its adverse effect on the stability of the system. Consequently, the design of a hold circuit involves a compromise between the requirements of stability and over-all dynamic performance on the one hand, and on the other hand, the desirability of a close approximation to the original time function and the reduction of ripple content in the output of the system.

It should be remarked that the hold circuits commonly employed in practice are generally of the so-called clamp type, which is one of the simplest forms of hold circuits. More sophisticated types of hold circuits based on the use of polynomial interpolating functions have been described by Porter and Stoneman.[7]

A complete treatment of hold circuits cannot ignore the random nature of the time function which the hold circuit is called upon to reconstruct. Such a treatment is outside the scope of the present paper. The brief discussion which follows is concerned chiefly with some of the more basic aspects of hold circuit design.

The generation of an approximation to the original time function between two sampling instants t_n and t_{n+1}, from its values at the preceding sampling instants $t_n, t_{n-1}, t_{n-2}, \ldots$, is essentially a problem in extrapolation or prediction. An effective, though not optimum, method of generating the desired approximation is based on the consideration of the power series expansion of $r(t)$ in the typical interval from $t_n = nT$ to $t_{n+1} = (n+1)T$

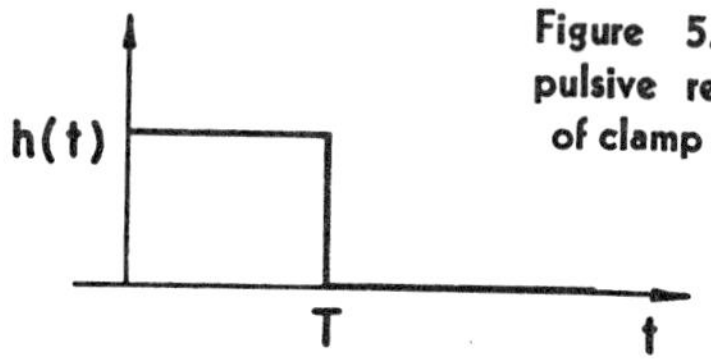

Figure 5. Impulsive response of clamp circuit

$$r(t) = r(nT) + r'(nT)(t-nT) + \frac{r''(nT)}{2}(t-nT)^2 + \ldots \quad (56)$$

where the primes indicate the derivatives of $r(t)$ at $t_n = nT$. To evaluate the coefficients of this series it is necessary to obtain the derivatives of the function $r(t)$ at the beginning of the interval in question. Since the information concerning $r(t)$ is available only at the sampling instants, these derivatives must be estimated from the sampled data. For instance, an estimate of the first derivative involving only two data pulses is given by

$$r'(nT) = \frac{1}{T}\{r[nT] - r[(n-1)T]\} \quad (57)$$

and the second derivative is given by

$$r''(nT) = \frac{1}{T}\{r'[nT] - r'[(n-1)T]\} = \frac{1}{T^2}\{r[nT] - 2r[(n-1)T] + r[(n-2)T]\} \quad (58)$$

Thus to obtain an estimate of a derivative of $r(t)$ the minimum number of data pulses which must be considered is equal to the order of the desired derivative plus one. This implies that the higher the order, the greater the delay before a reliable estimate of that derivative can be obtained. For this reason, an attempt to utilize the higher order derivatives of $r(t)$ for purposes of extrapolation meets with serious difficulties in maintaining system stability. Generally, only the first term in equation 56 is used, resulting in what is sometimes described as a boxcar or clamp circuit but which will be referred to here as a zero-order hold system. More generally, an nth order hold system is one in which the signal between successive sampling instants is approximated by an nth order polynomial.

Considering the zero-order hold system, it is evident that its impulsive response $h(t)$ must be as shown in Figure 5. By inspection, the Laplace transform of this time function is seen to be

$$H(s)=\frac{1}{s}-\frac{1}{s}\epsilon^{-Ts} \qquad (59)$$

The frequency response of this hold system is obtained by replacing the complex frequency s by $j\omega$, resulting in the following expression for the magnitude of the transfer function

$$|H(j\omega)|=\frac{2}{\omega}\left|\sin\frac{\omega T}{2}\right| \qquad (60)$$

This relation is plotted in Figure 6. It is observed that the hold system is essentially a low-pass filter which passes the low frequency spectrum of the impulse train and rejects the displaced high-frequency spectra resulting from the sampling process. An important property of the zero-order hold system is that the ripple at the output is zero if the input is a constant. In a similar way, the first order hold system has zero ripple output for an input function whose slope is a constant.

As is well known, if the signal does not contain frequencies higher than one-half the sampling frequency, perfect reproduction of the signal is obtained with an ideal low-pass filter (that is, one with unity gain and linear phase shift up to its cutoff frequency) whose cutoff frequency is equal to one-half the sampling frequency. For that matter, any low-pass network having roughly this characteristic can be used to extract most of the useful spectrum from the impulse train. It is even possible, though not advisable, to dispense with the hold circuit altogether, and rely on the low-pass characteristics of the forward circuit to perform the necessary smoothing of the sampled data.

System Design Using z-Transforms

The primary objectives in the design of closed-cycle control systems include the achievement of stability and an acceptable over-all dynamic performance. The standard technique of achieving these objectives consists in plotting the Nyquist diagram of the loop transfer function and adjusting the system parameters until the plot does not enclose the point -1.0. The margins by which such an enclosure is avoided constitute a measure of the damping of the system. Other more sophisticated techniques may be used if a better dynamic performance is desired.

In view of the fact that the starred transfer function is analogous to the conventional transfer function, the same basic technique may be applied in the case of sampled-data control systems. The function which is plotted is $GH^*(s)$ or $G^*(s)H^*(s)$ according as the denominator of the z-transform of the output is of the form $1+GH^*(s)$ or $1+G^*(s)H^*(s)$, see Table II. As usual, the complex frequency s is varied along a contour in the s-plane consisting of the imaginary axis and a semicircle enclosing the right-half of the plane. Since the starred transfer functions are periodic with period $j\omega_0$, the loci of the functions $GH^*(s)$ or $G^*(s)H^*(s)$ retrace themselves at each cycle, so that s need be varied only from $-j\omega_0/2$ to $j\omega_0/2$ in order to obtain the shape of the locus. Critical regions such as the vicinity of the origin in the s-plane are handled in the same manner as in the case of continuous-data systems.

Since the auxiliary variable z is defined as ϵ^{Ts}, it is evident that as s is assigned imaginary values over one complete cycle, z traces a unit circle in the z-plane. Thus, the loop transfer function $GH^*(s)$ can be plotted directly by expressing it in the form $GH^*(z)$ and varying z along the unit circle. To demonstrate the technique, the $GH^*(z)$ locus for the system shown in Figure 7 will be plotted. This system is seen to consist of a zero-order hold circuit and a simple linear component in the forward circuit. The feedback transmission is unity so that the loop transfer function is

$$G(s)H(s)=\frac{(1-\epsilon^{-s})}{s}\,\frac{1}{s(s+1)},\ T=1 \qquad (61)$$

Expanding this transform into partial fractions, there results

$$G(s)H(s)=(1-\epsilon^{-s})\left(\frac{1}{s^2}-\frac{1}{s}+\frac{1}{s+1}\right) \qquad (62)$$

On considering each term separately and obtaining the corresponding z-transforms from Table I, the starred loop transfer function is found to be

$$GH^*(z)=(1-z^{-1})\left[\frac{z^{-1}}{(1-z^{-1})^2}-\frac{0.632z^{-1}}{(1-z^{-1})(1-0.368z^{-1})}\right] \qquad (63)$$

which can be simplified to

$$GH^*(z)=\frac{0.264+0.368z}{(0.368-z)(1-z)} \qquad (64)$$

This function is plotted in Figure 8 where it is seen that for the constants chosen, the system is stable; but if the loop gain is increased by a factor of 1.5, the system becomes unstable.

If it were desired to improve the margin of stability or, for that matter, stabilize this system with a higher loop gain, the procedure would be to add lead networks just as in the case of a continuous-data system. The major difficulty encountered in this procedure is that the resulting starred loop transfer function is not related in a simple manner to the original function, for as was shown previously the starred transfer function of two networks in tandem is not equal to the product of respective starred transfer functions. Consequently, the insertion of a corrective network in the feedback loop requires the recalculation of the starred loop transfer function. The need for recalculation is inherent in the stabilization of sampled-data systems by the insertion of a corrective network in the feedback loop. Thus, as the art exists at the present time, the shaping procedure involves essentially a trial and error method with the plot of the Nyquist diagram for each trial set of system parameters used to assess the stability of the system.

Conclusions

The sampled-data feedback control system may be analyzed in a systematic manner by applying the z-transform method. Techniques of locus shaping similar to those commonly used in continuous systems may be applied by plotting the starred loop transfer function on the complex plane. This is done with no approximations other than those relating to the narrowness of the pulses constituting the pulse train. Once satisfactory loci are obtained by the addition of ap-

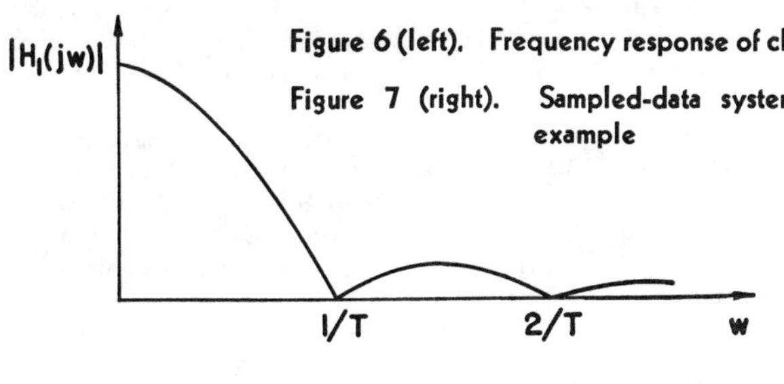

Figure 6 (left). Frequency response of clamp circuit

Figure 7 (right). Sampled-data system used in example

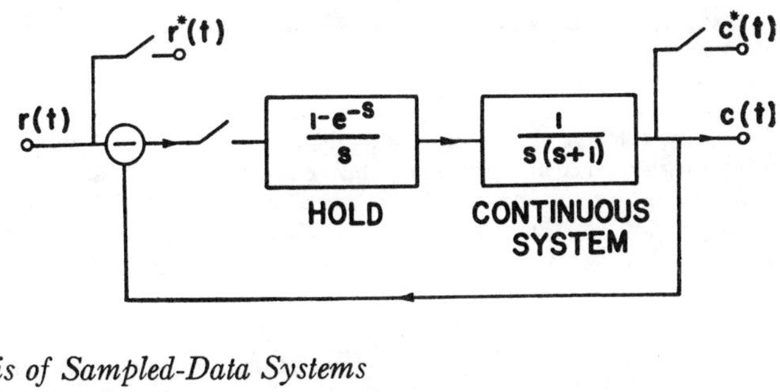

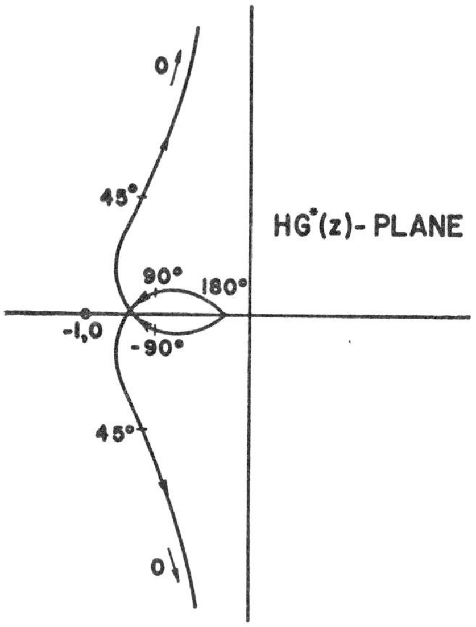

Figure 8. Plot of HG*(z) locus for system used in example

propriate networks, the transient performance of the system can be assessed by obtaining the time functions from a table of z-transforms or by expanding the z-transform of the output function into a power series which gives the ordinates at the sampling instants. The smoothness of the output can be estimated by use of the variable network analysis described in this paper.

One complication in the design of sampled-data systems is the relative difficulty of evaluating the effect of inserting corrective networks in the control loop. If this complication could be removed, locus shaping would be no more difficult than with continuous systems. Research now in progress is directed toward the devising of practical methods of locus shaping in the loop transfer function plane. Results to date indicate that the z-transform method, in conjunction with design techniques somewhat analogous to those used with conventional servomechanisms, furnishes a powerful tool for the analysis of linear sampled-data systems.

References

1. FUNDAMENTAL THEORY OF SERVOMECHANISMS (book), **L. A. MacColl.** D. Van Nostrand Company, Inc., New York, N. Y., chapter 10, 1945.

2. THEORY OF SERVOMECHANISMS (book), **H. M. James, N. B. Nichols, R. S. Phillips.** McGraw-Hill Book Company, Inc., New York, N. Y., chapter 5, 1947.

3. SAMPLED-DATA CONTROL SYSTEMS STUDIED THROUGH COMPARISON OF SAMPLING WITH AMPLITUDE MODULATION, **W. K. Linvill.** *AIEE Transactions*, volume 70, part II, 1951, pages 1779–88.

4. ANALYSIS OF DISCONTINUOUS SERVOMECHANISMS, **F. H. Raymond.** *Annales de Telecommunication* (Paris, France), volume 4, 1949, pages 250–56, 307–14, 347–57.

5. THEORY OF INTERMITTENT REGULATION, **Y. Z. Tsipkin.** *Avtomatika i Telemekhanika* (Moscow, USSR), volume 10, number 3, 1949, pages 189–224.

6. THE DYNAMICS OF AUTOMATIC CONTROLS (book), **R. C. Oldenbourg, H. Sartorius.** American Society of Mechanical Engineers New York, N. Y., 1948, chapter 5.

7. A NEW APPROACH TO THE DESIGN OF PULSE-MONITORED SERVO SYSTEMS, **A. Porter, F. Stoneman.** *Journal*, Institution of Electrical Engineers (London, England), volume 97, part II, 1950, pages 597–610.

8. A GENERAL THEORY OF SAMPLING SERVO SYSTEMS, **D. F. Lawden.** *Proceedings*, Institution of Electrical Engineers (London, England), volume 98, part IV, October 1951, pages 31–36.

9. APPLICATION OF FINITE DIFFERENCE OPERATORS TO LINEAR SYSTEMS, **B. M. Brown.** *Proceedings of the D.S.I.R. Conference on Automatic Control*, Butterworths Scientific Publications (London, England), 1951.

10. ANALYSIS OF A SAMPLING SERVOMECHANISM, **K. S. Miller, R. J. Schwarz.** *Journal of Applied Physics* (New York, N. Y.), volume 21, April 1950, pages 290–294.

11. THEORIE ANALYTIQUE DES PROBABILITÉS, PART 1: DU CALCUL DES FONCTIONS GENERATRICES (book), **P. S. Laplace.** Paris, France, 1812.

12. A LIST OF GENERALIZED LAPLACE TRANSFORMS, **W. M. Stone.** *Journal of Science*, Iowa State College (Ames, Iowa), volume 22, April 1948, pages 215–225.

13. TRANSIENTS IN LINEAR SYSTEMS (book), **M. F. Gardner, J. L. Barnes.** John Wiley and Sons, Inc., New York, N. Y., 1942, pages 354–356.

14. FREQUENCY ANALYSIS OF VARIABLE NETWORKS, **L. A. Zadeh.** *Proceedings*, Institute of Radio Engineers (New York, N. Y.), volume 38, March 1950, pages 291–299.

Discussion

John M. Salzer (Hughes Aircraft Company, Culver City, Calif.): The objectives of this paper are: (a) to unify the z-transform (Shannon, Hurewicz) and s-transform (Linvill) approaches to sampled-data systems; (b) to formulate input-output relations for various types of such systems; and (c) to treat such systems by considering the sampler a time-variant element.

The paper fills a clear need in this underpublished field, and it presents its topic concisely and illuminatingly. It brings together two viewpoints, (a) and (c), to bear on the same problem and shows the way toward systematization (b) of the solution.

Perhaps the most significant contribution of the paper is the variable network approach. Although the applicability of this approach was recognized before,[1] the authors' more recent investigations in the general field of time-varying systems are now made to bear directly on the problem of sampled-data systems. The importance of the generalization thus afforded should not be overlooked.

It is interesting to note that the variable network approach leads directly to the same expressions as the s-transform method. Both methods are predicated on the concept of using an arbitrary, characteristic input function $[r(t) = \epsilon^{st}]$, but by distinguishing a time-variant transfer function certain generalizations are made possible, as already noted. An interesting illustration of such a generalization is given in the section titled "Response to a Random Input."

There are several points and results in this paper which bear interesting relations to some of the work done by the discussor in connection with digital-analogue systems.[2] The use of starred s-transforms, such as $R^*(s)$, in place of infinite sums, is a welcome convenience.[3] This notation facilitates the manipulations in dealing with sampled-data systems and makes the systematizations of Table II of the paper easier to comprehend.

As noted in the paper, in the case of starred transforms (that is, in the case of sampled functions) the s- and z-transforms are exactly equivalent. Thus, the use of z-transforms involves no approximation, and it offers certain conveniences. One advantage is notational, for z is easier to write than ϵ^{st}. The other is that the infinite number of poles and zeros of the starred s-transforms are replaced by a finite set in the z-plane. Furthermore, the ambiguity at the point of infinity in the s-plane (due to essential singularity) is circumvented by the use of z-transforms.

In case the s-transform is not a starred transform, information is lost by the use of z-transform because this amounts to representing a continuous function, $c(t)$, by its samples, $c^*(t)$, just as it is done in numerical mathematics. But whereas in numerical work the sampling (or tabular) interval may be adjusted until such a representation is justified, in analyzing a given control system one is faced with a sampling rate already determined and the analysis must be made correct for the existing physical situation. For particular systems the sequence of output samples may not give a satisfactory picture so that it becomes necessary to study the behavior of the output also between sampling instants. Furthermore, and this is important, it is not always *a priori* obvious whether this is or is not the case.

Where the output behavior between samples is also of interest, the z-transform method is still applicable but must be augmented by separate investigation of the output during the sampling period. A separate solution based on initial conditions at the sampling instant may be used in analysis, but a synthesis procedure would hardly be fruitful along these lines.

The alternative solution is the s-transform approach. As noted by the authors, this method leads to transforms which are products of rational functions of s and z, and tables of corresponding transform pairs are not available. Nevertheless, the exact analysis is straightforward, even if somewhat laborious, and moreover, the frequency characteristics obtained may give a hint as to the nature of compensation needed to improve the response.

Whether the z-transform method is applicable or not in a particular case depends on the question of bandwidth. If the sampling rate is many times higher than the bandwidth of the input or of the system, then the z-transform solution is expected to be a suitable representation of the continuous output. It is presumed that the applications with which the authors concerned themselves were of this type. However, in the design of certain systems it is often desirable to use the lowest permissible sampling rate consistent with the specifications. In finding this limiting rate, one does not get a complete answer by the use of only z-transforms.

It may be noted that as far as stability is concerned either the z- or the s-transforms lead to exactly the same result, for only a divergent continuous function has a divergent sequence of samples. That this is so is demonstrated in Table II of the paper, where the corresponding denominators in both the s- and z-transform columns are identical.

To the numerous examples of sampled-data systems mentioned by the authors, the discussor wishes to add one: systems in which a digital computer is incorporated. As generally conceived today, digital computers operate on sampled data; therefore, their presence in the system requires sampling. Since the output of the digital computer is sampled also, the computer fits in between the sampler and the holding unit. If the digital computer is instructed to perform a linear difference equation on its sampled input, it can be represented by a transfer function which is rational in z. This result ties in with the methods of the paper.

For example, in the case of a digital computer equation 27 of the paper applies, because the data stay sampled through all numerical work. Thus, the transfer function of a composite digital program equals the product of the transfer functions of the component programs. The implication of this fact in system design is to be noted. Suppose that the stability of the system illustrated in Figure 8 of the paper is to be improved by a digital compensator, $W^*(s)$, inserted in either the forward or the feedback section. Since

$$WHG^*(z)=W^*(z)HG^*(z)$$

the new stability diagram is directly related to the old one so that the synthesis procedure is facilitated greatly. Of course, this is not meant to imply that digital compensation can do a better job than analogue; it only means that it is easier to see what a digital unit does. A somewhat academic example of digital compensation is worked out in chapter 4 of reference 2 of this discussion.

There is one comment concerning notation which may be found of interest: namely, it may be preferable to define z as being equal to ϵ^{-sT} rather than ϵ^{+sT}, when dealing with sampled-data systems. This is so because the latter corresponds to a time-advance operation, which has no physical meaning in a real-time application. In purely mathematical work one definition is as good as the other, and it is just unfortunate that in previous operational and transform work with difference equations the advance (ϵ^{+sT} rather than the delay (ϵ^{-sT}) operator was given a symbol. In consequence of this choice, z naturally will appear raised to negative powers, thereby diminishing the manipulative advantage of its usage. Table I of the paper illustrates this point. Of course, multiplication of both numerator and denominator by an appropriate power of z always can eliminate the negative powers of z (as was done in line 11 of Table I), but this is an additional step.

There are further reasons for which ϵ^{-sT} should be regarded the fundamental variable. For instance, in the investigation of stability of digital programs by conformal mapping the use ϵ^{-sT} leads to much simpler rules that that of ϵ^{+sT}.

REFERENCES

1. ANALYSIS AND DESIGN OF SAMPLED DATA CONTROL SYSTEMS (thesis), **W. K. Linvill.** Project Whirlwind *Report R-170*, Massachusetts Institute of Technology (Cambridge, Mass.), 1949.

2. TREATMENT OF DIGITAL CONTROL SYSTEMS AND NUMERICAL PROCESSES IN THE FREQUENCY DOMAIN (thesis), **John M. Salzer.** Digital Computer Laboratory (microfilmed report), Massachusetts Institute of Technology (Cambridge, Mass.), 1951.

3. Compares with the notation $R(s)$ used in reference 2; for example, pages 56 and 176.

B. M. Brown (Royal Naval College, London, England): An alternative technique is available for handling the general theory and problems of the type discussed in this paper. Instead of using Laplace transforms, which imply a limitation to input and output functions which are zero for negative time, this technique assumes functions of general type, and uses as transfer functions operators which are functions of the operator $D=d/dt$. Such a function $F(D)$ is usually a fraction, in which numerator and denominator are polynomials in D. Thus if input and output, u and x respectively, are connected by the relation $x=F(D)u$, where $F(D)=P(D)/Q(D)$, then x is understood to denote the general solution of the differential equation

$$Q(D)x=P(D)u$$

Such operators have provided a classical method for solving linear differential equations. If the coefficients are constant the operators in general can be manipulated algebraically, and this type of manipulation proves to be a very powerful tool.

If a linear system has a transfer function $F(D)$, then the stability is determined by the roots of $Q(\lambda)=0$. A steady-state solution can be obtained by expanding $F(D)$ in a series of ascending powers of D and operating on u. In many cases an adequate approximation is given by the first term of this series, which always can be written down by inspection. Thus if $F(D)$ is given, the main characteristics of the response can be inferred without the labour of evaluating particular solutions to particular inputs, whether by Laplace transform or other methods.

Operators of the type $F(D)$ have parallels in the form of functions of the operators E and Δ, with a complete set of analogous properties. These operators are defined by

$$Eu(t)=u(t+T)$$

and

$$\Delta u(t)=u(t+T)-u(t)$$

where T is constant. The three basic operators are connected by the relations

$$E=1+\Delta=\epsilon^{TD}$$

the latter being obtained by Taylor's theorem. Functions of E and Δ can be used for solving difference equations and for discussing systems based on such equations. A short account of the appropriate methods is given in reference 9 of the paper.

Now operators of the types $F(D)$, $F(E)$, and $F(\Delta)$ are all linear, which is to say that, denoting such an operator by Φ

$$\Phi(u+v)=\Phi u+\Phi v$$

They also have another important property of being time-invariant, which means that if $\Phi u(t)=x(t)$, then $\Phi u(t+t_0)=x(t+t_0)$, where t_0 is any constant. Because of this, they are commutative. They can be, and are in practice, applied both to continuous functions of t and to pulse trains.

Another operator S, the sampling operator, now is introduced whose effect is to convert a continuous function into a train of pulses. It is of course equivalent to multiplication by $\delta_T(t)$ in the notation of the paper. It easily is seen that S is linear, but not time-invariant and not in general commutative with functions of D, E, or Δ.

It will be shown briefly how the various processes described in the paper can be represented operationally. Consider first the effect of sampling a function $u(t)$ and then passing it through a network with transfer function $F(D)$. The resulting function is $F(D)Su(t)$ which is in general a continuous function. If this is sampled, either physically or for the purpose of analysis, the result is the pulse train $SF(D)Su(t)$. To determine the relation between the two pulse trains, let $f(t)$ be the response to a unit impulse input to the network. Then

$$\begin{aligned} SF(D)Su(t) &= SF(D)\sum_m u(mT)\delta(t-mT) \\ &= S\sum_m u(mT)F(D)\delta(t-mT) \\ &= S\sum_m u(mT)f(t-mT) \\ &= \sum_n\sum_m u(mT)f[(n-m)T]\delta(t-nT) \\ &= \sum_n\sum_k f(kT)u[(n-k)T]\delta(t-nT), \\ &\qquad\text{putting } n-m=k \\ &= \sum_n\left\{\sum_k f(kT)E^{-k}u(nT)\right\}\delta(t-nT) \\ &= \left\{\sum_k f(kT)E^{-k}\right\}Su(t) \end{aligned}$$

The operator in brackets is a function of E. If it is denoted by $F^*(E)$ we have the operational relation

$$SF(D)S=F^*(E)S \tag{1}$$

where

$$F^*(E)=\sum_k f(kT)E^{-k} \tag{2}$$

Consider the special case when $F(D) = 1/(D+a)$. Then $f(t)=\epsilon^{-at}$, so that

$$F^*(E)=\sum_{k=0}^{\infty}\epsilon^{-kaT}E^{-k}=\frac{1}{1-\epsilon^{-aT}E^{-1}} \tag{3}$$

As in the paper, the general operator can be dealt with by using partial fractions and a table similar to Table I.

It is now apparent that the operator E plays a part analogous to that of the transform variable z, the association being similar to that of D and s. It will be found further that most of the equations involving starred and unstarred functions of s given in the first part of the paper can be expressed in operational form. In particular, equation 1 of this discussion corresponds to equation 13 of the paper, while the equivalent of equation 27 in the paper would be written in the operational form

$$SF_1(D)SF_2(D)S = SF_1(D)F_2^*(E)S$$
$$= F_1^*(E)F_2^*(E)S \quad (4)$$

It is not easy to make a comparison of the relative merits of the two alternative approaches. So much depends on the notation with which a particular individual is familiar. It was claimed earlier that the use of operators implies greater generality, but this is perhaps of small account from a practical point of view. However, it may be an advantage to represent the operation of sampling by a special symbol.

As an example of the use of operators, consider system 4 in Table II of the paper. The circuit equation is easily seen to be

$$G(D)S[r(t)-H(D)c(t)] = c(t) \quad (5)$$

Operating with $H(D)$ and sampling

$$HG^*(E)[Sr(t)-SH(D)c(t)] = SH(D)c(t)$$

so that

$$SH(D)c(t) = \frac{HG^*(E)}{1+HG^*(E)}Sr(t)$$

Substituting in equation 5 and simplifying gives

$$c(t) = \frac{G(D)}{1+HG^*(E)}Sr(t)$$

and

$$Sc(t) = \frac{G^*(E)}{1+HG^*(E)}Sr(t)$$

It is of interest to observe that the process of clamping can be represented by the operator $(E^{-1}\Delta/D)S$. To prove this it is only necessary to point out that a clamped function is the integral of the sequence formed by the first differences of the sampled function.

William K. Linvill (Massachusetts Institute of Technology, Cambridge, Mass.): This paper makes a concise mathematical summary of the analysis of sampled-data systems. Table II is particularly helpful and illustrates the applicability of the analysis to a wide variety of system configurations. The easy interchangeability between the z-transform method and the Laplace transform method should receive more emphasis than the paper gives. When the sampler output is considered to be a train of modulated impulses rather than a sequence of ordinates of the sampler input, the sampler has all the properties of the familiar pulse-amplitude modulator and can be treated by conventional Laplace transforms. When the whole system is treated in the frequency domain from this point of view, there is no difference between the z-transform approach and the "old-fashioned" Laplace transform approach other than a change in variable $z=\epsilon^{sT}$. When the signals at any point are discrete samples, their transforms are periodic and the $z(=\epsilon^{sT})$ variable is the convenient one to use. When the signals at a point are continuous, their transforms are aperiodic and the s variable is the convenient one to use. The attitude on the part of the engineer that the z-transform and the Laplace transform methods are equivalent and that he can change from one to the other as the situation demands is mathematically correct as well as convenient.

Freedom in changing from the z to the s domain is often particularly convenient in obtaining time responses. For example, the result of equations 46 and 47 of the paper can be seen from elementary considerations in the frequency domain. The sampler is an impulse modulator. Since $G(s)$ represents a low-pass filter, only the pure signal and the pair of lowest frequency side bands from the sampler result in significant output. The pure signal input to the filter $G(s)$ is a step of amplitude $1/T$ and the two low-frequency side bands combine to form a cosine wave: $1/T(\epsilon^{j\omega_0 t}+\epsilon^{-j\omega_0 t})=2/T \cos \omega_0 t$ for $t>0$. The output resulting from the step is $(1/aT)(1-\epsilon^{-at})$ and the output from the cosine wave is calculated from elementary transient theory to be $2/T(a^2+\omega_0^2)[a \cos \omega_0 t+\omega_0 \sin \omega_0 t]$ for the steady-state component and $-2a\epsilon^{-at}/T(a^2+\omega_0^2)$ for the transient. Superposing all the output components gives

$$c(t) = \frac{1}{Ta}(1-\epsilon^{-at})+\frac{2}{T(a^2+\omega_0^2)}[a \cos \omega_0 t+\omega_0 \sin \omega_0 t - a\epsilon^{-at}]$$

The statement that the Laplace transformation procedure requires more labor than the other methods should be modified. To calculate the exact continuous time response is more laborious than to calculate a sequence of samples regardless of the method. The Laplace transform approach embraces both the s-domain and the z-domain pictures and from it the engineer can calculate the sampled response as easily as he can calculate it by any other method, but in addition he can get continuous signals exactly at the cost of considerable labor. Procedures have been worked out for obtaining simply an approximate continuous response and they will be described in a forthcoming paper.

J. R. Ragazzini and **L. A. Zadeh:** The authors wish to thank Dr. Salzer, Dr. Linvill, and Dr. Brown for their constructive discussions.

With regard to Dr. Salzer's comment on the variable network approach, it should be noted that the main feature of this approach is the characterization of a sampled-data system in terms of a transfer function $K(s;t)$ which involves both frequency and time. Such transfer functions do not appear in the report referred to by the discusser.[1]

In defining z as ϵ^{+sT} rather than ϵ^{-sT}, we have been motivated first by a desire to avoid conflict with the notation used by W. Hurewicz and others, and second by the fact that the alternative choice would make it inconvenient to use the only extensive table of z-transforms now available, namely, the table of so-called generalized Laplace transforms compiled by W. M. Stone. Otherwise, we are in complete agreement with Dr. Salzer's suggestion that it would be preferable to define z as being equal to ϵ^{-sT} rather than ϵ^{+sT}.

With regard to Dr. Linvill's statement to the effect that there is no difference between the z-transform and the conventional Laplace transform approaches, we believe that it would be more precise to say that the z-transform approach is a technique of analysis based on the Laplace transformation which is best suited for applications in which it is sufficient to know the values of the output at the sampling instants. By contrast, Dr. Linvill's approach leads to the expression for the Laplace transform of the continuous output, and does not yield directly the values of the output at the sampling instants. The method described in our paper achieves a unification of these approaches in the sense that it furnishes a systematic procedure for determining both the Laplace and z-transforms of the output, as illustrated in Table II. The connecting link between the two approaches is contained in the statement that a relation of the form $C(s)=G(s)R^*(s)$, where $C(s)$ and $G(s)$ are ordinary Laplace transforms and $R^*(s)$ is a starred transform (that is, z-transform), implies the relation $C^*(s)=G^*(s)R^*(s)$.

As we have pointed out in the paper, the expression for the output obtained by the use of the variable network approach also may be obtained from the expression for the Laplace transform of the output, and, in simple cases, the same results may be derived from elementary considerations in the manner indicated in Dr. Linvill's discussion. The main advantage of the variable network approach is that it yields the expression for a time-varying transfer function $K(s;t)$ which constitutes a much more explicit and flexible means of characterizing a system than the expression for the Laplace transform, $C(s)$ of the response to some particular input. Furthermore, $K(s;t)$ is, in general, more convenient to work with than $C(s)$. For example, one can readily express the mean-square value of the response to a random input in terms of $K(s;t)$, but not in terms of $C(s)$.

With reference to Dr. Brown's statement that the use of Laplace transforms implies limitation to input and output functions which vanish for negative time, it should be noted that, when such is not the case, it is merely necessary to employ the Fourier or bilateral Laplace transforms in place of the unilateral Laplace transforms. Thus, the applicability of the methods described in our paper is not restricted to input functions which vanish for negative t.

The operational approach presented by Dr. Brown is related to the z-transform approach in much the same manner as Heaviside's operational calculus is related to the conventional Laplace transformation. In particular, the operator E corresponds to z, the relation $SF(D)S=F^*(E)S$ is equivalent to the relation $C^*(s)=G^*(s)R^*(s)$, and the operation with a sampling operator S corresponds to the z-transformation. It is of interest to note that the operators employed by Dr. Brown may be regarded as special forms of so-called time-dependent Heaviside operators.[2]

A useful feature of the operational approach is that it places in direct evidence the operations performed on the operand. However, working with operators is more difficult than with z-transforms, since the latter require only purely algebraic manipulations. This is indeed the chief advantage of the z-transform method.

References

1. See reference 1 of John M. Salzer's discussion.
2. Time-Dependent Heaviside Operators, L. A. Zadeh. *Journal of Mathematics and Physics* (Cambridge, Mass.), volume 30, 1951, pages 73–78.

When Is a Linear Control System Optimal?

R. E. KALMAN
Research Institute for Advanced Studies (RIAS), Baltimore, Md.

The purpose of this paper is to formulate, study, and (in certain cases) resolve the Inverse Problem of Optimal Control Theory, which is the following: Given a control law, find all performance indices for which this control law is optimal.

Under the assumptions of (a) linear constant plant, (b) linear constant control law, (c) measurable state variables, (d) quadratic loss functions with constant coefficients, (e) single control variable, we give a complete analysis of this problem and obtain various explicit conditions for the optimality of a given control law. An interesting feature of the analysis is the central role of frequency-domain concepts, which have been ignored in optimal control theory until very recently. The discussion is presented in rigorous mathematical form.

The central conclusion is the following (Theorem 6): A stable control law is optimal if and only if the absolute value of the corresponding return difference is at least equal to one at all frequencies. This provides a beautifully simple connecting link between modern control theory and the classical point of view which regards feedback as a means of reducing component variations.

Introduction

The great interest in optimal control theory in recent years has brought with it a great deal of criticism as well. There are nagging doubts—particularly strongly felt by engineers—that the theory is overidealized, hence impractical. It is argued that the choice of the performance index to be optimized is arbitrary and subjective, perhaps only a matter of taste. If so, then it is pointless to devote too much effort to finding a control law which is the *best* in some narrow, individualistic sense—it would be more sensible to see approximate control laws which are not rigidly tied to a single performance index.

These are naive objections and cannot be accepted from the scientific point of view {1}.[1] They do contain, however, an important element of truth and suggest the following problem: *Instead of asking for a control law corresponding to a given performance criterion, one might seek to determine all performance criteria (if any) for which a given control law is optimal.* We might thereby discover general properties shared by all optimal control laws. We might be able to separate control laws which are optimal in some sense from those which are not optimal in any sense. If this plan of attack is successful, then the preceding objections will be irrelevant since the most important aspects of optimality will hold independently of the specific choice of a performance index {2}. This is what we shall do in the present paper.

The problem outlined in the foregoing has long been known in the calculus of variations, the "parent" of optimal control theory. It is *the inverse problem of the calculus of variations* [1, chapter 10, §1]:[2] Find all variational problems (if any) whose Euler equations are satisfied by a given family of curves. This is a difficult problem which has been the subject of numerous investigations {3}.

By analogy, we shall speak of the *inverse problem of optimal control theory*. Very little is known today about this problem. We shall not attempt here to give a complete analysis, but shall consider only a special (though large) class of problems which is of great interest in control engineering. Our main assumptions will be the following:

(*a*) The plant is governed by a linear differential equation with constant coefficients.

(*b*) The control law is linear and constant.

(*c*) All state variables can be directly measured.

(*d*) The loss functions are quadratic forms with constant coefficients in the state and control variables.

(*e*) There is only one control variable.

The first four of these assumptions are made in order to obtain explicit results. The last assumption can be removed, but only at the cost of a more refined analysis [2].

It is hoped that this paper will reduce the "gap" which exists today between optimal control theory and conventional control engineering practice.

There are many interesting and unexpected results. Let us emphasize some of these already here:

1 Every control law, stable or unstable, is optimal in some sense. To avoid such a trivial conclusion, the class of performance indices must be restricted. If—in addition to (*d*)—we make the usual assumption that the loss function does not contain cross products of the state variables with the control variable [3–8], it turns out that *a feedback system is optimal if and only if the absolute value of the return difference is at least 1 at all frequencies* (Theorem 6). This is a severe requirement.

The preceding criterion is well known in classical feedback theory: it means that sensitivity to component variations in the forward loop is diminished (not accentuated) by feedback. Thus a single criterion assures insensitivity with respect to component variations as well as optimal performance in the dynamical sense. This is a highly important result in the pure theory of control. In addition, it provides theoretical support for certain intuitive design procedures long used in control engineering.

2 Conditions of optimality can be expressed most conveniently by means of frequency-domain formulas (Theorem 5). This is a new trend in optimal control theory, heretofore rigidly confined to the time domain {4}. It is hoped that renewed interest in frequency-domain techniques will tend to break down the artificial dividing lines between conventional and modern control theory.

3 To obtain a "tight" control loop, the term representing control error in the definition of the loss function must be taken to be large relative to the term representing control energy. This leads to optimal control with high loop gains; the closed-loop poles of the system are then either near the open-loop zeros or near a Butterworth configuration (Theorem 11). Such a system has the attributes usually demanded from good control system design (moderate overshoot in response to a step input, pronounced low-pass frequency characteristic).

4 There have been many attempts [9–10] to prescribe universal closed-loop pole configurations for optimal single-loop control systems *independently of the open-loop transfer function.*

[1] Numbers in braces refer to special comments collected at the end of the paper.

[2] Numbers in brackets designate References at end of paper

Contributed by the Automatic Control Division of The American Society of Mechanical Engineers and presented at the Joint Automatic Control Division, Minneapolis, Minn., June 19–21, 1963. Manuscript received at ASME Headquarters, March 13, 1963.

Reprinted with permission from *J. Basic Eng.*, vol. 86, pp. 51–60, Mar. 1964.

These prescriptions are usually obtained from experimental analog-computer studies. They are rigorously confirmed by the present investigation only in the case of high loop gains, see (3) above. When a high loop gain is not possible or not desired, the optimal control law will always depend to some extent on the plant which is being controlled and no universal prescriptions can be made. In such cases, it is strongly recommended that the calculation of the control law proceed by the standard methods of optimal control theory, which take into account the properties of the plant in a quantitative way {5}.

Acknowledgments

The research, of which this paper forms a part began as a result of a conference with Dr. E. B. Stear of the Aeronautical Systems Division, Air Force Systems Command, Mr. P. A. Reynolds, of the Cornell Aeronautical Laboratories, and their associates. The idea of using frequency-domain methods arose during conversations with Professor S. Lefschetz. Many improvements in the paper were suggested by the author's colleagues at RIAS, particularly Dr. A. A. Frederickson. The work was supported in part by the U. S. Air Force under Contracts AF 49(638)-1026 and AF 33(657)-855 and by the National Aeronautical and Space Administration under Contract NASr-103.

Subdivision of the Problem

Implementing the plan outlined in the introduction will require a rather lengthy analysis. But the details of the arguments must not be allowed to obscure the ideas involved. For this reason, it is convenient to break up the discussion into six separate problems. The study of these problems will lead to the solution of the Inverse Problem of Optimal Control Theory under certain clearly defined conditions.

Problem A. What optimization problems lead to a constant, linear control law?

Problem B. How is this optimal control law explicitly computed?

Problem C. When is the optimal control law stable?

Problem D. What algebraic conditions are necessary and sufficient for the existence of a constant, linear, stable (optimal) control law?

Problem E. What is the most convenient form of the preceding conditions?

Problem F. What can be said about the pole-zero pattern of the closed-loop transfer function of an optimal system?

These problems are intentionally vaguely phrased; merely a guide to, and not the main object of, the following analysis.

Mathematical Description of the Plant

It is assumed that the *plant* (or *control object*) is a finite-dimensional, continuous-time, constant, linear dynamical system [11]. It is also assumed that only a single input to the plant is available for control purposes, and that all control variables can be measured directly {6}. (Assumptions (*a–c*) in the Introduction.)

The purpose of control is to return the state of the plant to the origin after it has been displaced from there by some extremal disturbance: we are concerned with a regulator system.

The control law is constant and linear. (Assumption (*d*) in the Introduction.)

The precise mathematical form of the preceding assumptions is:

The behavior of the plant is represented by the differential system

$$dx/dt = Fx + g\mu(t), \tag{1}$$

where x is a real n-vector, the *state* of the plant; $\mu(t)$ is a continuous, real-valued function of time, the *control function; F* is a real constant $n \times n$ matrix; and g is a real constant $n \times 1$ matrix, i.e., an n-vector. (Similar notations will be used throughout the paper without special comment. In general, capitals will denote matrices, lower-case letters vectors, and lower-case Greek letters scalars.)

The control law is given by

$$\mu(t) = -\langle k, x(t)\rangle,^{3} \tag{2}$$

where k is a real, constant n-vector of feedback coefficients, and $\langle k, x\rangle$ is the inner product. By abuse of language, it will be often convenient to talk of a "control law k" instead of the "control law $-\langle k, x\rangle$."

Substituting the control law (2) into (1) we obtain the free differential system representing the plant under closed-loop control:

$$dx/dt = (F - gk')x = F_k x. \tag{3}$$

Here the prime denotes the transpose. (The inner product $\langle k, x\rangle$ may be written also as $k'x$.) The abbreviation $F_k = F - gk'$, where k is any n-vector, will be used frequently.

The *resolvent* of the matrix F will be frequently used. This matrix-valued function of the complex variable s is defined by

$$\Phi(s) = (sI - F)^{-1} \; (I = \text{unit matrix}). \tag{4}$$

Clearly every element of $\Phi(s)$ is a rational function of s. $\Phi(s)$ may be regarded also as the formal Laplace transform of the matrix function $\exp Ft$ {7}.

With the aid of (4), it is easy to express transfer functions in vector-matrix notation. For instance, let η be the scalar $k'x$. Then the transfer function from μ to η is given by

$$\eta(s)/\mu(s) = k'\Phi(s)g. \tag{5}$$

We shall repeatedly use the notation $\psi(s) = det\,(sI - F)$ for the characteristic polynomial of the matrix F.

In analogy with $F_k = F - gk'$ we have then also the notations $\Phi_k(s) = (sI - F_k)^{-1}$ and $\psi_k(s) = det(sI - F_k)$.

It is frequently necessary to manipulate these frequency-domain expressions in the same way as one manipulates transfer functions in elementary control theory. To illustrate the algebraic steps involved, let us note some common formulas:

$$\begin{aligned}\psi_k(s) &= det(sI - F + gk') = det[(sI - F)\cdot(I + \Phi(s)gk')] \\ &= \psi(s)\,det(I + \Phi(s)gk') = \psi(s)(1 + k'\Phi(s)g),\end{aligned}$$

where the last step follows by a well-known matrix identity. Thus we have an explicit expression for the rational function

$$1 + k'\Phi(s)g = \psi_k(s)/\psi(s). \tag{6}$$

The quantity $T_k(s) = 1 + k'\Phi(s)g$ is the so-called *return difference* of classical feedback theory [20].

To express closed-loop transfer functions in terms of open-loop ones, we proceed as follows:

$$\begin{aligned}k'\Phi_k(s)g &= k'(sI - F + gk')^{-1}g \\ &= k'[(sI - F)(I + \Phi(s)gk')]^{-1}g \\ &= k'[I - \Phi(s)gk'/(1 + k'\Phi(s)g)]\Phi(s)g \\ &= k'\Phi(s)g\cdot[\psi(s)/\psi_k(s)].\end{aligned}$$

It should be noted that transfer functions—which express input-output relations—are independent of the choice of the (internal) state variables.

For instance, suppose the (numerical) state vector x is replaced by

$$\hat{x} = Tx,$$

where T is a nonsingular constant matrix. Then the matrices F, g, k in (1) and (2) must be replaced by

$$\hat{F} = TFT^{-1}, \quad \hat{g} = Tg, \quad \text{and} \quad \hat{k} = (T^{-1})'k.$$

[3] The minus sign in (2) is a notational convenience and a reminder that we are usually dealing with negative feedback.

The transfer function (5) is invariant under this change of coordinates because

$$\hat{k}'\hat{\Phi}(s)\hat{g} = k'T^{-1}(sI - TFT^{-1})^{-1}Tg$$
$$= k'T^{-1}[T(sI - F)T^{-1}]^{-1}Tg$$
$$= k'(sI - F)^{-1}g = k'\Phi(s)g.$$

Remark {4} is of direct relevance here.

For future purposes, it is very important to have a strict correspondence between time-domain and frequency-domain methods of system description. The frequency-domain form of (1) and (2) is the transfer function $k'\Phi(s)g$. However, knowledge of this transfer function will not uniquely identify the matrices F, g, and k appearing in (1) and (2) (even disregarding the lack of uniqueness due to the arbitrary choice of the basis for x—see Remark {4}) unless certain conditions are satisfied. These are [11]: (a) the plant is completely controllable and (b) the control law k is completely observable.

The first condition means that all state variables can be affected by some suitable choice of the control function $\mu(t)$. The second condition means that the control function $\mu(t)$ given by (2) can be identically zero only if the state is identically zero; in other words, the control law k is picked in such a way that any change from zero in the state variables is counteracted by some control action.

There is no loss of generality (as far as the problem discussed in this paper is concerned) in assuming that both of these conditions hold {8}.

In practically all the analysis which follows, we must assume that

The plant is completely controllable. (A_1)

This condition can be expressed in concrete form by [11]

$$\text{rank } [g, Fg, \ldots, F^{n-1}g] = n. \qquad (A_1')$$

On the other hand, the assumption that k is a completely observable control law, i.e., that [11]

$$\text{rank } [k, F'k, \ldots, (F')^{n-1}k] = n,$$

is not needed until much later (see Theorem 6).

Mathematical Formulation of the Optimization Problem

Our first objective ought to be to find all optimization problems which result in a constant, linear control law (Problem A). However, the general solution of this problem is not known at present. Therefore we shall merely give some sufficient conditions. In the next section we will see that these conditions imply that the control law is constant and linear.

Let us recall the mathematical definition of the dynamic optimization problem in control theory {9}. We denote by $x_\mu(t; x_0)$ the unique solution or *motion* of (1) corresponding to some fixed, continuous control function $\mu(t)$ and the initial state $x_0 = x_\mu(0; x_0)$. The *loss function* (or Lagrangian) L is an arbitrary smooth function of t, x, and μ. Suppose x_0 is a fixed initial state and $t_1 > 0$ a fixed value of the time. Then the integral

$$V(x_0, t_1; \mu) = \int_0^{t_1} L(t, x_\mu(t; x_0), \mu(t))dt \qquad (7)$$

is a continuous functional of the control function $\mu(t)$. As usual, V is called the *performance index* of the control system (1–2).

We ask: *For what continuous control function $\mu_*(t)$ (if any) is $V(x_0, t_1; \mu)$ a minimum?*

The minimum value of $V(x_0, t_1; \mu)$ will be denoted by $V_*(x_0, t_1)$.

The Principle of Optimality of the calculus of variations shows [3–4] that the function $\mu_*(t)$ (if it exists at all) may always be generated by a control law of the type

$$\mu_*(t) = -\chi(t, x(t)). \qquad (8)$$

Thus the precise formulation of Problem A is the following: *What conditions must be imposed on t_1 and L to assure that χ is constant (not explicitly dependent on t) and linear in x?*

Note that constancy and linearity of χ are entirely different properties.

If either $t_1 < \infty$ or L depends explicitly on t, we have a nonstationary situation and in general χ will not be constant. We assume therefore that $L \neq L(t)$ {10} and that $t_1 = \infty$.

The latter assumption must be made precise. Let Ω denote the set of all continuous functions $\mu(t)$ defined on the interval $[0, \infty)$ for which the functional

$$V(x_0, \infty; \mu) = \lim_{t_1 \to \infty} \int_0^{t_1} L(x_\mu(t; x_0), \mu(t))dt \qquad (9)$$

has a finite value. (Of course, Ω may be the empty set.)

We ask: *For what control function $\mu_*(t)$ in Ω (if any) is $V(x_0, \infty; \mu)$ a minimum?*

The minimum of $V(x_0, \infty; \mu)$ is written as $V_*(x_0, \infty)$.

It seems to be very difficult to give explicit conditions on L which are equivalent to the linearity of χ. For this reason, we shall base all further considerations on a simple and well-known sufficient condition: L is a quadratic form in the $n + 1$ variables (x, μ) {11}. Since we have required $L \neq L(t)$, the coefficients must be constants. In other words, the most general form of L that we shall study is given by

$$2L(x, \mu) = x'Qx + 2(r'x)\mu + \sigma\mu^2 \quad (Q, r, \sigma \text{ constants}). \qquad (10)$$

This is Assumption (d) in the Introduction.

With this preliminary analysis, we arrive at the following precise definition of the central problem of the paper:

Inverse Problem of Linear Optimal Control Theory. *Given a completely controllable constant linear plant (1) and constant linear control law (2). Determine all loss functions L of the form (10) such that the control law minimizes the performance index (9).*

Review of the Optimization Problem

Now we turn to Problem B. We seek an explicit expression for the minimum of (9) and the corresponding optimal control law. As the general theory of minimizing (7) is quite well known [3–4], we shall stress those aspects of the problem which result from letting $t_1 \to \infty$. This problem was solved in [3].

The loss function L cannot be completely arbitrary. We want to investigate what restrictions must be imposed on L for purely mathematical reasons. We shall also examine the physical significance of L.

The first restriction on L is a consequence of Pontryagin's "Maximum Principle" [4, 12]. According to this principle, the variational problem (7) has a solution only if the so-called *pre-Hamiltonian* function [4]

$$H(t, x, p, \mu) = L(t, x, \mu) + \langle p, Fx + g\mu \rangle$$

(where p is an n-vector, the *costate* of (1)) has an absolute minimum with respect to μ for every fixed value of (t, x, p).

Substituting (10) into H, it follows that H will have a minimum only if $\sigma \geq 0$. If $\sigma > 0$, then H has a unique minimum for all t, x, p. This is the so-called *regular case.* If $\sigma = 0$, then H can have a minimum if and only if $r'x = 0$ and $p'g = 0$, in which case H is independent of μ. This is the *singular case.* In the latter event, the Maximum Principle furnishes very little information about the proper choice of μ {12}.

To avoid complications which are of little interest in this paper, we shall consider only the regular case. (The same assumption is made in most of the classical literature on the calculus of variations.) Hence σ must be positive. We may set $\sigma = 1$ without loss of generality. Then (10) takes the form:

$$2L(x, \mu) = x'(Q - rr')x + (\mu + r'x)^2 \quad (Q = Q').$$

A second restriction is required to assure that the minimum value of (7) does not diverge to $-\infty$ as t_1 approaches some *finite* value. (In other words, we want to rule out the possibility of "conjugate points.") The standard way to avoid trouble is to assume that $Q - rr'$ is nonnegative definite. It is well known that a symmetric matrix $Q - rr'$ is nonnegative if and only if there is a $p \times n$ matrix H (where $p = \text{rank } Q - rr'$) such that $Q - rr' = H'H$. Consequently we shall write L in the form

$$2L(x, \mu) = \|Hx\|^2 + (\mu + r'x)^2. \tag{11}$$

Let us pause to examine the physical significance of (11). Clearly L is nonnegative. If L is positive, we incur a loss. The object of optimal control is to minimize this loss. The loss is zero if and only if both terms in L vanish separately. Therefore H is chosen in such a way that the state of the plant is "satisfactory" if and only if $Hx = 0$ {13}. The choice of r in L fixes the desired level $\mu = -r'x$ of the control variable.

In the rather intricate calculations which are to follow, it would be unpleasant to drag along the parameter r. Actually, r may be eliminated without loss of generality.

Let us change the control variable μ to

$$\bar{\mu} = \mu + \langle r, x\rangle.$$

Then (11) becomes

$$2\bar{L}(x, \bar{\mu}) = \|Hx\|^2 + \bar{\mu}^2 \tag{11a}$$

and (1) must be changed to

$$dx/dt = \bar{F}x + g\bar{\mu}, \qquad (\bar{F} = F - gr' = F_r), \tag{1a}$$

while k in (2) is to be replaced by

$$\bar{k} = k - r.$$

It is then clear that the problems (F, g, k, L) and $(\bar{F}, g, \bar{k}, \bar{L})$ are equivalent.

From now on, unless explicit mention is made to the contrary, all considerations will be restricted to the case $r = 0$, and the adjective "optimal" will always refer to minimizing (9) with respect to the loss function (11a). For the sake of simplicity, the bar on F, k, and L will be dropped.

Returning to the problem of minimizing (7), let us recall the results of the analysis given in [3–4].

Let $\Pi(t;\ t_1, 0) = P(t)$ be the unique symmetric solution of the Riccati-type matrix differential equation

$$-dP/dt = PF + F'P - Pgg'P + H'H \quad (P = P') \tag{12}$$

which satisfies the initial condition

$$\Pi(t_1;\ t_1, 0) = P(t_1) = 0.$$

Then the minimum of (7) is given explicitly by

$$2V_*(x_0, t_1) = \|x_0\|^2_{\Pi(0;\ t_1,\ 0)},^4$$

and the corresponding unique optimal control law is

$$\mu_*(t) = -\langle \Pi(t;\ t_1, 0)g, x(t)\rangle. \tag{13}$$

Up to this point, the analysis holds for every finite $t_1 > 0$. Additional arguments are needed to solve also the problem of minimizing (9).

(i) If the plant is completely controllable, it may be shown [3, Theorem 6.6] that

$$\lim_{t_1 \to \infty} \Pi(0;\ t_1, 0) = P_\infty$$

exists and is unique. In view of the constancy of the plant and of L, the choice of the origin of time in (11) is immaterial:

$$\Pi(0;\ t_1, 0) = \Pi(-t_1;\ 0, 0) \text{ for all } t_1 > 0.$$

Therefore P_∞ may be defined equivalently as

$$\lim_{t_1 \to -\infty} \Pi(t;\ 0, 0) = P_\infty. \tag{14}$$

[4] We use the notation $\|x\|^2_A$, where A is any symmetric matrix, for the quadratic form $x'Ax$.

This limit is readily evaluated numerically by computing the solution of (12) which starts at $P(0) = 0$ and letting $t \to -\infty$.

(ii) The control law (13), with $\Pi(t;\ t_1, 0)$ replaced by P_∞, generates functions $\mu^\infty(t)$ (dependent on x_0) which are always in Ω [3, Theorem 6.7]. Thus if $x^\infty(t)$ is the solution of (1) corresponding to $\mu^\infty(t)$, then

$$V(x_0, \infty;\ \mu^\infty) = (1/2)\|x_0\|^2_{P_\infty} = \lim_{t_1 \to \infty} \int_0^{t_1} L(x^\infty(t), \mu^\infty(t))dt < \infty.$$

Since L is nonnegative, the matrix P_∞ is nonnegative definite.

(iii) Of course, $\mu^\infty(t)$ is not necessarily optimal and therefore in general

$$V_*(x_0, \infty) \leqq V(x_0, \infty;\ \mu^\infty).$$

But in reality the strict inequality sign cannot hold for any x_0 [3, Theorem 6.7]. In other words, $\mu^\infty = \mu_*$.

Now we have obtained an explicit expression for the minimum of the performance index (9)

$$2V_*(x_0, \infty) = \|x_0\|^2_{P_\infty}; \tag{15}$$

and the corresponding optimal control law is given by

$$\begin{aligned} \mu_*(t) &= -\langle P_\infty g, x(t)\rangle \\ &= -\langle k_*, x(t)\rangle. \end{aligned} \tag{16}$$

The preceding results may be summarized as

THEOREM 1. (Solution of Problem B.) *Consider a completely controllable plant and the associated optimization problem (9), where L is given by (11a). This problem always has a solution, which is obtained by solving the differential equation (12) and then evaluating the limit (14). The minimum value of the performance index is given by (15). The optimal control law is given by (16).*

Stability of the Optimal Control Law

Optimality does not imply stability! In fact, let χ be any control law. Define L so that $L = 0$ when $\mu = -\chi(t, x)$ and positive for any other value of μ. Then the loss is identically zero if and only if the control law χ is used. Since L is nonnegative, $V_*(x_0, \infty)$ is also nonnegative for any x_0. It follows that the given control law χ—which is entirely arbitrary—is optimal and even unique.

To understand the difficulty raised by this example, let us examine more closely the physical significance of the condition $L \equiv 0$. Evidently this can happen only when the control law is $\mu = 0$. Then all solutions of (1) and (2) are of the form $x(t) = e^{Ft}x_0$. Consider now the linear subspace X_1 of the state space $X = R^n$ defined by

$$X_1 = \{x;\ \|He^{Ft}x\| \equiv 0\}.$$

If the state x_0 belongs to X_1, then the vector $x(t) = e^{Ft}x_0$ also belongs to X_1 for any t, since $e^{A(t+\tau)} = e^{At}e^{A\tau}$ for any matrix A and any scalars t, τ. Thus X_1 is invariant under the control law $\mu = 0$; in fact, X_1 is the largest subspace of X such that $L \equiv 0$ when x_0 is in X_1. Hence 0 is an optimal control law (conceivably not the only one) with respect to states in X_1. Actually, the optimal control law is unique by Theorem 1. *Thus the optimal control law throughout the subspace X_1 consists in setting $\mu = 0$.*

Going back for a moment to the case $r \neq 0$, it is clear that in general X_1 is given by

$$X_1 = \{x;\ \|He^{F_rt}x\| \equiv 0\} \qquad (F_r = F - gr').$$

As far as initial states in X_1 are concerned, the outcome of the optimization problem is determined a priori by the choice of r.

It is clear from these observations that there is no loss of generality in requiring

$$\textit{dimension } X_1 = 0. \tag{A_2}$$

This abstract mathematical condition is equivalent to the control-theoretical statement:

$$\textit{The pair } [F, H] \textit{ is completely observable.} \qquad (A_2')$$

In turn, this is equivalent to the concrete mathematical condition

$$\text{rank } [H', F', H', \ldots, (F')^{n-1}H'] = n. \qquad (A_2'')$$

These matters are discussed (with proofs) in [11].

In conventional language, (A_2') means the following: Suppose the p-vector $y = Hx$ denotes the outputs of the plant with respect to which the performance of the control system is to be optimized. Then y must not vanish identically along any free motion of the plant unless the initial state $x_0 = 0$. (The outputs y used for defining the performance index must be carefully differentiated from those outputs which are directly measured [13].

One might say that (A_2) assures the nondegeneracy of the statement of the optimal control problem.

If (A_2) holds, then L cannot be identically zero along any motion of (1). Then V_* is positive definite (not merely nonnegative definite) and its derivative $\dot{V}_*$ along optimal motions is $-L$. In other words, (A_2) implies that $V_* = (1/2)\|x\|^2_{P_\infty}$ is a Lyapunov function. By a theorem well known in the Lyapunov stability theory [14, Corollary 1.3; 15, Theorem 8] the desired result of this section follows immediately.

THEOREM 2. *If Assumptions (A_{1-2}) are satisfied, then P_∞ is positive definite and the optimal control law is (asymptotically) stable (i.e., all eigenvalues of $F - gk_*'$ have negative real parts).*

This may be regarded as the central theorem of linear optimal control theory. Under slight additional hypotheses it is valid also for the nonconsistant case [3, Theorem 6.10].

Our preceding analysis implies also a much stronger result:

THEOREM 3. (Solution of Problem C.) *Under Assumption (A_1), a necessary and sufficient condition for the stability of the optimal control law is that all eigenvalues of F restricted to X_1 have negative real parts.*

Algebraic Criterion for Optimality

Now we seek an explicit necessary and sufficient condition for a given control law k to be optimal (Problem D). Unfortunately, conditions (14) and (16) provided by Theorem 1 are inadequate for this purpose because P_∞ is defined only indirectly by the limit (14).

Let us observe, however, that by (14) P_∞ is an equilibrium state of the Riccati differential equation (12). Accordingly P_∞ satisfies the algebraic equation

$$-PF - F'P = H'H - Pgg'P, \qquad (17)$$

which is obtained by setting $dP/dt = 0$ in (12).

This does not characterize P_∞ completely because (17)—being a system of quadratic algebraic equations—does not have a unique solution in general. Even if P is required to be nonnegative definite, (17) may fail to have a unique solution {14}.

Fortunately, the difficulty may be removed with the help of Assumption (A_2). This provides the solution of Problem D:

THEOREM 4. (Algebraic Characterization of Optimality.) *Consider a completely controllable plant and the associated variational problem with H satisfying (A_2). Let k be a fixed control law. Then a (i) necessary and (ii) sufficient condition for k to be a stable optimal control law is that there exist a matrix P which satisfies the algebraic relations*

$$P = P' \textit{ is positive definite}, \qquad (18)$$

$$Pg = k, \qquad (19)$$

$$-PF_k - F_k'P = H'H + kk'. \qquad (20)$$

Proof of Theorem 4. (i) Suppose that $k = k^*$ is a stable optimal control law corresponding to some L which satisfies (A_2). By Theorem 1 there exists a symmetric matrix P_∞ which satisfies (14) and (16), and therefore also (17) and (19). Replacing Pg by k in (17), it follows that (17) and (19) together imply (20). By Theorem 2, P_∞ is positive definite. Hence optimality implies the existence of matrix P which satisfies (18)-(20).

(ii) Conversely, let k be a fixed control law. Suppose that we are given a matrix H which satisfies (A_2) and a matrix P which satisfies (18)-(20). Then P also satisfies (17). We want to show that P is equal to P_∞ of Theorems 1-2, for then the optimality of k follows from (19), and stability follows from (18) and (20). Consequently it is sufficient to prove

LEMMA 1. *If H satisfies (A_2), then (17) has a unique positive definite solution.*

Proof of Lemma 1. Let P be a positive definite solution of (17). Let $k = Pg$. Then the matrix F_k is stable. This is proved by introducing the scalar function

$$V(x) = \|x\|^2_P,$$

which is positive definite by hypothesis. Its derivative along the solutions of the differential equation

$$dx/dt = F_kx \qquad (21)$$

is given by

$$\dot{V} = x'[PF_k + F_k'P]x$$
$$= -\|Hx\|^2 - |g'Px|^2,$$

since P satisfies (17). Clearly $\dot{V}$ is nonpositive and is zero only if $g'Px = 0$, which implies that $k'x = 0$. It follows that $\dot{V}$ is identically zero along a solution $e^{F_kt}x_0$ of (17) only if

$$\|He^{F_kt}x_0\| = \|He^{Ft}x_0\| \equiv 0.$$

By (A_2) this can hold only if $x_0 = 0$. Hence $\dot{V}$ can vanish identically only along the trivial solution $x(t) \equiv 0$. The stability of F_k then follows immediately from the Lyapunov stability theory [14, Corollary 1.3].

Now suppose that (17) has two positive definite solutions P_i $(i = 1, 2)$. Let $k_i = P_ig$. Then $P_iF_{k_i} + F_{k_i}'P_i = -H'H$ by (17), and

$$P_1F_{k_1} + F'P_1 - (P_2F_{k_2} + F'P_2)'$$
$$= (P_1 - P_2)F_{k_1} + F_{k_2}'(P_1 - P_2)' = 0.$$

It is well known [16, chapter VIII] that the matrix equation $XA + BX = 0$ has a unique solution, namely $X = 0$, whenever

$$\lambda_j[A] + \lambda_k[B] \neq 0 \quad \text{for any pair } j, k. \qquad (22)$$

Since both F_1 and F_2 are stable matrices, condition (22) is obviously satisfied. Hence $P_1 - P_2 = 0$.

This completes the proof of Lemma 1.

Finally, by the Lyapunov stability theory, equation (20) together with (18) implies that k is a stable control law, i.e., that F_g is a stable matrix. Theorem 4 is proved.

Frequency-Domain Characterization of Optimality

Since F and g are usually known, Assumption (A_2) and the relations (18) may be regarded as constraints on the parameters H and k, the matrix P serving as a connecting link. We want to eliminate P. This is Problem E.

It is quite remarkable that a simple relation connecting H and k can be found at all. It is truly astounding that this relation *must be stated in the frequency-domain* if it is to be reasonably simple. This is the main result of the paper from which everything else will follow {15}.

The solution of Problem E is given by

THEOREM 5. (Frequency-Domain Characterization of Optimality.) *Consider a completely controllable plant and the associated variational problem, with L satisfying (A_2). Let k be a fixed control law. Then a (i) necessary and (ii) sufficient condition for k to be an optimal control law is that k be a stable control law and that the condition*

$$|1 + k'\Phi(i\omega)g|^2 = 1 + \|H\Phi(i\omega)g\|^2 \quad \text{(I)}$$

hold for all real ω.

Proof. (i) The assumptions being the same as in Theorem 4, there is a unique matrix P satisfying (18)-(20). We add and subtract sP from the left-hand side of (17) and obtain

$$P(sI - F) + (-sI - F')P = H'H - Pgg'P. \quad (23)$$

Then we multiply the right-hand side by $\Phi(s)g$ and the left-hand side by $g'\Phi'(-s)$

$$g'\Phi'(-s)Pg + g'P\Phi(s)g = g'\Phi'(-s)[H'H - Pgg'P]\Phi(s)g. \quad (24)$$

Recalling that $Pg = k$ by (19), we get

$$[1 + k'\Phi(-s)g][1 + k'\Phi(s)g] = 1 + g'\Phi'(-s)H'H\Phi(s)g.$$

Setting $s = i\omega$ gives (I).[5]

Finally, by Theorem 4, $k = Pg$ is necessarily a stable control law if P satisfies (17)-(20).

(ii) Suppose k is a given stable control law. Theorem 2 implies that given some H satisfying (A_2) equation (17) has a unique positive definite solution P_∞ and there is an optimal control law $k_* = P_\infty g$. Using Condition (I), we will prove that the matrix P_∞ so determined satisfies (19), in other words, that $k = k_*$. Then (20) will be also satisfied and it will follow by Theorem 4 that Condition (I) is sufficient for optimality.

We consider again (24), which is a consequence of (17), and let $s = i\omega$. We replace $\|H\Phi(i\omega)\|^2$ by its value given by (I). Introducing the abbreviations

$$\pi(i\omega) = g'P_\infty\Phi(i\omega)g,$$

$$\kappa(i\omega) = k'\Phi(i\omega)g,$$

and simplifying the resulting expressions we obtain

$$|1 + \pi|^2 = |1 + \kappa|^2.$$

Since the optimal control law corresponding to P_∞ is $k_* = P_\infty g$ it is clear that

$$\pi = \kappa_*.$$

In other words, the proof has been reduced to showing that

$$|1 + k'\Phi(i\omega)g|^2 = |1 + k_*\Phi(i\omega)g|^2 \quad (25)$$

implies $k = k_*$.

We recall the hypotheses that (a) the pair $[F, g]$ is completely controllable and that (b) k is a stable control law. We need to know also

LEMMA 2. *Suppose* $[F, g]$ *is completely controllable. Then one can always find a basis in the state space X such that F and g have the representation*

$$F = \begin{bmatrix} 0 & 1 & & & \\ & \cdot & \cdot & & \\ & & \cdot & \cdot & \\ & & & \cdot & \cdot \\ & & 0 & & 1 \\ -\alpha_1 & \cdot & \cdot & -\alpha_{n-1} & -\alpha_n \end{bmatrix}, \quad g = \begin{bmatrix} 0 \\ \cdot \\ \cdot \\ \cdot \\ 0 \\ 1 \end{bmatrix}, \quad (26)$$

where $\det (sI - F) = \psi(s) = s^n + \alpha_n s^{n-1} + \ldots + \alpha_1$.

Moreover, if

$$q'\Phi(i\omega)g = \frac{\gamma_n(i\omega)^{n-1} + \ldots + \gamma_1}{(i\omega)^n + \alpha_n(i\omega)^{n-1} + \ldots + \alpha_1}, \quad (27)$$

and F, g have the form (26), then the vector q has the representation

$$q = \begin{bmatrix} \gamma_1 \\ \cdot \\ \cdot \\ \cdot \\ \gamma_n \end{bmatrix} \quad (28)$$

In other words, if F and g have the canonical form (26), we can identify the components of the vector q with the numerator coefficients of the rational function (27).

Proof of Lemma 2. The canonical form (26) follows immediately from the definition of controllability [17]. Formula (27) can then be verified readily by elementary algebraic manipulations; for instance, by signal-flow-graph methods. For the significance and proof of this lemma see [11].

Another fact which we need here concerns the factorization of nonnegative polynomials. This is the main step in the method of *spectral factorization* [18, 19].

LEMMA 3. *Let* $\Theta(\omega^2)$ *be a polynomial in* ω^2 *with real coefficients that is nonnegative for all real* ω. *Then there exist q polynomials* $\nu_k(i\omega)$ $(1 \leq q \leq n)$ *with real coefficients such that*

$$\Theta(\omega^2) = \sum_{k=1}^{q} \nu_k(i\omega)\nu_k(-i\omega) = \sum_{k=1}^{q} |\nu_k(i\omega)|^2. \quad (29)$$

Moreover, we can always let $q = 1$ *and choose* $\nu_1(s)$ *so that all its zeros have nonpositive real parts. With these two restrictions we have the unique "factorization"* $\Theta(\omega^2) = |\nu_1(i\omega)|^2$.

Proof of Lemma 3. Everything follows easily by factoring $\Theta(\omega^2)$ according to classical algebra.

Returning to the proof of the theorem, we recall equation (6),

$$1 + k'\Phi(s)g = \psi_k(s)/\psi(s).$$

Hence (25) implies

$$|\psi_k(i\omega)|^2 = |\psi_{k_*}(i\omega)|^2 = \Theta(\omega^2).$$

In other words, the nonnegative polynomial $\Theta(\omega^2)$ of Lemma 3 has two different factorizations. By assumption, the zeros of $\psi_k(s)$ are in the left-half plane. By optimality and Theorem 2, the same is true concerning the zeros of $\psi_{k_*}(s)$. Hence

$$k'\Phi(i\omega)g = k_*'\Phi(i\omega)g. \quad (30)$$

By Lemma 2, we take F and g in the representation (26). Then (27) shows immediately that $k = k_*$.

This completes the proof of the theorem {16}.

Theorem 5 is not quite convenient as stated, because Assumption (A_2) is expressed in time-domain language. It is easy to see that Assumptions (A_{1-2}) are equivalent to the frequency-domain condition:

Rational functions $H\Phi(s)g$ *have no common cancelable factors* (B_{1-2})

The equivalence of this condition with (A_{1-2})—in other words, with the complete controllability of $[F, g]$ and the complete observability of $[F, H]$—is established in [11].

Theorem 3 holds if and only if all zeros of the common cancelable factors of $H\Phi(s)g$ have negative real parts.

Implications of Optimality

From Theorem 5 we can deduce a number of interesting relations between optimality and frequency-domain concepts. In this way we obtain a fully satisfactory solution of the Inverse Problem of Linear Optimal Control Theory.

From Condition (I) it is clear that a stable control law may be optimal only if the return difference $T_k(i\omega)$ satisfies the condition

$$|T_k(i\omega)| = |1 + k'\Phi(s)g|^2 > 1. \quad \text{(II)}$$

This condition may well fail to hold {17}. If it does hold, then H may be obtained according to Lemma 3 by factoring the nonnegative polynomial $\Gamma(\omega^2)$:

---

[5] The quadratic form $\|x\|^2_A$ for x complex and A real is defined, as usual, by

$$\|x\|^2_A = \sum_{i,j} \bar{x}_i a_{ij} x_j.$$

where $\bar{x}_i$ is the complex conjugate of x_i.

$$\Gamma(\omega^2)/|\psi(i\omega)^2| = |1 + k'\Phi(i\omega)g|^2 - 1 = \|H\Phi(i\omega)g\|^2. \tag{31}$$

Many different matrices H will satisfy (31) because there are many different factorizations of $\Gamma(\omega^2)$. However, not all H's obtained in this way define optimization problems which yield the control law k. Since k was assumed to be stable, the situation described in Theorem 3 must hold. Therefore (see remark following (B_{1-2})) the rational functions $H\Phi(s)g$ must not possess any common cancelable factor which has a zero with nonnegative real part. H's which do not satisfy this requirement must be discarded.

A proper choice of H is always possible. Using the unique factorization described at the end of Lemma 3, and Lemma 2, we can write

$$|1+k'\Phi(i\omega)g|^2 - 1 = |h'\Phi(i\omega)g|^2, \tag{32}$$

where all zeros of the transfer function $h'\Phi(s)g$ have nonpositive real parts.

We assume now (without loss of generality, see Section 3) that k is a completely observable control law. This is equivalent to the fact that the polynomials $\psi_k(s)$ and $\psi(s)$ are relatively prime. Since

$$|1 + k'\Phi(i\omega)g|^2 - 1 = |\psi_k(i\omega)/\psi(i\omega)|^2 - 1 = |h'\Phi(i\omega)g|^2, \tag{33}$$

the transfer function $h'\Phi(s)g$ has then no cancelable factors, condition (B_{1-2}) is satisfied, and therefore also (A_2). The matrix $H = h'$ so constructed satisfies the requirements of Theorem 5. Hence we have:

THEOREM 6. (Solution of the Inverse Problem of Linear Optimal Control Theory.) *Consider a completely controllable plant with a stable, completely observable control law k. Then k is a nondegenerate optimal control law if and only if Condition (II) is satisfied. In general, k will be optimal with respect to several H's, which are determined from (31) and must satisfy in addition the noncancellation conditions mentioned above* {18}.

The requirement $|T_k(i\omega)| > 1$ is a celebrated result of classical feedback theory [20]. It assures that the sensitivity of the system to component variations in the forward loop is diminished by the addition of feedback. The larger the value of $|T_k(i\omega)|$, the greater the effect of feedback in reducing sensitivity. By Theorem 6, the same condition also assures dynamic optimality. We have thus a beautifully simple relationship between the "classical" argument in favor of feedback and the "modern" concept of dynamic optimality.

It is well worth recording also the consequences of Theorems 5 and 6 when $r \neq 0$.

THEOREM 7. *Given any stable control law k, there exists a loss function (11) with H nonsingular for which k is optimal.*

Proof. Of course, this result hinges on the possibility of choosing r in a convenient way. Recalling the discussion of equivalent problems in Section 5, it follows that Condition (II) may be generalized to

$$|1 + (k' - r')\Phi_r(i\omega)g|^2 > 1. \tag{IIa}$$

We must show that r can be chosen in such a way that the strict inequality sign holds. Now

$$|1 + (k' - r')\Phi_r(i\omega)g|^2 = |1 + [\psi_k(i\omega) - \psi_r(i\omega)]/\psi_r(i\omega)|^2 = \left|\frac{\psi_k(i\omega)}{\psi_r(i\omega)}\right|^2 > 1, \tag{34}$$

from which it is obvious that the required r exists. Q.E.D.

THEOREM 8. *Consider a completely controllable plant with a given control law r. Suppose we wish to find a "better" control law k. In determining k an optimal compromise must be made between reducing the control error (as represented by the term $\|Hx\|^2$) and deviating from the given control law (as represented by the term $(\mu + r'x)^2$). Combining these terms additively to form the loss function (11), it follows that the control law k is "better" than the control law r if and only if the return differences satisfy the condition*

$$|T_k(i\omega)/T_r(i\omega)| > 1 \quad \text{for all real } \omega. \tag{IIb}$$

Proof. Condition (II) for the case $r \neq 0$ is given by (34). But

$$|T_k(i\omega)| = |\psi_k(i\omega)/\psi(i\omega)|. \tag{35}$$

The same holds for $T_r(i\omega)$ and (IIb) follows immediately.

Formula (33) implies also a useful arithmetic condition for optimality, which we state only for the case $r = 0$:

THEOREM 9. *A control law k is optimal in the sense of Theorem 5 if and only if*

(*a*) *$\psi_k(s)$ satisfies the Routh-Hurwitz conditions;*

(*b*) *$\Psi(\omega^2) = |\psi_k(i\omega)|^2 - |\psi(i\omega)|^2$ is a nonnegative polynomial in ω^2.*

In other words, it is possible to characterize optimality solely in terms of the open and closed-loop characteristic equations! This is related to the fact that the numerical values of k depend on the coordinate system chosen to describe the state variables, whereas ψ and ψ_k are independent of this arbitrary choice!

Condition (b) in Theorem 9 is equivalent to

(b') *$\Psi(\omega^2)$ has no real, positive root of odd multiplicity.*

To express (b') in the form of inequalities on the coefficients of $\Psi(\omega^2)$ is a classical problem in the theory of equations. By techniques based on Sturm's theorem, it is possible in principle to derive such inequalities (and to prove the Routh-Hurwitz conditions, see [16, Chapter XV]). This is a very difficult exercise in algebra; the general inequalities are not known today.

We shall give explicit inequalities corresponding to (a)-(b) only in the special cases $n = 2$ and $n = 3$. The derivations are elementary and therefore omitted.

Using the notations

$$\psi(s) = \det(sI - F) = s^n + \alpha_n s^{n-1} + \ldots + \alpha_1,$$

$$\psi_k(s) = \det(sI - F + gk') = s^n + \beta_n s^{n-1} + \ldots + \beta_1,$$

we have: Necessary and sufficient conditions for optimality of k are: $n = 2$:[6]

$$\begin{cases} \beta_1 > 1 \\ \beta_2 > 0 \end{cases} \tag{36}$$

$$\begin{cases} \beta_1^2 - \alpha_1^2 \geqq 0 \\ \beta_2^2 - \alpha_2^2 - 2(\beta_1 - \alpha_1) \geqq 0 \\ \text{both equal signs cannot hold simultaneously} \end{cases} \tag{37}$$

$n = 3$:

$$\begin{cases} \beta_1 > 0 \\ \beta_3 > 0 \\ \beta_2\beta_3 - \beta_1 > 0 \end{cases} \tag{38}$$

$$\begin{cases} \beta_1^2 - \beta_1^2 \geqq 0 \\ \beta_3^2 - \alpha_3^2 - 2(\beta_2 - \alpha_2) \geqq 0, \\ \text{Either } \beta_2^2 - \alpha_2^2 - 2(\beta_1\beta_3 - \alpha_1,\alpha_3) \geqq 0 \text{ or} \\ \beta_2^2 - \alpha_2^2 - 2(\beta_1\beta_3 - \alpha_1\alpha_3) = \\ \qquad - \sqrt{(\beta_1^2 - \alpha_1^2)[\beta_3^2 - \alpha_3^2 - 2(\beta_2 - \alpha_2)]}. \end{cases} \tag{39}$$

Asymptotic Properties of Optimal Control Laws

Now we turn to Problem F: *If L is given by*

$$2L(x, \mu) = \rho\|Hx\|^2 + \mu^2, \tag{40}$$

[6] These conditions were first presented by the writer in an oral discussion at the 1962 Joint Automatic Control Conference.

where H is fixed and ρ is variable parameter, how do the optimal control laws behave as $\rho \to \infty$? We assume of course that $\rho > 0$.

The solution of this problem is greatly simplified by a simple observation based on Condition (I) of Theorem 5: *The same control law is obtained if H is replaced by the matrix hh', where h is determined by*

$$\|H\Phi(i\omega)g\|^2 = |h'\Phi(i\omega)g|^2. \tag{41}$$

Since the left-hand side of (41) is a nonnegative polynomial in ω^2, the existence of h follows from Lemmas 2-3. The vector h is not uniquely determined by (41); it is again convenient to fix it by using the unique factorization mentioned in Lemma 3 {19}.

Replacing H by h' means passing from the loss function defined by (41) to that defined by

$$2L(x, \mu) = \rho\eta^2 + \mu^2, \tag{42}$$

where

$$\eta = \langle h, x\rangle = \sum_{i=1}^{n} h_i x_i. \tag{43}$$

If we choose the special coordinates described in Lemma 2, then

$$x_i = (d/dt)^{i-1}x_1 \ (i = 2, \ldots, n),$$

and every component of h_i is nonnegative since all zeros of $\sum_{i=1}^{n} h_i s^{i-1}$ must have negative real parts. Hence we have

THEOREM 10. *Consider a completely controllable plant with a single control variable. Without affecting the corresponding control law, every quadratic loss function (11a) may be replaced by (42), in which η is a linear combination with nonnegative coefficients of a certain state variable x_1 and its derivatives.*

Condition (I) is now of the form

$$|1 + k'\Phi(i\omega)g|^2 = 1 + \rho|h'\Phi(i\omega)g|^2. \tag{44}$$

It was first noticed by Chang [18, 19] that this equation admits a revealing interpretation in terms of root loci. Writing $\zeta(i\omega)$ to denote the numerator of the transfer function $h'\Phi(s)g$ (a polynomial with real coefficients of degree $m < n$), it is clear that (44) is equivalent to

$$\psi_k(s)\psi_k(-s) = \psi(s)\psi(-s) + \rho\zeta(s)\zeta(-s). \tag{45}$$

As $\rho \to \infty$ precisely $2m$ zeros of (45) tend to the zeros of $\zeta(s)\zeta(-s)$. The remaining $2(n - m)$ zeros tend to ∞ and are asymptotic to the zeros of the equation

$$s^{2(n-m)} = \rho. \tag{46}$$

Since all zeros of the polynomial $\psi_k(s)$ must be in the left-half plane, it follows that m zeros of $\psi_k(s)$ tend to the corresponding zeros of $\zeta(s)$ (which are in the left-half plane, or on the imaginary axis by the definition of h) while the remaining $n - m$ zeros of $\psi_k(s)$ tend asymptotically to a Butterworth pattern [9, 10, 19] of radius $\rho^{1/2(n-m)}$.

These observations may be summarized in the following form:

THEOREM 11. (Solution of Problem F). *Consider a completely controllable plant and the optimization problem (9) corresponding to the loss function (43). As $\rho \to \infty$, m closed-loop poles of the optimal control system tend to the m zero of $h'\Phi(s)g$, while the remainder tend to a Butterworth configuration of order $n - m$ and radius $\rho^{1/2(n-m)}$. The optimal closed-loop poles are asymptotically independent of the (open-loop) poles of the plant.*

This is a highly important result.

Note that the number $\rho^{1/2(n-m)}$ is closely related to the loop gain. At large values of ρ the return difference $|T_k(i\omega)|$ becomes very large so that the system becomes insensitive with respect to plant variations. At the same time, the dynamical behavior of the closed-loop system becomes independent of the uncontrolled dynamics of the plant.

The step response of a transfer function $G(s)$ with no zeros and a Butterworth pattern of poles has an overshoot from 0 to about 23 percent as $(n - m)$ increases from 1 to ∞ [10]. Moreover, the frequency response function

$$|G(i\omega)|^2 = \frac{1}{\omega^{2(n-m)} + \rho}$$

has an increasingly sharp low-pass characteristic as $(n - m) \to \infty$, the bandwidth being $\rho^{1/2(n-m)}$. (A high return difference requires large bandwidth.)

Moderate overshoot and low-pass frequency-response have always been regarded as typical of good servomechanism design. This fact is now "proved" with a rigorous theoretical analysis and brought within the framework of optimal control theory {20}.

It must be emphasized, however, that the influence of the plant parameters may be significant for moderate values of ρ. In such cases the machinery of optimal control theory (e.g., (14)) may lead to a control law which is not easily obtainable by the usual intuitive engineering design methods.

The essential idea of Theorem 11 is attributed to Chang [18–19], who called it the "root-square-locus" method {21}.

It is of some interest to give explicit formulas for the closed-loop characteristic equation of a system which is optimal with respect to the loss function (42). We shall do this only when $n = 2$. In this case the characteristic polynomial is written in the usual form

$$s^2 + \beta_2 s + \beta_1 = s^2 + 2\zeta_k\omega_k s + \omega_k^2,$$

where ζ_k is the (closed-loop) *damping ratio* and ω_k is the (closed-loop) *undamped natural frequency.*

We want an explicit relationship between ρ, ζ_k, and ω_k, given a fixed transfer function $h'\Phi(s)g$. These relations follow from (36)-(37) as well as from (44), which we can write also as

$$\left|\frac{-\omega^2 + 2\zeta_k\omega_k i\omega + \omega_k^2}{(i\omega - s_1)(i\omega - s_2)}\right|^2 = 1 + \rho|h'\Phi(i\omega)g|^2, \tag{47}$$

where s_1 and s_2 are the open-loop poles.

Case 1. $s_1 = s_2 = 0$. Then $\omega_k > 0$ and $\zeta_k \geqq 1/\sqrt{2}$.

Subcase. If $h'\Phi(s)g = 1/s^2$, then $\zeta_k = 1/\sqrt{2}$ and $\rho = \omega_k^4$.

Case 2. $s_1 = 0$, $s_2 = 1$. Then $\omega_k > 0$ and $\zeta_k \geqq \sqrt{\dfrac{1}{2} + \dfrac{1}{4\omega_k^2}}$.

Subcase. If $h'\Phi(s)g = 1/s(s - 1)$ then ζ_k attains its lower bound, while $\rho = \omega_k^4$.

Case 3. $s_1 = s_2 = -1$. Then $\omega_k \geqq 1$ and $\zeta_k \geqq \sqrt{\dfrac{1}{2} + \dfrac{1}{2\omega_k^2}}$

but both equal signs cannot hold simultaneously.

Subcase (a). If $h'(\Phi)(s)g = 1/(s^2 + 1)$, then $\rho = \omega_k^4 - 1$, $\omega_k > 1$, and ζ_k attains its lower bound.

Subcase (b). If $h'\Phi(s)g = s/(s + 1)^2$, then $\rho = \zeta_k^2 - 1$, $\zeta_k > 1$, and $\omega_k = 1$.

Case 4. $s_1 = i$ and $s_2 = -i$. Then $\omega_k \leqq 1$ and $\zeta_k \geqq \sqrt{\dfrac{1}{2} - \dfrac{1}{2\omega_k^2}}$, but again both equal signs cannot hold simultaneously.

Subcase (a). If $h'\Phi(s)g = 1/(s^2 + 1)$, then $\rho = \omega_k^4 - 1$, and ζ_k attains its lower bound.

Subcase (b). If $h'\Phi(s)g = s/(s^2 + 1)$, then $\rho^2 = 2(2\zeta_k^2 - 1)$ $\zeta_k > 0$, and $\omega_k = 1$.

Only in Case 4 is it possible to have a damping ratio less than $1/\sqrt{2}$ This is to be expected. If ρ is small, the performance index defined by (46) will be optimized and stability is achieved by introducing a small amount of damping. A large amount of damping would require too much control energy.

Thus in usual cases a second-order system can be optimal only if it has a damping ratio at least as high as $1/\sqrt{2}$. This confirms a well-known "rule-of-thumb" used in designing instrument servomechanisms, which calls for $\zeta_k \cong 0.7 - 0.8$.

It is interesting that the optimality conditions (39) do not put an upper limit on ζ_k.

References

1 P. Funk, "Variationsrechnung und ihre Anwendung in Physik und Technik," Springer, Berlin, 1962 (Grundlehren Series 94).

2 R. E. Kalman, "On the Inverse Problem of Optimal Control Theory" (to be published).

3 R. E. Kalman, "Contributions to the Theory of Optimal Control," *Bol. Soc. Mat. Mexicana*, 1960, pp. 102–119.

4 R. E. Kalman, "The Theory of Optimal Control and the Calculus of Variations," Proc RAND—Univ. Calif. Symp. on Optimization Theory, 1960; Univ. of Calif. Press, 1963, chap. 16.

5 R. E. Kalman, T. S. Englar, and R. S. Bucy, "Fundamental Study of Adaptive Control Systems," ASD Technical Report 61-27.

6 A. E. Bryson and W. F. Denham, "Multivariable Terminal Control for Minimum Mean Square Deviation From a Nominal Path," Proceedings of the Symposium on Vehicle Systems Optimization, Institute of the Aerospace Sciences, November, 1961.

7 E. B. Lee, "Design of Optimum Multivariable Control Systems," Journal of Basic Engineering, Trans. ASME, Series D, vol. 83, 1961, pp. 85–90.

8 C. W. Merriam, III, "A Class of Optimum Control Systems," *Journal of the Franklin Institute*, vol. 267, 1959, pp. 267–281.

9 D. Graham and R. C. Lathrop, "The Synthesis of 'Optimum' Transient Response: Criteria and Standard Forms," *Trans. AIEE*, vol. 72, part II, 1953, pp. 278–288.

10 D. T. McRuer, D. Graham, et al., "Performance Criteria for Linear Constant Coefficient Systems With Deterministic Inputs," Technical Report ASD-Technical Report 61-501, February, 1962.

11 R. E. Kalman, "Mathematical Description of Linear Dynamical Systems," SIAM J. Control, 1963.

12 L. S. Pontryagin, V. G. Boltyanskii, R. V. Gamkrelidze, and E. F. Mischenko, "The Mathematical Theory of Optimal Processes," Interscience Publishers, New York, N. Y., 1962.

13 K. J. Åström, J. E. Bertram, et al., "Current Status of Linear Optimal Control Theory," *SIAM J. Control*, 1963.

14 R. E. Kalman and J. E. Bertram, "Control System Analysis and Design Via the 'Second Method' of Lyapunov," Journal of Basic Engineering, Trans. ASME, Series D, vol. 82, 1960, p. 371.

15 J. P. LaSalle and S. Lefschetz, "Stability by Lyapunov's Direct Method," Academic Press, New York, N. Y., 1961.

16 F. R. Gantmakher. "The Theory cf Matrices," Chelsea, 1959.

17 R. E. Kalman, "Lyapunov Functions for the Problem of Lur'e in Automatic Control," *Proc. Nat. Acad. Sci.* USA, vol. 49, 1963, pp. 201–205.

18 S. S. L. Chang, "Root Square Locus Plot—a Geometrical Method for the Synthesis of Optimal Servosystems," IRE Convention Record, 1960.

19 S. S. L. Chang, "Synthesis of Optimum Control Systems," McGraw-Hill Book Co., Inc., New York, N. Y., 1961.

20 H. W. Bode, "Network Analysis and Feedback Amplifier Design," Van Nostrand and Co., Inc., New York, N. Y., 1945.

21 D. A. S. Fraser, "Nonparametric Methods in Statistics," John Wiley & Sons, Inc., New York, N. Y., 1957.

22 O. Bolza, "Lectures on the Calculus of Variations," Dover Press, New York, N. Y., 1960, pp. 31–32.

23 J. Douglas, "Solution of the Inverse Problem of the Calculus of Variations," *Trans. Am. Math. Soc.*, vol. 50, 1941, pp 71–128.

24 F. B. Hildebrand, "Methods of Applied Mathematics," Prentice-Hall, Inc., Englewood Cliffs, N. J., 1952.

25 A. A. Frederickson, to be published.

26 P. D. Joseph and J. Tou, "On Linear Control Theory," *Trans. AIEE*, vol. 80, part II, 1961, pp. 193–195.

27 R. E. Kalman, "Canonical Structure of Linear Dynamical Systems," *Proc. Nat. Acad Sci.* USA, vol. 48, 1962, pp. 596–600.

28 E. G. Gilbert, "Controllability and Observability in Multivariabl· Control Systems," *SIAM J. Control*, 1963.

29 G. A. Bliss, "Lectures on the Ca culus of Variations," Chicago Univ. Press, Chicago, Ill., 1946.

30 L. Berkovitz, "Variational Methods in Problems of Control and Programming," *J. Math. Anal. Appl.*, vol. 3, 1961, pp. 145–169.

31 V. M. Popov, "Absolute Stability of Nonlinear Systems of Automatic Control," *Avt. i Telemekh.*, vol. 22, 1961, pp. 961–979.

APPENDIX

{1} Optimal control theory must be regarded as a mathematical tool. A rigid definition of the performance index cannot and should not be avoided, because the power of mathematical reasoning is available only when problems are precisely stated. (If we seek approximations, then it must be precisely defined what constitutes a good or bad approximation.) It is true that the optimal control theory of today can solve only a few problems (mostly in the realm of linear mathematics), and that it is not applicable to many of the more complex and admittedly more important questions that interest the engineer. But this is not a defect in the conceptual foundations of the theory; it is merely an argument for more basic research to extend the applicability of the existing methods.

{2} The issue involved here is quite similar to the objections raised against parametric statistical procedures. To assume that a given statistical model has certain well-defined but unknown parameters (for instance, a Gaussian distribution with unknown mean and variance) is highly restrictive, and the resulting conclusions must not be interpreted too widely. The remedy is to use nonparametric statistics [21]. Then one can claim more general conclusions, but they will be necessarily less explicit than in the parametric case.

{3} The precise definition of the inverse problem of the calculus of variations is the following: *Given a family of curves which satisfy the vector differential equation*

$$(*) \qquad \ddot{x} = F(t, x, \dot{x}) \; (x, F = n\text{-vectors}, \quad \cdot = d/dt).$$

Determine all scalar functions $L(t, x, x)$ *such that every solution of* (*) *is a regular extremal of the ordinary variational problem*

$$\int L(t, x, x)dt;$$

in other words, determine all L *such that* (*) *is identical with the Euler equations*

$$\frac{d}{dt} L_x = L_x,$$

and $L_{\dot{x}\dot{x}}$ *is positive definite along every solution of* (*).

A solution of this problem always exists when $n = 1$ [22]. The case $n = 2$ has been investigated and settled by Douglas [23]. His results are much too complicated to be stated here. The problem is reduced to the solution of a system of first-order partial differential equations for the elements of the matrix $L_{\dot{x}\dot{x}}$, from which L is determined by quadratures. Not every family (*) is a regular extremal. For instance, there is no L (with L positive definite) for which the curves generated by

$$\ddot{x}_1 = x_1^2 + x_2^2, \quad \ddot{x}_2 = x_1$$

are extremal.

See also the interesting heuristic treatment of Hildebrand [24, Sect. 2.14–2.16].

{4} It seems that frequency-domain concepts are unavoidable in system theory when explicit conditions are desired. A classical example is of course Nyquist's stability criterion. While equivalent criteria can be stated in the time domain (all characteristic roots must have negative real parts) or even in terms of the system constants (the Routh-Hurwitz conditions), the frequency-domain Nyquist criterion is very elegant, simple to state, and often more useful than the others.

The deeper significance of the frequency-domain formulas is that they provide "coordinate-free" system description: since transfer functions refer to input-output relations, they are independent of the choice of the coordinates in state space. General results of optimal control theory must be of course independent of the arbitrary choice of coordinates.

A full discussion of the relations between the transfer-function and state-variable methods of describing linear dynamical systems may be found in [11].

{5} The practical significance of optimality conditions is explored in detail by Frederickson [25]. The reader should consult his paper also for a theoretical analysis of the so-called ITE^2 (integral of time $\times$ error squared) and IT^{2}E (integral of time squared $\times$ error squared) performance criteria [10].

{6} These assumptions are of course highly restrictive. One obtains a hierarchy of problems depending on the number of control variables and the number of state variables which can be measured directly.

If all state variables can be measured, the optimal controller does not contain dynamical elements because the best control action at any instant depends only on the values of the state variables at that instant. But if some control variables cannot be measured directly—which happens very often in practical problems—optimal control theory requires that the missing state variables be estimated from the known ones using Wiener filtering techniques [13, 26]. The Wiener filter will contain dynamical elements which are to be regarded as a part of the controller.

For example, if only one state variable can be measured then any optimal control loop can be specified by two transfer functions: the transfer function of the plant from control input to measured output and the transfer function of the controller from plant output to control input. Given the first transfer function, by the methods of this paper it is possible to obtain implicit conditions which must be satisfied by the second transfer function if it is to be optimal. No explicit form of these conditions is known (at present).

{7} The reader is reminded that in most of control theory (and also in this paper) there is no need to introduce the mathematical concept of a Laplace transform. All one requires are certain functions of a complex variable s. Only in rare cases is it useful to know that transfer functions can be interpreted as Laplace transforms, i.e., as an integral. In that case special restrictions must be imposed on s. No such restriction is needed or implied in the definition (4).

{8} It follows from the author's canonical decomposition theorem [27] (see also [11, 28]) that only one "part" of the plant is included in the control loop, namely that which is completely controllable and completely observable. Only this part is of interest in studying the optimality of the control law.

{9} In the classical calculus of variations, this problem is called the *Problem of Lagrange* or the *Problem of Mayer* or the *Problem of Bolza*. All three are equivalent [29, §69.]

{10} This assumption is not necessary. For instance, Frederickson [25] shows that every loss function of the form

$$L(t, x, \mu) = t^k\|x\|^2_{Q_1} + \mu^2 \text{ (}k\text{ positive integer, } Q_1 \text{ nonnegative definite)}$$

is strictly equivalent (yields the same minimum for (9) and the same optimal control law) to a constant loss function of the type

$$L(x, \mu) = \|x\|^2 Q_2 + \mu^2 \quad (Q_2 \text{ nonnegative definite}).$$

{11} This is a very special assumption. For example, if L is a homogeneous polynomial of degree $2k$ in (x, μ), then *under certain additional conditions* χ will again be linear in x. The explicit form and significance of these additional conditions on L are not known at present, however.

{12} The part of Pontryagin's maximum principle which is used here is equivalent to the classical necessary condition of Weierstrass. Historically, this condition was first stated for the ordinary problem (no constraints) of the calculus of variations [29, §9]. The extension of the Weierstrass condition to the problem of Lagrange [29, §78] has been shown [30] to be equivalent to Pontryagin's requirement that the pre-Hamiltonian H possess an absolute minimum with respect to μ for every (t, x, p). The Weierstrass, Pontryagin theory is needed here only to establish that $\sigma > 0$; the rest of the analysis proceeds in the spirit of the Hamilton-Jacobi-Carathéodory theory.

{13} Note that this requirement does not suffice to determine H uniquely. There is an essential arbitrariness involved here; in fact, the lack of a nice physical interpretation of the term $\|Hx\|^2$ has been a serious difficulty in the applications of optimal control theory. This difficulty is removed to a large extent in the present paper. See especially Section 10.

{14} Consider the matrices

$$F = \begin{bmatrix} 0 & 1 \\ 1 & 0 \end{bmatrix}, \quad g = \begin{bmatrix} 0 \\ 1 \end{bmatrix}, \quad H = [1 \ \ -1], \quad r = 0.$$

It is easily verified that the two symmetric matrices

$$P_1 = \begin{bmatrix} \sqrt{2} - 1 & -\sqrt{2} + 1 \\ -\sqrt{2} + 1 & \sqrt{2} - 1 \end{bmatrix},$$

$$P_2 = \begin{bmatrix} 3 + \sqrt{2} & 1 + \sqrt{2} \\ 1 + \sqrt{2} & 1 + \sqrt{2} \end{bmatrix}$$

are both solutions of (17). P_1 is nonnegative definite and P_2 is positive definite. P_1 is the one which corresponds to the limit (14). Condition (A_2) fails to hold, because

$$e^{Ft} = \begin{bmatrix} \cosh t & \sinh t \\ \sinh t & \cosh t \end{bmatrix}$$

and if $x_0 = \begin{bmatrix} 1 \\ 1 \end{bmatrix}$, then $\|He^{Ft}x_0\| \equiv 0$.

{15} The idea of using frequency-domain concepts in the present context is due to V. M. Popov [31]. By an extension of Popov's ideas, the writer has succeeded in obtaining a solution of the celebrated problem of Lur'e [17]. In fact, Theorem 4 is a variant of the Main Lemma used in [17], which has also other important applications in system theory.

{16} The assumption that "k is a stable control law" is an important part of Theorem 5. To see why, let us write

$$|1 + k'\Phi(i\omega)g|^2 = |1 + \nu(i\omega)|^2,$$

using Lemma 3. Suppose the rational function $\nu(i\omega) \neq k'\Phi(i\omega)g$; in other words, some zeros of $\nu(s)$ have positive real parts. By Lemma 2 there exists a vector q such that

$$\nu(i\omega) = q'\Phi(i\omega)g \quad (q \neq k),$$

and we may replace k by q without any effect on (I). Thus (I) is satisfied by many vectors. But only one of these corresponds to the optical control law, namely that which is determined by the special factorization mentioned in Lemma 3.

{17} Plotting the frequency-response function $k'\Phi(i\omega)g$ in the complex plane, it is easy to see that (II) can be satisfied only if $\lim_{\omega \to \infty} |i\omega k'\Phi(i\omega)g| > 0$. Using the canonical coordinate system it follows that the latter condition is satisfied if and only if $k_i \neq 0$ for $i = 1, \ldots, n$, which means that every single state variable must be fed back! This is a reasonable consequence of the theory: since all state variables are assumed to be measurable, some information would be discarded if a coefficient k_i were zero. Thus optimality requires using all available information.

{18} If $H \neq h'$ is a matrix consisting of more than one row, the condition $[F, H]$ = completely observable (i.e., (A_2')) is *not sufficient* to guarantee that the optimal control law is completely observable.

For instance, if $H = \text{diag}\,[h_{11}, \ldots, h_{nn}]$, $h_{ii} > 0$, and F, g have the canonical form (26), then

$$\|H\Phi(i\omega)g\|^2 = [h_{11} + h_{22}\omega^2 + \ldots + h_{nn}\omega^{2n-2}]/|\psi(i\omega)|^2.$$

By proper choice of the h_{ii} the numerator and denominator will have common factors. Then if

$$\|H\Phi(i\omega)g\|^2 = |h'\Phi(i\omega)g|^2,$$

where h' is the result of the special factorization mentioned in Lemma 3, $h'\Phi(i)g$ will also possess cancelable factors. Hence $[F, h']$ and consequently $[F, k']$ will not be completely observable.

{19} And then it follows further that $P_\infty(Q) - P_\infty(hh')$ is nonnegative definite for all Q. See [2].

{20} That frequency-domain methods are applicable just as easily to low or high-order systems has always been claimed as a major advantage for these methods. The present analysis shows that, *qualitatively speaking*, similar claims can be made also for time-domain methods. When it is a question of *accurately* computing an optimal control law, however, serious difficulties of a numerical nature may arise in dealing with high-order systems. If we had general design methods of the frequency-domain type—none exists today which is really general—it, too, would be subject to the same numerical difficulties.

{21} Chang's results were restricted to the optimization of the step response of the system. This inessential restriction arose solely because Chang used the older (frequency-domain) version of optimal control theory.

A General Formulation of the Nyquist Criterion

C. A. DESOER, FELLOW, IEEE

Abstract—The Nyquist diagram technique is examined under very general assumptions; in particular, the linear subsystem is represented by a convolution operator, thus, the case of any linear time-invariant distributed circuit is included. It is shown that if there are no encirclements of the critical point, then the impulse response of the closed-loop system is bounded and absolutely integrable on $[0, \infty)$; it also tends to zero as $t \to \infty$. For any initial state, the zero-input response of the closed-loop system is also bounded and goes to zero. If, on the other hand, there are one or more encirclements of the critical point, then the closed-loop impulse response tends asymptotically to a growing exponential.

Manuscript received September 6, 1964; revised October 26, 1964. The research reported in this paper was supported by the National Science Foundation under Grant GP-2413. This paper was presented at the Allerton Conference on September 28, 1964.

The author is with the Dept. of Electrical Engineering, University of California, Berkeley, Calif.

Introduction

THE NYQUIST CRITERION is proved for the single-loop feedback case. The purpose of the paper is to demonstrate the extreme generality of the criterion by constructing a proof which requires the least number of assumptions.[1] The main result is stated in the form of a theorem. The hypotheses of this theorem include most cases of engineering interest.

[1] The discussion of stability for the case where the transfer functions are not rational is far from trivial. Any reader who doubts this should consider the function defined for $t \geq 0$ by $e^t \sin(e^t)$ and note that its Laplace transform is analytic for *all* finite s. This example shows that the discussion of stability cannot be settled by "looking at the singularity that is the furthest to the right," which is a legitimate procedure with rational transfer functions.

Reprinted from *IEEE Trans. Circuit Theory*, vol. CT-12, pp. 230–234, June 1965.

Assumptions and Main Theorem

Following Nyquist [1], we consider the linear time-invariant single-loop feedback system shown in Fig. 1. It will be referred to as the closed-loop system. The block labeled k is a constant gain factor (i.e., independent of time and frequency), if its input is $\eta(t)$, and its output is $k\eta(t)$ where k is a fixed positive number. The block labeled G is linear, time invariant, and nonanticipative (causal), and it satisfies the following conditions:

(G.1) Its input-output relation relating the output y, the zero-input response z, and the input ξ is

$$y(t) = z(t) + \int_0^t g(t - \tau)\xi(\tau)\, d\tau \quad \text{for all} \quad t \geq 0. \tag{1}$$

(G.2) For all initial states, the zero-input response is bounded on $[0, \infty)$ and $z(t) \to z_\infty$ as $t \to \infty$, where z_∞ is a finite number which depends on the initial state. Let $z_M \triangleq \sup_{t \geq 0} |z(t)|$.

(G.3) The unit impulse response g is given by

$$g(t) = 1(t)[r + g_1(t)] \tag{2}$$

where the constant r is non-negative; $1(t)$ is the unit step function; g_1 is bounded on $[0, \infty)$, is an element of $L^1(0, \infty)$, and $g_1 \to 0$ as $t \to \infty$. When $r = 0$, for all initial states, z_∞ in (G.2) is zero. We write

$$\mathcal{L}[g(t)] \triangleq G(s) = \frac{r}{s} + G_1(s). \quad \text{Let } g_M = \sup_{t \geq 0} |g(t)|.$$

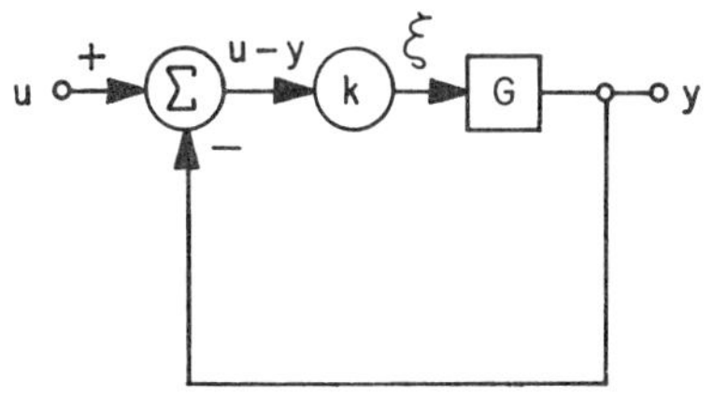

Fig. 1. Single-loop feedback system under consideration: the gain factor k is positive and the linear time-invariant subsystem G is characterized by a convolution operator [see (1)].

For ease of reference, we state formally the main result of this paper:

Theorem

Suppose the linear time-invariant single-loop feedback system shown on Fig. 1 satisfies the conditions (G.1), (G.2), and (G.3). If the Nyquist diagram[2] of $G(s)$ does not encircle or go through the critical point $(-1/k, 0)$, then

a) The impulse response of the closed-loop system is bounded, tends to zero as $t \to \infty$, and is an element of $L^1(0, \infty)$.

b) For any initial state, the zero-input response of the closed-loop system is bounded and goes to zero as $t \to \infty$.

c) For any initial state and for any bounded input, the response of the closed-loop system is bounded.

d) Let r be positive; then for any input u which tends to a constant u_∞ as $t \to \infty$, and for any initial state, the output y tends to u_∞ as $t \to \infty$. Let r be zero and $u \to 0$ as $t \to \infty$, then for any initial state, the output $y \to 0$.

If the Nyquist diagram of $G(s)$ encircles the critical point $(-1/k, 0)$ a finite number of times, then the impulse response of the closed-loop system grows exponentially as $t \to \infty$.

Comment: It should be stressed that the only assumption that is made concerning the box G is that it fulfills the conditions (G.1), (G.2), and (G.3). Such conditions are often fulfilled by the impulse response of systems described by ordinary differential equations, difference-differential equations, and those whose input-output relation is obtained through the solution of partial differential equations. The latter is the case for distributed circuits and for many control systems.

The analysis to follow applies to all cases where $r \geq 0$. For many circuit applications it turns out that $r = 0$ and that for initial states $z_\infty = 0$. The reader will have no difficulty in inserting the consequent simplifications in the proof.

Analysis: Let u be the bounded input applied to the system and let $u_M \triangleq \sup_{t \geq 0} |u(t)|$. The response of the closed-loop system starting from an arbitrary initial state is given by

$$y(t) = z(t) + k\int_0^t g(t - \tau)[u(\tau) - y(\tau)]\, d\tau \quad \text{for all} \quad t \geq 0. \tag{3}$$

The theorem will be proved in several steps. First, in order to be able to apply Laplace transform techniques to the integral equation (3), we establish that the solution is of exponential order; second, well-known facts concerning Laplace transforms are used to establish the uniqueness of the solution of (3); third, various tools of complex function theory and Fourier analysis are used to establish the properties of the impulse response of the closed-loop system and those of the zero-input response. The proof of the remaining assertions of the theorem follow easily.

Assertion: If (G.1), (G.2), and (G.3) hold, and if u is bounded, then

1) The output y is of exponential order and its Laplace transform $Y(s)$ is analytic for $Re\ s > kg_M$.

2) The output y, the solution of (3), is unique.

Proof: From (3) and the definitions of z_M, g_M, and u_M, we get

$$|y(t)| \leq (z_M + kg_M u_M t) + kg_M \int_0^t |y(\tau)|\, d\tau.$$

Hence, by the Gronwall-Bellman inequality [2], [3],

[2] The Nyquist diagram is the map under G of the imaginary axis from which the interval $[-j\epsilon, j\epsilon]$ has been removed and replaced by the semicircle $\{e^{j\theta}: -\pi/2 \leq \theta \leq \pi/2\}$; here ϵ is taken arbitrarily small.

$$|y(t)| \leq b(t) + k\int_0^t b(t-\xi)g_M e^{kg_M\xi}\, d\xi \quad \text{for all} \quad t \geq 0 \quad (4)$$

where $b(t) \triangleq z_M + kg_M u_M t$. Equation (4) implies that y is of exponential order and that its Laplace transform $Y(s)$ is an analytic function of s for $Re\ s > kg_M$. To establish uniqueness, suppose there were two responses y_1 and y_2. By subtraction we obtain from (3)

$$y_1(t) - y_2(t) = k\int_0^t g(t-\tau)[y_2(\tau) - y_1(\tau)]\, d\tau \quad \text{for all} \quad t \geq 0. \quad (5)$$

Now g_1 is zero for $t < 0$ and is in $L^1(0, \infty)$; therefore, the Laplace transform of g is analytic for $Re\ s > 0$ and goes to zero as $|s| \to \infty$ with $|\sphericalangle s| \leq \pi/2$ [4], [9]. From 1), y_1 and y_2 are of exponential order; hence, taking Laplace transforms of (5) we get

$$Y_1(s) - Y_2(s) = kG(s)[Y_2(s) - Y_1(s)] \qquad Re\ s > kg_M.$$

Therefore, $Y_1(s) - Y_2(s) = 0$ for all s in their domain of definition. By the uniqueness theorem of Laplace transforms [5], y_1 and y_2 are equal for almost all t in $[0, \infty)$. Since $y_1 - y_2$ is continuous, $y_1(t) = y_2(t)$ for all t in $[0, \infty)$. This completes the proof.

It might be worth noting that since g, u, and z are bounded their restriction to any finite interval, $(0, t)$, is an element of L^2, hence, the existence and uniqueness of the solution of (3) may also be established by iterative techniques [6].

Proof of the Theorem

To prove a) we recall that, by definition, h is the zero-state response of the system to a unit impulse applied at $t = 0$. By definition of g and from an examination of the configuration of the closed-loop system, to apply a unit impulse at the input of the closed-loop system is equivalent to having an identically zero input applied to the system but having G start from the state whose zero-input response is kg. Thus,

$$h(t) = kg(t) - k\int_0^t g(t-\tau)h(\tau)\, d\tau. \quad (6)$$

Let H be the Laplace transform of h; then

$$H(s) = \frac{kG(s)}{1 + kG(s)} \qquad Re\ s > kg_M. \quad (7)$$

Now, by the principle of the argument,[3] the denominator of $H(s)$ is $\neq 0$ for all $Re\ s \geq 0$ if, and only if, the Nyquist diagram of G does not encircle or go through the critical point $(-1/k, 0)$. By the assumption concerning the Nyquist diagram, the denominator of (7) has no zeros in the closed right-half plane. Let us rewrite (7) using (2). If we multiply the numerator and denominator by $s/(s + kr)$ we get

$$H(s) = \frac{k\left(\frac{r}{s} + G_1(s)\right)}{1 + k\left(\frac{r}{s} + G_1(s)\right)} = \frac{\frac{kr}{s+kr} + \frac{ks}{s+kr}G_1(s)}{1 + \frac{ks}{s+kr}G_1(s)}. \quad (8)$$

The denominator may be rewritten as

$$1 + kG_1(s) - k\frac{kr}{s+kr}G_1(s).$$

Observe that $\mathcal{L}^{-1}[kr/(s + kr)] = 1(t)kr\, e^{-krt}$, which is a function in $L^1(0, \infty)$. Since $g_1 \epsilon L^1(0, \infty)$ and since the product of the transforms of two L^1 functions is the transform of an L^1 function, the denominator is of the form "one plus the transform of a function in $L^1(0, \infty)$". The denominator has no zeros in the closed right-half plane. The numerator of (8) is also the transform of a function in $L^1(0, \infty)$. Hence, by a theorem of Paley-Wiener [8], it follows that h is in $L^1(0, \infty)$. Now h is bounded because (6) implies

$$h_M \triangleq \sup_{t\geq 0} |h(t)| \leq kg_M + kg_M\int_0^\infty |h(\tau)|\, d\tau < \infty.$$

To show that h tends to zero as $t \to \infty$, observe that (6) implies that

$$(h - kg)|_t^{t+\delta} = -k\int_0^t [g(t+\delta-\tau) - g(t-\tau)]h(\tau)\, d\tau - k\int_t^{t+\delta} g(t+\delta-\tau)h(\tau)\, d\tau.$$

Therefore, if we remember the form of g specified by (2), for all $t \geq 0$ and all $\delta > 0$,

$$|[h(t+\delta) - kg_1(t+\delta)] - [h(t) - kg_1(t)]| \leq kh_M\int_0^\infty |g_1(\xi+\delta) - g_1(\xi)|\, d\xi + k\delta g_M h_M. \quad (9)$$

Note that the right-hand side of (9) is independent of t. Since $g_1 \epsilon L^1(0, \infty)$, it follows that the first term of the right-hand side goes to zero as $\delta \to 0$ [9]. The same is obviously true of the second term. Consequently (9) implies that $h - kg_1$ is uniformly continuous on $[0, \infty)$. Since h and g_1 are in $L^1(0, \infty)$, so is $h - kg_1$; therefore, the uniform continuity implies that $\lim_{t\to\infty} [h(t) - kg_1(t)] = 0$ [11]. By (G.3) it follows that h tends to zero as $t \to \infty$.

Let us prove statement (b) of the theorem. The zero-input response of the closed-loop system z_c satisfies the equation

$$z_c(t) = z(t) - \int_0^t h(t-\tau)z(\tau)\, d\tau \quad \text{for all} \quad t \geq 0 \quad (10)$$

since $h \epsilon L^1(0, \infty)$ and z is bounded, z_c is bounded. It remains to show that z_c goes to zero as $t \to \infty$. For this purpose we need only show that the convolution integral tends to z_∞ since, by (G.2), $z(t) \to z_\infty$ as $t \to \infty$. The properties of h imply that for any $\epsilon > 0$ there is a $T(\epsilon) < \infty$ such that $t > T(\epsilon)$ implies $|h(t)| < \epsilon$ and

[3] Let C be a simple closed rectifiable positively oriented curve. Let C^* be the union of C_i, the interior of C, and of C itself. Let $f(z)$ be meromorphic in C^*, (i.e., have no other singularities than poles in C^*). If f has no zeros nor poles on C, then, when z describes C, the argument of $f(z)$ increases by $2\pi(Z_f - P_f)$ where Z_f, (P_f, resp.), is the number of zeros, (poles, resp.) of f in C_i.

$$\int_{T(\epsilon)}^{\infty} |h(t)|\, dt < \epsilon.$$

The properties of z imply that $|z(t)| \leq z_M < \infty$ for all t and that for any $\epsilon > 0$ there is a $T'(\epsilon) < \infty$ such that $t > T'(\epsilon)$ implies $|z(t) - z_\infty| < \epsilon$. Rewrite (10)

$$z_c(t) - z(t) = -\int_0^t h(\tau)[z(t-\tau) - z_\infty]\, d\tau - z_\infty \int_0^t h(\tau)\, d\tau. \tag{11}$$

From these considerations, we get the following inequalities: for any $t > T(\epsilon) + T'(\epsilon)$

$$\begin{aligned} |z_c(t) - z(t) + z_\infty \int_0^t h(\tau)\, d\tau| &\leq \int_0^{t-T'(\epsilon)} |h(\tau)|\, |z(t-\tau) - z_\infty|\, d\tau \\ &\quad + \int_{t-T'(\epsilon)}^{t} |h(\tau)|\, |z(t-\tau) - z_\infty|\, d\tau \\ &\leq \epsilon \int_0^{t-T'(\epsilon)} |h(\tau)|\, d\tau + (|z_M| \\ &\quad + |z_\infty|) \int_{t-T'(\epsilon)}^{t} |h(\tau)|\, d\tau. \end{aligned}$$

Changing the upper limit of integration of both integrals to ∞, we conclude that $t > T(\epsilon) + T'(\epsilon)$ implies that

$$|z_c(t) - z(t) + z_\infty \int_0^t h(\tau)\, d\tau| \leq \epsilon \left[\int_0^\infty |h(\tau)|\, d\tau + |z_M| + |z_\infty| \right]$$

that is

$$\lim_{t\to\infty} |z_c(t) - z(t) + z_\infty \int_0^t h(\tau)\, d\tau| = 0. \tag{12}$$

Now, since $h \in L^1$ and tends to zero as $t \to \infty$,

$$\lim_{t\to\infty} \int_0^t h(t)\, dt = \lim_{s\to 0} H(s) = 1$$

also by (G.2),

$$\lim_{t\to\infty} z(t) = z_\infty$$

hence, (12) gives

$$\lim_{t\to\infty} z_c(t) = 0.$$

Consider now statement (c) of the theorem. The configuration of the closed-loop system and (1) imply that the output y starting from an arbitrary initial state at time $t = 0$ and responding to an input u is given by

$$y(t) = z_c(t) + \int_0^t h(t-\tau)u(\tau)\, d\tau \quad \text{for all} \quad t \geq 0 \tag{13}$$

where z_c is the closed-loop zero-input response. If u is bounded then y is bounded; this follows from the boundedness of z_c and the fact that h is in $L^1(0, \infty)$. Incidentally, by a previous reasoning, $y - z_c$ is uniformly continuous on $[0, \infty)$. Thus, statement (c) is established. Since $z_c(t) \to 0$ as $t \to \infty$, statement (d) is equivalent to the assertion that $u(t) \to u_\infty$ implies that $\int_0^t h(t-\tau)u(\tau)d\tau \to u_\infty$. This implication has been proved in detail in proving (b). Therefore statement (d) holds.

Suppose now that the Nyquist diagram encircles $(-1/k, 0)$ a finite number of times. Since $G(s) \to 0$ as $|s| \to \infty$ with $|\measuredangle s| \leq \pi/2$ and since G is analytic in the open right-half plane, the principle of the argument [7] shows that $1 + kG(s)$ has a finite number of zeros in the open right-half plane. For simplicity of notation, we shall write the following expressions assuming that each pole is simple. By a partial fraction expansion we get

$$H(s) = \sum_{\nu=1}^{n'} \frac{b_\nu}{s - s_\nu} + H_1(s)$$

$$Re\, s_\nu > 0, \qquad \nu = 1, 2, \cdots, n$$

where $H_1(s)$ is analytic for $Re\, s > 0$. It can be easily verified that the behavior of $H(\sigma + j\omega)$ as $\omega \to \infty$ satisfies the conditions of Doetsch's theorem [10]. Therefore, we conclude that

$$h(t) \sim b_1 e^{s_1 t} \quad \text{as} \quad t \to \infty, \qquad Re\, s_1 > 0$$

where s_1 is the zero of $1 + kG(s)$ which has the largest real part. (If there are several such zeros, then the right-hand side must include the appropriate sum.) This completes the proof of the theorem.

For some applications it may be useful to be able to relate the norm of the output y to that of the input u and the zero-input response z.

Corollary: Let (G.1), (G.2), (G.3) hold and the Nyquist diagram satisfy the condition of the theorem. If, for some number $p \geq 1$, both z and u are elements of $L^p(0, \infty)$, then

$$||y||_p \leq (1 + ||h||_1)||z||_p + ||h||_1 \cdot ||u||_p. \tag{14}$$

When $p = \infty$, if we let $y_M = \sup_{t\geq 0}|y(t)|$, then, using previous notations,

$$y_M \leq (1 + ||h||_1)z_M + ||h||_1 u_M.$$

Proof: Observe that, for any $p \geq 1$, if h is in $L^1(0, \infty)$ and z is in $L^p(0, \infty)$, then $h * z$ is also in $L^p(0, \infty)$ and $||h * z||_p \leq ||h||_1 \cdot ||z||_p$ [12]. The inequalities above follow directly from the application of this fact to (10) and (12).

Conclusions

Under very general assumptions pertaining to the open-loop system, we have shown that if the Nyquist diagram satisfies the nonencirclement conditions then the zero-input response, the impulse response, and the complete response have all the usual properties associated with stable systems. The inequality (14) shows that if z is in L', then for all $p \geq 1$ (including $p = \infty$) the closed-loop system is L_p stable in the sense of I. W. Sandberg [13]. The results obtained here are essential for some recent extensions of Popov's criterion [11].

ACKNOWLEDGMENT

The author expresses his gratitude to Prof. R. W. Newcomb and to C. T. Chen for valuable comments on an earlier version of the manuscript.

REFERENCES

[1] Nyquist, H., Regeneration theory, *Bell; Sys. Tech. J.*, vol 2, Jan 1932, pp 126–147.
[2] Coddington, E. A., and N. Levinson, *Theory of Ordinary Differential Equations*, New York: McGraw-Hill, 1955, problem 1, p 37.
[3] Bourbaki, N., *Fonctions d'une Variable Réelle*, Paris: Hermann and Cie, 1961, ch 4, §1, no 4, Lemma 2.
[4] Doetsch, G., *Handbuch der Laplace Transformation*, Basel, Switzerland: Verlag Birkhäuser, vol I, 1950, p 162.
[5] Doetsch, G., *Ibid.*, p 72.
[6] Tricomi, F. G., *Integral Equations*, New York: Interscience, 1957, p 11.
[7] Hille, E., *Analytic Function Theory*, Boston, Mass.: Ginn, vol 1, 1959, p 252.
[8] Paley, R. E. A. C., and N. Wiener, *Fourier Transforms in the Complex Domain*, New York: Am. Mathematical Soc., 1934, pp 60–61.
[9] Goldberg, R. R., *Fourier Transforms*, New York: Cambridge, 1961, p 4.
[10] Doetsch, G., *op. cit.*, vol 2, p 150.
[11] Desoer, C. A., A generalization of the Popov criterion, *IEEE Trans. on Automatic Control, Short Papers*, vol 10, Apr 1965, pp 182–185.
[12] Dunford, N., and J. T. Schwarz, *Linear Operators*, New York: Interscience, vol 1, 1958, p 528, exercise 6.
[13] Sandberg, I. W., A frequency domain condition for the stability of feedback systems containing a single time-varying nonlinear element, *Bell Sys. Tech. J.*, vol 43, Jul 1964, pp 1601–1608.

Synthesis of feedback systems with large plant ignorance for prescribed time-domain tolerances†

ISAAC M. HOROWITZ

Department of Applied Mathematics, Weizmann Institute of Science, Rehovot, Israel, and Department of Electrical Engineering, University of Colorado, Boulder, Colorado

and MARCEL SIDI

Department of Applied Mathematics, Weizmann Institute of Science, Rehovot, Israel

[Received 15 September 1971]

There is given a minimum-phase plant transfer function, with prescribed bounds on its parameter values. The plant is imbedded in a two-degree-of-freedom feedback system, which is to be designed such that the system time response to a deterministic input lies within specified boundaries. Subject to the above, the design should be such as to minimize the effect of sensor white noise at the input to the plant. This report presents a design procedure for this purpose, based on frequency response concepts. The time-domain tolerances are translated into equivalent frequency response tolerances. The latter lead to bounds on the loop-transmission function $L(j\omega)$, in the form of continuous curves on the Nichols chart. Properties of $L(j\omega)$ which satisfy these bounds with minimum effect of sensor white noise are derived. The design procedure is quite transparent, providing the designer with the insight to make necessary trade-offs, at every step in the design process. The same design philosophy may be used to attenuate the effect of disturbances on plants with parameter ignorance.

1. Statement of the problem

This paper is devoted to the following problem. There is a single input–output ' plant ' imbedded in a linear ' two-degree-of-freedom feedback structure '. The term ' plant ' denotes the constrained part of the system whose output is the system output. The designation ' two-degree-of-freedom feedback structure ' indicates a system wherein the command input, $r(t)$ in fig. 1,

Fig. 1

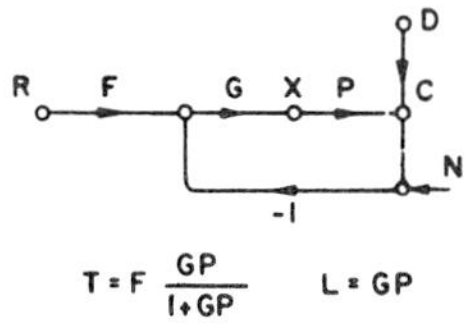

A canonic structure.

and the system output, $c(t)$, may be independently measured. In such a structure (Horowitz 1963) the system response to command inputs, and the

† Communicated by the Authors. This research was supported by NASA under Grant NGR 06-003-083.

Reprinted with permission from *Int. J. Contr.*, vol. 16, pp. 287–309, Feb. 1972.

system sensitivity to the plant, may be, to some extent, independently controlled. The structure shown in fig. 1 is of course only one of many possible canonic two-degree-of-freedom feedback structure. The plant parameters are not known precisely. Only the ranges of their values are known. For example, the plant transfer function may be a known function of elements of the set $X = \{x_1, x_2, \ldots, x_n\}$, but these elements are known only to lie in a given closed region in n-dimensional space. Strictly speaking, the design technique is applicable only to fixed parameter plants, but it is well known that for engineering purposes it is also applicable to ' slowly-varying ' plant parameters. It is less well known that the feedback can be quite effective even for rather fast-varying plants (Horowitz 1963). However, this is a topic requiring considerable separate treatment, so it is assumed in this paper that the plant is fixed, but there is on the designer's part bounded ignorance of the plant parameters.

Fig. 2

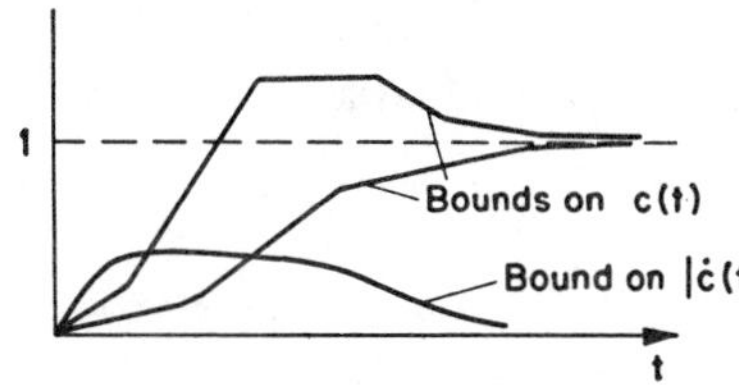

Tolerances on unit step response.

The system sensitivity to the ' plant ignorance ' is to be characterized by the resulting ignorance in the system time response to a deterministic time input. A unit step is chosen here, but any other input may be used The problem is to guarantee that the output ignorance is contained within prescribed bounds ; for example, those shown in fig. 2, for the case of the unit step input. It can be shown (Horowitz 1963) that if the plant is minimum-phase, then any such specifications, no matter how narrow the tolerances, may be approached as closely as desired. From this, it follows that it is easy to overdesign in minimum-phase systems. The ' price ' paid is the large ' bandwidth ' of the loop-transmission function, $L = GP(s)$, which in turn opens wider the ' window ' to the noise in the feedback return path, lumped as sensor noise N in fig. 1. In the high-frequency range where $|L(j\omega)| < 1$, but where $|P(j\omega)| < |L(j\omega)|$, the noise output at X in fig. 1 is amplified by $|L(j\omega)/P(j\omega)|$, which tends to be very large over a large bandwidth in such systems. The highly amplified noise then saturates the output stages of $G(s)$ or input stages of $P(s)$ for a large percentage of the time. This problem has been emphasized before.

1.1. *Optimization criteria*

This paper copes with the above problem by taking the response bounds as inviolate, but attempting to satisfy them with an $L(j\omega)$ whose magnitude as a function of frequency is decreased as fast as possible. Another important reason for doing this in all feedback systems is the difficulty of having the paper design correspond to reality in a frequency range where plant parasitics and higher-order modes tend to dominate (Bode 1945). Another approach to optimization would be to minimize an index into which enter both the spread in the response and the effect of the noise. Statistical methods have been very useful for such indices, for many problems in which the plant parameters are precisely known. Attempts to do the same for the present problem have been unsuccessful because of the need to obtain expectations over P of expressions like $P/(1+PM)$. The practice (Fleischer 1962) has been to neglect the ignorance of P in the denominator, and replace it there by some nominal P_0, but this is obviously a very poor approximation for plants with significant ignorance bounds.

1.2. *Principal steps in design procedure*

These are :

(1) Translation of time-domain bounds on $c(t)$ (such as those given in fig. 2) into bounds on $|T(j\omega)| \triangleq |C(j\omega)/R(j\omega)|$ of fig. 1.
(2) Derivation of bounds on $L(j\omega)$ from the bounds on $|T(j\omega)|$ and on $P(j\omega)$.
(3) Formulation of the optimum $L(s)$ from the results of Step 2.
(4) Derivation of the prefilter $F(s)$ of fig. 1.
(5) Modification, if necessary, of $L(s)$ and $F(s)$.

2. Design procedure

2.1. *Translation of time-domain bounds into bounds on* $\ln |T(j\omega)|$

In a minimum-phase system the magnitude of the frequency response $|T(j\omega)|$ completely specifies the transfer function $T(s)$, which in turn uniquely determines the system step response $c_s(t)$. Hence, bounds on $\ln |T(j\omega)|$ are just as good as those on both the magnitude and phase of $T(j\omega)$. But the rigorous translation of time-domain bounds into bounds on $|T(j\omega)|$ is, as yet, an unsolved problem. In practice, however, it has not been difficult to achieve a translation suitable for any specific numerical problem encountered. One may begin, for example, by assuming a simple second- or third-order system model for $T(s)$, and finding the bounds on the model parameters which correspond to the bounds on the time response. From the model parameter bounds one then determines the resulting bounds on $\ln |T(j\omega)|$. Suppose this step leads to the solid-line bounds B_u, B_l of fig. 3.

It is desirable, of course to increase the spread between B_u and B_l, but it will be seen that there is no advantage in doing so at isolated points. There is benefit only if the spread increases, on the whole, with increasing ω. One soon finds, with a little experimentation, that indicated modifications B_u', B_l' in fig. 3 are generally achievable. It is very helpful for such experimentation to have a computer programme for finding time response from the magnitude of the frequency response. Additional experimentation reveals that there is a definite limit to the permissible spread in the lower frequency range for a reasonably smooth curve of $|T(j\omega)|$. Subsequent design details provide one with an appreciation of the frequency ranges in which broadening of the bounds may or may not be important. Such ranges depend a great deal on the nature of the plant and of the ignorance of the plant. Hence it is best to obtain comparatively quickly estimates of B_u', B_l' and proceed with the design. The designer will subsequently understand whether it is worthwhile to return for better determination of bounds on $|T(j\omega)|$.

Fig. 3

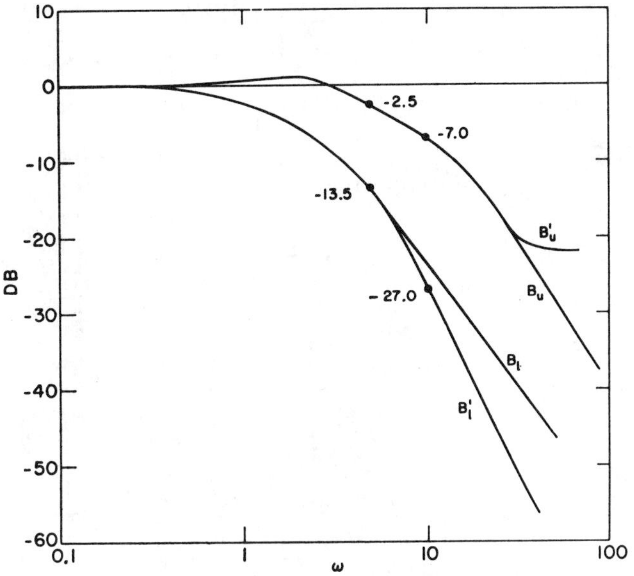

Derivation of bounds on $|T(j\omega)|$.

2.2. *Derivation of bounds on* $L(j\omega)$

2.2.1. *Templates of* $P(j\omega)$

It is assumed that the translation of time-domain into frequency-domain specifications has been accomplished and the latter are of the form shown in fig. 3. In fig. 1, $C=RT=RFL/(1+L)$, $L=GP$ and as there is no ignorance of F, G,

$$\Delta \ln |C(j\omega)| = \Delta \ln |T(j\omega)| = \Delta \ln \left|\frac{L(j\omega)}{1+L(j\omega)}\right| ; \quad \Delta \ln L = \Delta \ln P. \qquad (1\ a, b)$$

A specific value of frequency is chosen, say ω_1 r.p.s. The values of $P(j\omega_1)$ over the range of plant parameters are calculated and the bounds obtained. The procedure is illustrated for the case

$$P(s)=\frac{ka}{s(s+a)}; \quad 1 \leqslant k \leqslant 10 ; \quad 1 \leqslant a \leqslant 10. \qquad (2)$$

This is conveniently done on the plane of $\ln L(j\omega)=\ln |L| + j \arg L$, the abscissa in degrees and the ordinate in decibels (the Nichols chart). Thus, at $\omega=2$ r.p.s., $P(2j)$ lies within the boundaries given by A, B, C, D in fig. 4. Since $\ln L = \ln G + \ln P$, the pattern outlined by A, B, C, D may be translated (but not rotated) on the Nichols chart, the amount of translation being given by the value of $G(2j)$. For example, if a trial design of $L(2j)$ corresponds to the template of $P(2j)$ at A', B', C', D' in fig. 4, then

$$|G(2j)| = |L(2j)| - |P(2j)| = (-2{\cdot}0) - (-13{\cdot}0) = 11{\cdot}0 \text{ dB} ;$$
$$\arg G(2j) = \arg L(2j) - \arg P(2j) = (-60°) - (-153{\cdot}4°) = 93{\cdot}4°.$$

Fig. 4

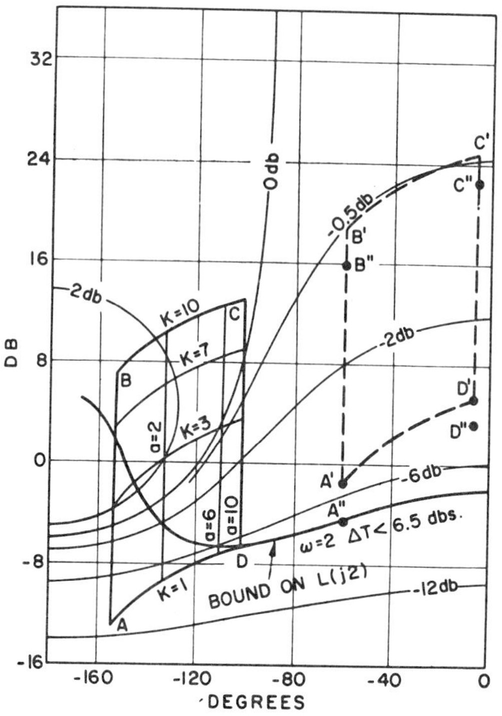

Range of $|P(j2)|$ and resulting bounds on $L(j2)$ on Nichols chart.

2.2.2. *Bounds on $L(j\omega)$ in the Nichols chart*

The templates of $P(j\omega)$ are manipulated to find the position of $L(j\omega)$ which results in the specifications of fig. 3 on $\ln|T(j\omega)|$ being satisfied. Taking the $\omega=2$ template, one tries, for example, positioning it, as shown in fig. 4, at A', B', C', D'. Contours of constant $\ln|L/(1+L)|$ are available on the Nichols chart. Using these contours, it is seen that the maximum change in $\ln|L/(1+L)|$ which, from eqn. (1 *a*), is the maximum change in $\ln|T|$ is, in this case, very closely $(-0{\cdot}49)-(-5{\cdot}7)=5{\cdot}2$ dB, the maximum being at the point C', the minimum at the point A'. The specifications of fig. 3 tolerate a change of 6·5 dB at $\omega=2$, so $|L(j2)|$ is in this case more than satisfactory. One may shift the template lower on the Nichols chart until the bounds on $\Delta\ln|T|$ correspond to 6·5 dB. This is achieved when the lower left corner of the template is at A'' in fig. 4. The template corners are at A'', B'', C'', D'', and the extreme values of $\ln|L/(1+L)|$ are at C'' $(-0{\cdot}7$ dB), $A''(-7{\cdot}2$ dB). If $L(2j)$ for condition A is chosen to be $-4{\cdot}2$ dB, arg $-60°$, then it is guaranteed that $\Delta\ln|T(j)|\leqslant 6{\cdot}5$ dB, over the entire range of plant parameter values. If $\arg L_A(2j)=-60°$, then 4·2 dB is the smallest magnitude of $L_A(2j)$ which satisfies the 3·2 dB specification for $\Delta\ln|T|$. Any larger magnitude is satisfactory, but represents, of course, overdesign at that frequency.

The manipulation of the $\omega=2$ template may be repeated along a new vertical line, and a corresponding new minimum of $|L_A(2j)|$ found. Sufficient points are obtained in this manner to permit drawing a continuous curve of the bound on $L_A(2j)$ as shown in fig. 4. The entire process may be repeated at other frequencies. Figure 5 shows the outline of the templates and the resulting bounds on $L_A(j\omega)$ for a number of frequencies. The template outlines are drawn in any convenient regions on the Nichols chart, since they are, in any case, translated later. In each case the permissible region is to the right of the curve. It is important to note that although condition A $(a=k=1)$ was chosen to generate the curves, any other set of values of a, k could have been chosen. However, once condition A was chosen at any one value of ω, this same condition A must be used for all the contours. If the bounds on L_A are satisfied, then automatically those on all other sets of parameter values, as encompassed by the templates, are also satisfied. This means that $\Delta \ln |T(j\omega)|$ will not exceed the specifications of fig. 3.

Fig. 5

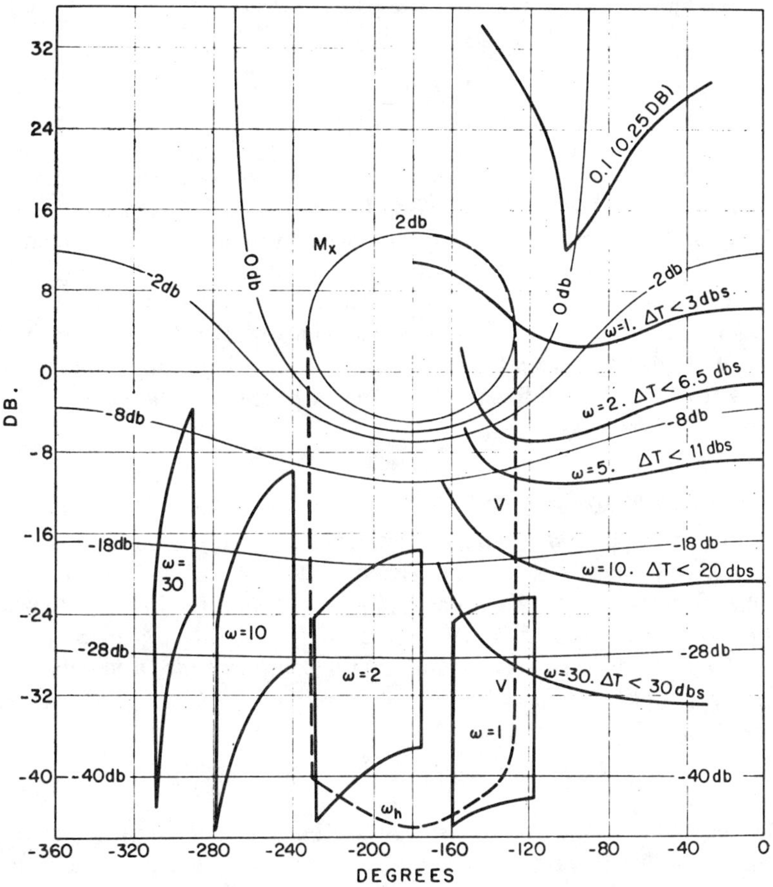

Derived bounds on $L(j\omega)$ on Nichols chart.

Since $P(s)$ is infinite at $\omega = 0$, the system is Type 1, and the zero frequency specification on $\Delta \ln |T|$ (assuming it is zero) can be satisfied with any finite value for $\lim_{s\to 0} sL(s)$. In practice there will be a requirement on the velocity constant which will give a lower bound on $\lim_{s\to 0} sL(s)$.

2.2.3. *System response to disturbances*

The system response to command inputs $r(t)$ (of fig. 1) is not the only response function of interest. There are, in most systems, also disturbances to be considered. The disturbance response (for D in fig. 1) is

$$C_D(s) = \frac{D(s)}{1+L(s)}. \tag{3}$$

It is necessary, of course, to choose $L(s)$ so that the disturbances are properly attenuated, and the technique of this report lends itself very readily for this purpose as detailed in § 5. For the present, only one aspect of this disturbance response problem will be considered, namely, that there will generally be a constraint on the damping factor of the pole pair nearest the $j\omega$ axis. This damping factor can be related to the peaking in

$$\left|\frac{L(j\omega)}{1+L(j\omega)}\right|.$$

Thus, using the single complex pole pair as a model, a peak of 8 dB corresponds closely to a damping factor $\zeta = 0{\cdot}2$; 2·7 dB to $\zeta = 0{\cdot}4$, etc. The usual constraint on the damping factor can therefore be translated into a constraint on the peak value of $|L/(1+L)|$. Suppose this happens to be 2 dB in the present example. If so, the contours in fig. 5 must be modified, as they now permit peaking greater than 2 dB. The required modifications are shown by the dashed lines. The parts of the contours rendered invalid because of the above requirement are to the left of the dashed lines. Note that a portion of the $|T| = 2$ dB locus is common to all contours.

2.2.4. *The single high-frequency boundary*

Sooner or later there is a frequency ω_h such that for all $\omega \geqslant \omega_h$ the boundaries become the contour V of fig. 5. The reason for this is that at large frequencies any rational function $P(s) = K\pi(s+z_i)/\pi(s+p_j)$ degenerates into Ks^{-e}, where e is the excess of poles of P over zeros of P. In the present example $P(j\omega) \to ka/(j\omega)^2$ at large ω. The plant template approaches a vertical line of length $|\Delta ka|_{\max} = 40$ dB. Also, at large frequencies $|L| \ll 1$ and eqn. (1 a) becomes

$$\Delta \ln |C(j\omega)| \to \Delta \ln L(j\omega) = \Delta \ln |P(j\omega)|. \tag{4}$$

Thus, the spread in $\ln C(j\omega)$ becomes equal to that in $\ln P(j\omega)$, which is acceptable when the allowed variation in $|T(j\omega)|$ exceeds the actual variation in $|P(j\omega)|$, and there is then no need of feedback in this frequency range. However, there is still the requirement of acceptable disturbance response, noted in 2.2.3., which provides the boundary V for all ω where this situation applies. In the present example, at large ω, $\Delta \ln |P(j\omega)| = 40$ dB, and from fig. 3 such a permitted change in $|T(j\omega)|$ is acceptable for $\omega \geqslant 60$ r.p.s. Hence, for all

$\omega \geq 60 = \omega_h$, the boundary is V of fig. 5. This reveals that there is no point in increasing the spread in the bounds on $|T(j\omega)|$ for $\omega > 60$ in fig. 3, and provides some insight on the problem considered in 2.1.

2.3. *Properties of optimum $L(j\omega)$*

The optimum design has been defined as that which satisfies the specifications and which, under a certain constraint, decreases as rapidly as possible with frequency. There is no limit on the latter if $e \triangleq$ the excess of poles over zeros of $L(\bullet)$ is allowed to be infinite. In practice, e must be finite, so the constraint of a fixed e value must be added. Section 2.2 in effect provides bounds on $L(j\omega)$ at each ω, although only a discrete number of ω values are displayed. The problem is to determine that $L(j\omega)$ which satisfies these boundaries and which at some very large ω is as small as possible. This problem has only been partially solved. Some important properties of the optimum $L(j\omega)$ have been derived. These properties are stated here and their proof will be presented in a subsequent paper.

1. *Case: Boundaries on $L(j\omega)$ have the property that $d|L|d\omega \leq 0$.* In this case the optimum L lies at each ω on its respective boundary. Also, such an $L(j\omega)$ exists and is unique.

In fig. 5 the low-frequency boundaries have some regions of positive slope. This is always the case because at low frequencies the templates of $P(j\omega)$ are almost vertical lines. However, if the system is Type 1 ($L(s)$ has one pole at the origin), then the optimum L often tends to pass through the boundaries in their negative slope regions.

2. *Case: Boundaries on $L(j\omega)$ have portions of both positive slope and of negative slope.* It is proven that a necessary condition for an optimum L which first crosses boundaries where the slopes are positive, followed by the crossing of boundaries where the slopes are negative, is that $L(j\omega)$ must lie on its respective boundary at each frequency. Such an $L(j\omega)$ function exists, but uniqueness has not been proven. This is the usual case.

The above theorems, plus practice and initiution, lead to the conjecture† that the infinitely complex ideal $L(j\omega)$ function with constrained e, and the additional constraint that the maximum permissible phase lag of L is $90e$ degrees, has the properties shown in fig. 6. Up to $\omega_x \leq \omega_h$ it lies on the boundary appropriate at each ω. For $\omega \geq \omega_x$ up to some $\omega_A > \omega_h$ it lies on V as shown. At ω_A the phase abruptly jumps from $-\theta_A$ to $-90e$ degrees. Hence $|L_A|$ goes to infinity on the vertical line $\theta = -\theta_A$ and returns along the vertical line $\theta = -90e$. The Nyquist plot of $L(j\omega)$ is shown for $e = 4$. In practice, one can approximate the above by a rational function as closely as desired. Equation 4 and the discussion in 2·4 give the designer a means of judging when the added complexity is justifiable.

2.4. *Practical guides in shaping of $L(j\omega)$*

The boundaries shown in fig. 7 are used to illustrate the procedure with $\omega_h = 8$ r.p.s., i.e. for all $\omega \geq 8$, L must lie to the right of the boundary marked V

† This has since been proven.

Fig. 6

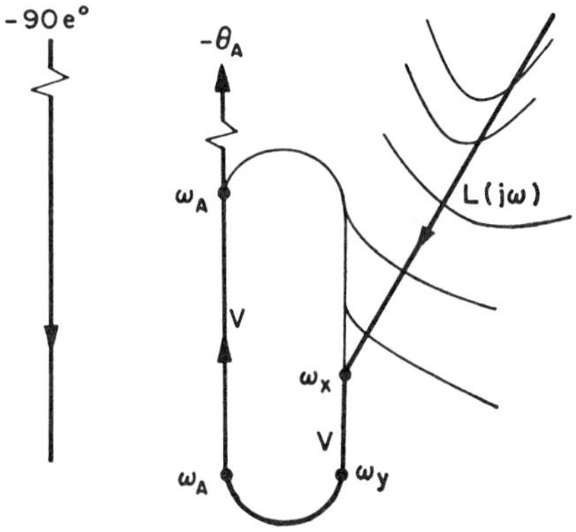

(a)

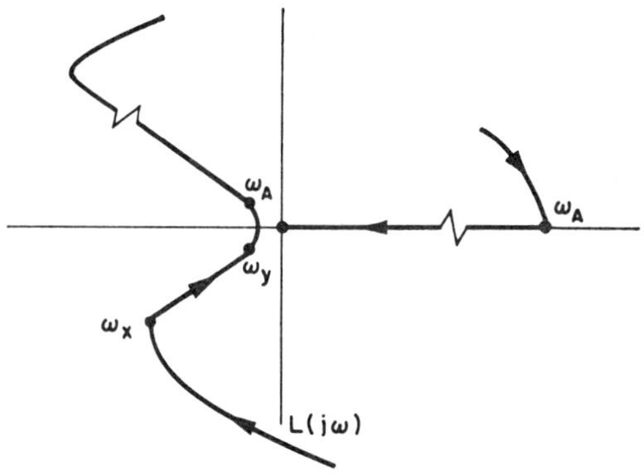

(b)

Conjectured ideal $L(j\omega)$ on (*a*) Nichols chart, (*b*) complex plane.

in fig. 7. It should be recognized that the phase at zero frequency is fixed at 0°, or $-90°$, etc., according as to whether the system is Type Zero, or One, etc. This may not correspond to the optimum $L(j\omega)$ if there was no such constraint. However, the ' loss ' due to this constraint can be made very small, because it is possible, at as low a frequency as desired, to have $L(j\omega)$ at the more favourable point, wherever it may happen to be. The practical limitation is the inconvenience of having poles and zeros very close to the origin. In fig. 7, whatever may be the value of L at zero r.p.s., it is easy to arrange that $L(j\,0{\cdot}5)$ have any desired value.

Consider the boundaries of fig. 7. Arbitrarily, suppose one tries to achieve, say, -26 dB at $\omega=\omega_h=8$. Why is this impractical? Note that at $\omega=4$, approximately -10 dB is needed for $|L|$. In order that $|L|$ decrease to -26 dB at $\omega=8$, L must have an average slope of $-26+10=-16$ dB per octave over this range of frequencies (between $\omega=4$ and $\omega=8$). But the average phase of L over this range is at best approximately $(-180-130)/2=-155°$. With such a phase there is associated an average slope of $-155/180\times 12\approx -10$ dB per octave which is significantly less than the assumed -16 dB per octave. A

Fig. 7

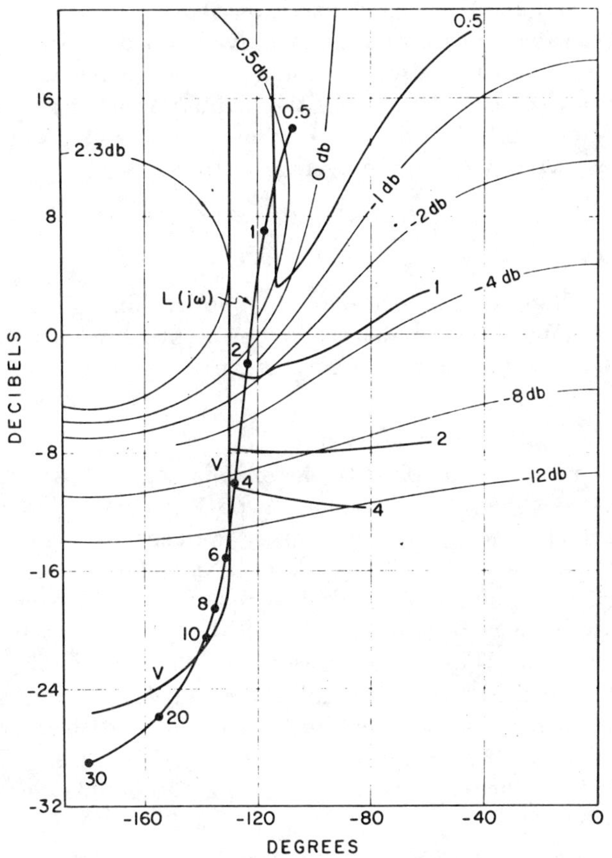

Example of practical shaping of $L(j\omega)$—Nichols chart.

value of -18 dB for $|L|$ at $\omega=8$ seems more reasonable. This value is checked in the same manner. The average phase is, at best, now $-130°$, so the average slope of $|L|$ is $130/180\times 12=-8\frac{2}{3}$ dB/octave. If $|L(j4)|=-10$ dB, then using the above slope, $|L(j8)|=-10\text{–}8\frac{2}{3}$, which is reasonably compatible with the assumption of -18 dB at $\omega=8$.

It is seen that the value of -10 dB at $\omega=4$ is a good starting point. It would be possible to use $|L(j4)|=-11$ dB providing arg. $L(j4)=-110°$. But then the average phase from $\omega=4$ to $\omega=8$ would only be $(-110-130)/2=-120°$, with an associated average slope of $-120/180\times 12=-8$ dB/octave, so that $|L(j8)|\approx -11-8=-19$, which is so close to $-18\frac{2}{3}$ as to make little difference. What of the other boundaries ? What points on $\omega=2$, 1, etc., should one aim for ? On the $\omega=2$ boundary the $-130°$ line is clearly the best, because the boundary is almost flat there. In any case the average slope for $|L|$ near $\omega=2$ is certainly such that if $|L(j4)|=-10$ dB, then $|L(j2)|$ will be greater than -8 dB, i.e. $(Lj2)$ might as well be on V. Similarly, for $L(j)$. As for $L(j\,0{\cdot}5)$ the designer need only make certain that arg $L(j\,0{\cdot}5)$ is close to $-110°$ or so. Working backwards from $|L(j4)|=-10$ dB, this means that $|L(j2)|$ will be approximately -1 dB, $|L(j1)|$ approximately 7 dB, and $|L(j\,0{\cdot}5)|$ approximately

15 dB, providing it is arranged to have approximately $-130°$ phase for L from $\omega=8$ to $\omega=1$, and about $-110°$ phase at $\omega=0{\cdot}5$.

How can the above phase values be simply obtained ? An average phase of $-130°$ may be obtained by alternating a lag corner frequency (lacf) with a lead corner frequency (lecf). Let $1+\alpha$ be the number of octaves under consideration, with a slope of -6 dB/octave over one octave and a slope of -12 dB/octave over α octaves. Then the average phase lag is

$$(\arg L)_{\text{av}} \approx \frac{-(6+\alpha 12)}{1+\alpha} 180,$$

which is to be $-130°$ in the above example. Solving for α gives $\alpha=0{\cdot}8$. Thus, if one allows a slope of -12 dB/octave for one octave duration, he should allow a slope of -6 dB/octave for $1/0{\cdot}8=1{\cdot}25$ octaves.

2.4.1. *Rational function approximation*

The above results are applied to the example of fig. 7 as follows. About $-110°$ is desired at $\omega=0{\cdot}5$. This is a Type 1 system, so assign a lacf (lag corner frequency) at ω_1, a lecf (lead corner frequency) at $2\omega_1$, such that the asymptotic slope of -12 dB/octave is over one octave, a lacf at $2^{1\cdot 25}(2\omega_1)$ such that the asymptotic slope of -6 dB/octave is over $1{\cdot}25$ octaves, etc. Try various values of ω_1, until ω_1 is found such that the net result of an infinite series of the above leads to $-110°$ phase at $\omega=0{\cdot}5$. To simplify the numbers, $2{\cdot}5$ was used instead of $2^{1\cdot 25}=2{\cdot}37$ and $\omega_1=1$, which is a conservative choice. In accordance with the above procedure, the lacf at $\omega=1$ is followed by a lecf at $\omega=2$, a lacf at $\omega=(2{\cdot}5)2=5$, and a lecf at (2) (5) = 10 r.p.s. This procedure is halted at 10 r.p.s., because near $\omega=10$ (see fig. 7) a gradual decrease in phase

Fig. 8

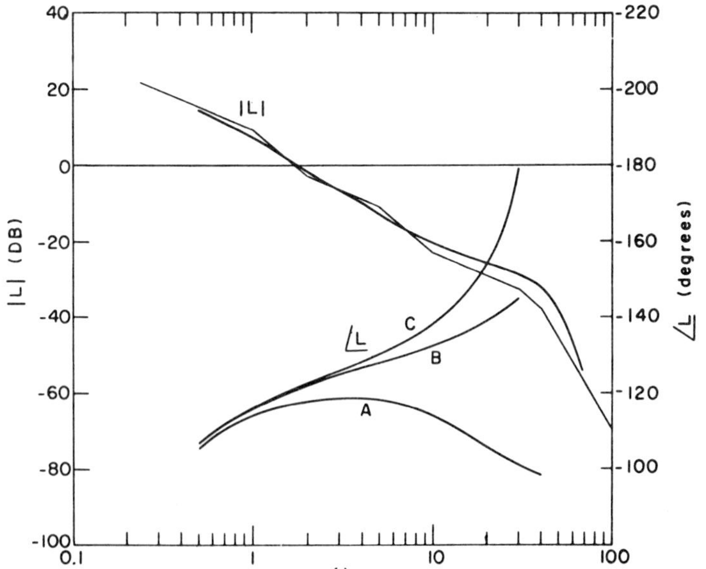

Example of practical shaping of $L(j\omega)$—Bode plot.

is permitted. The level of $|L|$ is moved vertically until $|L(j4)| = -10$ dB. The phase lag of the design, so far, is Curve A in fig. 8.

The next lacf will be set at a somewhat higher frequency than would result from the above formula, because it will be followed by two more lacfs, in order to have a final asymptote of -24 dB/octaves, corresponding to an excess of 4 poles over zeros for $L(s)$. The situation at $\omega = 10$ is examined. At present $\arg L(j10) = -114°$, and from fig. 7, it can be $\approx -140°$ if $|L(j10)| > -26$ dB. Hence 26° more lag is tolerable at $\omega = 10$. A lacf at $\omega = 30$ contributes $-18{\cdot}5°$ at $\omega = 10$, leaving $7{\cdot}5°$. The latter permits a complex pole pair at 4 r.p.s. if its damping factor is 0·2. The phase lag due to all poles and zeros, excepting the last complex pole pair, is given by Curve B in fig. 8, while the total phase lag is given by Curve C. The resulting L is also sketched in fig. 7. The boundaries are slightly violated for $6 < \omega < 10$. More significantly, for $\omega > 12$, L could have more phase lag, which would permit its faster reduction.

The following relation (Bode 1945) gives one an idea of the magnitude reduction available by increasing the phase lag :

$$\frac{2}{\pi}\int_0^\infty \theta d \ln \omega = -[\ln |L(0)| - \ln |L(\infty)|]. \tag{4}$$

Compare two designs, in which $|L(0)|$ is the same in both, but in one region $\theta_2 < \theta_1$ by, say, an average of 20° over one octave. The difference between the two, for the left side of (4) is

$$\frac{2}{\pi}\left(\frac{20}{57{\cdot}3}\right) \ln 2 = 0{\cdot}154 \text{ nepers} = 1{\cdot}34 \text{ dB}.$$

Equation (4) is useful for estimating whether, in any particular problem, it is justifiable to seek to improve a tentative design. Thus, in fig. 7, at $\omega = 0{\cdot}5$, 1, 2 the phase lag could be increased by 6°, 13°, 6°, respectively, so that the left side of (4) is increased in magnitude by about 1·7 dB. However, most of the resulting increase in the difference between $\ln |L(0)|$ and $\ln |L(\infty)|$ would be due to an increase in $|L(0)|$, rather than a decrease in $|L(\infty)|$. The reason is that $|L(j4)|$ cannot be decreased, and since the increase in phase lag is in the frequency range less than 4 r.p.s., the decrease in slope of $\ln |L(j\omega)|$ will occur primarily there. For this same reason, the increase in phase lag possible in the range $\omega > 12$ approximately is more appealing, for it occurs in the region $\omega > 4$, so most of the effect will be in the higher frequency range. In any case, the detailed shaping of $L(j\omega)$ tends to be somewhat onerous and it is very desirable to develop a computer programme for this purpose. The above techniques provide one with a first approximation.

3. Design example

It is useful at this point to apply the above steps to a significant design example in order to better appreciate the later steps in the design procedure.

3.1. *Design specifications*

The plant transfer function is given by

$$P(s) = \frac{k}{s(s^2 + S_p s + P_p)}$$

with $1 \leqslant k \leqslant 1000$, and the complex pole pair of P ranging anywhere in the rectangle M, N, Q, U of fig. 9 (*a*). The performance specifications require that the step response, characterizable by a dominant complex pole pair, be such that this complex pole pair lies within the region A, B, D, E, F, G in the complex plane of fig. 9 (*b*). This problem has been treated in the literature (Olson and Horowitz 1970) by the Dominant Poles Method.

Fig. 9

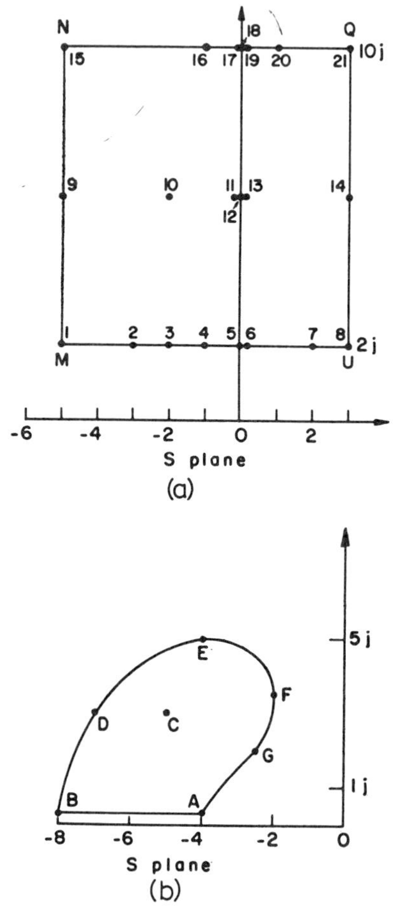

(*a*) Range of complex pole pair of $P(s)$. (*b*) Acceptable range of complex pole pair of second-order model of $T(s)$.

The first step was to translate the dominant-poles specifications of fig. 9 (*b*) into equivalent ones on $|T(j\omega)|$. A second-order system model was used, and the range of model parameters found which satisfies the domain specifications. In this example this is already available, in fig. 9 (*b*). The next step is to find the resulting range of variation of $|T(j\omega|$. These are shown in fig. 10 with the labels corresponding to those in fig. 9 (*a*). It is important to broaden the permissible range of $|T(j\omega)|$ in fig. 10 as much as possible, for clearly this permits design by an $L(j\omega)$ of smaller bandwidth. To broaden the permissible range of

$|T(j\omega)|$ one may proceed by trial and error, trying $|T(j\omega)|$ functions which progressively decrease faster as functions of frequency, until the time-response specifications are intolerably violated. Similarly, one tries $|T(j\omega)|$ functions which progressively decrease more slowly versus ω, until again the time-domain specifications are intolerably violated. In this way the significantly larger bounds shown by the dashed lines in fig. 10 were obtained.

Fig. 10

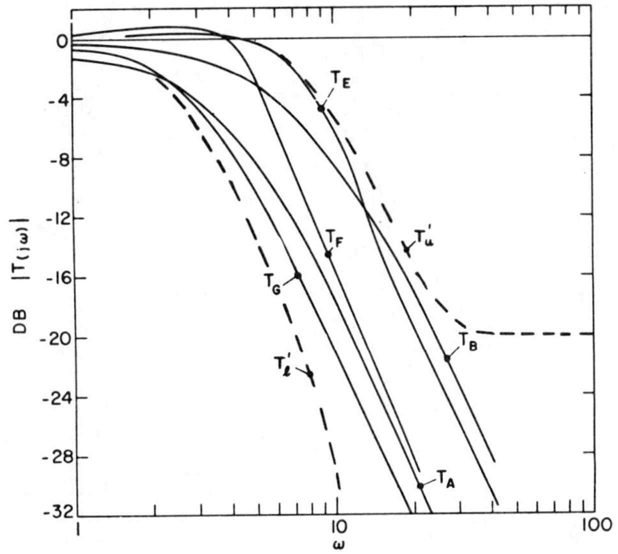

Bounds on $|T(j\omega)|$ corresponding to fig. 9 (*b*) (solid lines) and larger bounds by cut and try (dashed lines).

The procedure of the previous sections was then followed. Some of the plant templates are shown in fig. 11. Note that for $2 \leqslant \omega \leqslant 10$ they extend to infinity, because from fig. 9 (*a*) this range is included in the plant pole-range variation. The resulting boundaries on L and several alternative designs of L are shown in fig. 12. These were all done by hand calculation. It is interesting to compare the four L_n's of fig. 12. The larger phase lag of L_{n1} results in a larger value of $[\ln|L_n(0)| - \ln|L_n(\infty)|]$ (recall eqn. (4) and the discussion there). However, since this extra phase lag is in the low-frequency range, and the value at $\omega = 10$ is even higher than the rest, this difference means only a much larger $|L_{n1}(0)|$ than the rest. One should not make much of the small differences at $\omega = 100$ r.p.s., because the design was performed by hand calculations, which do not permit very precise optimum design.

In any case the resulting design leads to the changes in

$$\left|\frac{L(j\omega)}{1+L(j\omega)}\right| \triangleq |T'(j\omega)|$$

shown in fig. 13 (*a*). Most of the responses lie outside the permitted boundaries, which is not surprising, because so far the design only guarantees that the *change* in $|T(j\omega)|$ is no larger than the maximum change permitted in fig. 10.

Fig. 11

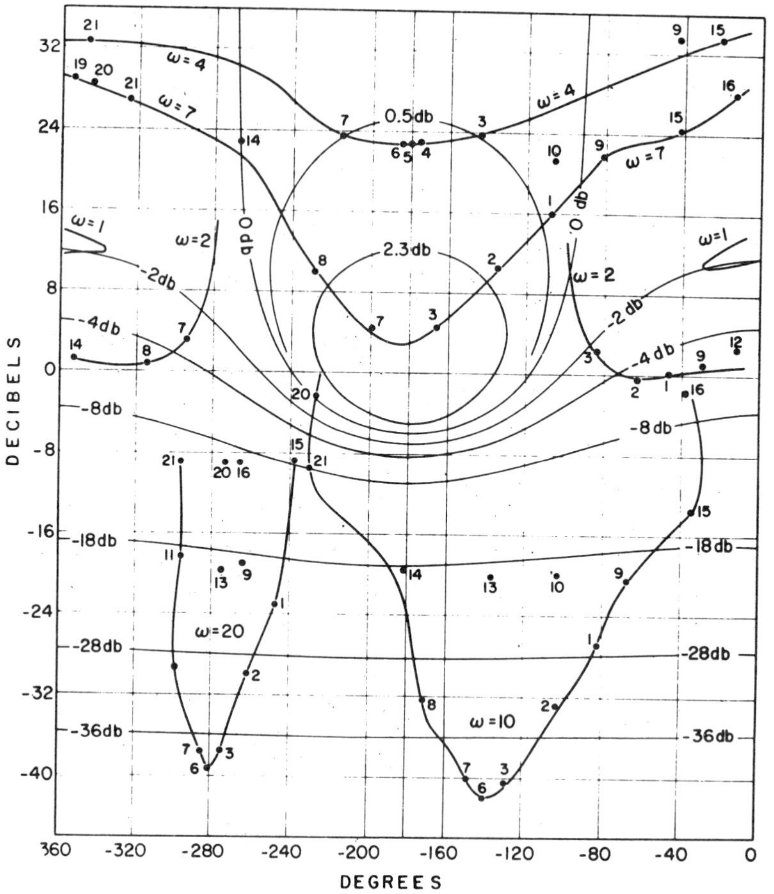

Plant templates at various frequencies.

Since $T = FT'$ (fig. 1), it is necessary to choose F so as to shift the spread in T' into the permissible spread of T. For example, at $\omega = 10$, $|T'|$ lies between 3·6 and $-3{\cdot}0$ dB. Since $|T|$ must lie below $-7{\cdot}5$ dB, $|F(j10)| = -11{\cdot}1$ dB. If L was properly chosen, it is guaranteed that $T(j10)$ does not range below its lower boundary T_l'. The prefilter F is thus determined. Note that $|F|$ uniquely determines arg F and the result can be approximated as closely as desired by a rational function.

The step responses resulting from fig. 13 (*b*) are shown in fig. 14. These responses fall within the time-response bounds corresponding to the complex pole range of fig. 9 (*b*). However, there are some time responses whose behaviour, as a function of time, may not be acceptable. The reference is to Curve 8, in which the first overshoot is below the final value. The corresponding frequency response marked ' 8 ' in fig. 13 (*b*) has a minimum followed by a peak which does not reach the $|T(0)|$ reference. This is denoted as the ' wobbling problem '. (It is interesting to note that reflection of the $|T(j\omega)|$ frequency response about the y axis at $\omega = 0$ gives a roughly qualitative picture

Fig. 12

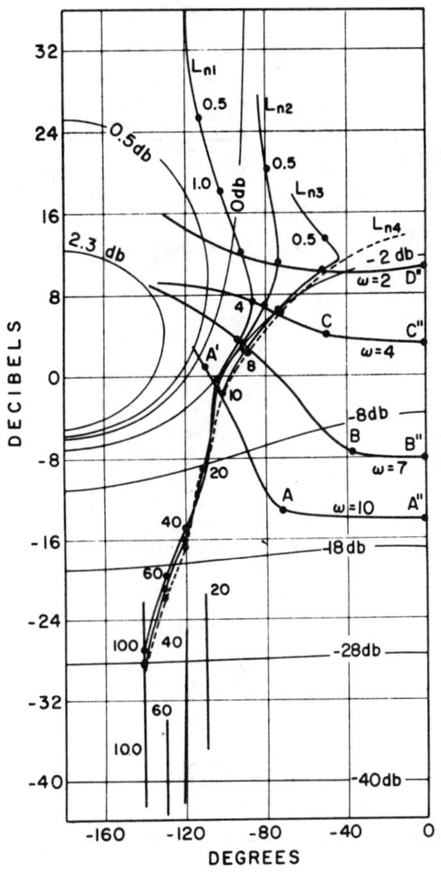

Bounds on $L(j\omega)$ and some $L(j\omega)$ designs.

of the system step response. This is especially true of the 'wobbling' phenomenon.) The wobbling problem will be next considered.

4. The wobbling problem

Case 8 in fig. 13 (*b*) is a good example of a 'wobble' in $|T(j\omega)|$. Evidently, at a low frequency (2 r.p.s.), Case 8 must be at the low end of the template of $P(j2)$ (see fig. 11). When this template is positioned to find the boundary of acceptable $L(j2)$, Case 8 lies near the low extreme of $|T(j2)|$. On the other hand, at $\omega = 3$, if the template of $P(j3)$ is calculated, it is found that Case 8 lies near the top of the template, towards the left side, which means that it will be near the high extreme of $|T(j3)|$. The occurrence of a wobble of this type may therefore be predicted when there are some plant conditions which exhibit this kind of behaviour.

How can the 'wobble' in the frequency response be eliminated? The simplest but least economical way is to increase the level of $|L|$ for all ω. The corrective effect is as follows (see fig. 15). At $\omega = 2$ the position of $L(j2)$ is, say,

Fig. 13

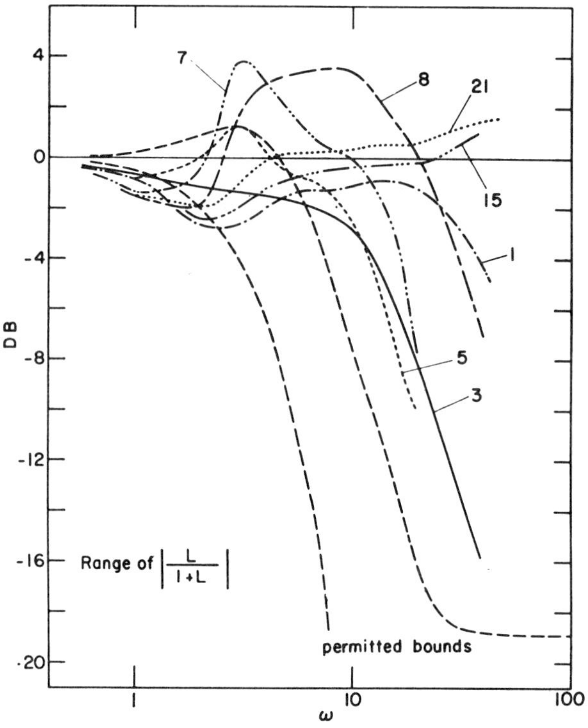

(a)

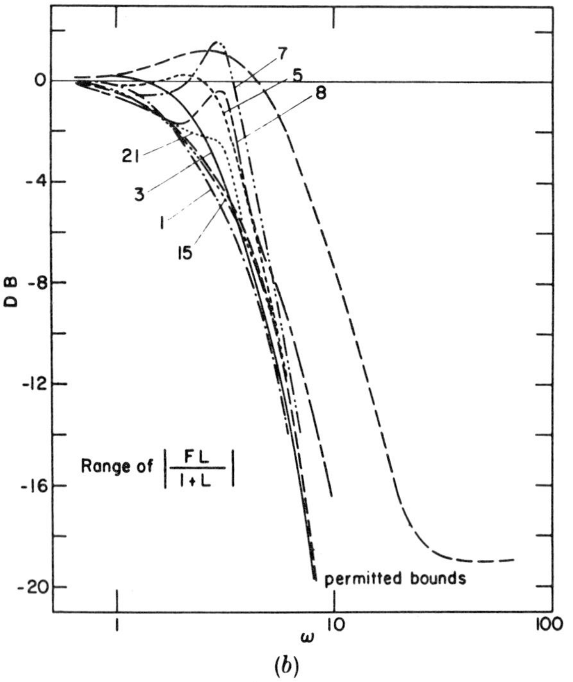

(b)

Range of $|T(j\omega)|$—first design.

Fig. 14

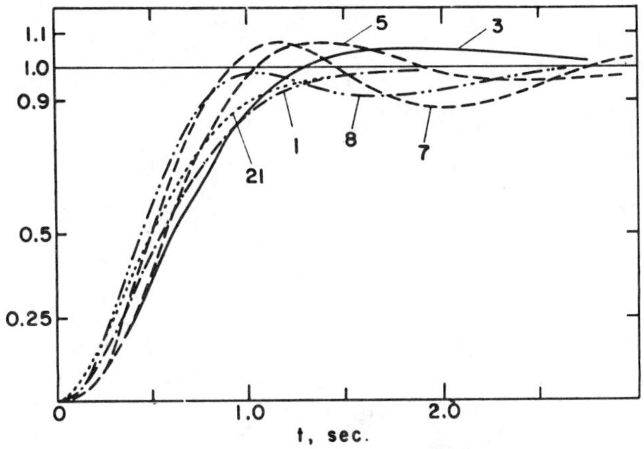

Step responses—first design.

in the neighbourhood of Q, i.e. in the low end, while at $\omega = 3$, $L(j3)$ is, say, at U, in the high end. Increase of $|L|$ at the same phase improves matters at both frequencies. It decreases $|T|$ at $\omega = 3$, and increases it at $\omega = 2$, both effects helping to straighten out the wobble. This method was used in the above design example, increasing $|L|$ by 2 dB, which almost completely eliminated the ' wobble '.

Fig. 15

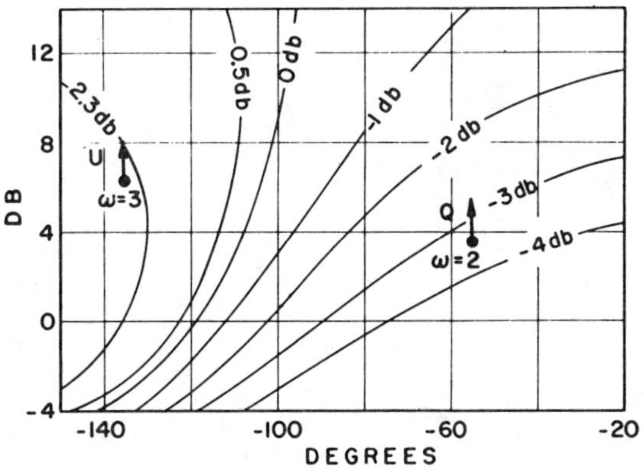

Effect of increase of $|L|$ on wobble.

It is certainly possible to eliminate the wobble in a more economical manner, i.e. with a smaller increase of $|L|$ at high frequencies. The two principal frequencies of the wobble, i.e. the minimum and maximum points, which were at $\omega = 2$, 3 for Case 8 in fig. 13 (*b*), are considered. Figure 16 (*a*) is used to present the argument, with extreme wobbling for Condition 1, between ω_1 and ω_2. Suppose L is changed at ω_1 such that $|T_1|$ is increased and $|T_2|$ is lowered, from points A_1, A_2 to points B_1, B_2, respectively. This by itself alleviates the

Fig. 16

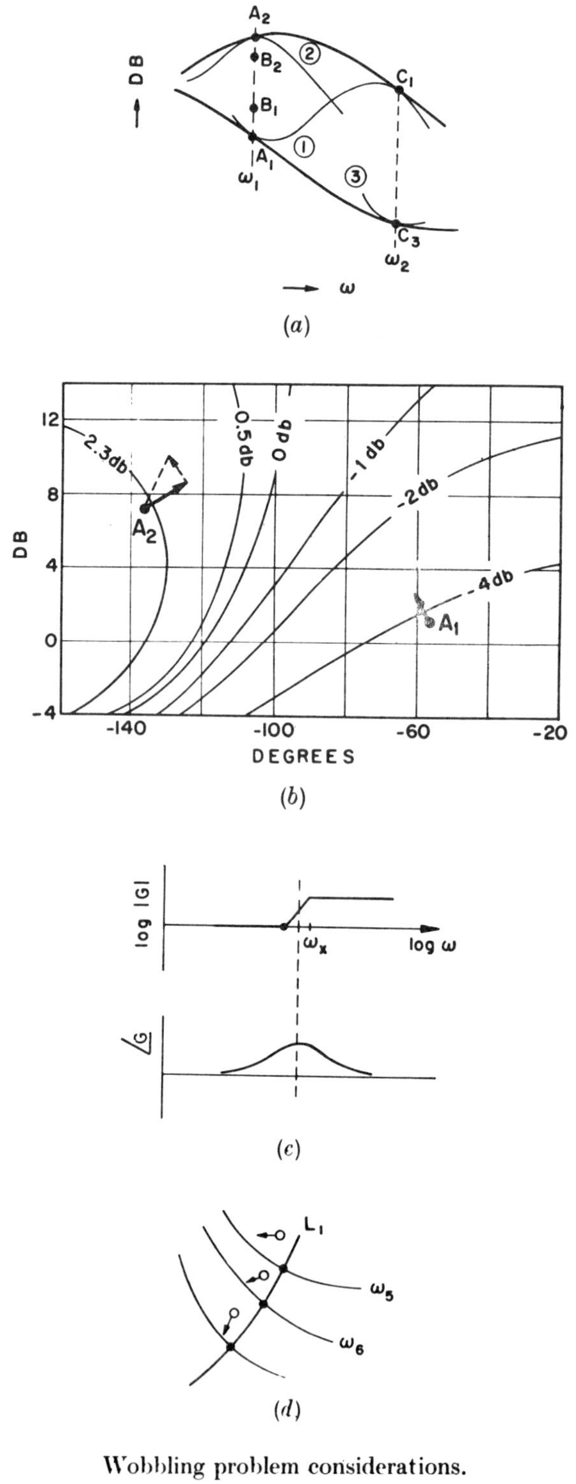

Wobbling problem considerations.

CON. U

wobbling problem in two ways. First, the difference in level between $T_1(j\omega_1)$ and $T_1(j\omega_2)$ is reduced by $(\log B_1 - \log A_1) \triangleq \delta_1$. Second, it is possible to improve matters by modifying the prefilter (F) value at ω_1. Let the new $|F(j\omega_1)|$ be larger than the old, by the amount $\log A_2 - \log B_2 \triangleq \delta_2$. The result is to restore $|T_2(j\omega_1)|$ back to the position A_2, and to increase $|T_1(j\omega_1)|$ precisely by the amount δ_2. Thus, the total improvement is $\delta_1 + \delta_2$. The same two effects occur at ω_2 if a change of L at ω_2 causes a decrease in $|T_1(j\omega_2)|$ and an increase in $|T_3(j\omega_2)|$.

There remain the following questions to be answered. How much of the improvement should be assigned to ω_1 and how much to ω_2? Whatever the amount assigned to either, how is it to be attained, i.e. how should L be changed at that frequency ? At any frequency one can find the net gradient of $|T|$ as follows. Consider fig. 16 (b) whose points A_1, A_2 correspond to the equivalent points in fig. 16 (a). The gradient of $|T|$ is, of course, normal to the contours of constant $|T|$. The solid arrows are drawn in the desired direction in each case, i.e. at A_2 it is desirable to decrease $|T_2|$, while at A_1 it is desirable to increase $|T_1|$. Let the length of the arrows be assumed proportional to the gradient magnitudes. Then the net gradient is the vector sum of the two arrows and gives the optimum direction for decreasing $|T|$ with least change in $|L|$ at that specific frequency. Superficially, it would seem that one could thus find the net gradients at each of ω_1, ω_2 and assign the burden of correction to each, in proportion to their net magnitudes. But the matter is not that simple, because a change in $|L|$ is associated to some extent with a change in arg L and the change cannot be local only. For example, suppose $\Delta L = 2$ dB, arg 30° is desired at $\omega_1 < \omega_2$. This can be achieved by means of a suitable ‘ finite line segment ’ (Bode 1945) properly placed (fig. 16 (c)). The phase lead exists for only a part of the frequency range, while the magnitude change persists for all $\omega > \omega_x$ and its benefits are therefore available for all $\omega > \omega_x$. Hence, if the ω_2 of fig. 16 (a) is not much larger than ω_1, it is certainly worth while maintaining the level of the correction (denoted by G) to ω_2. Also, it is clearly better to use fig. (16 (c) rather than increase the level of $|L|$ by the same amount for all ω, because fig. 16 (c) permits the desired phase lead to be simultaneously obtained, and so obtain a correction lined up with the net gradient calculated for the point ω_1. It is possible to make additional adjustments at ω_2, to try thereby to achieve a correction there, also lined up with the gradient.

The net ‘ loss ’ to the system, in the form of larger $|L|$ at high frequencies, is available from eqn. (4), when $|L(0)|$ is maintained at its former value. It is therefore desirable at higher frequencies, where correction is not necessary, to reduce $|G|$ back to zero dB. If that is possible, then there will be an associated phase lag which will cancel the phase lead in fig. 16 (c), and by eqn. (4) there will then be no net loss. This is impossible to do completely if the original design for L was indeed an optimum design. But it is at least possible to partially do so (see fig. 16 (d)). Let L_1 be the original optimum loop transmission which resulted in the wobbling problem. Let the circles represent the result of the correction which eliminated the wobbling. For simplicity, it is assumed ω_5 is sufficiently large so that the phase of the correction G is back to zero at ω_5, so the circles are vertically above the former points on L_1. A negative ‘ finite line-segment ’, if introduced here, would have the effect indicated by the arrows. It could, at least theoretically, be shaped optimally to reduce the

' loss ' as much as possible. It is certainly better to do this than to allow the correction, i.e. this higher level of $|L|$, to stand as is over this higher frequency range where it is not needed.

5. Application to disturbance attenuation

The same technique may be applied to the problem of disturbance attenuation accompanied by plant parameter ignorance. Consider the three disturbances of fig. 17, one by one,

$$T_{D3} = \frac{C}{D_3} = \frac{1}{1+L}, \quad \text{with} \quad L = GP_1P_2. \tag{6 a, b}$$

Let $l = 1/L$ and then

$$T_{D3} = \frac{C}{D_3} = \frac{l}{1+l}, \quad \ln\left|\frac{C}{D_3}\right| = \ln\left|\frac{l}{1+l}\right|. \tag{7 a, b}$$

The rotation of the Nichols chart by 180° is equivalent to the transformation $L = 1/l$. Hence, the Nichols chart may be so used for T_{D3}. Templates of $P = P_1P_2$ are found in the same manner as before and so are boundaries of $l(j\omega)$ to satisfy given frequency response specifications on T_{D3}, etc.

Fig. 17

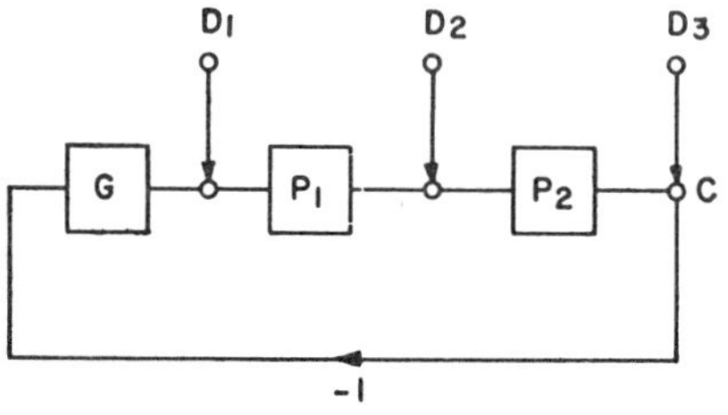

Three kinds of disturbances.

Consider

$$T_{D1} = \frac{C}{D_1} = \frac{P}{1+PG} = \frac{P_0}{(P_0/P)+P_0G} = \frac{P_0}{(P/P)+L_0} \tag{8}$$

where P_0 is any nominal plant transfer function. It may be more convenient to work in the complex plane rather than in the Nichols chart. At any given frequency the range of P_0/P may be found. Suppose it is as shown in fig. 18 (a) at $\omega = \omega_1$. Suppose also that $-L_0(j\omega_1)$ at point A_1 is under consideration. Then

$$T_{D1} = \frac{P_0(j\omega_1)}{AB} \tag{9}$$

where B may range anywhere inside or on $(P_0/P)(j\omega)$. One may then find the boundary of the $-L_0(j\omega_1)$ which satisfies the frequency response specifications on T_{D1}. The balance of the design is straightforward.

U 2

Fig. 18

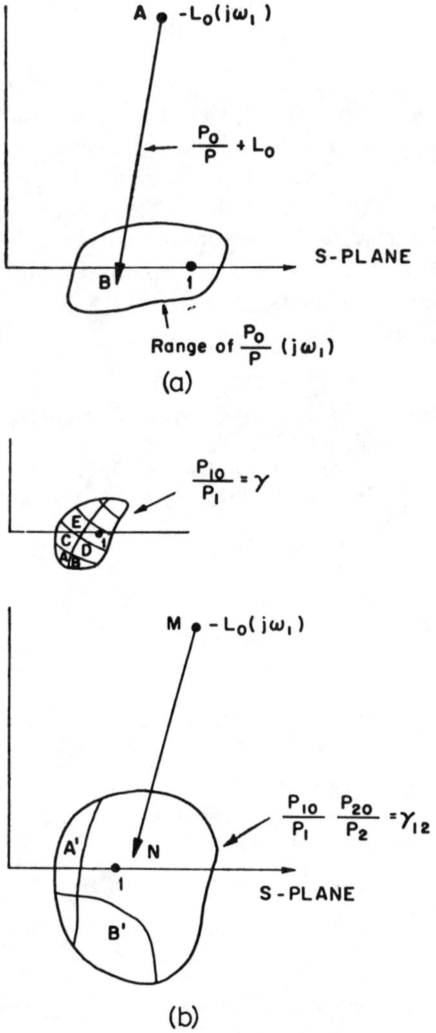

(*a*) Design technique for D_1. (*b*) Design technique for D_2.

Finally, consider

$$T_{D_2}=\frac{C}{D_2}=\frac{P_2}{1+P_1P_2G}=\frac{P_{20}(P_{10}/P_1)}{(P_{10}P_{20}/P_1P_2)+L_0}. \tag{10}$$

The boundaries of

$$\gamma_1 \triangleq \frac{P_{10}}{P_1}, \quad \frac{P_{10}}{P_1}\frac{P_{20}}{P_2} \triangleq \gamma_{12}$$

are obtained and sketched as in fig. 18 (*b*). The region A of γ_1 maps into the larger region A' of γ_{12}, B into B' and parts of A', B' may overlap. This is all at some specific frequency ω_1. From eqn. (10)

$$T_{D_2} = \frac{P_{20}\gamma_1}{MN}.$$

When the region A in γ_1 is considered, then the appropriate range of N, in fig. 18 (*b*), is A', etc. In this way boundaries of acceptable $-L_0(j\omega_1)$ may be obtained and the design continued by the methods of this paper.

Finally, if there are specifications on both the system response to commands, and its response to disturbances, it is possible by the means described to find the resulting boundaries of $L(j\omega)$ for each separately, and then take segments of each, such that both requirements are satisfied.

References

Bode, H. W., 1945, *Network Analysis and Feedback Amplifier Design* (New York : Van Nostrand), pp. 458, 472, 286, 338.

Fleischer, P., 1962, *I.R.E. Trans. autom. Control*, **7,** 2.

Horowitz, I. M., 1963, *Synthesis of Feedback Systems* (New York : Academic Press), pp. 246, 332, 441, 295.

Olson, D. E., and Horowitz, I. M., 1970, *Int. J. Control*, **12,** 545.

A Graphical Test for Checking the Stability of a Linear Time-Invariant Feedback System

FRANK M. CALLIER AND CHARLES A. DESOER

Abstract—A graphical test is developed for checking the condition $\inf_{\text{Re } s \geq 0} |1 + k\hat{g}(s)| > 0$ where k is a nonzero real constant and $\hat{g}$ is the sum of a finite number of right-half plane poles and the Laplace transform of an integrable function plus a series of delayed impulses. As a conseqence, $1 + k\hat{g}$ is, in Re $s \geq 0$, asymptotic to an almost periodic function, say $\hat{f}$, for $|s| \to \infty$. Theorem 1 gives a necessary and sufficient condition involving the curve $\{\hat{f}(j\omega)|\omega \in \mathbf{R}\}$ to ensure that $\inf_{\text{Re } s \geq 0} |\hat{f}(s)| > 0$; Corollary 1 gives a corresponding graphical test. Theorem 2 and Corollary 2 give a necessary and sufficient condition involving the curve $\{1 + k\hat{g}(j\omega)|\omega \in \mathbf{R}\}$ and a graphical test to ensure $\inf_{\text{Re } s \geq 0} |1 + k\hat{g}(s)| > 0$, a condition that guarantees the L^p stability of the feedback system for any $p \in [1, \infty]$.

Introduction

IT IS well known that the classical graphical test for stability [1] of linear time-invariant feedback systems is extremely important for two reasons: 1) it is based on experimental data that are easy to obtain with great accuracy, and 2) in case of instability it gives clear indications of the required design modifications. Recently, Willems [2], [3] developed a graphical test for a scalar linear time-invariant feedback system with constant feedback where the open-loop impulse response $g(t)$ belongs to the convolution algebra $\mathbf{A}$ [4] of integrable functions $\oplus$ impulses, and contains *equally spaced* impulses. This paper generalizes Willems' result in that: 1) the open-loop transfer function $\hat{g}(s)$ is the sum of a term in $\hat{\mathbf{A}}$ (i.e., the algebra of Laplace transforms of elements in $\mathbf{A}$) and a finite number of poles in the closed right-half plane, and 2) it does not require that the impulses of $g(t)$ be equally spaced. As a consequence, the function $s \to \hat{g}(s)$ is asymptotically almost periodic in Re $s \geq 0$ for $|s| \to \infty$, and the most elegant conformal mapping technique of Willems does not work. We have to rely heavily on the theory of almost periodic functions [6]–[8]. Therefore, the paper is organized as follows. In Section I, the problem is defined and the notation is laid out. In Section II, we concentrate on the solution of the problem,

considering only the almost periodic part of the open-loop transfer function. Finally, Section III gives the solution of the problem.

I. Description of the System and Assumptions

We consider a continuous-time scalar linear time-invariant feedback system with input u, error e, and output y. The latter are functions mapping $\mathbf{R}_+$ into $\mathbf{R}$ and satisfy

$$y = g * e \tag{1}$$

$$e = u - ky \tag{2}$$

where $*$ denotes the convolution operation, g is a real-valued distribution with support on $\mathbf{R}_+$, and k is a real nonzero constant.

Let $\hat{g}$ denote the Laplace transform of g. We assume that $\hat{g}$ has the following form:

$$\hat{g}(s) = \hat{g}_r(s) + \sum_{\alpha=1}^{l} \sum_{m=1}^{m_\alpha} r_{\alpha m}/(s - p_\alpha)^m \tag{3}$$

where

the poles p_α are either real with real residues or conjugate complex with complex conjugate residues; (4)

$$\text{Re } p_\alpha \geq 0, \qquad \text{for } \alpha = 1,2,\cdots,l; \tag{5}$$

g_r belongs to the convolution algebra $\mathbf{A}$ [4], i.e.,

$$g_r(t) = 0, \qquad\qquad \text{for } t < 0$$

$$g_r(t) = g_a(t) + \sum_{i=0}^{\infty} g_i \delta(t - t_i), \qquad \text{for } t \geq 0 \tag{6}$$

such that

$g_a(\cdot)$ is a real-valued function belonging to $L^1[0, \infty)$ (7)

$$g_i \in \mathbf{R}, \qquad \text{for } i = 0,1,2,\cdots, \tag{8}$$

$$\sum_{i=0}^{\infty} |g_i| < \infty \tag{9}$$

$$0 = t_0 < t_1 < \cdots < t_i < \cdots. \tag{10}^1$$

Note that g_r belongs to $\mathbf{A}$ if and only if its Laplace transform $\hat{g}_r$ belongs to the algebra $\hat{\mathbf{A}}$ with pointwise product. It is immediate that

Manuscript received January 6, 1972; revised April 28, 1972, and August 4, 1972. Paper recommended by J. C. Willems, Chairman of the IEEE S-CS Stability, Nonlinear, and Distributed Systems Committee. This work was supported in part by the National Aeronautics and Space Administration under Grant NGL-05-003-016 and in part by the Joint Services Electronics Program under Contract F44620-71-C-0087.

F. M. Callier is with the Department of Electrical Engineering and Computer Sciences and the Electronics Research Laboratory, University of California, Berkeley, Calif. 94720, and is also an "Aspirant" with the Belgian National Fund for Scientific Research, Brussels, Belgium.

C. A. Desoer is with the Department of Electrical Engineering and Computer Sciences and the Electronics Research Laboratory, University of California, Berkeley, Calif. 94720.

---

[1] It can be checked that the ordering of the t_i's in (10) can be replaced by $t_i > 0$ for $i = 1,2,\cdots$, both for the needed results from the algebra $\mathbf{A}$ and from the theory of almost periodic functions.

Reprinted from *IEEE Trans. Automat. Contr.*, vol. AC-17, pp. 773–780, Dec. 1972.

$\hat{g}_r(\cdot)$ is analytic in Re $s > 0$, bounded in Re $s \geq 0$ and each function $\omega \mapsto \hat{g}_r(\sigma + j\omega)$ with $s \triangleq \sigma + j\omega$ is uniformly continuous for $\sigma \geq 0$. (11)

It follows, therefore, that

$\hat{g}(\cdot)$ is meromorphic function in Re $s > 0$ [9, p. 217], well defined and continuous almost everywhere in Re $s \geq 0$. (12)

A necessary and sufficient condition that the closed-loop impulse response of the system defined by (1)–(10) is in $\boldsymbol{A}$ (this implies that the closed-loop system is L^p stable for $1 \leq p \leq \infty$) is

$$\inf_{\text{Re } s \geq 0} |1 + k\hat{g}(s)| > 0. \tag{13}$$

The proof follows easily using methods of [11] and [12]. It should be stressed that it has recently been established that, for any convolution feedback system whose closed-loop impulse response is in $\boldsymbol{A}$, $\hat{g}(s)$ can at most have isolated poles in Re $s > 0$ [5], [13].

The problem is to develop a graphical test for (13) based on the curve $\{1 + k\hat{g}(j\omega) | \omega \in \boldsymbol{R}\}$. Let

$$\hat{f}(s) \triangleq 1 + k \sum_{i=0}^{\infty} g_i e^{-st_i} \triangleq \sum_{i=0}^{\infty} f_i e^{-st_i}. \tag{14}$$

Then $\hat{f}(s)$ is a Dirichlet series with Dirichlet exponents $-t_i$ subject to (10) and Dirichlet coefficients f_i such that

$$f_0 = 1 + kg_0; f_i = kg_i, \qquad \text{for } i = 1,2,\cdots \tag{15}$$

where the coefficients g_i satisfy (8)–(9).

First we develop a condition expressed in terms of the curve $\{\hat{f}(j\omega)|\omega \in \boldsymbol{R}\}$, ensuring that $\inf_{\text{Re } s \geq 0} |\hat{f}(s)| > 0$; and then we use this result to develop the condition involving $\{1 + k\hat{g}(j\omega)|\omega \in \boldsymbol{R}\}$ that will ensure (13). Given $s = \sigma + j\omega$, we denote by V_σ the vertical line in $\boldsymbol{C}$ (i.e., the complex plane) with Re $s = \sigma$. Moreover, by $\bar{\hat{f}}(s)$ we mean the complex conjugate of $\hat{f}(s)$. Let

$n_P \triangleq$ the number of poles of $\hat{g}(s)$ counting multiplicities with Re $p_\alpha > 0$. (16)

II. A Necessary and Sufficient Condition Involving $\{\hat{f}(j\omega)|\omega \in \boldsymbol{R}\}$ to Ensure $\inf_{\text{Re } s \geq 0} |\hat{f}(s)| > 0$

Note that $\hat{f}$, defined by (14)–(15), is in $\hat{\boldsymbol{A}}$ as a consequence of (8)–(10) and can be uniformly approximated in Re $s \geq 0$ by a finite number of terms of the series (14). Hence,

$\hat{f}$ is bounded and uniformly continuous in Re $s \geq 0$ and $\hat{f}$ is analytic in Re $s > 0$. (17)

We now state some standard definitions [6], [7] and facts that streamline the proof of Theorem 1.

Given an infinite straight line L, a set $S \subset L$ is said to be *l-relatively dense on* L iff any open interval of length l on L contains at least one point of the set; moreover, a set $S \subset L$ is said to be *relatively dense on* L if, for some length l, S is l-relatively dense on L.

Given a set $D \subset \boldsymbol{R}$ (or $\subset \boldsymbol{C}$) and a complex-valued function h: $D \to \boldsymbol{C}$, an element τ of D is said to be an *ε-translation number of h on D* iff

$$|h(x + \tau) - h(x)| \leq \epsilon, \qquad \text{for all } x \in D.$$

A complex-valued function h of a real variable x is said to be *almost periodic* iff, given any $\epsilon > 0$, there exists a real number $l = l(\epsilon) > 0$ such that the set of ϵ-translation numbers $\tau = \tau(\epsilon)$ of h on $\boldsymbol{R}$ is l-relatively dense on $\boldsymbol{R}$. The number $l(\epsilon)$ is called the *density length*.

Let $-\infty \leq \alpha < \beta \leq \infty$. A complex-valued function h of a complex variable s, analytic in a (vertical) strip (α,β), is said to be *almost periodic in a strip* (α,β) ($[\alpha,\beta]$) iff, given any $\epsilon > 0$, there exists a real number $l = l(\epsilon) > 0$ such that the set of imaginary ϵ-translation numbers $j\tau = j\tau(\epsilon)$ of h on the strip (α,β) ($[\alpha,\beta]$) is l-relatively dense on the imaginary axis.

Note that this last definition requires that the functions $\omega \mapsto h(\sigma + j\omega)$ be almost periodic on *any* V_σ for $\sigma \in (\alpha,\beta)$ ($[\alpha,\beta]$) with an almost periodicity that is independent of σ, for $\sigma \in (\alpha,\beta)$ ($[\alpha,\beta]$).

Fact 1: The function $\hat{f}$ defined by (14)–(15) is almost periodic in the strip $[0,\infty)$.

Proof: As already noted, $\hat{f}$ can be uniformly approximated in the strip $[0,\infty)$ by a finite number of terms of the series (14), i.e., by an exponential polynomial $\hat{f}_N(s) \triangleq \sum_{i=0}^{N} f_i e^{-st_i}$. It is easy to show that the latter is an almost periodic function in the strip $[0,\infty)$ [8, p. 73]. Therefore, $\hat{f}$ is almost periodic in the strip $[0,\infty)$.

Let us now consider the distribution of zeros of $\hat{f}(s)$ in the strip $(0,\infty)$.

Fact 2: If $\hat{f}(s)$, defined by (14)–(15), has a zero $s_0 = \sigma_0 + j\omega_0$ in the strip $(0,\infty)$, then $\hat{f}(s)$ has infinitely many zeros in any strip (α,β) (with $0 < \alpha < \beta < \infty$) containing s_0, and their imaginary parts are relatively dense on the imaginary axis.

Proof: Without loss of generality, we assume that $\hat{f}(s)$ is not identically zero in Re $s \geq 0$. Since $\hat{f}(s)$ is analytic in Re $s > 0$, its zeros are isolated in Re $s > 0$; therefore, we can choose $0 < r < \sigma_0$ such that $|\hat{f}(s)| \geq m > 0$ on $|s - s_0| = r$. By Fact 1, for any $0 < \epsilon < m$ there exists a set of ϵ-translation numbers $j\tau = j\tau(\epsilon)$ of $\hat{f}$ on the strip $[0,\infty)$ that is $l(\epsilon)$-relatively dense on the imaginary axis. Hence, by $\hat{f}(s + j\tau) = \hat{f}(s + j\tau) - \hat{f}(s) + \hat{f}(s)$, it follows from (17) and Rouche's theorem (see [9, theorem 9.2.3, p. 254]) that $\hat{f}(s)$ has a zero in any disk $|s - (s_0 + j\tau)| < r$, which proves Fact 2. Q.E.D.

Definition of the Argument $\phi(s)$ of $\hat{f}(s)$

By definition,

$$\phi(s) = \arg \hat{f}(s) = \text{Im} \log \hat{f}(s), \qquad \text{in Re } s \geq 0 \tag{18}$$

with two additional conventions.

(A.1) Let L denote an oriented straight line in Re $s \geq 0$. By convention, we take $\phi(s)$, $s \in L$ as the right argument of $\hat{f}(s)$ on L, i.e., $\phi(s)$, $s \in L$ is an arbitrary branch of the argument, which is continuous except at the zeros of $\hat{f}(s)$ on L, while it is discontinuous with a jump of $+m\pi$, when s goes through a zero of $\hat{f}(s)$ of order m in the positive direction of L. At any discontinuity point we assign to ϕ the mean value of its one-sided limits. The function $\phi(s)$, $s \in L$ is then well defined (mod 2π) because of (17).

(A.2) Because $\hat{f}(j0)$ is real and because it will later be assumed to be nonzero, we pick for $\omega \mapsto \phi(j\omega)$, $\omega \in \boldsymbol{R}$ that branch of the argument such that $\phi(j0) = 0$ (or π), according to whether $f(j0)$ is positive (or negative, respectively).

Remarks

(R.1) It is important to observe that, by convention (A.1) and (17), the principle of the argument may be applied to $\hat{f}(s)$ on any rectangle in Re $s \geq 0$ that is oriented in clockwise sense and that has no zeros of $\hat{f}(s)$ on its corners.

(R.2) Because of (17) and (18), for any strip (α,β) in Re $s \geq 0$ such that $0 \leq \alpha < \beta \leq \infty$ and $\inf_{\beta \geq \text{Re}\, s \geq \alpha} |\hat{f}(s)| > 0$, $\phi(s)$ is well defined (mod 2π) and uniformly continuous in the strip $[\alpha,\beta]$ and analytic in the strip (α,β).

Since, by Fact 1, $\omega \mapsto \hat{f}(j\omega)$ is almost periodic, we have Fact 3.

Fact 3 [7]: Let $\hat{f}$ be defined by (14)–(15). If

$$\inf_{\omega \in \boldsymbol{R}} |\hat{f}(j\omega)| \triangleq K > 0, \tag{19}$$

then:

(a) $\omega \mapsto \phi(j\omega)$ is well defined on $\boldsymbol{R}$ and is of the form

$$\phi(j\omega) = \lambda\omega + h(j\omega) \tag{20}$$

where λ is a constant and $\omega \mapsto h(j\omega)$ is almost periodic; the constant λ will be called "the mean angular velocity of $\hat{f}(j\omega)$" (in the literature, the term "mean motion of $\hat{f}(j\omega)$" is used; however, this is borrowed from celestial mechanics. Note that $\lambda = \lim_{\omega\to\infty} [(\phi(j\omega) - \phi(-j\omega))/2\omega]$);

(b) if N is the least nonnegative integer such that

$$\sum_{N+1}^{\infty} |f_i| \leq K \sin(\delta/2), \qquad \text{for some } 0 < \delta < \pi, \tag{21}$$

then the mean angular velocity λ of $\hat{f}(j\omega)$ may be written in both the forms

$$\lambda = -h_0t_0 - h_1t_1 - \cdots - h_Nt_N \tag{22}$$

where the coefficients $h_0,h_1,\cdots,h_N$ are integers with sum 1 and

$$\lambda = -r_0t_0 - r_1t_1 - \cdots - r_Nt_N \tag{23}$$

where the coefficients $r_0,r_1,\cdots,r_N$ are nonnegative rationals with sum 1;

(c) with

$$\epsilon \leq K \sin(\delta/2), \qquad \delta < \pi \tag{24}$$

any ϵ-translation number $\tau(\epsilon)$ of $\omega \mapsto f(j\omega)$ satisfies

$$|\phi(j\omega + j\tau) - \phi(j\omega) - c_\tau 2\pi| \leq \delta, \qquad \text{for all } \omega \in \boldsymbol{R} \tag{25}$$

$$|\lambda\tau - c_\tau 2\pi| \leq \delta \tag{26}$$

where c_τ is an integer depending on τ;

(d) the function $\omega \to \phi(j\omega)$ is almost periodic if and only if the mean angular velocity λ of $\hat{f}(j\omega)$ is zero, or equivalently, if and only if there exists an increasing sequence $\{\omega_n\}_{n=-\infty}^{+\infty}$ satisfying

$$\cdots < \omega_{-n} < \cdots < \omega_{-1} < \omega_0 = 0 < \omega_1 < \cdots < \omega_n < \cdots \tag{27}$$

$$\omega_{-n} = -\omega_n, \qquad \text{for } n = 0,1,2,\cdots \tag{28}$$

$$\lim_{n\to\infty} \omega_n = \infty \tag{29}$$

such that

$$\phi(j\omega_n) = \phi(j0), \qquad \text{for } n = \cdots,-2,-1,0,1,2,\cdots. \tag{30}$$

Proof: Part (a) is a straightforward transcription of [7, p. 167, theorem 1]. Part (b): (21) implies that the mean angular velocities of $\hat{f}(j\omega)$ and $\hat{f}_N(j\omega) \triangleq \sum_{i=0}^{N} f_i e^{-j\omega t_i}$ are the same; for the latter exponential polynomial (22) and (23) are valid (see [7, pp. 170–176]). Part (c) follows from [7, pp. 168–170]. The first statement of part (d) is obvious from Part (a). The second statement is established as follows.

$\Rightarrow$) Since

$$\hat{f}(-j\omega) = \bar{\hat{f}}(j\omega), \qquad \text{for all } \omega \in \boldsymbol{R} \tag{31}$$

$$\phi(j\omega) - \phi(j0) = \phi(j0) - \phi(-j\omega), \qquad \text{for all } \omega \in \boldsymbol{R}. \tag{32}$$

So, unless $\phi(j\omega) \equiv \phi(j0)$, then for some $\omega' > 0$ either

$$\phi(j\omega') > \phi(j0) > \phi(-j\omega')$$

or

$$\phi(j\omega') < \phi(j0) < \phi(-j\omega').$$

Then (27)–(30) follow by the continuity and almost periodicity of $\phi(j\omega)$ on $\boldsymbol{R}$ and by (32).

$\Leftarrow$ The existence of the sequence $\{\omega_n\}_{n=-\infty}^{\infty}$ implies that $\phi(j\omega)$ is bounded on $\boldsymbol{R}$; hence, the mean angular velocity of $\hat{f}(j\omega)$ is zero, and thus, by (20), $\omega \mapsto \phi(j\omega)$ is almost periodic. Q.E.D.

Before we give Theorem 1, we give a last interesting result.

Fact 4: Let $\hat{f}$ be defined by (14)–(15). If

$$\inf_{\omega \in \boldsymbol{R}} |\hat{f}(j\omega)| \triangleq K > 0 \tag{19}$$

then, given any $\sigma > 0$, there exists a positive-real number C_σ depending on σ such that

$$|\phi(\sigma + j\omega) - \phi(j\omega)| < C_\sigma \text{ uniformly in } \omega.$$

Proof: Because of (19) and (17) there exists a $\sigma^* > 0$, $\sigma^* < \sigma$ such that $\inf_{\sigma^* \geq \text{Re}\, s \geq 0} |\hat{f}(s)| > 0$. So, by remark

(R.2) and convention (A.2), $\phi(s)$ is well defined and uniformly continuous in the strip $[0,\sigma^*]$ such that there exists a positive constant C_{σ^*} depending on σ^* for which

$$|\phi(\sigma^* + j\omega) - \phi(j\omega)| < C_{\sigma^*} \text{ uniformly in } \omega.$$

Observing that $[\sigma^*,\sigma]$ is a closed substrip of the strip $[0,\infty)$, in which $\hat{f}(s)$ is almost periodic by Fact 1, it follows that there exists a positive constant $C_{\sigma-\sigma^*}$ depending on $\sigma - \sigma^*$ such that

$$|\phi(\sigma + j\omega) - \phi(\sigma^* + j\omega)| < C_{\sigma-*_\sigma} \text{ uniformly in } \omega$$

[7, pp. 178–179, theorem 3(iv)]. Combining the two results, we obtain that with $C_\sigma = C_{\sigma^*} + C_{\sigma-\sigma^*}$ the fact is true. Q.E.D.

Theorem 1: Let $\hat{f}(s)$ be the Dirichlet series defined by (14)–(15). Under these conditions,

$$\inf_{\text{Re } s\geq 0} |\hat{f}(s)| > 0 \tag{33}$$

if and only if

$$\text{i) } f_0 = 1 + kg_0 \neq 0 \tag{34}$$

$$\text{ii) } \inf_{\omega \in R} |(\hat{f}j\omega) \triangleq K > 0 \tag{19}$$

iii) the mean angular velocity λ of $\hat{f}(j\omega)$ is zero. (35)

Proof: $\Leftarrow$ Observe that, because of (14)–(15), (17), and (34),

$$\lim_{\sigma\to\infty} \hat{f}(\sigma + j\omega) = f_0 \neq 0 \text{ uniformly in } \omega. \tag{36}$$

Thus there exists a $\tilde{\sigma} > 0$ such that

$$\inf_{\text{Re } s\geq\tilde{\sigma}} |\hat{f}(s)| > 0. \tag{37}$$

So, by remark (R.2), $\phi(s)$ is well defined (mod 2π) and uniformly continuous in the strip $[\tilde{\sigma},\infty)$. Hence, (36) implies, for any branch of $\phi(s)$,

$$\lim_{\sigma\to\infty} \phi(\sigma + j\omega) = \phi_\infty, \qquad \text{uniformly in } \omega \tag{38}$$

where $\phi_\infty = \arg f_0$ (mod 2π). Moreover, we can pick a $\sigma_1 > 0$ so large that

$$\sigma_1 \geq \tilde{\sigma} \tag{39}$$

and

$$|\phi(\sigma_1 + j\omega) - \phi_\infty| < 1, \qquad \text{uniformly in } \omega. \tag{40}$$

Finally, observe that

$$\hat{f}(s) \neq 0 \text{ in } \sigma_1 > \text{Re } s > 0 \Longrightarrow \inf_{\sigma_1 > \text{Re } s > 0} |\hat{f}(s)| > 0. \tag{41}$$

This can be proved using contradiction and [8, p. 71, theorem 3.6]. Therefore, in view of (19), (39), (37), and (41), we will have established (33) if we show that $\hat{f}(s) \neq 0$ in the strip $(0,\sigma_1)$. By contraposition of Fact 2, $\hat{f}(s) \neq 0$ in the strip $(0,\sigma_1)$ if we show that N, the number of zeros of $\hat{f}(s)$ in the strip $(0,\sigma_1)$, is bounded. Consider, therefore, a sequence of rectangles $\{R_n\}_{n=1}^{\infty}$ defined by $R_n \triangleq [0,\sigma_1] \times [-n,n]$ for $n = 0,1,2,\cdots$ and let the corresponding number of zeros of $\hat{f}(s)$ inside R_n be N_n for $n = 1,2,\cdots$. Observe that, because of (19), (37), and remark (R.1), the principle of the argument may be applied to each of these rectangles oriented in the clockwise sense. We show now that the sequence $\{\Delta\phi_n\}_{n=1}^{\infty}$ (where $\Delta\phi_n$ is the net increase in argument around the rectangle R_n) is bounded. This follows easily if one observes

a) that, by (19) and (35) and fact 3(d), $\omega \mapsto \phi(j\omega)$ is almost periodic, and hence bounded.

b) that, by (19) and Fact 4,

$$|\phi(\sigma_1 + j\omega) - \phi(j\omega)| < C_{\sigma_1}, \qquad \text{uniformly in } \omega.$$

c) that, by (40), any branch of $\omega \mapsto \phi(\sigma_1 + j\omega)$ is bounded. In view of this, it follows then that there exists a positive constant C such that

$$N = \lim_{n\to\infty} N_n = \lim_{n\to\infty} |\Delta\phi_n| < C. \tag{42}$$

$\Longrightarrow$ First, observe that the first equality of (36) still holds, so (33) implies (34). Next, (33) implies (19); hence, by Fact 3(a), $\omega \mapsto \phi(j\omega)$ is well defined and satisfies (20). Furthermore, by (33) and (17) and convention (A.2), $s \mapsto \phi(s)$ is well defined and uniformly continuous in Re $s \geq 0$. Hence, again (36) implies (38), and again we can pick a $\sigma_1 > 0$ such that (39) and (40) are true.

We claim now that $\omega \mapsto \phi(j\omega)$ is almost periodic. For this purpose, in view of (20), it is sufficient to show that $\phi(jn)$ for $n = 0,1,2,\cdots$ remains bounded as $n \to \infty$. Consider, therefore, the sequence of rectangles $\{R_n'\}_{n=1}^{\infty}$ defined by $R_n' \triangleq [0,\sigma_1] \times [0,n]$, $n = 1,2,\cdots$. By (33) and (17), it follows that the principle of the argument can be applied to each of these rectangles; hence, the net change in ϕ around each R_n' is zero for $n = 1,2,\cdots$. Now, by the uniform continuity of $s \mapsto \phi(s)$ in Re $s \geq 0$, there exists a constant C *independent of* n such that for any horizontal segment $H_n' \triangleq \{s = \sigma + jn: 0 \leq \sigma \leq \sigma_1\}$ for $n = 0,1,2,\cdots$: $|\phi(\sigma_1 + jn) - \phi(jn)| < C$. This fact, with (39), implies that the sequence $\{\phi(jn) - \phi(j)0\}_{n=0}^{n=\infty}$ is bounded. Hence, because $\phi(j0)$ is 0 or π by (A.2), the sequence $\{\phi(jn)\}_{n=0}^{\infty}$ is also bounded. So our claim is true, and by Fact 3(d) the mean angular velocity of $\hat{f}(j\omega)$ is zero, which implies (35). Q.E.D.

It is interesting to observe that under the conditions of Theorem 1 sgn $\hat{f}(j0)$ = sgn f_0 = sgn $(1 + kg_0)$. Hence, if $1 + kg_0 > 0$ (respectively, <0), then $\phi(j0) = 0$ (respectively, π).

Now we want to develop a graphical test involving $\{\hat{f}(j\omega)|\omega \in \mathbf{R}\}$ to ensure $\inf_{\text{Re } s\geq 0} |\hat{f}(s)| > 0$. Here, again, it will be the almost periodicity of $\omega \mapsto \hat{f}(j\omega)$ that will save us. We start giving some definitions and two facts.

Let $l(\epsilon)$ be the density length for the ϵ-translation numbers of $\omega \mapsto \hat{f}(j\omega)$. It is known that ϵ-translation numbers of $\hat{f}(j\omega)$ can be determined by diophantine analysis (see, e.g., [8, pp. 146–149]). From their pattern, a density length $l(\epsilon)$ can be determined.

Consider now (see Fig. 1) the path $\gamma(\epsilon)$ defined by

$$\gamma(\epsilon) \triangleq \{\hat{f}(j\omega)|\omega \in [0,l(\epsilon)]\} \tag{43}$$

and its closed ϵ-neighborhood $N(\epsilon)$ defined by

$$N(\epsilon) \triangleq \{x \in \mathbf{C}|\ |x - \hat{f}(j\omega)| \leq \epsilon;\ \omega \in [0,l(\epsilon)]\}. \tag{44}$$

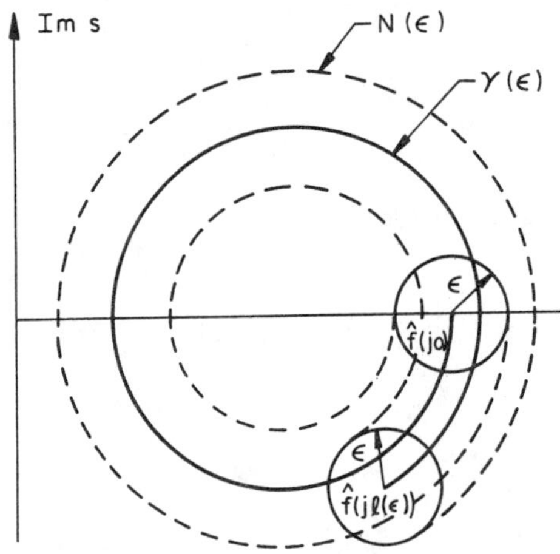

Fig. 1. The path $\gamma(\epsilon)$ and neighborhood $N(\epsilon)$.

Now we prove Fact 5, which allows us by the simple knowledge of the path $\gamma(\epsilon) = \{\hat{f}(j\omega)|\omega \in [0,l(\epsilon)]\}$ to locate the *closure* of the set $\{\hat{f}(j\omega)|\omega \in \boldsymbol{R}\}$, and Fact 6, which informs us about the minimal value of λ if it is nonzero.

Fact 5: Let $\hat{f}(j\omega)$ be given by (14)–(15) (setting $s = j\omega$). Consider the path $\gamma(\epsilon)$ and neighborhood $N(\epsilon)$ given by (43) and (44), respectively. Under these conditions

(a) for any $\epsilon > 0$, $N(\epsilon)$ contains the closure of the set $\{\hat{f}(j\omega)|\omega \in \boldsymbol{R}\}$;

(b) as $\epsilon \downarrow 0$, then $N(\epsilon)$ tends toward the closure of the set $\{\hat{f}(j\omega)|\omega \in \boldsymbol{R}\}$.

This fact follows by the almost periodicity of $\hat{f}(j\omega)$.

Fact 6: Let $\hat{f}(j\omega)$ be given by (14)–(15) (setting $s = j\omega$). Assume that

$$\inf_{\omega\in\boldsymbol{R}} |\hat{f}(j\omega)| \triangleq K > 0. \tag{19}$$

Under these conditions: (a) The set X, suggested by conditions (21)–(23) of Fact 3(b), is well defined. For convenience, we note that

$$X \triangleq \Big\{x = -\sum_{i=0}^{N} h_i t_i = -\sum_{i=0}^{N} r_i t_i;\ h_i \text{ are integers with } \sum_{i=0}^{N} h_i = 1;\ r_i \text{ are nonnegative rationals with } \sum_{i=0}^{N} r_i = 1;\ N \text{ is the least nonnegative integer such that } \sum_{n+1}^{\infty} |f_i| \le K \sin(\delta/2) \text{ some } 0 < \delta < \pi\Big\} \tag{45}$$

where $-t_i$ and f_i are the Dirichlet exponents and coefficients of $\hat{f}(s)$. (b) The set X has a finite number of nonzero elements and, if $N \geq 1$,[2] then the positive number $\lambda_{\min}$ given by

$$\lambda_{\min} \triangleq \min_{\substack{x\in X\\ x\neq 0}} |x| \tag{46}$$

is well defined. (c) If the mean angular velocity λ of $\hat{f}(j\omega)$ satisfies $|\lambda| < \lambda_{\min}$, then $\lambda = 0$.

Proof: (a) is an immediate consequence of (19). (b) is a consequence of the fact that the set $\{-t_i\}_{i=0}^{N}$ admits a *finite integral base*, i.e., a set of real numbers $\{\beta_j\}_{j=1}^{M}$ such that i) there exist no integers h_j, $j = 1,\cdots,M$, not all zero, such that $\sum_{j=1}^{N} h_j\beta_j = 0$ and ii) each number $-t_i$ can be expressed in a unique manner in the form $-t_i = \sum_{j=1}^{M} h_j^{(i)}\beta_j$ for $i = 0,1,\cdots,N$, where $h_j^{(i)}$ are integers (see [7, p. 146], [6, pp. 82–83]). Equivalently, the $N + 1$ numbers $-t_i$ can be represented by lattice points (i.e., with integer coordinates) in $\boldsymbol{R}^M$-space; indeed each point $-t_i$ may be represented by the M-vector $(h_1^{(i)},h_2^{(i)},\cdots,h_M^{(i)})$ with integer coordinates. Now (45) merely expresses the fact that the numbers x can be represented as a subset of lattice points in $\boldsymbol{R}^M$ that are in the closure of the convex hull of the $N + 1$ lattice points $h^{(i)}$, $i = 0,1,\cdots,N$, in $\boldsymbol{R}^M$. Hence, the set X is finite. The set $X - \{0\}$ is nonempty since $0 > -t_i \in X$ for $i = 1,2,\cdots,N$. Therefore, (b) follows. Concerning (c), observe that, because of Fact 3(b), the mean angular velocity λ of $\hat{f}(j\omega)$ belongs to X and also that 0 belongs to X; hence, (c) is a direct consequence of (b). Q.E.D.

As a final remark, observe that, because the ϵ-translation numbers are relatively dense on $\boldsymbol{R}$, it follows that, as soon as (19) is satisfied, we can pick a translation number $\tau(\epsilon)$ such that

$$\frac{\pi}{\tau(\epsilon)} \leq \lambda_{\min}. \tag{47}$$

We are now ready for a graphical test ensuring $\inf_{\mathrm{Re}\, s\geq 0} |\hat{f}(s)| > 0$.

Corollary 1: Let $\hat{f}(s)$ be the Dirichlet series defined by (14)–(15), and (8)–(10). Let $\gamma(\epsilon)$ and $N(\epsilon)$ be given by (43) and (44). Under these conditions,

$$\inf_{\mathrm{Re}\, s\geq 0} |\hat{f}(s)| > 0 \tag{33}$$

if and only if

$$\text{i) } f_0 = 1 + kg_0 \neq 0 \tag{34}$$

ii) the origin 0 of the complex plane is positioned with respect to $\{\hat{f}(j\omega)|\omega \in \boldsymbol{R}\}$ such that

a) there exists an $\epsilon > 0$ such that 0 does not belong to $N(\epsilon)$ (48)

b) for an $\epsilon > 0$, with $0 < \epsilon < K \triangleq \inf_{\omega\in\boldsymbol{R}} |\hat{f}(j\omega)|$, for which the corresponding ϵ-translation number $\tau(\epsilon)$ satisfies (47), where $\lambda_{\min}$ is defined by (45)–(46), $|\phi(j\tau) - \phi(j0)| < \pi$ must hold. (49)

Proof: Because of Theorem 1, we need only to show that (48) and (49) are equivalent to (19) and (35). Clearly, by Fact 5, (48) $\Longleftrightarrow$ (19). So we are left to prove the equivalence of (49) and (35) under the assumption of (19).

$\Longrightarrow$ We assume that (49) is true. Then $\epsilon < K$ implies $\epsilon \leq K \sin(\delta/2)$ with $\delta < \pi$. So, immediately by Fact 3(c), $|\phi(j\tau) - \phi(j0) - c_\tau \cdot 2\pi| \leq \delta < \pi$. Thus, by (49),

[2] The case $N = 0$ is immediate since then $\lambda = 0$ by Fact 3(b). For this reason, we assume $N \geq 1$ in the sequel.

$c_\tau = 0$, and hence by (26), $|\lambda\tau| \leq \delta$ or $|\lambda| \leq (\delta/\tau) < (\pi/\tau)$. So, by (47), $|\lambda| < \lambda_{\min}$, which by Fact 6(c) implies $\lambda = 0$. Q.E.D.

$\Leftarrow$ We assume that (35) is true. Let $0 < \epsilon < K$, i.e., $\epsilon \leq K \sin(\delta/2)$, $\delta < \pi$, and let $\tau(\epsilon)$ satisfy (47); then, immediately from Fact 3(c), $|c_\tau 2\pi| \leq \delta < \pi$, i.e., $c_\tau = 0$. Hence, from (25), $|\phi(j\tau) - \phi(j0)| \leq \delta < \pi$. Q.E.D.

Remarks

(R.3) It is important to observe that the knowledge of the density length $l(\epsilon)$ allows us to locate the closure of the set $\{\hat{f}(j\omega)|\omega \in \boldsymbol{R}\}$ and that the knowledge of a translation number $\tau(\epsilon)$ allows us to replace the condition $\lambda = 0$ by a condition on the increase in argument.

(R.4) If $\omega \mapsto \hat{f}(j\omega)$ is periodic with period ω_0, two important simplifications occur, i.e.,

a) $\{\hat{f}(j\omega); \omega \in \boldsymbol{R}\} = \{\hat{f}(j\omega); \omega \in [0,\omega_0]\}$.

b) if (19) is satisfied, then $\phi(j\omega) = \lambda\omega + h(j\omega)$ where $\omega \mapsto h(j\omega)$ is periodic with period ω_0.

Hence, $\lambda = 0 \Leftrightarrow \phi(j\omega_0) = \phi(j0)$, and hence, for the case that $\omega \mapsto \hat{f}(j\omega)$ is periodic with period ω_0, part ii) of Corollary 1 can be replaced by: the origin 0 of the complex plane is positioned with respect to $\{\hat{f}(j\omega)|\omega \in \boldsymbol{R}\}$ such that

a) 0 does not belong to $\{\hat{f}(j\omega); \omega \in [0,\omega_0]\}$

b) $\phi(j\omega_0) = \phi(j0)$.

III. A Necessary and Sufficient Condition on $\{1 + k\hat{g}(j\omega)|\omega \in \boldsymbol{R}\}$ to Ensure $\inf_{\operatorname{Re} s \geq 0} |1 + k\hat{g}(s)| > 0$

Definition of the Argument $\theta(s)$ of $1 + k\hat{g}(s)$ Subject to (3)–(10)

By definition,

$$\theta(s) = \arg [1 + k\hat{g}(s)] = \operatorname{Im} \log [1 + k\hat{g}(s)], \quad \text{in } \operatorname{Re} s \geq 0 \tag{50}$$

with two additional conventions:

(B.1) Let L denote a straight oriented line in $\operatorname{Re} s \geq 0$. By convention, we take $\theta(s)$, $s \in L$ as the right argument of $1 + k\hat{g}(s)$ on L, i.e., $\theta(s)$, $s \in L$ is an arbitrary branch of the argument, which is continuous except at the zeros and *poles* of $1 + kg(s)$ on L, while it is discontinuous with a jump of $+m\pi$, $(-m_\alpha\pi)$, when s passes, in the positive direction on L a zero (pole) of $1 + k\hat{g}(s)$ of order m, (m_α). At a discontinuity point we assign to θ the mean value of its one-sided limits. The function $\theta(s)$, $s \in L$ is then well defined (mod 2π) because of (12).

(B.2) Because $1 + k\hat{g}(s)$ is real for $s = \sigma \geq 0$ and meromorphic in $\operatorname{Re} s > 0$, there exists an interval $(0,\bar{\sigma})$ on which $1 + kg(\sigma)$ is real finite and different from zero. We pick for $\omega \mapsto \theta(j\omega)$ the branch of the argument such that $\theta(j0) \triangleq 0$ (or π) accordingly as $1 + k\hat{g}(\sigma)$ is positive (or negative) on $(0,\bar{\sigma})$.

Theorem 2: Given the system defined by (1)–(10), let $\hat{f}(s)$ be the Dirichlet series given by (14) and (15) and let n_P be given by (16). Under these conditions,

$$\inf_{\operatorname{Re} s \geq 0} |1 + k\hat{g}(s)| > 0 \tag{13}$$

if and only if

$$\text{i) } 1 + kg_0 \neq 0 \tag{34}$$

$$\text{ii) } \inf_{\omega \in \boldsymbol{R}} |1 + k\hat{g}(j\omega)| > 0 \tag{51}$$

iii) the mean angular velocity λ of

$$\omega \mapsto \hat{f}(j\omega) \text{ is zero} \tag{35}$$

$$\text{iv) } \lim_{\omega \to \infty} [\theta(j\omega) - \phi(j\omega)] = \theta(j0) - \phi(j0) + n_P\pi = b2\pi \tag{52}$$

where b is an integer.

Proof:

(a) Let us first study the asymptotic behavior of $1 + k\hat{g}(s)$. In view of (7), the Riemann–Lebesgue lemma implies $\hat{g}_a(s) \to 0$ as $|s| \to \infty$ in $\operatorname{Re} s \geq 0$; hence, by (3), (6), (14), and (15),

$$1 + k\hat{g}(s) \to \hat{f}(s) \text{ as } |s| \to \infty \text{ in } \operatorname{Re} s \geq 0. \tag{53}$$

An important conclusion is that, because of (53) and Fact 1, $\omega \mapsto 1 + k\hat{g}(j\omega)$ has an asymptotic almost-periodic behavior on $\boldsymbol{R}$ and $s \mapsto 1 + k\hat{g}(s)$ has an asymptotic almost-periodic behavior in $\operatorname{Re} s \geq 0$ (for $|s| \to \infty$).

(b) $\Leftarrow$. We first show that

$$\inf_{\operatorname{Re} s \geq 0} |(\hat{f}s)| > 0. \tag{33}$$

Indeed (51) and (53) imply $\lim \inf |\hat{f}(j\omega)| > 0$ as $|\omega| \to \infty$. Hence, since $\omega \mapsto \hat{f}(j\omega)$ is almost periodic on V_0 by Fact 1,

$$\inf_{\omega \in \boldsymbol{R}} |\hat{f}(j\omega)| \triangleq K > 0. \tag{19}$$

So by (34), (19), and (35), it follows that (33) is true by Theorem 1.

Observe that, by Fact 3(d), (19) and (35) are equivalent to the existence of a sequence $\{\omega_n\}_{n=-\infty}^{\infty}$ satisfying (27)–(30). Now choose ω_n with positive index from this sequence and a $\bar{\sigma} > 0$, both sufficiently large so that:

(a) the open rectangle $ABCD \triangleq (0,\bar{\sigma}) \times (-\omega_n,\omega_n)$ (Fig. 2), i) has all poles of $1 + k\hat{g}$ with $\operatorname{Re} p_\alpha > 0$ in the interior of $ABCD$, ii) has all poles of $1 + k\hat{g}$ with $\operatorname{Re} p_\alpha = 0$ on AB, iii) neither A nor B is the location of a pole of $1 + k\hat{g}$.

(b) in the complement of this rectangle with respect to $\{s|\operatorname{Re} s > 0\}$, $1 + k\hat{g}(s)$ is sufficiently close to $\hat{f}(s)$ such that $1 + k\hat{g}(s)$ is bounded away from zero by (53) and (33) in this complement. The principle of the argument can be applied to $ABCD$. Denote by $\Delta\theta_{AB}$ the net change in the argument on the oriented segment AB. By the principle of the argument along with (16), it follows that

$$\Delta\theta_{ABCDA} = (n_P - n_Z)2\pi \tag{54}$$

where n_Z is the number of zeros of $1 + k\hat{g}(s)$ inside $ABCD$. Remember that $\hat{f}(s)$ is analytic inside $ABCD$, continuous on the boundary $ABCDA$, and, by (33), bounded away from zero in $\operatorname{Re} s \geq 0$; hence, again by the principle of the argument,

$$\Delta\phi_{ABCDA} = 0. \tag{55}$$

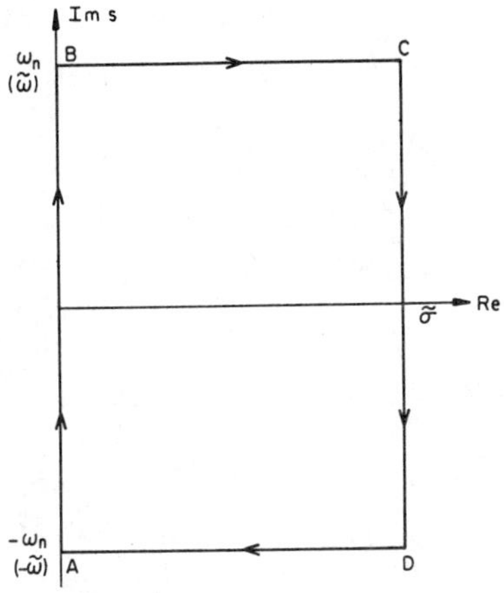

Fig. 2. The rectangle $ABCD$.

Moreover, since ω_n and $\tilde{\sigma}$ have been chosen sufficiently large, it follows from (53) that

$$\Delta\phi_{BCDA} \simeq \Delta\theta_{BCDA} \tag{56}$$

where $\simeq$ indicates that equality is reached as $\omega_n \to \infty$ and $\tilde{\sigma} \to \infty$. From conditions (28), (30), (52), the fact that $\theta(j\omega) - \theta(j0) = \theta(j0) - \theta(-j\omega)$ because $1 + k\hat{g}(j\omega) = \overline{1 + k\hat{g}(-j\omega)}$ and (51),

$$\Delta\phi_{AB} = 0 \tag{57}$$

$$\Delta\theta_{AB} \simeq n_P 2\pi. \tag{58}$$

Hence, (55)–(57) imply $\Delta\phi_{BCDA} \simeq \Delta\theta_{BCDA} \simeq 0$, which, along with (58) and (54), implies $n_Z = 0$. Thus, for sufficiently large ω_n and $\tilde{\sigma}$, $1 + k\hat{g}(s)$ has no zeros in $ABCD$. Furthermore, by construction, $1 + k\hat{g}(s)$ is bounded away from zero in the complement of $ABCD$ with respect to $\{s|\text{Re } s > 0\}$, and by (51), $1 + k\hat{g}(s)$ is bounded away from zero in the complement of $ABCD$ with respect to $\{s|\text{Re } s \geq 0\}$. Hence, (13) follows.

(c) $\Longrightarrow$. Immediately, (13) implies (51). Thus, because of (13) and (53), we can pick an $\omega = \tilde{\omega}$ and a $\sigma = \tilde{\sigma}$ so large that the rectangle $ABCD = (0,\tilde{\sigma}) \times (-\tilde{\omega},\tilde{\omega})$ (see Fig. 2) is such that $\hat{f}(s)$ is bounded away from zero in the complement of $ABCD$ with respect to $\{s|\text{Re } s \geq 0\}$ except on AB. Since, by Fact 1: $\omega \mapsto \hat{f}(\sigma + j\omega)$ is almost periodic on any line V_σ, $\sigma \in [0,\infty)$, it follows then that $\hat{f}(s)$ is bounded away from zero on all these V_σ. Hence,

$$\inf_{\text{Re } s \geq 0} |\hat{f}(s)| > 0, \tag{33}$$

which, by Theorem 1, implies (34), (19), and (35). Hence, because of Fact 3(d), there exists a sequence $\{\omega_n\}_{n=-\infty}^{\infty}$ such that (27)–(30) hold. We show now that (52) holds.

From now on, pick the parameters of $ABCD$ so that $\tilde{\omega}$ is an element of the above sequence with positive index and so that $\tilde{\omega}$ and $\tilde{\sigma}$ are so large that (53) holds; finally, all poles of $1 + k\hat{g}(s)$ with Re $p_\alpha > 0$ should be inside $ABCDA$ and all poles of $1 + k\hat{g}(s)$ with Re $p_\alpha = 0$ should be on AB, but neither A nor B should be the location of a pole. Again, the principle of the argument can be applied with $ABCDA$ oriented in clockwise sense. Hence, $\Delta\theta_{ABCDA} = n_P 2\pi$. Similarly, $\Delta\phi_{ABCDA} = 0$. By the construction of $ABCD$, again $\Delta\phi_{AB} = 0$ implies $\Delta\phi_{BCDA} = 0$. Hence, by (53), again $\Delta\theta_{BCDA} \simeq 0$ such that $\Delta\theta_{AB} \simeq n_P 2\pi$. Thus, for ω_n, $n > 0$ sufficiently large because $\theta(j\omega) - \theta(j0) = \theta(j0) - \theta(-j\omega)$ and (28), $\theta(j\omega_n) \simeq \theta(j0) + n_P\pi$. This implies, by (29) and (30), $\lim_{\omega\to\infty} [\theta(j\omega) - \phi(j\omega)] = \theta(j0) - \phi(j0) + n_P\pi$, which, because of (53), implies (52).

Q.E.D.

In order to establish a graphical test, it is interesting to observe that, because of (53), the validity of condition (52) can be determined in principle by considering $1 + k\hat{g}(j\omega)$ and $\hat{f}(j\omega)$ only over a *finite* interval. Moreover, given the neighborhood $N(\epsilon)$, defined by (44), it follows by the asymptotic and symmetric properties that:

(a) given any $\epsilon > 0$, there exists $\Omega(\epsilon) > 0$ such that

$$\omega \geq \Omega(\epsilon) \Longrightarrow |1 + k\hat{g}(j\omega) - \hat{f}(j\omega)| \leq \epsilon \tag{59}$$

$$\Longrightarrow 1 + k\hat{g}(j\omega) \in N(2\epsilon), \text{ where}$$

$$N(2\epsilon) \triangleq \{x \in \mathbf{C}|\ |x - \hat{f}(j\omega)| \leq 2\epsilon;\ \omega \in [0,l(\epsilon)]\} \tag{60}$$

(b) $\inf_{\omega\in R} |1 + k\hat{g}(j\omega)| > 0$

$\Longleftrightarrow$ the origin O of the complex plane is positioned with respect to $\{1 + k\hat{g}(j\omega)|\omega \in \boldsymbol{R}\}$ and $\{\hat{f}(j\omega)|\omega \in \boldsymbol{R}\}$ such that there exists an $\epsilon > 0$ such that

i) O does not belong to $N(2\epsilon)$

ii) O does not belong to $\{1 + k\hat{g}(j\omega)|\omega \in [0,\Omega(\epsilon)]\}$.

From this discussion, Theorem 2, Theorem 1, and Corollary 1, we conclude with the following graphical test.

Corollary 2 (Graphical Test): Given the system defined by (1)–(10). Let $\hat{f}(s)$ be the Dirichlet series defined by (14) and (15). Let $\gamma(\epsilon)$, $N(2\epsilon)$, $\Omega(\epsilon)$ be given by (43), (60), and (59). Under these conditions,

$$\inf_{\text{Re } s \geq 0} |1 + k\hat{g}(s)| > 0 \tag{13}$$

if and only if

i) $f_0 = 1 + kg_0 \neq 0$

ii) the origin O of the complex plane is positioned with respect to $\{\hat{f}(j\omega)|\omega \in \boldsymbol{R}\}$ and $\{1 + k\hat{g}(j\omega)|\omega \in \boldsymbol{R}\}$ such that

(a) there exists an $\epsilon > 0$ such that O does not belong to $N(2\epsilon)$ and $\{1 + k\hat{g}(j\omega)|\omega \in [0,\Omega(\epsilon)]\}$

(b) for an $\epsilon > 0$ with $0 < \epsilon < K \triangleq \inf_{\omega\in R} |\hat{f}(j\omega)|$, for which the corresponding ϵ-translation number $\tau(\epsilon)$ satisfies (47), where $\lambda_{\min}$ is defined by (45) and (46), then $|\phi(j\tau) - \phi(j0)| < \pi$ must hold.

(c) $\lim_{\omega\to\infty} [\theta(j\omega) - \phi(j\omega)] = \theta(j0) - \phi(j0) + n_P\pi = b2\pi$ where b is an integer. [Note that, by (16), n_P is the number of poles with *positive* real parts.]

Comment

a) It should be noted that the graphical test as given in Corollary 2 requires the knowledge *a priori* of the asymptotic part $f(s)$ of $1 + k\hat{g}(s)$. This, however, is the price we have to pay for admitting an almost periodic asymptote in the transfer function.

b) Willems' conditions [2], [3] are easily derived from Theorem 2, Corollary 2, and remark (R.4) if we take his assumptions, i.e., $|kg_0| < 1$; $\omega \mapsto f(j\omega)$ is periodic with period ω_0 and $\hat{g} \in \hat{A}$.

Then $\inf_{\mathrm{Re}\, s \geq 0} |1 + k\hat{g}(s)| > 0$ if and only if

$$\text{i) } \inf_{\omega \in R} |1 + k\hat{g}(j\omega)| > 0$$

$$\text{ii) } \lim_{n \to \infty} \theta(jn\omega_0) = \theta(j0) = 0, \qquad n = 0,1,2,\cdots.$$

Post Review Note

The authors are greatly indebted to the reviewers and Prof. J. C. Willems for bringing to their attention the fact that results analogous to Theorem 2 have been obtained by Davis [14] by techniques of functional analysis. Indeed, the ordered pair $\{\lambda, [\theta(j\omega) - \phi(j\omega)]_{-\infty}^{+\infty}/2\pi\}$ where ϕ, λ, θ are defined by (18), (20), and (50), respectively, corresponds to Davis' index of the time-invariant convolution operator $I + kG$, where G has a kernel g satisfying (3)–(10). The main concern of our paper was to obtain a graphical test for condition (13). This is a necessary and sufficient condition for the closed-loop impulse response to belong to A, which implies L^p-stability (any $p \in [1, \infty]$). Davis points out that the conditions of Theorem 2 are necessary and sufficient for L^2-stability. Extensions of these results to the multivariable case have been obtained by Davis [14] and Callier [15].

References

[1] H. Nyquist, "Regeneration theory," *Bell Syst. Tech. J.*, vol. 2, pp. 126–147, Jan. 1932.

[2] J. C. Willems, "Stability, instability, invertibility and causality," *SIAM J. Contr.*, vol. 7, no. 4, pp. 645–671, 1969. (See especially lemma 8.3, pp. 666–668.)

[3] ——, "The analysis of feedback systems," M.I.T. Press, Cambridge, Mass., Res. Monogr. 62, 1970, theorem 5.3, pp. 128–130.

[4] C. A. Desoer and M.-Y. Wu, "Stability of linear time-invariant systems," *IEEE Trans. Circuit Theory*, vol. CT-15, pp. 245–250, Sept. 1968.

[5] C. A. Desoer and F. M. Callier, "Convolution feedback systems," *SIAM J. Contr.*, vol. 15, Nov. 1972.

[6] H. Bohr, *Almost Periodic Functions.* New York: Chelsea, 1951. (See especially pp. 30–33, 82–83, 101.)

[7] B. Jessen and H. Thornehave, "Mean motions and zeros of almost periodic functions," *Acta Math.* (Upsala), vol. 77, pp. 137–279, 1945. (See especially pp. 143–148, 167–192.)

[8] C. Corduneanu, *Almost Periodic Functions.* New York: Interscience, 1961. (See especially pp. 69–73, 146–149.)

[9] E. Hille, *Analytic Function Theory,* vol. 1. Boston: Ginn, 1959.

[10] E. Hille and R. S. Phillips, *Functional Analysis and Semi-Groups*, rev. ed. Providence, R.I.: American Mathematical Society, 1957. (See especially p. 150.)

[11] C. A. Desoer and F. L. Lam, "On the input–output properties of linear time-invariant systems," *IEEE Trans. Circuit Theory* (Corresp.), vol. CT-19, pp. 60–62, Jan. 1972.

[12] C. A. Desoer and M. Vidyasagar, "General necessary conditions for input-output stability," *Proc. IEEE* (Lett.), vol. 59, pp. 1255–1256, Aug. 1971.

[13] C. A. Desoer and F. M. Callier, "Recent results in convolution feedback systems," in *Proc. 5th Asilomar Conf. Circuits and Systems*, 1971, pp. 252–255.

[14] J. H. Davis, "Encirclement conditions for stability and instability of feedback systems with delays," *Int. J. Contr.*, vol. 15, pp. 793–799, Apr. 1972.

[15] F. M. Callier, "On the input-output properties of convolution feedback systems," Ph.D. dissertation, Dep. Elec. Eng. Comput. Sci., Univ. Calif., Berkeley, June 1972.

On Simplifying a Graphical Stability Criterion for Linear Distributed Feedback Systems

F. M. CALLIER AND C. A. DESOER

Abstract—**In an earlier publication [1], Vidyasagar proposed to derive a standard Nyquist-type stability criterion [1, theorem 1] from a result about a graphical test developed by Callier and Desoer [2, theorem 2]. The attempt suffers from two major weaknesses which are detailed in the Appendix. Basically, Vidyasagar's concept is correct: namely, it is possible to give a graphical test which relies exclusively on the graph of $\measuredangle(1+k\hat{g}(j\omega))$, the phase of the return difference. We give below a correct statement and proof of such a graphical test.**

We shall use the same notation as in our previous paper [2]. We consider a continuous-time scalar linear time-invariant feedback system with constant feedback k and return difference $1+k\hat{g}(s)$. We assume conditions (1)–(10) of [2]. Thus

$$1+k\hat{g}(s)=k\hat{g}_a(s)+k\sum_{\alpha=1}^{l}\sum_{m=1}^{m_\alpha}\frac{r_m}{(s-p_\alpha)^m}+1+k\sum_{i=0}^{\infty}g_i e^{-st_i} \quad (1)$$

where $\hat{g}_a(s)$ is the Laplace transform of an L^1-function with support on $\boldsymbol{R}_+$, $\mathrm{Re}\,p_\alpha \geq 0$ for all α, $\Sigma_0^\infty|g_i|<\infty$, $t_0=0$, $t_i>0$ for $i>0$, and k is a real number.

We write the last two terms of (1) as

$$\sum_{i=0}^{\infty} f_i \exp(-st_i) \triangleq \hat{f}_{ap}(s).$$

(Note: we write here $\hat{f}_{ap}(s)$ instead of $\hat{f}(s)$ as in [2, eq. (14)] in order to distinguish it from Vidyasagar's $\hat{f}(s)$ [1, eq. (1)].) Following the prescriptions in [2, pp. 774 and 778], we define the phase curves

$$\theta(j\omega) \triangleq \measuredangle(1+k\hat{g}(j\omega)), \qquad \text{for } \omega\in\boldsymbol{R} \quad (2)$$

and

$$\phi(j\omega) \triangleq \measuredangle\hat{f}_{ap}(j\omega), \qquad \text{for } \omega\in\boldsymbol{R}. \quad (3)$$

We now state the new graphical test. It can be thought to be a new version of [2, corollary 2]; its most appealing feature is that it requires only the phase $\theta(j\omega)$ of $1+k\hat{g}(j\omega)$.

Graphical Test: Consider the system defined by [2, eq. (1)–(10)]. The *closed-loop* system has an impulse response in the algebra $\boldsymbol{A}$ (hence is L_p-stable for all $p\in[1,\infty]$) or, equivalently,

$$\inf_{\mathrm{Re}\,s>0}|1+k\hat{g}(s)|>0$$

if and only if

i) $\lim_{\mathrm{Re}\,s\to\infty}[1+k\hat{g}(s)]\neq 0$ or, equivalently, $1+kg_0\neq 0$ (4)

ii) $\inf_{\omega\in\boldsymbol{R}}|1+k\hat{g}(j\omega)|>0$ (5)

iii) $\omega\mapsto\theta(j\omega)$ is bounded on $\boldsymbol{R}_+$

iv) $$\lim_{\Omega\to\infty}\frac{1}{\Omega}\int_{\omega_0}^{\omega_0+\Omega}\theta(j\omega)d\omega-\lim_{\Omega\to\infty}\frac{1}{\Omega}\int_{-\omega_0-\Omega}^{-\omega_0}\theta(j\omega)d\omega=2n_p\pi \quad (6)$$

where ω_0 is any nonnegative number and, as in [2], n_p denotes the number of poles of $\hat{g}(s)$ in the *open* right-half plane, counting multiplicities.

Manuscript received August 11, 1975. This work was supported by the National Science Foundation under Grant GK-43024X and by the Belgian National Fund for Scientific Research.

F. M. Callier is with the Department of Mathematics, Facultes Universitaires de Namur, Belgium and the Belgian National Fund for Scientific Research, Brussels, Belgium.

C. A. Desoer is with the Department of Electrical Engineering and Computer Sciences and the Electronics Research Laboratory, University of California, Berkeley, CA 94720.

Comments:

I) All the comments of [1, p. 441, last paragraph of first column] apply.

II) As the example below suggests, the calculation of the averages in (6) is not difficult. Indeed, if i), ii), and iii) hold, then

$$A_+=\lim_{\Omega\to\infty}\frac{1}{\Omega}\int_{\omega_0}^{\omega_0+\Omega}\theta(j\omega)d\omega=k_+\pi, \text{ with } k_+=\text{integer}. \quad (7)$$

Of course, a similar result holds for A_-, the second expression in the left-hand side of (6). To see the truth of (7), note that first, by the Riemann–Lebesgue lemma, as $|\omega|\to\infty$, $[1+k\hat{g}(j\omega)]-\hat{f}_{ap}(j\omega)\to 0$; hence, as $|\omega|\to\infty$, $\theta(j\omega)-\phi(j\omega)\to 0 \pmod{2\pi}$. So $\delta(j\omega)\triangleq\theta(j\omega)-\phi(j\omega)$ is bounded and tends to an even multiple of π as $|\omega|\to\infty$; hence, for any fixed $\omega_0\geq 0$,

$$\lim_{\Omega\to\infty}\frac{1}{\Omega}\int_{\omega_0}^{\omega_0+\Omega}\delta(j\omega)d\omega=c \quad (8)$$

where c is an even multiple of π.

Second, by assumptions i)–iii), $\phi(j\omega)$ is almost periodic in ω; hence, its mean value over $[\omega_0,\omega_0+\Omega]$ is, in the limit as $\Omega\to\infty$, independent of ω_0 and equal to its mean value over $(-\infty,\infty)$ [3]. Now if $\phi(j0)=0$, $\omega\mapsto\phi(j\omega)$ is an odd function of ω, hence, its mean value is zero; if $\phi(j0)=\pi$, $\omega\mapsto\phi(j\omega)-\pi$ is an odd function of ω; hence, its mean value is π. These conclusions together with (8) establish the assertion (7) above.

III) With these facts in mind, checking condition iv) of the graphical test is quite simple: since A_+ is independent of ω_0, consider only ω_0 large enough so that the Nyquist plot is substantially almost periodic; then, in most cases, from the curve of $\theta(j\omega)$ versus ω [see, for example, Fig. 1, which treats $1+k\hat{g}(s)=1+50s\,(s+0.5)^{-1}(s^2+s+1)^{-1}-1.1\exp(-1.2s)+0.35\exp(-3.6s)$], the values of A_+ and A_- are readily obtained. In cases where the oscillations of θ are quite complicated, the left-hand side of (6) gives a completely unambiguous method for calculating A_+-A_-.

Proof: We show that our four conditions are equivalent to those of [2, theorem 2].

First, our i) and ii) are identical to i) and ii) of [2, theorem 2]. Second, our present iii) is equivalent to requiring that the mean angular velocity of $\hat{f}_{ap}(j\omega)$ be zero: indeed, we have asymptotically as $|\omega|\to\infty$

$$\theta(j\omega)\sim\phi(j\omega)\pmod{2\pi}$$

and

$$\phi(j\omega)=\lambda\omega+h(j\omega)$$

where λ is a constant and h is almost periodic (see [2, p. 775, eq. (20)]). Thus, an equivalent requirement is $\lambda=0$ which is precisely iii) of Theorem 2. Third, we show that our iv) is equivalent to iv) of Theorem 2. Using in iv) of Theorem 2 the symmetry properties of θ and ϕ, we obtain

$$\lim_{\omega\to\infty}\{[\theta(j\omega)-\phi(j\omega)]-[\theta(-j\omega)-\phi(-j\omega)]\}=2n_p\pi; \quad (9)$$

iv) of Theorem 2 also implies that as $\omega\to+\infty$ (and as $\omega\to-\infty$), $\theta(j\omega)-\phi(j\omega)$ approaches a *constant* which is an integral multiple of 2π. Now ϕ is almost periodic, so its mean over $[\omega_0,\Omega+\omega_0]$ and its mean over $[-\Omega-\omega_0,-\omega_0]$ tend, as $\Omega\to\infty$, to the same limit [3]. Hence, taking the mean of the expression of (9), we obtain our iv). Conversely, recalling the properties of θ and ϕ, it is easy to see that our iv) implies the old iv).

Thus, we have shown that our present four conditions, which only involve $1+k\hat{g}(s)$, are equivalent to the conditions of Theorem 2. / /

APPENDIX

The first difficulty with [1] is that as $|\omega|\to\infty$, $\theta(j\omega)$ tends modulo 2π to the almost periodic function $\phi(j\omega)$, defined in (3); hence, except when the latter function is a constant, the expression $\lim_{\omega\to\infty}\theta(j\omega)$ is *meaningless*. It is easy to see that the same conclusion holds for $\theta(j\omega)-\theta(-j\omega)$. Hence, [1, condition (9c)] has no meaning. As a consequence, the proof of necessity of [1, theorem 1] is false.

The second difficulty is in the development of the sufficiency proof of

Reprinted from *IEEE Trans. Automat. Contr.*, vol. AC-21, pp. 128–129, Feb. 1976.

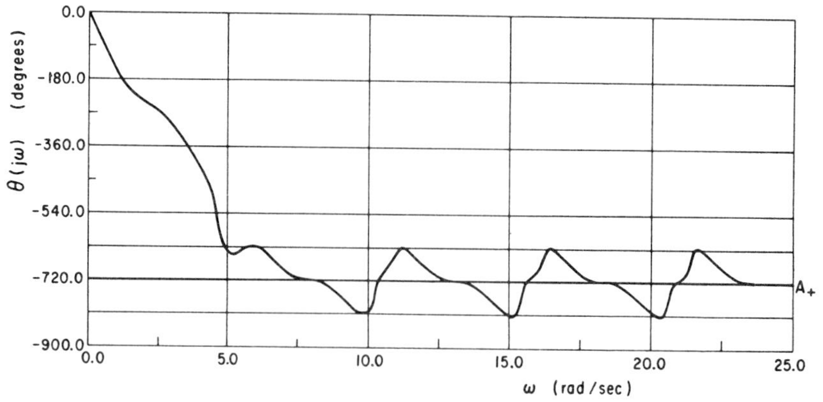

Fig. 1. $\theta(j\omega)$ versus ω for $1+k\hat{g}(s)=1+50s(s+0.5)^{-1}(s^2+s+1)^{-1}-1.1\exp(-1.2s)+0.35\exp(-3.6s)$.

the theorem of [1], namely, inequality (20), which can be written as (using notations of [1])

$$|\theta(j\omega)-\theta(-j\omega)-2\pi\nu_p|\leq 2\delta<\frac{\pi}{2} \tag{10}$$

for all $|\omega|$ sufficiently large. Clearly, this can be true only for some special cases; indeed, for large ω, θ is asymptotic to ϕ, i.e., $\theta(j\omega)\sim\phi(j\omega) = \measuredangle \hat{f}_{ap}(j\omega)\ (\mathrm{mod}\ 2\pi)$. Since the only requirement on the sequence $(f_i)_{i=0}^{\infty}$ is that it be in l^1, it is clear that the amplitude of the oscillations of θ can be arbitrarily large. Hence, [1, eq. (20)] does not hold in general. Vidyasagar's proof can be used for those cases where our (10) holds instead of his (9c). Note, however, that in the example above, $\omega\rightarrow\theta(j\omega)$ oscillates by more than $\pi/2$ above and below its asymptotic mean, so even (10) does not hold in general.

Acknowledgment

Our thanks go to Y. T. Wang, Department of Electrical Engineering and Computer Sciences, University of California, Berkeley, for computing the example.

References

[1] M. Vidyasagar, "Simplified graphical stability criteria for distributed feedback systems," *IEEE Trans. Automat. Contr.* (Tech. Notes and Corresp.), vol. AC-20, pp. 440–442, June 1975.

[2] F. M. Callier and C. A. Desoer, "A graphical test for checking the stability of a linear time-invariant feedback system," *IEEE Trans. Automat. Contr.*, vol. AC-17, pp. 773–780, Dec. 1972.

[3] C. Corduneanu, *Almost Periodic Functions.* New York: Wiley-Interscience, 1961.

Modern Wiener–Hopf Design of Optimal Controllers Part I: The Single-Input-Output Case

DANTE C. YOULA, FELLOW, IEEE, JOSEPH J. BONGIORNO, JR., MEMBER, IEEE, AND HAMID A. JABR, STUDENT MEMBER, IEEE

***Abstract*—An analytical feedback design technique is presented here for single-input-output processes which are characterized by their rational transfer functions. The design procedure accounts for the topological structure of the feedback system ensuring asymptotic stability for the closed-loop configuration. The plant or process being controlled can be unstable and/or nonminimum phase. The treatment of feedback sensor noise, disturbance inputs, and process saturation is another major contribution of this work.**

The cornerstone in the development is the selection of a performance index based on sound engineering considerations. It is these considerations, in fact, which ensure the existence of an optimal compensator for the system and make the performance index a natural one for the problem at hand.

I. Introduction

An analytical feedback design technique is presented for single-input-output processes which are characterized by their rational transfer functions. The design procedure accounts for the topological structure of the feedback system *and ensures the* asymptotic stability of the closed-loop configuration. The plant or process being controlled can be unstable and/or nonminimum phase. The treatment of feedback sensor noise, disturbance inputs, and process saturation is another major contribution of this work. The cornerstone of the development is the selection of a performance index based on sound engineering considerations. It is these considerations in fact which ensure the existence of an optimal compensator for the system and make the performance index a natural one for the problem at hand.

The classical treatment of the analytical feedback design problem by Newton is described in [1]. With his approach, which is inherently open loop, it is first necessary to find the transfer function $W_c(s)$ analytic in $\mathrm{Re}\,s \geqslant 0$ of the optimal equivalent cascade compensator. The transfer function $C(s)$ of the corresponding controller for the feedback loop is then calculated by means of the formula

$$C(s) = W_c(s)/[1 - F(s)P(s)W_c(s)].$$

Manuscript received January 9, 1975; revised October 16, 1975. Paper recommended by J. B. Pearson, Chairman of the IEEE S-CS Linear Systems Committee. This work was supported by the National Science Foundation under Grant ENG 74-13054 and is taken in part from a Ph.D. dissertation submitted by H. A. Jabr to the Faculty of the Polytechnic Institute of New York.

D. C. Youla and J. J. Bongiorno, Jr. are with the Department of Electrical Engineering and Electrophysics, Polytechnic Institute of New York, Long Island Center, Farmingdale, NY 11735.

H. A. Jabr was with the Department of Electrical Engineering and Electrophysics, Polytechnic Institute of New York, Long Island Center, Farmingdale, NY 11735. He is now with the University of Petroleum and Minerals, Dhaharan, Saudi Arabia.

$F(s)$ and $P(s)$ denote the transfer functions of the feedback sensor and plant, respectively. Unfortunately, this procedure is flawed because it can, and often does, yield a computed $C(s)$ which possesses a zero in $\mathrm{Re}\,s \geqslant 0$ coinciding with either a pole of the plant or feedback sensor. Clearly, if $C(s)$ possesses such a zero, the closed-loop system is unstable and the design is worthless. To exclude such a possibility Newton restricts the plant and feedback sensor to be asymptotically stable from the outset. In fact, several extensions of this idea to the multivariable case have already been made by Bongiorno and Weston [2], [3].

The earliest researchers to recognize the difficulty with right-half plane pole-zero cancellations within a feedback loop worked with sampled data systems [4]. The analogous treatment for continuous-time systems was presented by Bigelow [5].[1] His argument for ruling out pole-zero cancellations in $\mathrm{Re}\,s \geqslant 0$ is based on the fallacious reasoning that exact cancellation cannot be achieved in practice. Although the observation concerning what can be achieved in practice is of course true, it is also true that even if perfect cancellation were possible the system would nevertheless still possess unstable "hidden" modes. Despite the error in physical reasoning these two papers succeeded in focusing attention on several meaningful engineering problems.

The frequency-domain optimization procedure described herein is the first one to correctly account for the asymptotic stability of the closed-loop system and to correctly treat plants which are not asymptotically stable. It also supplies significant insight into the essential role played by the classical sensitivity function in feedback system design. Although confined to single-input-output systems, these ideas can be extended to the multivariable situation. This extension is nontrivial and is the subject of Part II. Just as in [6], the scalar solution provided the necessary insight and impetus required to effect the breakthrough in the multivariable case. It is, therefore appropriate that both cases be presented in the literature. Moreover, it is only in the single-input-output case that the unique role of the sensitivity function manifests itself so clearly.

The limitations imposed by feedback sensor noise have been known for some time. Horowitz [7] has proposed a design philosophy for single-input-output minimum-phase

[1]The paper by Bigelow was kindly brought to the attention of the authors by P. Sarachik.

Reprinted from *IEEE Trans. Automat. Contr.*, vol. AC-21, pp. 3–13, Feb. 1976.

stable plants which is quite imaginative but appears limited since it is modeled around a Bode two-terminal interstage equalization scheme. On the other hand, our approach takes the lumped character of the controller as an explicit constraint from the outset and nonminimum-phase and/or unstable plants offer no special obstacles.

A discussion of the relationship of our frequency-domain design procedure and some of the more popular state-variable techniques [14] is certainly in order and will be given in Part II. For now, we merely observe that the methods of this paper obviate the need to find state-variable representations and can handle stochastic inputs which are non-Gaussian and colored, as well as step and ramp-type disturbances. In addition, it permits the modeling and incorporation of feedback transducers such as tachometers, rate gyros, and accelerometers with nondynamical transfer functions.

II. Problem Statement and Preliminary Results

In this paper attention is restricted exclusively to the design of controllers for single-input-output finite-dimensional linear time-invariant plants embedded in an equivalent single-loop configuration shown in Fig. 1.[2] Suppose $y_d(s)$, the *desired* closed-loop output is related to $u_i(s)$, the *actual* input set-point signal in the linear fashion

$$y_d(s) = T_d(s)u_i(s)$$

via the *ideal* transfer function $T_d(s)$. The *prefilter* $H(s)$ can be selected in advance once and for all, but irrespective of the particular choice of criterion that is employed.[3]

$$u = H(u_i + n)$$

is the best available linear version of $y_d(s)$. Any reasonable performance measure must be based on the difference

$$e(s) = u(s) - y(s) \tag{1}$$

between the actual plant output $y(s)$ and the actual smoothed input $u(s)$ driving the loop. For a given plant and overall sensor $F(s)$ the design of the controller $C(s)$ should evolve from an appropriate minimization procedure subject to a power-like constraint on $r(s)$ to avoid plant saturation.

Plant disturbance $d(s)$ and measurement noise $m(s)$ are modeled in a perfectly general way by assuming that

$$y(s) = P(s)r(s) + P_0(s)d(s) \tag{2}$$

[2]To avoid proliferating symbols, all quantities are Laplace transforms, deterministic or otherwise, all stochastic processes are zero-mean second-order stationary with rational spectral densities and $\langle , \rangle$ denotes ensemble average.

[3]Function arguments are omitted wherever convenient.

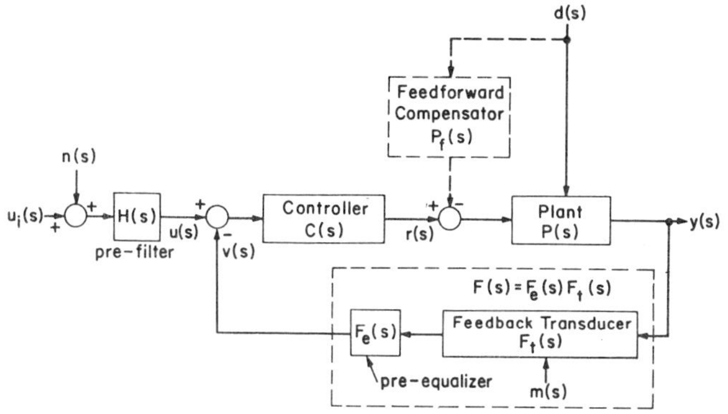

Fig. 1. Basic single-loop feedback configuration.

and

$$v(s) = F(s)y(s) + F_0(s)m(s) \tag{3}$$

where $P(s)$, $P_0(s)$, $F(s)$, and $F_0(s)$ are four real rational functions in the complex variable $s = \sigma + j\omega$. Moreover, by changing $P_0(s)$ into

$$P_0(s) - P(s)P_f(s) \tag{4}$$

it is also possible to envisage any desirable feedforward compensation $P_f(s)$.

Straightforward analysis yields

$$y = \frac{1-S}{F}(u - F_0 m) + SP_0 d, \tag{5}$$

$$r = \frac{1-S}{PF}(u - F_0 m - FP_0 d) \tag{6}$$

and

$$e = \left(\frac{F-1+S}{F}\right)u - SP_0 d + \left(\frac{1-S}{F}\right)F_0 m \tag{7}$$

where

$$S(s) = \frac{1}{1 + F(s)P(s)C(s)} \tag{8}$$

is the closed-loop sensitivity function. In process control, the actual choice of a reliable feedback transducer $F_t(s)$ is more or less dictated by the problem at hand. However, as explained in greater detail later, some low-power-level preequalization $F_e(s)$ is almost always necessary to model delay in the feedback path, to improve stability margin and to assure zero steady-state error. In other words

$$F(s) = F_e(s)F_t(s). \tag{9}$$

We therefore assume that $P_0(s)$, $F_0(s)$, $F(s)$, and $P(s)$ are prescribed in advance. Equations (5)–(7) reveal the possibilities for tradeoff in the various frequency bands. Observe, that with unity feedback ($F = 1$), $e(s)$ is the sum of the two errors

$$e_1(s) = S(u - P_0 d) \tag{10}$$

and

$$e_2(s) = (1 - S)F_0 m \tag{11}$$

whose different origins are betrayed by the prefactors $S(s)$ and 1-$S(s)$. The impossibility of making both $S(s)$ and $1-S(s)$ arbitrarily "small" over any frequency band is partly intrinsic and partly conditioned by the plant restrictions [8], [9]. This fundamental conflict is inevitable and largely responsible for a great deal of the difficulty surrounding practical feedback design.

Let

$$P(s)=\frac{n_p(s)}{d_p(s)} \tag{12}$$

$$F(s)=\frac{n_f(s)}{d_f(s)} \tag{13}$$

and

$$C(s)=\frac{n_c(s)}{d_c(s)} \tag{14}$$

where each numerator polynomial is relatively prime to its respective denominator mate. It is well known [10]–[12] that if the plant, controller and feedback sensor are free of unstable hidden modes, the closed loop of Fig. 1 is asymptotically stable iff the "reduced" characteristic polynomial

$$\varphi(s)=d_f(s)d_p(s)d_c(s)+n_f(s)n_p(s)n_c(s) \tag{15}$$

is strict Hurwitz; i.e., iff $\varphi(s)$ has no zeros in $\mathrm{Re}\, s\geq 0$. Hence, the pair $d_f(s)$, $n_p(s)$ as well as the pair $d_p(s)$, $n_f(s)$ must be devoid of common zeros in $\mathrm{Re}\, s\geq 0$ in which case $P(s)$ and $F(s)$ are said to be *admissible*.[4] Observe that once $H(s)$, $P(s)$, $F(s)$, $P_0(s)$, $F_0(s)$ and the statistics of $u_i(s)$, $n(s)$, $d(s)$, and $m(s)$ are specified, $y(s)$, $r(s)$, and $e(s)$ are uniquely determined by the choice of sensitivity function $S(s)$. Consequently, the following definition and its accompanying lemma have an obvious importance and are fundamental to our entire approach.

Definition 1: $S(s)$ is said to be *realizable* for an admissible pair $P(s)$, $F(s)$ if the closed-loop structure of Fig. 1 is asymptotically stable for some choice of controller $C(s)$ and possesses the sensitivity function $S(s)$.

Lemma 1 (Appendix): The function $S(s)\not\equiv 0$ is realizable for the admissible pair $P(s)$, $F(s)$ iff

1) $S(s)$ is analytic in $\mathrm{Re}\, s\geq 0$;
2) Every zero of the polynomial $d_f(s)d_p(s)$ in $\mathrm{Re}\, s\geq 0$ is a zero of $S(s)$ of *at least* the same multiplicity;
3) Every zero of the polynomial $n_f(s)n_p(s)$ in $\mathrm{Re}\, s\geq 0$ is a zero of $1-S(s)$ of *at least* the same multiplicity.

Let $G_i(-s^2)$, $G_n(-s^2)$, $G_u(-s^2)$, $G_d(-s^2)$, and $G_m(-s^2)$ denote the rational spectral densities of $u_i(s)$, $n(s)$, $u(s)$, $d(s)$, and $m(s)$, respectively. Setting aside for the moment all questions of convergence,[5]

$$2\pi jE_t=\int_{-j\infty}^{j\infty}\langle e_*(s)e(s)\rangle ds \tag{16}$$

is the usual quadratic measure of steady-state response. Similarly,[6] if $\boldsymbol{P}_s(s)$ represents the column-vector transfer matrix coupling the plant input $r(s)$ to those "sensitive" plant modes which must be especially protected against excessive dynamic excursions,

$$2\pi jE_s=\int_{-j\infty}^{j\infty}\langle r_*(s)\boldsymbol{P}_{s*}(s)\boldsymbol{P}_s(s)r(s)\rangle ds \tag{17}$$

is a proven useful penalty functional for saturation [1]. More explicitly,

$$2\pi jE_s=\int_{-j\infty}^{j\infty}Q(-s^2)\langle r_*(s)r(s)\rangle ds \tag{18}$$

where

$$Q(-s^2)=\boldsymbol{P}_{s*}(s)\boldsymbol{P}_s(s). \tag{19}$$

Thus,

$$E=E_t+kE_s. \tag{20}$$

k, a positive constant, serves as a weighted cost combining both factors. Using (6) and (7) and assuming all processes to be independent, a simple calculation yields the compact four-term expression

$$2\pi jE=\alpha+2\int_{-j\infty}^{j\infty}\frac{(F-1)S_*}{FF_*}G_u ds+\int_{-j\infty}^{j\infty}SS_*G_a ds+\int_{-j\infty}^{j\infty}(1-S)(1-S)_*G_b ds \tag{21}$$

where

$$\alpha=\int_{-j\infty}^{j\infty}\frac{(F-1)(F-1)_*}{FF_*}G_u ds, \tag{22}$$

$$G_a=\frac{G_u}{FF_*}+P_0P_{0*}G_d,\quad G_u=HH_*(G_i+G_n) \tag{23}$$

$$G_b=\frac{F_0F_{0*}}{FF_*}G_m+\frac{kQ}{PP_*}\left(P_0P_{0*}G_d+\frac{G_u+F_0F_{0*}G_m}{FF_*}\right). \tag{24}$$

Our entire physical discussion revolves around the implications of (21), and our assumptions are as follows.

Assumption 1: Rate gyros and tachometers are examples of practical sensing devices which are not modeled as dynamical systems.[7] Yet almost invariably, sensors are stable and their associated transfer functions $F_t(s)$ are analytic in $\mathrm{Re}\, s\geq 0$. For our purposes it suffices to restrict

[4]When $F_0(s)$, $H(s)$, $P_f(s)$, and $P_0(s)$ represent distinct physical blocks, these blocks must be stable: their transfer functions must be analytic in $\mathrm{Re}\, s\geq 0$. On the other hand if $F_0(s)$, $H(s)$, $P_f(s)$, and $P_0(s)$ are merely part of the paper modeling it is often possible to relax the analyticity requirements.

[5]If $A(s)$ is a real rational (or meromorphic) matrix in s, $A_*(s)\equiv A'(-s)$, the transpose of $A(-s)$.

[6]Column-vectors are written $\boldsymbol{a}$, $\boldsymbol{b}$, etc., and det A, A', $\bar{A}$, A^* $(\equiv\bar{A}')$ denote the determinant, transpose, complex conjugate, and adjoint of the matrix A, respectively. Note that for $A(s)$ real and meromorphic, $A_*(j\omega)=A^*(j\omega)$, ω real.

[7]A system with transfer function $A(s)$ is dynamical if $A(s)$ is proper; i.e., if $A(\infty)$ is finite.

$F(s)$ to be analytic on the finite $j\omega$-axis and to insist that the component of the cost α be finite. In particular, the integrand in (22) must be analytic on the $j\omega$-axis and $0(1/\omega^2)$ for $\omega^2 \to \infty$.

Suppose that parameter variations induce a change $\Delta\varphi(s)$ in the characteristic polynomial $\varphi(s)$. Clearly, if the nominal design is stable and structural changes are precluded

$$\eta(s) = \frac{\Delta\varphi(s)}{\varphi(s)}$$

is proper and analytic in $\mathrm{Re}\, s \geqslant 0$. Invoking the standard Nyquist argument it is immediately concluded that $\varphi(s) + \Delta\varphi(s)$, the reduced characteristic polynomial of the perturbed closed loop, is strict Hurwitz iff the normal plot of $\eta(j\omega)$ does not encircle the point $-1 + j0$ in a clockwise direction. It is imperative therefore that at the nominal setting $|\varphi(j\omega)|$ be comparably large over those frequency ranges where $|\Delta\varphi(j\omega)|$ is expected to be large. Unfortunately, it does not appear possible to translate any nontrivial stability-margin criteria directly into manageable integral restrictions reconcilable with E. However, once the formula for the optimal $S(s)$ is available, the role played by $F(s)$ in securing adequate stability margin will be clarified and further discussion along these lines is postponed until the next section.

Assumption 2: A pole of $P(s)$ in $\mathrm{Re}\, s > 0$ reveals true plant instability but a pole on the $j\omega$-axis is usually present because of intentional preconditioning and is not accidental. For example, with unity feedback ($F = 1$) and $d(s) = m(s) = 0$, a stable loop enclosing a plant whose transfer function possesses a pole of order ν at the origin will track any causal linear combination of the inputs 1, $t, \cdots, t^{\nu-1}$ with zero steady-state error. Similarly, if $s = j\omega_0$, ω_0 real, is a pole of order ν of $P(s)$, a unity-feedback stable loop will track any linear combination of $e^{j\omega_0 t}$, $te^{j\omega_0 t}, \cdots, t^{\nu-1}e^{j\omega_0 t}$ with zero steady-state error. These generalized ramp-modulated sinusoids constitute an important class of shape-deterministic information-bearing signals and play a key role in industrial applications. In a nonunity-feedback loop this perfect accuracy capability is lost unless $F_t(s)$ is also preconditioned compatibly. From (7) with $d(s) = m(s) = 0$,

$$e = \left(\frac{F - 1 + S}{F}\right)u. \tag{25}$$

Now according to Lemma 1, a finite pole $s = j\omega_0$ of $P(s)$ of multiplicity ν must be a *zero* of $S(s)$ of order at least ν. Thus, if $s = j\omega_0$ is *also* a zero of $F(s) - 1$ of order ν or greater, (25) shows that the loop is again capable of acquiring any linear combination of the inputs $e^{j\omega_0 t}$, $te^{j\omega_0 t}, \cdots, t^{\nu-1}e^{j\omega_0 t}$ with zero steady-state error. By setting $u(s) = m(s) = 0$ in (7) we obtain

$$e = -SP_0 d \tag{26}$$

the loop error under load disturbance $d(s)$. In many areas, such as process control, the recovery of steady state under load changes is a requirement of paramount importance. As is seen from (26), if the shape deterministic component of $P_0(s)d(s)$ is envisaged to be the transform of a sum of ramp-modulated sinusoids, bounded zero steady-state error is possible iff $e(s)$ vanishes at infinity and is analytic in $\mathrm{Re}\, s \geqslant 0$. Assuming SP_0 proper and $SP_0 d$ analytic in $\mathrm{Re}\, s \geqslant 0$ is evidently sufficient. In particular, reasoning as above, the $j\omega$-axis poles of $P_0(s)d(s)$, multiplicities included, must be contained in those of $P(s)$. Summing up, $(F-1)P$,

$$d_p d_{p*}\langle uu_* \rangle = d_p G_u d_{p*} \tag{27}$$

and

$$d_p d_{p*}\langle P_0 d d_* P_{0*} \rangle = d_p P_0 G_d P_{0*} d_{p*} \tag{28}$$

must be $j\omega$-analytic. Equivalently, in view of Assumption 1 and (23),

$$d_p G_a d_{p*} \tag{29}$$

is analytic on the finite $j\omega$-axis.

Assumption 3: In general, the effects of parameter uncertainty on $P(s)$ and $F(s)$ are more pronounced as ω increases and closed-loop sensitivity is an important consideration. This sensitivity is usually expressed in terms of the percentage change in the loop transfer function

$$T(s) = \frac{P(s)C(s)}{1 + F(s)P(s)C(s)}. \tag{30}$$

A straightforward calculation yields

$$\frac{\delta T}{T} = \frac{\delta(PC)}{PC} \cdot S - \frac{\delta F}{F} \cdot (1 - S) \tag{31}$$

and once again $S(j\omega)$ and $1 - S(j\omega)$ emerge as the pertinent gain functions for the forward and return links, respectively. Clearly then, to combat the adverse effects of high-frequency uncertainty in the modeling of $F(j\omega)$ and $P(j\omega)$ it is sound engineering practice to design $S(j\omega)$ proper and equal to 1 at $\omega = \infty$. This requirement is easily introduced into the analytic framework by imposing the restrictions $G_b(-s^2) \not\equiv 0$ and

$$G_b(-s^2) = 0(\omega^{2l}), \qquad l \geqslant 0 \tag{32}$$

for large ω^2.

Our final assumptions are fashioned for the express purpose of excluding from consideration certain mathematically possible but physically meaningless degeneracies. They are also motivated by Lemma 1, the structure of (21), and the requirement of finite cost.

Assumption 4: For large ω^2,

$$G_a(\omega^2) = 0(1/\omega^{2\nu}), \qquad \nu \geqslant 1. \tag{33}$$

Assumption 5: Q is analytic on the finite $j\omega$-axis, has no purely imaginary zeros in common with n_p, and the constant k is positive.

Assumption 6: Let

$$G = P_0 G_d P_{0*} + \frac{G_u + F_0 G_m F_{0*}}{FF_*}; \tag{34}$$

then

$$(d_p n_f) G (d_p n_f)_*$$

is analytic and nonzero on the finite $s = j\omega$-axis.

For later reference we record the useful formula

$$G_a + G_b = \left(1 + \frac{kQ}{PP_*}\right) G \tag{35}$$

which drops out of (23), (24), and (34).

III. The Wiener–Hopf Solution

Recall that any rational function $A(s)$ possesses a Laurent expansion constructed from all its poles, finite or infinite and as is customary, $\{A(s)\}_+$ denotes that part of the expansion associated with all the *finite* poles of $A(s)$ in $\mathrm{Re}\, s < 0$. Thus, $\{A(s)\}_+$ is analytic in $\mathrm{Re}\, s \geqslant 0$ and vanishes for $s = \infty$. The remainder of the expansion is written $\{A(s)\}_-$ and of course,

$$A(s) = \{A(s)\}_+ + \{A(s)\}_-.$$

Theorem 1 (Appendix): Let

$$d(s) = d_f(s) d_p(s) \tag{36}$$

$$n(s) = n_f(s) n_p(s) \tag{37}$$

$$\chi(s) = d(s) n(s) \tag{38}$$

and write

$$\chi(s) = \chi_l(s) \chi_r(s). \tag{39}$$

The polynomial $\chi_l(s)$ absorbs all the zeros of $\chi(s)$ in $\mathrm{Re}\, s < 0$ and $\chi_r(s)$ all those in $\mathrm{Re}\, s \geqslant 0$. Perform the spectral factorization

$$\chi_r \chi_{r*} (G_a + G_b) = \Omega \Omega_* \tag{40}$$

where $\Omega(s)$ is free of zeros and poles in $\mathrm{Re}\, s > 0$.

1) Under Assumptions 1–6, the optimal closed-loop sensitivity function $S_0(s)$ associated with any admissible pair $P(s)$, $F(s)$ is given by

$$S_0 = \frac{\left\{ \frac{\chi_r \chi_{r*}}{\Omega_*} \left(G_b - \frac{F-1}{FF_*} G_u \right) \right\}_+ + f}{\Omega}. \tag{41}$$

$f(s)$ a real polynomial. The requirements $E < \infty$ (finite cost) and $S_0(s)$ realizable for $P(s)$, $F(s)$ determine $f(s)$ *uniquely*.

2) The optimal controller $C_0(s)$ which realizes $S_0(s)$ for the pair $P(s), F(s)$ is obtained from the formula

$$C_0(s) = \frac{1 - S_0(s)}{P(s) F(s) S_0(s)} \tag{42}$$

and can be improper, unstable or both.[8] Nevertheless, the closed-loop structure is always asymptotically stable and $S_0(s)$ is proper and analytic in $\mathrm{Re}\, s \geqslant 0$. (Assumptions 1–6 actually force $\Omega(s)$ to be free of zeros in $\mathrm{Re}\, s \geqslant 0$.)

With exact arithmetic the finite zeros and poles of $P(s)F(s)$ in $\mathrm{Re}\, s \geqslant 0$ are cancelled exactly by the zeros of $S_0(s)$ and $1 - S_0(s)$, respectively. Thus, in any computer implementation of (41) and (42) it is necessary that all these exact arithmetic cancellations in $\mathrm{Re}\, s \geqslant 0$ be effected automatically by suitable preparation. Failure to do so will result in a nonstrict-Hurwitz stability polynomial $\varphi(s)$ and a corresponding unstable closed-loop design.

An examination of (41) reveals that the zeros of $\Omega(s)$ and the poles of

$$\left\{ \frac{\chi_r \chi_{r*}}{\Omega_*} \left(G_b - \frac{F-1}{FF_*} G_u \right) \right\}_+ \tag{43}$$

constitute the poles of $S_0(s)$. Since the poles of $S_0(s)$ are all zeros of $\varphi(s)$, the stability margin of the optimal design is ascertainable *in advance*. This important feature cannot be overemphasized. From the formula

$$\Omega \Omega_* = \chi_r \chi_{r*} \left(1 + \frac{kQ}{PP_*}\right) G \tag{44}$$

it is seen that the zeros of $\chi_r \chi_{r*} G$ and $1 + kQ/PP_*$ in $\mathrm{Re}\, s < 0$ emerge as poles of $S_0(s)$. The locations of these zeros depend on the choice of $F(s)$, the spectral density $G(-s^2)$ and the value of k. Changing k means compromising saturation (and accuracy). A more detailed analysis shows generally that the *negative images* of the right-half plane poles of $P(s)$ and $F(s)$ are zeros of $\chi_r \chi_{r*}$ and therefore poles of $S_0(s)$ unless $G(-s^2)$ is properly preconditioned. If some of these poles lie close to the $s = j\omega$-axis, it may be impossible to attain adequate stability margin. This difficulty can be circumvented by simply incorporating the offending poles into $G(-s^2)$. Hence, the rule, any pole of $P(s)F(s)$ in $\mathrm{Re}\, s > 0$ which lies "too close" to the imaginary axis must be made a pole of $G(-s^2)$ of exactly twice the multiplicity. Last, we mention that delay τ in the feedback path can be simulated by introducing right-half plane zeros into $F_e(s)$ through one of the many available rational function approximations to $e^{-s\tau}$.

IV. Example

The theory developed in the preceding sections is now used to design the controller $C(s)$ for the system shown in Fig. 2. Since the theory is based on rational transfer

[8] $C(s)$ is proper if the integer l in Assumption 3 equals the order of the zero of $F(s)P(s)$ at infinity. This is often the case.

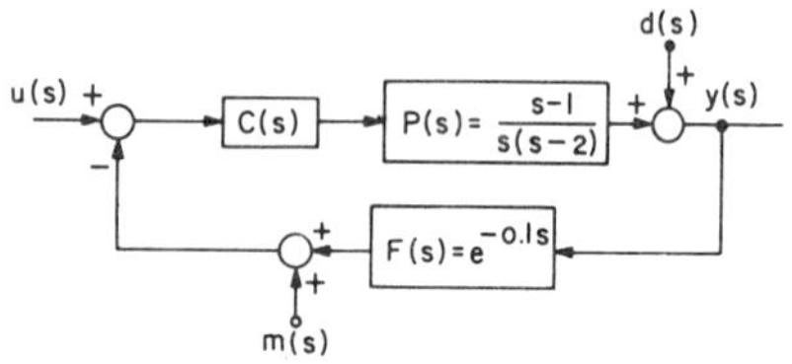

Fig. 2. Example.

functions, the first step is the selection of a suitable approximation for the ideal delay represented by $F(s) = e^{-0.1s}$. Highly satisfactory results are obtained with the second-order Padé approximation

$$F(s)=\frac{\frac{12}{(0.1)^2}-\frac{6}{(0.1)}s+s^2}{\frac{12}{(0.1)^2}+\frac{6}{(0.1)}s+s^2}\equiv\frac{p_f(-s)}{p_f(s)}. \tag{45}$$

Note that $F(s)$ and $P(s)$ are an admissible pair and (45) satisfies the condition $F-1=0$ at $s=0$, the only pole of $P(s)$ on the imaginary axis.

Because of the plant pole at the origin and the choice of rational approximation for $F(s)$, the closed loop is capable of following step inputs u with zero steady-state error when $m=d=0$. The simplest example calls for

$$G_u=-\frac{1}{s^2}. \tag{46}$$

For the remaining spectral densities we choose

$$G_d=\frac{1}{100-s^2} \tag{47}$$

and

$$G_m=1. \tag{48}$$

We also assume that the plant input is the signal most likely to cause saturation and put $Q=1$. The only remaining quantities needed for the calculation of the optimal controller are k, F_0, and P_0. Comparing Figs. 1 and 2, it is seen that $F_0=P_0=1$. With regard to k, we note that the performance index E is actually an auxilary cost function. The design objective is to minimize E_t subject to the constraint $E_s \leqslant N_s$, N_s a specified bound. Thus, k is a Lagrangian multiplier chosen to meet the design objectives.

The first step in the design of the optimal controller $C(s)$ is the determination of S_0 given by (41). For the determination of the optimal sensitivity function we need the quantities χ_r, Ω, G_a, and G_b. From (45) and Fig. 2 it follows that

$$\chi=n_pd_pn_fd_f=s(1-s)(2-s)p_f(s)p_f(-s) \tag{49}$$

and

$$\chi_r=s(1-s)(2-s)p_f(-s). \tag{50}$$

Substitution of the given data into (23), (24), (34), and (35) yields

$$G_a=G_u+G_d=\frac{-2(50-s^2)}{s^2(100-s^2)} \tag{51}$$

$$G_b=G_m+\frac{k}{PP_*}(G_m+G_u+G_d)=1+\frac{k(4-s^2)p_1(s)}{(1-s^2)(100-s^2)} \tag{52}$$

and

$$G_a+G_b=\frac{-kp_1(s)p_2(s)}{s^2(100-s^2)(1-s^2)} \tag{53}$$

where

$$p_1(s)=100-102s^2+s^4 \tag{54}$$

and

$$p_2(s)=\frac{1}{k}-\left(\frac{1}{k}+4\right)s^2+s^4. \tag{55}$$

It now follows from (40) that

$$\Omega=\frac{\sqrt{k}\;p_1^+p_2^+(2+s)p_f(s)}{10+s} \tag{56}$$

where

$$p_1^+=10+\sqrt{122}\;s+s^2 \tag{57}$$

and

$$p_2^+=\frac{1}{\sqrt{k}}+\sqrt{\frac{1}{k}+\frac{2}{\sqrt{k}}+4}\;s+s^2 \tag{58}$$

are the factors containing all the zeros of $p_1(s)$ and $p_2(s)$ in $\mathrm{Re}\,s<0$, respectively.

In addition,

$$\frac{(F-1)G_u}{FF_*}=\frac{120}{sp_f(s)} \tag{59}$$

where

$$\left\{\frac{\chi_r\chi_{r*}}{\Omega_*}\left(G_b-\frac{F-1}{FF_*}G_u\right)\right\}_+=\frac{k_0}{10+s} \tag{60}$$

$$k_0=-\left.\frac{\sqrt{k}\;s^2(2+s)(4-s^2)p_f(s)p_1^+(s)}{p_2^+(-s)}\right|_{s=-10} \tag{61}$$

We now find that

$$S_0=\frac{k_0+(10+s)f(s)}{\sqrt{k}\;(2+s)p_f(s)p_1^+(s)p_2^+(s)}\equiv\frac{h(s)}{g(s)} \tag{62}$$

in which the sixth-degree polynomial $f(s)$ is uniquely determined by the interpolatory conditions

$$S_0(0)=S_0(2)=0 \tag{63}$$

$$S_0(1)=S_0(z_0)=S_0(\bar{z}_0)=1 \tag{64}$$

$$1-S_0(s)=0\left(\frac{1}{s^2}\right), \quad |s| \text{ large.} \tag{65}$$

In (64), z_0 and $\bar{z}_0$ are the zeros of $p_f(-s)$.

Due to roundoff error, the computed polynomial $f(s)$ will, in general, not satisfy conditions (63)–(65) exactly. However, we know from the theory that the poles of $F(s)$ and $P(s)$ in Re $s \geqslant 0$ must be zeros of $S_0(s)$ and the zeros of $F(s)$ and $P(s)$ in Re$s \geqslant 0$ must be zeros of $1-S_0(s)$. The computations are therefore conditioned so that

$$h(s)=s(s-2)h_1(s) \tag{66}$$

and

$$g(s)-h(s)=(s-1)(s-z_0)(s-\bar{z}_0)h_2(s). \tag{67}$$

This is accomplished by dividing the computed $h(s)$ by $s(s-2)$, setting $h_1(s)$ equal to the quotient and ignoring the remainder.[9] The same procedure is followed in obtaining (67), and (42) then yields

$$C_0(s)=\frac{p_f(s)h_2(s)}{h_1(s)} \tag{68}$$

for the optimal controller.

The design described above depends parametrically on k. The values of E_t and E_s have been computed for various values of k and the results are shown in Fig. 3. It is clear from the curves that the choice $k=4$ leads to a suitable compromise between the desire to minimize E_t while limiting E_s. (Note that all transfer functions in the frequency domain and all signals in the time domain are taken to be dimensionless quantities but time is measured in seconds. It follows that E_t and E_s have the dimensions of seconds.) The transient response of the optimally designed system to a unit step input has also been investigated. The error and plant input responses for several values of k are shown in Fig. 4 and Fig. 5. Since these responses are obtained with $d=m=0$ they do not, and should not, reflect the optimality of the design. They do show, however, that reasonable transient performance is obtained with the choice $k=4$.

It has been pointed out in Assumption 1 that $|\phi(j\omega)|$ should be large or, equivalently, its reciprocal should be small for good stability margin. We have in fact computed and plotted $\phi^{-1}(j\omega)$ for several values of ω in the range zero to infinity. The results are shown in Fig. 6 and are highly satisfactory. With $k=4$, $|\phi^{-1}(j\omega)| \leqslant 10^{-4}$ and the system remains stable no matter what the phase of $\Delta\phi(j\omega)$

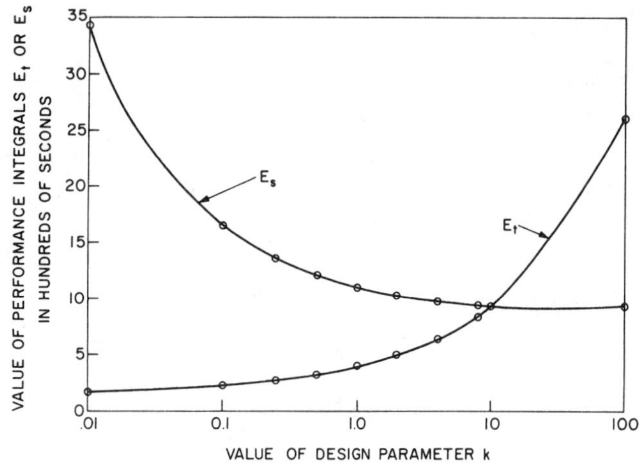

Fig. 3. Variation of performance integrals.

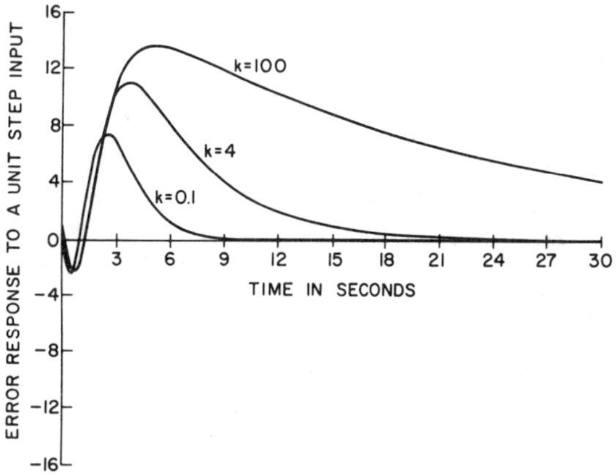

Fig. 4. Error responses.

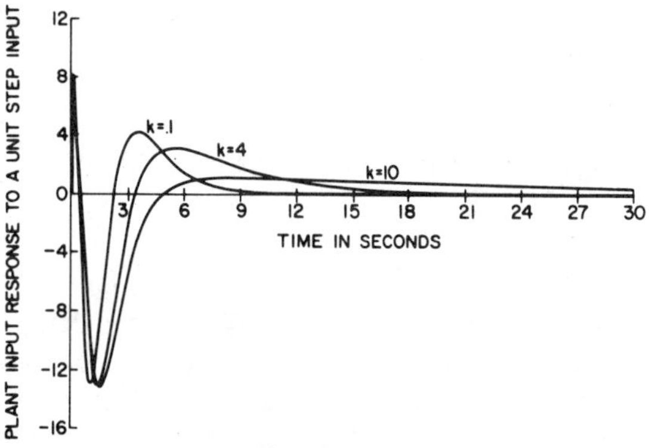

Fig. 5. Plant input responses.

provided only that $|\Delta\phi(j\omega)| < 10\,000$. For completeness, plots are also shown in Fig. 7 of $|S_0(j\omega)|$ versus ω for several choices of k.

Evidently, in the light of these observations, the choice $k=4$ makes engineering sense and the final step in the design is to compute the optimal controller transfer function with $k=4$. Using (68) we get

$$C_0(s)=\frac{K(s-\sigma_1)(s-\sigma_2)(s-s_0)(s-\bar{s}_0)}{(s-\rho_1)(s-\rho_2)(s-\rho_3)(s-s_p)(s-\bar{s}_p)}, \tag{69}$$

[9]The accuracy of the computations on a digital computer is such that this remainder is quite small (coefficients less than 10^{-5} in this example).

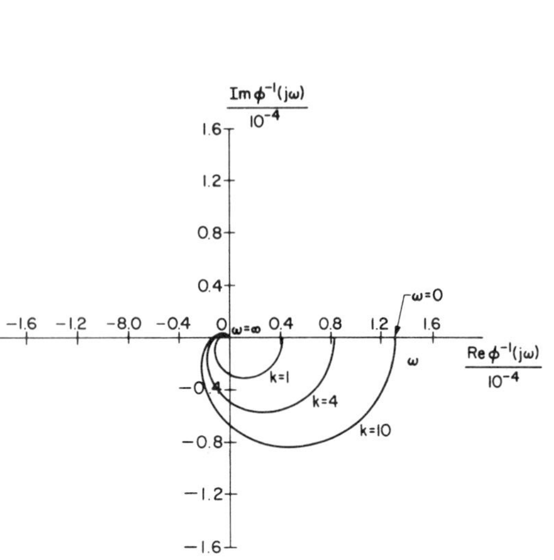

Fig. 6. Nyquist plot of $\phi^{-1}(j\omega)$.

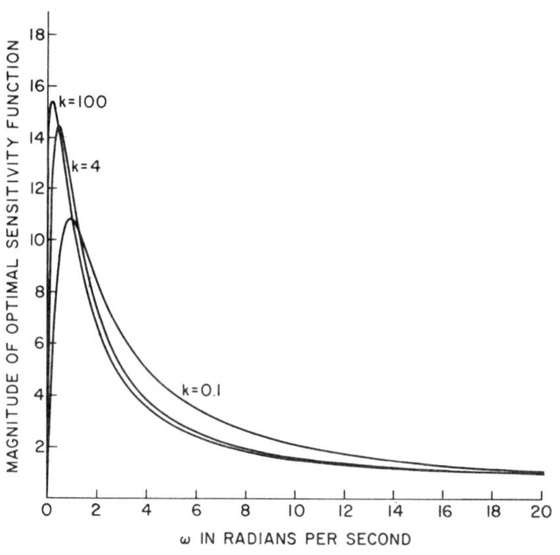

Fig. 7. Sensitivity function amplitude response.

where

$$\left.\begin{aligned} K&=67.228808647\\ \sigma_1&=0.014874634\\ \sigma_2&=-9.9999638\\ \rho_1&=2.413271030575\\ \rho_2&=-9.9806403944\\ \rho_3&=-33.65463165144\\ s_0&=-30+j17.320508076\\ s_p&=-18.05732390209+j14.991623794.\end{aligned}\right\} \tag{70}$$

The reader has probably noticed that σ_2 and ρ_2 are very nearly equal. Although we have in fact verified theoretically that these two quantities cannot be equal, it is nevertheless natural to inquire whether any significant deterioration in performance results by putting $\sigma_2=\rho_2$ and using the suboptimal controller

$$C(s)=\frac{67.2(s-0.015)(s^2+60s+1200)}{(s-2.4)(s+33.7)(s^2+36s+549)}. \tag{71}$$

Another aspect of the design which should be clarified is the use of the Padé approximation (45) for the delay $e^{-0.1s}$ in the feedback loop. These points have been taken up and the results are presented in Table I. A comparison of the first two columns in the table reveals that the use of the Padé approximation is certainly satisfactory while a comparison of the last two shows that the use of the suboptimal controller is justified. This is gratifying since no analog controller can be designed to the accuracy demanded by the values in (70).

We have also studied the stability margin with respect to variations in the delay $\tau=0.1$ s. With the suboptimal controller the feedback loop remains stable for $0\leqslant\tau\leqslant 0.155$ s. This stability margin is clearly satisfactory and the example indicates that the design procedure is a practical one.

One final point. It is quite obvious that the design equations are substantially simpler if $F(s)=1$ is used

TABLE I
COMPARISON OF RESULTS

	Optimal $C(s)$ Padé		Suboptimal $C(s)$
	Approximation for $F(s)$	$F(s)=e^{-0.1s}$	$F(s)=e^{-0.1s}$
E_t	646.9	646.1	676.8
E_s	986.7	957.6	952.2

instead of the Padé approximation and the delay is ignored. However, when the corresponding controller is employed it is found that the system remains stable only for $0\leqslant\tau\leqslant 0.08$ s. Thus, with an actual delay $\tau=0.1$ s the system designed optimally with $F=1$ would be unstable. This facility to incorporate delay is of significant practical value.

V. Discussion

It appears from Fig. 4 that the transient performance of the optimally compensated loop in our example is poor. In fact, for $k=4$ a peak error response of 10.7 is obtained. Is this poor transient performance a consequence of the design procedure, inherent limitations imposed by the plant, or both? To answer this question the example described in the previous section is considered once again but with $G_m=G_d=k=0$. (Note that although the conditions $k>0$ and $G_b(-s^2)\not\equiv 0$ are violated, it is still possible to obtain an optimal solution. Optimal solutions can exist for cases which do not satisfy our assumptions on the data. Assumptions 1–6 are *sufficient* to guarantee the existence of an optimal controller and they hold in most cases of interest.)

The optimal solution obtained for $G_m=G_d=k=0$ is the one which minimizes the integral square error with a unit step input. The optimal controller in this case is

$$C_0=\frac{-\hat{K}(s-\sigma_3)(s-s_0)(s-\bar{s}_0)}{(s-\rho_4)(s-\rho_5)} \tag{72}$$

where s_0 is given in (70) and

$$\left.\begin{aligned}\hat{K}&=1.136452161649\\ \sigma_3&=0.240139\\ \rho_4&=56.64885134963\\ \rho_5&=9.55199217963.\end{aligned}\right\} \tag{73}$$

The error response to a unit step input with this controller in the system is shown in Fig. 8. The initial value of the error is $e(0)=-7.33$ and differs from unity because with $G_m=G_d=k=0$ the performance index is finite and $S(\infty)\neq 1$. In fact, the optimal sensitivity function is

$$S_0=-\tilde{K}\frac{s(s-2)(s-\rho_4)(s-\rho_5)}{(s+1)(s+2)(s-s_0)(s-\bar{s}_0)} \tag{74}$$

where

$$\tilde{K}=-7.328575728765. \tag{75}$$

It is clear from Fig. 8 that even in the best of circumstances, no disturbance inputs, no measurement noise, and no plant saturation constraints, the best possible transient performance is poor. The reason is that this particular nonminimum-phase unstable plant is one of the most difficult to control irrespective of whether the policy is optimal or suboptimal. Indeed, since it is impossible to stabilize this plant $P(s)=(s-1)/s(s-2)$ by means of any dynamical stable compensation whatsoever [6], lead-lag methods are futile. In our opinion, a design methodology which can accomodate disturbance inputs, feedback sensor noise, rms restrictions on plant inputs, and also yield results as encouraging as those shown in Figs. 4 and 5, is a valuable engineering tool.

APPENDIX

Proof of Lemma 1: The controller $C(s)=n_c(s)/d_c(s)$ is determined from the formula

$$S(s)=\frac{1}{1+P(s)F(s)C(s)}=\frac{d_f(s)d_p(s)d_c(s)}{\varphi(s)} \tag{76}$$

$$\varphi(s)=d_f(s)d_p(s)d_c(s)+n_f(s)n_p(s)n_c(s). \tag{77}$$

What must be shown is that $\varphi(s)$ is strict Hurwitz. According to Assumption 1, $S(s)$ is analytic in Re $s\geqslant 0$ and any zero s_0 of $\varphi(s)$ in Re $s\geqslant 0$ must be a zero of $d_f(s)d_p(s)d_c(s)$ and therefore of $n_f(s)n_p(s)n_c(s)$. If it is a zero of $d_f(s)d_p(s)$, it cannot be a zero of $n_f(s)n_p(s)$ because $P(s)$ and $F(s)$ are assumed to be admissible. Thus, s_0 must be a zero of $n_c(s)$ and consequently not one of $d_c(s)$ which is relatively prime to $n_c(s)$. But this means that the multiplicity of $s=s_0$ as a zero of $S(s)$ is less than its multiplicity as a zero of $d_f(s)d_p(s)$ which contradicts Assumption 2. If instead s_0 is assumed to be a zero of $d_c(s)$, it then follows that it is a zero of $n_f(s)n_p(s)$, but not a zero of $n_c(s)$. However, the expression

$$1-S(s)=\frac{n_f(s)n_p(s)n_c(s)}{\varphi(s)} \tag{78}$$

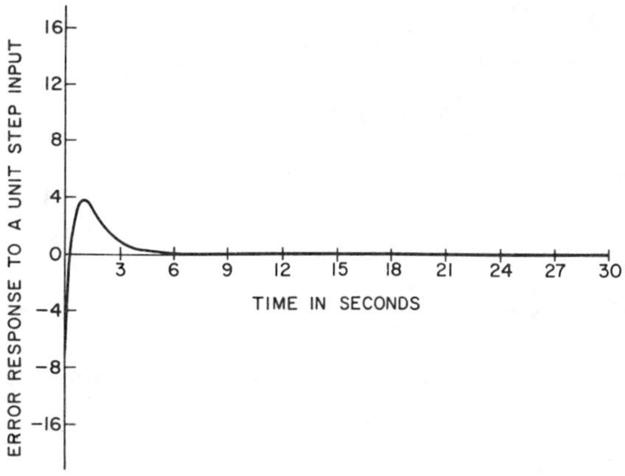

Fig. 8. Optimal error response.

then reveals that the multiplicity of $s=s_0$ as a zero of $1-S(s)$ is less than its multiplicity as a zero of $n_f(s)n_p(s)$, a contradiction with Assumption 3. Q.E.D.[10]

Proof of Theorem 1: In (21), the candidate functions $S(s)$ must all be realizable for the prescribed admissible pair $P(s)$, $F(s)$, Hence, if $S_0(s)$ is minimizing and ϵ is any reai number,

$$S(s)=S_0(s)+\epsilon\chi_r(s)\delta(s)$$

is a legitimate competitor provided $\delta(s)$ is analytic in Re$s\geqslant 0$ and the resulting cost is finite. The proof of this assertion is simple. Both $S_0(s)$ and $S(s)$ must include all the zeros of $d_f(s)d_p(s)$ in Re $s\geqslant 0$ and so must the difference $S-S_0$. Again, all the zeros of $n_f(s)n_p(s)$ in Re$s\geqslant 0$ must be zeros of $1-S_0(s)$ and $1-S(s)$ and therefore of $(1-S_0)-(1-S)=S-S_0$. But $d_f(s)d_p(s)$ and $n_f(s)n_p(s)$ are relatively prime in Re$s\geqslant 0$ and it follows that $S(s)-S_0(s)$ is divisible by

$$(d_fd_p)_r\cdot(n_fn_p)_r=\chi_r.$$

This quotient $\epsilon\delta(s)$ is analytic in Re$s\geqslant 0$ and the order of its zero at $s=\infty$ must be sufficiently high to guarantee the finiteness of E. To exploit the optimality of $S_0(s)$, we set

$$\left.\frac{dE}{d\epsilon}\right|_{\epsilon=0}=0 \tag{79}$$

and use the standard Wiener–Hopf variational argument [3] to obtain

$$\chi_{r*}S_0(G_a+G_b)-\chi_{r*}\left(G_b-\frac{F-1}{FF_*}G_u\right)=X_*(s) \tag{80}$$

$X(s)$ analytic in Re$s\geqslant 0$. Performing the spectral factorization

$$\chi_r\chi_{r*}(G_a+G_b)=\Omega\Omega_* \tag{81}$$

where $\Omega(s)$ is free of zeros and poles in Re$s>0$ and dividing both sides of (80) by Ω_*/χ_r gives, after re-

[10]The proof of necessity follows immediately from (76)+(78) and is trivial.

arrangement,

$$\Omega S_0 - \left\{ \frac{\chi_r \chi_{r*}}{\Omega_*} \left(G_b - \frac{F-1}{FF_*} G_u \right) \right\}_+ = \frac{\chi_r X_*}{\Omega_*} + \left\{ \frac{\chi_r \chi_{r*}}{\Omega_*} \left(G_b - \frac{F-1}{FF_*} G_u \right) \right\}_- \tag{82}$$

Using (35) and (38) it is seen that

$$\chi\chi_*(G_a + G_b) = (n_p n_{p*} + kQ d_p d_{p*}) \cdot (d_p n_f) G (d_p n_f)_* \cdot (d_f d_{f*}) \tag{82a}$$

and invoking Assumptions 1, 5, and 6 we conclude that $\Omega(s)$ is actually free of zeros and poles in $\mathrm{Re}\, s \geqslant 0$. Thus, $S_0(s)\Omega(s)$ must be analytic in $\mathrm{Re}\, s \geqslant 0$. But then the left-hand side of (82) is also analytic in $\mathrm{Re}\, s \geqslant 0$ and equals the right-hand side which is analytic in $\mathrm{Re}\, s < 0$. Being analytic in the entire finite s-plane,

$$\Omega S_0 - \left\{ \frac{\chi_r \chi_{r*}}{\Omega_*} \left(G_b - \frac{F-1}{FF_*} G_u \right) \right\}_+ = f(s) \tag{83}$$

$f(s)$ a real polynomial; or

$$S_0 = \frac{\left\{ \frac{\chi_r \chi_{r*}}{\Omega_*} \left(G_b - \frac{F-1}{FF_*} G_u \right) \right\}_+ + f}{\Omega}, \tag{84}$$

which is (41).

Clearly, $S_0(s)$ is analytic in $\mathrm{Re}\, s \geqslant 0$. Since $G_b(\omega^2) = 0(\omega^{2l})$, $l \geqslant 0$, the convergence of (21) forces

$$1 - S_0(j\omega) = 0(1/\omega^{l+1}). \tag{85}$$

Write

$$\left\{ \frac{\chi_r \chi_{r*}}{\Omega_*} \left(G_b - \frac{F-1}{FF_*} G_u \right) \right\}_+ = \frac{h(s)}{g(s)} \tag{86}$$

and

$$\Omega(s) = \frac{a(s)}{b(s)}. \tag{87}$$

$h(s)$, $g(s)$, $a(s)$, and $b(s)$ are four real polynomials. Then, as is easily checked,

$$\text{degree } g \geqslant \text{degree } h \tag{88}$$

$$\text{degree } a = \text{degree } b + \text{degree } \chi_r + l \tag{89}$$

and

$$S_0 = \frac{(h + gf)b}{ag}. \tag{90}$$

To insure a proper $S_0(s)$, we must impose the degree restriction[11]

$$\delta(f) \leqslant \delta(a) - \delta(b) \tag{91}$$

or, using (89),

$$\delta(f) \leqslant \delta(\chi_r) + l. \tag{92}$$

To guarantee that $S_0(s)$ be realizable for $P(s)$, $F(s)$ every zero of $(d_f d_p)_r$ must be a zero of $S_0(s)$ and every zero of $(n_f n_p)_r$ must be a zero of $1 - S_0(s)$. Coupling this with (85) we get a total of $\delta(\chi_r) + l + 1$ interpolatory constraints on $f(s)$ which is one more than its permitted maximum degree, $\delta(\chi_r) + l$. Thus, $f(s)$ is the unique *Lagrange interpolation* polynomial [13] satisfying these conditions and if a minimizing $S_0(s)$ exists, it must be the one given by (84) because the cost functional is quadratic in $S(s)$.

Now part 2 is obviously correct and to complete the proof of Theorem 1 it suffices to show that $X_*(s)$, as given by (84), is actually analytic in $\mathrm{Re}\, s \leqslant 0$. Rearranging (80) with the aid of (81) and (84) leads to

$$\frac{\Omega\Omega_*}{\chi_r} \left(\frac{\{\Psi\}_+ + f}{\Omega} \right) - \frac{\Omega_*}{\chi_r} \Psi = \frac{\Omega_*}{\chi_r} (f - \{\Psi\}_-) \tag{93}$$

where

$$\Psi = \frac{\chi_r \chi_{r*}}{\Omega_*} \left(G_b - \frac{F-1}{FF_*} Gu \right). \tag{94}$$

It is apparent that (93) is analytic in $\mathrm{Re}\, s < 0$ and it only remains to show that the same is true on the $s = j\omega$-axis. We observe first that the analyticity of $\{\Psi\}_-$ for $s = j\omega$ is implied by Assumption 2, (82a), and Assumption 6. Thus, (93) is analytic on the $j\omega$-axis if the purely imaginary zeros of χ_r are also zeros of $f - \{\Psi\}_-$ of at least the same multiplicities. But this is automatic whenever f is chosen to make $S_0(s)$ realizable for the pair $F(s)$, $P(s)$. For suppose that $s = j\omega_0$ is a zero of χ_r of order ν. Then, invoking Assumption 1, it is either a pole of P or a zero of FP of order ν.[12] Suppose it is a pole of P. Since the only $j\omega$-poles of G_b are either zeros of F or zeros of P, (94) shows that $s = j\omega_0$ is a zero of Ψ of order at least ν. It now follows from the identity

$$\{\Psi\}_+ + f = \Psi + (f - \{\Psi\}_-) \tag{95}$$

that $s = j\omega_0$ is a zero of $f - \{\Psi\}_-$ of multiplicity ν or higher [see (84)].

Suppose instead that $s = j\omega_0$ is a zero of χ_r which is a zero of FP of order ν. A direct calculation yields

$$1 - S_0 = \left(1 - \frac{\Psi}{\Omega} \right) - \frac{1}{\Omega} (f - \{\Psi\}_-) \tag{96}$$

and from (81) and (94) we obtain

$$1 - \frac{\Psi}{\Omega} = \frac{G_a + \frac{F-1}{FF_*} G_u}{G_a + G_b}. \tag{97}$$

With the aid of (82a) and Assumption 6 it is seen that

[11] $\delta(\cdot) \equiv$ degree $(\cdot)$.

[12] According to Assumption 1, F is $j\omega$-analytic.

$s=j\omega_0$ is a zero of the right-hand side of (97) of order ν or more. Since f has been constructed to make S_0 realizable for F and P, $s=j\omega_0$ is a zero of $1-S_0$ of order at least ν and therefore, in view of (96), a zero of $f-\{\Psi\}_-$ of multiplicity ν or greater. Q.E.D.

REFERENCES

[1] G. C. Newton, Jr., L.A. Gould, and J. F. Kaiser, *Analytical Design of Linear Feedback Controls*. New York: Wiley, 1957.

[2] J. J. Bongiorno, Jr., "Minimum sensitivity design of linear multivariable feedback control systems by matrix spectral factorization," *IEEE Trans. Automat. Contr.*, vol. AC-14, pp. 665–673, Dec. 1969.

[3] J. E. Weston and J. J. Bongiorno, Jr., "Extension of analytical design techniques to multivariable feedback control systems," *IEEE Trans. Automat. Contr.*, vol. AC-17, pp. 613–620, Oct. 1972.

[4] J. R. Ragazzini and G. F. Franklin, *Sampled-Data Control Systems*. New York: McGraw-Hill, 1958, pp. 155–158.

[5] S. C. Bigelow, "The design of analog computer compensated control systems," *AIEE Trans.* (Appl. Ind.), vol. 77, pp. 409–415, Nov. 1958.

[6] D. C. Youla, J. J. Bongiorno, Jr., and C.N. Lu, "Single-loop feedback-stabilization of linear multivariable dynamical plants," *Automatica*, vol. 10, pp. 159–173, Mar. 1974.

[7] I. Horowitz, "Optimum loop transfer function in single-loop minimum-phase feedback systems," *Int. J. Contr.* vol. 18, no. 1, pp. 97–113, 1973.

[8] H. W. Bode, *Network Analysis and Feedback Amplifier Design*. New York: Van Nostrand, 1945.

[9] D. C. Youla, "The modern design of optimal multivariable controllers via classical techniques," proposal to Nat. Science Foundation, Dec. 1973.

[10] ——, "Modern classical feedback control theory: Part I," Rome Air Development Center, Griffiss Air Force Base, NY, Tech. Rep. RADC-TR-70-98, June 1970.

[11] C. T. Chen, *Introduction to Linear System Theory*. New York: Holt, Rinehart and Winston, 1970.

[12] H. H. Rosenbrock, *State-Space and Multivariable Theory*. New York: Wiley Interscience, 1970.

[13] F. R. Gantmacher, *The Theory of Matrices*, vol. I. New York: Chelsea, 1960.

[14] C. D. Johnson, "Accommodation of external disturbances in linear regulator and servomechanism problems," *IEEE Trans. Automat. Contr.* (Special Issue on Linear-Quadratic-Gaussian Problem), vol. AC-16, pp. 635–644, Dec. 1971.

The encirclement condition
An approach using algebraic topology†

R. DECARLO‡ and R. SAEKS‡

The usual proof of the Nyquist theorem depends heavily on the argument principle. The argument principle, however, supplies unneeded information in that it counts the number of encirclements of ' -1 '. System stability requires only a binary decision on the number of encirclements. Using homotopy theory, a branch of algebraic topology, we construct new proofs of the classical Nyquist criteria along with the more recent linear multivariable results. In both cases the proof is essentially the same. Moreover, we believe our point of view to be more intuitive and capable of generalization to systems characterized by functions of several complex variables.

1. Introduction

The concepts delineated in this paper arose in part from an introductory study of Riemann surfaces. Associated with an analytic function is a Riemann surface. It has the property that the image of simply connected regions in the complex plane are simply connected on the Riemann surface.

The point made here is that the Nyquist criterion is trivial for simply-connected regions. Moreover, if one can work on the Riemann surface, this triviality carries over to the general case. To illustrate the point, let Fig. 1 (*a*) be the image of the right half-plane under an analytic map. The region is not simply-connected. Figure 1 (*b*) shows the ' same region ' as it might appear on an appropriate Riemann surface. Here the region is simply-connected.

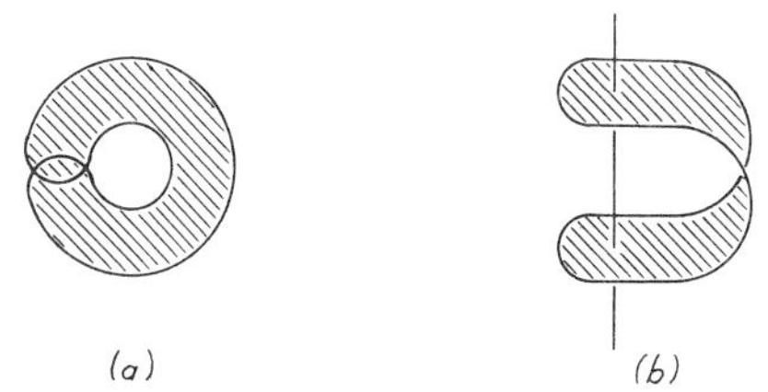

Figure 1.

Under the hypothesis that f is bounded at infinity, the boundary of the region in Fig. 1 (*b*) is the image of the imaginary axis as is the darkened line in Fig. 1 (*a*).

Now remove ' -1 ' (this may be a set of points) from the Riemann surface. The essential argument we need is that the Nyquist contour in the complex plane is homotopic to zero if and only if ' -1 ' is *not* in the interior of its image on the Riemann surface.

Received 11 June 1976 ; revision received 3 August 1976.

† Supported in part by AFOSR Grant 74–2631d.

‡ Department of Electrical Engineering, Texas Technical University, Lubbock, Texas 79409, U.S.A.

Reprinted with permission from *Int. J. Contr.*, vol. 26, pp. 279–287, Aug. 1977.

Although motivated by the intrinsic properties of the Riemann surface, this paper drops any further discussion of the concept so as to simplify the exposition. Instead, the paper exploits the fact that the Nyquist contour is a simply closed curve in the complex plane. Mathematically we draw only on the intuitive concept of homotopic triviality as found in algebraic topology.

In the sequel we prove the classical stability results via homotopy theory. In particular, we utilize covering space theory. We believe our analysis is clearer and more intuitive than has hitherto appeared. Moreover, we believe that this research indicates that the nub of the Nyquist criteria is in fact homotopy theory. In a future paper we will generalize these results to functions of several complex variables and their application to the stability of multi-dimensional digital filters.

2. Mathematical preliminaries

Firstly, let $\mathbb{C}$, $\mathbb{C}_+$ and $\mathring{\mathbb{C}}_+$ be the complex plane, the closed right half-plane, and the open right half-plane respectively. Let $\mathring{\mathbb{C}}_- = \mathbb{C} - \mathbb{C}_+$. Basic to homotopy theory is the concept of a path. A path or a curve in the complex plane is a continuous function of bounded variation $\gamma : [0, 1] \to \mathbb{C}$. γ is thus called a rectifiable curve. γ is a closed path if $\gamma(0) = \gamma(1)$. γ is a simple closed path if γ is a closed path and has no self-intersections. The image of $I = [0, 1]$ under γ is called the trace of γ and is denoted by $\{\gamma\}$.

Two closed curves γ_0 and γ_1 are homotopic ($\gamma_0 \sim \gamma_1$) in $\mathbb{C}$ if there exists a continuous function $\Gamma : I \times I \to \mathbb{C}$ such that

(a) $\quad \Gamma(s, 0) = \gamma_0(s) \qquad 0 \leqslant s \leqslant 1$

(b) $\quad \Gamma(s, 1) = \gamma_1(s) \qquad 0 \leqslant s \leqslant 1$

(c) $\quad \Gamma(0, t) = \Gamma(1, t) \qquad 0 \leqslant t \leqslant 1$

Intuitively, γ_0 is homotopic to γ_1 if one can continuously deform γ_0 into γ_1. Moreover, it is easily shown that the homotopy relation is an equivalence relation (Hocking and Young 1961, Massey 1967).

Another important property of a closed curve is its index or degree. The index of a closed curve, γ, with respect to a point a not in $\{\gamma\}$ is

$$n(\gamma\,;\ a) = \frac{1}{2\pi i} \int_\gamma (z-a)^{-1}\, dz$$

Observe that

$$\int_\gamma (z-a)^{-1}\, dz = \int_\gamma d\,[\ln(z-a)] = \int_\gamma d\,[\ln|(z-a)|] + i \int_\gamma d\,[\arg(z-a)]$$
$$= i \int_\gamma d\,[\arg(z-a)]$$

This integral therefore measures i times the net increase in angle that the ray r of Fig. 2 accumulates as its tip traverses the trace of γ.

Following the comments of Barman and Katzenelson (1974), for the integral to be well defined it is necessary to specify the appropriate branch of arg $(z-a)$ at each point of the integration. We will assume the choice of branch as outlined in the paper by Barman and Katzenelson (1974).

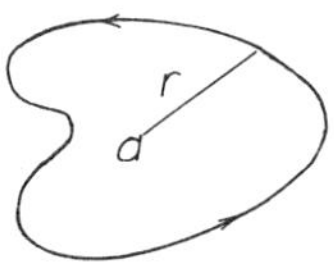

Figure 2.

Finally, we point out that this definition of index (encirclement) is a special case (i.e. in the plane) of the general topological concept of Brouwer degree (Hocking and Young 1961, Massey 1967, Milnor 1965).

At any rate, intuition for the approach stems in part from the observation that $n(\gamma\,;\ a)=0$ if and only if γ is homotopic to a point in $\mathbb{C}-\{a\}$ (cf. prop. 5.4 of Conway 1973). Simply then, a closed curve γ does not encircle the point ' -1 ' if and only if γ is homotopic to a point in $\mathbb{C}-\{-1\}$. We will henceforth refer to such a γ as being homotopically trivial.

Conversely, γ encircles ' -1 ' if and only if γ *cannot* be continuously deformed to a point in $\mathbb{C}-\{-1\}$. These ideas indicate that the Nyquist encirclement condition is fundamentally a homotopy concept.

To further illucidate the point, let $\hat{g}(s)$ be a rational transfer function depicting the open-loop gain of a scalar single-loop feedback system. Suppose all poles of $\hat{g}(s)$ are in $\mathring{\mathbb{C}}_-$ and $\hat{g}(\infty)\leqslant M<\infty$. Via the Nyquist criteria, the closed-loop system is stable if and only if $\hat{h}(s)=\hat{g}(s)/[1+\hat{g}(s)]$ is stable ; if and only if the image of the imaginary axis, under $\hat{g}(s)$ [the Nyquist plot of $\hat{g}(s)$] does not pass through nor encircle ' -1 '.

Specifically, the encirclement of ' -1 ' by the Nyquist plot implies there exists at least one s_0 in $\mathring{\mathbb{C}}_+$ such that $\hat{g}(s_0)=-1$. Thus the Nyquist contour is homotopically trivial in $\mathbb{C}_+-\{\hat{g}^{-1}(-1)\}$ if and only if the Nyquist plot is homotopically trivial in $\hat{g}(\mathbb{C}_+)-\{-1\}$.

Motivation behind this approach also arose from a close scrutiny of the classical proof of the Nyquist criteria which depends on the argument principle. The argument principle supplies unnecessary although specific information, in that it counts the number of times ' -1 ' is encircled. This may account for the apparent difficulty in generalizing the Nyquist criteria. Nevertheless, the affinity between homotopy and encirclement ideas led the authors to a minor study of algebraic topology.

In our setting, algebraic topology establishes a topologically invariant relationship between a metric space, X, and an algebraic group called the fundamental group of X, denoted by $\pi(X)$. The relationship is topologically invariant in that homoeomorphic spaces have isomorphic fundamental groups.

Specifically, the fundamental group is a set of equivalence classes of closed curves. Each equivalence class consists of a set of curves homotopically equivalent. The group operation is ' concatenation ' of curves.

For example, the fundamental group of $\mathbb{C}$ consists of one element, $i_{\mathbb{C}}$, the identity, since all closed curves are homotopic to zero. If $X=\mathbb{C}-\{-1\}$, then $\pi(X)$ has a countable number of elements : i_X (the identity) equal to the equivalence class of all closed curves not encircling ' -1 ' and the remaining elements, μ_n $(n=1, 2, 3, \ldots)$ consisting of the equivalence class of all closed curves encircling ' -1 ', n times. Moreover, μ_i concatenated with μ_k is equal to the element μ_{k+i}.

Now let X and Y be metric spaces. Let $f: X \to Y$ be locally homoeomorphic. In particular, assume that for each point y in Y there exists an open neighbourhood G of y such that each connected component of $f^{-1}(G)$ is homoeomorphic to G under the map f. Under this condition X is said to be a covering space of Y (Conway 1973, Hocking and Young 1961). Also let $\pi(X)$ and $\pi(Y)$ be the fundamental groups associated with X and Y respectively. With these assumptions, f effects a group isomorphism (i.e. a one-to-one onto mapping preserving group operations) ϕ_f between $\pi(X)$ and a subgroup of $\pi(Y)$ as in the following diagram (Hocking and Young 1961, Massey 1967):
F is the functor which establishes the relationship between a topological space and its fundamental group.

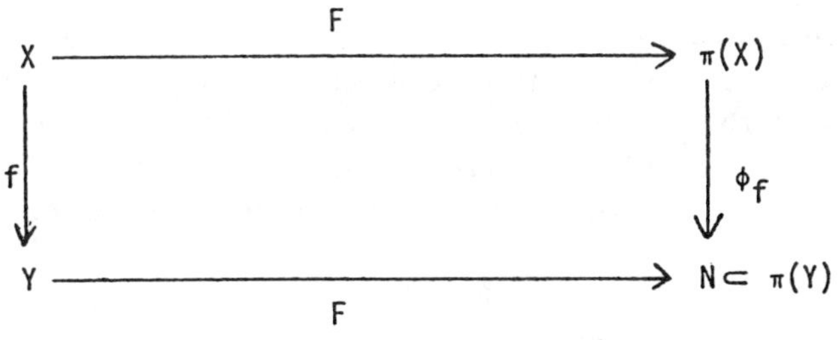

Figure 3.

Before judiciously tailoring the complex plane so as to apply the above result, we distinguish between a critical point and a critical value. A point z_0 in $\mathbb{C}$ is a critical point of a differentiable function f if $f'(z_0)=0$. A critical value of f is any point $w=f(z_0)$ whenever z_0 is a critical point.

Now suppose $f: \mathbb{C} \to \mathbb{C}$ is a rational function whose set of poles is $P=\{p_1, \ldots, p_n\}$. Let $Q=\{q_1, \ldots, q_m\}$ be the set of all points in $\mathbb{C}$ such that $f(q_i)$ is a critical value of f. Note that there may be q_i's which are not critical points. To see this, consider $g(z)=z^2(z-a)$. $g'(0)=0$ implies ' 0 ' is a critical value of g, but $g(a)=0$ with $g'(a) \neq 0$. Finally, define $T=\{t_i | t_i = f^{-1}(-1), i=1, \ldots, s\}$. Note also that since f is a rational function, P, Q and T are finite sets. Define $X=\mathbb{C}-\{P \cup Q \cup T\}$ and define $Y=f(X)$.

Lemma 1

Under the above hypothesis, X is a covering space of Y.

Proof

For X to be a covering space of Y, each y in Y must have an open neighbourhood G_y such that each component of $f^{-1}(G_y)$ is homoeomorphic to G_y. Using the inverse function theorem (Rudin 1973) we construct such a neighbourhood.

Let $\{x_1, \ldots, x_k\}=f^{-1}(y)$ where again the finiteness of this set is a consequence of the rationality of f. Let $W_1, \ldots, W_k$ be disjoint open neighbourhoods of $x_1, \ldots, x_k$ respectively. Since f is analytic on X and since $f'(x) \neq 0$ for all x in X, the inverse function theorem guarantees that there exist open neighbourhoods

$U_i \subset W_i$ $(i=1, \ldots, k)$ such that U_i is homoeomorphic to $V_i = f(U_i)$, where it follows that V_i is an open neighbourhood of y.

Thus $f^{-1}(V_1 \cup \ldots \cup V_k) = U_1 \cup \ldots \cup U_m$ Define $V = V_1 \cap \ldots \cap V_k$. Clearly V is an open neighbourhood of y and $f^{-1}(V) \subset U_1 \cup \ldots \cup U_k$. Since each U_i is homoeomorphic to $V_i \supset V$, $f^{-1}(V) \subset U_i$ is homoeomorphic to V.

Therefore each y in Y has an open neighbourhood G_y such that $f^{-1}(G_y)$ has each of its components homoeomorphic to G_y. It follows that X is a covering space of Y.

Corollary

The fundamental group $\pi(X)$ of X is isomorphic to a subgroup N of $\pi(Y)$.

This corollary says that a closed curve in X is homotopically trivial if and only if its image under f is homotopically trivial.

3. The scalar Nyquist criterion

In this section we apply the above corollary to an ' ugly ' Nyquist contour. After proving the Nyquist theorem, using this ' ugly ' contour, we relate it to the usual Nyquist contour. This will establish the classical result.

Let $\hat{g}(s)$ be a rational function which represents the open-loop gain of a scalar, single-loop unity feedback system. We assume $\hat{g}(s) \not\equiv 0$. Thus the closed-loop system has a transfer function $\hat{h}(s) = \hat{g}(s)(1+\hat{g}(s))^{-1}$. We will say that the closed-loop system $\hat{h}(s)$ is stable if and only if $\hat{h}(s)$ has all its poles in $\mathring{\mathbb{C}}_-$ and $h(\infty) < \infty$.

Let $P = \{p_1, \ldots, p_n\}$ be the set of poles of $\hat{g}(s)$ and let $Q = \{q_1, \ldots, q_m\}$ be the set of points q_i such that $\hat{g}(q_i)$ is a critical value of $\hat{g}$. Define $T = \{t_i | t_i = f^{-1}(-1), i = 1, \ldots, s\}$. Finally, let $X = \mathbb{C} - \{P \cup Q \cup T\}$ and let $Y = f(X)$. Lemma 1 implies X is a covering space of Y under the mapping f.

Assume for the present that $\hat{g}(i\omega) \neq$ ' -1 ' for $-\infty \leqslant \omega \leqslant \infty$. The first task is to construct the ' ugly ' Nyquist contour as well as the classical contour. Define the ugly contour to be γ_R, where $\gamma_R : I \to X \subset \mathbb{C}$ is a path whose trace is illustrated in Fig. 4 (*a*). Note that R is chosen strictly greater than $\max(|p_i|, |q_j|, |t_k|)$ for $1 \leqslant i \leqslant n$, $1 \leqslant j \leqslant m$, and $1 \leqslant k \leqslant s$. The indentations, along the imaginary axis into the right half-plane, are of radius $0 < \epsilon < \epsilon_0$. These semicircular indentations are made around all points of P lying on the imaginary axis and around all points q_i of Q lying on the $i\omega$-axis with $q_i \notin T$. The other ' indentations ' (again of radius ϵ, $0 < \epsilon < \epsilon_0$) are slits into $\mathring{\mathbb{C}}_+$ which encircle all points of P and all points q_i of Q $(q_i \notin T)$ which are in $\mathbb{C}_+$ so as to eliminate these points from the interior of the contour. We have also labelled these slits $\mu_1, \ldots, \mu_r$ where each μ_i maps an appropriate subinterval of I onto the specified subset of $\{\gamma_R\}$. The parallel lines, connecting a pole in $\mathring{\mathbb{C}}_+$ with the semicircular portion of γ_R, are actually the same line segment (slit) traversed in opposite directions. Note that we have indicated the usual counter-clockwise orientation to the path. Thus the only points encircled by γ_R are points of T which are in $\mathring{\mathbb{C}}_+$.

Lemma 2

Under the above assumptions on $\hat{g}$ and γ_R, $\hat{h}(s)$ is stable if and only if the path $\hat{g} \circ \gamma_R$ does not encircle ' -1 '.

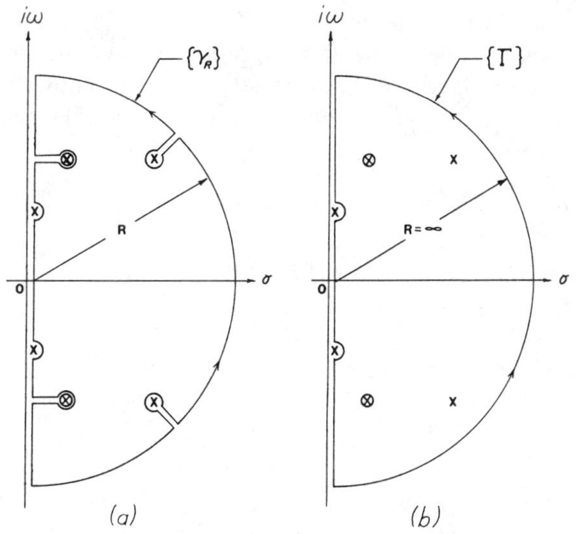

Figure 4. × indicates a point of P ; ⊗ indicates a point of Q. Γ denotes the classical Nyquist contour where $\Gamma : I \to \mathcal{C} \cup \{\infty\}$ as indicated in (*b*).

Proof

Since $\hat{g}(i\omega) \neq -1$, $-\infty \leqslant \omega \leqslant \infty$, there is a finite R such that γ_R encircles all points of T lying in $\mathcal{C}_+$. This fact, together with g being analytic on X, implies that the statements of the lemma are well defined.

Suppose $\hat{h}(s)$ is stable. Then $\hat{h}(s)$ has all poles in $\mathring{\mathcal{C}}_-$. Equivalently $\hat{g}(s) \neq -1$ for all s in $\mathcal{C}_+$. Thus γ_R does not encircle any points of T, implying that γ_R is homotopically trivial in X.

By the corollary to Lemma 1, $\hat{g}\circ\gamma_R$ is homotopically trivial in Y. Conversely, suppose that $\hat{g}\circ\gamma_R$ does not encircle '-1'. Then $\hat{g}\circ\gamma_R$ is homotopically trivial in Y. The same corollary implies that γ_R does not encircle any points of T. Thus all points of X which map to '-1' are in $\mathring{\mathcal{C}}_-$.

At this stage let us compare the information of the Nyquist plot, $\hat{g}\circ\Gamma$, with the 'ugly' Nyquist plot, $\hat{g}\circ\gamma_R$.

Lemma 3

Let n be the number of poles of $\hat{g}$ in $\mathring{\mathcal{C}}_+$, then

$$\frac{1}{2\pi i}\int_{\hat{g}\circ\Gamma}(z-1)^{-1}\,dz=\frac{1}{2\pi i}\int_{\hat{g}\circ\gamma_R}(z-1)^{-1}\,dz+n$$

Proof

Consider that

$$\frac{1}{2\pi i}\int_{\hat{g}\circ\gamma_R}(z-1)^{-1}\,dz=\frac{1}{2\pi i}\int_{\hat{g}\circ\Gamma}(z-1)^{-1}\,dz+\sum_{k=1}^{r}\int_{\hat{g}\circ\mu_k}(z-1)^{-1}\,dz$$

But

$$\int_{\hat{g}\circ\mu_k}(z-1)^{-1}\,dz=\int_{\mu_k}[\hat{g}(z)-1]^{-1}\hat{g}'(z)\,dz$$

If μ_k encircles a point of Q, then $[\hat{g}(z)-1]^{-1}\hat{g}'(z)$ is analytic in the region bounded by μ_k and thus the integral approaches zero uniformly for arbitrarily small ϵ. Consequently the integral is zero at these points.

If μ_k encircles a pole of $\hat{g}(z)$, then since $[\hat{g}(z)-1]^{-1}\hat{g}'(z)$ is analytic in the region bounded by μ_k :

$$\int_{\mu_k} [\hat{g}(z)-1]^{-1}\hat{g}'(z)\, dz = \int_{\mu_k} d\,[\ln(\hat{g}(z)-1)] = \ln[\hat{g}(z)-1]\big|_{\mu_k} = 2\pi i$$

for a suitable branch of the logarithm. The integral comes out as negative $2\pi i$ since μ_k was traversed in the clockwise direction. The conclusion of the lemma now follows.

At this point let us remove the restriction that $\hat{g}(i\omega) \neq -1$ for $-\infty \leqslant \omega \leqslant \infty$. We now give a proof of the classical Nyquist criterion using the above concepts.

Theorem 1

Let $\hat{g}(s)$ be as above with the earlier restriction removed. Then $\hat{h}(s)$ is stable if and only if the Nyquist plot of $\hat{g}(s)$ does not pass through ' -1 ' and encircles ' -1 ' exactly n times, where n is the number of poles of $\hat{g}(s)$ in $\mathring{\mathbb{C}}_+$.

Proof

Suppose $\hat{h}(s)$ is stable, then all poles of $\hat{h}(s)$ are in $\mathring{\mathbb{C}}_-$ and $\hat{h}(\infty) < \infty$. Thus $\hat{g}(\infty) \neq -1$ and $\hat{g}(s) \neq -1$ for all s in $\mathbb{C}_+$. Therefore via Lemmas 2 and 3 the Nyquist plot encircles ' -1 ' exactly n times.

Conversely, suppose the Nyquist plot encircles ' -1 ' exactly n times and does not pass through ' -1 '. Thus $\hat{g}(\infty) \neq -1$, which implies $\hat{h}(\infty) < \infty$. Moreover, since $\hat{g} \circ \Gamma$ encircles ' -1 ' n times and there are n poles of $\hat{g}(s)$ in $\mathring{\mathbb{C}}_+$, we know that $\hat{g} \circ \gamma_R$ is homotopically trivial. Thus γ_R is homotopically trivial. Consequently there are no points t_i in $\mathbb{C}_+$ such that $\hat{g}(t_i) = -1$. Thus $\hat{h}(s)$ is stable.

4. Matrix case

Let the entries of an $n \times n$ matrix $\hat{G}(s)$ be rational functions in the complex variable s. Suppose that $\hat{G}(s)$ depicts the open-loop gain of the single-loop feedback system of Fig. 5.

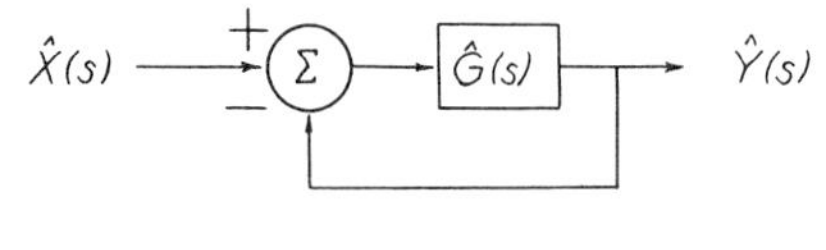

Figure 5.

$\hat{x}(s)$ and $\hat{y}(s)$ are n vectors whose entries are also rational functions of s which represent the input and output of the system respectively.

This article assumes that each entry of $\hat{G}(s)$ is bounded at $x = \infty$. Thus $\hat{G}(s)$ is a mapping, $\hat{G}(\cdot) : \mathbb{C} \to \mathbb{C}^{n \times n}$, analytic on $\mathbb{C}$ except at a finite number of points, the poles of its entries.

For Fig. 5 to be well defined we require that $\det[I+\hat{G}(s)] \not\equiv 0$. Thus there exists a closed-loop convolution operator, H, such that $y = H*x$. Moreover the Laplace transform of H, $\hat{H}(s)$ satisfies

$$\hat{H}(s) = \hat{G}(s)[I+\hat{G}(s)]^{-1}$$

For the system of Fig. 5 to be stable, $\hat{H}(s)$ must have all its poles in $\mathring{\mathbb{C}}_-$ and have all its entries bounded at $s = \infty$.

Under the assumptions on $\hat{G}(s)$, the following factorization is valid :

$$\hat{G}(s) = N(s)D^{-1}(s)$$

where $N(s)$ and $D(s)$ are right co-prime, polynomial matrices in s with $\det[D(s)] \not\equiv 0$. Moreover, s_0 is a pole of $\hat{G}(s)$ if and only if it is a zero of $\det[D(s)]$ (Wang 1971).

Desoer and Schulman (1972) have shown that the closed-loop operator H is stable if and only if $\det[N(s)+D(s)] \neq 0$ for s in $\mathbb{C}_+$ and $\det[I+G(\infty)] \neq 0$. Using this fact, we state and prove the following.

Theorem 2

H is stable if and only if (1) the Nyquist plot of $\det[N(s)+D(s)]$ does not encircle nor pass through ' 0 ', and (2) $\det[I+\hat{G}(\infty)] \neq 0$.

Proof

By hypothesis we require $\det[I+G(\infty)] \neq 0$. Therefore we must only verify that $\det[N(s)+D(s)] \neq 0$ for $\text{Re}(s) \geqslant 0$ if and only if the Nyquist plot of $\det[N(s)+D(s)]$ does not pass through nor encircle ' 0 '.

Now the Nyquist plot of $\det[N(s)+D(s)]$ passes through ' 0 ' if and only if $\det[N(s)+D(s)]$ has a zero on the imaginary axis—i.e. if and only if the closed-loop system has a pole on the imaginary axis.

Finally, assume that the Nyquist plot of $\det[N(s)+D(s)]$ does not pass through ' 0 '. Observe that $\det[N(s)+D(s)]$ is a polynomial and thus a rational function. As shown in Theorem 1, appropriately define X and Y so that X is a covering space of Y under the map $\det[N(\cdot)+D(\cdot)]$. The above lemmas imply that the Nyquist plot of $\det[N(s)+D(s)]$ is homotopically trivial if and only if there exists no point s in $\mathring{\mathbb{C}}_+$ such that $\det[N(s)+D(s)] = 0$. The assertion of the theorem now follows.

Observe that if one assumes the open-loop gain to be stable [i.e. $\hat{G}(s)$ has all poles in $\mathring{\mathbb{C}}_+$], then $\det[I+\hat{G}(s)]$ can replace $\det[N(s)+D(s)]$ in the above theorem. This follows, since for all s in $\mathbb{C}_+$,

$$\det[N(s)+D(s)] = \det[I+\hat{G}(s)] \det[D(s)]$$

with $\det[D(s)] \not\equiv 0$. Thus, in $\mathbb{C}_+$, $\det[N(s)+D(s)]$ has a zero if and only if $\det[I+\hat{G}(s)]$ has a zero.

Finally, it is worthwhile to cite the relationship between the above formulated multivariable Nyquist criterion and that formulated by Barman and Katznelson. For this purpose we let $\lambda_j(iw)$; $j = 1, \ldots, n$; denote the n eigenvalues of $\hat{G}(iw)$. In general parameterization of these functions by iw is not uniquely determined but one can always formulate such a function.

Moreover these functions are piecewise analytic and can be concatenated together in such a way as to form a closed curve which Barman and Katznelson term the Nyquist plot of $\hat{G}(s)$.

Now, since

$$\det [I+\hat{G}(iw)] = \prod_{j=1}^{n} [1+\lambda_j(iw)]$$

and the degree of a product is the sum of the degrees of the individual factors and also equals the degree of the concatenation of the factors, the degree of the Barman and Katznelson plot with respect to ' -1 ' coincides with the degree of our plot with respect to ' 0 '. As such, even though the two plots are different, their degrees coincide and hence either serves as a stability test.

Acknowledgments

The authors would like to acknowledge the contribution of Dr. John Murray (Department of Mathematics, Texas Tech University) whose continuous flow of counter examples helped to shape the ideas presented herein.

References

Barman, John F., and Katzenelson, Jacob, 1974, *Int. J. Control*, **20,** 593.
Conway, John B., 1973, *Functions of One Complex Variables* (New York : Springer-Verlag).
Desoer, Charles A., and Schulman, J. D., 1972, Memorandum No. ERL–M346, College of Engineering, University of California, Berkeley, California.
Hocking, John G., and Young, Gail S., 1961, *Topology* (Reading, Mass.: Addison-Wesley Inc.).
Massey, William S., 1967, *Algebraic Topology: An Introduction* (New York : Harcourt, Brace & World Inc.).
Milnor, John W., 1965, *Topology from the Differential Viewpoint* (University Press of Virginia).
Rudin, Walter, 1973, *Functional Analysis* (New York : McGraw-Hill Inc.).
Springer, George, 1957, *Introduction to Riemann Surfaces* (Reading, Mass.: Addison-Wesley Inc.).
Wang, S. H., 1971, Memorandum No. ERL–M309, Electronics Research Laboratory, University of California, Berkeley, California.

Part III
Extensions to Nonlinear, Time-Varying and Stochastic Systems

The great success of frequency-response methods for the analysis and design of linear feedback systems inevitably led to frequency-response attacks on nonlinear feedback control problems. Work by Krylov and Bogoliubov on "harmonic balance" methods for problems in nonlinear mechanics had shown the way (Bogoliubov and Mitropolsky [7]; Minorsky [36]). The describing function method—a quasi-linearization technique based on simple physical ideas—was developed more or less simultaneously and independently in Russia by Goldfarb [19], in England by Daniel and Tustin [48], by Oppelt [41] in Germany, by Kochenburger [30] in the United States, and by Dutilh [16] in France. Comprehensive descriptions of the use of the describing function method in control systems analysis and design are given in the books by Gelb and Vander Velde [18] and Atherton [3].

The Describing Function Method and Harmonic Balance Techniques

The standard describing function method (Grensted [20], Gelb and Vander Velde [18], Holtzmann [23] is applied to a nonlinear feedback loop such as that shown in Fig. 1(a). Here N is a frequency-independent nonlinearity whose input-output characteristic has odd symmetry, and $g(s)$ is the transfer function of a linear time-invariant dynamical system with low-pass filter characteristics. Suppose that the feedback loop is broken at the input to the nonlinearity, as shown in Fig. 1(b), and an input

$$e_i = a \sin \omega t$$

applied at point #1. The describing function of the nonlinearity gives its complex first-harmonic gain as

$$N(a) = M(a) \exp [j\Psi(a)]$$

so that the output of the nonlinearity has a first harmonic given by

$$e_n = M(a)\, a \sin [\omega t + \Psi(a)].$$

The first harmonic of the signal which is returned to the other side of the break point at #2 is thus given by

$$e_0 = |g(j\omega)|\, M(a)\, a \sin [\omega t + \pi + \Psi(a) + \text{phase}\, g(j\omega)].$$

To see whether the closed-loop system of Fig. 1(a) has a sustained oscillation one can now attempt to strike a balance between the input sinusoid at #1 and the first harmonic in the returned signal at #2. If the linear dynamical part of the system being considered severely attenuates higher harmonics, then it seems reasonable to hope that any balance found in amplitude and frequency will closely approximate an actual periodic

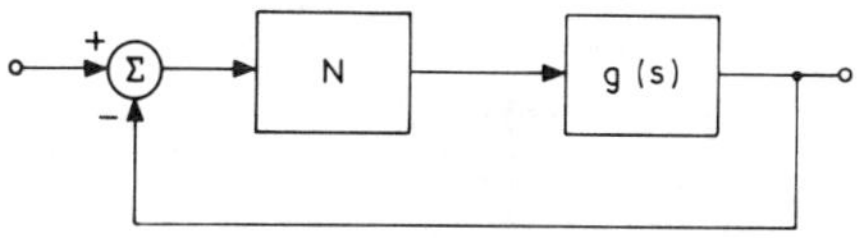

(a)

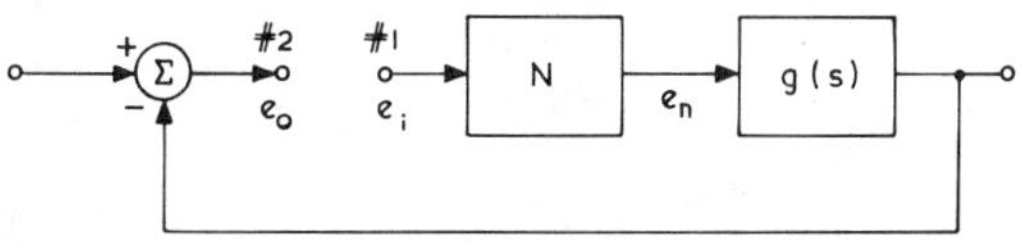

(b)

Fig. 1.

solution of the nonlinear equations governing closed-loop behavior.

The condition for first harmonic balance can be written as

$$1 + g(j\omega)\, N(a) = 0 \tag{3.1}$$

or

$$g(j\omega) = \frac{-1}{N(a)} \tag{3.2}$$

which is usually called the describing function method equation. Its great attraction is that its solution may be investigated graphically using the Nyquist diagram for the linear dynamical subsystem involved in the loop. As shown in Fig. 2 the Nyquist locus $g(j\omega)$, calibrated in frequency ω, and the inverse describing-function locus $-1/N(a)$, calibrated in amplitude a, are both drawn on the same complex gain plane and the result inspected to see whether any intersections exist. Such an intersection, like that shown in Fig. 2(a) would correspond to values of frequency ω and amplitude a which would satisfy the harmonic balance equation (3.2), and thus indicate a possible closed-loop periodic behavior. If no intersection exists, as in Fig. 2(b) and (c), an obvious extension of the Nyquist stability criterion is invoked to predict stable or unstable closed-loop behavior according as any points on the inverse describing-function locus are or are not encircled an appropriate number of times by the complete Nyquist locus drawn for positive and negative frequencies. Furthermore, the way in which an intersecting Nyquist locus and inverse describing-function locus sit with respect to each other can be used to consider the stability or instability of a limit cycle associated with the intersection. For example, in Fig. 3 the limit cycles associated with the intersection points A and C would be judged to be stable and that associated with B deemed unstable.

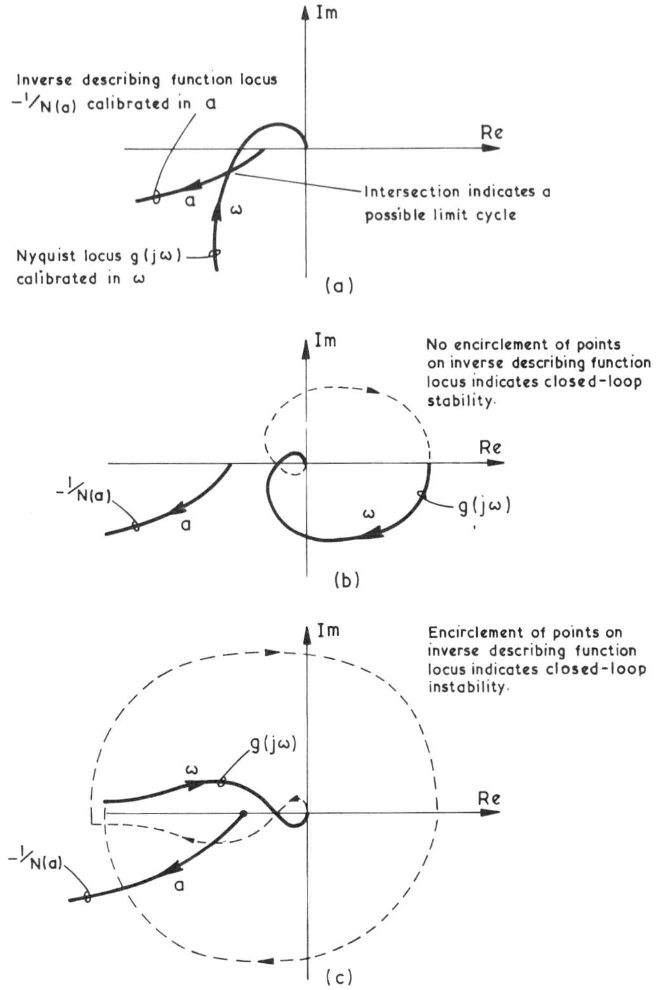

In each case g(jω) is a Nyquist locus for an open loop stable plant.

Fig. 2.

First-order describing-function analyses naturally fail to give correct predictions under certain conditions. In general, one may say that the predictions of the simple describing-function approach tend to be optimistic in that they may indicate closed-loop stability when the system is actually unstable rather than the other way about. Examples of the failure of the method are given by Willems [54] and Fitts [17]. That great care is needed in its application is clear from the fact that an example of the failure of the first-order describing function method has been given in a situation involving a simple nonlinearity and a low-pass transfer function for which, at first sight, it appears eminently applicable (Rapp and Mees [44]). Investigations have therefore been made of the conditions under which a use of the describing-function method is justified. Johnson [24] made a study of the accuracy of the describing-function method based on earlier work by Bulgakov [13]; he considered the use of second-harmonic terms to correct first-order predictions and to gauge accuracy. Bass [4] made the first attempt to give a rigorous treatment of the mathematical validity of the method. He considered systems whose behavior may be described by a vector differential equation of the form

$$\ddot{x} = f(x, \dot{x})$$

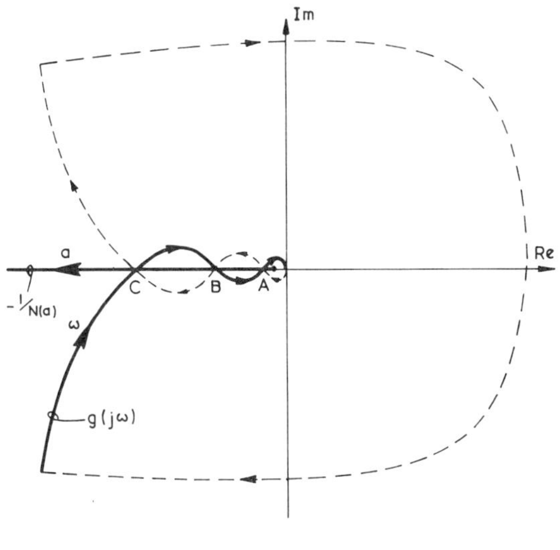

g(jω) is the Nyquist locus for an open-loop stable plant.

Fig. 3.

where

$$f(-x, -\dot{x}) = -f(x, \dot{x}).$$

On normalizing in terms of a period T (if one exists) b putting

$$\Theta = \gamma t$$

where

$$\gamma = \frac{2\pi}{T},$$

he then considered the equation

$$\gamma^2 \frac{d^2x}{d\Theta^2} = f\left(x, \gamma \frac{dx}{d\Theta}\right)$$

and broke this into linear and nonlinear parts to obtain

$$\gamma^2 \frac{d^2x}{d\Theta^2} + \gamma C_1 \frac{dx}{d\Theta} + C_2 x = \Phi\left(x, \frac{\gamma dx}{d\Theta}\right). \qquad (3.3$$

Taking $x_0(\Theta)$ as the first-harmonic term in the Fourier ex pansion of the vector $x(\Theta)$, he then considered the equation

$$\gamma^2 \frac{d^2x_0}{d\Theta^2} + \gamma C_1 \frac{dx_0}{d\Theta} + C_2 x_0 = \Phi\left(x_0, \gamma \frac{dx_0}{d\Theta}\right) \qquad (3.4$$

and asked the question, under what circumstances does th fact that (3.4) has exactly one periodic solution imply tha (3.3) has at least one periodic solution? Bass showed that $\Phi(x, \dot{x})$ is smooth, then under appropriate conditions (th most important of which is that the "low-pass filter" hypothe sis of the standard describing function technique is satisfiec a periodic solution of (3.4) does indeed imply a periodic solu tion of (3.3). Although the restriction to smooth nonlinear ties ruled out many of the forms of nonlinearity of greates practical interest, Bass's work revived theoretical interest i the technique and gave some moral support to the many er gineers using it. Sandberg [46] attacked the problem usin the tools of functional analysis applied to a space of periodi functions square integrable over a period, and found cond

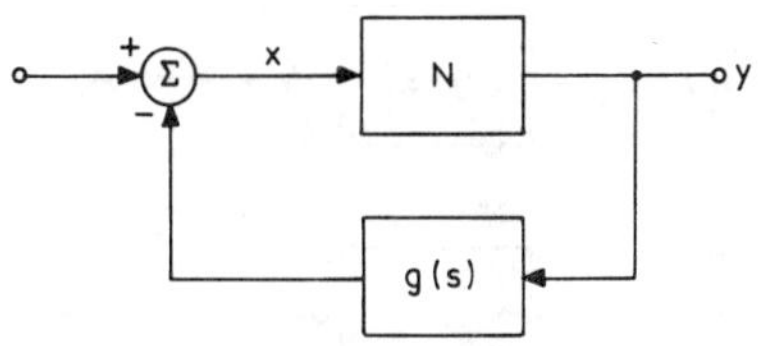

Fig. 4.

tions that guaranteed that a linearized operator of the type extracted by a describing-function analysis is a contraction mapping in the whole space. The fixed point corresponding to such a contraction mapping would correspond to a periodic oscillation of the closed-loop system. He also gave conditions under which subharmonics cannot occur. Holtzmann [22] also made an investigation using a functional analysis approach, looking for contraction mappings in the vicinity of the first-harmonic approximate solution. Bergen and Franks [6] gave tests for the validity of the method in which vague requirements such as "the linear plant is a sufficiently good low-pass filter" or "the nonlinearity is not too nonlinear" were replaced by precise statements which enabled appropriate numerical tests to be carried out on a system being investigated. Kudrewicz [32] made a similar type of study of the validity of the describing-function method. Some interesting work in this area was also done by Williamson [56]. A good discussion of describing functions for slope-bounded nonlinearities has been given by Mees and Bergen [35] who showed how to give error bounds for oscillation predictions and how to find ranges of frequency and amplitude over which oscillation is impossible.

An obviously important generalization of the simple first-order describing-function method is to replace the simple describing-function giving the effect of the nonlinearity in terms of the first harmonic in its output by a more comprehensive description giving the effect in terms of any desired finite number of harmonics. Ways of doing this for bias (zero-frequency) terms and a few harmonics, using what are usually known as "multiple-input describing-functions," are well described in the books by Gelb and Vander Velde [18] and by Atherton [3]. Mees [33] showed how this extension could be done in terms of a describing-function matrix which gives a straightforward algorithmic procedure for proceeding to incorporate terms of higher harmonic order in an analysis. In Fig. 4 let the input to the nonlinearity N be

$$x = \mathrm{Re}\left\{\sum_{r=0}^{\infty} a_r e^{jr\omega t}\right\}$$

and put

$$a = (a_0, a_1, a_2, \cdots)^T$$

$$a^m = (a_0, a_1, \cdots, a_m)^T$$

where T denotes transposition. If c is the analogous vector of complex Fourier coefficients of the output y from the nonlinearity, then the describing-function matrix N is defined so that

$$Na = c$$

and

$$N^m a^m = c^m$$

where N^m consists of the first m rows and first m columns of the matrix N. The top left-hand element n_{11} of N is the standard first-harmonic describing-function for the nonlinearity, and the matrix N has elements

$$n_{kj} = \frac{[c_k(a^j) - c_k(a^{j-1})]}{a_j}$$

constructed in such a way that, at each stage in an investigation using the describing-function matrix, the incorporation of another harmonic only requires the calculation of another row and column of N. Hence, one may easily proceed from an investigation of harmonic balance of one order to that at a higher order. For the system of Fig. 4 let a diagonal matrix G be defined as

$$G = \mathrm{diag}\,[g(0), g(j\omega), g(j2\omega), \cdots].$$

Then the condition for there to be an exactly periodic oscillation with period $2\pi/\omega$ is that the equation

$$(GN + 1)\,a = 0$$

should have a solution

$$\Psi = \begin{bmatrix}\omega\\ a\end{bmatrix}.$$

An mth-order describing-function method tries to find a solution

$$\Psi_m = \begin{bmatrix}\omega\\ a^m\end{bmatrix}$$

to the reduced equation

$$(G^m N^m + 1)\,a = 0$$

and assumes that if one exists it is close to the solution Ψ. Such an equation can, of course, no longer be solved by a simple graphical technique, and computer-generated solution methods using hill-climbing or other systematic search techniques are required. Mees [33] used the describing-function matrix in an investigation of mth-order harmonic balance methods and established the following pair of results.

1) If a closed-loop oscillation exists, then some finite order of describing function solution will predict it.

2) Under certain conditions the existence of an mth-order describing-function equation solution will guarantee the existence of a higher order solution. He showed how to obtain bounds on the error of a solution of given order, and studied the problem of determining when a finite-order describing-function method can predict a specific periodic solution for a given system. Mees [34] has also used techniques based on the describing-function matrix to study the problem of limit cycle stability. Unlike earlier limit cycle stability tests using describing-functions, this approach has a built-in "reliability guide" and indicates when a higher order approximation needs to be used.

The result of the investigations by Bass, Sandberg, Holtzmann, Bergen and Franks, Kudrewicz and Mees has been to put the describing-function method on a sound basis and, in the describing-function matrix, to provide a flexible and powerful tool for the study of closed-loop behavior in terms of harmonic balances.

Aizerman's Conjecture and Kalman's Conjecture

Many important results in nonlinear feedback theory stem from work on what is called, in the Russian literature, the problem of "absolute stability." This concerns the stability of the class of systems, illustrated by Fig. 5 formed by associating a given linear dynamic system with a set of sector-bounded nonlinearities, that is of a type where the nonlinearity is confined to the sector bounded by lines of slope k_1 and k_2 with $k_2 > k_1$. If the nonlinearity is replaced in turn by linear gains of k_1 then k_2, the stability of the resulting pair of linear closed-loop systems can be easily checked by standard linear techniques. One is then led to ask, what can be inferred about the stability of the set of systems corresponding to the admissible set of sector-bounded nonlinearities from the knowledge that both of these "bounding" linear systems are stable? The system is said to be *absolutely stable* if it is in fact stable for all such sector-bounded nonlinearities. In 1949 Aizerman [1] put forward the conjecture that the system would be absolutely stable if, when the nonlinearity were replaced by a linear gain k, the resulting linear system was stable for

$$k_1 < k < k_2.$$

Pliss [42] demonstrated that this conjecture does not generally hold by providing a counterexample. Further counterexamples have been provided by Hahn [21], Fitts [17] and Willems [55]. Aizerman's conjecture has also been discussed by Dewey and Jury [15].

In 1957 Kalman [28] conjectured that if the *slope* of the nonlinearity were bounded by k_1^1 and k_2^1, then the system would be absolutely stable if the corresponding linear system were to be stable for

$$k_1^1 < k < k_2^1.$$

A counterexample to Kalman's conjecture has been provided by Willems [55].

The discovery of counterexamples to these conjectures shows that one cannot hope to merely reduce problems in nonlinear closed-loop stability to the investigation of a set of related linear problems. Nevertheless, they had an important influence, and work on the problem of absolute stability led directly to Popov's classic work on the frequency-response approach to the stability of nonlinear feedback systems.

Popov Stability Criterion

In 1961 Popov [43] essentially discovered a class of systems for which the Aizerman conjecture is true; this is the class with the "multiplier property" described below. Popov's Stability Criterion marked an important advance in the application of frequency-response methods to nonlinear feedback system stability determination since it was a true sufficiency condition for stability. Unlike the first-order describing function method for certain situations, it never predicts that a system will be closed-loop stable if it is really unstable. In the generalized form given by Brockett and Willems [10] it may be stated as follows. The system analyzed is shown in Fig. 6, and it is assumed that

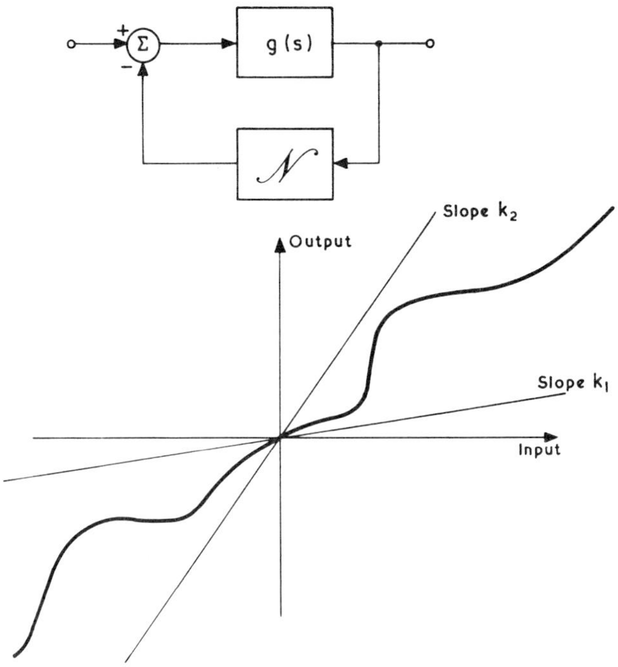

The nonlinearities in $\mathcal{N}$ must have output – input characteristics which lie between lines of slope k_1 and k_2 and which have continuity and differentiability properties sufficient to guarantee a unique solution to the differential equation describing closed-loop behaviour.

Fig. 5.

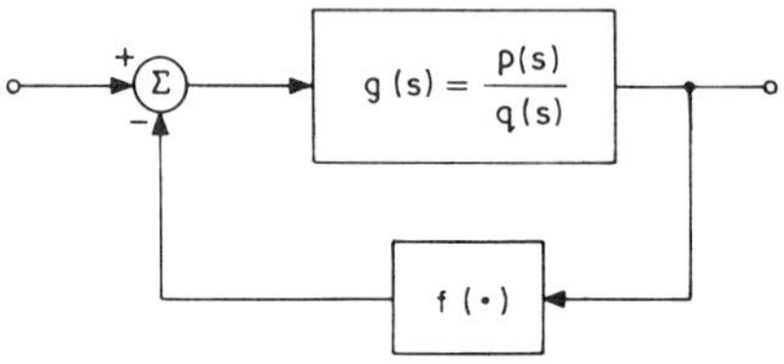

Fig. 6.

1) $p(s)$ and $q(s)$ are polynomials without common factors;
2) that the degree of $q(s)$ exceeds that of $p(s)$;
3) that $q(s)$ does not vanish in the closed right-half-plane; and
4) that the nonlinearity f is sufficiently smooth to ensure the existence of a unique solution to the governing differential equation.

Popov Stability Criterion

The null solution of the differential equation governing the behavior of the system shown in Fig. 6 is asymptotically stable in the large if

1) the nonlinear function satisfies

$$f(0) = 0$$

and

$$0 < \frac{f(u)}{u} < k_m, \qquad \text{for all } u \neq 0,$$

2) there is some constant α such that

$$(1+\alpha s)\, g(s) + \frac{1}{k_m}$$

is a positive real function.

Positive real functions play an important role in frequency-response attacks on nonlinear feedback system stability. They were first used in the analysis of passive linear electrical networks and are defined as follows.

Positive Real Function

A rational function $z(s)$ of the complex variable s which is real for all real s is said to be positive real if

1) $\mathrm{Re}\, z(j\omega) \geqslant 0$, for all real ω,
2) $z(s)$ has no right-half-plane poles,
3) all the imaginary-axis poles of $z(s)$ are simple, and the residue of $z(s)$ at each one of them is real and positive.

Positive real functions and their reciprocals are stable. In particular

$$g(s) = \frac{p(s)}{q(s)}$$

is positive real if

1) $\mathrm{Re}\, g(j\omega) \geqslant 0$, for all real ω,
2) both the polynomials $p(s)$ and $[p(s) + q(s)]$ have all their zeros in the left-half-plane $\mathrm{Re}\, s \leqslant 0$.

The basic reference for positive real functions is Wienberg and Slepian [53]; they have also been discussed by Jury [27].

The term $(1+\alpha s)$ which occurs in the above statement of the Popov stability criterion is called a frequency-domain multiplier. Its presence leads to the use of a modified polar frequency-response plot or "Popov diagram" for the investigation of closed-loop stability. For stability given an appropriately sector-bounded nonlinearity it is sufficient that

$$\mathrm{Re}\left[(1+\alpha j\omega)\, g(j\omega) + \frac{1}{k_m}\right] \geqslant 0$$

for all real ω.

If we put

$$\mathrm{Re}\, g(j\omega) + j\omega\, \mathrm{Im}\, g(j\omega) = X + jY,$$

then we will have that

$$\mathrm{Re}\,[(1+\alpha j\omega)\, g(j\omega)] = X - \alpha Y,$$

and so it will be sufficient for closed-loop stability that

$$X - \alpha Y + \frac{1}{k_m} \geqslant 0.$$

Now the straight line defined by

$$X - \alpha Y + \frac{1}{k_m} = 0,$$

which may be called the Popov line, is the equation of a straight line of slope $1/\alpha$ passing through the point $-1/k_m$ on the real axis. The Popov locus is a plot of

$$M(j\omega) = \mathrm{Re}\, g(j\omega) + j\omega\, \mathrm{Im}\, g(j\omega)$$

in the complex plane. In terms of this plot the Popov stability criterion assumes the succinct form:

It is sufficient for closed-loop stability that the Popov locus lie to the right of the Popov line.

The relationship between the Popov stability criterion and the Aizerman conjecture is easily seen in terms of the Popov plot. Asymptotic stability of a corresponding linear system for all values of gain in the range

$$0 < k < k_m$$

implies that the Popov plot does not intersect the negative real axis to the left of the point $-1/k_m$, since the Nyquist plot and the Popov plot cross the real axis at the same point. Thus, for any system for which the Popov stability criterion is satisfied, the Aizerman conjecture will hold true. One can therefore regard the Popov criterion as singling out from the class of "sector-bounded nonlinear" systems a subclass of nonlinear systems for which the Aizerman conjecture is correct.

Brockett [11] has given an interesting nonlinear circuit-based physical interpretation of the Popov stability criterion.

Parabola Test

The standard form of testing for closed-loop stability via the Popov Criterion is to see whether the Popov locus lies to one side of the Popov line. This makes the investigation of the absolute stability of conditionally stable systems awkward. To deal with this situation, Bergen and Sapiro [5] showed how to replace the Popov line by a parabola in terms of which the conditionally stable sector of absolute stability can be found in a straightforward way.

Popov's beautiful and powerful result aroused great interest and enthusiasm and caused a surge of work on the frequency-response approach to nonlinear feedback problems. The most important results to emerge from this activity were the various forms of "circle criteria" which arose from the work of Rozenwasser [45], Bongiorno [8], [9], Narendra and Goldwyn [39], Kudrewicz [31], Sandberg [46] and Zames [59]. The basic circle criterion results will be given for the system shown in Fig. 7. Its structure and the nature of the dynamical block are the same as considered for the Popov criterion, but the feedback block $k(x,t)$ may now be a time-varying nonlinearity, where x is a suitable state vector for the dynamical block. For such a system the following results can be established.

1) The null solution of the governing nonlinear differential equation is uniformly stable if

$$k_1 < k(x,t) < k_2$$

for all x and t and if

$$\frac{k_2 g(s) + 1}{k_1 g(s) + 1} = F(s)$$

is positive real.

2) The null solution is uniformly asymptotically stable in the large if there exists an $\epsilon > 0$, however small, such that

$$k_1 + \epsilon \leqslant k(x,t) \leqslant k_2 - \epsilon$$

and if $F(s)$, defined in 1) above, is positive real.

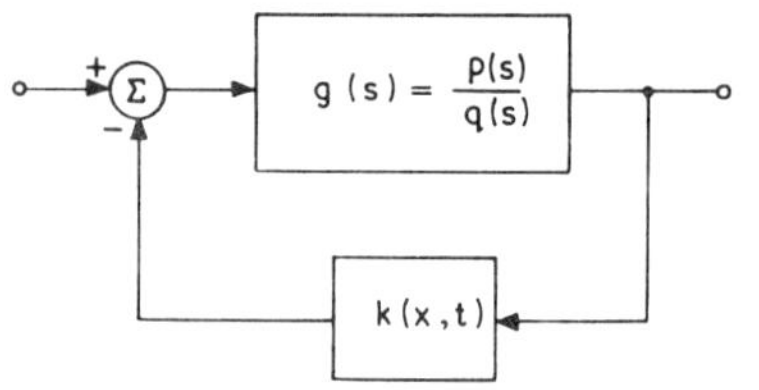

Fig. 7.

3) If $k(x, t) = k(x)$ is time-invariant and if

$$k_1 < k(x) < k_2$$

for all x and $F(s)$, defined in 1) above, is positive real, then the null solution is asymptotically stable in the large.

Results of this sort are called circle criteria because of the following graphical interpretation. Put

$$g(j\omega) = U + jV.$$

Then (Narendra and Taylor [40]) one has that

$$\operatorname{Re}\left[\frac{1 + k_2 g(j\omega)}{1 + k_1 g(j\omega)}\right] = \frac{1 + (k_1 + k_2) U + k_1 k_2 (U^2 + V^2)}{(1 + k_1 U)^2 + (k_2 V)^2}.$$

If neither k_1 nor k_2 is zero, then the numerator of this expression can be written as

$$\begin{aligned} \text{numerator} &= k_1 k_2 \{[U + \tfrac{1}{2}(k_1^{-1} + k_2^{-1})]^2 \\ &\quad + V^2 - \tfrac{1}{2}(k_1^{-1} - k_2^{-1})^2\} \\ &\triangleq k_1 k_2 \{[U - v_0]^2 + V^2 - \rho_0^2\}. \end{aligned}$$

Thus

$$\operatorname{Re}\left[\frac{k_2 g(j\omega) + 1}{k_1 g(j\omega) + 1}\right] > 0, \qquad \text{for all real } \omega \tag{3.5}$$

implies that

$$k_1 k_2 \{[U - v_0]^2 + V^2 - \rho_0^2\} > 0$$

and, provided that $k_1 \neq 0$ and $k_2 \neq 0$, the numerator term obviously vanishes on the circle in the complex gain plane defined by

$$(U - v_0)^2 + V^2 = \rho_0^2$$

whose U-axis intercepts are $(v_0 \pm \rho_0)$, where

$$v_0 + \rho_0 = -k_1^{-1} \quad \text{and} \quad v_0 - \rho_0 = -k_2^{-1}.$$

Thus the numerator term vanishes on a circle C with center at $-(k_1 + k_2)/2k_1k_2$ and with radius $|k_1 - k_2|/2k_1k_2$, that is, a circle having as a diameter that segment of the real axis joining the points

$$\left(\frac{-1}{k_1}, 0\right) \quad \text{and} \quad \left(-\frac{1}{k_2}, 0\right).$$

The region in the gain plane (U, V - plane) which corresponds to a positive numerator will obviously depend on the signs of k_1 and k_2.

1) If $\operatorname{sgn} k_1 = \operatorname{sgn} k_2$ $(k_1 k_2 > 0)$, then the numerator will be positive outside the circle. In this case for (3.5) to be satisfied, the Nyquist locus for $g(s)$ must not have any point inside the circle C.

2) If $\operatorname{sgn} k_1 = -\operatorname{sgn} k_2$, then the numerator will be positive inside the circle C, and the Nyquist locus for $g(s)$ must not have any point outside the circle C for (3.5) to be satisfied.

In order to interpret these stability criteria in terms of Nyquist diagrams for $g(s)$, an additional condition must be invoked, since the satisfaction of (3.5) is not sufficient for the positive realness of $F(s)$. The additional condition required is that the zeros of the polynomial $p(s) + kq(s)$ must have negative real parts for $k_1 < k < k_2$. For the case where $k_1 < 0 < k_2$, this condition will be satisfied if the Nyquist plot of $g(s)$ does not leave the circle C. If k_1 and k_2 have the same sign, then an application of the standard Nyquist criterion shows that the Nyquist plot of $g(s)$ must encircle C as many times in an anticlockwise direction as there are right-half plane poles of $g(s)$. Collecting all this together we have the following, stated for the case $k_1 > 0$, $k_2 > 0$, and $k_2 > k_1$, and illustrated in Fig. 3.8.

Circle Criteria for Closed-Loop Stability

Let $D(k_1, k_2)$ and $D[k_1, k_2]$ denote the open and closed disks in the g-plane having as a diameter the join of the points

$$\left(-\frac{1}{k_1} + j0\right) \quad \text{and} \quad \left(-\frac{1}{k_2} + j0\right).$$

1) Then the system shown in Fig. 7 and detailed above will be stable in the sense that outputs are bounded for all initial conditions if the Nyquist locus Γ of $g(s)$ does not intersect the disk $D(k_1, k_2)$ and encircles it p_0 times in an anticlockwise direction, where p_0 is the number of right-half plane poles of $g(s)$.

2) This same system will be stable in the sense that all sets of initial conditions lead to outputs that approach zero as $t \to \infty$, if Γ does not intersect the disk $D[k_1, k_2]$ and encircles it p_0 times in an anticlockwise direction.

The various possibilities for different signs of k_1 and k_2 are described in detail by Narendra and Taylor [40], who also discuss what happens when $k_1 = 0$ or $k_2 = 0$. In both of these cases the circle degenerates into a straight line. If $k_1 = 0$, then this implies that

$$1 + k_2 \operatorname{Re} g(j\omega) > 0$$

and the Nyquist plot of $g(j\omega)$ must lie strictly to the right of a vertical line passing through $-k_2^{-1} < 0$. If $k_2 = 0$, then we must have that

$$1 - |k_1| \operatorname{Re} g(j\omega) > 0,$$

and the Nyquist plot of $g(j\omega)$ must lie strictly to the left of a vertical line passing through $-k_1^{-1} < 0$.

The Popov criterion and circle criterion as described above give sufficient criteria for a class of nonlinear feedback systems to be closed-loop stable. To complete the description of the behavior of these systems in frequency-response terms, it is important to have the complementary conditions defining when the closed-loop system will be unstable. Such conditions have been given by Brockett and Lee [12] who treat the circle criterion case in detail, and explain how their method can be extended to other stability criteria to derive appropriate instability counterparts. Their instability complements

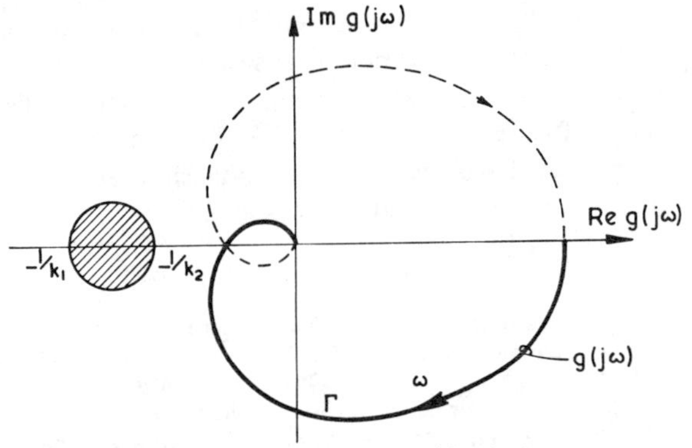

Γ is Nyquist locus of an open-loop stable plant. No encirclement or penetration of critical disc thus implies closed-loop stability.

Fig. 8.

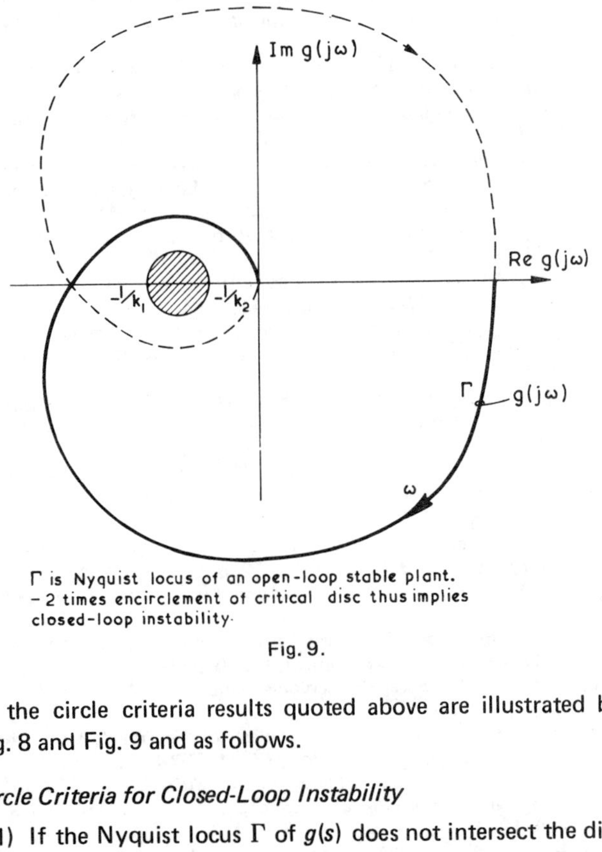

Γ is Nyquist locus of an open-loop stable plant. – 2 times encirclement of critical disc thus implies closed-loop instability.

Fig. 9.

to the circle criteria results quoted above are illustrated by Fig. 8 and Fig. 9 and as follows.

Circle Criteria for Closed-Loop Instability

1) If the Nyquist locus Γ of $g(s)$ does not intersect the disk $D(k_1, k_2)$ and encircles it fewer than p_0 times in an anticlockwise direction, then the system of Fig. 7 will be unstable in the sense that one or more sets of initial conditions will lead to outputs which do not approach zero as $t \to \infty$.

2) If Γ does not intersect the disk $D[k_1, k_2]$ and encircles it fewer than p_0 times in the anticlockwise direction, then the closed-loop system will be unstable in the sense that one or more initial conditions will lead to outputs which grow without bound as $t \to \infty$.

Circuit Analogy for the Circle Criterion

Brockett [11] has given the following interesting network interpretation of the circle criterion. The feedback system of Fig. 10(a) and the network of Fig. 10(b) can be shown to have their behavior described by the same differential equation.

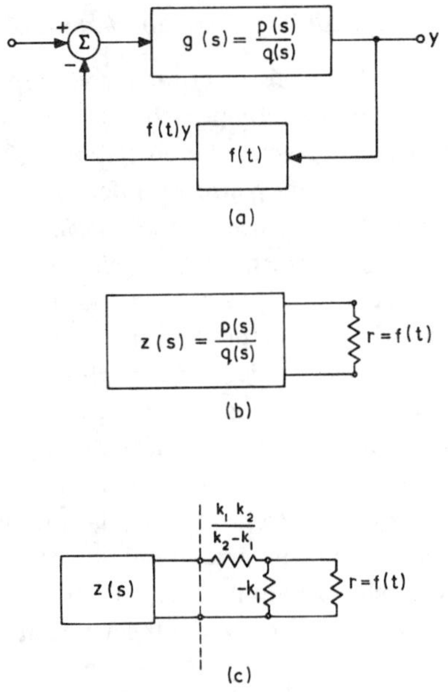

Fig. 10.

Furthermore, the voltage and current at the input terminals of a passive network consisting of linear constant inductors, capacitors, and resistors can be shown to be related by an impedance function which is a positive real function. Thus, if in Fig. 10(b) $z(s)$ is a positive real passive network impedance function, and $f(t)$ is always positive, we will have bounded solutions since we are dealing with a passive network. This gives an interpretation of the circle criterion for $k_2 = 0$ and $k_1 = \infty$. Now consider Fig. 10(c). If $f(t)$ is bounded between k_2 and k_1, then the total resistance to the right of the dotted line is always positive. A suitable translation of this gives a network interpretation of the general circle criterion.

The work of Zames [58], [59], Brockett and Willems [10], and Narendra and Neuman [37] showed how sufficient conditions for nonlinear stability for feedback systems having monotonic and odd-monotonic nonlinearities could be expressed in terms of the transfer function $g(s)$ of the linear part of the system and a frequency-domain multiplier $z(s)$ such that $g(s)\, z(s)$ was a positive real function. Finding such multipliers by means of a geometric construction was investigated by Narendra and Cho [38] who established the following criterion.

Off-Axis Circle Criterion

If any circle can be drawn which intersects the negative real axis of the complex gain plane at the points $(-1/k_1 + j0)$ and $(-1/k_2 + j0)$ in such a way that the Nyquist plot for $g(s)$ lies outside the circle and does not completely encircle it, then the nonlinear feedback system of Fig. 6, in which $g(s)$ is open-loop stable, will be asymptotically stable for all real-valued functions $f(\cdot)$ satisfying

$$k_1 < \frac{f(y_1) - f(y_2)}{y_1 - y_2} < k_2$$

where k_1 and k_2 are positive constants. (Note that these "off-axis" circles are *not* restricted to having their centers on the real axis.)

Comparison of the Various Approaches

The advantages of the circle criteria and Popov criterion over the describing-function approach are that they give true sufficiency conditions for closed-loop stability. Their principal disadvantage is that they give no information as to what happens when the Nyquist locus enters the forbidden regions of the gain plane. By contrast, the describing-function method will give an estimate of both amplitude and frequency of the oscillation involved when it predicts instability. A further advantage of the describing-function method is that it can handle certain important types of nonlinearity—such as rectangular hysteresis and backlash—which are excluded by the restriction of the circle and Popov criteria to sector-bounded nonlinearities. Both the Popov and circle criteria are often far too conservative in their prediction of stability. In particular for the circle criterion, if $k_1 = 0$, then the relevant circle becomes a half-plane which the Nyquist locus must not penetrate, and if $k_2 = \infty$, the edge of the appropriate circle will touch the origin of the complex gain plane, placing a strong restriction on the high-frequency behavior of the Nyquist diagram.

Unlike the conservatism of the Popov and circle criteria, the describing-function approach is sometimes over-optimistic in its stability predictions. However, since it retains quite a lot of information about the nonlinearity, it tends to make its predictions in some detail. By contrast the circle and Popov criteria make safe predictions but, having thrown away a lot of detailed information about the nonlinearity, cannot make predictions giving any details of expected behavior such as the amplitude and frequency of closed-loop oscillations in the event of instability. As advised by Mees [34], it therefore seems prudent in practice to use a combination of methods. Since both the circle criterion and the describing-function use the same Nyquist diagram, one could use the circle criterion to demonstrate the possibility of instability associated with a limit cycle at some frequency for which the Nyquist diagram penetrates a circle or half plane and then use the describing-function approach to make a more detailed investigation of the suspected limit cycle. An important link between the describing-function and circle criterion has been established by Cook [14] who has shown that for sector-bounded nonlinearities the inverse describing-function locus lies inside the circular disk used in the circle criterion approach.

The Popov approach deals only with nonlinear systems and requires the linear subsystem involved to be stable, but the circle criterion handles both time-varying and nonlinear feedback around a dynamical system which can be open-loop unstable. There are important links between the Popov and circle criterion methods and Lyapunov methods for stability investigation (Kalman [29], Aizerman and Gantmacher [2]). In particular, Popov has shown that his results subsume those obtainable via the use of a Lyapunov function consisting of a quadratic form plus an integral of the nonlinearity, and Yakubovitch [57] established the converse result that if the Popov criterion was satisfied together with some additional constraints, then there exists a Lyapunov function consisting of a quadratic form plus an integral of the nonlinear term. Jury and Lee [26] have discussed the extension of Popov's method to a class of multinonlinear systems.

Nonlinear sampled-data systems have been studied by Tsypkin [50], [51] and Vidal [52]. Tsypkin [49] and Jury and Lee [25] have discussed the extension of Popov's criterion to nonlinear sampled-data systems.

References

[1] M. A. Aizerman, "On a problem concerning the stability in the large of dynamic systems," *Usp. Mat. Nauk.*, 4, 187-188, 1949.

[2] M. A. Aizerman, and F. R. Gantmacher, *Absolute Stability of Regulator Systems*, San Francisco: Holden-Day, 1964.

[3] D. P. Atherton, *Nonlinear Control Engineering*, London: Van Nostrand Reinhold, 1975.

[4] R. W. Bass, "Mathematical legitimacy of equivalent linearization by describing functions," *Proc. First IFAC World Congress*, Moscow, Butterworth Scientific Publishers, London, 2074-2083, 1960.

[5] A. R. Bergen and M. A. Sapiro, "The parabola test for absolute stability," *IEEE Trans. Automat. Control*, AC-12, 312-314, 1967.

[6] A. R. Bergen and R. L. Franks, "Justification of the describing function method," *SIAM J. Control*, 9, 568-569, 1971.

[7] N. N. Bogoliubov and Y. A. Mitropolsky, *Asymptotic Methods in the Theory of Nonlinear Oscillations*, Moscow, 1958. English translation published by Gordon and Breach, New York, 1961.

[8] J. J. Bongiorno, Jr., "An extension of the Nyquist-Barkhausen stability criterion to linear lumped-parameter systems with time-varying elements," *IEEE Trans. Automat. Control*, AC-8, 166-172, 1963.

[9] —, "Real frequency stability criteria for linear time-varying systems," *Proc. IEEE*, 52, 832-841, 1964.

[10] R. W. Brockett and J. L. Willems, "Frequency domain stability criteria," *IEEE Trans. Automat. Control*, AC-10, 255-261 and 407-413, 1965.

[11] R. W. Brockett, "The status of stability theory for deterministic systems," *IEEE Trans. Automat. Control*, AC-11, 596-606, 1966.

[12] R. W. Brockett and H. B. Lee, "Frequency-domain instability criteria for time-varying and nonlinear systems," *Proc. IEEE*, 55, 604-619, 1967.

[13] B. V. Bulgakov, "Periodic processes in free pseudo-linear oscillatory systems," *J. Franklin Inst.*, 235, 591-616, 1943.

[14] P. A. Cook, "Describing function for a sector nonlinearity," *Proc. IEE*, 120, 143-144, 1973.

[15] A. G. Dewey and E. I. Jury, "A note on Aizerman's conjecture," *IEEE Trans. Automat. Control*, AC-10, 482-483, 1965.

[16] J. Dutilh, "Theorie des servomechanisms a relais," *Onde Elec.*, 438-445, 1950.

[17] R. Fitts, "Two counter-examples to Aizerman's conjecture," *IEEE Trans. Automat. Control*, AC-11, 553-556, 1966.

[18] A. Gelb and W. E. Vander Velde, *Multiple-Input Describing Functions and Nonlinear System Design.* New York: McGraw-Hill, 1968.

[19] L. C. Goldfarb, "On some nonlinear phenomena in regulatory systems," *Avtomatika i Telemekhanika*, 8(5), 349-383, 1947.

[20] P. E. W. Grensted, "Frequency response methods applied to nonlinear systems," in *Progress in Control Engineering*, Vol. I, New York: Academic Press, 103-141, 1962.

[21] W. Hahn, *Theory and Application of Liapunov's Direct Method.* Englewood Cliffs, NJ: Prentice-Hall, 1963.

[22] J. M. Holtzmann, "Contraction maps and equivalent linearization," *Bell Syst. Tech. J.*, 46, 2405-2435, 1967.

[23] —, *Nonlinear System Theory.* New York: Prentice-Hall, 1970.

[24] B. C. Johnson, "Sinusoidal analysis of feedback control systems containing nonlinear elements," *Trans. AIEE*, Part II, 71, 169-181, 1952.

[25] E. I. Jury and B. W. Lee, "On the stability of a certain class of nonlinear sampled-data systems," *IEEE Trans. Automat. Control*, AC-9, 51-61, 1964.

[26] —, "A stability theory for multinonlinear systems," *Proc. Third World Congress IFAC*, London, Session 28, Paper 28a, 1966.

[27] E. I. Jury, *Inners and Stability of Dynamic Systems.* New York: Wiley, 1974.

[28] R. E. Kalman, "Physical and mathematical mechanisms of instability in nonlinear automatic control systems," *Trans. ASME*, 79, 553–566, 1957.

[29] ——, "Liapunov functions for the problem of Lur'e in automatic control," *Proc. Nat. Acad. of Science USA*, 49, 201–205, 1963.

[30] R. J. Kochenburger, "A frequency response method for analysing and synthesizing contactor servomechanisms," *Trans. AIEE*, 69, 270–283, 1950.

[31] J. Kudrewicz, "Stability of nonlinear systems with feedback," *Avtomatika i Telemekhanika*, 25, 8, 1964.

[32] ——, "Theorems on the existence of periodic vibrations based upon the describing function method," *Proc. Fourth IFAC World Congress*, Warsaw, Session 41, pp. 46–60, 1969.

[33] A. I. Mees, "The describing function matrix," *J. Inst. Math. Appl.*, 10, 49–67, 1972.

[34] ——, "Limit cycle stability," *J. Inst. Maths. Appl.*, 11, 281–295, 1973.

[35] A. I. Mees and A. R. Bergen, "Describing functions revisited," *IEEE Trans. Automat. Control*, AC-20, 473–478, 1975.

[36] N. Minorsky, *Theory of Nonlinear Control Systems*. New York: McGraw-Hill, 1969.

[37] K. S. Narendra and C. P. Neuman, "Stability of a class of differential equations with a single monotonic nonlinearity," *SIAM J. Control*, 4(2), 1966.

[38] K. S. Narendra and Y. S. Cho, "An off-axis circle criterion for the stability of feedback systems with a monotonic nonlinearity," *IEEE Trans. Automat. Control*, AC-13, 413–416, 1968.

[39] K. S. Narendra and R. M. Goldwyn, "A geometrical criterion for the stability of certain nonlinear nonautonomous systems," *IEEE Trans. Circuit Theory*, CT-11(3), 406–408, 1964.

[40] K. S. Narendra and J. H. Taylor, *Frequency Domain Criteria for Absolute Stability*, New York: Academic Press, 1973.

[41] W. Oppelt, "Locus curve method for regulators with friction," *Z. Deut. Ingr.*, Berlin, 90, 179–183, 1948.

[42] V. A. Pliss, "Necessary and sufficient conditions for the global stability of a certain system of three differential equations," *Dokl. Akad. Nauk SSSR*, 120, 4, 1958.

[43] V. M. Popov, "Absolute stability of nonlinear systems of automatic control," *Automation and Remote Control*, 21, 961–979, 1961.

[44] P. E. Rapp and A. I. Mees, "Spurious predictions of limit cycles in a non-linear feedback system by the describing function method," *Int. J. Control*, 26, 821–829, 1977.

[45] E. N. Rozenwasser, "The absolute stability of nonlinear systems," *Avtomat. i. Telemekh.*, 24(3), 283–294, 1963.

[46] I. W. Sandberg, "A frequency domain condition for the stability of systems containing a single time-varying nonlinear element," *Bell Syst. Tech. J.*, 43, 1901–1908, 1964.

[47] ——, "On the response of nonlinear control systems to periodic input signals," *Bell Syst. Tech. J.*, 43, 911–926, 1964.

[48] A. Tustin, "The effects of backlash and of speed dependent friction on the stability of closed-cycle control systems," *J. IEE*, 94, Part II, 143–151, 1947.

[49] Ya. Z. Tsypkin, "On the stability in the large of nonlinear sampled-data systems," *Dokl. Akad. Nauk.*, 145, 52–55, 1962.

[50] Ya. Z. Tsypkin and Yu. S. Popkov, *Theory of Nonlinear Sampled-Data Systems*. Moscow: Publishing House "Science," 1973.

[51] Ya. Z. Tsypkin, *Relay Control Systems*. Moscow: Publishing House "Science," 1974.

[52] P. Vidal, *Nonlinear Sampled-Data Systems*. New York: Gordon and Breach, 1970.

[53] L. Wienberg and P. Slepian, "Positive real matrices," *J. Math. and Mechanics*, 9, 71–83, 1960.

[54] J. C. Willems, *Proc. Fourth Allerton Conference on Circuit and System Theory*, p. 836, 1966.

[55] ——, *The Analysis of Feedback Systems*. Cambridge, MA: M.I.T. Press, 1971.

[56] D. Williamson, "Periodic motion in nonlinear systems," *IEEE Trans. Automat. Control*, AC-20, 479–485, 1975.

[57] V. A. Yacubovich, "Solution of certain matrix inequalities occuring in the theory of automatic controls," *Dokl. Acad. Nauk SSSR*, 143, 1304–1307, 1962.

[58] G. Zames, "On the stability of nonlinear, time-varying feedback systems," *Proc. NEC*, 20, 726–730, 1964.

[59] ——, "On the input-output stability of time-varying non-linear feedback systems," *IEEE Trans. Automat. Control*, AC-11, 228–238 and 465–476, 1966.

A Frequency Response Method for Analyzing and Synthesizing Contactor Servomechanisms

RALPH J. KOCHENBURGER
ASSOCIATE AIEE

THIS paper introduces a procedure for synthesizing contactor servomechanisms in which the frequency response of the system is employed. In this respect it represents a radical departure from the techniques used previously to handle the analysis and synthesis of such discontinuous servomechanisms. While these earlier methods all involve step-by-step procedures based upon the transient response, the method proposed here permits the analysis and synthesis procedure to be determined from a knowledge of the response of the components to sinusoidal signals of various amplitudes and frequencies.

The successful application of the proposed method is based upon an approximation which is valid for most of the physical systems encountered in practice. This approximation permits the discontinuous contactor to be represented in terms of a linear describing function. The limitations imposed upon the use of this approximation are discussed in the paper.

Although the proposed method can be profitably applied to both the analysis and synthesis of contactor servomechanisms, it is the synthesis problem which is particularly facilitated by this approach. Instances are described in the paper where a synthesis procedure based on this method resulted in a selection of design constants which greatly enhanced the performance of a representative contactor servomechanism.

Servomechanisms and feed-back control systems in general, may be classified as either continuous types or discontinuous types. Most of the existing literature concerning feed-back systems deals only with the types in which control is continuous, particularly when problems of analysis and synthesis are discussed. The scarcity of published treatments dealing with systems in which control is discontinuous is due, in some part, to the difficulties encountered when such systems are subjected to a rigorous mathematical treatment. On the other hand, discontinuous controls represent a substantial number of the systems used in practice, and methods for analyzing and, still more important, synthesizing them would be of decided practical interest.

Figure 1 is a block diagram representing a simple feed-back control system. Such a system may be subdivided into the error-detecting means, the controller, and the servomotor and output-load combination as shown. It is assumed that a direct feed-back path is employed, and that no additional component need be introduced to represent dynamic factors which modify the feed-back signal. The case when such an additional component need be considered in the feedback can, however, be handled as well by the general method described here. The symbolism used to describe the input and output signals of the various components is indicated in Figure 1.

In the more familiar linear continuous systems, the relationship between the correction and error signals may be expressed as a continuous function. If the controller characteristic is plotted in terms of the quiescent response, or steady-state response to various nonvarying error signals, the relation between the correction signal D and the quiescent value of the error $\mathcal{E}$, called $\mathcal{E}_q$, may be plotted as in Figure 2(A). In discontinuous systems, this relationship cannot be expressed by such a continuous curve. In the discontinuous type of system discussed here, and specifically the contactor type of servomechanism, the D versus $\mathcal{E}_q$ relationship is itself discontinuous, as shown in Figure 2(B). In other words, as the error of the system varies in some continuous manner, the correction signal applied to the servomotor varies in discrete jumps.

Paper 50-44, recommended by the AIEE Committee on Feedback-Control Systems and approved by the AIEE Technical Program Committee for presentation at the AIEE Winter General Meeting, New York, N. Y., January 30-February 3, 1950. Manuscript submitted October 26, 1949; made available for printing December 1, 1949.

RALPH J. KOCHENBURGER is with the University of Connecticut, Storrs, Conn.

The material described in this paper represents some of the results obtained as part of a doctoral thesis research program conducted by the author at the Massachusetts Institute of Technology. The aid of various members of the Electrical Engineering Department and Servomechanisms Laboratory staffs and of H. K. Weiss of the Aberdeen Proving Grounds is gratefully acknowledged. The suggestions and criticisms furnished by Dr. Gordon S. Brown, Director of the Servomechanisms Laboratory, in his capacity as thesis supervisor were particularly helpful. Acknowledgment is due to the United States Air Forces, Air Materiel Command, Armament Laboratory, Wright Field, who sponsored the project under which this work was done.

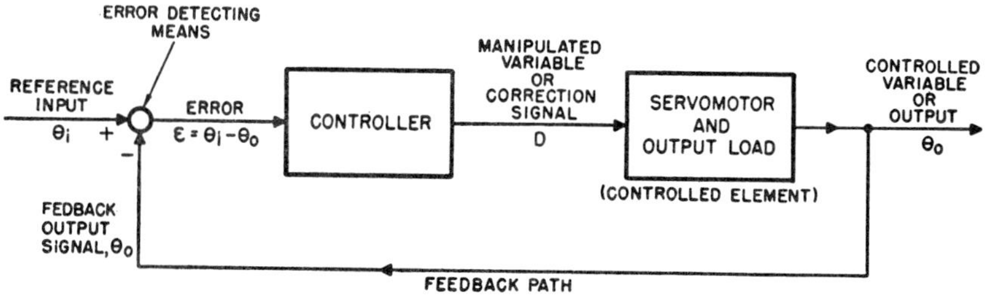

Figure 1. General form of single-loop servomechanism

Reprinted from *AIEE Trans.*, vol. 69, pp. 270–284, 1950.

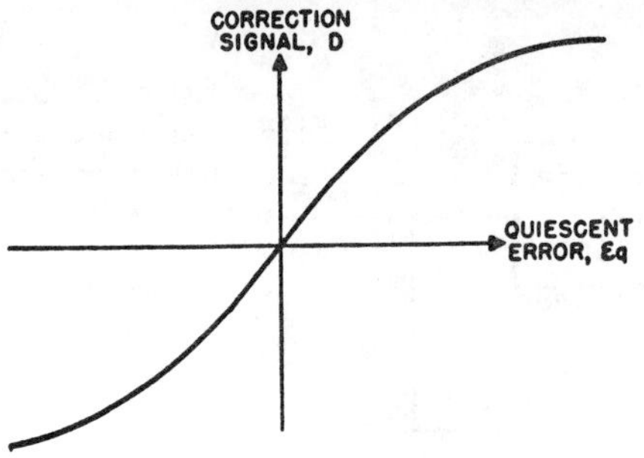

(a) CONTINUOUS SERVOMECHANISM

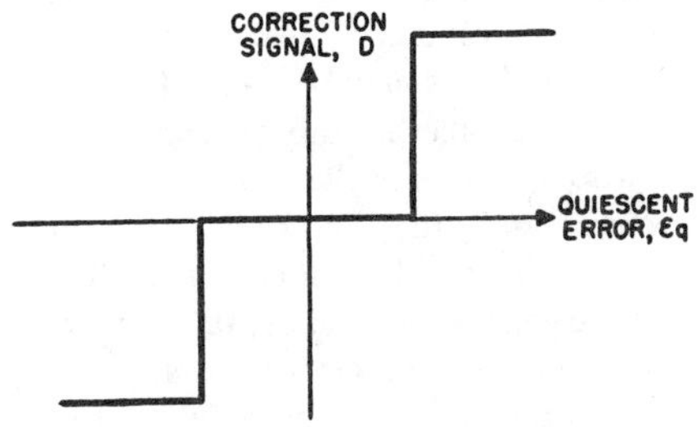

(b) CONTACTOR SERVOMECHANISM

Figure 2. Typical controller relations

The type of controller characteristic shown in Figure 2(B) is found in those systems which employ mechanically or hydraulically actuated electrical contactors, electromagnetic relays, electronic-control circuits of the trigger or flip-flop type, certain types of mechanical clutches, and some hydraulic and pneumatic valves. These devices are distinguished by an all-or-nothing characteristic. Their actual characteristics may be more complicated than shown, but will still possess the distinguishing feature of producing sudden jumps in the value of correction signal D. Because one of the most frequent applications of contactor servomechanisms involves electromagnetic relays, this general class is sometimes described as relay servomechanisms. Contactor servomechanisms have found widespread employment in both military and industrial fields. They frequently possess advantages over continuous types in economy of weight, bulk, complexity, and cost of control equipment. One of the major practical objections to their use has been the nonlinearity of the response relationship. Only the simplest versions have been amenable to analysis. It has been difficult to analyze their performance characteristics and to synthesize design constants and compensating networks which will provide a specified performance.

One of the earliest analyses of contactor-type servomechanisms was published by Hazen[1] in 1934. He employed the direct differential-equation method for analyzing performance and a number of characteristics peculiar to contactor types were demonstrated. This method becomes cumbersome when the system is at all complicated because a new equation must be established and solved for each switching cycle or correction interval initiated by the contactor.

The phase-plane method of analysis provided a simple graphical approach. This method has been employed by various authors[2,3] in connection with other forms of nonlinear systems. It was applied to contactor servomechanisms by Weiss[4] and MacColl[5] and the analyses of certain types of such servomechanisms were shown to be greatly facilitated. Unfortunately, the method is limited to systems possessing relatively few energy-storage elements. A recent AIEE paper by Kahn,[6] based on the differential-equation approach, proposes relatively simple graphical constructions to eliminate some of the computational labor associated with the analysis of such systems.

There are two basic disadvantages to these methods of treatment, which might be characterized as solutions in the time domain. One disadvantage is the great difficulty of treating systems of apparently elementary physical configuration which have only a few energy-storage elements. The second and more significant disadvantage from the standpoint

Figure 3. Typical contactor servomechanism for positional control

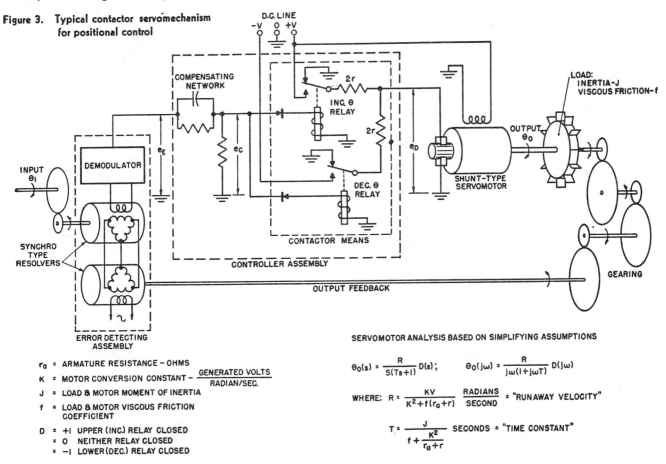

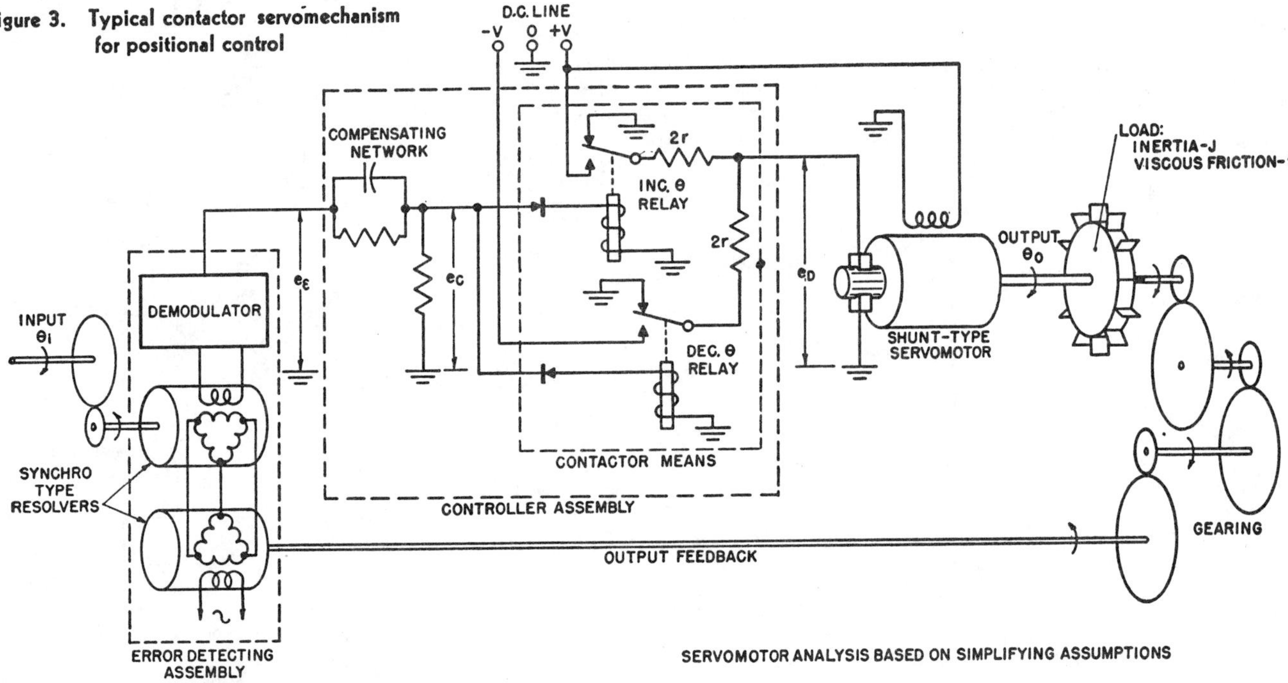

r_a = ARMATURE RESISTANCE – OHMS

K = MOTOR CONVERSION CONSTANT – $\dfrac{\text{GENERATED VOLTS}}{\text{RADIAN/SEC.}}$

J = LOAD & MOTOR MOMENT OF INERTIA

f = LOAD & MOTOR VISCOUS FRICTION COEFFICIENT

D = +1 UPPER (INC.) RELAY CLOSED
= 0 NEITHER RELAY CLOSED
= –1 LOWER (DEC.) RELAY CLOSED

SERVOMOTOR ANALYSIS BASED ON SIMPLIFYING ASSUMPTIONS

$$\theta_o(s) = \frac{R}{s(Ts+1)} D(s); \qquad \theta_o(j\omega) = \frac{R}{j\omega(1+j\omega T)} D(j\omega)$$

$$\text{WHERE: } R = \frac{KV}{K^2+f(r_a+r)} \ \frac{\text{RADIANS}}{\text{SECOND}} = \text{"RUNAWAY VELOCITY"}$$

$$T = \frac{J}{f+\dfrac{K^2}{r_a+r}} \ \text{SECONDS} = \text{"TIME CONSTANT"}$$

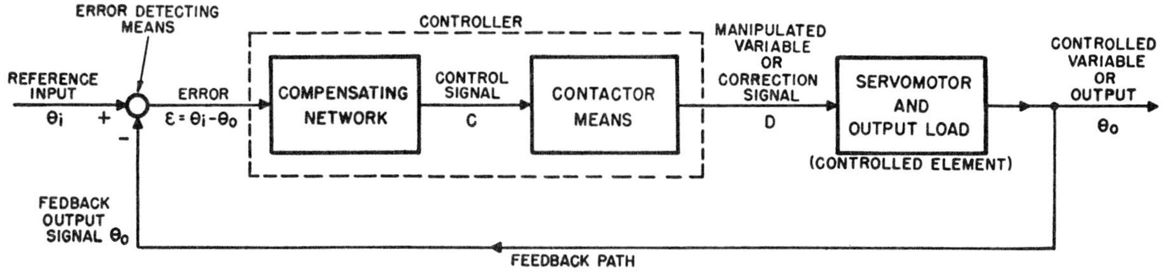

Figure 4. General form of contactor servomechanism

of usefulness is the fact that the methods are not directly adaptable to system synthesis.

It is the purpose of this paper to present an analysis and synthesis procedure in which the frequency response of the system is employed in a manner[7] analogous to its use with continuous servomechanisms. Results obtained by the method have been compared with those obtained by more cumbersome exact methods and with test data* and the agreement has been found sufficient for most engineering applications. The method is not limited by any inherent dynamic complexity, provided the system can be described by a control loop as shown in Figure 1. Furthermore, the proposed method is particularly adapted to synthesis and permits the selection of compensating networks suitable for the attainment of given performance requirements.

*The contactor servomechanism simulator used to obtain the test data was purposely slow to provide ease of measurement: the slow response indicated in the examples should not be considered as generally typical of contactor servomechanisms.

General Configuration of a Contactor Servomechanism

Figure 3 illustrates a typical contactor servomechanism for controlling angular position. In this example, the various signals are represented as voltage equivalents; that is, the voltage e_ε is an indication of the angular error ε. A simple lead-type compensating network is shown in this example.

The compensating network converts the error signal to a new form, here called the *control signal*, before application to the contactor means. When no compensating networks are employed, ε and

C are identical. In almost all cases, the introduction of a suitable compensating network results in improved performance. Networks of mechanical, hydraulic, or electrical forms may be used. In the contactor servomechanism of Figure 3, the controller includes the compensating networks and the succeeding contactor means. This is illustrated again in Figure 4 as a general block diagram of a single-loop contactor servomechanism.

In some cases, compensating networks may be inserted between the contactor means and the servomotor. This is usually less practical than the arrangement shown in Figure 4 because of the

Figure 5 (below). Typical contactor characteristics

Figure 6 (right). Typical electrical phase-lead compensating networks for cascade insertion in control system

$$\frac{e_2}{e_1}(j\omega) = \frac{R_2}{R_0+R_1+R_2} \frac{1+j\omega\tau_a}{1+j\omega\frac{\tau_a}{\alpha}}$$

WHERE: $\tau_a = R_1 C_1$ SECONDS

$\alpha = 1 + \frac{R_1}{R_0+R_2}$ = ATTENUATION FACTOR

(a) SIMPLE PHASE-LEAD COMPENSATING NETWORK

(a) NO INACTIVE ZONE
$C_\Delta = 0$

(b) WITH INACTIVE ZONE, C_Δ
$C_h = 0$

(c) WITH INACTIVE ZONE, C_Δ AND HYSTERESIS ZONE, C_h

$T_1 \triangleq R_3 C_3 = R_1 C_1$ REQUIRED CONDITION, $T_2 \triangleq \frac{L_2}{R_2}$

$$\frac{e_2}{e_1} = \frac{R_2+R_3}{R_0+R_1+R_2+R_3} \frac{1+2\mathfrak{f}_1 j\left(\frac{\omega}{\omega_1}\right)-\left(\frac{\omega}{\omega_1}\right)^2}{1+2\mathfrak{f}_2 j\left(\frac{\omega}{\omega_2}\right)-\left(\frac{\omega}{\omega_2}\right)^2}$$

WHERE: $\omega_1 = \sqrt{\frac{1+\frac{R_3}{R_2}}{T_1 T_2}}$ $\mathfrak{f}_1 = \frac{R_2(T_1+T_2)}{2\omega_1(R_2+R_3)}$

$\omega_2 = \sqrt{\frac{1+\frac{R_0+R_1+R_3}{R_2}}{T_1 T_2}}$ $\mathfrak{f}_2 = \frac{R_2(T_1+T_2)+R_0 T_1}{2\omega_2(R_0+R_1+R_2+R_3)}$

(b) RESONANT LEAD NETWORK

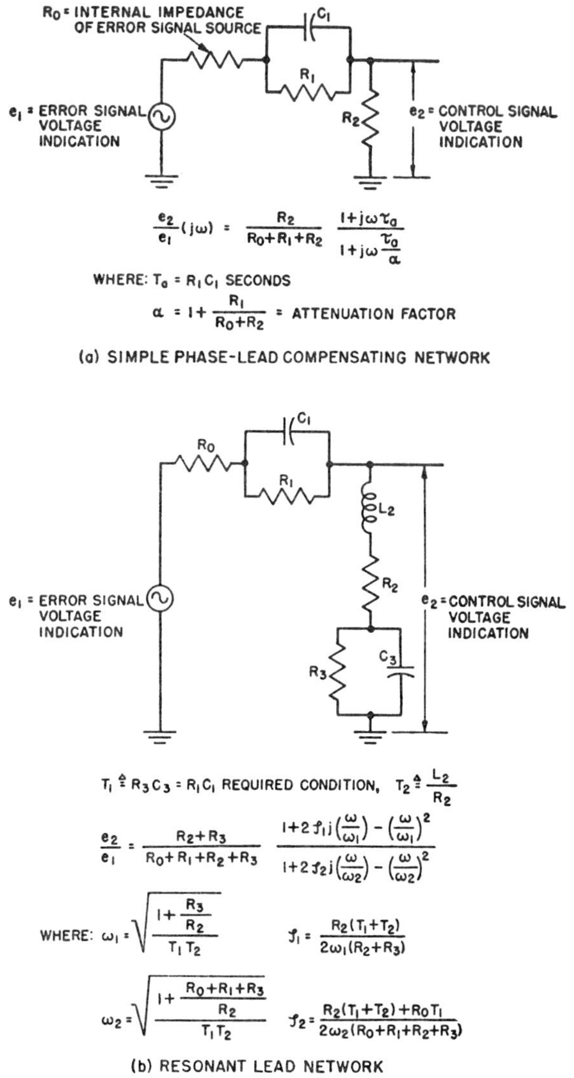

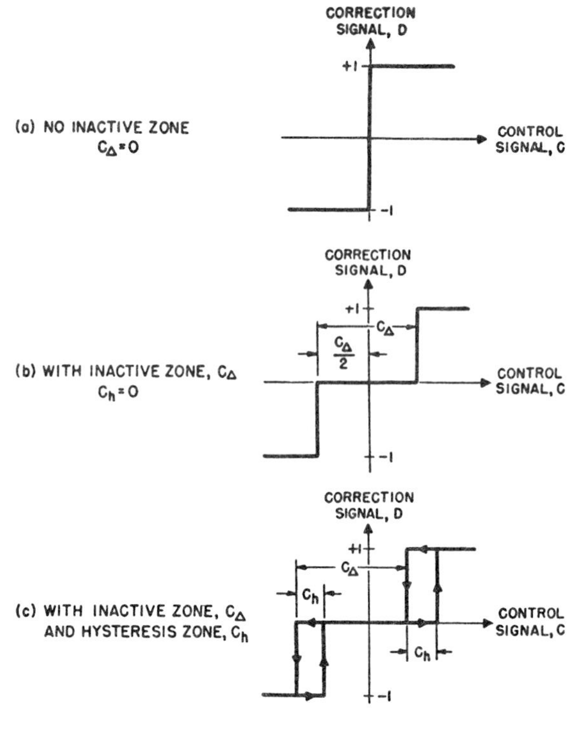

higher power level at which the network is operated. When the network is directly cascaded with the servomotor and appears after the contactor means, its characteristics are generally lumped with those of the servomotor for purposes of analysis.

The contactor may be considered as a discontinuous power amplifier. The relay shown in Figure 3 represents one particular type. The relationship between C and D might follow one of the characteristics shown in Figure 5. In these diagrams, symmetrical operation is assumed in that the corrective efforts associated with positive and negative correction are identical in magnitude. It is convenient to express the correction signal D in dimensionless units, assigning it the value $D=+1$ when positive correction is initiated by the contactor and causes the servomotor to increase the output θ_o and $D=-1$ when negative correction is initiated.

In Figure 5(A), a relationship is shown where the contactor will initiate either positive or negative correction, depending on the algebraic sign of the control signal C. In this case, the *inactive zone* or range of error within which no corrective effort arises is zero. In Figure 5(B) an inactive zone, C_Δ, is introduced and the control signal must have a magnitude greater than $C_\Delta/2$ before corrective effort is initiated; otherwise the correction signal will merely be expressed by $D=0$. An inactive zone may be unavoidable because of physical limitations, but often it is purposely introduced because it contributes to dynamic stability. A system using a contactor possessing the characteristic of Figure 5(A) will always oscillate about some equilibrium point while one having an inactive zone as in Figure 5(B) can be designed to remain in a state of rest when no significant disturbance is applied. Since the inactive zone represents the range of permissible error within which no corrective action is initiated, it should not be excessively large. On the other hand, there is no point in making it smaller than the accuracy requirements of the application might stipulate. One of the basic problems of system synthesis is the selection of compensating networks which will permit adequate dynamic stability for some specified range of inactive zone. This problem becomes more difficult as the specified range of inactive zone becomes smaller.

Many contactors possess a hysteresis effect. This means that the control signal necessary to initiate correction is greater than that necessary to cease correction. In the case of electromagnetic relays, for example, the coil current of an already-closed relay must usually be reduced to some value lower than that which originally caused the relay to close before the relay will reopen. Figure 5(C) illustrates the effect as designated by the symbol C_h.

It can be shown that a hysteresis effect generally adversely affects the dynamic stability.

More complicated types of contactor characteristics are met in practice; for example, nonsymmetrical corrective action, or multistep contactors. These will not be discussed in detail but the general method of treatment to be introduced is applicable to them as well.

The other components of the contactor servomechanism, as shown in Figures 3 and 4, are the servomotor and the error-detecting means. Both of these usually exist in essentially the same form as in continuous systems. In a contactor servomechanism, however, it is rarely necessary to design for continuously variable control of speed. This greatly simplifies the equipment.

Performance Criteria of a Contactor Servomechanism

The performance criteria of contactor servomechanisms are basically the same as for continuous types. Static accuracy is one of the major design considerations. It is the possible range of error which can exist when the servomechanism is in a state of rest and which will not be sufficient to initiate corrective action. The static accuracy is therefore met by keeping the range of the inactive zone within specified limits.

Dynamic accuracy defines the extent to which errors are minimized when the system is responding to a disturbance. Such errors are best minimized by designing a system that will possess adequate speed of response and relative stability.

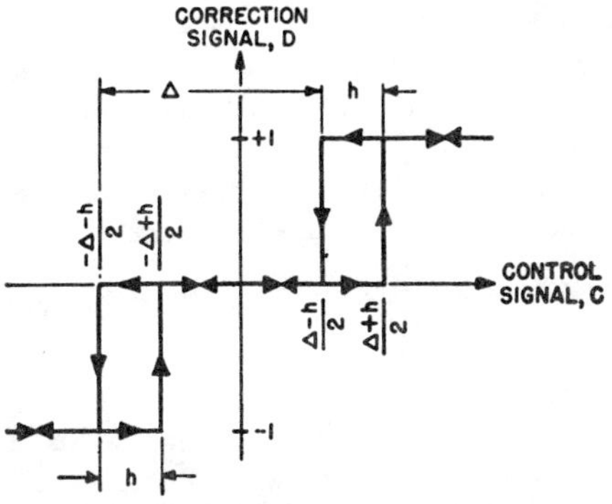

Figure 7. Dimensionless representation of contactor characteristics (case involving both inactive zone and hysteresis)

Speed of response deals with the rapidity by which errors are reduced to a tolerable level following some disturbance. The fastest response may be obtained by:

1. Using a runaway velocity that is as large as the stability limitations and servomotor capabilities permit.
2. Having the frequencies associated with any damped transient oscillation as high as possible.
3. Having adequate degree of stability for transient oscillations of amplitude greater than the region of error tolerance.

Stability is the tendency of a system to approach an equilibrium condition without excessive oscillation. Absolute stability is descriptive of a system incapable of self-sustained oscillations. Degree of stability refers to the rate with which transient oscillations disappear after a disturbance. A distinction must be made between the stability requirements imposed on nonlinear systems and those imposed on linear types. For the former, continuous self-sustained oscillations of a small amplitude may be permissible. For the latter, the amplitude of any self-sustained oscillations would tend to increase to an undesirably high value.

For contactor servomechanisms, performance requirements may be met by specifying a range of inactive zone consistent with the static accuracy requirements and a runaway velocity consistent with the desired speed of response. Once these are chosen, the major problem remaining is the selection of components which will provide adequate stability. The remainder of this paper is devoted primarily to the problem of stability.

Mathematical Representation of Characteristics

Transfer Functions

The assumption commonly employed in the study of continuous servomechanisms, that all components possess linear characteristics, will be applied to all of the components of a contactor servomechanism except the contactor. Each of these linear components may then be described in terms of its transfer functions or ratios of output to input.

Servomotor Characteristics

The transfer function of the servomotor, designated as $G_s(s)$, is defined by the ratio

$$G_s(s)=\frac{\theta_o(s)}{D(s)} \tag{1}$$

where $\theta_o(s)$ and $D(s)$ are the Laplace transforms of the output $\theta_o(t)$ and the

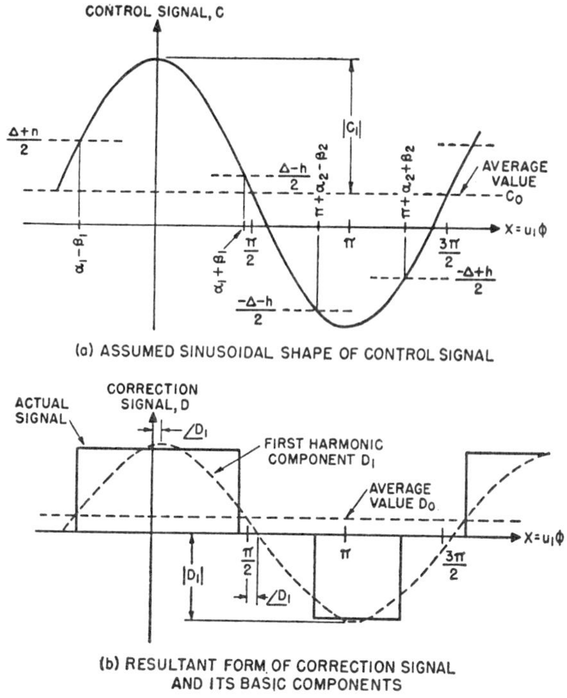

Figure 8 (left). Relation of correction signal to control signal for a simple contactor with hysteresis

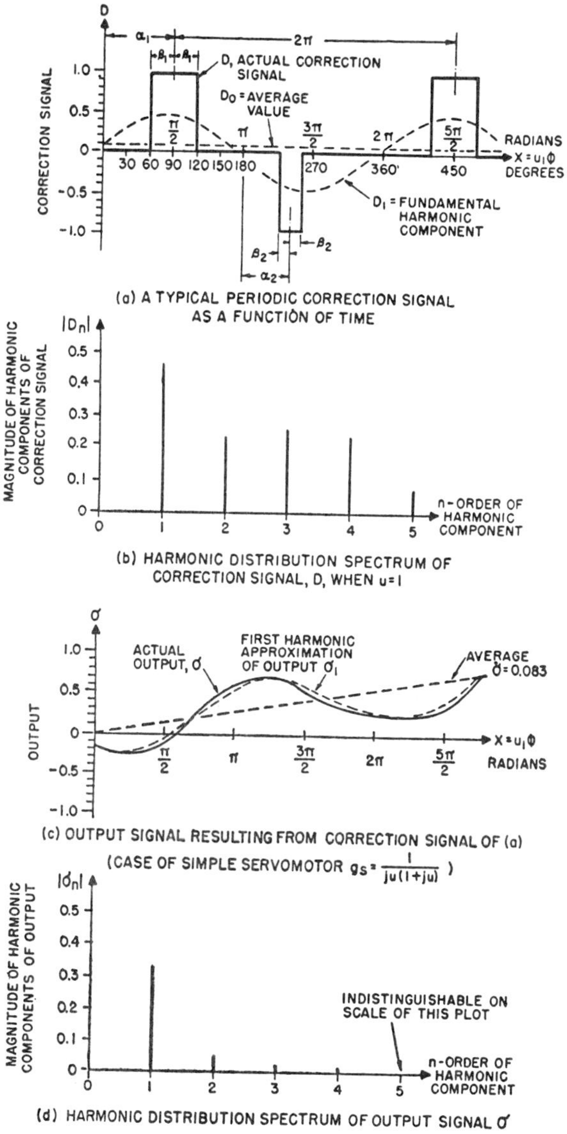

Figure 9 (right). Comparison—exact response of servomotor with that obtained from fundamental harmonic approximation

correction signal $D(t)$, subject to zero initial conditions. When the polynomials of the transfer function are factored, it will appear as

$$G_s(s)=\frac{\theta_o(s)}{D(s)}=\frac{R(1+\tau_1 s)(1+\tau_2 s)\ldots}{s(1+T_1 s)(1+T_2 s)(1+T_3 s)\ldots}\quad \text{units of output quantity} \qquad (2)$$

The τ's and T's are time constants which may be either real or complex. Equation 2 applies to the most common form of servomotor which approaches the condition of a constant output rate of R output units per second. The quantity R is the runaway velocity for a given correction signal applied for a sufficiently long time. The linear factor s in the denominator of the transfer function represents a single-order pole at the origin of the complex s plane and identifies a system having a sustained rate for a constant input signal. The servomotor or equivalent may have other forms of transfer function; for example, in regulator applications, there may be no pole at the origin while, in other applications a higher-order pole may exist. Only transfer functions of the form given in equation 2 are treated herein although the method is generally applicable to any form.

The transfer function also might be described in terms of its steady-state response to various real frequencies by substituting the imaginary quantity $j\omega$ for the operator s ($\omega=2\pi f$=angular frequency).

Equation 2 then assumes the form

$$G_s(j\omega)=\frac{\theta_o(j\omega)}{D(j\omega)}=\frac{R(1+j\omega\tau_1)(1+j\omega\tau_2)\ldots}{j\omega(1+j\omega T_1)(1+j\omega T_2)(1+j\omega T_3)\ldots} \qquad (3)$$

One advantage of the frequency-function form is the fact that, when the component being considered is not practically subject to an analysis based upon its design constants, the complex transfer function $G(j\omega)$ may often be expressed in graphical form on the basis of actual tests. The method of analysis and synthesis to be described here possesses the advantage that such graphical data may be directly employed. It is not necessary to convert $G(j\omega)$ to an analytic form.

The type of servomotor and load combination shown in Figure 3 has an elementary transfer function if, for example, coulomb friction, armature reaction and armature inductance are neglected. In this case, $G_s(j\omega)$ becomes

$$G_s(j\omega)=\frac{R}{j\omega(1+j\omega T)} \qquad (4)$$

where the relations for determining the runaway velocity R and the time constant T are given in Figure 3. For many engineering purposes, this simplified form of relationship is adequate for analysis and synthesis. Similar transfer functions arise in many other servomotors.

Compensating Networks

The characteristics of the compensating network may similarly be expressed in terms of a transfer function $G_c(j\omega)$ as

$$G_c(j\omega)=\frac{(1+j\omega\tau_a)(1+j\omega\tau_b)\ldots}{(1+j\omega T_a)(1+j\omega T_b)\ldots}=\frac{C(j\omega)}{\mathcal{E}(j\omega)} \qquad (5)$$

It will be noted that at zero frequency $G_c(j\omega)$ is unity. This is because both C and $\mathcal{E}$ are expressed in units of the output quanity; C being described in terms of the equivalent value of $\mathcal{E}$ under quiescent

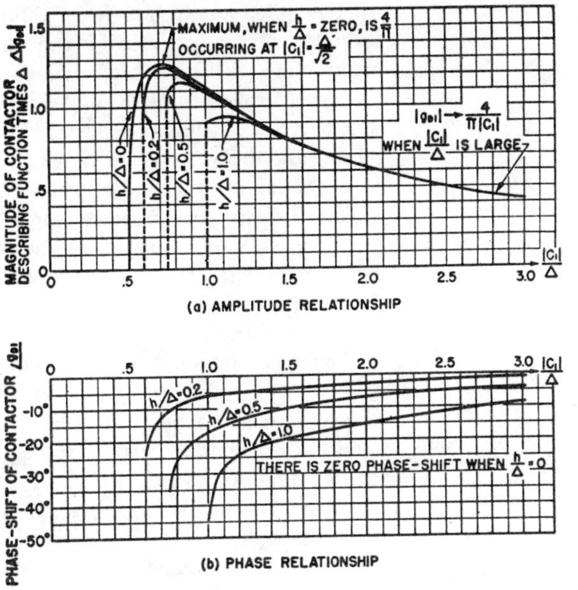

Figure 10 (left). Plot of the fundamental harmonic transfer function g_D—simple contactor with hysteresis ratio h/Δ, for case of zero input velocity ($d\delta/dt=0$) and zero load torque ($\delta_L=0$)

conditions. Any attenuation or amplification occurring within the controller is described in terms of its effect on the range of inactive zone. This range is the sole measure of the zero-frequency gain of the system.

Figure 6 shows two common forms of compensating network for producing a phase-lead effect. For these networks, the transfer functions are given by

$$G_c(j\omega)=\frac{1+j\omega\tau_a}{1+j\omega\frac{\tau_a}{\alpha}} \quad \text{network of Figure 6(A)} \qquad (6)$$

and

$$G_c(j\omega)=\frac{1+2\zeta_1 j\left(\frac{\omega}{\omega_1}\right)-\left(\frac{\omega}{\omega_1}\right)^2}{1+2\zeta_2 j\left(\frac{\omega}{\omega_2}\right)-\left(\frac{\omega}{\omega_2}\right)^2} \quad \text{network of Figure 6(B)} \qquad (7)$$

where

ζ_1, ζ_2 = numerator and denominator damping ratios, respectively
ω_1, ω_2 = numerator and denominator resonant frequencies, respectively

In the network of Figure 6(A), called a simple phase-lead network, the transfer function given in equation 6 includes the attenuation factor α, computed as shown in the diagram. The higher the value of α the more effective phase-lead effect is obtained. However, a high value of α results in a relative increase in the transmission of high-frequency noise. Some engineering compromise concerning its value is therefore required in practice.

Since the phase-lead effect of the circuit shown in Figure 6(A) cannot exceed 90 degrees, it may be inadequate for some applications. The resonant lead network shown in Figure 6(B) may then be employed. Equation 7 represents the transfer function of this latter network. Examples will be given where the use of these compensating networks materially improve system performance.

The Over-all Loop Transfer Function

Since the components represented by G_s and G_c are essentially linear and have transfer functions which depend only upon the applied frequency, they are called the frequency-variant portions of the system. On the other hand, the contactor, considered as having no dynamic lag but having a discontinuous characteristic, is nonlinear and therefore dependent on signal amplitude. Any dynamic lag action occurring in a physical contactor is conveniently lumped with either the servomotor or compensating network. The contactor represents the amplitude-variant portion of the system, and its describing function G_D, although independent of frequency, is dependent upon the control signal C. Other nonlinear effects such as backlash may be treated similarly in terms of amplitude-variant describing functions.

The over-all loop transfer function $G(j\omega)$ or combined transfer function of all linear and frequency-variant components is particularly significant. With the arrangement shown in Figure 4, this would merely be

$$G(j\omega)=G_s(j\omega)G_c(j\omega)=\frac{C(j\omega)}{D(j\omega)}_{\theta_1=\text{constant}}$$

$$=\text{loop transfer function} \qquad (8)$$

It will be shown how the loop transfer function and the contactor describing function may be used together to determine the performance characteristics of the control system.

Dimensionless Notation

The mechanics of analyzing and synthesizing contactor servomechanisms are simplified and the results obtained acquire more general utility if a dimensionless form of notation is used. This procedure is employed in many engineering fields and the system of notation proposed here is an expansion and modification of that introduced by Weiss.[4]

As a first step select a convenient time base t_b seconds. Then divide all variables and constants having the dimensions of time by t_b in order to obtain the corresponding dimensionless value; for example, $\phi=t/t_b$=elapsed time. A convenient time base is frequently obtained

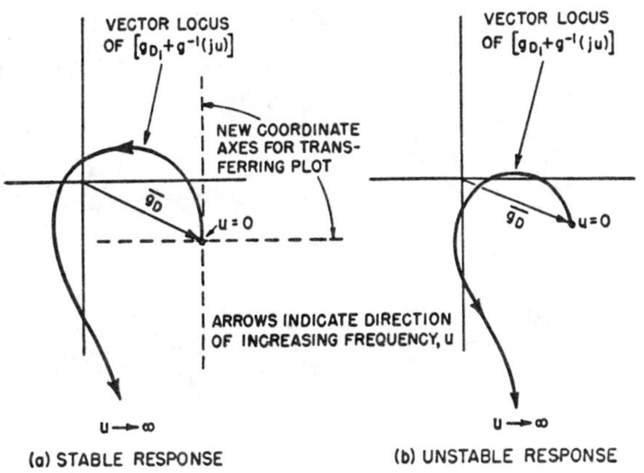

Figure 11 (left). Inverse response-function loci for single-loop servomechanisms

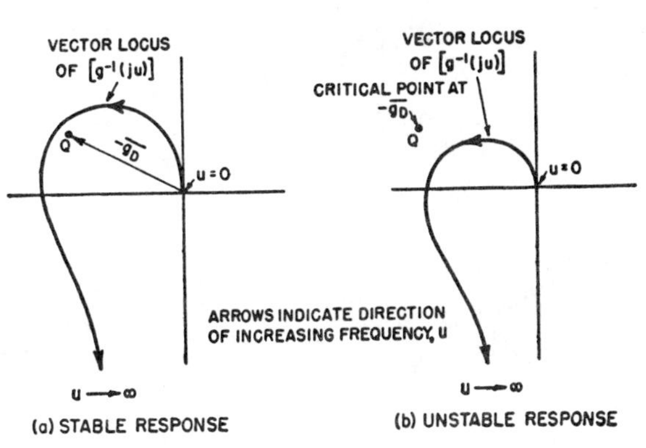

Figure 12 (right). Inverse transfer-function loci for single-loop servomechanisms

Table I. Dimensional and Dimensionless Symbols Used

	Quantity	Dimensional Symbol	Units	Dimensionless Symbol
Time Units	Time base	t_b	Seconds	
	Elapsed time	t	Seconds	$\phi = t/t_b$
	Time derivative operator	$p = d/dt$	Seconds^{-1}	$\lambda = t_b p = d/d\phi$
	Applied angular frequency	ω	Seconds^{-1}	$u = \omega t_b$
Signals in Control System	Signal base	$B = Rt_b$	Output-Units	
	Output	θ_o	Output-Units	$\sigma = \theta_o/B$
	Input	θ_i	Output-Units	$\delta = \theta_i/B$
	Error	$\mathcal{E} = \theta_i - \theta_o$	Output-Units	$\varepsilon = \mathcal{E}/B = \delta - \sigma$
	Control signal	C	Output-Units	$c = C/B$
	Correction signal	D	Dimensionless	D (same)
System Properties	Runaway velocity	R	Output-Units / Seconds	Unity
	Inactive zone	C_Δ	Output-Units	$\Delta = C_\Delta/B$
	Hysteresis range	C_h	Output-Units	$h = C_h/B$
	Transfer functions:			
	Of servomotor	$G_s = \dfrac{\theta_o}{D}$	Output-Units	$g_s = \dfrac{\sigma}{D}$
	Of compensating network	$G_c = \dfrac{C}{\mathcal{E}}$	Dimensionless	$g_c = \dfrac{c}{\varepsilon}$
	Over-all loop	$G = G_s G_c$	Output-Units	$g = g_s g_c$
	Describing function of contactor	G_D where $D = G_D(C)$		g_D where $D = g_D(c)$
	Transfer function properties: Time constant			
	In numerator	τ	Seconds	$\rho = \dfrac{\tau}{t_b}$
	In denominator	T	Seconds	$\gamma = \dfrac{T}{t_b}$
	Natural frequency	$\omega_1, \omega_2, \ldots$	Seconds^{-1}	$u_1 = \omega_1 t_b$, $u_2 = \omega_2 t_b \ldots$
	Damping ratio associated with a natural frequency	$\zeta_1, \zeta_2, \ldots$	Dimensionless	ζ_1, ζ_2 .... (same)
	Attentuation factor of a compensating network	α	Dimensionless	α (same)

by setting $t_b = |T_1|$, where T_1 is the smallest time constant of the servomotor. In equation 4, for example, the only time constant T is naturally the lowest and $t_b = T$.

The next step is to select an output signal base B. All signals, such as the output θ_o, are divided by B in order to obtain the dimensionless equivalents, for example, the dimensionless output is expressed as $\sigma = \theta_o/B$. The inactive zone and hysteresis ranges, C_Δ and C_h, are dimensionlessly expressed as: $\Delta = C_\Delta/B$, $h = C_h/B$. The most convenient signal base B is the product of the runaway velocity and the time base, namely Rt_b. Table I summarizes the dimensional and dimensionless notation used.

In dimensionless form, the transfer functions of the servomotor and compensating network given in equations 3 and 5 become

$$g_s(ju) = \frac{(1+ju\rho_1)(1+ju\rho_2)\ldots\ldots}{ju(1+ju\gamma_1)(1+ju\gamma_2)\ldots} \qquad \text{(3A)}$$

$$g_c(ju) = \frac{(1+ju\rho_a)(1+ju\rho_b)\ldots\ldots}{(1+ju\gamma_a)(1+ju\gamma_b)\ldots\ldots} \qquad \text{(5A)}$$

The transfer function of the simple second-order servomotor expressed in equation 4 now is

$$g_s(ju) = \frac{1}{ju(1+ju)} \qquad \text{(4A)}$$

The simple lead-compensating network and the resonant lead-controller network shown in Figures 6(A) and 6(B) now have the following dimensionless forms

$$g_c(ju) = \frac{1+ju\rho_a}{1+ju\dfrac{\rho_a}{\alpha}} \qquad \text{(6A)}$$

$$g_c(ju) = \frac{1+2\zeta_1 j\left(\dfrac{u}{u_1}\right) - \left(\dfrac{u}{u_1}\right)^2}{1+2\zeta_1 j\left(\dfrac{u}{u_2}\right) - \left(\dfrac{u}{u_2}\right)^2} \qquad \text{(7A)}$$

The Frequency-Response Method of Analysis and Synthesis

The frequency-response method of analysis and synthesis has been found to be a practical means for treating essentially linear servomechanisms.[7,8,9] By this method it is possible to determine whether the system possesses absolute stability; that is, whether it is capable of maintaining self-sustained oscillations. By various rules-of-thumb, it also is possible to reach qualitative conclusions concerning the degree of stability which are adequate for most engineering purposes. This technique uses frequency loci arranged in various forms to suit the convenience of the user; the well-known polar-locus plots are one example.

In view of the successful application of the frequency-response method to linear systems, its application to contactor servomechanisms appears desirable. The nonlinear relationship describing the contactor operation has impeded such an application. In the preceding sections it was necessary to express this relationship in terms of a describing function; it could not be expressed in terms of a linear transfer function. The frequency-response method is therefore not applicable unless certain assumptions are made.

In order to determine whether an adaptation of the frequency-response method might not be applied, let it be assumed that a sinusoidal control signal is applied to a typical contactor. Suppose that the contactor has the more general characteristic shown in Figure 7. If the control signal c is of the form

$$c = c_0 + |c_1| \cos u\phi \qquad (9)$$

the contactor will initiate a positive correction when $c = \Delta/2 + h/2$, cease correction when $c = \Delta/2 - h/2$, initiate negative correction when $c = -\Delta/2 - h/2$, and cease correction when $c = -\Delta/2 + h/2$. These instants of time are designated by the angles, $u\phi = \alpha_1 - \beta_1$, $= \alpha_1 + \beta_1$, $= \pi + \alpha_2 - \beta_2$, and $= \pi + \alpha_2 + \beta_2$, respectively. This is shown in Figure 8(A). The angles $2\beta_1$ and $2\beta_2$ represent the duration of the positive and negative pulses, respectively; the angles α_1 and α_2 represent the phase lags associated with the respective pulses.

Figure 8(B) shows the rectangular form of the resultant periodic correction signal

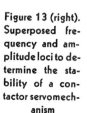

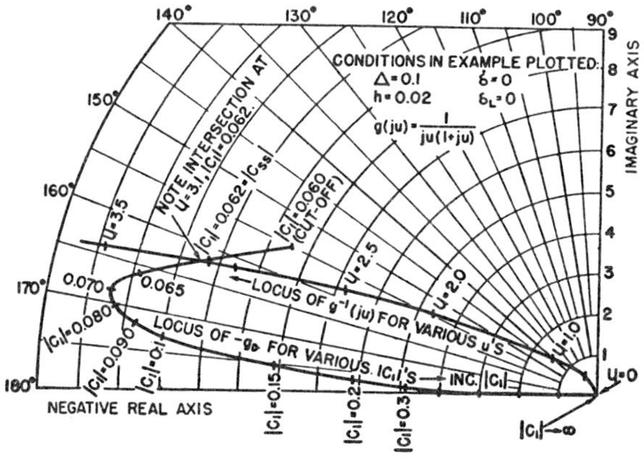

Figure 13 (right). Superposed frequency and amplitude loci to determine the stability of a contactor servomechanism

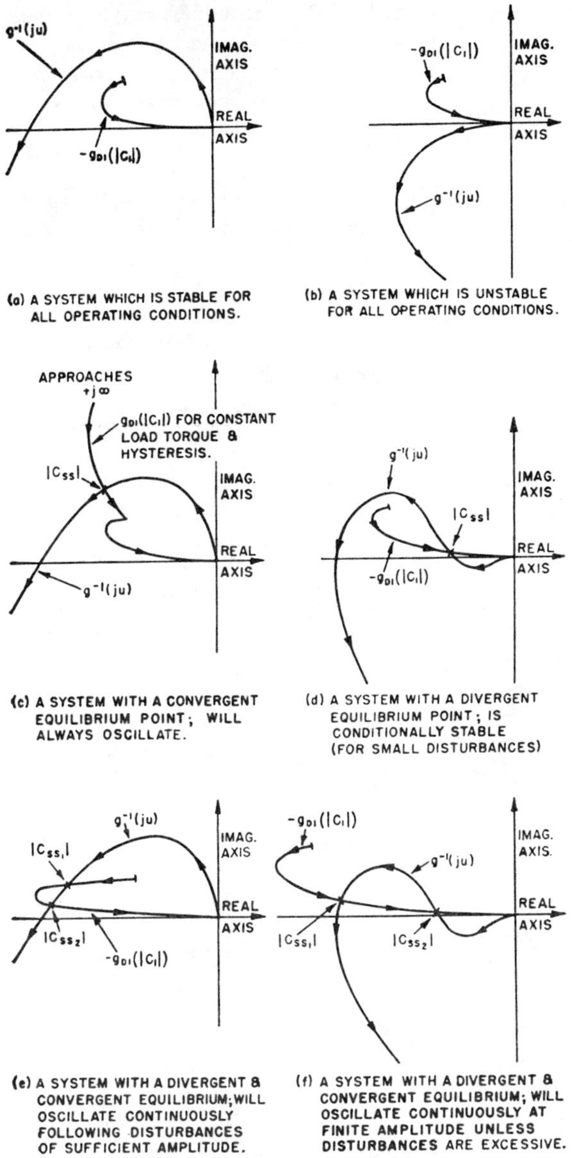

Figure 14 (left). Significance of various relative configurations of the loci

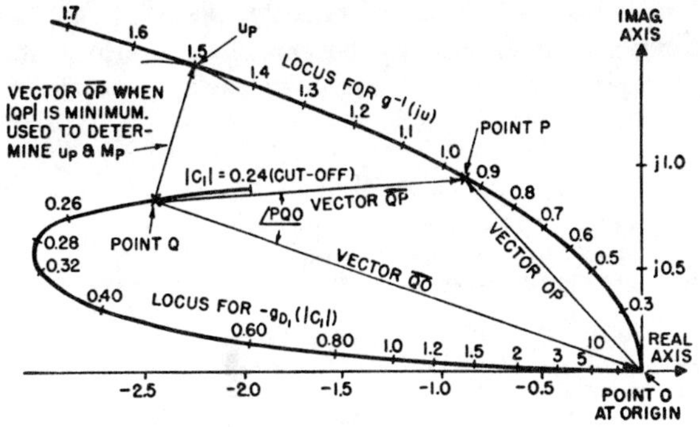

Figure 15 (right). Vector relationships in loci diagram (used to determine relative stability)

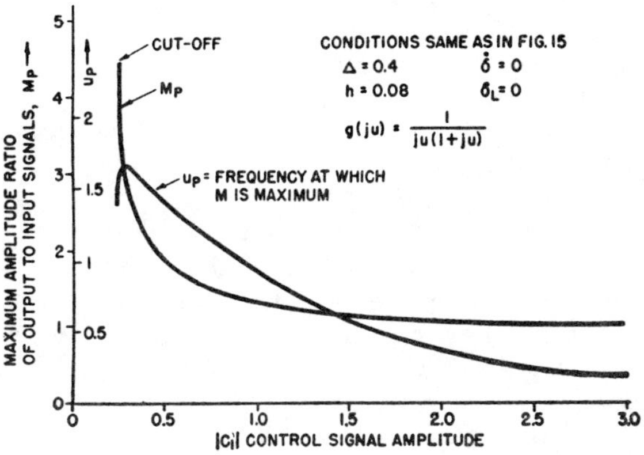

Figure 16 (right). Values of M_p and u_p (used in determining relative stability and speed of response)

D. The broken-line relation plotted in Figure 8(B) shows the average or zero-frequency component D_0 and fundamental harmonic component D_1 of this rectangularly shaped signal. Higher harmonic components which contribute to the corners of the rectangular shape are not shown.

If the correction signal consisted only of D_0 and D_1, only sinusoidally varying signals would exist throughout the system when sinusoidal inputs were applied. The contactor would then appear as a quasi-linear transfer device in that it would operate as a linear amplifier for any given constant amplitude of control signal. It would not operate as a truly linear device because of the nonlinear relationship between input and output amplitudes. Considering the contactor as such a quasi-linear device will permit the frequency-response method to be used in determining the system stability for any given control signal amplitude. The approximation which permits the higher harmonic components to be neglected so that the quasi-linear representation of the contactor may be employed must now be justified.

Figure 9 shows the relative importance of the harmonic components of the signals in a typical contactor servomechanism. Figure 9(A) shows a typical rectangular correction signal resulting from a periodic control signal. Figure 9(B) represents the harmonic spectrum associated with this correction signal. It is assumed, for example, that the servomotor has the typical transfer function given in equation 4, and that the fundamental frequency of the control signal is designated by the relation $u=1$. Under these considerations, an exact determination of the resultant servomotor output σ obtained by a mathematical determination of the repeated transients, would appear as plotted by the solid-line curve of Figure 9(C). The harmonic distribution of this output signal is shown plotted in Figure 9(D). It may be seen that, while the original correction signal D possessed higher harmonic components of significant amplitudes (referring back to Figure 9(B), these higher harmonic components have relatively small amplitudes, compared with the fundamental, when measured as part of the output signal.

The minor importance of the role played by the higher harmonic components also is demonstrated by the broken-line curve of the output response in Figure 9(C). This curve, designated as σ_1, represents the output response which would have been obtained if only the average and fundamental components of the correction signal had been present. It may be seen that this latter response curve is a fairly good approximation of the exact response represented by the solid-line curve.

If the higher-harmonic components may be considered negligible as far as the output signal is concerned, their contribution to the error and control signals will generally have minor significance. This in turn tends to justify the original assumption of a truly sinusoidal control signal.

It is therefore proposed that the frequency-response method of analysis be used where the contactor characteristic is described in terms of a quasi-linear describing-function g_D where the subscript *1* is used to indicate that the describing function takes into account only the fundamental harmonic component. This function neglects the higher harmonics with the following justifications:

1. The normal frequency spectrum of a rectangular wave involves progressively smaller amplitudes for increasing orders of the harmonic components.

2. Most servomotors serve as effective low-pass filters and minimize the importance of the higher-harmonic components.

Justification (1) above is valid for most cases but becomes less applicable under conditions where the pulse widths associated with the correction signals are short compared with the duration of the intervals between pulses. A periodic impulse signal of zero pulse width has odd harmonic components of equal magnitudes. Justification (2) was demonstrated using the example of an elementary servomotor; more complicated servomotors should serve as still more effective low-pass filters. On the other hand, it is conceivable that when servomotors exhibit marked resonance effects, the validity of the approximation may suffer under certain conditions where one of the neglected harmonic components might have a frequency near resonance and its effect on performance might therefore be particularly prominent.

At any rate, the previously-mentioned approximation is proposed so that the frequency-response method can be employed. Some conclusions concerning the general accuracy of the method may be reached by the comparisons given herein between the results thus obtained with those obtained by more exact methods of computation or by actual test. It should be kept in mind that the method proposed is an engineering approximation and that, even in the case of the better-understood continuous linear servomechanisms, conclusions regarding stability that are accurate to within 10-20 per cent are frequently satisfactory.

The Quasi-Linear Representation of the Contactor Describing-Function

The contactor may be approximately represented in the manner just described and cases involving the application of constant rates of input change or constant load disturbances may be taken into account. This entails additional mathematical complication because the duration of positive and negative corrective pulses will differ ($\beta_1 \neq \beta_2$). For brevity, only the case where symmetrical corrective operation occurs ($\beta_1=\beta_2$) will be discussed. This implies the condition of zero average load torque and zero average rate-of-change of input.

Under this latter condition, the input signal δ may be of the form

$$\delta=\delta_0+\delta_1 \cos u\phi \tag{10}$$

In order to determine the relative stability of the system when subjected to such an input signal, only the steady-state response need be considered when the frequency-response method is employed. Under such steady-state conditions, since the average value of input is constant, the average value of the output σ_0 also is constant. This can be the case only if the average component of the correction signal D_0 is zero, since from equation 2, the presence of an average component of D would result in an integrating action because of the s factor in the numerator of $G_s(s)$ and a $D_0\phi$ term would appear in the corresponding time solution for the response. The assumed sinusoidal nature of the control signal was expressed by equation 9. The average value of D or D_0 is given by

$$D_0=\frac{\beta_1-\beta_2}{2\pi} \tag{11}$$

Since, for this case $D_0=0_0$, $\beta_1=\beta_2$, and the operation is symmetrical. But, from the trigonometric relations shown in Figure 8

$$\beta_1=\frac{1}{2}\left\{\cos^{-1}\left[\frac{\Delta-h-2c_0}{2|c_1|}\right]+\cos^{-1}\left[\frac{\Delta+h-2c_0}{2|c_1|}\right]\right\} \tag{12A}$$

$$\beta_2=\frac{1}{2}\left\{\cos^{-1}\left[\frac{\Delta-h+2c_0}{2|c_1|}\right]+\cos^{-1}\times\left[\frac{\Delta+h+2c_0}{2|c_1|}\right]\right\} \tag{12B}$$

Since $\beta_1=\beta_2$ the average value of control signal c_0 must be zero, in which case

$$\beta=\beta_1=\beta_2=\frac{1}{2}\left\{\cos^{-1}\left(\frac{\Delta-h}{2|c_1|}\right)+\cos^{-1}\left(\frac{\Delta+h}{2|c_1|}\right)\right\} \tag{13}$$

Similarly, the phase-lag angles α_1 and α_2 shown in Figure 8 will be equal and will be

$$\alpha=\alpha_1=\alpha_2=\frac{1}{2}\left\{\cos^{-1}\left(\frac{\Delta-h}{2|c_1|}\right)-\cos^{-1}\left(\frac{\Delta+h}{2|c_1|}\right)\right\} \tag{14}$$

The foregoing results indicate that, for the case of an input disturbance represented by equation 9 and with zero average load torque, there will be zero average component of control signal. This also is based on the original assumption that the contactor exerts equal amounts of positive and negative corrective effort. Therefore, c_0 is zero and equation 10 simply becomes

$$c=|c_1| \cos u\phi \tag{15}$$

Since any average component of the error $\mathcal{E}$ or $\mathcal{E}_0$ would result in a finite value of c_0, the average error for the condition just considered will be zero.

By means of a Fourier analysis of the rectangular corrective pulse shown in Figure 8, the fundamental harmonic component may be shown to be

$$D_1=|D_1| \cos (u\phi+\underline{/D_1}) \tag{16A}$$

where

$$|D_1|=\frac{2}{\pi}\sqrt{\sin^2\beta_1+\sin^2\beta_2+2\sin\beta_1\sin\beta_2\times\cos(\alpha_1-\alpha_2)} \tag{16B}$$

$$\underline{/D_1}=-\tan^{-1}\frac{\sin\alpha_1\sin\beta_1+\sin\alpha_2\sin\beta_2}{\cos\alpha_1\sin\beta_1+\cos\alpha_2\sin\beta_2} \tag{16C}$$

If the fact that $\alpha=\alpha_1=\alpha_2$ and $\beta=\beta_1=\beta_2$ is considered, these equations acquire the simpler form

$$|D_1|=\frac{4}{\pi}\sin\beta \tag{17A}$$

$$\underline{/D_1}=-\alpha \tag{17B}$$

where the values of α and β are given in equations 13 and 14.

The contactor describing function, g_{D_1} may now be expressed in a manner similar to that used to describe transfer functions of linear components, that is, as the mathematical ratio of the output and input quantities, or

$$g_{D_1}=\frac{D_1}{c_1} \tag{18A}$$

which is written in vector form as

$$g_{D_1}=\frac{|D_1|}{|c_1|}\underline{/D_1}=\frac{4}{\pi}\frac{\sin\beta}{|c_1|}\underline{/-\alpha} \tag{18B}$$

The above expression represents the describing function for the quasi-linear approximate equivalent of the contactor. The angles α and β given in equations 13 and 14 are functions of the inactive-zone range Δ, the hysteresis range h, and the control-signal amplitude $|c_1|$. The amplitude and phase angle associated with the function g_{D_1} may be conveniently plotted as a function of the ratio $|c_1|/\Delta$ for various ratios of the quantity h/Δ representing the hysteresis effect. This has been done in Figure 10.

Figure 10 shows the amplitude and phase angle associated with the contactor describing-function for various control-signal amplitudes and various conditions of contactor hysteresis. It may be noted that the describing function is independent of the frequency u. However, a phase lag is involved because of the hysteresis effect. When the control amplitude $|c_1|$ is less than $(\Delta+h)/2$, it is insufficient to actuate the contactor and, as shown in the diagram, the magnitude of g_{D_1} remains zero.

Stability Criteria for Contactor Servomechanisms

In view of the approximation proposed, the contactor servomechanism may be considered as equivalent to a system involving all linear components if a single constant signal amplitude $|c_1|$ is considered at a time. Under these conditions the describing function g_{D_1} may be treated in the same manner as a conventional transfer function. The ratio of the output response of the servomechanism shown in Figure 4 to a sinusoidally varying control signal of some dimensionless frequency u and of fixed amplitude $|c_1|$ would then be given by

$$\sigma(ju) = g_{D_1} g(ju) \varepsilon(ju) \tag{19}$$

where

$$g(ju) = g_c(ju) g_s(ju)$$

= loop transfer function

The error by definition is

$$\varepsilon(ju) = \delta(ju) - \sigma(ju) \tag{20}$$

If equations 19 and 20 are combined, the response ratio is conveniently given in inverse form as

$$\frac{\delta}{\sigma}(ju) = \frac{g^{-1}(ju) + g_{D1}}{g_D} \tag{21}$$

where

$$g^{-1}(ju) = \frac{1}{g(ju)}$$

A system having an inverse response ratio as in equation 21 will be stable if, for a polar locus of $\delta/\sigma(ju)$ drawn for the complete range of frequencies, $-\infty < u < +\infty$, the origin of the plot always appears to the left of this locus as the locus is traversed in the direction of increasing frequency. This criterion is merely a simplified version of the well-known Nyquist criteria for stability. It applies only to single-loop systems.

Since only the orientation of the locus with respect to the origin is of interest, the criterion given could be applied as well to a locus representing merely the numerator of equation 21. Therefore only the locus of $g^{-1}(ju)+g_{D_1}$ need be plotted, since the quantity g_{D_1} appearing in the denominator of equation 21 is independent of frequency and simply represents a scale factor. This has been done in constructing the typical locus of Figure 11. In this example Figure 11(A) represents a stable system which fulfills the criterion. On the other hand the case represented by Figure 11(B) is unstable.

In the case of the loci of $g^{-1}(ju)+g_{D_1}$ shown in Figure 11, the origin was the critical point whose location with respect to the locus determined stability. However, it is convenient to shift the coordinate axes along the vector g_{D_1}. These translated axes are shown as broken lines in Figure 11. In Figure 12, the coordinate axes have been translated in this fashion and the point which was formerly the origin is now the point Q located at the tip of the vector $-g_{D_1}$. If such translated axes are used, the stability criterion given may be revised as follows:

If a polar locus of the inverse-loop transfer function $g^{-1}(ju)$ is drawn over the range of frequencies, u, and if a critical point Q is located at the tip of the describing-function vector $-g_{D_1}$ the system will be stable provided the point Q always appears to the left of the locus as the latter is traversed from zero to infinite frequency. Figure 12 demonstrates the application of the above criterion.

The foregoing test for absolute stability may be made for any specified value of control-signal amplitude $|c_1|$. It might in fact be found that the system will be stable for some amplitudes and unstable for others. The location of the point Q is dependent on the value of $|c_1|$. In order to obtain a complete picture of the stability, it is necessary that a second locus be drawn connecting the points Q over the complete amplitude range being considered. This curve will be referred to as the amplitude locus to distinguish it from the frequency locus plotted for the function $g^{-1}(ju)$.

The amplitude locus is drawn by plotting the tips of the vector values of the function $-g_{D_1}$ and connecting them by a curve. The two loci are superposed on the same graph and their relative orientation determines the stability characteristics of the system.

Figure 13 is an example of the superposed loci. The frequency locus shown is that representing the simple-loop transfer function given by the equation

$$g(ju) = \frac{1}{ju(1+ju)} \text{ or } g^{-1}(ju) = ju(1+ju) \tag{22}$$

The amplitude locus of Figure 13 represents the contactor describing function under conditions of a zero-average input velocity ($\delta=0$) and zero-average load torque. It was obtained from Figure 10 and represents a hysteresis effect given by $h/\Delta=0.2$.

In the case shown in Figure 13, the two loci intersect at the amplitude $|c_1|=0.062$. From the criterion just given, operating points on the amplitude locus corresponding to lower values of $|c_1|$, $0.060<|c_1|<0.062$, are unstable. Oscillations existing at these amplitudes will result in a tendency for the amplitude to increase. Operating points corresponding to higher values of $|c_1|$, that is, $|c_1|>0.062$, are stable. Oscillations existing at these amplitudes will result in a tendency for the amplitude to decrease. At the intersection itself, where $|c_1|=0.062$, the oscillations will tend to be maintained at this amplitude because this intersection corresponds to the borderline condition of stability.

The intersection point of the two loci is described as an equilibrium point. Because of the fact that higher amplitudes of oscillation decrease and lower amplitudes increase, the system's operating point tends to converge at this equilibrium point, it is therefore described as a point of convergent equilibrium.

The graphical construction shown in Figure 13 indicates that any initial disturbance sufficient to initiate the contactor, that is, $|c_1|>0.060$, will result in oscillations which will approach a self-sustained condition with an amplitude and frequency corresponding to the intersection point of the two loci. Disturbances less than sufficient to trip the contactor are beyond the cut-off point of the amplitude locus, where $g_{D_1}=0$, and naturally no oscillations result.

From Figure 13, the self-sustained oscillations will correspond to a dimensionless control-signal amplitude of $|c_1|=0.062$ (the error amplitude is the same since $g_c=1$) and a dimensionless frequency ratio given by $u=3.1$. The graphical construction which provides this result depends upon the basic approximation mentioned previously. It is therefore interesting to compare the predicted result with that actually observed or computed by more exact methods. Such calculations show that the actual conditions of steady-state self-sustained oscillations would be given by $|c_1|=0.066$ and $u=3.2$. The agreements concerning amplitude and frequency are within $6^1/_2$ per cent and 3 per cent respectively.

Convergent and Divergent Equilibrium

The preceding section illustrated an intersection of loci that indicated a con-

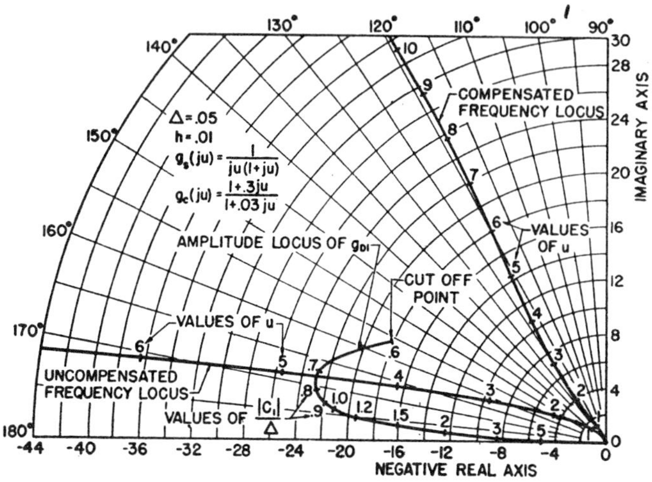

Figure 17. Loci diagrams illustrating stability improvement resulting from use of a phase-lead compensating network

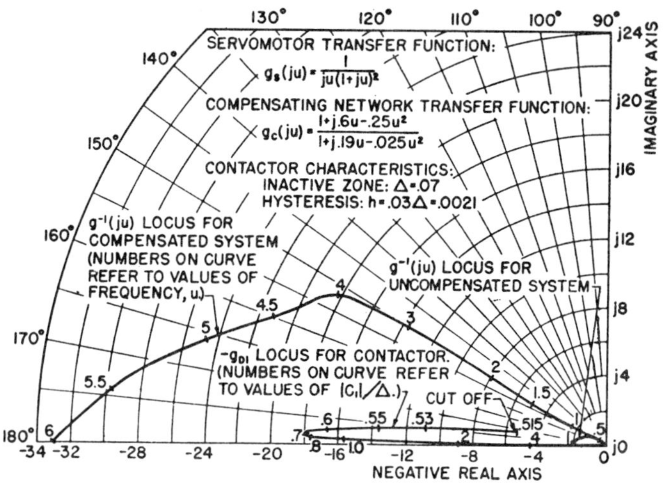

Figure 18. Loci plots for contactor servomechanism with critically damped servomotor

vergent condition of equilibrium. Figure 14 illustrates other possible configurations of the loci, some of which involve one or more intersections. In general, these intersections indicate convergent equilibrium if a slight increase in $|c_1|$ from its value at the intersection causes the locus of $-g_{D1}$ to enter the stable region and if a slight decrease causes it to enter the unstable region. In this event, self-sustained oscillations may result. If the intersections possess the converse properties, the equilibrium condition is divergent; it then does not correspond to a condition of self-sustained oscillation, but merely represents an amplitude boundary. The operating point will always tend to shift away from such a divergent equilibrium point. It may be noted from Figure 14 that the loci always intersect at the origin, corresponding to the condition that $|c_1| \rightarrow \infty$ and $u \rightarrow 0$. The origin equilibrium points are divergent in Figures 14(A), (C), and (E) and the amplitude of any oscillations which might arise will tend to decrease until either a convergent equilibrium point is reached or the contactor cut-off point, as marked by the abrupt termination of the amplitude locus is reached. The origin equilibrium points in Figures 14(B), (D), and (F) are convergent, indicating that if these systems are subjected to disturbances of sufficient magnitude, destructive oscillations will result.

It also might be noted that, in Figure 10, the amplitude of g_{D1} is plotted in terms of the quantity Δg_{D1}. This function is therefore inversely proportional to Δ for a given amplitude ratio $|c_1|/\Delta$. The inactive-zone range Δ appears as a reciprocal scale factor affecting the amplitude locus. The scale of this locus may be varied by changing the inactive-zone range, and the stability characteristics of the system may thus be altered. In the cases shown in Figures 13 and 14(A) and (E), the response can always be made stable for all conditions of operation by making the inactive-zone sufficiently large.

Degree of Stability

In many applications of contactor systems, a specification that requires merely a stable system is inadequate. The requirement that any transient oscillation following the correction of disturbance shall involve sufficient damping also is imposed. In other words the degree of stability is of importance.

In the case of linear servomechanisms, a rule-of-thumb procedure has been developed[7] which gives an indication of the degree of stability from the frequency-response loci. This procedure is to determine the peak value M_p of the output-input ratio $M=|\theta_o/\theta_i|=|\sigma|/|\delta|$. In general, it is found that satisfactory damping exists if $M_p<1.3$, the exact limit imposed depending upon the application. This rule-of-thumb method must be used with caution. When it is backed up by the designer's past experience, successful system designs are obtained.

It is proposed that a similar rule-of-thumb criterion be used to determine the degree of stability of contactor servomechanisms. Figures 15 and 16 show how this might be done. Figure 15 contains the two loci shown previously in Figure 13. However, the inactive-zone range has been increased to a value of $\Delta=0.4$. Under this condition, the system will possess absolute stability, as shown by the fact that the loci do not intersect.

The peak ratio of output-to-input amplitudes M_p may be determined for a given control-signal amplitude $|c_1|$ by graphical means now to be described. Equation 21 may be inverted and rewritten as

$$\frac{\sigma}{\delta}(ju)=\frac{g_{D1}}{g^{-1}(ju)+g_{D1}}=\frac{\text{output}}{\text{input}} \tag{23}$$

In Figure 15 the quantity g_{D1} is represented by the vector $\boldsymbol{QO}$ and the quantity $g^{-1}(ju)$ by the vector $\boldsymbol{OP}$. The sum appearing in the denominator of 23 will therefore be represented by the vector sum $(\boldsymbol{QO}+\boldsymbol{OP})$ or by the connecting vector $\boldsymbol{QP}$. The output-input ratio is therefore expressed by the vector ratio

$$\frac{\sigma}{\delta}(ju)=\frac{\boldsymbol{QO}}{\boldsymbol{QP}} \tag{24}$$

The amplitude ratio or value of M is merely

$$M=\left|\frac{\sigma}{\delta}(ju)\right|=\frac{\text{length of } \boldsymbol{QO} \text{ vector}}{\text{length of } \boldsymbol{QP} \text{ vector}} \tag{25}$$

For a given value of $|c_1|$ the vector length $|\boldsymbol{QO}|$ is constant. Therefore M_p or the peak value of M over the frequency range is given by

$$M_p=\left|\frac{\boldsymbol{QO}}{\boldsymbol{QP}}\right|_{\min}=\frac{\text{length of } \boldsymbol{QO} \text{ vector}}{\text{minimum length of } \boldsymbol{QP} \text{ vector}} \tag{26}$$

The minimum length of the $\boldsymbol{QP}$ vector is found by drawing an arc of shortest possible radius, tangent to the frequency-response locus from the point Q as a center. The frequency u at the point of tangency of the $\boldsymbol{QP}_{\min}$ vector with the frequency-variant locus is designated as the peak frequency u_p.

The values of M_p and u_p determined over the entire range of control-signal amplitude $|c_1|$ provide a complete picture of degree of stability. This is shown in Figure 16. For the case considered in the examples, the values of M_p and u_p increase with a decrease in control-signal amplitude. This indicates that during the beginning of a correction process involving high control-signal amplitudes, the system would act as though it possessed adequate response damping and had a relatively low natural frequency. On the other hand, as the correction process approached completion, the degree of stability would become poor and the frequency associated with the transient oscillations would increase. This is a common characteristic of uncompensated contactor servomechanisms. When an actual servomechanism having the properties represented by Figures 15 and 16 was subjected to a large disturbance, the initial correction process appeared well damped but slow with a moderate initial overshoot, but the final portion of the correction process appeared poorly damped but more rapid. Eight positive and eight negative corrective impulses were initiated by the contactor before the correction process ceased and the error finally remained within the inactive zone.

The foregoing example represents a servomechanism possessing a low degree of stability, as evidenced by the value of M_p approaching 4.5 before the cut-off point is reached. It has been found from experimental tests on various types of contactor systems that an M_p of 2.0 near the cut-off point and of 1.3 for higher control-signal amplitudes provides a satisfactory degree of relative stability for most applications.

In the example shown, the degree of stability was poor in spite of the large inactive zone. It is obvious that compensating networks are desirable to improve the response in even the most elementary types of contactor servomechanisms.

Application of a Simple Phase-Lead Type Compensating Network

The example in the preceding section involved a low degree of stability in spite of the large inactive zone employed ($\Delta=0.4$). In most practical applications, a smaller inactive zone would be specified because of accuracy considerations and a typical value might be given by: $\Delta=0.05$. In that case, the amplitude locus would appear as in Figure 17. The uncompensated frequency locus is the same as in the preceding example. Because of the decrease in Δ, the loci intersect and self-sustained oscillations occur. The point of intersection indicates that these oscillations involve a control-signal amplitude $|c_1|=0.74\Delta=0.35$, at a frequency $u=4.70$. Experimental tests indicate that the control-signal amplitude of oscillation (which also equals the error and output amplitudes since no compensation is assumed) is given by $|c_1|=0.040$ at a measured frequency $u=4.30$. The discrepancy between calculated values and test values is only 12 and 10 per cent, respectively.

A compensating network of the form shown in Figure 6(A) was employed to improve stability. An attenuation factor $\alpha=10$ was specified since this represents a practical compromise between the problem of obtaining a large phase lead and that of minimizing the amplification of noise signals. Plotting loci curves corresponding to various trial values of the time constant ratio ρ_a, given in equation 6A shows that the best stability characteristics are obtained when $\rho_a=0.3$. The dimensionless transfer function of the compensating network is then

$$g_c(ju)=\frac{1+0.3ju}{1+0.03ju} \tag{27}$$

The compensated frequency locus shown in Figure 17 is based on the network of equation 27. The frequency and amplitude loci no longer intersect and self-sustained oscillations will not occur. Furthermore, if the rule-of-thumb criterion for degree of stability is used as described previously, the value of M_p is a maximum when the control-signal amplitude $|c_1|$ is just at the cut-off point and is given by $M_{p\max}=1.76$. In view of the previous discussion on degree of stability, the compensated system should be adequately stable.

An experimental version of this servomechanism confirmed the results predicted above. The test equipment involved a runaway velocity R of 30 degrees per second and a time constant T of 2.3 seconds, giving a signal base of the dimensionless notation as $B=RT=69$ degrees. The actual inactive zone was 3.5 degrees (or $\Delta=C_\Delta/B=3.5/69=0.05$). The compensating network had a numerator time constant τ_a of equation 6 given by $\tau_a=\rho_a t_b=\rho_a T=0.3\times 2.30=0.69$ seconds. The electrical constants for the network of Figure 6(A) are $R_0=4{,}000$ ohms, $R_1=1.45$ megohms, $R_2=157{,}000$ ohms, and $C_1=1.0$ microfarad. When this compensating network was used, a sudden input change of 360 degrees resulted in an initial error overshoot of 15 degrees and then an undershoot of two degrees. The error then remained within the inactive-zone range. Such a response would be considered to have adequate degree of stability for most applications.

This experimental test not only confirmed the conclusions reached from the loci diagram, but also demonstrated that the addition of the compensating network resulted in a spectacular improvement in the transient response. It is interesting to note that the optimum value of the numerator time constant $\tau_a=0.69$ seconds selected on the basis of the loci diagram was also the optimum when experimentally selected by trial-and-error means.

Application of a Resonant Phase-Lead Type of Compensating Network

A contactor servomechanism possessing more complicated dynamic characteristics has also been investigated. The servomotor transfer function corresponding to equation 3 was

$$G_s(j\omega)=\frac{30}{j\omega(1+2.3j\omega)^2}\text{ degrees} \tag{28}$$

The runaway velocity was $R=30$ degrees per second as before. The basic time constant was again $T=2.30$ seconds. However, the transfer-function term involving the time constant is now second order and the servomotor response is critically damped. The dimensionless transfer function of the servomotor then is reduced to

$$g_s(ju)=\frac{1}{ju(1+ju)^2} \tag{29}$$

The uncompensated frequency locus in Figure 18 corresponds to the loop transfer function of the servomechanism without the compensating network. The amplitude loci curve of Figure 18 corresponds to a contactor inactive-zone range of $\Delta=0.07$ and a hysteresis effect given by $h=0.03\ \Delta=0.021$. This ratio of h to Δ represents a typical practical minimum for many applications. The two loci intersect at a value of control-signal amplitude $|c_1|=9.5\Delta=0.66$ which is relatively large. This would correspond to self-sustained oscillations with an error amplitude of 46 degrees. It would be necessary to increase the inactive-zone range to an impractically high value $\Delta=0.63$ or a static error range of $\pm B\Delta/2=\pm 69\times 0.63/2=\pm 22$ degrees in order to suppress these oscillations. The need for a compensating network is obvious.

Trial constructions of loci indicated that suitable compensation was not obtainable with a simple lead controller of the type shown in Figure 6(A). A resonant lead network similar to that shown in Figure 6(B) was therefore used.* The

*The actual compensating network possessed the same characteristics as that of Figure 6(B); however, a circuit arrangement employing electronic feedback was used. This was done in order to avoid the use of the impractically high values of inductance and capacitance which would otherwise have been required.

characteristics were selected by trial-and-error, graphical constructions of the frequency locus being employed. It was found that a resonant lead controller having a transfer function of the form stated in equations 7 and 7A provided the best response with the following constants

$\zeta_1=0.6$ $\zeta_2=0.6$

$u_1=2$ $u_2=6.3$

$\omega_1=\frac{u_1}{t_b}=0.87\frac{\text{radians}}{\text{second}}$ $\omega_2=\frac{u_2}{t_b}=2.76\frac{\text{radians}}{\text{second}}$

$$\text{attenuation constant } \frac{\omega_2^2}{\omega_1^2}=10$$

With a compensating network of this type the frequency-response curve is that described as the compensated-frequency locus in Figure 18. Since no intersections of the amplitude and frequency loci occur, the system is stable. The maximum value of M_p is determined graphically as $M_{p\max}=2.5$. This value is somewhat higher than that specified previously but indicates that a reasonable degree of relative stability might be expected.

Experimental tests incorporating this compensating network with a critically damped servomotor having a transfer function of the form given in equation 29 were conducted. The transient response appeared satisfactory. A sudden input change of 360 degrees resulted in an initial error overshoot of 27 degrees, a subsequent undershoot of 13 degrees, an overshoot of seven degrees, and then an undershoot of two degrees before the correction process was completed. The total correction process described involved a time interval of 37 seconds; half of this time involved the initial correction process prior to the first overshoot when the speed of response is limited by the value of runaway velocity. In view of the inherently slow response of the servomotor (purposely made so to provide ease of measurement), the performance may be considered satisfactory.

The results described above corresponded to an inactive-zone range of 4.6 degrees ($\Delta=0.07$). From Figure 18, a reduction in the inactive-zone range to a value given by $\mathcal{E}_\Delta=2.5$ degrees ($\Delta=0.038$) would be just sufficient to cause the two loci curves to intersect and self-sustained oscillations to result. This change in inactive zone would be represented by a simple increase in the scale of the amplitude loci curve by the factor 0.07/0.038. The loci curves indicate that these oscillations would have a frequency given by $u=5.9$ or $\omega=ut_b=2.56$ radians per second or a period of $2\pi/\omega=2.45$ seconds, and a control-signal amplitude given by $|c_1|=0.027$. The corresponding dimensional error amplitude would be $|\mathcal{E}|=B|c_1|/g_c(j5.9)=0.76$ degrees.

Actual tests indicated that it was necessary to reduce the inactive-zone range to a value of $\mathcal{E}_\Delta=2.7$ degrees before self-sustained oscillations could occur. This is within 8 per cent of the predicted value of 2.5 degrees. The observed period of oscillation was 2.7 seconds, or 10 per cent longer than the predicted value of 2.45 seconds, and the error amplitude was 3/4 degree or equal to the predicted value of 0.76 degrees as closely as could be determined in view of the accuracy of measurement.

The condition of self-sustained oscillations obtained with the smaller inactive zone might be acceptable for some applications of contactor servomechanisms. On the other hand if the application's specifications prohibit such oscillations, an 80 per cent increase in inactive-zone range would provide the reasonably well-damped transient response described previously. It is to be noted that the error amplitude associated with self-sustained oscillations can be considerably smaller than the inactive-zone range when a phase-lead type compensating network is employed.

The effectiveness of the compensating network is best demonstrated by the fact that, in the case of the uncompensated system, an inactive-zone range given by $\Delta=0.63$ was required to prevent the occurrence of excessive self-sustained oscillations. With the addition of the compensating network an inactive-zone range of $\Delta=0.038$ was sufficient to prevent oscillation. This is a permissible improvement in static accuracy by a factor of seventeen.

Experimental Verification of the Theory

The examples previously mentioned represented several cases where the predicted performance was compared with that obtained by actual experimental tests. These tests were performed on a model of a contactor servomechanism designed to simulate actual systems. This simulator employed a shunt-type d-c motor as the servomotor and operated essentially as shown by Figure 3. The actual circuit details were, however, considerably more complicated than shown in that diagram. Various adjustable dynamic characteristics and contactor characteristics were provided and extraneous factors which might lead to incorrect results were minimized by suitable design. The simulator was designed so that the inactive-zone range and hysteresis range could be adjusted, so that the servomotor transfer function could assume varied forms including those involving finite time delays, and so that various compensating networks could be introduced. The details of construction of this device and that of the electronic-feedback type resonant-lead controller mentioned in the preceding section are not discussed here since they are not directly pertinent to the subject matter.

The instances given where the results predicted by the theory were compared with experimentally observed data represent only several examples of a large number of such tests made for various types of contactor servomechanism problems. In general, the percentage agreement was the same as shown in these examples. It was considered desirable that the results obtained by the simulator be of a form which could be visually recorded so that electrical recording instruments would not generally be required. For this reason, the relatively slow runaway velocity of 30 degrees per second and the basic time constant of 2.30 seconds were chosen. By employing proper scale factors, faster servomechanisms may still be represented by the simulator. The purposely slow response of the simulator should be kept in mind when evaluating the results described in the preceding sections; the dimensional performance figures given are not necessarily typical.

Conclusions

The investigation described in this paper leads to the following basic conclusions:

A frequency-response method of analysis and synthesis may be adapted to contactor servomechanisms by employing a simple approximation. This method is usually capable of providing sufficiently accurate results for most engineering applications.

The performance of contactor servomechanisms can be materially improved, in even the simplest cases, by the introduction of suitable compensating networks. The proposed frequency-response method of treatment is particularly adaptable to the selection of such networks.

The approximate method of treatment used here in application to contactor servomechanisms also is generally applicable to the analysis and synthesis of other nonlinear systems. It might prove of particular value if the nonlinear effects, such as backlash, coulomb friction, saturation, and so forth, appearing in essentially linear servomechanisms were treated by this means. It is hoped that the technique introduced here will contribute to the more effective employment of contactor servomechanisms in control applications.

References

1. Theory of Servomechanisms, **H. L. Hazen.** *Journal,* Franklin Institute (Philadelphia, Pa.), volume 218, number 3, September 1934, pages 279–330.

2. Theory of Oscillation (book), **A. A. Andronow, C. E. Chaikin.** Moscow, 1937. English Edition edited by Solomon Lefschetz. Princeton University Press, Princeton, N. J., 1949.

3. Introduction to Non-Linear Mechanics (book), **Nicholas Minorsky.** J. W. Edwards Brothers, Ann Arbor, Mich.

4. Analysis of Relay Servomechanisms, **H. K. Weiss.** *Journal of the Aeronautical Sciences* (New York, N. Y.), volume 13, July 1946.

5. Fundamental Theory of Servomechanisms (book), **L. A. MacColl.** D. Van Nostrand Company, New York, N. Y., appendix—Study of a Simple On-Off Servomechanism, 1945.

6 An Analysis of Relay Servomechanisms, **D. A. Kahn.** *AIEE Transactions,* volume 68, part II, 1949, pages 1079–88.

7. Principles of Servomechanisms (book), **G. S. Brown, D. P. Campbell.** John Wiley and Sons, New York, N. Y., 1948.

8. Fundamental Theory of Servomechanisms (book), **L. A. MacColl.** D. Van Nostrand Company, New York, N. Y., chapter I-VII, 1945.

9. Analysis and Synthesis of Linear Servomechanisms (book), **A. C. Hall.** Technology Press, Cambridge, Mass., 1943.

Discussion

George A. Philbrick (George A. Philbrick Researches, Boston, Mass.): Since many readers of this able and intelligent paper will not previously have come across its author, it is appropriate to mention an earlier, and unpublished, contribution by him. While working with the Propeller Division of Curtiss-Wright Corporation prior to 1946, Kochenburger prepared a skillful analysis of a compound automatic control problem in turbo-prop regulation. This analysis was happily received and applied in a related project by the present writer

The paper under discussion treats a fundamentally nonlinear servomechanism, which it appears to handle successfully by a harmonic method. It will thus give great comfort to frequency enthusiasts. If some of the comments which follow are at best dispassionate, attribute them to the fact that this writer is an enthusiast from another camp altogether.

Items which it is felt belong in the list of references include a paper by A. Ivanoff;[1] and the recently translated book, Dynamics of Automatic Control, by Oldenbourg and Sartorius.[2] Ivanoff studied the combined influences of inertness and static friction, under sinusoidal performance, in a manner related to the Kochenburger approach; the compensatory effects of inertness, for example, were clearly shown by him. In the Oldenbourg book, which contains many pioneering elements, similar nonlinear phenomena also are introduced into otherwise linear control loops, and the stability and performance evaluated through consideration of the behavior of the fundamental frequency, as is done in the present paper. A recent noteworthy paper in this same field was prepared by T. A. Rogers of the University of California.[3]

A more serious omission, from the writer's point of view, is the absence of any reference to the method of analogy as a tool of analysis and synthesis in the study of systems of this general type. The current availability of analogue computing components, as a concrete fact, requires the qualification, even the revision, of many of the statements in the paper. Such components are regularly employed in our laboratory, and elsewhere, to represent regulatory systems of which those described in this paper form a special case. In a few minutes after receipt of this paper the first example described was set up, operated, and the conclusions corroborated quantitatively through oscilloscope displays. The computing assemblage is shown in Figure 1 of the discussion. Straightforward additions lead to the second and slightly more involved example. All the components exhibited are perfectly standard catalog items.

An interesting outcome of our brief experience with the analog representation of this problem was the observation that substantially the same compensating characteristic is optimum when the nonlinear contactor-unit is replaced by the simplest linear approximation. As to the form of the time responses themselves, which are important for many applications, all will agree that these do not come readily from any frequency method. The analog of course, on the other hand, gives time responses directly for either discrete or random stimuli, and frequency responses as well for those who want them. In a more intricate nonlinear control or servo system, of which perhaps the mechanism discussed is a minor component, the applicability of the author's approach may be open to some additional doubt, whereas the abilities of the analog are inherently unaffected by the extent or complexity of the primary structure under study.

References

1. Theoretical Foundations of the Automatic Regulation of Temperature, **A. Ivanoff.** *Journal,* Institute of Fuel (London, England), February 1934.

2. Dynamics of Automatic Control (book), **Oldenbourg, Sartorius.** Translated by Dr. H. L. Mason. *American Society of Mechanical Engineers* (New York, N. Y.), February 1948.

3. Relay Servomechanisms, **T. A. Rogers.** *Paper 50-S-13, American Society of Mechanical Engineers* (New York, N. Y.), 1950.

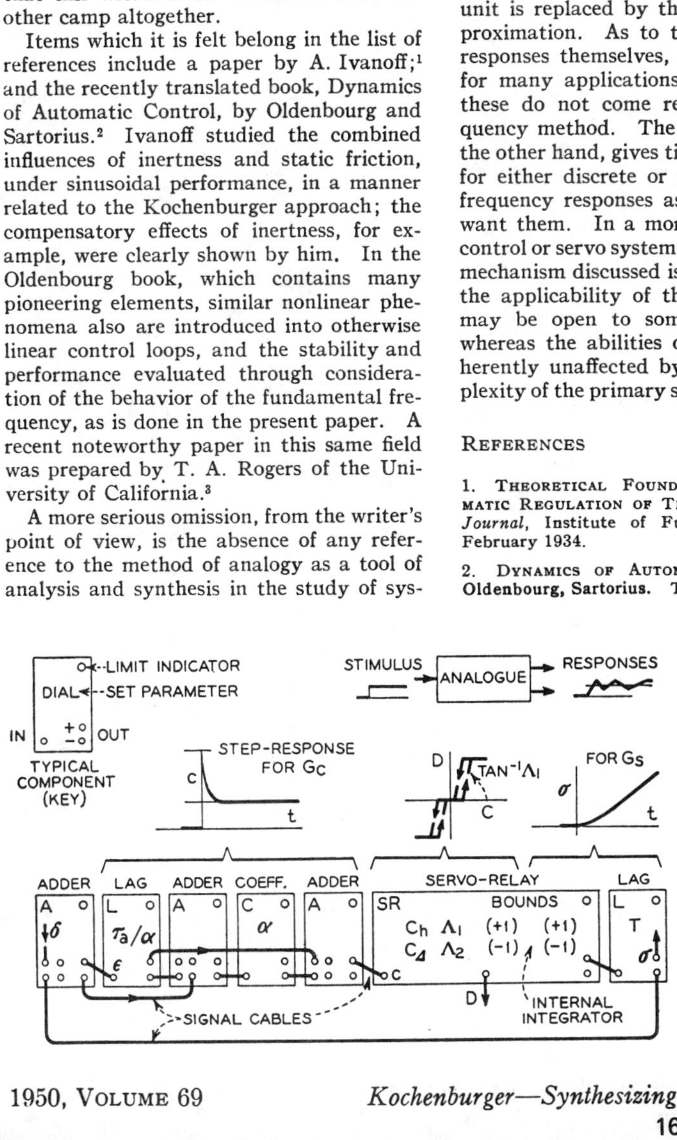

Figure 1. Analog computing assembly for the contactor servomechanism

Ralph J. Kochenburger: The author appreciates the constructive comments made by Mr. Philbrick in his discussion of this paper and wishes to thank him for calling attention to an earlier unpublished work in the field of feedback control systems. Several interesting points were raised in his discussion which warrant further clarification.

Mr. Philbrick classifies this paper as belonging to the "camp of frequency-response enthusiasts." There has been an unfortunate tendency to group engineers studying feedback control systems into two groups those interested in the transient response of such systems and those interested in the frequency response. Such a distinction is fallacious since all of these engineers are interested in the transient response of the system they are studying. It however happens that, in complicated feedback control systems, the operational calculus necessary for a direct approach involves computations which become unduly cumbersome and the seemingly "round-about" method of first studying the response of the system to sinusoidal disturbances and then predicting the transient response from these results represents a more practical approach. This is particularly the case when the system contains components whose input-output relationships are not readily subject to analytic representations but which can be described in terms of experimentally derived data.

It might be kept in mind that the Nyquist criteria, upon which the frequency response method is based, are no more than means for determining whether any objectionable terms exist in the transient response relationship. In its most frequently applied form, the locus of the transfer function is plotted for various values of "real frequency," that is, the substitution is made that $s=j\omega$ where s is the Laplace transformation operator. This form permits the question to be answered—is the system stable? It is however possible to use this general method to determine how stable the system is as well. If it is not only specified that it be stable but that its response involve no oscillatory components with damping ratios less that some specified value, ζ, it is merely necessary to draw a new transfer locus using the substitution, $s=\zeta\omega_n \pm j\sqrt{1-\zeta^2}\omega_n$ over the complete range of frequencies, ω_n, and then to apply the same graphical test as before. If the criteria are fulfilled for such a complex frequency locus, then all damping ratios involved in the frequency function will be greater than the specified value ζ. Sometimes this second procedure is tedious and for this reason the engineer frequently determines the response function for the range of real frequencies only and then employs various well known rules-of-thumb to make approximate predictions covering the nature of the transient response.

Mr. Philbrick mentions two earlier contributions where other problems in nonlinear dynamics employ a similar approximation by which all but the average and fundamental frequency components of a nonsinusoidal periodic function are ignored. Such an approximation method has been used frequently and is generally well-known. The author consequently did not cite all of the contributions where such a procedure is employed. The paper under discussion merely suggests a combination of this procedure and of the Nyquist method which is particularly applicable to nonlinear servomechanisms. The reference given in the discussion to a recent paper by T. A. Rogers is of particular interest. The author has not yet had the opportunity to examine this contribution.

The discussion points out the omission of the analogue method for studying feedback control systems. The author agrees that this method should have been accorded more emphasis since it constitutes a practical means of attack in many instances. As a matter of fact, mention was made in the paper of a simulator or analogue device employed by the author to check the validity of the proposed method in the case of several specific problems. It is felt that the analytic and analogue approaches complement each other and that there is need for both in control system design. The analytic approach has an advantage in that it not only determines the nature of the response itself, but also shows which design factors are the cause of its various features. It consequently gives direct information leading to the synthesis of an improved system.

Analogue methods show the nature of the system response but the synthesis problem still involves a trial-and-error variation of design constants. Furthermore, the experimental facilities involved in such an approach may be expensive. Their use may well be justified in a laboratory dealing with a number of related control problems. In the case of industrial concerns which encounter problems in feedback control systems at only infrequent intervals, there is some question regarding their economic justification.

It is appreciated that Mr. Philbrick used his analogue computor to check some of the results presented in the paper. More quantitative information concerning the correlation of the two methods would have been of interest.

The discussion mentions that a prediction of the time response does not come readily from a frequency response method. Methods by which the general nature of the time response can be predicted from a knowledge of the frequency response have been mentioned. If an actual picture of the time response is desired, this too may be obtained by a method developed by Dr. George W. Floyd and described in Chapter 11 of reference 1 of the paper. In regard to elements of doubt regarding the applicability of the proposed method to more involved systems, it is true that, in view of space limitation, the paper discussed only the application to a basic single loop system. An extension of this method applicable to a multiloop system should follow directly and also should be valid provided the Nyquist criteria are correctly applied. The simple form of these criteria given in the paper holds only for single-loop systems with stable components. In any case, some check should be made in any given problem concerning the validity of the approximation upon which this method is based.

In conclusion, the author wishes to thank Mr. Philbrick for his discussion and for the number of interesting suggestions he has made.

ABSOLUTE STABILITY OF NONLINEAR SYSTEMS OF AUTOMATIC CONTROL

V. M. Popov (Bucharest)

Translated from Avtomatika i Telemekhanika, Vol. 22, No. 8,
pp. 961-979, August, 1961
Original article submitted January 17, 1961

The problem of absolute stability of an "indirect control" system with a single nonlinearity is investigated by using a method which differs from the second method of Lyapunov. The main condition of the obtained criterion of absolute stability is expressed in terms of the transfer function of the system linear part. It is also shown that by forming the standard Lyapunov function - "a quadratic form plus the integral of the nonlinearity" it is not possible in the case considered here to obtain a wider stability domain than the one obtained from the presented criterion. Graphical criteria of absolute continuity ~~are also~~ given by means of the phase-amplitude characteristic or by what is known as the modified phase-amplitude characteristic" of the system linear part.

In the present paper the absolute stability is investigated of nonlinear systems of "indirect control." The existing literature in this field (see [1] for example) deals exclusively with a direct application of Lyapunov's method. In this paper the solution is obtained by a different method, and this enables one to get new results.

It is assumed that the reader is not familiar with the author's previous publications. Therefore, not only the most general results are given here but also a very simple example shall be considered.

By using a new method the author has also investigated the absolute stability of other types of systems of differential equations (for example,of the system of "direct control"), as well as of other classes of nonlinear functions (for example,of functions whose graph is contained within a sector). In all these cases the absolute stability of the system with several nonlinearities is also studied (the case of systems with many controlling devices).

In his most recent papers now in press, the author has studied the stability in certain critical cases and also the stability of systems of differential equations with an "aftereffect".

1. Statement of the Problem

Systems of "indirect control" are considered which can be described by the following system of differential equations:

$$\frac{dx_l}{dt} = \sum_{k=1}^{n} a_{lk}x_k + b_l\varphi(\sigma) \qquad (l = 1, 2, \ldots, n), \tag{1.1}$$

$$\frac{d\xi}{dt} = \varphi(\sigma), \tag{1.2}$$

$$\sigma = \sum_{l=1}^{n} c_l x_l - \gamma\xi, \tag{1.3}$$

where a_{lk}, b_l, c_l, and γ are constant, and $\varphi(\sigma)$ is a function of class A*, that is,a continuous function satisfying the condition

$$\varphi(0) = 0 \tag{1.4}$$

and also the inequality

* It is assumed that the quantity σ_* introduced in [6] always vanishes. It should just be mentioned that if $\sigma_* \neq 0$, the trivial solution of the system (1.1)-(1.3) cannot be asymptotically stable.

$$\varphi(\sigma)\sigma > 0 \text{ for } \sigma \neq 0 \tag{1.5}$$

The system (1.1)-(1.3) admits the trivial solution

$$x_l = \xi = \sigma = 0, \tag{1.6}$$

whose stability is under investigation.

It is assumed that the trivial solution of the linear system with constant coefficients

$$\frac{dy_l}{dt} = \sum_{k=1}^{n} a_{lk} y_k \qquad (l = 1, 2, \ldots, n), \tag{1.7}$$

where a_{lk} are the same as in (1.1), is asymptotically stable, or (which is equivalent) that all real parts of the eigenvalues of the matrix (a_{lk}) are negative. The conditions are being sought which would be satisfied by the quantities a_{lk}, b_l, c_l, and γ in order that the trivial solution of the system (1.1)-(1.3) be asymptotically stable, whatever the function $\varphi(\sigma)$ of the class A (in other words, a condition of asymptotic absolute stability of the trivial solution). As we know to achieve this, it is necessary that*

$$\gamma > 0. \tag{1.8}$$

We shall therefore consider in the sequel the inequality (1.8) to be satisfied.

2. Introductory Definitions. Formulation of Criterion of Absolute Stability

Consider the functions $\psi_{lm}(t)$ ($l = 1, 2, \ldots, n$; $m = 1, 2, \ldots, n$), defined when $t \geq 0$, and being the solutions of the equations

$$\frac{d\psi_{lm}(t)}{dt} = \sum_{k=1}^{n} a_{lk} \psi_{km}(t) \qquad \begin{pmatrix} l = 1, 2, \ldots, n \\ m = 1, 2, \ldots, n \end{pmatrix} \tag{2.1}$$

together with the initial conditions

$$\psi_{lm}(0) = \delta_{lm} \quad (l = 1, 2, \ldots, n;\ m = 1, 2, \ldots, n), \tag{2.2}$$

where $\delta_{lm} = 0$ when $l \neq m$, and $\delta_{lm} = 1$ when $l = m$.

The functions $\psi_{lm}(t)$ form the fundamental system of solutions for the system (1.7).

Let $x_l(t)$, $\xi(t)$ be the solution of the equations (1.1)-(1.3)** which satisfies the initial conditions $x_l(0) = x_{l0}$, $\xi(0) = \xi_0$, and let $\varphi[\sigma(t)]$ be a function of t obtained by substituting the function $\sigma(t) = \sum c_l x_l(t) - \gamma\xi(t)$ in $\varphi(\sigma)$ [see (1.3)].

As a solution of the system (1.1) we obtain

$$x_l(t) = \sum_{m=1}^{n} \psi_{lm}(t) x_{m0} + \sum_{m=1}^{n} \int_0^t \psi_{lm}(t-\zeta)\, b_m \varphi(\sigma(\zeta))\, d\zeta. \tag{2.3}$$

It follows from (1.3) that

$$\sigma(t) = \sum_{m=1}^{n} \mu_m(t) x_{m0} - \int_0^t \nu(t-\zeta)\, \varphi(\sigma(\zeta))\, d\zeta - \gamma\xi(t), \tag{2.4}$$

---

*If $\gamma < 0$, the trivial solution is unstable when $\varphi(\sigma) = h\sigma$, $h>0$. If $\gamma = 0$, the condition $\xi(t) = 0$ is not satisfied for all solutions of the system.

** The existence of solutions is a consequence of the assumptions made in section 1. But their uniqueness is not assumed in the sequel. A solution can always be extended in view of the conditions for stability as formulated below.

where

$$\mu_m(t) = \sum_{l=1}^{n} c_l \psi_{lm}(t), \qquad (2.5)$$

$$v(t) = -\sum_{l=1}^{n} \sum_{m=1}^{n} c_l \psi_{lm}(t)\, b_m. \qquad (2.6)$$

In agreement with our assumptions the trivial solution of the system (1.7) is asymptotically stable, and therefore two positive constants K_0 and K_1 can be found such that [see (2.1) and (2.2)] for all $t \geq 0$ the inequality

$$|\psi_{lm}(t)| < K_1 e^{-K_0 t}, \qquad t \geq 0 \qquad \begin{pmatrix} l = 1, 2, \ldots, n, \\ m = 1, 2, \ldots, n \end{pmatrix}. \qquad (2.7)$$

takes place.

Therefore, for $v(t)$ [see (2.6)] the inequality

$$|v(t)| < K_2 e^{-K_0 t} \quad (t \geq 0), \qquad (2.8)$$

is valid where

$$K_2 = \sum_{l=1}^{n} |c_l| \sum_{l=1}^{n} |b_l|\, K_1.$$

We note that in view of the inequality (2.7), the Fourier transform of the function $v(t)$ given by the formula

$$N(j\omega) = \int_0^{\infty} e^{-j\omega t} v(t)\, dt \qquad (j = \sqrt{-1}). \qquad (2.9)$$

must exist.

We introduce the function

$$G(j\omega) = N(j\omega) + \frac{\gamma}{j\omega}, \qquad (2.10)$$

which shall be called the transfer function of the system linear part (see Appendix 1).

Now the following theorem can be stated.

Theorem. If a nonnegative quantity q exists such that for all real w the inequality*

$$\mathrm{Re}\,(1 + j\omega q)\, G(j\omega) \geq 0, \qquad (2.11)$$

takes place, then the trivial solution of the system (1.1)-(1.3) is asymptotically absolutely stable provided the assumptions made in Section 1 remain valid.

* ReX (or ImX) denotes the real (or, respectively, imaginary) part of a complex quantity X.

3. Proof of the Theorem in Section 2

Consider again the solution x_l (t), ξ (t), σ (t) of the system (1.1)-(1.3) as well as the function φ (σ (l)), corresponding to it. For any positive quantity T we define auxiliary functions

$$\varphi_T(t) = \begin{cases} \varphi(\sigma(t)) & \text{for } 0 \leqslant t \leqslant T, \\ 0 & \text{for } t > T, \end{cases} \tag{3.1}$$

$$\lambda_T(t) = -\int_0^t \nu(t-\zeta)\,\varphi_T(\zeta)\,d\zeta - q\int_0^t \frac{d\nu(t-\zeta)}{dt}\varphi_T(\zeta)d\zeta - q[\nu(0)+\gamma]\,\varphi_T(t), \tag{3.2}$$

where q is the quantity occurring in the theorem, and v (t) is given by the formula (2.6); it follows that [see (2.2)]

$$\nu(0) = -\sum_{l=1}^{n} c_l b_l. \tag{3.3}$$

It can easily be seen that the function λ_T (t) is bounded for all $0 \le t \ge T$. When $t > T$, the inequality (see Appendix 1)

$$|\lambda_T(t)| < K_3 e^{-K_4 t} \quad (K_3 > 0,\ t > T), \tag{3.4}$$

takes place in which K_3 is independent of t. This guarantees the existence of the Fourier transform

$$L_T(j\omega) = \int_0^\infty e^{-j\omega t}\lambda_T(t)\,dt. \tag{3.5}$$

There exists also the transform

$$F_T(j\omega) = \int_0^\infty e^{-j\omega t}\varphi_T(t)\,dt. \tag{3.6}$$

In view of (2.6), (2.1), and (2.7) the Fourier transform of the function dv (t)/ dt exists and can be written as [see (2.9)]

$$\int_0^\infty e^{-j\omega t}\frac{d\nu(t)}{dt}dt = j\omega N(j\omega) - \nu(0), \tag{3.7}$$

Therefore, by taking the Fourier transform of (3.2) [see (3.5), (3.6), and (3.7)] we obtain

$$L_T(j\omega) = -[(1 + j\omega q)N(j\omega) + q\gamma]\,F_T(j\omega). \tag{3.8}$$

The following function of T is introduced:

$$\rho(T) = \int_0^\infty \lambda_T(t)\,\varphi_T(t)\,dt. \tag{3.9}$$

The Parseval formula can be applied in (3.9) because the function $\varphi_T(t)$ is continuous for $0 \le t \le T$ and it vanishes for $t > T$, and the function $\lambda_T(t)$ is also continuous for $0 \le t \le T$, and for $t > T$ the inequality (3.4) takes place. We now obtain

$$\rho(T) = \frac{1}{2\pi} \int_{-\infty}^{\infty} L_T(j\omega)\, \overline{F_T(j\omega)}\, d\omega, \tag{3.10}$$

where $\overline{F_T(j\omega)}$ is the conjugate complex of $F_T(j\omega)$.

By replacing $L_T(j\omega)$ by (3.8) in (3.10), and by taking into account that

$$F_T(j\omega)\, \overline{F_T(j\omega)} = |F_T(j\omega)|^2, \tag{3.11}$$

we obtain

$$\rho(T) = -\frac{1}{2\pi} \int_{-\infty}^{\infty} |F_T(j\omega)|^2 [(1 + j\omega q) N(j\omega) + q\gamma]\, d\omega. \tag{3.12}$$

By comparing their real parts we obtain

$$\rho(T) = -\frac{1}{2\pi} \int_{-\infty}^{\infty} |F_T(j\omega)|^2 \operatorname{Re} [(1 + j\omega q) N(j\omega) + q\gamma]\, d\omega. \tag{3.13}$$

Observing that [see (2.10) and (2.11)]

$$\operatorname{Re} [(1 + j\omega q) N(j\omega) + q\gamma] = \operatorname{Re} (1 + j\omega q)\left(N(j\omega) + \frac{\gamma}{j\omega}\right) = \operatorname{Re} (1 + j\omega q) G(j\omega) \geqslant 0, \tag{3.14}$$

gives the inequality

$$\rho(T) \le 0. \tag{3.15}$$

By substituting (3.1) into (3.9) we obtain

$$\rho(T) = \int_0^T \lambda_T(t)\, \varphi(\sigma(t))\, dt \leqslant 0. \tag{3.16}$$

By substituting the expression for $\varphi_T(t)$ into (3.2) and by applying the formula (2.4) as well as the formula

$$\frac{d\sigma(t)}{dt} = \sum_{m=1}^{n} \frac{d\mu_m(t)}{dt} x_{m0} - \int_0^t \frac{d\nu(t-\zeta)}{dt} \varphi(\sigma(\zeta))\, d\zeta - [\nu(0) + \gamma]\, \varphi(\sigma(t)), \tag{3.17}$$

easily following from (2.4), we obtain within the interval $0 \le t \le T$

$$\lambda_T(t) = \sigma(t) + q\frac{d\sigma(t)}{dt} + \gamma\, \xi(t) - \sum_{m=1}^{n} \left(\mu_m(t) + q\frac{d\mu_m(t)}{dt}\right) x_{m0}. \tag{3.18}$$

By substituting this expression into (3.16) we obtain

$$\int_0^T \varphi(\sigma(t))\,\sigma(t)\,dt + q\int_0^T \varphi(\sigma(t))\frac{d\sigma(t)}{dt}\,dt + \gamma\int_0^T \varphi(\sigma(t))\,\xi(t)\,dt$$

$$-\sum_{m=1}^{n} x_{m0}\int_0^T \left(\mu_m(t) + q\,\frac{d\mu_m(t)}{dt}\right)\varphi(\sigma(t))\,dt \leqslant 0. \tag{3.19}$$

Each term of the expression (3.19) shall be considered in turn. For the first term we have the inequality [see (1.4) and (1.5)]

$$-\int_0^T \varphi(\sigma(t))\,\sigma(t)\,dt \leqslant 0. \tag{3.20}$$

The second term can be rewritten with the aid of the identity

$$\int_0^T \varphi(\sigma(t))\frac{d\sigma(t)}{dt}\,dt = F(\sigma(T)) - F(\sigma(0)), \tag{3.21}$$

where

$$F(\sigma) = \int_0^\sigma \varphi(\sigma)\,d\sigma.$$

In the case when $\varphi(\sigma)$ belongs to the class A [see (1.4) and (1.5)], the condition

$$F(\sigma) \geq 0 \tag{3.22}$$

is fulfilled, with the equality only taking place when $\sigma = 0$. As q is nonnegative, one has, of course, the inequality

$$-qF(\sigma(T)) \leq 0. \tag{3.23}$$

The third term can be rewritten as follows [see (1.2)]:

$$\int_0^T \varphi(\sigma(t))\,\xi(t)\,dt = \int_0^T \frac{d\xi(t)}{dt}\,\xi(t)\,dt = \frac{1}{2}\xi^2(T) - \frac{1}{2}\xi_0^2. \tag{3.24}$$

As $\gamma > 0$ [see (1.8)] we have

$$-\frac{1}{2}\gamma\xi^2(T) \leqslant 0. \tag{3.25}$$

As far as the remaining terms are concerned we note [see Appendix 3] that there exists a positive quantity K_4 such that the inequality:

$$\left|\int_0^T \left(\mu_m(t) + q\,\frac{d\mu_m(t)}{dt}\right)\varphi(\sigma(t))\,dt\right| \leqslant \frac{1}{n}K_4 \sup_{0<\zeta<T}|\xi(\zeta)| \quad (m = 1, 2, \ldots n). \tag{3.26}$$

takes place.

Using the identities (3.21) and (3.24) as well as the inequalities (3.26), one is able to rewrite the inequality (3.19) as

$$\int_0^T \varphi(\sigma(t))\,\sigma(t)\,dt + qF(\sigma(T)) + \frac{1}{2}\gamma\xi^2(T)$$

$$-K_4 \max_{m=1,2,\dots,n} (|x_{mo}|) \sup_{0\leqslant\zeta\leqslant T} |\xi(\zeta)| \leqslant qF(\sigma(0)) + \frac{1}{2}\gamma\xi_0^2. \tag{3.27}$$

We shall show that the trivial solution of the system (1.1)-(1.3) is stable. To this end we combine the inequalities (3.27), (3.20), and (3.23)

$$\frac{1}{2}\gamma\xi^2(T) - K_4 \max_{m=1,2,\dots,n} (|x_{mo}|) \sup_{0\leqslant\zeta\leqslant T} |\xi(\zeta)| \leqslant qF(\sigma(0)) + \frac{1}{2}\gamma\xi_0^2. \tag{3.28}$$

Let t be an arbitrary positive quantity. The inequality (3.28) is valid for any T > 0. In particular, (3.25) remains valid for T (t) such that the inequality

$$0 \leq T(t) \leq t \tag{3.29}$$

takes place, and also the equality

$$|\xi(T(t))| = \sup_{0\leqslant\zeta\leqslant t} |\xi(\zeta)|. \tag{3.30}$$

Such a quantity T (t), of course, exists. It is easy to see that in view of (3.29) the inequalities

$$|\xi(T(t))| \leqslant \sup_{0\leqslant\zeta\leqslant T(t)} |\xi(\zeta)| \leqslant \sup_{0\leqslant\zeta\leqslant t} |\xi(\zeta)|. \tag{3.31}$$

take place.

By comparing (3.31) and (3.30) we obtain

$$|\xi(T(t))| = \sup_{0\leqslant\zeta\leqslant T(t)} |\xi(\zeta)|. \tag{3.32}$$

When considering (3.28) for T = T (t) and by using (3.32) we obtain

$$\frac{1}{2}\gamma\xi^2(T(t)) - K_4 \max_{m=1,2,\dots,n} (|x_{mo}|)\,|\xi(T(t))| - qF(\sigma(0)) - \frac{1}{2}\gamma\xi_0^2 \leqslant 0. \ (3.33) \tag{3.33}$$

The polynomial of the variable $|\xi(T(t))|$ in the lefthand side of the inequality (3.33) has real roots of opposite sign, when made equal to zero. The inequality (3.33) is equivalent to the inequality

$$|\xi(T(t))| \leqslant \frac{1}{\gamma} K_4 \max_{m=1,2,\dots,n} (|x_{mo}|) + \frac{1}{\gamma}\sqrt{K_4^2 \left(\max_{m=1,2,\dots,n} (|x_{mo}|)\right)^2 + 2\gamma\left(qF(\sigma(0)) + \frac{1}{2}\gamma\xi_0^2\right)}, \tag{3.34}$$

which is valid for all t > 0.

One can find two positive quantities K_5 and K_6 [see Appendix 4] such that for all t > 0 the inequality

$$|x_l(t)| \leqslant K_5 \max_{m=1,2,\dots,n} (|x_{mo}|) + K_6 \sup_{0\leqslant\zeta\leqslant t} |\xi(\zeta)|. \tag{3.35}$$

takes place.

By applying (3.30), (3.34), and (3.35) we finally obtain

$$|\xi(t)| \leqslant \frac{1}{\gamma} K_4 \max_{m=1,2,\ldots,n} (|x_{m0}|) +$$

$$\frac{1}{\gamma} + \sqrt{K_4^2 (\max_{m=1,2,\ldots,n} (x_{m0}|))^2 + 2\gamma (qF(\sigma(0)) + \frac{1}{2}\gamma\xi_0^2)}, \tag{3.36}$$

$$|x_l(t)| \leqslant \left(K_5 + \frac{1}{\gamma} K_4 K_6\right) \max_{m=1,2,\ldots,n} (|x_{m0}|)$$

$$+ \frac{1}{\gamma} K_6 \sqrt{K_4^2 (\max_{m=1,2,\ldots,n} (|x_{m0}|))^2 + 2\gamma\left(qF(\sigma(0)) + \frac{1}{2}\gamma\xi_0^2\right)}. \tag{3.37}$$

Let ϵ be an arbitrary positive quantity. There exists than a $\delta > 0$ such that when $|x_{l0}| < \delta$ and $|\xi_0| < \delta$, the righthand sides of the inequalities (3.36) and (3.37) are less than ϵ* and therefore the inequalities $|x_l(t)| < \epsilon$ and $|\xi(t)| < \epsilon$ take place. Consequently, the trivial solution of the system (1.1)-(1.3) is stable according to Lyapunov. Moreover, it follows from (3.36) and (3.37) that all the solutions of the system are bounded. This implies that all the solutions of the system (1.1)-(1.3) can be extended for all $t > 0$.

It shall be shown now that the trivial solution is also asymptotically stable for any $\varphi(\sigma)$ of the class A. We combine for this purpose the inequalities (3.27), (3.23), and (3.25):

$$\int_0^T \varphi(\sigma(t))\,\sigma(t)\,dt \leqslant K_4 \max_{m=1,2,\ldots,n} (|x_{m0}|) \sup_{0\leqslant\zeta\leqslant T} |\xi(\zeta)| + qF(\sigma(0)) + \frac{1}{2}\gamma\xi_0^2. \tag{3.38}$$

By making use of (3.36)

$$\int_0^T \varphi(\sigma(t))\,\sigma(t)\,dt \leqslant f_1(x_{m0}, \xi_0), \tag{3.39}$$

where $f_1(x_{m0}, \xi_0)$ is a specified function of the variables x_{m0} and ξ_0.

Taking into account the reaction [see (1.1), (1.3)]

$$\frac{d\sigma(t)}{dt} = \sum_{l=1}^{n} c_l \frac{dx_l}{dt} - \gamma\frac{d\xi}{dt} = \sum_{l=1}^{n} c_l \left(\sum_{k=1}^{n} a_{lk}x_k + b_l\varphi(\sigma)\right) - \gamma\varphi(\sigma), \tag{3.40}$$

[in the above formula x_k and ξ satisfy the inequalities (3.37) and (3.36), σ is determined by the equation (1.3) and $\varphi(\sigma)$ is a continuous function of σ], we obtain the inequality

$$\left|\frac{d\sigma(t)}{dt}\right| < f_2(x_{m0}, \xi_0), \tag{3.41}$$

where $f_2(x_{m0}, \xi_0)$ does not depend on t.

By using (3.39) and (3.41) we obtain [see Appendix 5]

$$\lim_{t\to\infty} \sigma(t) = 0 \tag{3.42}$$

---

* Here we make use of the fact that $F(\sigma(0))$ is a continuous function of $\sigma(0)$, vanishing when $\sigma(0) = 0$, and also of the equality $\sigma(0) = \sum_{l=1}^{n} c_l x_{l0} - \gamma\xi_0$ [see (1.3)].

and also

$$\lim_{t\to\infty} \varphi(\sigma(t)) = 0. \tag{3.43}$$

because $\varphi(\sigma)$ is a continuous function.

From (3.43) and from the equations (2.3) one obtains [see Appendix 6]

$$\lim_{t\to\infty} x_l(t) = 0. \tag{3.44}$$

The relation (1.3) implies [see (3.42) and (3.44)]

$$\lim_{t\to\infty} \xi(t) = \lim_{t\to\infty} \frac{1}{\gamma}\Big(\sum_{l=1}^{n} x_l(t) - \sigma t\Big) = 0. \tag{3.45}$$

The theorem has thus been proved.

4. Comparing the Results with the Results Obtainable with the Aid of Lyapunov Functions of Known Kind

It is of interest to compare the criteria (2.11) of absolute stability with the ones which can be obtained by constructing a Lyapunov function of the kind described as a "quadratic form plus the integral of the nonlinearity" [6-8]. We shall show that the latter are included in the criteria of the theorem in section 2, that is, if for the system under investigation there exists a Lyapunov function of the above kind, then a nonnegative quantity q also exists such that the inequality (2.11) takes place.

By differentiating the equation (1.3) we obtain a system equivalent to the (1.1)-(1.3):

$$\begin{aligned} \frac{dx_l}{dt} &= \sum_{k=1}^{n} a_{lk}x_k + b_l\varphi(\sigma) \qquad (l = 1, 2, \ldots, n), \\ \frac{d\sigma}{dt} &= \sum_{l=1}^{n} c_l\Big(\sum_{k=1}^{n} a_{lk}x_k + b_l\varphi(\sigma)\Big) - \gamma\varphi(\sigma). \end{aligned} \tag{4.1}$$

It is shown in Appendix 7 that the most general form of a negative definite Lyapunov function which is of the kind described as a "quadratic form plus the integral of the nonlinearity" and which can be formed for the system (4.1) takes the form

$$V = \sum_{l=1}^{n}\sum_{m=1}^{n} x_l r_{lm} x_m - \alpha\Big(\sigma - \sum_{l=1}^{n} c_l x_l\Big)^2 - 2\beta\int_0^{\sigma}\varphi(\sigma)\,d\sigma, \tag{4.2}$$

with the parameters r_{lm}, α, β satisfying the conditions:

$$r_{lm} = r_{ml}, \ \alpha \geqslant 0, \ \beta \geqslant 0, \ \alpha + \beta > 0. \tag{4.3}$$

The derivative of this function which, in accordance with the system (1.4)*

$$\frac{1}{2}\frac{dV}{dt} = W(x_l, \sigma) = \sum_{l=1}^{n}\sum_{m=1}^{n} x_l r_{lm}\Big(\sum_{k=1}^{n} a_{mk}x_k + b_m\varphi(\sigma)\Big)$$

$$+ \alpha\gamma\varphi(\sigma)\Big(\sigma - \sum_{l=1}^{n} c_l x_l\Big) - \beta\varphi(\sigma)\Big(\sum_{l=1}^{n} c_l\Big(\sum_{k=1}^{n} a_{lk}x_k + b_l\varphi(\sigma)\Big) - \gamma\varphi(\sigma)\Big) \tag{4.4}$$

must be positive definite for all functions $\varphi(\sigma)$ of the class A, and in particular when

---

* We note that $\frac{d}{dt}\big(\sigma - \sum_{l=1}^{n} c_l x_l\big) = -\gamma\varphi(\sigma)$.

$$\varphi(\sigma) = h\sigma, \ h>0. \tag{4.5}$$

By putting (4.5) in (4.4) we obtain a quadratic form of real variables x_l and σ which must be positive definite. This implies that for all complex values of x_l and σ not vanishing simultaneously the inequality

$$\begin{aligned}\mathrm{Re}\Big\{\sum_{l=1}^{n}\sum_{m=1}^{n}\bar{x}_l r_{lm}\Big(\sum_{k=1}^{n} a_{mk}x_k + b_m h\sigma\Big) + \alpha\gamma h\bar{\sigma}\Big(\sigma - \sum_{l=1}^{n} c_l x_l\Big)\\ -\beta h\bar{\sigma}\Big(\sum_{l=1}^{n} c_l\Big(\sum_{k=1}^{n} a_{lk}x_k + b_l h\sigma\Big) - \gamma h\sigma\Big)\Big\} > 0,\end{aligned} \tag{4.6}$$

is valid, the quantities $\bar{x}_l$ and $\bar{\sigma}$ being conjugate to x_l and σ. That this is so can be seen by putting in (4.6) $x_l = u_l + jv_l$, $\sigma = \mu + j\nu$, with u_l, v_l, μ, and ν real; the left-hand side of (4.6) assumes the form $\frac{1}{2}(W_0(u_l, \mu) + W_0(v_l, \nu))$, where W_0 is the quadratic form (4.4) with $\varphi(\sigma) = h\sigma$. Thus, if u_l, v_l, μ, and ν do not vanish simultaneously, we have the inequality (4.6).

The inequality (4.6) is satisfied in the particular case of

$$\begin{aligned}\sigma &= \frac{1}{h},\\ x &= M_l(j\omega) \qquad (l = 1, 2, \ldots, n),\end{aligned} \tag{4.7}$$

where $M_l(j\omega)$ satisfy the system of simultaneous equations

$$j\omega M_l(j\omega) = \sum_{k=1}^{n} a_{lk}M_k(j\omega) + b_l \qquad (l = 1, 2, \ldots, n). \tag{4.8}$$

The system (4.8) has a unique solution for any real ω as according to our assumptions (see section 1) the matrix (a_{lk}) has no purely imaginary eigenvalues.

By taking Fourier transforms of the system (2.1) including (2.2) we obtain

$$j\omega F\{\psi_{lm}(t)\} = \sum_{k=1}^{n} a_{lk}F\{\psi_{km}(t)\} + \delta_{lm} \quad \begin{pmatrix} l = 1, 2, \ldots, n\\ m = 1, 2, \ldots, n\end{pmatrix}, \tag{4.9}$$

where

$$F\{\psi_{lm}(t)\} = \int_0^{\infty} e^{-j\omega t}\psi_{lm}(t)\,dt. \tag{4.10}$$

By comparing (4.9) and (4.8) we obtain

$$M_l(j\omega) = \sum_{m=1}^{n} F\{\psi_{lm}(t)\}\,b_m = \sum_{m=1}^{n}\int_0^{\infty} e^{-j\omega t}\psi_{lm}(t)\,b_m dt. \tag{4.11}$$

Substituting (4.7) into (4.6) and using the relations (4.8) we obtain

$$\begin{aligned}\mathrm{Re}\Big\{\sum_{l=1}^{n}\sum_{m=1}^{n}\overline{M_l(j\omega)}\,r_{lm}j\omega M_m(j\omega) + \alpha\gamma\Big(\frac{1}{h} - \sum_{l=1}^{n} c_l M_l(j\omega)\Big)\\ -\beta\Big(\sum_{l=1}^{n} c_l j\omega M_l(j\omega) - \gamma\Big)\Big\} > 0.\end{aligned} \tag{4.12}$$

But [see (4.11), (2.6), (2.9)]

$$\sum_{l=1}^{n} c_l M_l(j\omega) = \sum_{l=1}^{n}\sum_{m=1}^{n}\int_0^{\infty} e^{-j\omega t} c_l \Psi_{lm}(t)\, b_m dt = -\int_0^{\infty} e^{-j\omega t} \nu(t)\, dt = -N(j\omega). \tag{4.13}$$

In view of $r_{lm} = r_{ml}$, we have*

$$\operatorname{Re}\sum_{l=1}^{n}\sum_{m=1}^{n} \overline{M_l(j\omega)}\, r_{lm}\, j\omega M_m(j\omega) = \operatorname{Re}\left\{\frac{1}{2} j\omega \sum_{l=1}^{n}\sum_{m=1}^{n}\left(\overline{M_l(j\omega)}\, M_m(j\omega) + M_l(j\omega)\,\overline{M_m(j\omega)}\right) r_{lm}\right\} = 0. \tag{4.14}$$

The inequality (4.12) can therefore be rewritten as

$$\frac{\alpha\gamma}{h} + \operatorname{Re}(\alpha\gamma + j\omega\beta)\, N(j\omega) + \beta\gamma > 0 \tag{4.15}$$

or [see (2.10)]

$$\frac{\alpha\gamma}{h} + \operatorname{Re}(\alpha\gamma + j\omega\beta)\, G(j\omega) > 0. \tag{4.16}$$

The above consideration remain valid for any real ω. Thus, it has been shown that for a Lyapunov function of the considered kind to exist it is necessary that the inequality (4.16) be valid for all $h>0$ and for any ω.

If $\alpha \neq 0$, [see (4.3)] and thus if $\alpha\gamma > 0$ [see (1.8)], from (4,16) must follow the inequality

$$\operatorname{Re}\left(1 + j\omega\frac{\beta}{\alpha\gamma}\right) G(j\omega) \geqslant 0. \tag{4.17}$$

Indeed, should the inequality (4.17) be invalid for some $\omega = \omega_0$, then a positive quantity h exists such that the inequality (4.16) will not take place for $\omega = \omega_0$. The necessary condition (4.17) is identical with the inequality (2,11) if $q = \beta/\alpha\gamma > 0$.

If $\alpha = 0$, we obtain from (4,3) and (4,16) the inequalities

$$\beta > 0, \tag{4.18}$$

$$\operatorname{Re} j\omega G(j\omega) > 0. \tag{4.19}$$

We shall now consider certain properties of the function $N(j\omega)$ [see (2.9)]. The function $N(j\omega)$ is a continuous function of ω in view of the inequality (2.8). By the Riemann-Lebesque Lemma

$$\lim_{|\omega|\to\infty} N(j\omega) = 0. \tag{4.20}$$

Therefore, there exists a positive number P_1 such that for any ω

$$\operatorname{Re} N(j\omega) \succ -P_1. \tag{4.21}$$

By the Riemann-Lebesque Lemma we also obtain** [see (3.3)]

$$\lim_{|\omega|\to\infty} j\omega N(j\omega) = \nu(0) = -\sum_{l=1}^{n} c_l b_l. \tag{4.22}$$

*We note that $\operatorname{Im}\left(\overline{M_l(j\omega)}\, M_m(j\omega) + M_l(j\omega)\,\overline{M_m(j\omega)}\right) \equiv 0$.

**From the relations (2.6), (2.1) and (2.7) it is easy to find that the integral $\int_0^{\infty}\left|\frac{d\nu(t)}{dt}\right| dt$ must converge.

It follows from (4.21), (4.22) and (2.10) that

$$\operatorname{Re} G(j\omega) = \operatorname{Re} N(j\omega) > -P_1, \tag{4.23}$$

$$\lim_{|\omega|\to\infty} j\omega G(j\omega) = \lim_{|\omega|\to\infty} j\omega N(j\omega) + \gamma = -\sum_{l=1}^{n} c_l b_l + \gamma > 0. \tag{4.24}$$

The latter is a necessary condition and can be obtained from (4.6) and (4.18) by putting $x_l = 0$, $\sigma = 1/h$, $\alpha = 0$. It follows from (4.19), (4.24), and from the continuity of the function $G(j\omega)$ that a positive quantity P_2 can be found such that for any real ω the inequality

$$\operatorname{Re} j\omega G(j\omega) > P_2. \tag{4.25}$$

takes place.

By multiplying the inequality (4.25) by $2P_1/P_2$ and by adding the result to the inequality (4.23), we obtain

$$\operatorname{Re}\left(1 + 2\frac{P_1}{P_2} j\omega\right) G(j\omega) > -P_1 + 2P_1 > 0. \tag{4.26}$$

The latter implies that the inequality (2.11) is valid (as a strong inequality) when $q = 2P_1/P_2 > 0$.

Thus it has been proved that the inequality (2.11) suffices for the trivial solution of the system described in section 1 to be absolutely asymptotically stable and also to be a necessary condition for the existenec of a Lyapunov function of the considered type.

Remarks. (1) In order to construct a Lyapunov function of the "quadratic form" type (that is of the kind as in (4.2) with $\beta = 0$) it is necessary that the inequality (4.17) be valid with $\beta = 0$, that is that

$$\operatorname{Re} G(j\omega) \geq 0 \tag{4.27}$$

for any real ω.

The condition (4.27) is sufficient for the absolute asymptotic stability of the trivial solution of the system under investigation, as in this case the inequality (2.11) occurs for $q = 0$.

(2) Most of the Lyapunov functions so far constructed in [8] are of the kind as in (4.2), with $\alpha = 0$. That is why it is necessary that the inequality (4.19) be valid; the latter is also sufficient for the absolute stability of the system trivial solution.

The condition (4.19) can also be written for any real positive ω as

$$\operatorname{Im} G(j\omega) < 0, \tag{4.28}$$

This follows from the relation [see (2.9) and (2.10)]

$$\operatorname{Im} G(j\omega) = -\operatorname{Im} G(-j\omega) \tag{4.29}$$

and from the inequality [see (2.10), (3.7), and (1.8)].

$$[\operatorname{Re} j\omega G(j\omega)]_{\omega=0} = \gamma > 0. \tag{4.30}$$

(3) It would be interesting to find the general solution of the following inverse problem: If the condition (2.11) is satisfied is it always possible to construct a Lyapunov function of the kind as in (4.2)? For some relatively simple cases the answer is in the affirmative.

5. Various Analytic and Graphic Forms of the (2.11) Criterion

The function $(1 + j\omega q)G(j\omega)$ can be written as

$$(1 + j\omega q) G'(j\omega) = \frac{P(j\omega)}{Q(j\omega)}, \tag{5.1}$$

(see Appendix 1) with P (jω) and Q (jω) being polynomials of jω. The condition (2.11) can now be written as

$$\mathrm{Re} P(j\omega) Q(-j\omega) \geqslant 0 \tag{5.2}$$

or

$$R(x) \geqslant 0, \ x = \omega^2, \tag{5.3}$$

where R (x) is a polynomial of the variable x. The condition (2.11) is reduced, therefore, to a polynomial of x being nonnegative for x ≥ 0. The solution can be obtained by using standard algebraic methods.

An arbitrary nonnegative parameter q appears in the criterion, which can be selected in a suitable manner in every specific case. * The algebraic methods for obtaining the optimal values of q are quite straightforward.

The following graphical criteria of absolute asymptotic stability are of special interest in practical applications.

The locus of the points (u, v) in the plane of (u, v) such that

$$u(\omega) = \mathrm{Re}\, G(j\omega), \ v(\omega) = \omega \mathrm{Im}\, G(j\omega) \tag{5.4}$$

shall be called the "modified phase-amplitude characteristic" (M.P. A.C.). Directly from (2.11) we obtain the inequality

$$u(\omega) + qv(\omega) \geqslant 0, \ q \geqslant 0, \tag{5.5}$$

which means that the M. P.A.C. is in a half-plane.

A graphical criterion (Fig. 1). If there is a straight line situated either in the first and the third quadrants of the (u, v) plane or it is the ordinate axis**, and in addition it is such that the M.P.A.C. is "on the right" of this straight line, then the trivial solution of the investigated system is absolutely asymptotically stable. One may add that the M.P.A.C. is "on the right" of this straight line if any point of the M.P.A.C. is either on the straight line or it is in the half-plane bounded by this straight line and containing the point (+∞, 0).***

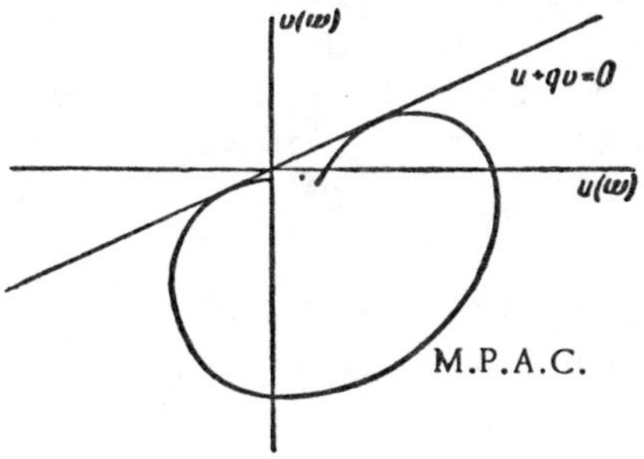

Fig. 1.

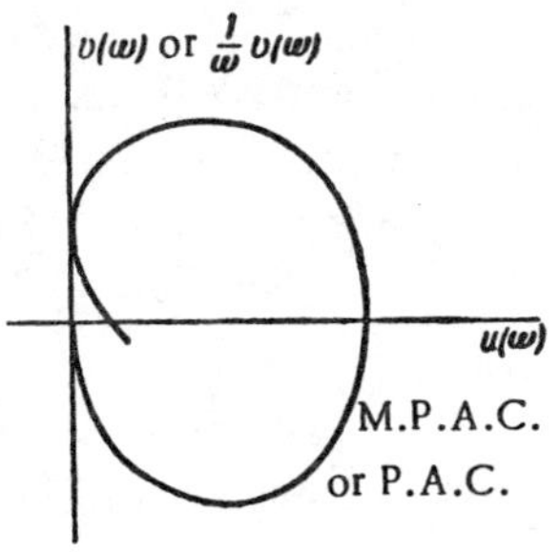

Fig. 2.

* We note that in the criteria (4.27) or (4.28) which described the results obtainable by the usual kind of Lyapunov function (see Remarks (1) and (2), there is no arbitrary parameter.

** Such a straight line obviously passes through the origin. Its equation is of the form u + qv = 0 with q ≥ 0.

*** Or, otherwise, that the inequality (5.5) takes place.

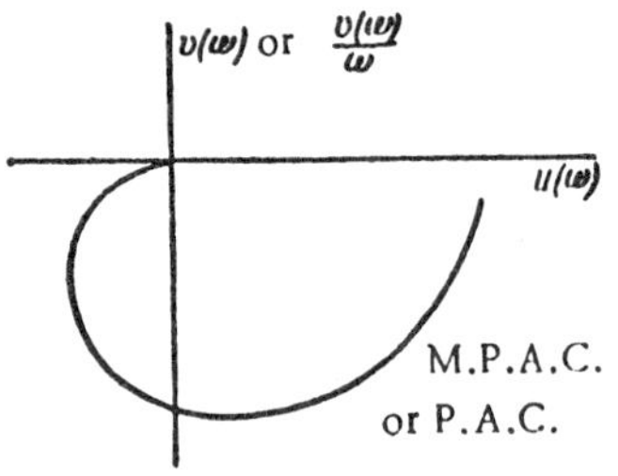

Fig. 3.

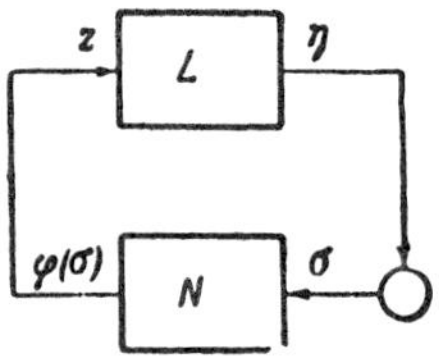

Fig. 4.

The ordinary phase-amplitude characteristic can also be made use of in order to obtain simplified graphical criteria of absolute stability.

The following graphical criterion is obtained from the condition (4.27).

Simplified graphical criterion No. 1. If all the points of the ordinary (or modified) phase-amplitude characteristic are situated "on the right" of the ordinate axis, the trival solution of the system under investigation is asymptotically absolutely stable. (Fig. 2)

It is necessary that this graphical criterion be satisfied in order that a Lyapunov function of the "quadratic form" kind may exist [see Remark (1)].

From the sufficient condition (4.28) of stability another simplified graphical criterion is obtained.

Simplified grapical criterion No. 2. If, when $\omega > 0$, all the points of the ordinary (or modified) P.A.C. are situated in the third or the fourth quadrant or on the negative ordinate semi-axis, then the trivial solution of the system under investigation is asymptotically absolutely stable (Fig. 3).

It is necessary that this criterion be fulfilled in order that a Lyapunov function (5.3) with $\alpha = 0$ may exist [see Remark (2)].

We should like to mention that no simple method exists to express the general graphical criterion (Fig. 1) by means of the ordinary P.A.C. Knowing the ordinary P.A.C., one is able to obtain the modified P.A.C. by multiplying the ordinate of each point by the corresponding value of the variable.

6. Concluding Remarks

The majority of the arguments developed in the preceding sections can be applied with practically no alterations to more general cases mentioned in the introduction, and results of similar nature are obtained.

The fact that in the criteria only the transfer function of the system linear part appears, apart from the simple assumptions of section 1, seems to constitute the main characteristic of the achieved results. The latter need not be evaluated with the aid of the formula (2.9) but can be obtained by more direct methods which have been developed for linear systems of automatic control. The graphical criteria of absolute stability developed above are also applicable when nothing but its linearity and independence are known about the linear block of the system, its phase-amplitude characteristic being determined experimentally.

The author wishes to express his thanks to the collective of research-workers in the field of ordinary differential equations of the Mathematical Institute of the Academy of Sciences of the Romanian National Republic, in particular to Professor A. Khalan, for the interest they have shown and for their valuable remarks.

APPENDIX 1

The investigated system can always be represented in the form of a block diagram as in Fig. 4 where the linear block is denoted by L, the latter described by the system of equations

$$\frac{dx_l}{dt} = \sum_{k=1}^{n} a_{lk}x_k + b_l z \quad (l = 1, 2, \ldots, n),$$

$$\frac{d\xi}{dt} = z,$$

$$\eta = -\sum_{l=1}^{n} c_l x_l + \gamma\xi, \tag{I.1}$$

and N representing the nonlinear block. The input and the output quantities of the linear and nonlinear blocks are related by the equations

$$\eta = -\sigma, \quad z = \varphi(\sigma). \tag{I.2}$$

Let $z^0(t)$ be a known function such that the integral $\int_0^\infty | z^0(t) |$ exists, and let $L\{z^0(t)\}$ be its Laplace transform

$$L\{z^0(t)\} = \int_0^\infty e^{-st} z^0(t)\, dt, \quad \text{Re } s \geqslant 0. \tag{I.3}$$

Let further $x^0_l(t)$, $\xi^0(t)$, $\eta^0(t)$ be the solution of (I.1) when $z = z^0(t)$ and when the initial conditions are all nul. It follows from the assumptions in section 1 that $L\{x^0_l(t)\}$ exists at least for Re $s \geq 0$, and $L\{\xi^0(t)\}$ and $L\{\eta^0(t)\}$ exist for Re $s > 0$.

Taking Laplace transforms of (I.1) we obtain

$$sL\{x_l^0(t)\} = \sum_{k=1}^{n} a_{lk} L\{x_k^0(t)\} + b_l L\{z^0(t)\}, \quad \text{Re } s \geqslant 0 \quad (l = 1, 2, \ldots, n). \tag{I.4}$$

$$sL\{\xi^0(t)\} = L\{z^0(t)\}, \quad \text{Re } s > 0, \tag{I.5}$$

$$L\{\eta^0(t)\} = -\sum_{l=1}^{n} c_l L\{x_l^0(t)\} + \gamma L\{\xi^0(t)\}, \quad \text{Re } s > 0. \tag{I.6}$$

The system of simultaneous equations (I.4) has a unique solution when Re $s > 0$ (see the assumptions in section 1).

Now taking Laplace transforms of the system (2.1) with the initial conditions (2.2):

$$sL\{\psi_{lm}(t)\} = \sum_{k=1}^{n} a_{lk} L\{\psi_{km}(t)\} + \delta_{lm}, \quad \text{Re } s \geqslant 0 \quad \begin{pmatrix} l = 1, 2, \ldots, n \\ m = 1, 2, \ldots, n \end{pmatrix}. \tag{I.7}$$

By comparing (I.4) and (I.7) we obtain

$$L\{x_l^0(t)\} = \left(\sum_{m=1}^{n} L\{\psi_{lm}(t)\}\, b_m\right) L\{z^0(t)\}, \quad \text{Re } s \geqslant 0 \quad (l = 1, 2, \ldots, n). \tag{I.8}$$

Using (I.5),(I.6), and (I.80)gives

$$L\{\eta^0(t)\} = \widetilde{G}(s)\, L\{z^0(t)\}, \quad \text{Re } s > 0, \tag{I.9}$$

where

$$\widetilde{G}(s) = N(s) + \frac{\gamma}{s}, \quad \text{Re } s > 0, \tag{I.10}$$

$$N(s) = -\sum_{l=1}^{n} \sum_{m=1}^{n} c_l L\{\psi_{lm}(t)\}\, b_m, \quad \text{Re } s \geqslant 0. \tag{I.11}$$

The function $\widetilde{G}(s)$ defined by the equations (I.10)-(I.11) is the transfer function of the system linear block. The function $\widetilde{G}(s)$ is obtained in the form of a rational function of s. The above considerations are only valid when Re

$s > 0$; we shall say nevertheless that G (s) is a transfer function if it is a rational function defined in the whole s-plane and obtained as the analytic continuation of the $\tilde{G}$ (s) function.

It should be mentioned that the function $L\{\psi_{lm}(t)\}$ exists when Re $s = 0$ and that when $s = j\omega$ (ω real), then $L\{\psi_{lm}(t)\} = F\{\psi_{lm}(t)\}$ [see (4.10)]. By comparing (I.11) with (2.6) and (2.9) we see that when $s = j\omega$ the function (I.11) is equal to the function of (2.9). Therefore, the function (2.10) is equal to the above defined function G (s) with $s = j\omega$.

APPENDIX 2

By using (3.1) and (3.2) we obtain for $t > T$

$$\lambda_T(t) = -\int_0^T \left(\nu(t-\zeta) + q\frac{d\nu(t-\zeta)}{dt}\right)\varphi(\sigma(\zeta))\,d\zeta. \tag{II.1}$$

But [see (2.6), (2.1) and (2.7)]

$$\left|\nu(t) + q\frac{d\nu(t)}{dt}\right| \leqslant \sum_{l=1}^{n}|c_l|\left(1 + q\sum_{k=1}^{n}\sum_{m=1}^{n}|a_{km}|\right)\sum_{i=1}^{n}|b_i|K_1 e^{-K_0 t}. \tag{II.2}$$

Therefore,

$$|\lambda_T(t)| \leqslant \sup_{0<\zeta<T}|\varphi(\sigma(\zeta))|\int_0^T\left|\nu(t-\zeta) + q\frac{d\nu(t-\zeta)}{dt}\right|d\zeta$$

$$\leqslant \sup_{0<\zeta<T}|\varphi(\sigma(\zeta))|\sum_{l=1}^{n}|c_l|\left(1 + q\sum_{k=1}^{n}\sum_{m=1}^{n}|a_{km}|\right)\sum_{i=1}^{n}|b_i|K_1\int_0^T e^{-K_0(t-\zeta)}\,d\zeta. \tag{II.3}$$

This gives the inequality (3.4), where

$$K_3 = \sup_{0<\zeta<T}|\varphi(\sigma(\zeta))|\sum_{l=1}^{n}|c_l|\left(1 + q\sum_{k=1}^{n}\sum_{m=1}^{n}|a_{km}|\right)\sum_{i=1}^{n}|b_i|\frac{K_1}{K_0}\left(e^{K_0 T} - 1\right). \tag{II.4}$$

For a specified solution of the system and for a given T, K_3 is a constant.

Therefore the Fourier transformation (3.5) exists.

APPENDIX 3

From the equation (1.2) we obtain

$$E = \int_0^T\left(\mu_m(t) + q\frac{d\mu_m(t)}{dt}\right)\varphi_T(\sigma(t))\,dt = \int_0^T\left(\mu_m(t) + q\frac{d\mu_m(t)}{dt}\right)\frac{d\xi(t)}{dt}\,dt. \tag{III.1}$$

The integration by parts gives

$$E = \left[\left(\mu_m(t) + q\frac{d\mu_m(t)}{dt}\right)\xi(t)\right]_0^T - \int_0^T \xi(t)\left(\frac{d\mu_m(t)}{dt} + q\frac{d^2\mu_m(t)}{dt^2}\right)dt, \tag{III.2}$$

and hence, in view of $|\xi(T)| \leqslant \sup_{0<\zeta<T}|\xi(\zeta)|$ и $|\xi(0)| \leqslant \sup_{0<\zeta<T}|\xi(\zeta)|$, it follows that

$$E| \leqslant \sup_{0<\zeta<T}|\xi(\zeta)|\left(2\sup_{0<t<T}\left|\mu_m(t) + q\frac{d\mu_m(t)}{dt}\right| + \int_0^T\left|\frac{d\mu_m(t)}{dt} + q\frac{d^2\mu_m(t)}{dt^2}\right|dt\right). \tag{III.3}$$

But [see (2.5), (2.1), and (2.7)]

$$\left|\mu_m(t) + q\frac{d\mu_m(t)}{dt}\right| \leqslant \sum_{l=1}^{n}|c_l|\left(1 + q\sum_{k=1}^{n}\sum_{m=1}^{n}|a_{km}|\right)K_1, \tag{III.4}$$

$$\left|\frac{d\mu_m(t)}{dt} + q\frac{d^2\mu_m(t)}{dt^2}\right| \leqslant \sum_{l=1}^{n}|c_l|\left(1 + q\sum_{k=1}^{n}\sum_{m=1}^{n}|a_{km}|\right)\sum_{k'=1}^{n}\sum_{m'=1}^{n}|a_{k'm'}|K_1 e^{-K_0 t}. \tag{III.5}$$

By substituting (III.4) and (III.5) into (III.3) and by using the inequality

$$\int_0^T e^{-K_0 t}\,dt < \int_0^\infty e^{-K_0 t}\,dt = \frac{1}{K_0}, \tag{III.6}$$

we obtain the inequality (3.26), where

$$\frac{1}{n} K_4 = \sum_{l=1}^{n} |c_l| \left(1 + q \sum_{k=1}^{n} \sum_{m=1}^{n} |a_{km}|\right)\left(2 + \frac{1}{K_0} \sum_{k'=1}^{n} \sum_{m'=1}^{n} |a_{k'm'}|\right) K_1. \tag{III.7}$$

APPENDIX 4

By replacing $\varphi(\sigma(\xi))$ in (2.3) by $d\xi(\zeta)/d\zeta$ [see (1.2)] and by integrating by parts we obtain

$$x_l(t) = \sum_{m=1}^{n} \psi_{lm}(t)\, x_{m0} + \sum_{m=1}^{n} b_m \left[\psi_{lm}(t-\zeta)\,\xi(\zeta)\right]_{\xi=0}^{\zeta=t} - \sum_{m=1}^{n} b_m \int_0^t \xi(\zeta)\, \frac{d\psi_{lm}(t-\zeta)}{d\zeta}\, d\zeta. \tag{IV.1}$$

From (2.1) and (2.7) it follows that

$$|x_l(t)| \leqslant K_1 n \max(|x_{m0}|) + \sup|\xi(\zeta)|\, K_1 \sum_{m=1}^{n} |b_m| \left(2 + \sum_{l=1}^{n} \sum_{k=1}^{n} |a_{lk}| \int_0^t e^{-K_0(t-\zeta)}\, d\zeta\right). \tag{IV.2}$$

As $\int_0^t e^{-K_0(t-\zeta)}\, d\zeta \leqslant \int_{-\infty}^t e^{-K_0(t-\zeta)}\, d\zeta = \frac{1}{K_0}$, we obtain the inequality (3.35) where

$$K_5 = nK_1,$$

$$K_6 = K_1 \sum_{m=1}^{n} |b_m| \left(2 + \frac{1}{K_0} \sum_{l=1}^{n} \sum_{k=1}^{n} |a_{lk}|\right).$$

APPENDIX 5

The result (3.42) could be obtained by making use of a lemma published by Barbalat [9]. Below we shall give a more direct proof.

We assume for this purpose that (3.42) is not true. Then a positive quantity δ and a sequence of quantities t_i must exist such that

$$|\sigma(t_i)| > \delta, \quad t_i > 0, \quad \lim_{i\to\infty} t_i = +\infty. \tag{V.1}$$

Let the solution in question [see (3.41), (3.36), (3.37), and (1.3)] be

$$\left|\frac{d\sigma(t)}{dt}\right| < M_1. \quad |\sigma(t)| < M_2. \tag{V.2}$$

The sequence t_k can be selected such that

$$t_k - t_{k-1} > \frac{\delta}{M_1}, \quad t_1 > \frac{\delta}{2M_1}. \tag{V.3}$$

When $|t - t_k| < \frac{\delta}{2M_1}$ we have

$$M_2 > |\sigma(t)| = \left|\sigma(t_k) + \int_{t_k}^{t} \frac{d\sigma(t)}{dt}\, dt\right| > |\sigma(t_k)| - M_1|t - t_k| > \frac{1}{2}\delta. \tag{V.4}$$

We also have [see (1.4) and (1.5)]

$$\int_0^T \varphi(\sigma(t))\,\sigma(t)\, dt \geqslant \sum_{k=1}^{N(T)} \int_{t_k - \frac{\delta}{2M_1}}^{t_k + \frac{\delta}{2M_1}} \varphi(\sigma(t))\,\sigma(t)\, dt, \tag{V.5}$$

where N (T) is an index such that $t_{N(T)} + \frac{\delta}{2M_1} \leqslant T$ and $t_{N(T)+1} + \frac{\delta}{2M_1} > T$.

Obviously

$$\lim_{T\to\infty} N(T) = \infty. \tag{V.6}$$

Let $\inf\limits_{\frac{\delta}{2}<|\sigma|<M_2} |\varphi(\sigma)| = m$. Then we obtain from (V.5) [see (1.5)]

$$\int_0^t \varphi(\sigma(t))\,\sigma(t)\,dt \geq N(T)\frac{\delta}{M_1}\cdot\frac{\delta}{2}m. \tag{V.7}$$

In view of (V.6)

$$\lim_{T\to\infty}\int_0^T \varphi(\sigma(t))\,\sigma(t)\,dt = \infty, \tag{V.8}$$

which contradicts (3.39), and so (3.42) is proved.

APPENDIX 6

In order to prove the relation (3.44) [see (2.3)] it is sufficient, in view of (2.7), to prove that

$$\overline{\lim_{t\to\infty}}\int_0^t \psi_{lm}(t-\zeta)\,\varphi(\sigma(\zeta))\,d\zeta = 0. \tag{VI.1}$$

follows from (3.44).

According to (2.7) we have

$$\left|\int_0^t \psi_{ml}(t-\zeta)\,\varphi(\sigma(\zeta))\,d\zeta\right| \leqslant K_1\int_0^t e^{-K_0(t-\zeta)}\,|\varphi(\sigma(\zeta))| \tag{VI.2}$$

By applying de l 'Hopital rule (see, for example, [10]) we obtain [see (3.43)]

$$\lim_{t\to\infty}\int_0^t e^{-K_0(t-\zeta)}\,|\varphi(\sigma(\zeta))|\,d\zeta = \lim_{t\to\infty}\frac{\int_0^t e^{K_0\zeta}\,|\varphi(\sigma(\zeta))|\,d\zeta}{e^{K_0 t}} = \frac{1}{K_0}\lim_{t\to\infty}|\varphi(\sigma(t))| = 0, \tag{VI.3}$$

and hence follows (VI.1).

APPENDIX 7

It can easily be seen that the most general negative definite Lyapunov function of the type "a quadratic form plus the integral of the nonlinearity" can be represented as

$$V = \sum_{l=1}^{n}\sum_{m=1}^{n} x_l r_{lm} x_m - \alpha\left(\sigma - \sum_{l=1}^{n} c_l x_l\right)^2 - 2\beta\int_0^\sigma \varphi(\sigma)\,d\sigma + 2\sigma\sum_{l=1}^{n} f_l x_l, \tag{VII.1}$$

with r_{lm}, α, β, f_l being constants. The derivative of the V function by virtue of (4.1) assumes the form

$$\frac{1}{2}\frac{dV}{dt} = W(x_l, \sigma) + \sigma\sum_{l=1}^{n} f_l\left(\sum_{k=1}^{n} a_{lk}x_k + b_l\varphi(\sigma)\right)$$
$$+\sum_{l=1}^{n} f_l x_l\left[\sum_{l=1}^{n} c_l\left(\sum_{k=1}^{n} a_{lk}x_k + b_l\varphi(\sigma)\right) - \gamma\varphi(\sigma)\right], \tag{VII.2}$$

where $W(x_l, \sigma)$ is given by the expression (4.4).

We shall show that the equalities

$$f_l = 0 \quad (l = 1, 2, \ldots, n) \tag{VIII.3}$$

are necessary. We note that the function $\frac{1}{2}\,dV/dt$ is positive when

$$x_l = x_l^0 = \varepsilon\int_0^\infty \psi_{lm}(t)\,dt \quad (l = 1, 2, \ldots, n) \tag{VII.4}$$

$$\varphi(\sigma) = \varepsilon^2\sigma, \tag{VII.5}$$

$$\sigma = 1, \tag{VII.6}$$

where m is one of the integers 1, 2, . . . , n; ψ_{lm} (t) the functions introduced in section 2, and ϵ an arbitrary (positive or negative) quantity. The function (VII.5) is of course of the class A. By integrating (2.1) we obtain, in view of ψ_{lm}(t) [see also (2.2)],

$$-\psi_{lm}(0) = -\delta_{lm} = \sum_{k=1}^{n} a_{lk} \int_0^\infty \psi_{km}(t)\,dt. \tag{VII.7}$$

Consequently [see (VII.4)]

$$\sum_{k=1}^{n} a_{lk} x_k^0 = -\varepsilon\delta_{lm}. \tag{VII.8}$$

It is easily seen that for the values of (VII.4)-(VII.6) the function $\frac{1}{2}$ dV/dt can be written as

$$\frac{1}{2}\frac{dV}{dt} = \left(\sum_{l=1}^{n} f_l \sum_{k=1}^{n} a_{lk} x_k^0\right)\varepsilon + O(\varepsilon^2), \tag{VII.9}$$

in which $0(\epsilon^2)$ denotes terms with the property $|0(\epsilon^2)| < K\epsilon^2$, with K being a constant.

From (VII.9) using (VII.8) we obtain

$$\frac{1}{2}\frac{dV}{dt} = -f_m\varepsilon + O(\varepsilon^2). \tag{VII.10}$$

If $f_m \neq 0$, then for a sufficiently small ϵ the expression (VII.10) has the sign of $-f_m\epsilon$; the latter, however, is arbitrary because the sign of ϵ is also arbitrary. It is therefore necessary that $f_m = 0$ be true. As m was taken as arbitrary we see that the equalities (VII.3) must be true.

The function (4.2) is negative when $x_l = 0, \sigma = 1, \varphi(\sigma) = h\sigma, h > 0$. This gives the inequality

$$-\alpha - h\beta < 0 \text{ for any } h > 0, \tag{VII.11}$$

which proves finally the relations (4.3).

LITERATURE CITED

1. A. I. Lur'e and E. N. Rozenvasser, Methods of constructing Lyapunov functions of the nonlinear control systems - theory, Proc. of the First International Conference on Automatic Control, Acad. Sci. USSR Press (1961). Sci. Press (1961).
2. V. M. Popov, Criterii de stabilitate pentru sistemele neliniare de reglare automata pe utikizarea transformatei Laplace. Studii si Cercetarii de Energetica. Anul. IX. No. 4, 1959.
3. V. M. Popov, Criterii suficiente de stabilitate asimptotica in mare pentru sistemele neliniare cu mai multe organe oe executie. Studii si Cercetari de Energetica, Anul. IX, No. 4, 1959.
4. V. M. Popov, Nouveaux criteriums pe stabilite por les systemes automatiques non-lineaires. Revue d'Electrotechnique et d'Energetique, vol. V, No. 1, 1960.
5. V. M. Popov, Noi criterii grafice pentru stabilitatea starii stationare a sistemelor automati neliniare. Studii si Cerletari de Energetica. Anul. X, No. 3, 1960.
6. A. M. Letov, The stability of nonlinear systems under control, Gostekhizdat (1951).
7. A. I. Lur'e, Some nonlinear problems in the theory of automatic control, Gostekhizdat (1951).
8. V. A. Yakubovich, Nonlinear differential equations of automatic control systems with a single controlling device, Bull. Leningrad Univ., No. 7 (1960).
9. I. Barbalat, Systemes d'équations différentielles d'oscillatíons non linéaires. Revue de mathematiques pures et appliquées. Acad. R. P. R., vol. 4.,No. 2, 1959.
10. Miron Nicolescu, Analiză Matematică, Vol. II, Bucaresti Editura Tehnică, 1958.

ON THE STABILITY OF NONLINEAR AUTOMATIC CONTROL SYSTEMS WITH LAGGING ARGUMENT

V. M. Popov, and A. Halanay

(Bucharest)

Translated from Avtomatika i Telemekhanika, Vol. 23, No. 7,
pp. 849-851, July, 1962
Original article submitted January 5, 1962

The present paper contains an application of the method of V. M. Popov [1] to the problem of stability of some systems with lagging argument.

We investigate systems of the form

$$\frac{dx}{dt} = Ax(t) + Bx(t-r) + l\varphi[\sigma(t-r)], \qquad \sigma = (c, x), \tag{1}$$

where A and B are square matrices, l and $\underline{c}$ are vectors, φ and σ are scalars; we assume that A, B, l and $\underline{c}$ are constants.

A special case of this system was studied in [2].

We shall assume that the equation $\det(A + e^{-\lambda r}B - \lambda I) = 0$ (I is the unit matrix) has roots in the half-plane $\mathrm{Re}\,\lambda \le -\alpha \le 0$. It is known (for example, see [3]) that in this case the solution of the homogeneous system

$$\frac{dz}{dt} = Az(t) + Bz(t-r) \tag{2}$$

is estimated by $|z(t, v)| \le \beta e^{-\alpha' t}\|v\|$, $\alpha' < \alpha$, where $\underline{v}$ is the initial function given in $[-r, 0]$.

With respect to function φ it is assumed that it is continuous and that there exist constants h_1 and $h_2 < k$ such that $h_1\sigma^2 \leqslant \sigma\varphi(\sigma) \leqslant h_2\sigma^2$.

Let

$$G(j\omega) = e^{-j\omega r}[c(A + e^{-j\omega r}B - j\omega I)^{-1}l] \qquad (j = \sqrt{-1}).$$

Theorem. If there exists $q > 0$ such that

$$\frac{1}{k} + \mathrm{Re}\,(1 + j\omega q)\,G(j\omega) \geqslant 0$$

for all real ω, then the trivial solution of system (1) is asymptotically stable [under suitable assumptions with respect to the eigenvalues of the matrix $(A + e^{-\lambda r}B - \lambda I)$ and with respect to function φ].

Proof. Let x(t) be an arbitrary solution of system (1), and let $\sigma(t) = (c, x(t))$.

Let us define the functions

$$\varphi_T(t) = \begin{cases} \varphi[\sigma(t)] & \text{when } 0 \leqslant t \leqslant T, \\ 0 & \text{when } -r \leqslant t < 0,\ T < t, \end{cases}$$

$$\psi(t) = \begin{cases} \varphi[\sigma(t)] & \text{when} -r \leqslant t \leqslant 0, \\ 0 & \text{when } t > 0 \end{cases}$$

and let us consider the system

$$\frac{du}{dt} = Au(t) + Bu(t-r) + l\psi(t-r). \quad (3)$$

Let w(t) be the solution of the system

$$\frac{dw}{dt} = Aw(t) + Bw(t-r) + l\varphi_T(t-r),$$

satisfying zero initial conditions.

We have $w(t) = x(t) - u(t)$ when $-r \leq t \leq T$, where u(t) is the solution of system (3) satisfying the same initial conditions as x(t).

Let

$$\rho(T) = \int_0^T \left[(c, w(t)) - \frac{1}{k}\varphi_T(t) + q\left(c, \frac{dw}{dt}\right)\right]\varphi_T(t)\,dt$$

$$= \int_0^\infty \left[(c, w(t)) - \frac{1}{k}\varphi_T(t) + q\left(c, \frac{dw}{dt}\right)\right]\varphi_T(t)\,dt$$

and

$$\tilde{w} = \int_0^\infty e^{-j\omega t} w(t)\,dt, \qquad \tilde{\varphi}_T = \int_0^\infty e^{-j\omega t}\varphi_T(t)\,dt.$$

Then on the basis of the known formulas of Fourier transform theory we can write

$$\rho(T) = \frac{1}{2\pi}\int_{-\infty}^{\infty} \mathrm{Re}\left\{(c, \tilde{w}) - \frac{1}{k}\tilde{\varphi}_T + q(c, j\omega\tilde{w})\right\}\tilde{\varphi}_T^*\,d\omega,$$

where $\tilde{\varphi}_T^*$ is the complex conjugate of $\tilde{\varphi}_T$.

Taking into account the system of equations for w, we obtain that

$$\tilde{w} = -e^{-j\omega r}(A + e^{-j\omega r}B - j\omega I)^{-1} l\tilde{\varphi}_T.$$

Hence it follows that

$$\rho(T) = \frac{1}{2\pi}\int_{-\infty}^{\infty} \mathrm{Re}\left\{\frac{1}{k} + (1 + j\omega q)G\right\}|\varphi_T|^2\,d\omega$$

and from the conditions in the theorem it ensues that $\rho(T) \leq 0$.

But $w(t) = x(t) - u(t)$, and $(c, w) = (c, x) - (c, u) = \sigma - (c, u)$. We obtain the inequality

$$\int_0^T \left\{\sigma(t) - \frac{1}{k}\varphi[\sigma(t)] + q\frac{d\sigma(t)}{dt}\right\}\varphi[\sigma(t)]\,dt$$

$$\leqslant \int_0^T \left\{(c, u(t)) + q\left(c, \frac{du(t)}{dt}\right)\right\}\varphi[\sigma(t)]\,dt.$$

From the conditions $h_1\sigma^2 \leq \sigma\varphi(\sigma) \leq h_2\sigma^2$, $h_2 < k$, it follows that

$$\varphi(\sigma)\left(\sigma - \frac{1}{k}\varphi(\sigma)\right) \leqslant h_3\sigma^2, \quad h_3 = \frac{k - h_2}{k}h_1, \qquad \int_0^{\sigma(T)} \varphi(\sigma)\,d\sigma \geqslant \frac{h_1^2}{2}\sigma^2(T).$$

The obtained inequality gives

$$q\frac{h_1}{2}\sigma^2(T) + h_3\int_0^T \sigma^2(t)\,dt \leqslant q\int_0^{\sigma(0)} \varphi(\sigma)\,d\sigma$$

$$+ \int_0^T \left\{(c, u(t)) + q\left(c, \frac{du(t)}{dt}\right)\right\}\varphi[\sigma(t)]\,dt.$$

From the inequality

$$|u(t)| \leqslant \gamma e^{-\alpha' t}\|v\|, \left|\frac{du}{dt}\right| \leqslant \gamma e^{-\alpha' t}\|v\|, \ |\varphi(\sigma)| \leqslant h_2(\sigma)$$

it follows that

$$\left|\int_0^T \left\{(c, u(t)) + q\left(c, \frac{du}{dt}\right)\right\}\varphi[\sigma(t)]\,dt\right| \leqslant \beta_1 \sup_{0<t<T}|\sigma(t)|\,\|v\|.$$

Thus, the inequality

$$\frac{qh_1}{2}\sigma^2(T) + h_3\int_0^T \sigma^2(t)\,dt \leqslant q\int_0^{\sigma(0)} \varphi(\sigma)\,d\sigma + \beta_1\|v\|\sup_{0<t<T}|\sigma(t)|$$

is correct.

From the inequality

$$\frac{qh_1}{2}\sigma^2(T) \leqslant q\int_0^{\sigma(0)} \varphi(\sigma)\,d\sigma + \beta_1\|v\|\sup_{0<t<T}|\sigma(t)|$$

we obtain, by means of the same reasoning as in [1], that $|\sigma(t)| \leq \alpha_1(\|v\|)$.

We have the formula of "variation of parameters" (see [4], [5]):

$$x(t) = X(t, 0)\,x(0) + \int_{-r}^{0} X(t, \alpha + r)\,Bx(\alpha)\,d\alpha$$

$$+ \int_0^t X(t, \alpha)\,l\varphi[\sigma(\alpha - r)]\,d\alpha, \tag{4}$$

where $X(t, \sigma)$ is the solution of system (2) such that $X(t, \sigma) \equiv 0$ when $\sigma - r \leq t < \sigma$, $X(\sigma, \sigma) = I$.

From this formula and from the estimate obtained for σ, it follows* that $|x(t)| \leq \alpha_2 (\|v\|)$. Hence it follows $\left|\frac{d\sigma}{dt}\right| \leqslant \alpha_3 (\|v\|)$ and then from $\int_0^T \sigma^2(t)\,dt \leqslant C$ we obtain, as in [1], that $\lim_{t\to\infty} \sigma(t) = 0$. Then, by using formula (4) once again, we conclude* that $\lim_{t\to\infty} x(t) = 0$, and the theorem is proved.

LITERATURE CITED

1. V. M. Popov, "On the absolute stability of nonlinear automatic control systems." Avtomatika i telemekhanika, 22, No. 8 (1961).
2. B. S. Razumikhin, "Stability of nonlinear automatic control systems with lag." Inzhenernyi sb., 29 (1960).
3. N. N. Krasovskii, Certain Problems in the Theory of Stability of Motion [in Russian]. Fizmatgiz (1959).
4. R. Bellman and K. Cooke, Stability Theory and Adjoint Operators for Linear Differential-Difference Equations. Trans. Amer. Math. Soc. Vol. 92, No. 3 (Sept., 1950).
5. A. Halanay, "Periodic solutions of linear systems with lag." Revue de Math. pure et appliquees. Acad. R.S.R., vol. VI, No. 1 (1961).

All abbreviations of periodicals in the above bibliography are letter-by-letter transliterations of the abbreviations as given in the original Russian journal. *Some or all of this periodical literature may well be available in English translation.*

*Since $\|X(t, \sigma)\| < \beta_3 e^{-\alpha'(t-\sigma)}$ when $t > \sigma$.

A Geometrical Criterion for the Stability of Certain Nonlinear Nonautonomous Systems

In this communication the existence of "Common Liapunov Functions" (CLF's) for certain nonlinear systems is discussed and the results interpreted geometrically to provide a simple criterion assuring the stability of such systems. For a negative feedback system with a linear time-invariant part with transfer function $G(s)$ in the forward path and a nonlinear gain $k(\sigma, t)$ in the feedback path, the criterion provides a simple method of obtaining a range $\underline{k} < k(\sigma, t) < \bar{k}$ within which the system is absolutely stable.

Such a system is shown in Fig. 1, and for k constant the over all transfer function is called $G_k(s)$ where

$$\frac{1}{G_k} = \frac{1}{G} + k. \tag{1}$$

It is assumed that for k constant and $\underline{k} \le k \le \bar{k}$ the system is stable. For convenience, with $\hat{k}$ constant ($\underline{k} \le \hat{k} \le \bar{k}$) define

$$l(\sigma, t) = k(\sigma, t) - \hat{k}$$

$$\bar{l} = \bar{k} - \hat{k} \ge 0 \tag{2}$$

and

$$\underline{l} = \hat{k} - \underline{k} \ge 0.$$

With the above one is assured that $H(s) \equiv G_{\hat{k}}(s)$ is the transfer function of a stable system. It is assumed then that this system may be represented as

$$\dot{\mathbf{x}} = \mathbf{F}\mathbf{x} + \mathbf{g}u$$

$$u = -l(\sigma, t)\sigma \tag{3}$$

$$\sigma = \mathbf{h}'\mathbf{x}$$

where

$$H(s) = \mathbf{h}'(s\mathbf{I} - \mathbf{F})^{-1}\mathbf{g}. \tag{4}$$

System (3) may be represented as

$$\dot{\mathbf{x}} = \hat{\mathbf{F}}(l)\mathbf{x} \tag{5}$$

where

$$\hat{\mathbf{F}}(l) = \mathbf{F} - l\mathbf{g}\mathbf{h}'. \tag{6}$$

The concept of a CLF [1], [2] may be stated generally in terms of (5). With $l = 0$ ($k = \hat{k}$) the system is stable and it is required to determine a Liapunov function $V(\mathbf{x})$ showing stability of a constant coefficient system with $-\underline{l} \le l \le \bar{l}$. If one finds a positive definite $V(\mathbf{x})$ *independent* of l such that for $-\underline{l} \le l \le \bar{l}$ ($\dot{V}\mathbf{x}$) is negative definite, then $V(\mathbf{x})$ is called a CLF and shows stability for $-\underline{l} \le l(\sigma, t) \le \bar{l}$ (or $\underline{k} \le k(\sigma, t) \le \bar{k}$). The approach used here is to construct a CLF having a quadratic form $V = \mathbf{x}'\mathbf{P}\mathbf{x}$. In the remainder of this paper CLF will refer only to quadratic-type Common Liapunov Functions. Razumikhin [3] and Roitenberg [4] have used a similar approach in attempting to pick the elements of a $\mathbf{P}$ matrix, but their work fails to give a recipe for constructing a $\mathbf{P}$ matrix or the entire range within which l (or k) may lie.

Taking the Liapunov function $V = \mathbf{x}'\mathbf{P}\mathbf{x}$, one can write

$$\dot{V} = -\mathbf{x}'[\mathbf{R} + (\mathbf{q} + l\mathbf{h})(\mathbf{q} + l\mathbf{h})' + (\underline{l} + l)(\bar{l} - l)\mathbf{h}\mathbf{h}']\mathbf{x} \tag{7}$$

if $\mathbf{P}$ and $\mathbf{q}$ simultaneously satisfy

$$\mathbf{F}'\mathbf{P} + \mathbf{P}\mathbf{F} = -\mathbf{Q} = -[\mathbf{R} + \mathbf{q}\mathbf{q}' + \underline{l}\bar{l}\mathbf{h}\mathbf{h}'] \tag{8}$$

Manuscript received November 26, 1963; revised February 12, 1964. The work reported in this communication was supported in whole or in part by the Office of Naval Research, Contract NONR-1866(16).

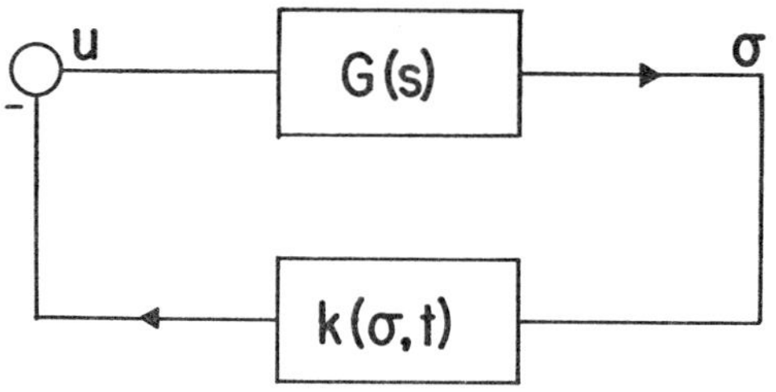

Fig. 1—Time-varying system.

and

$$\mathbf{P}\mathbf{g} = \mathbf{q} + \tfrac{1}{2}(\bar{l} - \underline{l})\mathbf{h} \tag{9}$$

with $\mathbf{R} \ge 0$, *i.e.*, $\mathbf{R}$ positive semidefinite. It is clear that the $\mathbf{P}$ of (8) must be positive definite if $\mathbf{Q}$ is positive definite, *i.e.*, $\mathbf{Q} > 0$, as it is now assumed that the system with $l = 0$ is asymptotically stable. (With ($\mathbf{F}$, $\mathbf{h}'$) completely observable, one can show $\mathbf{P} > 0$ even with $\mathbf{R} = 0$ [2].) Eq. (8) insures that the $V = \mathbf{x}'\mathbf{P}\mathbf{x}$ is a Liapunov function and (9) insures that it is a CLF, *i.e.*, independent of l.

Eq. (8) may be written as

$$\mathbf{Q} = \mathbf{T}^{+}\mathbf{P} + \mathbf{P}\mathbf{T} \tag{10}$$

where

$$\mathbf{T} = (i\omega\mathbf{I} - \mathbf{F}) \text{ and } \mathbf{T}^{+} = (-i\omega\mathbf{I} - \mathbf{F}'), \quad (\omega \text{ real}). \tag{11}$$

This is equivalent to

$$\mathbf{g}'\mathbf{T}^{+-1}\mathbf{Q}\mathbf{T}^{-1}\mathbf{g} = \mathbf{g}'\mathbf{P}\mathbf{T}^{-1}\mathbf{g} + \mathbf{g}'\mathbf{T}^{+-1}\mathbf{P}\mathbf{g}. \tag{12}$$

With (9), (12) becomes

$$1 + (\bar{l} - \underline{l})\, Re\, H(i\omega) - \underline{l}\bar{l}\, |H(i\omega)|^2 = \|\mathbf{T}^{-1}\mathbf{g}\|_{\mathbf{R}}^2 + |\mathbf{q}'\mathbf{T}^{-1}\mathbf{g} - 1|^2 \ge 0. \tag{13}$$

Hence (13) is necessary for the simultaneous solution of (8) and (9). One can also show [2], [5] that with ($\mathbf{F}$, $\mathbf{g}$) completely controllable, it is also a sufficient condition. Hence there exists a CLF in the range $-\underline{l}$ to $\bar{l}$(or $\underline{k}$ to $\bar{k}$) showing stability. In terms of (1) and the configuration of Fig. 1, (13) may be written as

$$\left|\frac{1}{G_{\underline{k}}}\right|^2 + \left|\frac{1}{G_{\bar{k}}}\right|^2 - (\bar{k} - \underline{k})^2 \ge 0 \tag{14}$$

or

$$\left|\frac{1}{G(i\omega)} + \underline{k}\right|^2 + \left|\frac{1}{G(i\omega)} + \bar{k}\right|^2 \ge (\bar{k} - \underline{k})^2. \tag{15}$$

Condition (15) may be interpreted geometrically and forms a simple, elegant, and effective method of determining a range of total stability of time-varying systems using the frequency response plot of the open-loop time-invariant system.

Geometrical Interpretation

The problem of stability may be stated in a variety of ways.

1) Given a plot of $1/G(i\omega)$ and $\underline{k}$ and $\bar{k}$, determine whether a CLF exists in the range $\underline{k} \le k \le \bar{k}$.
2) Given $G_{\underline{k}}(i\omega)$, determine the maximum range of k, *i.e.*, determine $\Delta = \bar{k} - \underline{k}$.
3) Given a mean value of k_m and $G_{k_m}(i\omega)$, determine the range $\pm\Delta/2$.

For 1), if $G(i\omega)$ and $\underline{k}$ are specified, the maximum range Δ can be obtained geometrically from the fact that the circle on $(-\underline{k}, 0)$, $(-\bar{k}, 0)$ as diameter lies *outside* the curve $1/G(i\omega)$ and is tangent to it at only one point, as shown in Fig. 2. (The circle may lie inside the curve for cases in which points on the real axis lying within the

Reprinted from *IEEE Trans. Circuit Theory*, vol. CT-11, pp. 406–408, Sept. 1964.

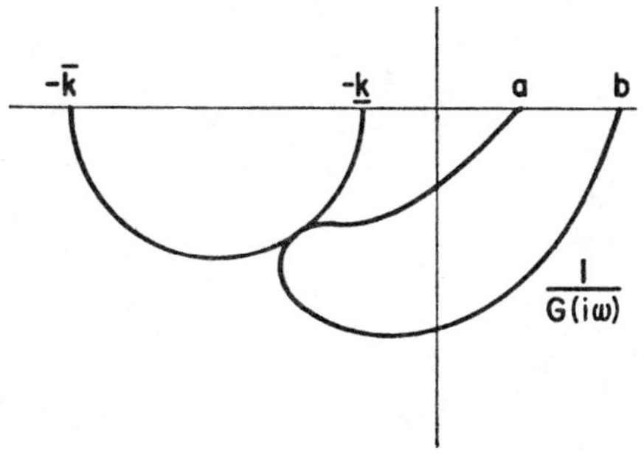

Fig. 2—Geometric interpretation of (15).

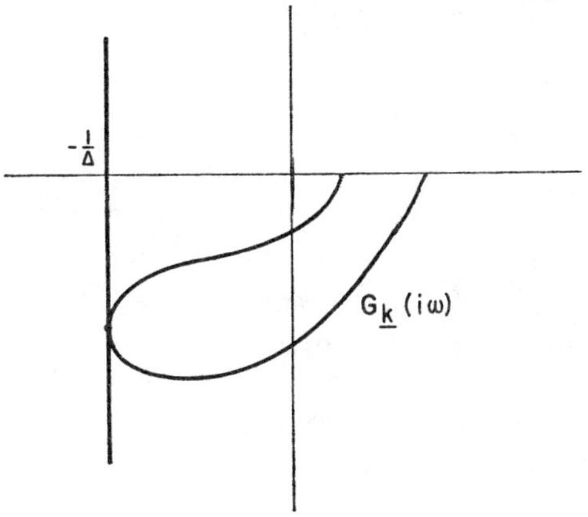

Fig. 3—Geometric interpretation of (17).

curve correspond to stable gains.) The Nyquist stability criterion *if k were constant* would demand that the points $(-\underline{k}, 0)$ and $(-\bar{k}, 0)$ not be encircled. (In Fig. 2 it is clear that the system is unstable for all constant gains corresponding to the range a to b.)

For 2) it is assumed the $G_{\underline{k}}$ is given. Using

$$\frac{1}{G_{\bar{k}}} - \frac{1}{G_{\underline{k}}} = \Delta \geq 0 \tag{16}$$

it follows from (15) that

$$1 + \Delta \, Re \, G_{\underline{k}}(i\omega) \geq 0 \quad \text{or} \quad Re\left[\frac{1}{\Delta} + G_{\underline{k}}\right] \geq 0, \quad (\omega \text{ real}). \tag{17}$$

Condition (17) may be interpreted in another way. For example, if $\underline{k} = 0$ so that $G_{\underline{k}} = G$, (17) is the condition that $1/\bar{k} + G(s)$ be a positive real function, *e.g.*, a driving-point impedance function. Condition (17) may be interpreted geometrically also. If $G_{\underline{k}}(i\omega)$ is given, the ordinate through $(-1/\Delta, 0)$ which is just tangent to the curve $G_{\underline{k}}$ gives the maximum Δ. This is shown in Fig. 3. If the upper

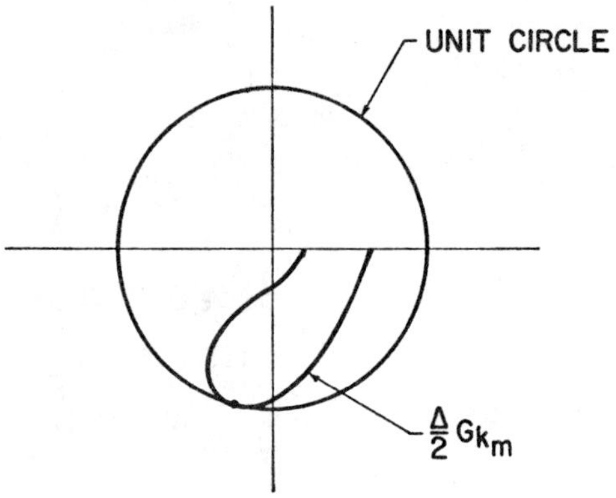

Fig. 4—Geometric interpretation of (19).

limit of gain $\bar{k}$ is specified, the range Δ is given by

$$Re\left[\frac{1}{\Delta} - G_{\bar{k}}\right] \geq 0, \quad (\omega \text{ real}). \tag{18}$$

In this case the ordinate through $(1/\Delta, 0)$ is tangent to $G_{\bar{k}}$.

For 3) one is given k_m and $G_{k_m}(i\omega)$, where k_m is interpreted as a "mean" value of gain. The range on k is now from $k_m - \Delta/2$ to $k_m + \Delta/2$, or the variation is $\pm\Delta/2$. For this case (11) becomes

$$1 - \left(\frac{\Delta}{2}\right)^2 |G_{k_m}|^2 \geq 0 \quad \text{or} \quad |G_{k_m}| \frac{\Delta}{2} \leq 1. \tag{19}$$

This implies that the frequency response $\Delta/2 \, G_{k_m}$ is tangent to the unit circle at the maximum value of Δ and lies completely within it as depicted in Fig. 4. This special case of (19) has been given by Bongiorno [6] without using the simplicity of the Liapunov function derivation.

The conditions obtained in the various cases insure the existence of a quadratic-type Liapunov function in the various cases and are hence sufficient, but not necessary, for absolute stability.

K. S. Narendra
Harvard University
Cambridge, Mass.
R. M. Goldwyn
Rice University
Houston, Tex.

References

[1] R. M. Goldwyn and K. S. Narendra, "Stability of certain nonlinear differential equations," IEEE Trans. on Automatic Control, vol. AC-8, pp. 381–382; October, 1963.
[2] K. S. Narendra and R. M. Goldwyn, "Existence of quadratic type Liapunov functions for a class of nonlinear systems," *Intern. J. Engrg. Sci.*, to be published.
[3] B. S. Razumchin, "On the application of Liapunov's method to stability problems," *Prinklad. Mat. Mekh.*, vol. 22, pp. 338–349; May–June, 1958.
[4] J. N. Roitenberg, "On a method of constructing Liapunov functions for linear systems with variable coefficients," *Prinklad. Mat. Mekh.*, vol. 22, pp. 167–172; March–April, 1958.
[5] R. E. Kalman, "Liapunov functions for the problem of Lur'e in automatic control," *Proc. Natl. Acad. Sci.*, vol. 49, pp. 201–205; February, 1963.
[6] J. J. Bongiorno, Jr., "An extension of the Nyquist-Barkhausen stability criterion to linear lumped-parameter systems with time-varying elements," IEEE Trans. on Automatic Control, vol. AC-8, pp. 166–170; April, 1963.

A Frequency-Domain Condition for the Stability of Feedback Systems Containing a Single Time-Varying Nonlinear Element

By I. W. SANDBERG

(Manuscript received May 6, 1964)

It is proved that a condition similar to the Nyquist criterion guarantees the stability (in an important sense) of a large class of feedback systems containing a single time-varying nonlinear element. In the case of principal interest, the condition is satisfied if the locus of a certain complex-valued function (a) is bounded away from a particular disk located in the complex plane, and (b) does not encircle the disk.

I. INTRODUCTION

The now well-known techniques introduced by Lyapunov have led to many very interesting results concerning the stability of time-varying nonlinear feedback systems governed by systems of differential equations. However, these methods have by no means led to a definitive theory of stability for even the simplest nontrivial time-varying nonlinear feedback systems. The general problem is, of course, one of considerable difficulty.

The unparalleled utility of the Nyquist stability criterion for single-loop, linear, time-invariant feedback systems is directly attributable to the fact that it is an explicit frequency-domain condition. The Nyquist locus not only indicates the stability or instability of a system, it presents the information in such a way as to aid the designer in arriving at a suitable design. The criterion is useful even in cases in which the system is so complicated that a sufficiently accurate analysis is not feasible, since experimental measurements can be used to construct the loop-gain locus.

The primary purpose of this article is to point out that some recently obtained mathematical results,[1] not involving the theory of Lyapunov, imply that a condition similar to, and possessing the advantages of, the Nyquist criterion guarantees the stability (in an important sense) of feedback systems containing a single time-varying nonlinear element.*,†

II. THE PHYSICAL SYSTEM AND DEFINITION OF $\mathcal{L}_2$-STABILITY

Consider the feedback system of Fig. 1. We shall restrict our discussion throughout to cases in which g_1, f, u, and v denote real-valued measurable functions of t defined for $t \geqq 0$.

The block labeled ψ is assumed to represent a memoryless time-varying (not necessarily linear) element that introduces the constraint $u(t) = \psi[f(t),t]$, in which $\psi(x,t)$ is a function of x and t with the

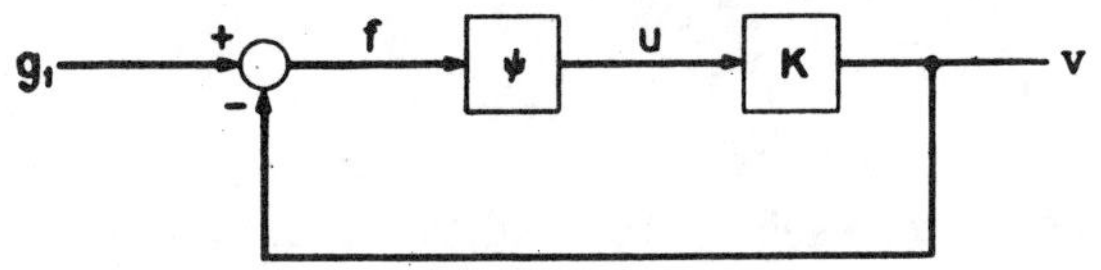

Fig. 1 — Nonlinear feedback system.

properties that $\psi(0,t) = 0$ for $t \geqq 0$ and there exist a positive constant β and a real constant α such that

$$\alpha \leqq \frac{\psi(x,t)}{x} \leqq \beta, \qquad t \geqq 0$$

for all real $x \neq 0$. In particular, we permit the extreme cases in which $\psi(x,t)$ is either independent of t or linear in x [i.e., $\psi(x,t) = \psi(1,t)x$].

The block labeled **K** represents the linear time-invariant portion of the forward path. It is assumed to introduce the constraint

$$v(t) = \int_0^t k(t-\tau)u(\tau)d\tau - g_2(t), \qquad t \geqq 0$$

in which k and g_2 are real-valued functions such that

$$\int_0^\infty |k(t)|\,dt < \infty, \qquad \int_0^\infty |g_2(t)|^2\,dt < \infty. \qquad (1)$$

* The results of Ref. 1 relate to feedback systems containing an arbitrary finite number of time-varying nonlinear elements, but, with the exception of the case discussed here, they do not admit of a simple geometric interpretation.

† For results concerned with frequency-domain conditions for the global asymptotic stability (a sense of stability that is different from the one considered here) of nonlinear systems, see, for example, Refs. 2–4.

The function g_2 takes into account the initial conditions at $t = 0$. Our assumptions regarding **K** are satisfied, for example, if, as is often the case, u and v are related by a differential equation of the form

$$\sum_{n=0}^{N} a_n \frac{d^n v}{dt^n} = \sum_{n=0}^{N-1} b_n \frac{d^n u}{dt^n}, \qquad t \geqq 0$$

in which the a_n and the b_n are constants with $a_N \neq 0$, and

$$\sum_{n=0}^{N} a_n s^n \neq 0 \quad \text{for} \quad \operatorname{Re}[s] \geqq 0.$$

However, we *do not* require that u and v be related by a differential equation (or by a system of differential equations).

Assumption: We shall assume throughout that the response v is well defined and satisfies the inequality

$$\int_0^t |v(\tau)|^2 \, d\tau < \infty \tag{2}$$

for all *finite* $t > 0$, for each initial-condition function g_2 that meets the conditions stated above and each input g_1 such that

$$\int_0^\infty |g_1(t)|^2 \, dt < \infty.$$

Although this assumption plays an important role in the proof of the theorem to be presented, from an engineering viewpoint it is a trivial restriction (see Ref. 5).

Definition: We shall say that the feedback system of Fig. 1 is "$\mathfrak{L}_2$-stable" if and only if there exists a positive constant ρ with the property that the response v satisfies

$$\left(\int_0^\infty |v(t)|^2 \, dt\right)^{\frac{1}{2}} \leqq \rho \left(\int_0^\infty |g_1(t) + g_2(t)|^2 \, dt\right)^{\frac{1}{2}} + \left(\int_0^\infty |g_2(t)|^2 \, dt\right)^{\frac{1}{2}}$$

for every initial-condition function g_2 that meets the conditions stated above, and every input g_1 such that

$$\int_0^\infty |g_1(t)|^2 \, dt < \infty.$$

In particular, if the system is $\mathfrak{L}_2$-stable, then the response is square-integrable whenever the input is square-integrable.

It can be shown* that the response $v(t)$ approaches zero as $t \to \infty$ for any square-integrable input g_1, provided that the system is $\mathfrak{L}_2$-stable,

* See the proof of Theorem 6 of Ref. 1.

$g_2(t) \to 0$ as $t \to \infty$, and

$$\int_0^\infty | k(t) |^2 dt < \infty. \tag{3}$$

In addition, it follows at once from the Schwarz inequality that the response $v(t)$ is uniformly bounded on $[0, \infty)$ for any square-integrable input g_1, provided that the system is $\mathfrak{L}_2$-stable, $g_2(t)$ is uniformly bounded on $[0, \infty)$, and (3) is satisfied.

III. SUFFICIENT CONDITIONS FOR $\mathfrak{L}_2$-STABILITY

Theorem: Let

$$K(i\omega) = \int_0^\infty k(t)e^{-i\omega t} dt, \qquad -\infty < \omega < \infty.$$

The feedback system of Fig. 1 is $\mathfrak{L}_2$-stable if one of the following three conditions is satisfied:

(i) $\alpha > 0$; and the locus of $K(i\omega)$ for $-\infty < \omega < \infty$ (a) lies outside the circle C_1 of radius $\frac{1}{2}(\alpha^{-1} - \beta^{-1})$ centered on the real axis of the complex plane at $[-\frac{1}{2}(\alpha^{-1} + \beta^{-1}),0]$, and (b) does not encircle C_1 (see Fig. 2)

(ii) $\alpha = 0$, and $Re[K(i\omega)] > -\beta^{-1}$ for all real ω

(iii) $\alpha < 0$, and the locus of $K(i\omega)$ for $-\infty < \omega < \infty$ is contained within the circle C_2 of radius $\frac{1}{2}(\beta^{-1} - \alpha^{-1})$ centered on the real axis of the complex plane at $[-\frac{1}{2}(\alpha^{-1} + \beta^{-1}),0]$ (see Fig. 3).

Proof: Note first that

$$\int_0^\infty | u(t) |^2 dt \leqq \max(\beta^2, | \alpha |^2) \int_0^\infty | f(t) |^2 dt,$$

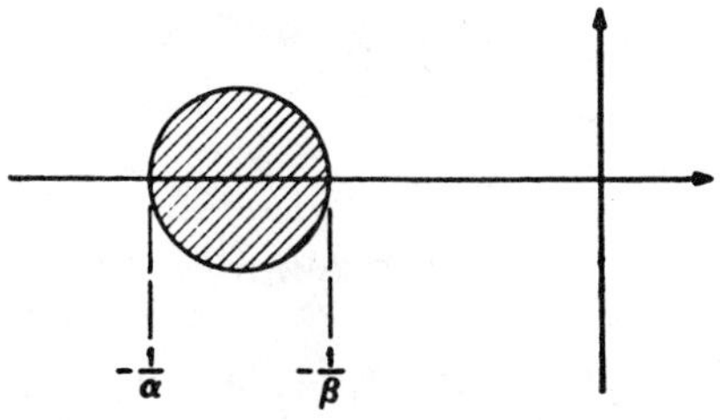

Fig. 2 — Location of the "critical circle" C_1 in the complex plane ($\alpha > 0$). The feedback system is $\mathfrak{L}_2$-stable if the locus of $K(i\omega)$ for $-\infty < \omega < \infty$ lies outside C_1 and does not encircle C_1.

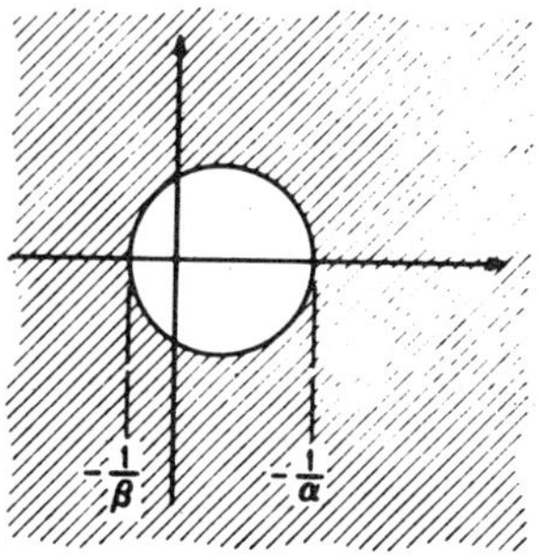

Fig. 3 — Location of the "critical circle" C_2 in the complex plane ($\alpha < 0$). The feedback system is $\mathfrak{L}_2$-stable if the locus of $K(i\omega)$ for $-\infty < \omega < \infty$ is contained within C_2.

and hence, by a well-known result,

$$\int_0^\infty \left| \int_0^t k(t-\tau)u(\tau)d\tau \right|^2 dt \leqq \left(\int_0^\infty | k(t) | dt \right)^2 \int_0^\infty | u(t) |^2 dt$$
$$\leqq \max\left(\beta^2, | \alpha |^2\right)\left(\int_0^\infty | k(t) | dt \right)^2 \int_0^\infty | f(t) |^2 dt.$$

Using Minkowski's inequality,

$$\left(\int_0^\infty | v(t) |^2 dt \right)^{\frac{1}{2}} \leqq \left(\int_0^\infty \left| \int_0^t k(t-\tau)u(\tau)d\tau \right|^2 dt \right)^{\frac{1}{2}}$$
$$+ \left(\int_0^\infty | g_2(t) |^2 dt \right)^{\frac{1}{2}} \leqq \max(\beta, | \alpha |) \int_0^\infty | k(t) | dt$$
$$\left(\int_0^\infty | f(t) |^2 dt \right)^{\frac{1}{2}} + \left(\int_0^\infty | g_2(t) |^2 dt \right)^{\frac{1}{2}}.$$

Consider now the relation between $(g_1 + g_2)$ and f:

$$g_1(t) + g_2(t) = f(t) + \int_0^t k(t-\tau)\psi[f(\tau),\tau]d\tau, \qquad t \geqq 0$$

and suppose that

$$\int_0^\infty | g_1(t) + g_2(t) |^2 dt < \infty.$$

According to the results of Ref. 1, our assumptions* imply that there

* In Ref. 1 it is assumed that

$$\int_0^t | f(\tau) |^2 d\tau < \infty$$

exists a positive constant ρ_1 (which does not depend upon g_1 or g_2) such that

$$\int_0^\infty |f(t)|^2 \, dt < \rho_1 \int_0^\infty |g_1(t) + g_2(t)|^2 \, dt$$

provided that, with

$$K(s) = \int_0^\infty k(t)e^{-st} \, dt$$

and $\omega = \mathrm{Im}[s]$,

(i) $1 + \frac{1}{2}(\alpha + \beta)K(s) \neq 0$ for $\mathrm{Re}[s] \geqq 0$, and

(ii) $\frac{1}{2}(\beta - \alpha) \max_{-\infty<\omega<\infty} |K(i\omega)[1 + \frac{1}{2}(\alpha + \beta)K(i\omega)]^{-1}| < 1$.

Thus the feedback system of Fig. 1 is $\mathfrak{L}_2$-stable if conditions (i) and (ii) are satisfied.

According to the well-known theorem of complex-function theory that leads to the Nyquist criterion, condition (i) is satisfied if (and only if) the polar plot of $K(i\omega)$ for $-\infty < \omega < \infty$ does not encircle or pass through the point $[-2(\alpha + \beta)^{-1},0]$. It can easily be verified that condition (ii) is met if one of the following three conditions is satisfied.

(a) $\alpha > 0$, and the locus of $K(i\omega)$ for $-\infty < \omega < \infty$ lies outside the circle C_1 of radius $\frac{1}{2}(\alpha^{-1} - \beta^{-1})$ centered in the complex plane at $[-\frac{1}{2}(\alpha^{-1} + \beta^{-1}),0]$.

(b) $\alpha = 0$, and $\mathrm{Re}[K(i\omega)] > -\beta^{-1}$ for all real ω.

(c) $\alpha < 0$, and the locus of $K(i\omega)$ for $-\infty < \omega < \infty$ is contained within the circle C_2 of radius $\frac{1}{2}(\beta^{-1} - \alpha^{-1})$ centered in the complex plane at $[-\frac{1}{2}(\alpha^{-1} + \beta^{-1}),0]$.

If $\alpha > 0$, the point $[-2(\alpha + \beta)^{-1},0]$ lies on the real-axis diameter of C_1, while if condition (b) or (c) is met, it is impossible for the polar plot of $K(i\omega)$ to encircle the point $[-2(\alpha + \beta)^{-1},0]$. Therefore, the conditions of the theorem guarantee that the feedback system is $\mathfrak{L}_2$-stable.

Remarks

With regard to the necessity of our sufficient conditions for $\mathfrak{L}_2$-stability, consider, for example, the case in which $\alpha > 0$ and suppose, for simplicity, that v and u are related by a differential equation of the type mentioned in Section II. Then, a moment's reflection shows that there exists a $\psi(x,t)$, in fact a $\psi(x,t)$ which is independent of t and linear in x,

---

for all finite $t > 0$. Our assumption that (2) is satisfied for all finite $t > 0$ implies that this condition is met.

that satisfies our assumptions and for which the feedback system is *not* $\mathcal{L}_2$-stable, provided that for some value of ω, $K(i\omega)$ is a point on the real-axis diameter of C_1. This clearly shows that the condition is in the correct "ball park." Similar remarks can be made concerning our conditions for the cases in which $\alpha < 0$ and $\alpha = 0$.

IV. FURTHER PROPERTIES OF THE FEEDBACK SYSTEM OF FIG. 1

It is possible to say much more about the properties of the feedback system on the basis of frequency-domain information if our assumptions regarding $\psi(x,t)$ are strengthened.

For example, suppose that

$$\alpha \leqq \frac{\psi(x_1,t) - \psi(x_2,t)}{x_1 - x_2} \leqq \beta, \qquad \psi(0,t) = 0 \tag{4}$$

for $t \geqq 0$ and all real $x_1 \neq x_2$, and that one of the three conditions of our theorem is met. Let g_1 and $\hat{g}_1$ denote two arbitrary input functions such that

$$\int_0^t |g_1(\tau)|^2 d\tau < \infty \quad \text{and} \quad \int_0^t |\hat{g}_1(\tau)|^2 d\tau < \infty$$

for all finite $t > 0$, and

$$\int_0^\infty |g_1(\tau) - \hat{g}_1(\tau)|^2 d\tau < \infty.$$

Let v and $\hat{v}$, respectively, denote the (assumed well defined) responses due to g_1 and $\hat{g}_1$. Then if

$$\int_0^t |v(\tau)|^2 d\tau < \infty \quad \text{and} \quad \int_0^t |\hat{v}(\tau)|^2 d\tau < \infty$$

for all finite $t > 0$, and the assumptions of Section II are met, it follows* that

$$\int_0^\infty |v(\tau) - \hat{v}(\tau)|^2 d\tau < \infty$$

and that there exists a positive constant λ (which does not depend upon g_1 or $\hat{g}_1$) such that

$$\int_0^\infty |v(\tau) - \hat{v}(\tau)|^2 d\tau \leqq \lambda \int_0^\infty |g_1(\tau) - \hat{g}_1(\tau)|^2 d\tau.$$

---

* Consider Theorem 1 of Ref. 6 with $h_1(t) = f_1(t) = 0$ for $t < 0$.

Suppose now that $\psi(x,t)$ satisfies (4) and is either independent of t or periodic in t with period T for each x, and that one of the three conditions of our theorem is met. Assume that the initial-condition function $g_2(t)$ approaches zero as $t \to \infty$, and that the input $g_1(t)$ applied at $t = 0$ is a bounded periodic function with period T. Then it can be shown* that there exists a bounded periodic function p, with period T, which is independent of g_2 and such that the (assumed well defined) response $v(t)$ approaches $p(t)$ as $t \to \infty$, provided that the conditions of Section II are met, (2) is satisfied for all finite $t > 0$, and

$$\int_0^\infty \left| \int_t^\infty | k(\tau) | \, d\tau \right|^2 dt < \infty, \qquad \int_0^\infty | (1 + t)k(t) |^2 \, dt < \infty. \tag{5}$$

Observe that the conditions of (5) are satisfied if u and v are related by a differential equation of the form described in Section II.

REFERENCES

1. Sandberg, I. W., On the $\mathcal{L}_2$-Boundedness of Solutions of Nonlinear Functional Equations, B.S.T.J., this issue, p. 1581.
2. Popov, V. M., Absolute Stability of Nonlinear Systems of Automatic Control, Avtomatika i Telemekhanika, **22**, Aug., 1961, pp. 961–978.
3. Kalman, R. E., Lyapunov Functions For the Problem of Lur'e in Automatic Control, Proc. Natl. Acad. Sci., **49**, Feb., 1963, pp. 201–205.
4. Rekasius, Z. V., A Stability Criterion for Feedback Systems with One Nonlinear Element, Trans. IEEE-PTGAC, **AC9**, Jan., 1964, pp. 46–50.
5. Tricomi, F. G., *Integral Equations*, Interscience Publishing, Inc., New York, 1957, p. 46.
6. Sandberg, I. W., and Beneš, V. E., On the Properties of Nonlinear Integral Equations That Arise in the Theory of Dynamical Systems, to be published.

* See Theorem 3 of Ref. 6.

A FREQUENCY CRITERION FOR ABSOLUTE PROCESS STABILITY IN NONLINEAR AUTOMATIC CONTROL SYSTEMS

(UDC 62-503.12)

B. N. Naumov and Ya. Z. Tsypkin

Moscow

Translated from Avtomatika i Telemekhanika, Vol. 25, No. 6, pp. 852-867, June, 1964

A frequency criterion is formulated for absolute process stability in nonlinear automatic control systems which is similar to the usual frequency criterion for linear automatic control systems. The proposed criterion is based on a generalization of V. M. Popov's absolute equilibrium state stability condition as a case of absolute process stability in nonlinear systems. Amplitude-phase and logarithmic frequency characteristics are used to investigate absolute process stability. Methods are also presented for the synthesis of stabilizing devices which provide absolute process stability and a degree of stability not less than a given one.

A large class of nonlinear automatic control systems may be reduced to a structure which is a combination of a nonlinear element NE and a linear part LP (Fig. 1). Absolute equilibrium state stability in similar nonlinear systems is understood to be asymptotic equilibrium state stability in the Lyapunov sense for any continuous characteristics of a nonlinear element belonging to a specific class and for any instantaneous disturbances.

The problem of absolute equilibrium state stability in nonlinear systems, first presented in 1944 by A. I. Lur'e and V. N. Postnikov [1], was studied on the basis of the Lyapunov direct method in the papers by A. I. Lur'e [2], A. M. Letov [3], I. G. Malkin [4], E. N. Rozenvasser [5], and others.

Comparatively recently, the papers of V. M. Popov [6-8] appeared, in which to solve this problem the Parseval' formula and the theory of positive-definite functions were brought in, which made it possible to express the absolute equilibrium state stability conditions by functions related to the frequency characteristic of the linear part of the system. V. M. Popov's results were refined and extended for the critical cases in the paper by V. A. Yakubovich [9].

The relation between the V. M. Popov method and the Lyapunov direct method is established in papers by V. A. Yakubovich [9, 10], E. N. Rozenvasser [11], and R. Kalman [12]. All of these results are summarized in the book by M. A. Aizerman and F. R. Gantmakher [13].

One must emphasize, however, that in many cases absolute equilibrium state stability is not sufficient to guarantee a normal operation of the nonlinear automatic control system for various driving and disturbing influences. Therefore it is very important to guarantee stability of the processes initiated by various outside influences together with equilibrium state stability of the nonlinear system.

The aim of the present paper is to find the conditions for which in nonlinear control systems not only will the equilibrium state but also the processes initiated by outside influences be absolutely stable, and to state these conditions in the form of a simple frequency criterion suitable for practical applications.

A frequency criterion for absolute process stability reduces the absolute stability problem to the investigation of some linearized system, obtained from the nonlinear system by replacing the nonlinear element by a linear one, on the basis of investigating the amplitude-phase or logarithmic frequency characteristics.

Using logarithmic frequency characteristics makes it possible to synthesize very simply a stabilizing device which guarantees realization of the required sufficient conditions for process stability and a degree of stability not less than the given one. The examples presented illustrate the practical use of the frequency criterion for absolute process stability and the method for synthesizing stabilizing devices.

1. Nonlinear Automatic Control System Equation

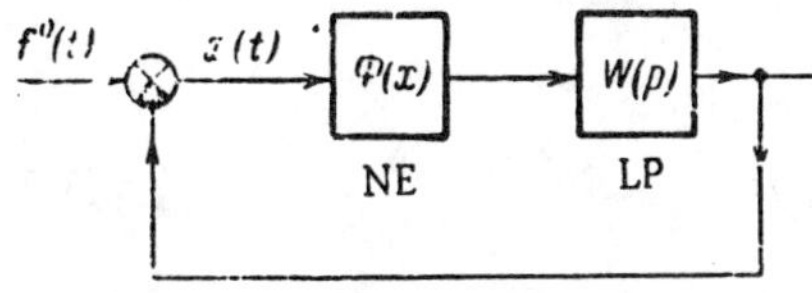

Fig. 1.

Let us assume that a bounded outside influence $f^{\circ}(t)$ is applied to the nonlinear automatic control system under consideration for $t \geq t_0$, where it is possible that $t_0 \leq 0$ (Fig. 1). Then its integral equation with respect to the error $x(t)$ may be represented in the form

$$x(t) = f^{\circ}(t) - \int_{t_0}^{t} w(t-\lambda)\,\Phi[x(\lambda)]\,d\lambda. \tag{1.1}$$

By applying a bilateral Laplace transform to both sides, we get

$$X(p) = F^{\circ}(p) - W(p)L\{\Phi[x(t)]\}. \tag{1.2}$$

In Eqs. (1.1) and (1.2), $w(t)$ and $W(p)$ denote the pulse response and corresponding transfer function of the linear part of the system, $\Phi(x)$ is the nonlinear element characteristic.

Depending on the character of the poles of the transfer function $W(p)$, the linear part may be stable, neutral, or unstable. In order to include all these cases, let us derive an equivalent transformation of Eqs. (1.1) and (1.2). Let us represent $\Phi(x)$ in the form:

$$\Phi(x) = \Phi_{tr}(x) + rx. \tag{1.3}$$

By substituting (1.3) in (1.2), after the elementary transformations we get

$$X(p) = F_{tr}(p) - W_{tr}(p)L\{\Phi_{tr}(x(t))\}, \tag{1.4}$$

where

$$F_{tr}(p) = \frac{F^{\circ}(p)}{1 + rW(p)} = L\{f_{tr}(t)\}, \tag{1.5}$$

$$W_{tr}(p) = \frac{W(p)}{1 + rW(p)}. \tag{1.6}$$

Let us assume that there exists a minimum r for which all the poles of the transfer function $W_{tr}(p)$ (1.6) have negative real parts. This means that the transformed linear part of the system is stable. If we go from the equation regarding representation (1.4) to the original and if we take into account that $f_{tr}(t)$ is applied at the moment $t = t_0 \leq 0$, we get the integral equation of the transferred system in the form

$$x(t) = f_{tr}(t) - \int_{t_0}^{t} w_{tr}(t-\lambda)\,\Phi_{tr}[x(\lambda)]\,d\lambda, \tag{1.7}$$

where, as it is easy to show, if we start from relationships (1.5) and (1.6) after going over to the original:

$$w_{tr}(t) = L^{-1}\{W_{tr}(p)\}, \tag{1.8}$$

$$f_{tr}(t) = f^{\circ}(t) - r\int_{t_0}^{t} w_{tr}(t-\lambda)\,f_{tr}(\lambda)\,d\lambda. \tag{1.9}$$

It is apparent that when $f^{\circ}(t)$ is bounded and the transformed linear part is stable it follows from (1.9) that $f_{tr}(t)$ is also bounded. For $r = 0$ we have $f_{tr}(t) = f^{\circ}(t)$, and Eq. (1.7) becomes Eq. (1.1). The block diagram of the transformed system corresponding to Eq. (1.7) is represented in Fig. 2.

The integral Eq. (1.7) describes the variation process in the error $x(t)$ due to the bounded outside influence applied to the system at the moment of time $t = t_0$. In particular, the case when $t = -\infty$ corresponds to an unbounded long-acting outside influence. In this case, if there exists the unique bounded process $x(t) = x^{\circ}(t)$:

$$x^{\circ}(t) = f_{tr}(t) - \int_{-\infty}^{t} w_{tr}(t-\lambda)\,\Phi_{tr}[x^{\circ}(\lambda)]\,d\lambda, \tag{1.10}$$

then it is possible, by analogy with linear systems, to call this a forced process.

In Eq. (1.10), if we substitute t − λ for the variable of integration λ, the equation for the forced process (1.10) may also be written in the following form:

$$x^{\circ}(t) = f_{\mathrm{tr}}(t) - \int_{0}^{\infty} w_{\mathrm{tr}}(\lambda)\, \Phi_{\mathrm{tr}}[x^{\circ}(t-\lambda)]\, d\lambda. \tag{1.11}$$

Describing the processes by using integral equations is convenient because not only are systems with lumped parameters included, but also some classes of systems with distributed parameters for fixed boundary conditions.

2. The Deviation Equation

To investigate the stability of processes $x(t)$, let us assume that at the moment $t = 0$ the initial conditions are disturbed in the linear part of the system. Let us designate the reaction of the transformed linear part to this disturbance by $f_{\mathrm{i}}(t)$ (Fig. 2).

Since the transformed linear part is stable:

$$\lim f_{\mathrm{i}}(t) = 0 \quad \text{or} \quad \int_{0}^{\infty} |f_{\mathrm{i}}(t)|\, dt = M_1 < \infty. \tag{2.1}$$

On account of the influence of these disturbances, the process $x(t)$ for $t \geq 0$ is changed by the value $\xi(t)$ and in place of Eq. (1.11) we have

$$x(t) + \xi(t) = f_{\mathrm{tr}}(t) + f_{\mathrm{i}}(t) - \int_{t_0}^{t} w_{\mathrm{tr}}(t-\lambda)\, \Phi_{\mathrm{tr}}\{x(\lambda) + \xi(\lambda)\}\, d\lambda, \tag{2.2}$$

where

$$\xi(t) \equiv 0 \ \text{for} \ t < 0. \tag{2.3}$$

Subtracting Eq. (1.7) from Eq. (2.2) we get an expression for the deviation $\xi(t)$ from the process being investigated:

$$\xi(t) = f_{\mathrm{i}}(t) - \int_{t_0}^{t} w_{\mathrm{tr}}(t-\lambda)\, \Psi[\xi(\lambda); \lambda]\, d\lambda, \tag{2.4}$$

where

$$\Psi[\xi(t); t] = \Phi_{\mathrm{tr}}[x(t) + \xi(t)] - \Phi_{\mathrm{tr}}[x(t)]. \tag{2.5}$$

Taking into account (2.3), let us write Eq. (2.4) in the form

$$\xi(t) = f_{\mathrm{i}}(t) - \int_{0}^{t} w_{\mathrm{tr}}(t-\lambda)\, \Psi[\xi(\lambda); \lambda]\, d\lambda. \tag{2.6}$$

The block diagram represented in Fig. 3 corresponds to the deviation equation (2.6). This block diagram differs from the one in Fig. 2 in that the nonlinear element with stationary characteristic $\Phi_{\mathrm{tr}}(x)$ is replaced by the nonlinear element with a nonstationary characteristic $\Psi[\xi(t), t]$ which depends on the value $x(t)$ and defines the process being investigated.

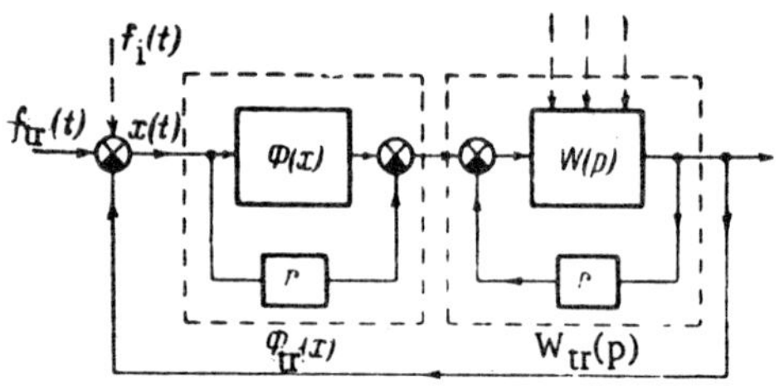

Fig. 2

It follows from (2.5) that the nonstationary characteristic possesses such properties that

$$\Psi[0; t] = 0. \tag{2.7}$$

3. Frequency Criterion for Absolute Process Stability

The conditions for absolute process stability, as shown in the Supplement, may be stated in the following way. In order that the process in the nonlinear system (Fig. 1), initiated by a bounded outside influence $f_{\mathrm{tr}}(t)$,

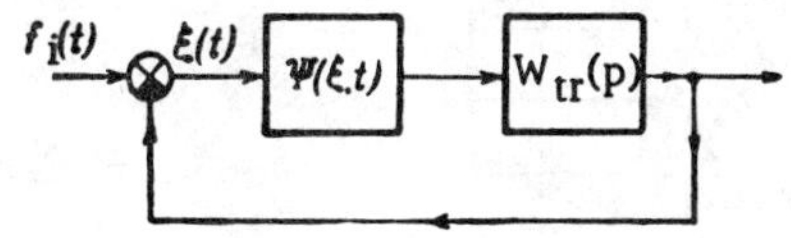

Fig. 3.

be absolutely stable, it is sufficient for a given r for the transformed linear part to be stable, for the linear part frequency characteristic $W(j\omega)$ to satisfy the condition

$$\mathrm{Re}\frac{W(j\omega)}{1+rW(j\omega)}+\frac{1}{k-r}\geqslant 0 \quad (0\leqslant\omega<\infty), \tag{3.1}$$

and for the derivative of the nonlinear characteristic $\Phi(x)$ to belong to the region $(r+\varepsilon, k-\varepsilon)$, i.e.,

$$r+\varepsilon\leqslant\frac{d\Phi(x)}{dx}\leqslant k-\varepsilon, \tag{3.2}$$

where ε is an arbitrarily small positive value and k is a positive value satisfying inequality (3.1).

For the case when the linear part is stable, having assumed in (3.1) that $r = 0$, we get

$$\mathrm{Re}\,W(j\omega)+1/k\geqslant 0 \quad (0\leqslant\omega<\infty) \tag{3.3}$$

or

$$\mathrm{Re}\,kW(j\omega)+1\geqslant 0 \quad (0\leqslant\omega<\infty). \tag{3.4}$$

Geometrically, on the plane of the frequency characteristic $kW(j\omega)$ of the open linearized system obtained from the original nonlinear system (Fig. 1) by substituting for the nonlinear element a linear amplifier with an amplification factor k, this means that $kW(j\omega)$ may be situated to the right of the straight line $U(\omega) = -1$.

To formulate the frequency criterion for absolute stability in the general case when $r \neq 0$, let us transform inequality (3.1). If we multiply the left side of inequality (3.1) by $A = k/r > 0$, we get

$$\mathrm{Re}\frac{kW(j\omega)}{A+kW(j\omega)}+\frac{1}{A-1}\geqslant 0 \quad (0\leqslant\omega<\infty), \tag{3.5}$$

where

$$kW(j\omega)=U(\omega)+jV(\omega). \tag{3.6}$$

Let us find on the U, V plane the locus of the points which correspond to a replacement of the inequality sign in (3.5) by an equality sign. If we substitute (3.6) into the left side of (3.5), find the real part and set it to zero, we get the equation for the desired curves

$$\left[U(\omega)+\frac{1}{2}(A+1)\right]^2+V^2(\omega)=\frac{1}{4}(A-1)^2. \tag{3.7}$$

It is easy to show that (3.7) defines a family of circles passing through the point $-1; j0$, having a radius $R=(A-1)/2$ and situated to the left of the straight line $U(\omega) = -1$ (Fig. 4). To each circle corresponds its own value $A=k/r\geq 1$.

That inequality (3.5) will be satisfied outside of the A-circles is easily established by assuming that $U(\omega) = V(\omega) = 0$ for $k > 0$, $r > 0$. Condition (3.5) and the condition for stability of the transformed linear part will be satisfied if the frequency characteristic $kW(j\omega)$ is found outside the corresponding A-circle.

For $A = 1$ the A-circle degenerates into the point $-1, j0$ and the sufficient condition for absolute stability of the nonlinear system becomes a necessary and sufficient condition for stability of some linear system for $k = r$.

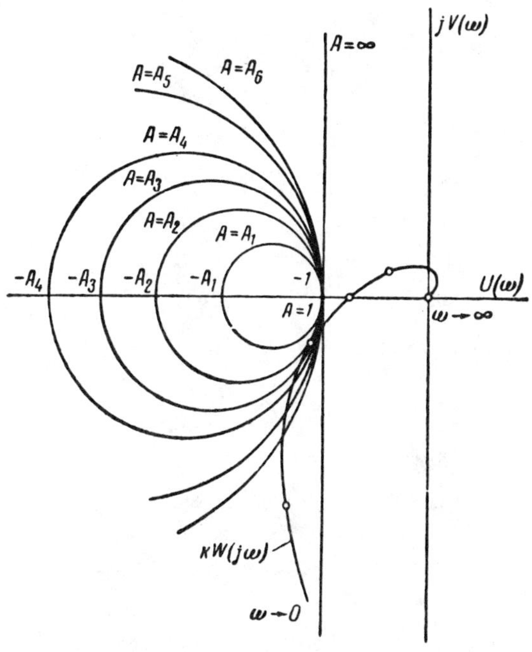

Fig. 4.

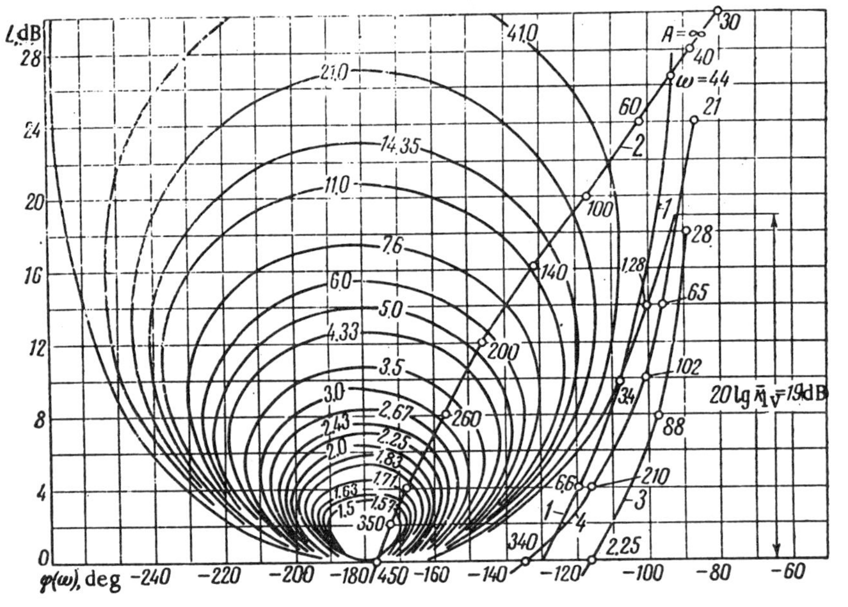

Fig. 5.

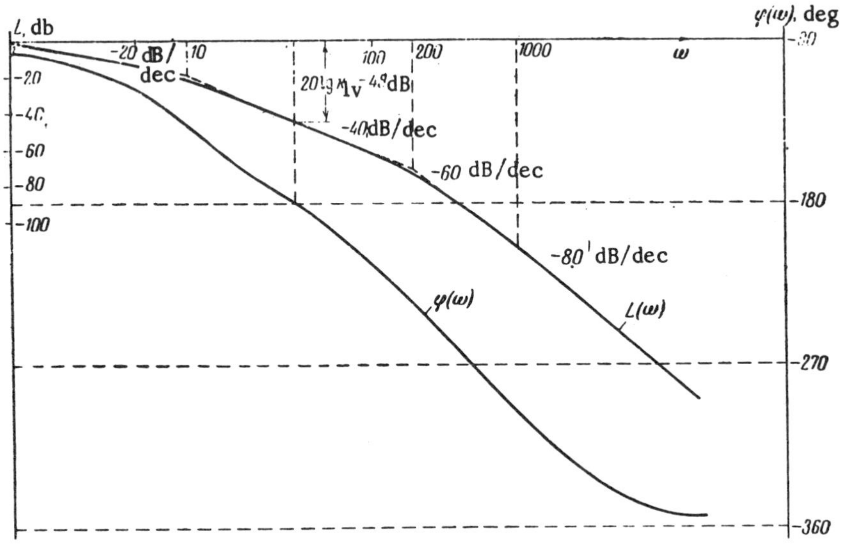

Fig. 6.

For A = ∞ the A-circle becomes a circle of infinite radius and from (3.5) (after getting rid of the indeterminate form) we get condition (3.3).

Now it is possible to make the following simple statement of the frequency criterion for absolute process stability in nonlinear automatic control systems.

So that the processes in nonlinear systems are absolutely stable, it is sufficient for the derivative of the nonlinear element characteristic $d\Phi/dx$ to belong to the region $(r + \varepsilon;\ k - \varepsilon)$, where $\varepsilon > 0$ is an arbitrarily small number, and for the open linear system frequency characteristic $kW(j\omega)$ which satisfies the Nyquist frequency criterion, to be found outside the corresponding A-circle, where $A = k/r$.

It is apparent that for realizing the frequency criterion for absolute process stability, not only the processes possible in the system but also the equilibrium state will be stable.

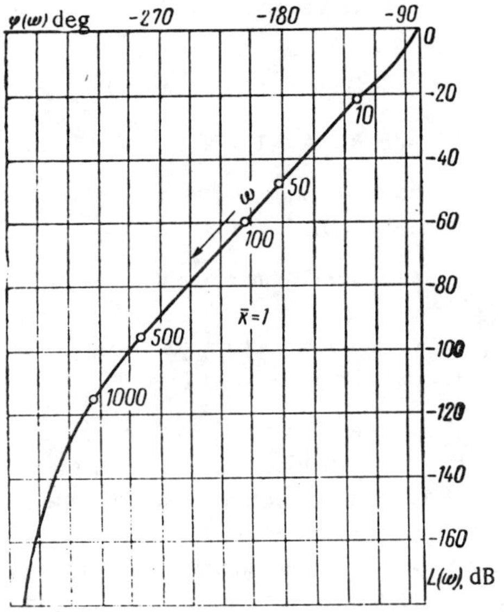

Fig. 7.

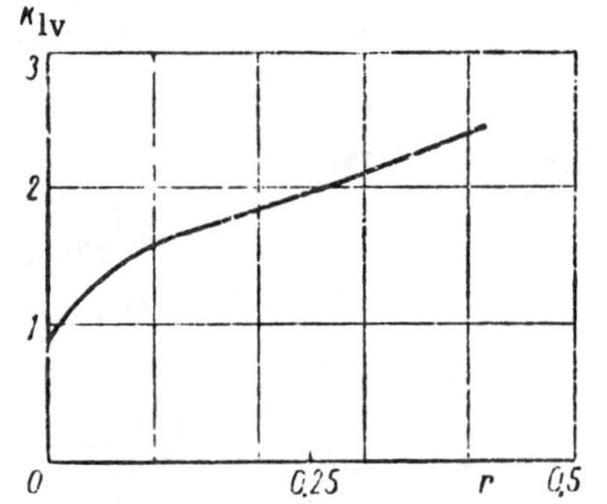

Fig. 8.

In this way the frequency criterion of process stability distinguishes a class of systems in which the equilibrium state stability also depends on process stability.

In this sense the character of this class of systems is similar to the character of linear systems.

The conditions for absolute process stability in nonlinear continuous systems are more rigid in comparison with the conditions for equilibrium state stability. On one hand, they impose additional restrictions on the derivative of the nonlinear element characteristic. On the other hand, they correspond to the special case of the V. M. Popov condition where $q = 0$ [7].

A condition similar to condition (3.3) which defines the condition for equilibrium state stability for nonlinear systems with a nonstationary characteristic was obtained by the more rigorous means of V. A. Yakubovich [9, 10] and E. N. Rozenvasser [11]. For sampled-data systems a condition similar to (3.1) was obtained in [14].

The paper by V. A. Yakubovich [15], with which the authors became familiar after writing the present article, contains a rigorous proof of the criterion for absolute process stability which includes a wider class of systems with less strict restrictions imposed on the nonlinear characteristics.

4. Analysis of Absolute Process Stability

The problem of absolute process stability consists of verifying the realization of the frequency criterion.

If the frequency characteristic of the linearized system $kW(j\omega)$ is given, then it is easy to determine the set of regions $(r+\varepsilon;\ k-\varepsilon)$ to which the derivative of the nonlinear element characteristic must belong. For this purpose it is convenient to use the network of A-circles (Fig. 4). If we are given the $\underline{k}$ values and if we represent on this network the frequency characteristic $kW(j\omega)$ of the open linear system, we shall determine the parameter $A = k/r$ of the A-circle to which the frequency characteristic is tangent. If we know the values of $\underline{k}$ and A it is easy to determine the corresponding value of $\underline{r}$. In this way we may obtain the relationship $k = Q(r)$.

Logarithmic frequency characteristics are usually used in automatic control system calculation, since in many cases it is considerably simpler to plot them than the usual frequency characteristics $kW(j\omega)$.

To find the relationship $k = Q(r)$ in this case, instead of the circle diagrams in Fig. 5* it is necessary to have the same diagrams in Cartesian coordinates on the plane $L(\omega) = 20 \log |kW(j\omega)|$ and $\varphi(\omega)$, which are shown in Fig. 5. Then, to find the relationship $k = Q(r)$ it is necessary:

1. To plot the logarithmic amplitude- and phase-frequency characteristics for $\bar{k} = kk_v = 1$, where k_v is the amplification factor of the linear part of the system;

2. To re-plot them on the $L(\omega)$, $\varphi(\omega)$ plane for various $\underline{k}$ and to determine the indices of the A-curves tangent to the logarithmic characteristics;

3. Knowing the value of A, to find the value of $\underline{r}$ corresponding to various values of $\bar{k} = kk_v$.

---

* Let us note that the networks of A-circles (Fig. 4) and A-curves (Fig. 5) for various values of A coincide with the circle diagrams used for plotting the closed system real frequency characteristics with respect to the open system amplitude-phase characteristics.

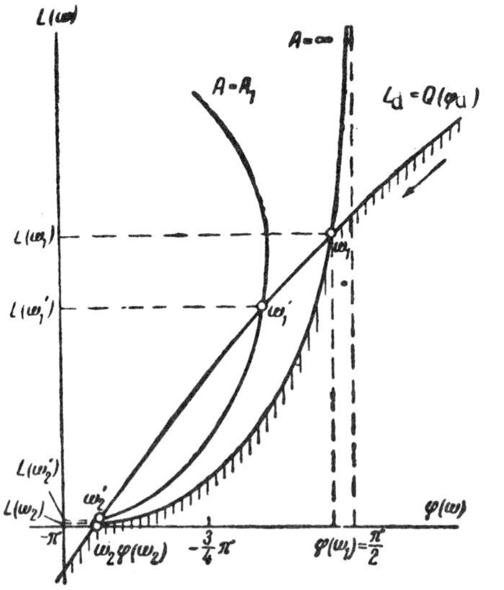

Fig. 9.

Let us consider an example. Let the transfer function of the linear part of a servo system have the form

$$kW(p) = \frac{kk_v}{p(T_g p + 1)(T_m T_y p^2 + T_m p + 1)}, \tag{4.1}$$

where $k_v = 10$; $T_g = 0.005$ sec; $T_m = 0.1$ sec; $T_y = 0.001$ sec.

Let us find the limiting value $\bar{k}_{1v}$, and for a given k_v, let us determine the relationship $k = Q(r)$.

Let us plot the log amplitude-frequency characteristic $L(\omega)$ and phase-frequency characteristic $\varphi(\omega)$ for $k = 1$ (Fig. 6) and, with respect to these, the log frequency characteristic in Cartesian coordinates on the $L(\omega)$, $\varphi(\omega)$ plane, for $\bar{k} = 1$ (Fig. 7).

It is convenient to plot the characteristic $L(\omega) = f[\varphi(\omega)]$ on transparent paper with the same scale on the axes as for the A-curves (Fig. 5). Let us shift the curve obtained up along the axis of ordinates until it is tangent to one of the A-curves. Let us determine the value of the upward shift in decibels which matches the increase in the amplification factor $\bar{k}$ by a corresponding number of decibels.

It is easy to determine the amplification factor limiting value $\bar{k}_{1v}$ of the region $(0, k_{1v})$ from the condition that $L = f(\varphi)$ is tangent to the logarithmic A-curve corresponding to $A = \infty$, which will be equal to 19 dB or 8.90. Knowing the numerical value of A and $k_v = 10$, we compute the corresponding values of k and r, with respect to which the curve $k = Q(r)$ is plotted (Fig. 8).

5. Synthesis of Stabilizing Devices which Provide Absolute Process Stability

In a number of cases it may be shown that for the nonlinear system being investigated it is necessary to have the values of $\bar{k}$ and r be somewhat different from the corresponding values of $\bar{k}$ which define the sectors and regions $(k - \varepsilon, r + \varepsilon)$ of the nonlinear characteristic $\Phi(x)$ and its derivative $\Phi'(x)$, which are computed with the aid of the methods stated in the previous section.

In this case the logarithmic frequency characteristic represented in Cartesian coordinates will intersect the A-curve (for $A = \infty$) at the points ω_1 and ω_2 (Fig. 9). This means that in order to fulfill the sufficient conditions for absolute stability, it is necessary to introduce a stabilizing device which changes the log frequency characteristic plotted for a given value of $\bar{k}$ to the frequency band ω_1, ω_2. In the frequency band $\omega < \omega_2$ and $\omega > \omega_1$, the sufficient conditions for process stability are satisfied.

Then the log frequency characteristic shaded in Fig. 9 may be considered to be the desired one $L_d = f(\varphi_d)$.

In practice, it is more convenient to find the log frequency characteristics of the stabilizing device by using $L_d(\omega)$ $[\varphi_d(\omega) \equiv \varphi(\omega)]$ for the log amplitude-frequency characteristic, having determined it beforehand from $L_d = (\varphi_d)$ (Fig. 10).

Now the problem reduces to finding that stabilizer (series or shunt), for which the log amplitude-frequency characteristic of the synthesized system would coincide with $L_d(\omega)$ or lie inside the shaded region (Fig. 10).

After finding the logarithmic characteristic of the stabilizer it is necessary to plot the phase-frequency characteristic or the characteristic $L = f(\varphi)$ of the synthesized system and to verify that the sufficient condition for absolute process stability is satisfied.

If it is necessary to provide certain required values of k and r, then instead of considering the A-curve for $A = \infty$ for synthesizing the stabilizer, it is necessary to consider the A-curve for $A = A_1$ (Figs. 9, 10).

Let us look at an example. Let the transfer function of a nonlinear system for the automatic control of motor speed have the form

$$kW(p) = \frac{kk_v}{(T_g p + 1)(T_m T_y p^2 + T_m p + 1)}, \tag{5.1}$$

where $\bar{k} = kk_v = 100$; $T_g = 0.005$ sec; $T_m = 0.1$ sec; $T_y = 0.001$ sec.

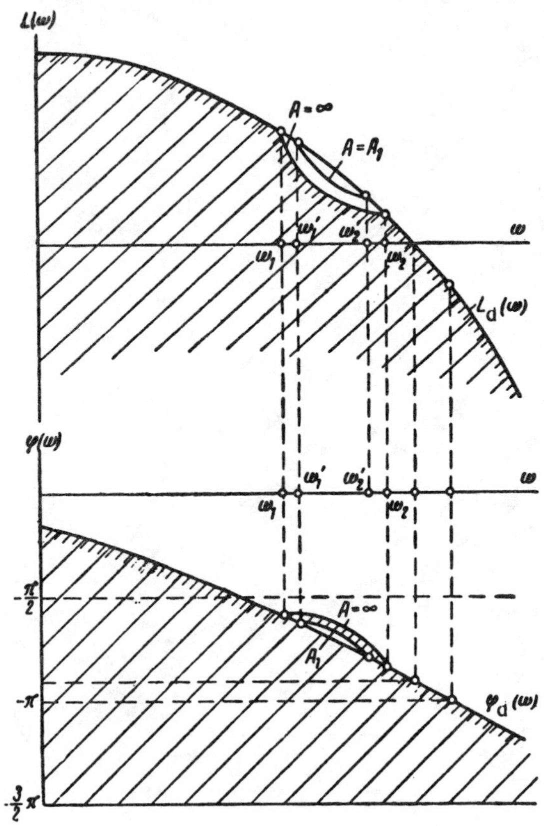

Fig. 10.

By using the log frequency characteristic, let us verify that the sufficient conditions for absolute process stability are fulfilled for $\bar{k}$ = 100 and r = 0, r_1 = 9.1, and in the case when they are not fulfilled, let us specify the necessary stabilizing device.

The log amplitude- and phase-frequency characteristics corresponding to kW(p) for $\bar{k}$ = 100 are shown in Fig. 11, and in Fig. 5 the same log frequency characteristic L = $f(\varphi)$ is represented in Cartesian coordinates (curve 2).

From studying the relative position of the curve L = $f(\varphi)$ and the A-curves (Fig. 5) for A = 100/0 = ∞, A_1 = 100/9.1 = 11, it follows that the necessary and sufficient conditions for stability of the linearized system having a transfer function kW(p) are satisfied, but the sufficient conditions for absolute process stability in a nonlinear system are not satisfied (for A = ∞, A_1 = 11).

In Fig. 11 are also represented the desired log amplitude-frequency $L_d(\omega)$, $L_{d1}(\omega)$ and phase-frequency characteristics $\varphi_d(\omega)$, $\varphi_{d1}(\omega)$ corresponding to A = ∞, A_1 = 11, in addition to the characteristics of the original system. Now it is easy to determine the log amplitude-frequency characteristic $L_k(\omega)$ of the stabilizer, which has a transfer function

$$W_k(p) = \frac{(T_2p+1)(T_3p+1)}{(T_1p+1)(T_4p+1)}, \qquad (5.2)$$

where

$$T_1 = \frac{1}{\omega_1^k}, \quad T_2 = \frac{1}{\omega_2^k}, \quad T_3 = \frac{1}{\omega_3^k}, \quad T_4 = \frac{1}{\omega_4^k}.$$

For A = ∞, T_1 = 0.435 sec; T_2 = 0.1 sec; T_3 = 0.005 sec; T_4 = 0.0016 sec.

Let us verify that the sufficient conditions for process stability are satisfied in a nonlinear system containing the stabilizer found with transfer function (5.2) and with parameters corresponding to A = ∞. Let us plot the log frequency

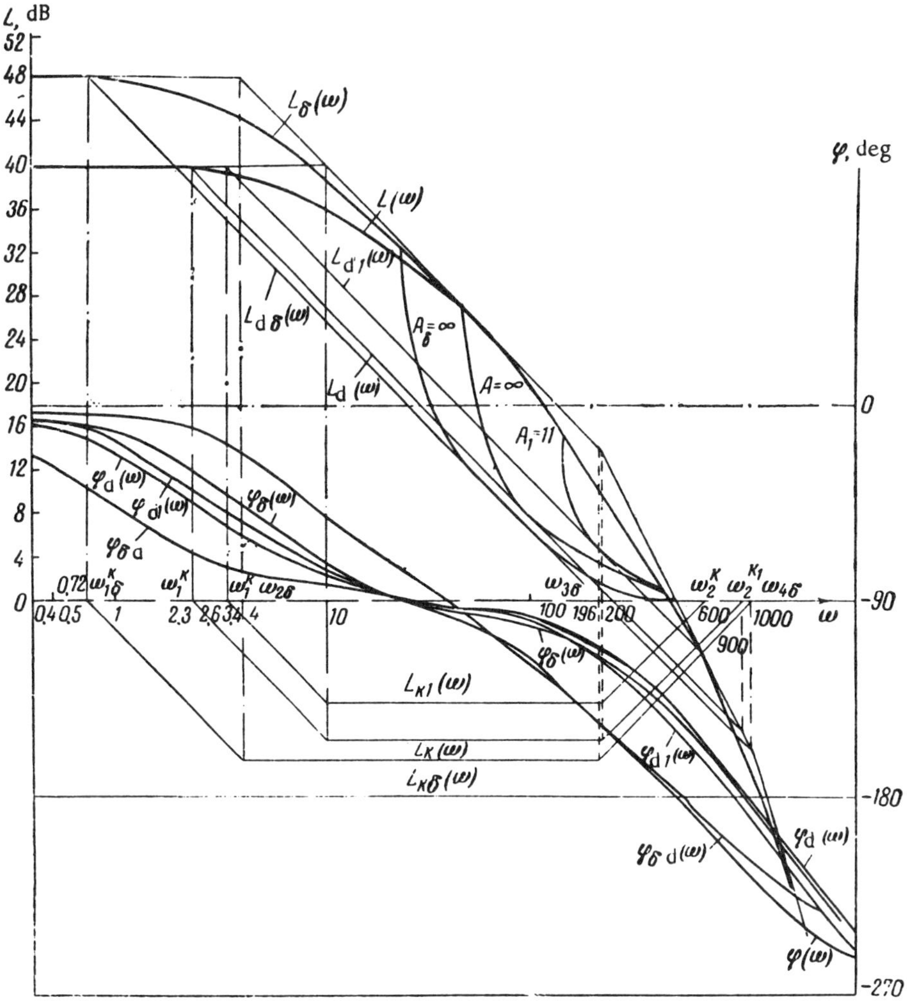

Fig. 11.

characteristic of the synthesized system in Cartesian coordinates (Fig. 5, curve 3). It is easy to see that after introducing the stabilizer, the sufficient conditions for stability for $\bar{k} = 100$ and $A = \infty$ are satisfied, and also, there even exists a safety factor equal to $+\Delta\bar{k} = 6.5$ dB. For this, $k = 211.3$.

One should note that for the stabilizer obtained the sufficient conditions for absolute process stability will also be fulfilled for $k = 100$ and $A_1 = 11$.

Similarly, the stabilizer parameters may be found which guarantee that the sufficient conditions for process stability are satisfied for $A_1 = 11$ (see curve 4, Fig. 5). These parameters will be:

$T_1 = 0.284$ sec; $T_2 = 0.1$ sec; $T_3 = 0.005$ sec; $T_4 = 0.0011$ sec.

6. Synthesis of Stabilizing Devices which Provide a Degree of Stability not Less than a Given One

Above, a frequency criterion was formulated for absolute process stability in nonlinear systems. Let us find the sufficient condition for which, in order to be satisfied, the system will have a degree of stability not less than the given one, i.e., the process deviation will satisfy the condition

$$|\xi(t)| < M_0 e^{-\delta_0 t}, \tag{6.1}$$

where M_0 is a constant, δ_0 is the given degree of stability.

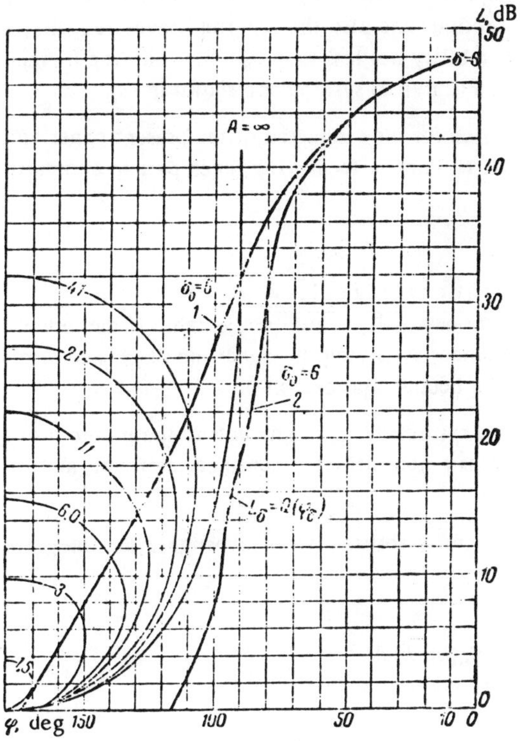

Fig. 12.

If we multiply the left- and right-hand sides of (2.6) by $e^{\delta_0 t}$ and the integrand by $e^{-\delta_0\lambda}e^{\delta_0\lambda}$, we get

$$\bar{\xi}(t) = \bar{f}_i(t) - \int_{t_0}^{t} \bar{w}_{tr}(t-\lambda)\bar{\Psi}[\bar{\xi}(\lambda);\lambda]\,d\lambda, \tag{6.2}$$

where

$$\bar{\xi}(t) = \xi(t)\,e^{\delta_0 t}, \tag{6.3}$$

$$\bar{f}_i(t) = f_i(t)\,e^{\delta_0 t}, \tag{6.4}$$

$$\bar{w}_{tr}(t-\lambda) = w_{tr}(t-\lambda)\,e^{\delta_0(t-\lambda)}, \tag{6.5}$$

$$\bar{\Psi}[\bar{\xi}(\lambda);\lambda] = \Psi[\xi(\lambda);\lambda]\,e^{\delta_0\lambda} \tag{6.6}$$

and δ_0 is less than the degree of stability of the transformed linear part.

In this case

$$\lim_{t\to\infty} \bar{f}_i(t) = \lim_{t\to\infty} f_i(t)\,e^{\delta_0 t} = 0. \tag{6.7}$$

If the system described by Eq. (6.2) has absolute equilibrium state stability, then

$$\lim_{t\to\infty} \bar{\xi}(t) = \lim_{t\to\infty} \xi(t)\,e^{\delta_0 t} = 0 \tag{6.8}$$

and, consequently, inequality (6.1) will be satisfied.

It is easy to show that condition (S.21) is satisfied, and for the function $\bar{\Psi}[\bar{\xi}(t);t]$

$$\varepsilon \leqslant \frac{\bar{\Psi}[\bar{\xi}(t);t]}{\bar{\xi}(t)} \leqslant k - r - \varepsilon. \tag{6.9}$$

Actually, if we substitute in (6.9) the appropriate expressions from (6.3) and (6.6) we get (S.21)

$$\varepsilon \leqslant \frac{\Psi[\xi(t);t]}{\xi(t)} \leqslant k - r - \varepsilon. \tag{6.10}$$

If we compare the integral equation (6.2) to Eq. (2.6), we see that the only difference in them is contained in the main part, whose spectral function has the following form

$$\int_0^\infty w_{tr}(t)\,e^{\delta_0 t}\,e^{-j\omega t} = W_{tr}(j\omega - \delta_0) = \frac{W(j\omega - \delta_0)}{1 + rW(j\omega - \delta_0)}. \tag{6.11}$$

Therefore, the sufficient condition, for which the degree of stability of the nonlinear system will not be less than the given one, is represented in the form

$$\mathrm{Re}\,\frac{W(j\omega - \delta_0)}{1 + rW(j\omega - \delta_0)} + \frac{1}{k - r} \geqslant 0 \quad (0 \leqslant \omega < \infty). \tag{6.12}$$

Also, the degree of stability of the transformed linear part must not be less than δ_0, and the derivative of the nonlinear characteristic $\Phi'(x)$ must belong to the region $(r + \varepsilon;\, k - \varepsilon)$.*

If we use the log frequency characteristic method and plot, as follows from (6.12), the displaced amplitude- and phase-frequency characteristics $L_\delta(\omega)$ and $\varphi_\delta(\omega)$, and next $L_\delta = f(\varphi_\delta)$, we may use the methods presented in the previous section for the synthesis of a stabilizer for a system having a degree of stability not less than the given one.

---

*For discrete systems, a condition similar to (6.12) is established in [17], and for continuous systems, in [15], both for bounded and for vanishing influences. For the latter case in [15], more general conditions are obtained.

In Fig. 11 are shown the displaced amplitude- and phase-frequency characteristics $L_\delta(\omega)$ and $\varphi_\delta(\omega)$ when $\delta_0 = 6$ for the system investigated as the example in the previous section, and also the log amplitude-frequency characteristic of the synthesized stabilizer which provides a degree of stability not less than $\delta_0 = 6$. The log frequency characteristics $L_\delta = f(\varphi_\delta)$ for the original (curve 1) and synthesized (curve 2) systems are shown in Fig. 12.

The authors express their deep appreciation to V. A. Yakubovich for his discussion of the present paper and for a number of valuable observations, and also to V. I. Dimkov and N. N. Popova for having taken part in computing the examples.

APPENDIX

Proof of the Sufficiency Criterion for Absolute Process Stability

The process $x(t)$ being studied and, in particular, the forced process will be absolutely stable if the deviation $\xi(t)$ is asymptotically stable (in the Lyapunov sense) for any disturbances satisfying the condition (2.1), and also if to any outside influence $f_{tr}(t)$ bounded for $t_0 \leq t < \infty$ there corresponds a bounded process $x(t)$.

The problem of absolute process stability in automatic control systems (Fig. 2) amounts to the problem of absolute equilibrium state stability in the system (Fig. 3) which contains a nonstationary nonlinear element, and to the problem of establishing the fact that $x(t)$ is bounded for $t_0 \leq t < \infty$.

In order to determine the sufficient conditions for absolute process stability, let us investigate the integral equation related to the deviation

$$\xi(t) = f_i(t) - \int_0^t w_{tr}(t-\lambda)\,\Psi[\xi(\lambda);\lambda]\,d\lambda. \tag{S.1}$$

Since the transformed linear part, whose transfer function equals $W_{tr}(p)$, is stable, then

$$\lim_{t\to\infty} w_{tr}(t) = 0. \tag{S.2}$$

If we consider that

$$\frac{1}{k-r}\Psi[\xi(t);t] = \frac{1}{k-r}\int_0^t \Psi[\xi(\lambda);\lambda]\,\delta(t-\lambda)\,d\lambda, \tag{S.3}$$

where $\delta(t)$ is the delta-function, and if we compute (S.3) from (S.1) we get

$$\xi(t) - \frac{1}{k-r}\Psi[\xi(t);t] = f_i - \int_0^t \left[w_{tr}(t-\lambda) + \frac{\delta(t-\lambda)}{k-r}\right]\Psi[\xi(\lambda);\lambda]\,d\lambda. \tag{S.4}$$

If we multiply both sides of (S.4) by $\Psi[\xi(t);t]$ and integrate with respect to time from 0 to T, we have

$$\int_0^T \Psi[\xi(t);t]\left[\xi(t) - \frac{\Psi[\xi(t);t]}{k-r}\right]dt - \int_0^T \Psi[\xi(t);t] - f_i(t)\,dt$$
$$+ \int_0^T\int_0^t \left[w_{tr}(t-\lambda) + \frac{\delta(t-\lambda)}{k-r}\right]\Psi[\xi(\lambda);\lambda]\,\Psi[\xi(t);t]\,d\lambda\,dt = 0. \tag{S.5}$$

First, let us find the condition which is satisfied when the third term in (S.5) has a nonnegative value, i.e.,

$$\int_0^T\int_0^t \left[w_{tr}(t-\lambda) + \frac{\delta(t-\lambda)}{k-r}\right]\Psi[\xi(\lambda),\lambda]\,\Psi[\xi(t),t]\,d\lambda\,dt \geqslant 0. \tag{S.6}$$

For this, we shall use S. Bokhner's theorem [17], according to which, in order that for any $y(\lambda)$ and $y(t)$ and any $T > 0$

$$\int_0^T\int_0^T \bar{\varphi}(t-\lambda)\, y(\lambda)\, y(t)\, d\lambda\, dt \geqslant 0, \tag{S.7}$$

where $\bar{\varphi}(t) = \varphi(-t)$ is an even function, there is necessary and sufficient satisfaction of the inequality

$$\operatorname{Re} \bar{F}(j\omega) \geqslant 0 \qquad (0 \leqslant \omega < \infty), \tag{S.8}$$

where

$$\bar{F}(j\omega) = \int_{-\infty}^{\infty} \bar{\varphi}(t)\, e^{-j\omega t}\, dt. \tag{S.9}$$

Let us denote

$$\bar{\varphi}(t) = \frac{\varphi(t) + \varphi(-t)}{2}, \tag{S.10}$$

where

$$\varphi(t) \equiv 0 \quad \text{for } t < 0, \tag{S.11}$$

$$\varphi(-t) \equiv 0 \quad \text{for } t > 0. \tag{S.12}$$

Let us substitute (S.10) in (S.7), and then with regard to (S.11) and (S.12) we get

$$\int_0^T\int_0^T \frac{\varphi(t) + \varphi(-t)}{2}\, y(\lambda)\, y(t)\, d\lambda\, dt = \frac{1}{2}\left[\int_0^T\int_0^t \varphi(t-\lambda)\, y(\lambda)\, y(t)\, d\lambda\, dt + \int_0^T\int_0^\lambda \varphi(\lambda - t)\, y(\lambda)\, y(t)\, d\lambda\, dt\right]. \tag{S.13}$$

Since the integrals in the square brackets are equal to each other, we get

$$\int_0^T\int_0^T \bar{\varphi}(t-\lambda)\, y(\lambda)\, y(t)\, d\lambda\, dt = \int_0^T\int_0^t \varphi(t-\lambda)\, y(\lambda)\, y(t)\, d\lambda\, dt. \tag{S.14}$$

If we assume in the right-hand side of (S.14)

$$\varphi(t) = w_{tr}(t) + \frac{\delta(t)}{k-r}, \tag{S.15}$$

$$y(\lambda) = \Psi[\xi(\lambda);\ \lambda], \tag{S.16}$$

$$y(t) = \Psi[\xi(t);\ t], \tag{S.17}$$

from (S.9) we get the necessary and sufficient condition for satisfying (S.6)

$$\operatorname{Re} W_{tr}(j\omega) + \frac{1}{k-r} \geqslant 0 \quad (0 \leqslant \omega < \infty), \tag{S.18}$$

where $W_{tr}(j\omega) = \int_0^\infty w_{tr}(t)\, e^{-j\omega t}\, dt$ is the frequency characteristic of the transformed linear part of the system.

If we now assume that condition (S.18) is satisfied and if we discard the third term in (S.5), we get the inequality

$$\int_0^T \Psi[\xi(t);\ t]\left[\xi(t) - \frac{\Psi[\xi(t);\ t]}{k-r}\right] dt \leqslant \int_0^T \Psi[\xi(t);\ t]\, f_i(t)\, dt. \tag{S.19}$$

Let us take advantage of Theorem 1 in V. M. Popov's paper [8], according to which [see Eq. (S.4)] for satisfying the condition (S.18) the value $|\xi(t) - (k-r)^{-1}\Psi[\xi(t);\ t] - f_i(t)|$ is bounded, i.e.,

$$\left|\xi(t) - \frac{1}{k-r}\Psi[\xi(t);\ t] - f_i(t)\right| < M. \tag{S.20}$$

If $\Psi[\xi(t); t]$ belongs to the sector $[\varepsilon; k - r - \varepsilon]$, i.e.,

$$\varepsilon \leqslant \frac{\Psi[\xi(t); t]}{\xi(t)} \leqslant k - r - \varepsilon, \tag{S.21}$$

where ε is an arbitrarily small positive number and $\lim_{t \to \infty} f_i(t) = 0$, then from (S.20) it follows that $|\xi(t)|$ is also bounded.*

But if $|\xi(t)|$ is bounded, then it is easy to show, by differentiating Eq. (S.1) with respect to t, that $|\xi'(t)|$ is also bounded. From the boundedness of $|\xi(t)|$, the boundedness of $\Psi[\xi(t); t]$ also follows, i.e., $|\Psi[\xi(t); t]| \leq C_1$. Therefore the right-hand side of inequality (S.19) may be evaluated in the following way:

$$\int_0^T \Psi[\xi(t); t] f_i(t)\, dt \leqslant \int_0^T |\Psi[\xi(t); t]|\, |f_i(t)|\, dt \leqslant C_1 \int_0^\infty |f_i(t)|\, dt. \tag{S.22}$$

If we take (2.1) into account, we get

$$C_1 \int_0^\infty |f_i(t)|\, dt = M_1 C_1 = C \tag{S.23}$$

and consequently,

$$\int_0^T \Psi[\xi(t); t] \left[\xi(t) - \frac{\Psi[\xi(t); t]}{k - r}\right] dt \leqslant C, \tag{S.24}$$

where $C > 0$ is not dependent on T.

If the nonstationary nonlinear characteristic $\Psi[\xi(t); t]$ belongs to the sector $[\varepsilon; k - r - \varepsilon]$, then the left-hand side of (S.24) will always be positive and will increase indefinitely as $|\xi(t)|$ increases indefinitely.

If we let T go to infinity in (S.24) and if we use, as in [6, 7, and 13], Barbalat's lemma which also holds for this case, we conclude that for satisfying condition (S.18), the equality

$$\lim_{t \to \infty} \xi(t) = 0. \tag{S.25}$$

occurs.

If we apply Theorem 1 of paper [8] to the equation obtained from the process equation (1.7) by a transformation to a form similar to the one considered above, i.e., to the equation

$$x(t) - \frac{\Phi_{tr}(x)}{k - r} = f_{tr}(t) - \int_{t_0}^{t} \left[W_{tr}(t - \lambda) + \frac{\delta(t - \lambda)}{k - r}\right] \Phi_{tr}[x(\lambda)]\, d\lambda, \tag{S.26}$$

it is easy to show that condition (S.18) guarantees boundedness of

$$\left| x(t) - \frac{\Phi_{tr}(x)}{k - r} - f_{tr}(t) \right| < M_2, \tag{S.27}$$

from which it is easy to conclude that for $|f_{tr}(t)| < M_3$ the value $|x(t)|$ is bounded.†

Thus, in order for the processes in a nonlinear system to be stable, besides inequality (S.18) being satisfied, the nonstationary characteristic $\Psi[\xi(t); t]$ should belong to the sector $[\varepsilon; k - r - \varepsilon]$. We shall express this condition by means of the stationary characteristic of the original nonlinear system.

If we take equality (1.3) into consideration, the expression $\Psi[\xi(t); t]$ may be represented in the form

$$\Psi[\xi(t); t] = \Phi[x(t) + \xi(t)] - \Phi[x(t)] - r\xi(t).$$

*If it is presupposed that $|\bar{\Psi}(\xi(t), t)| < N$, then the fact that $|\xi(t)|$ is bounded follows directly from Eq. (S.1), and in this case it is not necessary to include the V. M. Popov theorem.

†See the footnote on page 847 of paper [8].

By substituting $\Psi[\xi(t);t]$ in (S.21) and adding r to both sides of the inequality, we get

$$r+\varepsilon \leqslant \frac{\Phi[x(t)+\xi(t)]-\Phi[x(t)]}{\xi(t)} \leqslant k-\varepsilon. \quad (S.28)$$

It is apparent, since this follows from the Lagrange theorem of the mean:

$$\frac{\Phi[x(t)+\xi(t)]}{\xi(t)}=\Phi'[x(t)+\theta\xi(t)] \quad (0 \leqslant \theta \leqslant 1), \quad (S.29)$$

that inequality (S.28) will be satisfied for any $x(t)$ if

$$\Phi(0)=0 \text{ and } r+\varepsilon \leqslant d\Phi(x)/dx \leqslant k-\varepsilon, \quad (S.30)$$

i.e., if the derivative of the nonlinear element characteristic $d\Phi/dx$ belongs to the region $(r+\varepsilon;\ k-\varepsilon)$. In addition, it is apparent that the characteristic $\Phi(x)$ itself will also belong to the sector $(r+\varepsilon;\ k-\varepsilon)$.

LITERATURE CITED

1. A. I. Lur'e, and V. N. Postnikov, On the theory of control system stability [in Russian], Prikl. matem. i mekhan. 8, 3 (1944).
2. A. I. Lur'e, Some Nonlinear Problems in Automatic Control Theory [in Russian], Gostekhizdat (1951).
3. A. M. Letov, Stability of Nonlinear Control Systems [in Russian], Fizmatgiz (1962).
4. I. G. Malkin, The Theory of Motion Stability [in Russian], Gostekhizdat (1952).
5. E. N. Rozenvasser, Some problems in the theory of nonlinear control systems [in Russian], Candidate dissertation, Gor'kovsk gos. univ. (1961).
6. V. M. Popov, Criterii de stabilitate pentru sistemele nelineare de reglare automata bazate pe utilizarea transformatei Laplace, Studii si cercetari de energetica, Acad. R.P.R., ann. IX, 1 (1959).
7. V. M. Popov, Absolute stability of nonlinear automatic control systems [in Russian], Avtomatika i telemekhanika, 22, 8 (1961).
8. V. M. Popov, Sur certains unéqalites intégrales concernant la théorie du reglage automatique, Compt. Rend., 256, 17 (1963).
9. V. A. Yakubovich, Absolute stability of nonlinear control systems in critical cases [in Russian], Avtomatika i telemekhanika, 24, 3, 6 (1963).
10. V. A. Yakubovich, Absolute stability frequency conditions in nonlinear control systems with hysteresis nonlinearity [in Russian], Doklady Akad. Nauk SSSR, 149, 2 (1963).
11. E. N. Rozenvasser, Absolute stability of nonlinear systems [in Russian], Avtomatika i telemekhanika, 24, 3 (1963).
12. R. E. Kalman, Liapunov functions for the problem of Lur'e in automatic control, Proc. Nat. Acad. Sci. USA, 49, 2 (1963).
13. M. A. Aizerman and F. R. Gantmakher, Absolute Stability of Control Systems [in Russian], Izd. Akad. Nauk SSSR (1963).
14. Ya. Z. Tsypkin, Absolute equilibrium state and process stability in nonlinear automatic sampled-data systems [in Russian], Avtomatika i telemekhanika, 24, 12 (1963).
15. V. A. Yakubovich, A matrix inequality method in the theory of nonlinear control systems. I. Absolute stability of forced vibrations [in Russian], Avtomatika i telemekhanika, 25, 7 (1964).
16. Ya. Z. Tsypkin, Basic theory of nonlinear sampled-data systems [in Russian], Reports on the Second International Congress, International Federation on Automatic Control, Basel (1962).
17. C. Bokhner, Lectures on Fourier Integrals [in Russian], Fizmatgiz (1962).

All abbreviations of periodicals in the above bibliography are letter-by-letter transliterations of the abbreviations as given in the original Russian journal. *Some or all of this periodical literature may well be available in English translation.*

Frequency Domain Stability Criteria—Part I

R. W. BROCKETT, MEMBER, IEEE AND J. L. WILLEMS

Abstract—**The objective of this paper is to illustrate the limitations of the generalized Popov Theorem in establishing the stability of a loop containing a single nonlinearity, and to use the Liapunov Theory to give a new frequency domain stability criterion for such systems. The new criterion differs from Popov's in that less restrictive assumptions are made on the linear part, and stronger assumptions are made on the nonlinearity. In this paper, it is assumed that the nonlinearity is monotone increasing. The approach used here is quite general, however, and in a companion paper various other restrictions are considered.**

I. Introduction

Although a great deal has been written about the stability of systems containing a single instantaneous nonlinearity in an otherwise linear loop, most of the results which do not depend in an essential way on the order of the equation are special cases of a rather simple theorem due, in essence, to Popov. This result, stated in Theorem I, makes more restrictive assumptions on the linear part of the system than would seem to be necessary on the basis of linear theory, i.e., it does not verify Aizerman's conjecture. On the other hand, the assumptions made on the nonlinearity are quite unrestrictive. The object of this paper is to make a critical evaluation of Popov's Theorem and then to establish a new criterion which enables one to enlarge the class of systems which can be treated, provided it is possible to constrain the slope of the nonlinearity.

The system under consideration is shown in Fig. 1.

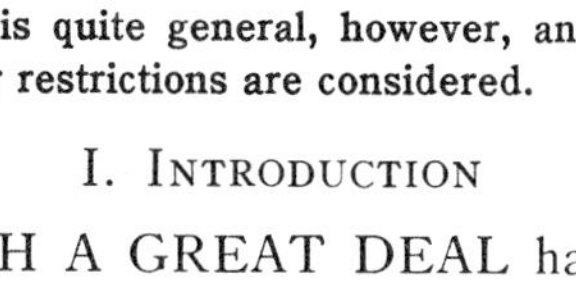

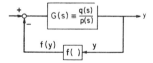

Fig. 1. Block diagram of the system under consideration.

It is assumed that $p(s)$ and $q(s)$ are polynomials without common factors and that the degree of $p(s)$ exceeds that of $q(s)$. It is also assumed that the nonlinearity f is sufficiently smooth to insure the existence of a unique solution of the governing differential equation. Notice that if x is defined by the differential equation $q(D)x=y$, then the differential equation governing the behavior of x is simply

$$p(D)x + f(q(D)x) = 0; \quad D \equiv d/dt. \tag{1}$$

Thus the stability of the closed-loop system shown in Fig. 1 can be observed by studying this scalar equation.

Manuscript received October 5, 1964; revised March 29, 1965. The work reported in this paper was supported in part by the National Aeronautics and Space Administration under Contract No. NsG-496 with the center for Space Research.

The authors are with the Dept of Electrical Engineering, Massachusetts Institute of Technology, Cambridge, Mass.

II. The Generalized Popov Theorem

If $f(y)$ is a continuous function of y, and if $0 < yf(y) < ky^2$, then f will be said to belong to the class A_k, hereafter written as $f \in A_k$. If $Z(s)$ is any rational function of s which is real for all real s, then $Z(s)$ is said to be *positive real* if (1) Re $Z(j\omega) \geq 0$ for all real ω, (2) $Z(s)$ has no right half-plane poles, and (3) all the imaginary axis poles of $Z(s)$ are simple and the residue of $Z(s)$ at each one of them is real and positive. These two definitions are amalgamated in the following theorem.

Theorem 1

The null solution of the system shown in Fig. 1 is ASIL (asymptotically stable in the large) if $f \in A_k$ and there exists an α such that $(1+\alpha s)G(s)+1/k$ is positive real.

The original theorem of this type appearing in Popov [1] considered the special case where $G(s)$ contains a pure integration and $k=\infty$. In that case α can be assumed positive without loss of generality. The idea of restricting f to belong to the class A_k appeared, about a year later, in a paper by Popov and Halaney [2]. Rozenvasser [3], Narendra and Goldwyn [4], and Rekasius [5] also treated this case, getting essentially equivalent results.

These authors made special assumptions about the nature of the imaginary axis poles and usually restricted α to be non-negative. Some work on relaxing the assumptions on the imaginary axis poles has been done by Yakubovich [6]. A complete survey of the Russian work done before 1964 can be formed in the recent monograph by Aizerman and Gantmacher [7]. These authors also remark[1] that positive realness can be used in stating the conditions for stability. A proof of the theorem in the form given here appears in Willems [8].

In order to use this theorem on a given system, one must determine if there exists an α such that $(1+\alpha s)G(s)+1/k$ is positive real. This is easily done when Popov's modified polar plot is used. In the modified polar plot ω Im $G(j\omega)$ is plotted as a function of Re $G(j\omega)$ instead of plotting Im $G(j\omega)$ vs. Re $G(j\omega)$, as is done in the ordinary polar (Nyquist) plot. From

$$\text{Re } (1+\alpha j\omega)G(j\omega) + 1/k = \text{Re } G(j\omega) - \alpha\omega \text{ Im } G(j\omega) + 1/k \tag{2}$$

it is seen that Re $(1+\alpha j\omega)G(j\omega)+1/k \geq 0$ for all ω if, and only if, the modified polar plot lies to the right of a straight line passing through the $-1/k$ point having slope $1/\alpha$ (Fig. 2). If there is no straight line passing

[1] See [7], p 79.

Reprinted from *IEEE Trans. Automat. Contr.*, vol. AC-10, pp, 255–261, July 1965.

through the $-1/k$ point such that the modified polar plot always lies to the right, then Theorem 1 cannot predict stability for all $f \in A_k$, although it may predict stability for some smaller class of nonlinearities. Assuming that $G(s)$ is stable, the only remaining thing to be done, in connection with establishing the positive realness of $(1+\alpha s)G(s)+1/k$, is to check the residues of the imaginary axis poles.

It is interesting to compare Popov's result with the usual Nyquist criterion. First, recall that the system $G(s)$ will be stable for any linear feedback in A_k if, and only if, the Nyquist plot avoids the part of the negative real axis which lies to the left of the $-1/k$ point as shown in Fig. 3. For the special case where the Nyquist plot lies to the right of the vertical line passing through the $-1/k$ point, it is clear that by taking α to be zero, it is possible to make $(1+\alpha s)G(s)+1/k$ positive real, and in this case the generalized Popov criterion and the Nyquist criterion agree.

It is of some interest to examine the case where $f \in A_\infty$ in more detail. The important question here is, "Under what circumstances can one find an α such that $(1+\alpha s)G(s)$ is positive real" Notice that in this case α must be non-negative because positive real functions and their reciprocals are stable. The Nyquist plot of a positive real function lies entirely in the right half-plane. Since the effect of the factor $(1+\alpha s)$ is to rotate each point on the Nyquist plot of $G(s)$ in the counter-clockwise direction, it is clear that it will not be possible to find an α such that $(1+\alpha s)G(s)$ is positive real, if the Nyquist plot of $G(s)$ enters the second quadrant.

Even if the Nyquist plot of $G(s)$ does not enter the second quadrant, it may be impossible to find an α such that $(1+\alpha s)(G)(s)$ is positive real. If it avoids both the second and the first quadrants, however, then one can always make Re $(1+\alpha j\omega)G(j\omega) \geq 0$ by taking α sufficiently large. What this means is that if $0 \geq \arg G(j\omega)$ for $0 \leq \omega \leq \infty$ then the null solution will be ASIL for all $f \in A_\infty$ if, and only if, it is ASIL for all negative linear feedback.

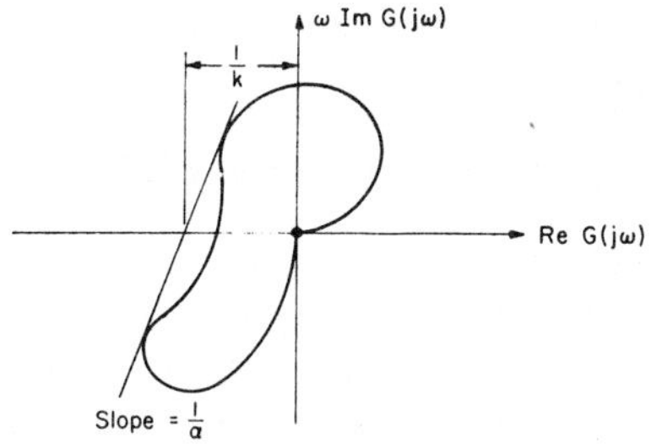

Fig. 2. A modified polar plot.

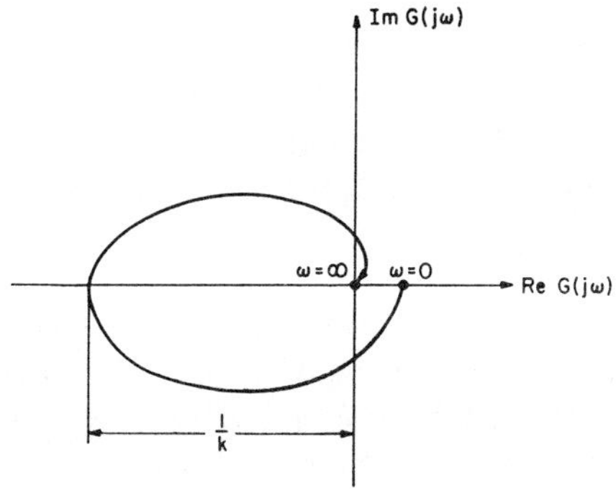

Fig. 3. The Nyquist plot of a system for which the Popov criterion is necessary and sufficient.

III. Examples and Limitations

Before discussing ways of extending Theorem 1 it seems appropriate to examine some examples which illustrate its power and its limitations.

One special form of (1), which has been examined repeatedly, is

$$p(D)y + f(y) = 0. \tag{3}$$

This corresponds to a system obtained by applying nonlinear feedback around a system with no zeros. In particular, for systems with 2, 3, and 4 poles [11],

$$y^{(2)}+ay^{(1)}+f(y)=0;\ a>0 \tag{4}$$

$$y^{(3)}+ay^{(2)}+by^{(1)}+f(y)=0;\ a,b>0 \tag{5}$$

$$y^{(4)}+ay^{(3)}+by^{(2)}+cy^{(1)}+f(y)=0;\ a,b,c,ab-c,>0. \tag{6}$$

The modified polar plots of these systems are shown in Fig. 4–6. By examining the plot corresponding to (4), it is seen that it lies to the right of a line passing through the origin having slope $1/a$. Therefore, from Theorem 1 it follows that the null solution of this system is ASIL for all $f \in A_\infty$. This is a well known result.

The modified polar plot of $1/(s^3+as^2+bs)$ intersects the negative rela axis at $-1/ab$ just as its Nyquist plot does, and thus it will certainly not be possible to take k to be greater than ab. Is it possible to use Theorem 1 to prove stability for $f \in A_{ab}$? To show that it is, it must be shown that the modified polar plot lies to the right of a line passing through the $-1/ab$ point. Clearly, if such a line exists it must have the same slope as the modified polar plot has at that point. A short calculation shows that this slope is b/a; with a little further calculation one can show that the modified polar plot actually lies to the right of this line, and therefore, that the null solution of the third-order system is ASIL for all $f \in A_{ab}$. This result has also appeared before, but this explanation of why α should be b/a seems to be new.

For the fourth-order system the modified polar may take either of the shapes shown in Fig. 6. It crosses the negative real axis at $-a^2/(abc-c^2)$; however, it is not always possible to find a straight line through the point such that the modified polar plot is always on the right. The slope of the modified polar plot at the point where it crosses the negative real axis is $ac/(ab-2c)$. The modified polar plot will lie to the right of this line if, and only if, one imposes the additional constraint $a^3-(2ab-2c)>0$. Thus in the fourth-order case, unlike the second- and third-order cases, it is not always possible to prove asymptotic stability in the large for as wide a class as would be predicted on the basis of linear theory.

It is interesting to note that the conditions $a^3-(2ab-2c)>0$ can be given a simple interpretation in the root plane. If one replaces $f(\ddot{x})$ by the linear term $\ddot{x}(abc-c^2)/a^2$, then the system has a pair of imaginary axis poles at $\omega=\pm j\sqrt{c/a}$. The remaining poles satisfy

$$s^2 + as + (ab - c)/a = 0. \qquad (7)$$

Since the real and imaginary parts of the roots of this equation are

$$\mathrm{Re}\, s_i = -a/2; \quad \mathrm{Im} = \pm\sqrt{b - a^2/4 - c/a} \qquad (8)$$

it follows that the inequality $a^3-2(ab-c)>0$ implies that the two roots with nonzero real parts must lie in a wedge bounded by two lines making a 45° angle with the real axis (Fig. 7).

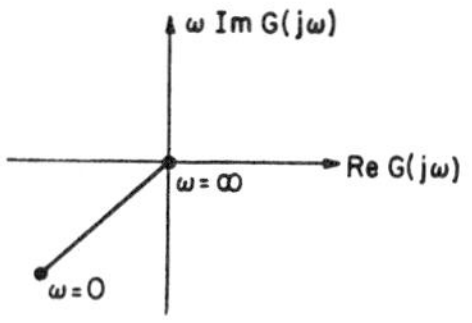

Fig. 4. The modified polar plot of a second-order system.

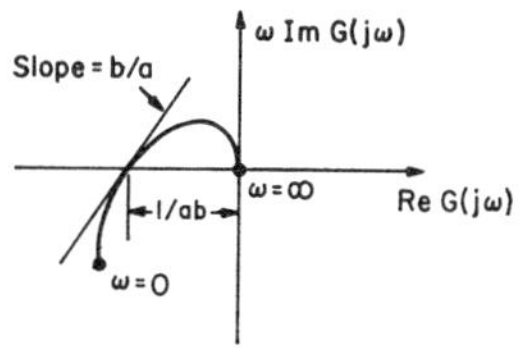

Fig. 5. Modified polar plot of a third-order system.

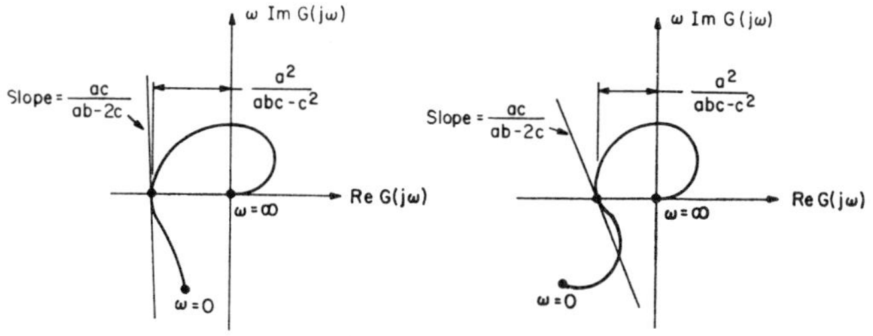

Fig. 6. Two possible forms of the modified polar plot of a fourth-order system.

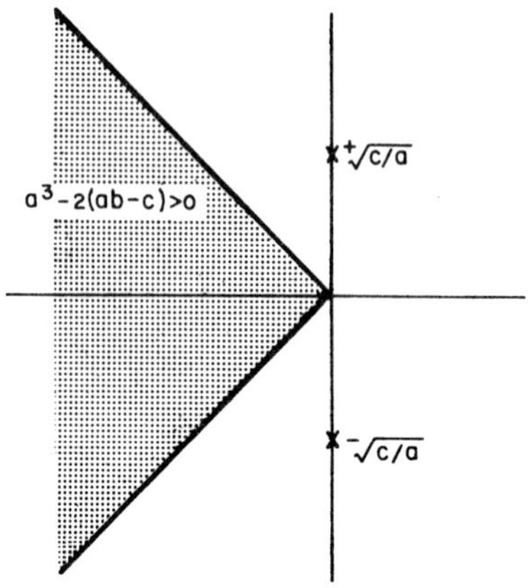

Fig. 7. Admissible pole location for Aizerman's conjecture to be verified.

An even worse situation is illustrated by the two equations

$$x^{(3)} + ax^{(2)} + bx^{(1)} + cx + f(x^{(2)}) = 0; \; ab - c > 0 \qquad (9)$$

$$x^{(4)} + ax^{(3)} + bx^{(2)} + cx^{(1)} + dx + f(x^{(2)}) = 0;$$
$$abc - c^2 - a^2 d > 0. \qquad (10)$$

The null solutions of the linearized versions of both these equations are ASIL for all positive k, yet the generalized Popov cannot predict stability for $f \in A_\infty$, regardless of any additional assumptions placed on the coefficients. One of the objectives of this paper is to develop a method of dealing with such equations. These examples will be considered again.

IV. A Reformulation of the Aizerman Conjecture

In terms of scalar equations, the Aizerman conjecture suggests that if the null solution of the linearized equation

$$p(D)x + k^* q(D)x = 0 \qquad (11)$$

is ASIL for all $k_1<k^*<k_2$, then the null solution of the nonlinear equation (1) should also be ASIL if $k_1<f(y)/y<k_2$ for all y. Even though examples have been given which show that the Aizerman conjecture is not true, it remains as an upper limit which one strives for. The objective here is to reformulate this conjecture in such a way as to place in evidence the relationship between it and what the Popov Theorem proves; this will also provide the motivation for the work in later sections.

It can be seen that without loss of generality one can always assume that the linearized system is stable over the range $0<k^*<k$, since if the original equation is stable over the range $k_1<k^*<k_2$, then it can be trans formed into

$$(p(D) + k_1 q(D))x + kq(D)x = 0 \qquad (12)$$

which is stable over the range $0<k<k_2-k_1$.

Theorem 1 can be regarded as an attempt to verify Aizerman's conjecture. As such, it works in some cases and not in others; the relationship between the information it provides and the Aizerman conjecture is considerably clarified by the following theorem.

Theorem 2

The null solution of (11) is stable for all k^* in the range $0<k^*<k$ if, and only if, there exists a rational positive real function $Z(s)$ such that $Z(s)(G(s)+1/k)$ is positive real.

Proof: Assume such a $Z(s)$ exists; write it as $m(s)/n(s)$. Since the sum of two positive real functions is, itself, a real function, it follows that for all positive k^* the quantity $Z(s)(G(s)+1/k)+k^*Z(s)$ is positive real. The numerator of this rational function is

$$m(s)(p(s)(1 + kk^*) + kq(s)).$$

Since the numerator and denominator polynomials of a positive real function must have their zeros in the half plane Re $s \leq 0$, we see that $p(s)(1+kk^*)+kq(s)$ is a polynomial of the stable type. By dividing this by $(1+kk^*)$, it is seen that the null solution of (11) is indeed stable for the specified range of gains.

The converse is a little more difficult. It can be seen that since the null solution of $p(D)x+k^*q(D)x=0$ is stable for all $0<k^*<k$, it follows that the null solution of

$$p(D)x + k^*(p(D) + kq(D))x = 0 \tag{13}$$

is stable for all $0<k^*<\infty$. In view of this, it follows that the phase plot of $(p(s)+kq(s))/p(s)$ always lies between plus and minus 180°; if this were not the case, there would be instability for some k^* (Fig. 8).

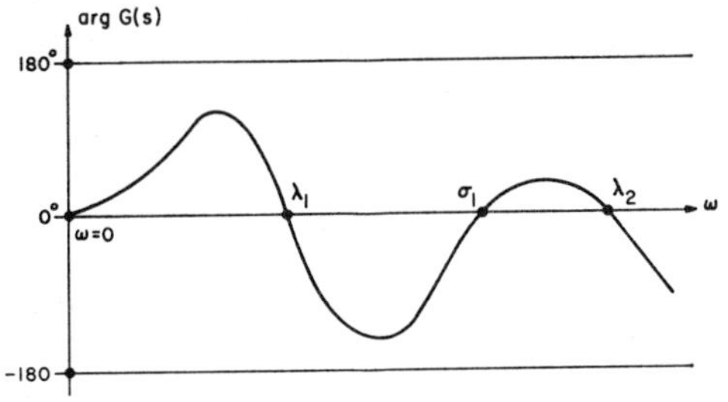

Fig. 8. The argument of a system which is stable for all positive linear feedback.

Identify the points $\lambda_1, \lambda_2, \cdots, \lambda_n$ at which the phase curve crosses the 0° line from below. Define β to be -1, if the first nonzero value of the phase curve is positive, and let it be $+1$ if its first nonzero value is negative. Define $Z(s)$ in terms of these quantities by

$$Z(s) = s\beta\pi_i(s^2 + \lambda_i^2)/\pi_i(s^2 + \sigma_i^2) \tag{14}$$

Clearly, $Z(s)$ is positive real since its poles and zeros alternate and lie on the imaginary axis. Moreover, from the way $Z(s)$ has been constructed, it follows that the phase angle of $Z(s)(G(s)+1/k)$ always lies between plus and minus 90°. To show that $Z(s)(G(s)+1/k)$ is positive real it remains only to show that the residues at the imaginary poles are real and positive. The only poles which need to be checked are those of $Z(s)$, since any imaginary axis poles of $G(s)$ will be canceled by the zeros of $Z(s)$; however, since the argument of $G(s)$ is zero at all poles of $Z(s)$, we see that the residues are, indeed, real and positive.

Now, consider the following restatement of the generalized Popov theorem.

Theorem 1 (Alternate form)

The null solution of (1) is ASIL if there exists a positive real function of the form $(1+\alpha s)^{\pm 1}$ such that $(1+\alpha s)^{\pm 1}(G(s)+1/k)$ is positive real.

Proof: To establish the equivalence between this and Theorem 1, as it was originally stated, observe that Re $(1+\alpha j\omega)G(j\omega)+1/k=$ Re $(1+\alpha j\omega)(G(j\omega)+1/k)$, and the argument of $(1+\alpha j\omega)$ equals that of $(1-\alpha j\omega)^{-1}$. In view of this, it is obvious that moving the $1/k$ term inside the parenthesis does not alter anything, and that taking the minus sign for an exponent of $(1+\alpha s)$ is equivalent to permitting α to be negative.

The main conclusion which these results lead to is that Aizerman's conjecture asserts that a system *should* be stable with any $f \in \boldsymbol{A}_k$ if there exists *any* positive real multiplier $Z(s)$ such that $Z(s)(G(s)+1/k)$ is positive real. Theorem 1 asserts that the system *will* be stable with any $f \in \boldsymbol{A}_k$ if there exists a positive real multiplier *of the special form* $(1+\alpha s)^{\pm 1}$ such that

$$(1 + \alpha s)^{\pm 1}(G(s) + 1/k)$$

is positive real. The problem is, then, one of seeking ways to generalize the class of admissable multipliers. In Section V one such result is described.

V. A New Result on Monotone Nonlinearities[2]

In order to make further progress in establishing the stability of (1), it will be necessary to make additional assumptions on the form of the nonlinearity. In particular, it is convenient to deal with the class of functions $\boldsymbol{M}_k$ having the properties (1) $f(0)=0$, (2) $0 \leq df(y)/dy < k$, and (3) $f^{-1}(y)$ exist. Clearly, $\boldsymbol{M}_k$ is a subclass of $\boldsymbol{A}_k$; every member of $\boldsymbol{M}_k$ is monotone increasing, and $\boldsymbol{M}_\infty$ is just the class of all invertible functions passing through the origin. The following theorem gives a stability criterion valid when f is thus restricted.

Theorem 3

The null solution of the system shown in Fig. 1 is ASIL if $f \in M_k$, and there exists a positive real multiplier of the form

$$Z(s) = a_0 s + \sum_{i=1} a_i(s + z_i)/(c_i s + z_i); \quad c_i \leq 1 \tag{15}$$

such that $(Z(s))^{\pm 1}(G(s)+1/k)$ is positive real. (a_i, c_i, and z_i real and positive.)

Proof: Since the proof is somewhat involved, a number of preliminary results will be established first.

Lemma 1: Let $n(D)$ be a polynomial in D and assume that the null solution of $n(D)x=0$ is ASIL. If the null solution of

$$n(D)p(D)x + f(n(D)q(D)x) = 0 \tag{16}$$

is ASIL, then so is the null solution of the lower-order equation

$$p(D)x + f(q(D)x) = 0. \tag{17}$$

Proof: If $\phi(t)$ is a solution of (16), then $n(D)\phi(t)$ is a solution of (17). If all solutions of (16) are asymptotically stable, then $n(D)\phi(t)$ is bounded and tends to zero for any choice of $\phi(t)$ satisfying (16). Since the zeros of $n(D)$ lie in the left half-plane, it follows that if $n(D)\phi(t)$

[2] Similar results have recently been obtained by Zames [9], [10], using the methods of functional analysis, and a somewhat different definition of stability.

is bounded and tends to zero, then the same must be true of $\phi(t)$.

Lemma 2: The null solution of (16) is ASIL for all $f \in \boldsymbol{M}_\infty$ if, and only if, the null solution of

$$n(D)q(D)x + f(n(D)p(D)x) = 0 \tag{18}$$

is ASIL for all $f \in \boldsymbol{M}_\infty$.

Proof: If $f \in \boldsymbol{M}_\infty$, then f has an inverse, f^{-1}, which also belongs to $\boldsymbol{M}_\infty$. Since any solution of (16) is also a solution of

$$n(D)q(D)x + f^{-1}(n(D)p(D)x) = 0 \tag{19}$$

and conversely; the result follows.

Lemma 3: If the positive realness of $Z(s)G(s)$ for some $Z(s)$ of a given form implies that the null solution of (16) is ASIL for all $f \in \boldsymbol{M}_\infty$, then the positive realness of $(Z(s))^{\pm 1}(G(s)+1/k)$ implies that the null solution of (16) is ASIL for all $f \in \boldsymbol{M}_k$.

Proof: Since the stability properties of (16) and (18) are the same, it follows that if the positive realness of $Z(s)G(s)$ implies stability for $f \in \boldsymbol{M}_\infty$, then the positive realness of $Z(s)(G(s))^{-1}$ implies stability for all $f \in \boldsymbol{M}_\infty$. Since the reciprocal of a positive real function is positive real, this latter condition can be expressed by saying $(Z(s))^{-1}G(s)$ is positive real.

If $f \in \boldsymbol{M}_k$, then f^{-1} exist, and (16) is equivalent to

$$p(D)x + g(q(D)x + p(D)x/k) = 0 \tag{20}$$

where g is defined through its inverse by

$$g^{-1}(y) = f^{-1}(y) - y/k. \tag{21}$$

Since the slope of f^{-1} is always greater than $1/k$, it follows that $g \in \boldsymbol{M}_\infty$. Therefore, if (20) is asymptotically stable in the large for $g \in \boldsymbol{M}_\infty$, it follows that (16) is asymptotically stable in the large for $f \in \boldsymbol{M}_k$. The transfer function associated with (20) is $(G(s)+1/k)$, and so by our previous remarks the lemma is proven.

Lemma 4: Let $\mathbf{x}^*$ be a state vector for

$$n(D)p(D)x + m(D)q(D)x = 0 \tag{22}$$

which has the components x, $x^{(1)}$, etc., and let

$$(Evm(D)q(D)n(-D)p(-D))^-$$

denote the right half-plane spectral factor of the even part of $m(D)q(D)n(-D)p(-D)$. If $m(s)q(s)/n(s)p(s)$ is positive real, and if $m(s)q(s)$, $n(s)p(s)$, and

$$(Evm(s)q(s)n(-s)p(-s))^-$$

have no common factors, then the line integral

$$V(\mathbf{x}^*) = \int_{t(0)}^{t(\mathbf{x}^*)} m(D)q(D)xn(D)p(D)x - ((Evm(D)q(D)n(-D)p(-D))^-x)^2\,dt \tag{23}$$

is independent of path and is a positive definite function of $\mathbf{x}^*$.

Proof: That this integral is independent of path has been shown earlier [11]. To see that it is positive definite, note that the fact that $m(s)q(s)/n(s)p(s)$ is positive real, implies that (22) is asymptotically stable.[3] Let $\phi(\mathbf{x}^*)$ denote the solution of (22) which starts at $\mathbf{x}^*$. Along this particular path $V(\mathbf{x}^*)$ is given by

$$V(\mathbf{x}^*) = \int_0^\infty (p(D)\phi(\mathbf{x}^*))^2 + ((Evm(D)q(D)n(-D)p(-D)^-\phi(x^*))^2\,dt. \tag{24}$$

Clearly, $V(x^*)$ is positive semidefinite; to see that it is positive definite observe that if it is to be zero, then there must be a solution to (22) along which $p(D)\phi$ and $(Evm(D)q(D)n(-D)p(-D))^-\phi$ vanish identically. In view of (22) it follows that $n(D)p(D)\phi$ can vanish only if $m(D)q(D)\phi$ does also; hence, if $m(D)q(D)$, $n(D)p(D)$, and $(Evm(D)q(D)n(-D)p(-D))$ have no common factors, as assumed, $V(\mathbf{x}^*)$ is positive for all $\mathbf{x}^* \in 0$.

Lemma 5: The null solutions of the autonomous differential equation

$$\dot{\mathbf{x}} = \boldsymbol{f}(\mathbf{x});\ \boldsymbol{f}(0) = 0 \tag{25}$$

is ASIL, if there exists a positive definite radially unbounded $V(\mathbf{x})$, having continuous first partial derivatives, and a $\dot{V}(\mathbf{x})$, which is nonpositive and not identically zero along any solution of $\dot{\boldsymbol{x}} = \boldsymbol{f}(\boldsymbol{x})$, which does not, itself, tend to the origin.

Proof: LaSalle [13] has shown that under the given hypothesis all solutions tend to the largest invariant set in the set of points for which

$$\dot{V}(\mathbf{x}) = 0. \tag{26}$$

If $\dot{V}(\mathbf{x})$ only vanishes along solutions which tend to the origin, it follows by a continuity argument that x goes to the origin, and hence that the hypothesis insures asymptotic stability in the large.

In view of Lemma 3, it follows that if it can be shown that the existence of a $Z(s)$, of the given form which makes $Z(s)G(s)$ positive real, implies the stability of (1) for all $f \in \boldsymbol{M}_\infty$, then the theorem will be established. This last phase of the proof is largely calculations.

Let $\mathbf{x}$ be a state vector for (16), having the components x, $x^{(1)}$, etc. If the degree of $m(D)q(D)+n(D)p(D)$ exceeds that of $n(D)p(D)+n(D)q(D)$, then $\mathbf{x}^*$ will be a vector of higher dimension than $\mathbf{x}$; however, if $Z(s)G(s)$, is positive real, it will have at most one more component. By using (16) it will be possible to express this additional component in terms of the components of $\mathbf{x}$, so that in any case it will be possible to write $\mathbf{x}^* = T(\mathbf{x})$, provided only that $Z(s)G(s)$ is positive real.

Suppose there exists a $Z(s)$ of the given form such that $Z(s)G(s)$ is positive real. Write $Z(s)$ as $m(s)/n(s)$ with $m(s)$ and $n(s)$ being polynomials without common factors. Multiply (16) by $m(D)q(D)x$ and subtract $((Evm(D)q(D)n(-D)p(-D))^-x)^2$ from each side to get

[3] See Weinberg and Slepian [12] for a proof.

$$m(D)q(D)xn(D)p(D)x - ((Evm(D)q(D)n(-D)p(-D))^{-}x)^2 + m(D)q(D)xf(n(D)q(D)x) = -((Evm(D)q(D)n(-D)p(-D))^{-}x)^2. \quad (27)$$

Integrating this from $t(0)$ to $t(\mathbf{x}^*)$, and using $T(\mathbf{x})$ for $\mathbf{x}^*$ gives[4]

$$V(T(\mathbf{x})) + \int_{t(0)}^{t(x^*)} m(D)q(D)xf(n(D)q(D)x)\,dt = \int_{t(0)}^{t(\mathbf{x}^*)} ((Evm(D)q(D)n(-D)p(-D))^{-}x)^2\,dt \quad (28)$$

where V is defined by (23).

From (15) it follows that the zeros of $n(s)$ lie at $-z_i/c_i$. Introduce the notation $n_i(s) = n(s)/(c_i s + z_i)$, and notice that $m(s)$ can be expressed as

$$m(s) = a_0 sn(s) + a_1(s + z_1)n_1(s) \cdots a_r(s + z_v)n_v(s). \quad (29)$$

Define $G(x^*)$ as

$$G(\mathbf{x}^*) = \int_{t(0)}^{t(\mathbf{x}^*)} a_0 D_n(D)q(D)f(n(D)q(D)x) + \sum_{i=1}^{v} a_i(1 - c_i)Dn_i(D)q(D)xf(z_i n_i(D)q(D)x)\,dt \quad (30)$$

and observe that even though $G(\mathbf{x}^*)$ is expressed as a integral, it is only a function of $\mathbf{x}^*$, since each term in it is of the form $a_i\int f(y)dy$. Clearly, $G(\mathbf{x}^*) = G(T(\mathbf{x}))$ is nonnegative.

Inserting G into (28) gives, after some manipulation,

$$V(T(\mathbf{x})) + G(T(\mathbf{x})) = \int_{t(0)}^{t(\mathbf{x}^*)} -((Evm(D)q(D)n(-D)p(-D))^{-}x)^2 \left(\sum_{i=1}^{v} a_i c_i)n(D)q(D)xf(n(D)q(D)x)\right) - \left(\sum_{i=1}^{v} a_i(1 - c_i)Dn_i(D)q(D)x(f(n(D)q(D)x)) - f(z_i n_i(D)q(D)x)\right) dt. \quad (31)$$

Taking $V(T(\mathbf{x}))+G(T(\mathbf{x})$ to be a Liapunov function, it is clear that its derivative is simply the integrand on the right side of (31). The first term in the integrand is never positive; the second is of the form $-ayf(y)$, with a positive, and is, likewise, never positive. Each term in the last sum is of the form

$$-cz(f(z+w) - f(w)) = -c((z+w) - w)(f(z+w) - f(w)).$$

Because f is assumed to monotone, these terms are also never positive.

To complete the proof, it remains only to note that the derivatives of the proposed Liapunov function is identically zero only if $n(D)x \equiv 0$. Since $n(D)$ has all its zeros in the left half plane, this and Lemma 5 imply that the null solution of (16) is ASIL.

VI. Interpretation and Examples

Some study of the class of functions which can be represented by expansions of the form given by (15) seems appropriate. Actually, this expansion defines the most general driving point impedance which can be constructed from linear inductors and resistors; such functions have been studied in considerable detail by circuit theorists. The reciprocal also has a circuit theoretic interpretation; it defines the most general driving point impedance which can be synthesized from capacitors and resistors. It may be shown that the poles and zeros of any $Z(s)$ of the form given by (15) lie on the negative real axis and interlace (Fig. 9).

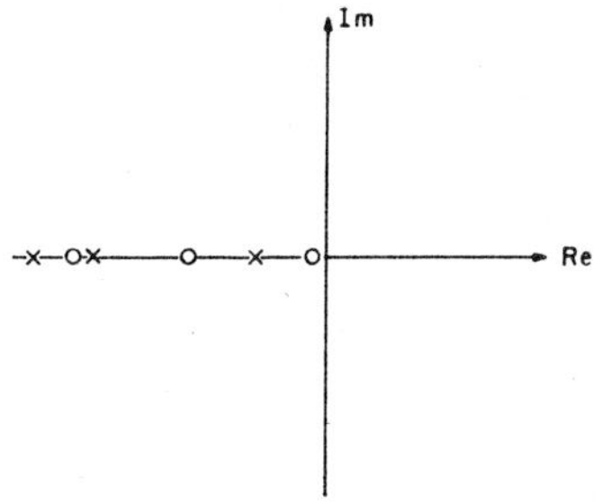

Fig. 9. An RL driving point impedance.

It is clear that the assumption of monotonicity and Theorem 3 makes it possible to prove stability in some cases where Theorem 1 cannot be used. Unfortunately, it is still impossible to prove stability in all the cases where linear theory is predicted. These points will be illustrated further. The question of determining exactly how far Theorem 3 goes toward filling the gap between what Theorem 1 proves, and what the Aizerman conjecture suggests, however, remains largely unresolved.

Before returning to the examples, it seems worth while to point out one special case in Theorem 3 which covers a number of interesting cases.

Corollary: The null solution of the system shown in Fig. 1 is ASIL if $f \in \boldsymbol{M}_k$ and if

$$((1 + \alpha s)/(\beta + \gamma s))^{\pm 1}(G(s) + 1/k)$$

is positive real.

This is an obvious specialization to the case where $v = 1$. Now consider the third-order system

$$x^{(3)} + ax^{(2)} + bx^{(1)} + cx + f(x^{(2)}) = 0. \quad (32)$$

Stability may be proven for all $f \in \boldsymbol{M}_\infty$ by taking $Z(s)$ to be of the form $(as+b)/s$.

[4] The notation used here should not be interpreted as implying that the integration is to be done along a solution of the given equation. Equations (28)–(30) should be viewed as an explanation of the fact that the derivative of the left side of (31) evaluated along solutions of (16) is, in fact, the integrand on the right side of (31).

Theorem 3 is not capable of establishing the asymptotic stability of

$$x^{(4)} + ax^{(3)} + bx^{(2)} + cx^{(1)} + f(x) = 0 \qquad (33)$$

for the full range predicted by linear theory, but the restrictions on a, b, and c are somewhat weaker than those implied by the Popov theorem. In fact, a necessary and sufficient condition for Theorem 3 to predict stability for all $f \in M(abc-c^2)/a^2$ is that either

$$a^3 - 2(ab - c) \geq 0 \quad \text{or} \quad ab - 2c \geq 0. \qquad (34)$$

This means that when $f(x) = x(abc - c_2)/a_2$ the roots should lie within either a wedge or a semicircular disk of radius $\sqrt{c/a}$, Fig. 10.

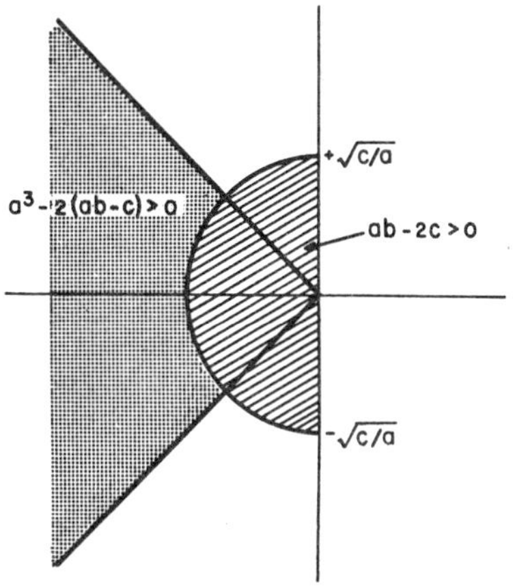

Fig. 10. Admissible pole locations for the monotone theorem to prove stability.

Additional examples could be given illustrating application of Theorem 3, however, it seems just as important to indicate clearly those cases where it is least effective. Consider the equation

$$y^{(4)} + ay^{(3)} + by^{(2)} + cy^{(1)} + dy + f(y^{(2)}) = 0;$$
$$a, b, c, d, abc - c^2 - a^2d > 0. \qquad (35)$$

To see that there exists no $Z(s)$ of the form given by (15), such that $(Z(s))^{+1}s_2/(s^4+as^3+bs^2+cs+d)$ is positive real, observe that such a $Z(s)$ would have to pave a pole at the origin and a pole at infinity, which is not possible for a $Z(s)$ of the given form. It is of some interest to note that a detailed analog computer study of this equation, with $f(y) = y^3$, indicates that for moderately large initial conditions, (35) actually has limit cycles. (See Fitts [14].)

VII. Conclusions

On the basis of the analysis done on the generalized Popov Theorem, it is clear that it gives a stability criterion which is considerably more restrictive that that which would be predicted on the basis of linear theory. The relationship between the information it provides and the Nyquist criterion is clarified by Theorem 2. As a first step in the development of a more general theory which will enable one to place further restrictions on the nonlinear part, and in this way relax the restrictions on the linear part, the authors introduced the assumption of monotonicity, and developed a corresponding frequency domain stability criterion. Additional stability criteria imposing different restrictions on the nonlinearity will be given in the second part of the paper.

Acknowledgment

The authors would like to thank Prof. G. Zames of M.I.T., Cambridge, Mass., for contributing numerous ideas and suggestions to their research. They would also like to thank Prof. R. E. Kalman of Stanford University, Calif., and K. Meyer of Brown University, Providence, R. I., for pointing out several errors in an earlier draft.

References

[1] Popov, V. M., Absolute stability of nonlinear systems of automatic control, *Automation and Remote Control*, vol 22, no 8, Mar 1962, pp 857–875. (Russian original published in Aug 1961.)

[2] Popov, V. M., and A. Halaney, On the stability of nonlinear automatic control systems with lagging arguments, *Automation and Remote Control*, vol 23, no 7, Feb 1963, pp 783–786. (Russian original published in Jul 1962.)

[3] Rozenvasser, E. N., The absolute stability of nonlinear systems, *Automation and Remote Control*, vol 24, no 3, Oct 1963, pp 283–294. (Russian original published in Mar 1963.)

[4] Narendra, K. S., and R. M. Goldwyn, Existence of quadratic type Liapunov functions for a class of nonlinear systems, Tech. Rept. no. 415, Cruft Laboratory, Harvard University, Cambridge, Mass., Aug 1963.

[5] Rekasius, Z. V., A stability criterion for feedback systems with one nonlinear element, *IEEE Trans. on Automatic Control*, vol AC-9, Jan 1964, pp 46–50.

[6] Yakubovich, V. A., Absolute stability of nonlinear control systems in critical cases, Parts I and II, *Automation and Remote Control*, vol 24, nos 3 and 6, Oct 1963 and Jan 1964, pp 273–282 and 655–668. (Russian originals published in Mar and Jun 1963.)

[7] Aizerman, M. A., and R. F. Gantmacher, On critical cases in the theory of absolute stability of controlled systems, *Automation and Control*, vol 24, no 6, Jan 1964, pp 669–674. (Russian original published in Jun 1963).

[8] Willems, J. L., The stability of systems containing a single nonlinearity, S.M. thesis, MIT, Cambridge, Mass., Jul 1964.

[9] Zames, G., Nonlinear time-varying systems—Contracting transformations for iteration and stability, Electronic Systems Lab. Rept., MIT, Cambridge, Mass., 1964.

[10] —— On the stability of nonlinear time-varying feedback systems, *1964 Proc. NEC*, pp 725–730.

[11] Brockett, R. W., On the stability of nonlinear feedback systems, *IEEE Trans. Applications and Industry*, vol AP-83, Nov 1964, pp 443–449.

[12] Weinberg, L., and P. Slepian, Positive real matrices, *J. Math. Mech.*, vol 9, no 1, 1960, pp 71–83.

[13] LaSalle, J. P., Some extensions of Liapunov's second method, *IRE Trans. on Circuit Theory*, vol CT-7, Dec 1960, pp 520–527.

[14] Fitts, D., Summary of results on the stability of a fourth-order differential equation with monotonic nonlinearity, Internal Memorandum, Electronic Systems Laboratory, MIT, Cambridge, Mass., 1964.

Frequency Domain Stability Criteria—Part II

R. W. BROCKETT, MEMBER, IEEE, AND J. L. WILLEMS

Abstract—**In Part I of this paper a detailed analysis was made of the type of information Popov's Theorem gives about the stability of a closed-loop system containing a single instantaneous nonlinearity, and a new stability theorem, useful when the nonlinearity is monotone, was given. In this part a general approach for generating stability criteria is described and several specific results are obtained. In particular, an improved criterion valid when *f* is an odd function is given, and criteria valid when *f* is a power law nonlinearity are also developed. Several examples are included to illustrate the theory.**

Manuscript received October 5, 1964; revised July 7, 1965. This work was supported in part by the National Aeronautics and Space Administration under Contract NsG-498 with the Center for Space Research.

The authors are with the Dept. of Electrical Engineering, Massachusetts Institute of Technology, Cambridge, Mass.

I. Introduction

It was shown in Part I[1] that a linear system having a transfer function $G(s)$ is stable for *all linear* feedback in $\boldsymbol{A}_k$ if and only if there exists a positive real function $Z(s)$ such that $Z(s)\ (G(s)+1/k)$ is positive real. (See Part I for notation.) It was also shown that Popov's Theorem can be viewed as predicting stability for *all* $f \in \boldsymbol{A}_k$ if there exists a positive real multiplier of the special form $Z(s)=(1+\alpha s)^{\pm 1}$ such that

[1] R. W. Brockett and J. L. Willems, "Frequency domain stability criteria—Part I," *IEEE Transactions on Automatic Control*, vol. AC-10, pp. 255–261, July 1965.

Reprinted from *IEEE Trans. Automat. Contr.*, vol. AC-10, pp. 407–413, Oct. 1965.

$Z(s)$ $(G(s)+1/k)$ is positive real, and a new stability theorem was given which states that if the nonlinearity $f \in \boldsymbol{M}_k$ then stability is assured provided there exists a $Z(s)$ of the form of a RC or RL impedance such that $Z(s)$ $(G(s)+1/k)$ is positive real. In this paper the stability of the nonlinear feedback loop is examined from the point of view of determining what assumptions should be made on the nonlinearity in order to make the conditions for nonlinear stability approach those predicted by linear theory. The principal new results are given in Theorems 4, 5, and 6.

As in Part I, the stability of the closed-loop system will be studied by studying the stability of the solutions of the scalar equation

$$p(D)x + f(q(D)x) = 0. \tag{1}$$

It is assumed throughout that $f(0)=0$, that f is monotone increasing, and that f has a continuous inverse; in short, $f \in \boldsymbol{M}_\infty$. Additional assumptions will be imposed on f as required. The fact that the assumptions on f are more restrictive than those used in the Popov Theorem is partially compensated for by the fact that it will no longer be necessary to assume that the degree of $q(D)$ is less than that of $p(D)$.

Some use will be made of the lemmas used in proving Theorem 3. In particular, the stability of (1) will be established by proving the stability of the related equations

$$n(D)p(D)x + f(n(D)q(D)x) = 0 \tag{2}$$

$$n(D)q(D)x + f^{-1}(n(D)p(D)x) = 0. \tag{3}$$

As was shown in Lemma 3, if the nonlinearity is invertible then it is possible to get information about the cases where f is restricted to lie in a sector by treating the unrestricted case and then transforming.

II. A Class of Positive Real Functions

In what follows, considerable use will be made of a special group of positive real functions. Let $\boldsymbol{Z}_c$ denote the class of rational functions which can be expressed in the form

$$Z(s) = a_0 s + \sum_{i=1}^{v} a_i(s + z_i)/(c_i s + z_i) \tag{4}$$

with all constants being non-negative and $c_i \leq c$. For example, if $c=0$ then this sum reduces to a term of the form $Z(s)=as+b$ which is only a slight generalization of the multiplier appearing in the Popov Theorem. If $c=1$ then this is simply the class of functions appearing in Theorem 3.

The stability criteria to be derived here are stated in terms of the existence of a multiplier $Z(s)$ which makes $(Z(s))^{\pm 1}(G(s)+1/k)$ a *positive real product*. By this terminology it is meant that $(Z(s))^{\pm 1}(G(s)+1/k)$ is positive real in the ordinary sense and that $Z(s)$ and $(G(s)+1/k)$ do not have common imaginary axis poles and zeros.

Whether or not there exists a $Z(s)$ of a certain type which makes $Z(s)G(s)$ positive real depends to a large extent on the phase angle of $G(s)$ and the type of phase angles which $Z(s)$ is capable of generating. The product $Z(s)G(s)$ can not be positive real unless its phase angle, i.e., the sum of the phase angles of $Z(s)$ and $G(s)$, lies between 90° and $-90°$. If the phase angle of $G(s)$ lies outside these limits then the phase of $Z(s)$ must be selected in such a way to compensate. Moreover, the rate at which the phase of $G(s)$ varies, and the extent to which it varies, determines what characteristics the phase of $Z(s)$ must have. For this reason a knowledge of the phase characteristics of the functions defined by (4) is useful.

For $Z(s) \in \boldsymbol{Z}_0$, the Popov multiplier, the phase angle is just that of a first-order lead term; it starts at zero and increases monotonically to 90°. For $Z(s) \in \boldsymbol{Z}_1$, the class of multipliers occurring in Theorem 3, the phase angle is again restricted to lie between 0 and 90° but need not be monotone increasing. Notice that this means that if the phase plot of $G(s)+1/k$ both exceeds 90° and falls below $-90°$ then Theorems 1 and 3 cannot predict stability. Otherwise stated, a necessary condition for the application of Theorems 1 and 3 is that the Nyquist plot of $G(s)+1/k$ be restricted to 3 quadrants.

If $c>1$ then the phase angle of functions in $\boldsymbol{Z}_c$ can be negative. The minimum value which can be achieved is limited however, and only approaches $-90°$ as c approaches infinity. In the special case where $v=1$ and $c_1=c$, the functions in $\boldsymbol{Z}_c$ assume the form

$$Z(s) = [a_0 s(cs + z) + a_1(s + z)]/(cs + z). \tag{5}$$

The possible zero configurations for $c=2$ and $z=1$ are shown in Fig. 1. For lower values of c the possible zero configurations lie inside the circle shown.

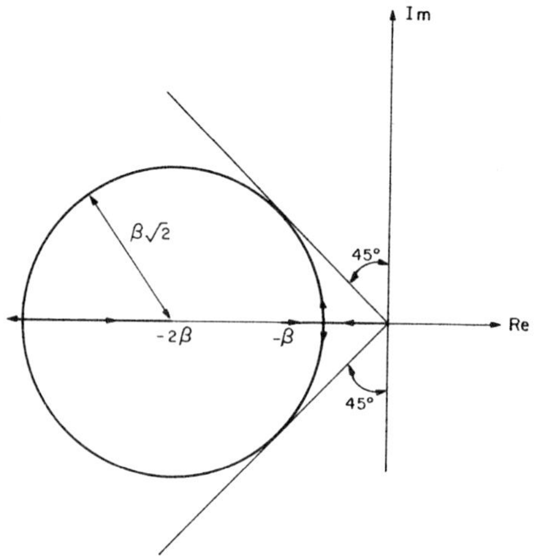

Fig. 1. Possible zero locations for (5); $\beta = z/2$.

An analysis of the $Z(s)$ defined by (5) shows that the phase starts at 0°, assumes a minimum value of $\tan^{-1}((1-c)/2\sqrt{c})$ for $c \geq 1$, and then goes to 90° as ω approaches infinity. Since any $Z(s)$ in $\boldsymbol{Z}_c$ can be expressed as a sum of terms of this type, and since the argument of a sum of complex numbers can not exceed the maximum argument of its individual terms, it follows that the minimum phase angle of any $Z(s)\in \boldsymbol{Z}_c$ is not less than $\tan^{-1}((1-c)/2\sqrt{c})$, $c\geq 1$.

III. Two General Results on Stability

In searching for sufficient conditions for the stability of equation (1) it is evident that there is some trade-off between the class of admissible multipliers [the admissible form of $Z(s)$] and the restrictions placed on the nonlinearity f. The following lemma isolates the basic problem.

Lemma 6: If $f\in \boldsymbol{A}_\infty$ then the null solution of (1) is ASIL if there exists a positive real multiplier $Z(s) = m(s)/n(s)$ such that $Z(s)G(s)$ is a positive real product and

$$\int_{t(0)}^{t(x)} m(D)yf(n(D)y)\,dt = G(x) + \int_{t(0)}^{t(x)} g(x)\,dt \quad (6)$$

with $G(x)\geq 0$, and $g(x)\geq 0$. Here $y=q(D)x$ and x is a vector whose components are $x, x^{(1)}, \cdots, x^{(\beta-1)}$, β being the degree of $m(D)q(D)+n(D)p(D)$.

Proof: In view of Lemma 1 it is enough to show that the null solution of (2) is ASIL. In order to construct a Liapunov function for (2), multiply by $m(D)q(D)x$, subtract $((Evm(D)q(D)n(-D)p(-D))^{-}x)^2$ from both sides, and integrate the result to get

$$\int_{t(0)}^{t(x)} m(D)q(D)xn(D)p(D)x - ((Evm(D)q(D)n(-D)p(-D))^{-}x)^2\,dt + G(x)$$
$$= -\int_{t(0)}^{t(x)} ((Evm(D)q(D)n(-D)p(-D))^{-}x)^2 + g(x)\,dt. \quad (7)$$

In view of Lemma 4 and the assumptions made on $G(x)$, the quantity on the right side of (7) is a positive definite function of x. If the degree of $n(D)p(D) + n(D)q(D)$ equals that of $n(D)p(D)+m(D)q(D)$ then x is a state vector for (2). If, on the other hand, the degree of $n(D)p(D) + n(D)q(D)$ is less than $n(D)p(D) + m(D)q(D)$ it can not be more than one less, because the denominator and numerator of a positive real function differ in degree by one or zero. Thus (2) can be used to express x in terms of a state vector for (2). In either case the quantity on the left side of (7) is a positive definite function of the state vector associated with (2).

Its derivative, the integrand of the term on the right, is obviously negative semidefinite; this shows that the null solution of (2) is at least (weakly) stable. To show that it is actually asymptotically stable, note that the derivative, given by

$$\dot{V} = -(Evm(D)q(D)n(-D)p(-D))^{-}x)^2 - g(x) \quad (8)$$

vanishes identically only if

$$n(D)x = 0 \quad (9)$$

and thus by Lemma 5 asymptotic stability exists.

Using Lemma 6 it is very easy to prove either Theorem 1 or 3 and other theorems of that form. (See Theorem 6 below.) If monotonicity is assumed, however, it is possible to establish an even more direct connection between the class of admissible multipliers and the form of the nonlinearity.

Lemma 7: If $f\in \boldsymbol{M}_\infty$ then the null solution of (1) is ASIL if there exists a $Z(s)\in \boldsymbol{Z}_c$ and constants $b\geq 0$ and $d\geq 0$, depending only on c, such that $Z(s)G(s)$ is a positive real product and the inequality

$$(\dot{y} + y)f(c\dot{y} + y) - b\dot{y}f(dy) \geq 0 \quad (10)$$

holds for all y and $\dot{y}$.

Proof: From Lemma 7 it follows that it is enough to show that

$$\int_{t(0)}^{t(x)} m(D)yf(n(D)y)\,dt = G(x) + \int_{t(0)}^{t(x)} g(x)\,dt \quad (11)$$

with $G(x)\geq 0$ and $g(x)\geq 0$. Assume $Z(s)\in \boldsymbol{Z}_c$. Expand its numerator $m(s)$ as

$$m(s) = a_0 sn(s) + a_1(s+z_1)n_1(s) + a_2(s+z_2)n_2(s) \cdots + a_v(s+z_v)n_v(s) \quad (12)$$

where $n(s)$ is the denominator of $Z(s)$ and $n_i(s) = n(s)/(c_i s+z_i)$.

In terms of this notation the integral on the right side of (11) can be expressed as

$$\int_{t(0)}^{t(x)} m(D)yf(n(D)y)\,dt = \int_{t(0)}^{t(x)} a_0 Dn(D)yf(n(D)y) + \sum_{i=1}^{v} a_i(D+z_i)n_i(D)yf((c_iD+z_i)n_i(D)y)\,dt. \quad (13)$$

The first term on the right is of the form $\int f(z)dz$ and thus can be put in $G(x)$. A typical term in the remaining sum can be written as

$$\int_{t(0)}^{t(x)} a_i(D+z_i)n_i(D)yf((c_iD+z_i)n_i(D)y)\,dt$$
$$= \int_{t(0)}^{t(\ )} a_i((c_i/c)D+z_i)n_i(D)yf((c_iD+z_i)n_i(D)y) - a_ibDn_i(D)yf(dz_in_i(D)y)\,dt$$
$$+ \int_{t(0)}^{t(x)} a_i(1-c_i/c)Dn_i(D)y(f((c_iD+z_i)n_i(D)y) - f(z_in_i(D)y)\,dt$$
$$+ \int_{t(0)}^{t(x)} a_i(1-c_i/c)Dn_i(D)yf(z_in_i(D)y) + a_ibDn_i(D)yf(dz_in_i(D)y)\,dt. \quad (14)$$

The integrand of the first term on the right is positive by virtue of inequality (10); that of the second term is positive because f is monotone. The last term clearly integrates to give a positive function. Thus, if $g_i(x)$ is taken to be the sum of the first two integrands and if

$G_i(\mathbf{x})$ is taken to be the last integral, then it is clear that the sum of the $g_i(\mathbf{x})$ makes a suitable choice for $g(\mathbf{x})$ and a sum of the $G_i(\mathbf{x})$ plus the first term on the right side of (13) makes a suitable choice for G. Since the requirements of Lemma 6 are met this completes the proof.

In the Sections IV and V Lemma 6 is used to get more explicit stability criteria.

IV. Odd Monotone Nonlinearities

If $f(y) = -f(-y)$ then f is said to be an odd function. If $f \in \boldsymbol{M}_k$ is odd then f will be said to belong to the class $\boldsymbol{O}_k$. Theorem 4 gives a stability criterion which is somewhat stronger than that given by Theorem 3, provided that f is odd.

Theorem 4

If $f \in \boldsymbol{O}_k$ then the null solution of (1) is ASIL if there exists a $Z(s) \in \boldsymbol{Z}_2$ such that $(Z(s))^{\pm 1}(G(s)+1/k)$ is a positive real product.

Proof: The case where $f \in \boldsymbol{O}_k$ can be reduced to the case where $f \in 0_\infty$ in exactly the same way as it was in proving Theorem 3. If $f \in \boldsymbol{O}_k$ then define g by the equation

$$g^{-1}(y) = f^{-1}(y) - y/k. \tag{15}$$

Notice that g and its inverse belong to $\boldsymbol{O}_\infty$ for the inverse of an odd function is odd and the inverse of a function in $\boldsymbol{M}_k$ has a slope everywhere greater than $1/k$. Notice that all solutions of (2) are solutions of the equations

$$n(D)p(D)x + g(n(D)q(D)x + n(D)p(D)x/k) = 0 \tag{16}$$

$$n(D)q(D)x + n(D)p(D)x/k + g^{-1}(n(D)q(D)x) = 0. \tag{17}$$

If it can be shown that the null solutions of these equations are stable for all $g \in 0_\infty$ then the theorem will be proven.

From Lemma 7 it follows that if it can be shown that there exists $b>0$ and $d>0$ such that inequality (10) holds with $c=2$ then (16) will be stable if $Z(s)(G(s)+1/k)$ is a positive real product, and (17) will be stable if $Z(s)(G(s)+1/k)^{-1}$ is a positive real product. Since the reciprocal of a positive real function is a positive real function it follows that if inequality (10) can be established with $c=2$ then the proof will be complete.

Consider inequality (10) with $c=2$ and $b=d=1$. In this case it becomes

$$(\dot{y} + y)f(2\dot{y} + y) - \dot{y}f(y) \geq 0. \tag{18}$$

Let $z = 2\dot{y} + y$ and write inequality (18) in the two equivalent forms

$$1/2(z + y)(f(z) - f(-y)) - zf(y) \geq 0 \tag{19}$$

$$1/2(z - y)(f(z) - f(y)) + yf(z) \geq 0. \tag{20}$$

The first makes it obvious that the desired result holds if y and z have different signs whereas the second makes it obvious that the desired result holds if they have the same sign. This completes the proof.

As an example of where Theorem 4 can be used to predict stability where the previous results fail, consider a fourth-order system having a transfer function

$$G(s) = (10s+1)(2s+1)/(s^2+20s+400)(2s^2+5s+4). \tag{21}$$

The phase curve of $G(s)$ is shown in Fig. 2.

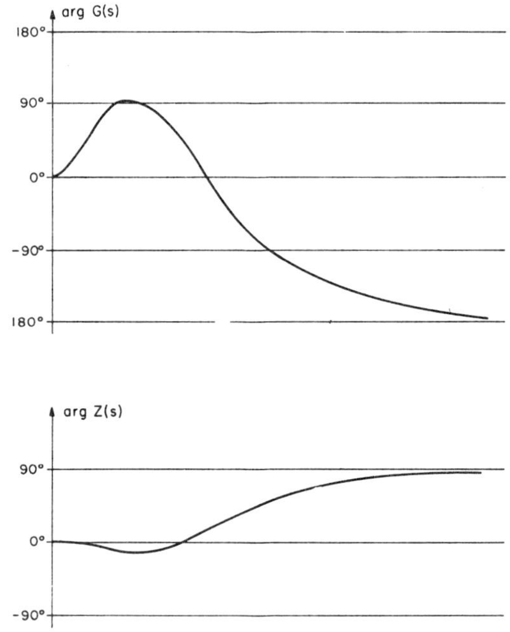

Fig. 2. The phase angles for G and Z for a fourth-order example.

Since the Nyquist diagram is not restricted to three quadrants it is clear that Theorems 1 and 3 will not work. Yet, if $f \in \boldsymbol{O}_\infty$ it is possible to prove stability; a suitable choice for $Z(s) \in \boldsymbol{Z}_2$ is

$$Z(s) = (2s^2 + 5s + 4)/(2s + 1). \tag{22}$$

The phase curve of $Z(s)$ is sketched in Fig. 2.

Of course Theorem 4 will not predict stability for all four pole systems whose linearized equations are stable. The maximum phase lag associated with a Z_2 multiplier is approximately 19.5°. In view of this it is clear that if the phase approaches 180° at high frequency then the maximum phase lead must be less than 109.5° if Theorem 4 is to be used. Even this is only a necessary condition on $G(s)$; no really interesting sufficient conditions have yet been found.

V. Stronger Assumptions on the Nonlinearity

From Lemma 6 it follows that one way to get a stability theorem allows a more general class of multipliers is to make assumptions on f which will allow inequality (10) to be satisfied for larger values of c. One type of nonlinearity which immediately suggests itself is the power law. For example, if $f(y) = ky^3$, $k>0$, what is the best choice of b and d, and what is the corresponding value of c? In this case inequality (10) becomes

$$k(\dot{y} + y)(c\dot{y} + y)^3 - kb\dot{y}(dy)^3 \geq 0. \quad (23)$$

If this is multiplied by $1/ky^4$, it becomes, on substituting z for $\dot{y}/y$,

$$(z + 1)(cz + 1)^3 - bd^3z \geq 0. \quad (24)$$

It may be shown that if bd^3 is taken to be 64 then c may be taken to be 9 and that this is the highest value of c for which inequality (23) can be validated, regardless of the choice of bd^3. The details of this argument may be found in Willems [8], Part I.

For the general power law, where $f(y)$ is given by

$$f(y) = k \mid y \mid^u \operatorname{sgn}(y) \quad (25)$$

it is not known what the best values of b and d are nor is it known what the corresponding value of c is. Other special cases which have been worked out are $u=2$, for which the best value of c is $10+6\sqrt{3}$, and $u=5$, for which the best value of c is 5.

The best value of c associated with the power u is the same as that associated with the power $1/u$. To prove this, start by considering the uth power equivalent of inequality (25) which is

$$(z + 1) \mid cz + 1 \mid^u \operatorname{sgn}(cz + 1) - bd^uz \geq 0. \quad (26)$$

This inequality is assumed to hold for all z. By taking the uth root of both terms this becomes

$$(cz + 1) \mid z + 1 \mid^{1/u} \operatorname{sgn}(z + 1) - \mathrm{d}\mathrm{b}^{1/u}z^{1/u} \geq 0. \quad (27)$$

Multiply this by $z^{-1-1/u}$ to get

$$(c + 1/z) \mid 1 + 1/z \mid^{1/u} \operatorname{sgn}(z + 1) - db^{1/u}/z \geq 0. \quad (28)$$

Let $w=1/cz$ and divide inequality (28) by c. This shows that the value of c with a given u is the same as that associated with $1/u$, but it also shows that if $b=d$ then the same values of b and d are appropriate for both u and $1/u$.

Let $\phi(u)$ denote the best value of c associated with a given u. A sketch of this function is shown in Fig. 3.

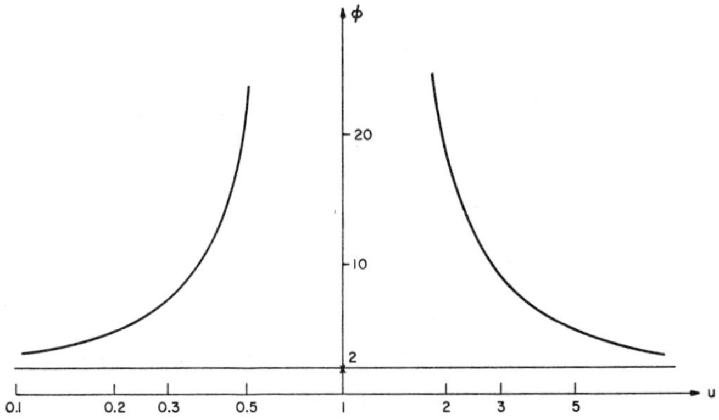

Fig. 3. A sketch of the function $\phi(u)$.

This sketch is only approximate; it is based on the data given above and some additional numerical work. Notice that as u approaches infinity $\phi(u)$ approaches 2, the value used for functions of class $\boldsymbol{O}_k$.

On the basis of Lemma 7 it follows that the equation

$$p(D)x + k \mid q(D)x \mid^u \operatorname{sgn}(q(D)x) = 0; \quad k \geq 0 \quad (29)$$

is stable if there exists a $Z(s) \in \boldsymbol{Z}_{\phi(u)}$ such that $(Z(s))^{\pm 1}G(s)$ is a positive real product. However, it is possible to prove a considerably more general result if the proper classification of nonlinear functions is used.

The function $f(y)$ will be said to belong to the class $\boldsymbol{P}_\infty(u)$ if it is odd and if for all $|y| \geq |z|$

$$\mid y/z \mid^{1/u} \leq \mid f(y)/f(z) \mid \leq \mid y/z \mid^u. \quad (30)$$

These are the functions which lie between a $1/u$ power law and a u power law. It has already been shown that the inequalities

$$(\dot{y}+y)\phi(u)\dot{y}+y \mid^u \operatorname{sgn}(\phi\dot{y}+y) - b\dot{y} \mid by \mid^u \operatorname{sgn}(y) \geq 0 \quad (31)$$

$$(\dot{y}+y) \mid \phi\dot{y}+y \mid^{1/u} \operatorname{sgn}(\phi\dot{y}+y) - b\dot{y} \mid by \mid^{1/u} \operatorname{sgn}(y) \geq 0 \quad (32)$$

both hold for a suitable choice of b. Since a function $f \in \boldsymbol{P}_\infty(u)$ lies between these two extremes it follows that for $f \in \boldsymbol{P}_\infty(u)$

$$(\dot{y} + y)f(\phi(u)\dot{y} + y) - b\dot{y}f(by) \geq 0. \quad (33)$$

The functions in $\boldsymbol{P}_\infty(u)$ are permitted to have infinite gains. In order to modify this theory in such a way as to treat systems for which the gain is limited, it is only necessary to re-examine the steps leading to (16). Define the set $\boldsymbol{P}_k(u)$ by saying that $f \in \boldsymbol{P}_k(u)$ if $f^{-1}(y) - y/k$ belongs to $\boldsymbol{P}_\infty(u)$. In terms of this notation, Theorem 5 summarizes the results of this section.

Theorem 5

If $f \in \boldsymbol{P}_k(u)$ then the null solution of (1) is ASIL if there exists a $Z(s) \in \boldsymbol{Z}_{\phi(u)}$ such that $(Z(s))^{\pm 1}(G(s)+1/k)$ is a positive real product.

Notice that this theorem actually includes Theorem 4 as a special case.

VI. Other Sufficient Conditions

While the assumptions made on the nonlinearity in the previous theorems have been natural enough, they are but a few of the many which could be used. For example, they say nothing about what improvement, if any, can be made on the Popov Theorem if f is monotone, and in $\boldsymbol{A}_k$ but not in $\boldsymbol{M}_k$ so that Theorem 4 cannot be used. Likewise, if $f \in \boldsymbol{A}_k$ and $\boldsymbol{O}_\infty$, can Theorem 1 be improved upon? The following theorem treats the first case.

Theorem 6

If $f \in \boldsymbol{M}_\infty$ and $\boldsymbol{A}_k$ then the null solution of (1) is ASIL if there exists a $Z(s) \in \boldsymbol{Z}_1$ such that $Z(s)(G(s)+Z(0)/kG(s))$ is a positive real product.

Proof: If (2) is multiplied by $m(D)q(D)x + n(D)p(D)xZ(0)/k$ and then integrated, this result can be written as

$$\int_{t(0)}^{t(x)} (m(D)q(D)x + n(D)p(D)xZ(0)/k)n(D)p(D)x$$
$$-((Ev(m(D)q(D)(n(D)p(D)Z(0)/k)n(-D)p(-D))^{-}x)^2$$
$$+f(n(D)q(D)x)(m(D)q(D)x-f(n(D)q(D)x)Z(0)/k)\,dt$$
$$=\int_{t(0)}^{t(x)} ((Ev(m(D)q(D)$$
$$+n(D)p(D)Z(0)/k)n(-D)p(-D))^{-}x)^2 \quad (34)$$

provided the term appearing on the right is subtracted from both sides. The integral containing the nonlinear term can be rewritten as

$$\int_{t(0)}^{t(x)} f(n(D)q(D)x)(m(D)q(D)x-f(n(D)q(D)x)Z(0)/k)\,dt$$
$$=\int_{t(0)}^{t(x)} f(n(D)q(D)x)(Z(0)n(D)q(D)x-f(n(D)q(D)x)/k)$$
$$+\int_{t(0)}^{t(x)} (m(D)q(D)x$$
$$-n(D)q(D)xZ(0))f(n(D)q(D)x)\,dt. \quad (35)$$

The integrand of the first term on the right is clearly positive. If it can be shown that the second term can be expressed as a sum of the form $G(\mathbf{x}+g(\mathbf{x})$ as in Lemma 5, then the theorem will be proven. Notice however, that the ratio $(m(D)q(D)-n(D)q(D)Z(0))/n(D)q(D)=m(D)/n(D)-Z(0)$ is, itself, a $\boldsymbol{Z}_1$ function; to prove this merely examine a typical term in (4).

In the proof of Theorem 3 it was shown if $m(s)$ $n(s)$ $\in\boldsymbol{Z}_1$ then the integral

$$\int_{t(0)}^{t(x)} m(D)q(D)xf(n(D)q(D)x\,dt=G(\mathbf{x})+\int_{t(0)}^{t(x)} g(\mathbf{x})\,dt \quad (36)$$

with $G(x)\geq 0$ and $g(x)\geq 0$; the remaining details are left to the reader.

Corresponding results, valid when $f\in\boldsymbol{A}_k$ and $\boldsymbol{O}_\infty$ or $\boldsymbol{P}_\infty(u)$ are given in reference [8] of Part I. Other possibilities, such as $f\in\boldsymbol{M}_{k'}$, and $f\in\boldsymbol{A}_k$, $k'>k$, have not been worked out; however, the way to proceed seems clear.

VII. Linearization

Certainly one of the most interesting questions in stability theory is, "When it is possible to determine the stability properties of a nonlinear system by looking at some linearized version of it?" The question is complicated because of various types of linearizations which can be used. In this paper, the results obtained from the Liapunov theory have compared with those predicted heuristicly by 1) total linearization, [the Aizerman problem] and 2) local linearization [linearization at each point on the nonlinearity]. No comparison was made with the describing function linearization, although this would seem to be a worthwhile thing to do.

Consider a transfer function $G(s)$ which is stable for all linear feedback in $\boldsymbol{A}_\infty$. The results obtained here suggest that if the phase angle always lags then this system will be stable for any nonlinear feedback of the correct sign. If the phase approaches 180° at high frequencies and is positive for some range of frequencies then it still may be possible to prove stability for all $f\in A_\infty$ if the phase lead never exceeds 90°. If the phase angle of such a system exceeds 90° then it seems that linearization must be used with more caution. Roughly speaking, the larger and the more rapid the phase angle excursions, the less likely it is that linearization techniques will accurately predict stability behavior.

VIII. Conclusions

In Parts I and II of this paper a detailed study of the stability of a class of nonlinear feedback systems has been made. Sufficient conditions for asymptotic stability in the large have been given in terms of the existence of a multiplier $Z(s)$ of a certain class, which can make the product $Z(s)G(s)$ positive real. The class of multipliers is defined by (4) and the stability criteria are listed in the following.

The null solution of (1) will be ASIL if:

1) $f\in\boldsymbol{A}_k$ and there exists a positive real function $Z(s)\in\boldsymbol{Z}_0$ such that $(Z(s))^{\pm1}(G(s)+1/k)$ is a positive real product.
2) $f\in\boldsymbol{M}_k$ and there exists a positive real function $Z(s)\in\boldsymbol{Z}_1$ such that $(Z(s))^{\pm1}(G(s)+1/k)$ is a positive real product.
3) $f\in\boldsymbol{O}_k$ and there exists a positive real function $Z(s)\in\boldsymbol{Z}_2$ such that $(Z(s))^{\pm}(G(s)+1/k)$ is a positive real product.
4) $f\in\boldsymbol{P}_k(u)$ and there exists a positive real function $Z(s)\in\boldsymbol{Z}_{\phi(u)}$ such that $(Z(s))^{\pm1}(G(s)+1/k)$ is a positive real product.
5) $f\in\boldsymbol{A}_k$ and $f\in\boldsymbol{M}_\infty$ and there exists a positive real function $Z(s)\in\boldsymbol{Z}_1$ such that $(Z(s))(G(s)+Z(0)/kG(s))$ is a positive real product.

On the basis of the criteria given, it seems clear that the cases in which Aizerman type linearization can give wrong answers are those for which the phase angle exceeds 90° or those for which the phase angle changes rapidly from a positive value to a large (∼180°) negative value. It seems that any type of linearization can give a wrong answer if the phase angle approaches 180° as ω approaches zero or if the phase changes rapidly from near 180° to near −180°.

A great deal more work is required to translate the given stability criteria into engineering terms. This, and an investigation of the necessary conditions for stability, seem to be two worthwhile areas for future study.

Appendix

The object of this Appendix is to describe in more detail the procedure used for calculating $\dot{V}$ in the various proofs in Parts I and II of this paper. Basically what is done is to first define a scalar function $V(\mathbf{x})$ by a line integral which is independent of path; e.g.,

$$V(\mathbf{x}) = \int_{t(0)}^{t(\mathbf{x})} p(D)xq(D)x - ((Evq(D)p(-D))^{-}x)^2\, dt. \quad (37)$$

Of course, t need not be identified with time but it should be understood that in evaluating $V(\mathbf{x})$ a path is traversed which starts at $\mathbf{x}=O$ and ends at $\mathbf{x}$ and that $t(\mathbf{x})$ depends on the particular path chosen. Now let $\mathbf{x}$ and $\mathbf{x}_0$ be points on the trajectory of the equation along whose solutions $\dot{V}(\mathbf{x})$ is to be calculated; e.g.,

$$p(D)x = 0 \quad \text{or} \quad \dot{\mathbf{x}} = A\mathbf{x}. \quad (38)$$

Suppose that the state at time t is $\mathbf{x}$ and the state at time $t+\Delta t$ is $\mathbf{x}_0$. Then clearly

$$V(\mathbf{x}) - V(\mathbf{x}_0) = \int_{t}^{t+\Delta t} p(D)xq(D)x - ((Evq(D)p(-D))^{-}x)^2\, dt \quad (39)$$

provided that *now* $x(t)$, the path of integration, is a solution of (38) and t is identified with time. By taking the limit,

$$\dot{V}(\mathbf{x}, \dot{\mathbf{x}}) = p(D)xq(D) - ((Evq(D)p(-D)x)^{-}x)^2\, dt \quad (40)$$

and, using (38),

$$\dot{V}(\mathbf{x}, \dot{\mathbf{x}}) = -((Evq(D)p(-D))^{-}x)^2. \quad (41)$$

Similar reasoning applies in the more complicated cases.

The reason for showing a dependency on $\dot{\mathbf{x}}$ in $\dot{V}$ is that in the event that $q(D)$ is of the same degree as $p(D)$, the nth derivative of x will appear in $\dot{V}$. This can, of course, always be eliminated by using the equation of motion but it often simplifies things not to do so. This is particularly true in proving the Popov Theorem (see Brockett [11], Part I).

On the Input-Output Stability of Time-Varying Nonlinear Feedback Systems

Part I: Conditions Derived Using Concepts of Loop Gain, Conicity, and Positivity

G. ZAMES, MEMBER, IEEE

Abstract—The object of this paper is to outline a stability theory for input-output problems using functional methods. More particularly, the aim is to derive open loop conditions for the boundedness and continuity of feedback systems, without, at the beginning, placing restrictions on linearity or time invariance.

It will be recalled that, in the special case of a linear time invariant feedback system, stability can be assessed using Nyquist's criterion; roughly speaking, stability depends on the amounts by which signals are amplified and delayed in flowing around the loop. An attempt is made here to show that similar considerations govern the behavior of feedback systems in general—that stability of nonlinear time-varying feedback systems can often be assessed from certain gross features of input-output behavior, which are related to amplification and delay.

This paper is divided into two parts: Part I contains general theorems, free of restrictions on linearity or time invariance; Part II, which will appear in a later issue, contains applications to a loop with one nonlinear element. There are three main results in Part I, which follow the introduction of concepts of *gain*, *conicity*, *positivity*, and *strong positivity:*

THEOREM 1: If the open loop gain is less than one, then the closed loop is bounded.

THEOREM 2: If the open loop can be factored into two, suitably proportioned, conic relations, then the closed loop is bounded.

THEOREM 3: If the open loop can be factored into two positive relations, one of which is strongly positive and has finite gain, then the closed loop is bounded.

Results analogous to Theorems 1–3, but with boundedness replaced by continuity, are also obtained.

I. Introduction

FEEDBACK, broadly speaking, affects a system in one of two opposing ways: depending on circumstances it is either degenerative or regenerative—either stabilizing or destabilizing. In trying to gain some perspective on the qualitative behavior of feedback systems we might ask: What are the kinds of feedback that are stabilizing? What kinds lead to a stable system? Can some of the effects of feedback on stability be described without assuming a very specific system representation?

Part I of this paper is devoted to the system of Fig. 1, which consists of two elements in a feedback loop.[1] This simple configuration is a model for many controllers, amplifiers, and modulators; its range of application will be extended to include multi-element and distributed systems, by allowing the system variables to be multidimensional or infinite-dimensional.

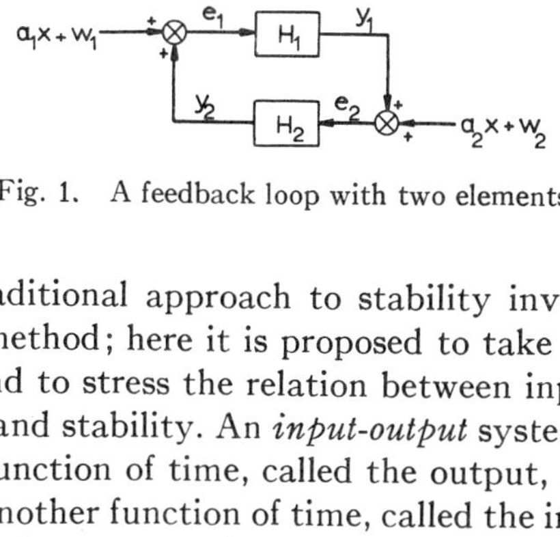

Fig. 1. A feedback loop with two elements.

The traditional approach to stability involves Lyapunov's method; here it is proposed to take a different course, and to stress the relation between input-output behavior and stability. An *input-output* system is one in which a function of time, called the output, is required to track another function of time, called the input; more generally the output might be required to track some function of the input. In order to behave properly an input-output system must usually have two properties:

1) Bounded inputs must produce bounded outputs—i.e., the system must be nonexplosive.

2) Outputs must not be critically sensitive to small changes in inputs—changes such as those caused by noise.

Manuscript received December 29, 1964; revised October 1, 1965; February 2, 1966. This work was carried out at the M.I.T. Electronic Systems Laboratory in part under support extended by NASA under Contract NsG-496 with the Center for Space Research. Parts of this paper were presented at the 1964 National Electronics Conference, Chicago, Ill., and at the 1964 International Conference on Microwaves, Circuit Theory, and Information Theory, Tokyo, Japan.
The author is with the Department of Electrical Engineering, Massachusetts Institute of Technology, Cambridge, Mass.

[1] The system of Fig. 1 has a *single* input x, multiplied by constants a_1 and a_2, and added in at *two* points. This arrangement has been chosen because it is symmetrical and thus convenient for analysis; it also remains invariant under some of the transformations that will be needed. Of course, a single input loop can be obtained by setting a_1 or a_2 to zero. The terms w_1 and w_2 are fixed bias functions, which will be used to account for the effects of initial conditions. The variables e_1, e_2, y_1, and y_2 are outputs.

Reprinted from *IEEE Trans. Automat. Contr.*, vol. AC-11, pp. 228–238, Apr. 1966.

These two properties will form the basis of the definition of stability presented in this paper. It is desired to find conditions on the elements $\boldsymbol{H}_1$ and $\boldsymbol{H}_2$ (in Fig. 1) which will ensure that the overall loop will remain stable after $\boldsymbol{H}_1$ and $\boldsymbol{H}_2$ are interconnected. It is customary to refer to $\boldsymbol{H}_1$ and $\boldsymbol{H}_2$ prior to interconnection as the "open-loop" elements, and to the interconnected structure as the "closed loop." The problem to be considered here can therefore be described as seeking *open-loop conditions for closed-loop stability*.

Although the problem at hand is posed as a feedback problem, it can equally well be interpreted as a problem in networks; it will be found, for example, that the equations of the system of Fig. 1 have the same form as those of the circuit of Fig. 2, which consists of two elements in series with a voltage source, and in parallel with a current source.[2]

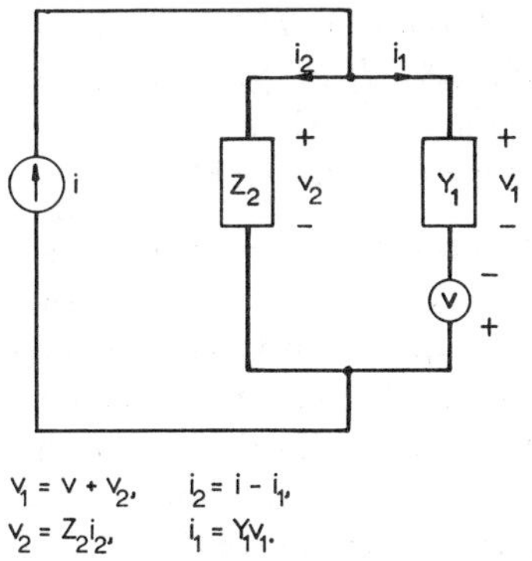

Fig. 2. A circuit equivalent to the loop of Fig. 1.

1.1 Historical Note

The problem of Lyapunov stability has a substantial history with which the names of Lur'e, Malkin, Yakubowitch, Kalman, and many others, are associated. On the other hand, functional methods for stability received less attention until relatively recently, although some versions of the well-known Popov [1] theorem might be considered as fitting into this category.

The present paper has its origin in studies [2a, b] of nonlinear distortion in bandlimited feedback loops, in which contraction methods were used to prove the existence and stability of an inversion scheme. The author's application of contraction methods to more general stability problems was inspired in part by conversations with Narendra during 1962–1963; using Lyapunov's method, Narendra and Goldwyn [3] later obtained a result similar to the circle condition of Part II of this paper.

The key results of this paper, in a somewhat different formulation, were first presented in 1964 [2d, e]. Many of these results are paralleled in the work of Brockett and Willems [4], who use Lyapunov based methods. Several others have obtained similar or related results by functional methods: Sandberg [5a] extended the nonlinear distortion theory mentioned above; later [5b] he obtained a stability theorem similar to Theorem 1 of this paper. Kudrewicz [6] has obtained circle conditions by fixed point methods. Contraction methods for incrementally positive operators have been developed by Zarantonello [7], Kolodner [8], Minty [9], and Browder [10]. A stability condition for linear time-varying systems has been described by Bongiorno [11].

2. Formulation of the Problem

There are several preliminaries to settle, namely, to specify a system model, to define stability, and to write feedback equations. What is a suitable mathematical model of a feedback element? A "black box" point of view towards defining a model will be taken. That is to say, only input-output behavior, which is a purely external property, will be considered; details of internal structure which underlie this behavior will be omitted. Accordingly, throughout Part I, a feedback element will be represented by an abstract relation, which can be interpreted as a mapping from a space of input functions into a space of output functions. More concrete representations, involving convolution integrals, characteristic graphs, etc., will be considered in Part II.

Some of the elementary notions of functional analysis will be used, though limitations of space prevent an introduction to this subject.[3] Among the concepts which will be needed and used freely are those of an abstract relation, a normed linear space, an inner product space, and the L_p spaces.

The practice of omitting the quantifier "for all" shall be utilized. For example, the statement

$$\text{"}-x^2 \leq x^2 (x \in X)\text{"}$$

is to be read:

$$\text{"for all } x \in X,\ -x^2 \leq x^2.\text{"}$$

CONVENTION: *Any expression containing a condition of the type "$x \in X$," free of quantifiers, holds* for all $x \in X$.

2.1 The Extended Normed Linear Space X_e

In order to specify what is meant by a system, a suitable space of input and output functions will first be defined.[4] Since unstable systems will be involved, this space must contain functions which "explode," i.e., which grow without bound as time increases [for example, the exponential exp (t)]. Such functions are not contained in the spaces commonly used in analysis, for example, in the L_p spaces. Therefore it is necessary to

[2] It is assumed that the source voltage v and the source current i are inputs, with $v = a_1 x + w_1$ and $i = a_2 x + w_2$; the currents and voltages in the two elements are outputs.

[3] A good reference is Kolmogorov and Fomin [12].

[4] The space of input functions will equal the space of output functions.

construct a special space, which will be called X_e. X_e, will contain both "well-behaved" and "exploding" functions, which will be distinguished from each other by assigning finite norms to the former and infinite norms to the latter. X_e will be an extension, or enlargement, of an associated normed linear space X in the following sense. Each finite-time truncation of every function in X_e will lie in X; in other words, the restriction of $x \in X_e$ to a finite time interval, say to $[0, t]$, will have a finite norm—but this norm may grow without limit as $t \to \infty$.

First a time interval T and a range of input or output values V will be fixed.

DEFINITION: *T is a given subinterval of the reals, of the type $[t_0, \infty)$ or $(-\infty, \infty)$. V is a given linear space.*

[For example, in the analysis of multielement (or distributed) networks, V is multidimensional (or infinite-dimensional).] Second, the notion of a truncated function is introduced.

NOTATION: *Let x be any function mapping T into V, that is, $x: T \to V$; let t be any point in T; then the symbol x_t denotes the* truncated function, *$x_t: T \to V$, which assumes the values $x_t(\tau) = x(\tau)$ for $\tau < t$ and $x_t(\tau) = 0$ elsewhere.*

(A truncated function is shown in Fig. 3.) Next, the space X is defined.

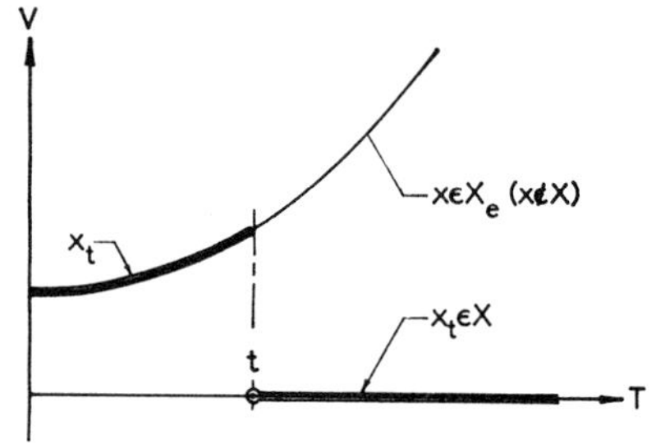

Fig. 3. A truncated function.

DEFINITION: *X is a space consisting of functions of the type $x: T \to V$; the following assumptions are made concerning X:*

(1) *X is a normed linear space; the norm of $x \in X$ is denoted by $\|x\|$.*
(2) *If $x \in X$ then $x_t \in X$ for all $t \in T$.*
(3) *If $x: T \to V$, and if $x_t \in X$ for all $t \in T$, then:*
 (a) *$\|x_t\|$ is a nondecreasing function of $t \in T$.*
 (b) *If $\lim_{t\to\infty} \|x_t\|$ exists, then $x \in X$ and the limit equals $\|x\|$.*

(For example, it can be verified that assumptions (1)–(3) are satisfied by the L_p spaces.) Next, X_e is defined.

DEFINITION: *The* extension *of X, denoted by X_e, is the space consisting of those functions whose truncations lie in X, that is, $X_e = \{x \mid x: T \to V$, and $x_t \in X$ for all $t \in T\}$.* (NOTE: X_e is a linear space.) *An* extended norm, *denoted $\|x\|_e$, is assigned to each $x \in X_e$ as follows: $\|x\|_e = \|x\|$ if $x \in X$, and $\|x\|_e = \infty$ if $x \notin X$.*

The point of assumptions (2)–(3) on X can now be appreciated; these assumptions make it possible to determine whether or not an element $x \in X_e$ has a finite norm, by observing whether or not $\lim_{t\to\infty} \|x_t\|$ exists. For example:

EXAMPLE 1: Let $L_2[0, \infty)$ be the normed linear space consisting of those real-valued functions x on $[0, \infty)$ for which the integral $\int_0^\infty x^2(t)dt$ exists, and let this integral equal $\|x\|^2$. Let $X = L_2[0, \infty)$, and let $L_{2e} = X_e$; that is, L_{2e} is the extension of $L_2[0, \infty)$. Let x be the function on $[0, \infty)$ given by $x(t) = \exp(t)$. Is $\|x\|_e$ finite, that is, is x in X? No, because $\|x_t\|$ grows without limit as $t \to \infty$, or in other words, $\|x\|_e = \infty$.

2.2 Input-Output Relations

The mathematical model of an input-output system will be a relation on X_e:

DEFINITION: *A* relation *$\boldsymbol{H}$ on X_e is any subset of the product space $X_e \times X_e$. If (x, y) is any pair belonging to $\boldsymbol{H}$ then y will be said to be* $\boldsymbol{H}$-related *to x; y will also be said to be an* image of x under $\boldsymbol{H}$.[5]

In other words, a relation is a set of pairs of functions in X_e. It will be convenient to refer to the first element in any pair as an input, and to the second element as an output, even though the reverse interpretation is sometimes more appropriate. A relation can also be thought of as a mapping, which maps some (not necessarily all) inputs into outputs. In general, a relation is multivalued; i.e., a single input can be mapped into many outputs.

The concept of state, which is essential to Lyapunov's method, will not be used here. This does not mean that initial conditions cannot be considered. One way of accounting for various initial conditions is to represent a system by a multi-valued relation, in which each input is paired with many outputs, one output per initial condition. Another possibility is to introduce a separate relation for each initial condition.

Note that the restrictions placed on X_e tend to limit, a priori, the class of allowable systems. In particular, the requirement that truncated outputs have finite norms means, roughly speaking, that only systems having infinite "escape times," i.e., systems which do not blow up in finite time, shall be considered.

Some additional nomenclature follows:

DEFINITION: *If $\boldsymbol{H}$ is a relation on X_e, then the* domain *of $\boldsymbol{H}$ denoted $Do(\boldsymbol{H})$, and the* range *of $\boldsymbol{H}$ denoted $Ra(\boldsymbol{H})$, are the sets,*

$Do(\boldsymbol{H}) = \{x \mid x \in X_e$, *and there exists* $y \in X_e$ *such that* $(x, y) \in \boldsymbol{H}\}$

$Ra(\boldsymbol{H}) = \{y \mid y \in X_e$, *and there exists* $x \in X_e$ *such that* $(x, y) \in \boldsymbol{H}\}$

[5] In general x can have *many* images.

NOTATION: *If* H *is a relation on* X_e, *and if* x *is a given element of* X_e, *then the symbol* Hx *denotes an* image *of* x *under* H.[5]

The idea here is to use a special symbol for an element instead of indicating that the element belongs to a certain set. For example, the statement, "there exists Hx having property P" is shorthand for "there exists $y \in \text{Ra}(H)$, such that y is an image of x, and y has property P."[6]

Observing that Hx is, according to the definitions used here, a function on T, the following symbol for the value of Hx at time t is adopted:

NOTATION: *The symbol* $Hx(t)$ *denotes the value assumed by the function* Hx *at time* $t \in T$.

Occasionally a special type of relation, called an operator, will be used:

DEFINITION: *An* operator H *is a relation on* X_e *which satisfies two conditions: 1)* $\text{Do}(H) = X_e$. *2)* H *is single-valued; that is, if* x, y, *and* z *are elements of* X_e, *and if* y *and* z *are images of* x *under* H, *then* $y = z$.

2.3 The Class $\mathcal{R}$

DEFINITION: $\mathcal{R}$ *is the class of those relations* H *on* X_e *having the property that the zero element, denoted* o, *lies in* $\text{Do}(H)$, *and* $Ho = o$.

The assumption that H maps zero into zero simplifies many derivations; if this condition is not met at the outset, it can be obtained by adding a compensating bias to the feedback equations.

If H and K are relations in $\mathcal{R}$, and c is a real constant, then the *sum* $(H+K)$, the *product* cH, and the *composition product* KH of K *following* H, are defined in the usual way,[7] and are relations in $\mathcal{R}$. The *inverse of* H in $\mathcal{R}$, denoted by H^{-1}, *always exists*. The *identity operator* on X_e is denoted by I.

2.4 Input-Output Stability

The term "stable" has been used in a variety of ways, to indicate that a system is somehow well behaved. A system shall be called stable if it is well behaved in two respects: (1) It is bounded, i.e., not explosive. (2) it is continuous, i.e., not critically sensitive to noise.

DEFINITION: *A* subset Y *of* X_e is bounded *if there exists* $A > 0$ *such that, for all* $y \in Y$, $\|y\|_e < A$. *A* relation H *on* X_e is bounded[8] *if the image under* H *of every bounded subset of* X_e *is a bounded subset of* X_e.

[6] In keeping with the usual convention used here, any statement containing Hx free of quantifiers holds *for all* x in $\text{Ra}(H)$. For example, "$Hx > 1$ $(x \in X_e)$" means that "for all x in X_e, and for all Hx in $\text{Ra}(H)$, $Hx > 1$."

[7] In particular, $\text{Do}(H+K) = \text{Do}(H) \cap \text{Do}(K)$. Note that $\mathcal{R}$ is not a linear space; for example, if $\text{Do}(H) \neq \text{Do}(K)$ then $\text{Do}[(H+K)-K] \neq \text{Do}(H)$.

[8] This definition implies that inputs of finite norm produce outputs of finite norm. More than that, it implies that the sort of situation is avoided in which a bounded sequence of inputs, say $\|x_n\| < 1$ where $n = 1, 2, \cdots$, produces a sequence of outputs having norms that are finite but increasing without limit, say $\|Hx_n\| = n$.

DEFINITION: *A relation* H *on* X_e *is* continuous *if* H *has the following property: Given any* $x \in X$ *(that is,* $\|x\|_e < \infty$*), and any* $\Delta > 0$, *there exists* $\delta > 0$ *such that, for all* $y \in X$, *if* $\|x - y\| < \delta$ *then* $\|Hx - Hy\| < \Delta$.

DEFINITION: *A relation* H *on* X_e *is* input-output stable *if* H *is bounded and continuous.*

2.5 Feedback Equations

Although negative feedback loops will be of interest, the positive feedback configuration of Fig. 1 has been chosen because it is symmetrical.[1] The equations describing this system, to be known as the FEEDBACK EQUATIONS, are:

$$e_1 = w_1 + a_1 x + y_2 \tag{1a}$$

$$e_2 = w_2 + a_2 x + y_1 \tag{1b}$$

$$y_2 = H_2 e_2 \tag{2a}$$

$$y_1 = H_1 e_1 \tag{2b}$$

in which it is assumed that:

H_1 and H_2 are relations in $\mathcal{R}$
a_1 and a_2 are real constants
w_1 and w_2 are fixed biases in X
x in X_e is an input
e_1 and e_2 in X_e are (error) outputs
y_1 and y_2 in X_e are outputs.

(The biases are used to compensate for nonzero zero-input responses and, in particular, for the effects of initial conditions.) The *closed-loop relations* E_1, E_2, F_1, and F_2, are now defined as follows.

DEFINITION: E_1 *is the relation that relates* e_1 *to* x *or, more precisely,* $E_1 = \{(x, e_1) \mid (x, e_1) \in X_e \times X_e$, *and there exist* e_2, y_1, y_2, $H_1 e_1$, *and* $H_2 e_2$, *all in* X_e, *such that* (1) *and* (2) *are satisfied.*$\}$ *Similarly* E_2 *relates* e_2 *to* x; F_1 *relates* y_1 *to* x; F_2 *relates* y_2 *to* x.

All the prerequisites are now assembled for defining the problem of interest which is: *Find conditions on* H_1 *and* H_2 *which ensure that* E_1, E_2, F_1, *and* F_2 *are bounded or stable.* In general it will be enough to be concerned with E_1 and E_2 only, and to neglect F_1 and F_2, since every $F_2 x$ is related to some $E_1 x$ by the equation $F_2 x = E_1 x - a_1 x - w_1$, so that F_2 is bounded (or stable) whenever E_1 is, and similarly for F_1 vs. E_2.

It should be noted that by posing the feedback problem in terms of relations (rather than in terms of operators) all questions of existence and uniqueness of solutions are avoided. For the results to be practically significant, it must usually be known from some other source[9] that solutions exist and are unique (and have infinite "escape times").

[9] Existence and stability can frequently be deduced from entirely separate assumptions. For example, existence can often be deduced, by iteration methods, solely from the fact that (loosely speaking) the open loop delays signals; stability can not. (The connection between existence and generalized delay is discussed in G. Zames, "Realizability conditions for nonlinear feedback systems," *IEEE Trans. on Circuit Theory,* vol. CF-11, pp. 186–194, June 1964.)

3. Small Loop Gain Conditions

To secure a foothold on this problem a simple situation is sought in which it seems likely, on intuitive grounds, that the feedback system will be stable. Such a situation occurs when the open loop attenuates all signals. This intuitive idea will be formalized in Theorem 1; in later sections, a more comprehensive theory will be derived from Theorem 1.

To express this idea, a measure of attenuation, i.e., a notion of gain, is needed.

3.1 Gains

Gain will be measured in terms of the ratio of the norm of a truncated output to the norm of the related, truncated input.

DEFINITION: *The* gain *of a relation* $\boldsymbol{H}$ *in* $\mathcal{R}$, *denoted by* $g(\boldsymbol{H})$, *is*

$$g(\boldsymbol{H}) = \sup \frac{\|(\boldsymbol{H}x)_t\|}{\|x_t\|} \tag{3}$$

where the supremum is taken over all x *in* $Do(\boldsymbol{H})$, *all* $\boldsymbol{H}x$ *in* $Ra(\boldsymbol{H})$, *and all* t *in* T *for which* $x_t \neq 0$.

In other words, the supremum is taken over all possible input-output pairs, and over *all possible truncations.* The reason for using truncated (rather than whole) functions is that the norms of truncated functions are known to be finite *a priori.*

It can be verified that gains have all the properties of norms. In addition, if $\boldsymbol{H}$ and $\boldsymbol{K}$ belong to $\mathcal{R}$ then $g(\boldsymbol{KH}) \leq g(\boldsymbol{K})g(\boldsymbol{H})$. Gains also satisfy the following inequalities:

$$\|(\boldsymbol{H}x)_t\| \leq g(\boldsymbol{H})\cdot\|x_t\| \qquad [x \in Do(\boldsymbol{H}); t \in T] \tag{4}$$

$$\|\boldsymbol{H}x\|_e \leq g(\boldsymbol{H})\cdot\|x\|_e \qquad [x \in \mathrm{Do}(\boldsymbol{H})] \tag{5}$$

where (4) is implied by (3), and (5) is derived from (4) by taking the limit as $t \to \infty$.

If $g(\boldsymbol{H}) < \infty$ then (5) implies that $\boldsymbol{H}$ is bounded. In fact, conditions for boundedness will be derived using the notion of gain and inequalities such as (5). In a similar way, conditions for continuity will be derived using the notion of incremental gain, which is defined as follows:

DEFINITION: *The* incremental gain *of any* $\boldsymbol{H}$ *in* $\mathcal{R}$, *denoted by* $\tilde{g}(\boldsymbol{H})$, *is*

$$\tilde{g}(\boldsymbol{H}) = \sup \frac{\|(\boldsymbol{H}x)_t - (\boldsymbol{H}y)_t\|}{\|x_t - y_t\|} \tag{6}$$

where the supremum is taken over all x *and* y *in* $Do(\boldsymbol{H})$, *all* $\boldsymbol{H}x$ *and* $\boldsymbol{H}y$ *in* $Ra(\boldsymbol{H})$, *and all* t *in* T *for which* $x_t \neq y_t$.

Incremental gains have all the properties of norms, and satisfy the inequalities

$$\tilde{g}(\boldsymbol{KH}) \leq \tilde{g}(\boldsymbol{K})\cdot\tilde{g}(\boldsymbol{H}) \tag{7}$$

$$\|(\boldsymbol{H}x)_t - (\boldsymbol{H}y)_t\| \leq \tilde{g}(\boldsymbol{H})\cdot\|x_t - y_t\| \quad [x, y \in \mathrm{Do}(\boldsymbol{H}); t \in T] \tag{8}$$

$$\|\boldsymbol{H}x - \boldsymbol{H}y\|_e \leq \tilde{g}(\boldsymbol{H})\cdot\|x - y\|_e \quad [x, y \in \mathrm{Do}(\boldsymbol{H})]. \tag{9}$$

In the Feedback Equations (1)–(2), the product $g(\boldsymbol{H}_1)\cdot g(\boldsymbol{H}_2)$ will be called the *open-loop gain-product,* and similarly, $\tilde{g}(\boldsymbol{H}_1)\cdot\tilde{g}(\boldsymbol{H}_2)$ will be called the *incremental open-loop gain-product.*

3.2 A Stability Theorem

Consider the Feedback Equations (1)–(2).

THEOREM 1:[10] *a) If* $g(\boldsymbol{H}_1)\cdot g(\boldsymbol{H}_2) < 1$, *then the closed loop relations* $\boldsymbol{E}_1$ *and* $\boldsymbol{E}_2$ *are bounded. b) If* $\tilde{g}(\boldsymbol{H}_1)\cdot\tilde{g}(\boldsymbol{H}_2) < 1$, *then* $\boldsymbol{E}_1$ *and* $\boldsymbol{E}_2$ *are input-output stable.*

Theorem 1 is inspired by the well known Contraction Principle.[11]

PROOF OF THEOREM 1: (a) Since eqs. (1)–(2) are symmetrical in the subscripts 1 and 2, it is enough to consider $\boldsymbol{E}_1$. This proof will consist of showing that there are positive constants a, b, and c, with the property that any pair (x, e_1) belonging to $\boldsymbol{E}_1$ [and so being a solution of eqs. (1)–(2)], satisfies the inequality

$$\|e_1\| \leq a\|w_1\| + b\|w_2\| + c\|x\|. \tag{10}$$

It will follow that if x is confined to a bounded region, say $\|x\| \leq A$, then e_1 will also be confined to a bounded region, in this case $\|e_1\| \leq a\|w_1\| + b\|w_2\| + cA$. Thus $\boldsymbol{E}_1$ will be bounded.

PROOF OF INEQUALITY (10): If (x, e_1) belongs to $\boldsymbol{E}_1$ then, after truncating eqs. (1a) and (1b), and using the triangle inequality to bound their norms, the following inequalities are obtained:

$$\|e_{1t}\| \leq \|w_{1t}\| + |a_1|\cdot\|x_t\| + \|y_{2t}\| \qquad (t \in T) \tag{10a}$$

$$\|e_{2t}\| \leq \|w_{2t}\| + |a_2|\cdot\|x_t\| + \|y_{1t}\| \qquad (t \in T) \tag{10b}$$

Furthermore, applying Inequality (4) to eqs. (2), the following is obtained, for each t in T:

$$\|y_{2t}\| \leq g(\boldsymbol{H}_2)\cdot\|e_{2t}\| \tag{11a}$$

$$\|y_{1t}\| \leq g(\boldsymbol{H}_1)\cdot\|e_{1t}\|. \tag{11b}$$

Letting $g(\boldsymbol{H}_1) \triangleq \alpha$ and $g(\boldsymbol{H}_2) \triangleq \beta$, and applying (11a) to (10a) and (11b) to (10b), the following inequalities are obtained:

$$\|e_{1t}\| \leq \|w_{1t}\| + |a_1|\cdot\|x_t\| + \beta\|e_{2t}\| \qquad (t \in T) \tag{12a}$$

$$\|e_{2t}\| \leq \|w_{2t}\| + |a_2|\cdot\|x_t\| + \alpha\|e_{1t}\| \qquad (t \in T). \tag{12b}$$

Applying (12b) to $\|e_{2t}\|$ in (12a), and rearranging,

$$(1 - \alpha\beta)\|e_{1t}\| \leq \|w_{1t}\| + \beta\|w_{2t}\| + (|a_1| + \beta|a_2|)\|x_t\| \qquad (t \in T). \tag{13}$$

[10] A variation of Theorem 1 was originally presented in [2d]. A related continuity theorem was used in [2c]. An independent, related result is Sandberg's [5b].

[11] If X is a complete space, if all relations are in fact operators, and if the hypothesis of Theorem 1b holds, then the Contraction Principle implies existence and uniqueness of solutions—a matter that has been disregarded here.

Since $(1-\alpha\beta)>0$ (as $\alpha\beta<1$, by hypothesis), Inequality (13) can be divided by $(1-\alpha\beta)$; after dividing and taking the limit of both sides as $t\rightarrow\infty$, the Inequality (10) remains. Q.E.D.

(b) Let (x', e_1') and (x'', e_1'') be any two pairs belonging to $\boldsymbol{E}_1$. Proceeding as in Part (a) an inequality of the form $\|e_1''-e_1'\|\leq c\|x''-x'\|$ is obtained, which implies that $\boldsymbol{E}_1$ is continuous. Moreover, since the hypothesis of Part (b) implies the hypothesis of Part (a), $\boldsymbol{E}_1$ is bounded too. Therefore $\boldsymbol{E}_1$ is input-output stable.

EXAMPLE 2: In eqs. (1)–(2) (and in Fig. 1) let one of the two relations, say $\boldsymbol{H}_1$, be the identity on L_{2e}. (L_{2e} is defined in Example 1.) Let the other relation, $\boldsymbol{H}_2$ on L_{2e}, be given by the equation $\boldsymbol{H}_2x(t)=kN[x(t)]$, where $k>0$ is a constant, and N is a function whose graph is shown in Fig. 4. *For what values of k are the closed loop relations (a) bounded? (b) stable?*

(a) First the gain is calculated.

$$g(\boldsymbol{H}_2) = \sup\left\{\int_0^\infty N^2[x(t)]\,dt \Big/ \int_0^\infty x^2(t)\,dt\right\}^{1/2}$$

$$= k \sup_{x \text{ real}} \left|\frac{N(x)}{x}\right| = k$$

where the first sup is over $[x\in \mathrm{Do}(\boldsymbol{H});\ \boldsymbol{H}x\in \mathrm{Ra}(\boldsymbol{H});\ t\in T,\ x_t\neq 0]$. That is, $g(\boldsymbol{H})$ is k times the supremum of the absolute slopes of lines drawn from the origin to points on the graph of N. Here $g(\boldsymbol{H})=k$, so Theorem 1 implies *boundedness for* $k<1$. This example is trivial in at least one respect, namely, in that H has no memory; examples with memory will be given in Part II.

(*b*) $\tilde{g}(\boldsymbol{H})$ can be worked out to be k times the supremum of the absolute *Lipschitzian* slopes of N, that is, $\tilde{g}(\boldsymbol{H})=k\ \sup_{x,\,y \text{ real}}|N(x)-N(y)/x-y|=2k$. *The closed loop is therefore stable for* $k<1/2$.

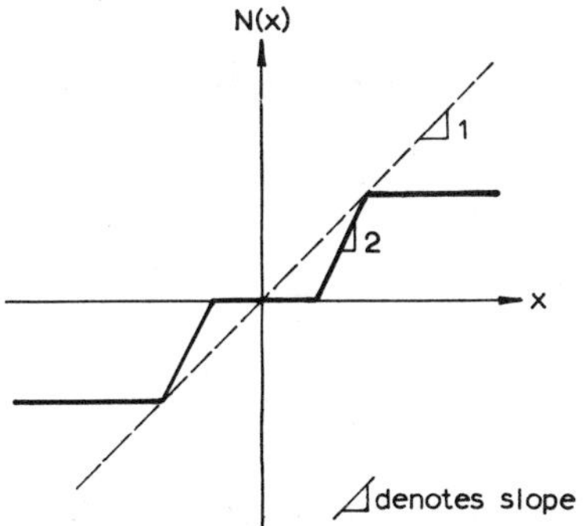

Fig. 4. Graph of the relation in Example 2.

4. Conditions Involving Conic Relations

The usefulness of Theorem 1 is limited by the condition that the open-loop gain-product be less than one—a condition seldom met in practice. However, a reduced gain product can often be obtained by transforming the feedback equations. For example, if $c\boldsymbol{I}$ is added to and subtracted from $\boldsymbol{H}_2$, as shown in Fig. 5, then e_2 remains unaffected; however, $\boldsymbol{H}_1$ is changed into a new relation $\boldsymbol{H}_1'$, as in effect $-c\boldsymbol{I}$ appears in feedback around $\boldsymbol{H}_1$. Under what conditions does this transformation give a gain product less than one? It will appear that a sufficient condition is that the input-output relations of the open loop elements be confined to certain "conic" regions in the product space $X_e \times X_e$.

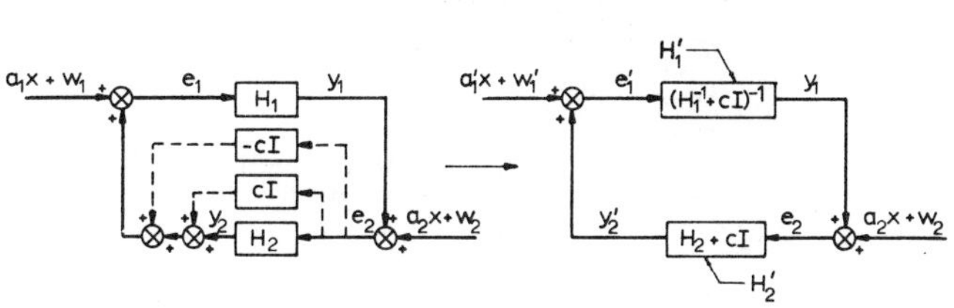

Fig. 5. A transformation.

RESTRICTION: *In the remainder of this paper, assume that X is an inner-product space, that* $\langle x, y\rangle$ *denotes the inner product on X, and that* $\langle x, x\rangle=\|x\|^2$.

This restriction is made with the intention of working mainly in the extended $L_2[0, \infty)$ norm,[12] with $\langle x, y\rangle =\int_0^\infty x(t)y(t)dt$.

4.1 Definitions of Conic and Positive Relations

DEFINITION: *A relation* $\boldsymbol{H}$ *in* $\mathcal{R}$ *is* interior conic *if there are real constants* $r\geq 0$ *and c for which the inequality*

$$\|(\boldsymbol{H}x)_t - cx_t\| \leq r\|x_t\| \quad [x\in \mathrm{Do}(\boldsymbol{H}); t\in T] \quad (14)$$

is satisfied. $\boldsymbol{H}$ *is* exterior conic *if the inequality sign in* (14) *is reversed.* $\boldsymbol{H}$ *is* conic *if it is exterior conic or interior conic. The constant c will be called the* center parameter *of* $\boldsymbol{H}$, and r will be *called the* radius parameter.

The truncated output $(\boldsymbol{H}x)_t$ of a conic relation lies either inside or outside a sphere in X, with center proportional to the truncated input x_t and radius proportional to $\|x_t\|$. The region thus determined in $X_e\times X_e$ will be called a "cone," a term suggested by the following special case:

EXAMPLE 3: Let $\boldsymbol{H}$ be a relation on L_{2e} (see Example 1); let $\boldsymbol{H}x(t)$ be a function of $x(t)$, say $\boldsymbol{H}x(t)=N[x(t)]$, where N has a graph in the plane; then, as shown in Fig. 6, the graph lies inside or outside a conic sector of the plane, with a center line of slope c and boundaries of slopes $c-r$ and $c+r$. More generally, for $\boldsymbol{H}$ to be conic [without $\boldsymbol{H}x(t)$ necessarily being a function of $x(t)$, that is, if $\boldsymbol{H}$ has memory], it is enough for the point $[x(t), \boldsymbol{H}x(t)]$ to be confined to a sector of the plane. In this case, it will be said that $\boldsymbol{H}$ is *instantaneously confined to a sector of the plane.*

Inequality (14) can be expressed in the form $\|(\boldsymbol{H}x)_t-cx_t\|^2-r\|x_t\|^2\leq 0$. If norms are expressed in

[12] However, in engineering applications it is often more interesting to prove stability in the L_∞ norm. The present theory has been extended in that direction in the author's [2f]. The idea is [2f] is to transform L_2 functions into L_∞ functions by means of exponential weighting factors.

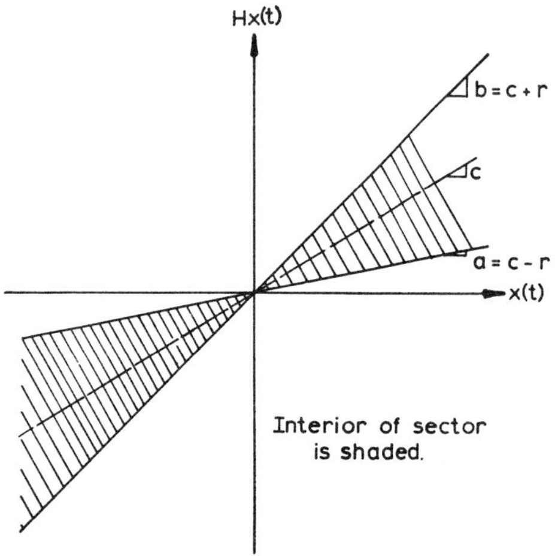

Fig. 6. A conic sector in the plane.

terms of inner products then, after factoring, there is obtained the equivalent inequality

$$\langle (Hx)_t - ax_t, (Hx)_t - bx_t \rangle \le 0 \quad [x \in \mathrm{Do}(H); t \in T] \quad (15)$$

where $a=c-r$ and $b=c+r$. It will often be desirable to manipulate inequalities such as (15), and a notation inspired by Fig. 6 is introduced:

NOTATION: *A conic relation* H *is said to be* inside the sector $\{a, b\}$, *if* $a \le b$ *and if Inequality (15) holds.* H *is* outside the sector $\{a, b\}$ *if* $a \le b$ *and if (15) holds with the inequality sign reversed.*

The following relationship will frequently be used: If H is interior (exterior) conic with center c and radius r then H is inside (outside) the sector $\{c-r, c+r\}$. Conversely, if H is inside (outside) the sector $\{a, b\}$, then H is interior (exterior) conic, with center $(b+a)/2$ and radius $(b-a)/2$.

DEFINITION: *A relation* H *in* $\mathcal{R}$ *is* positive[13] *if*

$$\langle x_t, (Hx)_t \rangle \ge 0 \qquad [x \in \mathrm{Do}(H); t \in T]. \qquad (16)$$

A positive relation can be regarded as degenerately conic, with a sector from 0 to ∞. [Compare (15) and (16).] For example, the relation H on L_{2e} is positive if it is instantaneously confined (see Example 3) to the first and third quadrants of the plane.

4.2 Some Properties of Conic Relations

Some simple properties will be listed. It will be assumed, in these properties, that H and H_1 are conic relations; that H is inside the sector $\{a, b\}$, with $b>0$; that H_1 is inside $\{a_1, b_1\}$ with $b_1>0$; and that $k \ge 0$ is a constant.

(i) *I is inside $\{1, 1\}$.*
(ii) *kH is inside $\{ka, kb\}$; $-H$ is inside $\{-b, -a\}$.*
(iii) SUM RULE: *$(H+H_1)$ is inside $\{a+a_1, b+b_1\}$.*
(iv) INVERSE RULE

CASE 1a: *If $a>0$ then H^{-1} is inside $\{1/b, 1/a\}$.*
CASE 1b: *If $a<0$ then H^{-1} is outside $\{1/a, 1/b\}$.*
CASE 2: *If $a=0$ then $(H^{-1}-(1/b)I)$ is positive.*

(v) *Properties (ii), (iii), and (iv) remain valid with the terms "inside { }" and "outside { }" interchanged throughout.*
(vi) *$g(H) \le max(|a|, |b|)$. Hence if H is in $\{-r, r\}$ then $g(H) \le r$.*

The proofs are in Appendix A. One consequence of these properties is that it is relatively easy to estimate conic bounds for simple interconnections, where it might be more difficult, say, to find Lyapunov functions.

[13] Short for "positive semidefinite." The terms "passive" and "nondissipative" have also been used.

4.3 A Theorem on Boundedness

Consider the feedback system of Fig. 1, and suppose that H_2 is confined to a sector $\{a, b\}$. It is desirable to find a condition on H_1 which will ensure the boundedness of the closed loop. A condition will be found, which places H_1 inside or outside a sector depending on a and b, and which requires either H_1 or H_2 to be bounded away from the edge of its sector by an arbitrarily small amount, Δ or δ.

THEOREM 2a: *[In eqs. (1)–(2)] Let H_1 and H_2 be conic relations. Let Δ and δ be constants, of which one is strictly positive and one is zero. Suppose that*

(I) *$-H_2$ is inside the sector $\{a+\Delta, b-\Delta\}$ where $b>0$, and,*
(II) *H_1 satisfies one of the following conditions.*

CASE 1a: *If $a>0$ then H_1 is outside*

$$\left\{-\frac{1}{a} - \delta, -\frac{1}{b} + \delta\right\}.$$

CASE 1b: *If $a<0$ then H_1 is inside*

$$\left\{-\frac{1}{b} + \delta, -\frac{1}{a} - \delta\right\}.$$

CASE 2: *If $a=0$ then*

$$H_1 + \left(\frac{1}{b} - \delta\right)I$$

is positive; in addition, if $\Delta=0$ then $g(H_1) < \infty$.

Then E_1 and E_2 are bounded.

The proof of Theorem 2a is in Appendix B. Note that the minus sign in front of H_2 reflects an interest in *negative* feedback.

EXAMPLE 4: If H_1 and H_2 are relations on L_{2e} instantaneously confined to sectors of the plane (as in Example 3), then the closed loop will be bounded if the sectors are related as in Fig. 7. (More realistic examples will be discussed in Part II.)

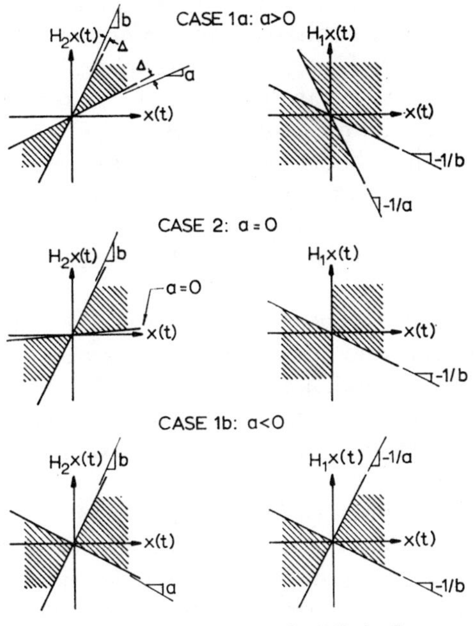

Fig. 7. Mutually admissible sectors for H_2 and H_1

4.4 *Incrementally Conic and Positive Relations*

Next, it is desired to find a stability result similar to the preceding theorem on boundedness. To this end the recent steps are repeated with all definitions replaced by their "incremental" counterparts.

DEFINITION: *A relation H in $\mathcal{R}$ is* incrementally interior (exterior) *conic if there are real constants $r>0$ and c for which the inequality*

$$\|(Hx - Hy)_t - c(x-y)_t\| \leq r\|(x-y)_t\| \quad [x, y \in \mathrm{Do}(H); t \in T] \tag{17}$$

is satisfied (with inequality sign reversed). An incrementally conic relation H is incrementally inside (outside) *the sector $\{a, b\}$, if $a \leq b$ and if the inequality*

$$\langle (Hx - Hy)_t - a(x-y)_t, (Hx - Hy)_t - b(x-y)_t\rangle \leq 0 \quad [x, y \in \mathrm{Do}(H); t \in T] \tag{18}$$

is satisfied (with inequality sign reversed). A relation H in $\mathcal{R}$ is incrementally positive[14] if

$$\langle (x-y)_t, (Hx - Hy)_t\rangle \geq 0 \quad [x, y \in \mathrm{Do}(H); t \in T]. \tag{19}$$

EXAMPLE 5: Consider the relation H on L_{2e}, with $Hx(t) = N[x(t)]$, where N is a function having a graph in the plane. If N is incrementally inside $\{a, b\}$ then N satisfies the Lipschitz conditions, $a(x-y) \leq N(x) - N(y) \leq b(x-y)$. Thus N lies in a sector of the plane, as in the nonincremental case (see Fig. 6), and in addition has upper and lower bounds to its slope.

Incrementally conic relations have properties similar to those of conic relations (see Section 4.2).

[14] The terms "monotone" and "incrementally passive" have also been used.

THEOREM 2b: *Let H_1 and H_2 be incrementally conic relations. Let Δ and δ be constants, of which one is strictly positive and one is zero. Suppose that,*

(I) *$-H_2$ is incrementally inside the sector $\{a+\Delta, b-\Delta\}$, where $b>0$, and,*
(II) *H_1 satisfies one of the following conditions:*

CASE 1a: *If $a>0$ then H_1 is incrementally outside*

$$\left\{-\frac{1}{a} - \delta, \; -\frac{1}{b} + \delta\right\}.$$

CASE 1b: *If $a<0$ then H_1 is incrementally inside*

$$\left\{-\frac{1}{b} + \delta, \; -\frac{1}{a} - \delta\right\}.$$

CASE 2: *If $a=0$ then*

$$H_1 + \left\{\frac{1}{b} - \delta\right\} I$$

is incrementally positive; in addition, if $\Delta = 0$ then $\tilde{g}(H_1) < \infty$.

Then E_1 and E_2 are input-output stable.

The proof is similar to that of Theorem 1a, and is omitted.

5. Conditions Involving Positive Relations

A special case of Theorem 2, of interest in the theory of passive networks, is obtained by, in effect, letting $a=0$ and $b \to \infty$. Both relations then become positive; also, one of the two relations becomes strongly positive, i.e.:

DEFINITION: *A relation H in $\mathcal{R}$ is* strongly (incrementally) positive *if, for some $\sigma>0$, the relation $(H-\sigma I)$ is (incrementally) positive.*

The theorem, whose proof is in Appendix C, is:

THEOREM 3:[15] (a) [In eqs. (1)–(2)] If H_1 and $-H_2$ are positive, and if $-H_2$ is strongly positive and has finite gain, then E_1 and E_2 are bounded. (b) If H_1 and $-H_2$ are incrementally positive, and if $-H_2$ is strongly incrementally positive and has finite incremental gain, then E_1 and E_2 are input-output stable.

For example, if H_2 on L_{2e} is instantaneously confined to a sector of the plane, then, under the provisions of Theorem 3, the sector of H_2 lies in the first and third quadrants, and is bounded away from both axes.

5.1 *Positivity and Passivity in Networks*

A passive element is one that always absorbs energy. *Is a network consisting of passive elements necessarily stable?* An attempt will be made to answer this question for the special case of the circuit of Fig. 2.

First, an elaboration is given on what is meant by a

[15] A variation of this result was originally presented in [2d]. Kolodner [8] has obtained related results, with a restriction of linearity on one of the elements.

passive element. Consider an element having a current i and a voltage v; the absorbed energy is the integral $\int_0^\infty i(t)v(t)dt$, and the condition for passivity is that this integral be non-negative. Now, let $\mathbf{Z}$ be a relation mapping i into v; by analogy with the linear theory, it is natural to think of $\mathbf{Z}$ as an *impedance relation;* suppose $\mathbf{Z}$ is defined on L_{2e}, where the energy integral equals the inner product $\langle i, v\rangle$; then passivity of the element is equivalent to positivity of $\mathbf{Z}$. Similarly, if $\mathbf{Y}$ on L_{2e} is an admittance relation, which maps v into i, then passivity is equivalent to positivity of $\mathbf{Y}$.

Now consider the circuit of Fig. 2. This circuit consists of an element characterized by an impedance relation $\mathbf{Z}_2$, an element characterized by an admittance relation $\mathbf{Y}_1$, a voltage source v, and a current source i. The equations of this circuit are,

$$v_1 = v + v_2 \tag{20a}$$

$$i_2 = i - i_1 \tag{20b}$$

$$v_2 = \mathbf{Z}_2 i_2 \tag{21a}$$

$$i_1 = \mathbf{Y}_1 v_1. \tag{21b}$$

It is observed that these equations have the same form as the Feedback Equations, provided that the sources i and v are constrained by the equations $v=a_1x+w_1$, and $i=a_2x+w_2$. (By letting $a_1=0$ the familiar "parallel circuit" is obtained. Similarly, by letting $a_2=0$ the "series circuit" is obtained.) Thus there is a correspondence between the feedback system and the network considered here. Corresponding to the closed loop relation $\mathbf{E}_1$ there is a voltage transfer relation mapping v into v_1. Similarly, corresponding to $\mathbf{E}_2$ there is a current transfer relation mapping i into i_2. If Theorem 3 is now applied to eqs. (20)–(21) it may be concluded that: *If both elements are passive, and if, in addition, the relation of one of the elements is strongly positive and has finite gain, then the network transfer relations are bounded.*

6. Conclusions

The main result here is Theorem 2. This theorem provides sufficient conditions for continuity and boundedness of the closed loop, without restricting the open loop to be linear or time invariant. Theorem 2 includes Theorems 1 and 3 as special cases. However, all three theorems are equivalent, in the sense that each can be derived from any of the others by a suitable transformation.

There are resemblances between Theorem 2 and Nyquist's Criterion. For example, consider the following, easily derived, limiting form of Theorem 2: "If $\mathbf{H}_2=k\mathbf{I}$ then a sufficient condition for boundedness of the closed loop is that $\mathbf{H}_1$ be bounded away from the critical value $-(1/k)\mathbf{I}$, in the sense that

$$\left\|\left(\mathbf{H}_1x - \frac{1}{k}x\right)_t\right\| \geq \delta\|x_t\|$$

for all x in X_e and t in T, where δ is an arbitrarily small positive constant." In fact, the conic sectors defined here resemble the disk-shaped regions on a Nyquist chart. However, Theorem 2 differs from Nyquist's Criterion in two important respects: (1) Unlike Nyquist's Criterion, Theorem 2 is not necessary, which is hardly surprising, since bounds on $\mathbf{H}_1$ and $\mathbf{H}_2$ are assumed in place of a more detailed characterization. (2) Nyquist's criterion assesses stability from observation of only the eigenfunctions exp (jwt), where Theorem 2 involves *all* inputs in X_e.

There is also a resemblance between the use of the notions of gain and inner product as discussed here, and the use of attenuation and phaseshift in the linear theory. A further discussion of this topic is postponed to Part II, where linear systems will be examined in some detail.

One of the broader implications of the theory developed here concerns the use of functional analysis for the study of poorly defined systems. It seems possible, from only coarse information about a system, and perhaps even without knowing details of internal structure, to make useful assessments of qualitative behavior.

Appendix

A. Proofs of Properties (i–vi)

Properties (i, ii). These two properties are immediately implied by the inequalities

$$\langle(\mathbf{I}x)_t - 1\cdot x_t, (\mathbf{I}x)_t - 1\cdot x_t\rangle = 0$$

$$\langle(c\mathbf{H}x)_t - cax_t, (c\mathbf{H}x)_t - cbx_t\rangle = c^2\langle(\mathbf{H}x)_t - ax_t, (\mathbf{H}x)_t - bx_t\rangle \leq 0$$

in which c is a (positive or negative) real constant.

Property (iii). It is enough to show that $(\mathbf{H}+\mathbf{H}_1)$ has center $\frac{1}{2}(b+b_1+a+a_1)$ and radius $\frac{1}{2}(b+b_1-a-a_1)$; the following inequalities establish this:

$$\left\|[(\mathbf{H}+\mathbf{H}_1)x]_t - \tfrac{1}{2}(b+b_1+a+a_1)x_t\right\| \leq \left\|(\mathbf{H}x)_t - \tfrac{1}{2}(b+a)x_t\right\| + \left\|(\mathbf{H}_1x)_t - \tfrac{1}{2}(b_1+a_1)\right\| \quad \text{(Triangle Ineq.)} \tag{A1a}$$

$$\leq \tfrac{1}{2}(b-a)\|x_t\| + \tfrac{1}{2}(b_1-a_1)\|x_t\| = \tfrac{1}{2}(b+b_1-a-a_1)\|x_t\| \tag{A1b}$$

where eq. (A1b) follows from eq. (A1a) since $\mathbf{H}$ has center $\frac{1}{2}(b+a)$ and radius $\frac{1}{2}(b-a)$, and since $\mathbf{H}_1$ has center $\frac{1}{2}(b_1+a_1)$ and radius $\frac{1}{2}(b_1-a_1)$.

Property (iv).

CASES 1a AND 1b: Here $a\neq 0$ and $b>0$, and

$$\left\langle(\mathbf{H}^{-1}x)_t - \frac{1}{b}x_t, (\mathbf{H}^{-1}x)_t - \frac{1}{a}x_t\right\rangle = \left\langle y_t - \frac{1}{b}(\mathbf{H}y)_t, y_t - \frac{1}{a}(\mathbf{H}y)_t\right\rangle = \frac{1}{ab}\langle(\mathbf{H}y)_t - ay_t, (\mathbf{H}y)_t - by_t\rangle$$

where $H^{-1}x=y$ and $x=Hy$. Since, by hypothesis, H is inside $\{a, b\}$ and $b>0$, the sign of the last expression is opposite to that of a. Thus the Inverse Rule is obtained.

CASE 2: Here $a=0$. The property is implied by the inequality,

$$\left\langle x_t, (H^{-1}x)_t - \frac{1}{b}x_t \right\rangle = \frac{1}{b}\langle (Hy)_t, by_t - (Hy)_t\rangle \geq 0.$$

Property (v). Simply reverse all the inequality signs.

Property (vi).

$$\begin{aligned}\|(Hx)_t\| &\leq \|(Hx)_t - \tfrac{1}{2}(b+a)x_t\| \\ &\quad + \|\tfrac{1}{2}(b+a)x_t\| \text{ (Triangle Ineq.)} \quad \text{(A2a)} \\ &\leq \tfrac{1}{2}(b-a)\|x_t\| + \tfrac{1}{2}|b+a|\cdot\|x_t\| \quad \text{(A2b)} \\ &= \max(|a|, |b|)\cdot\|x_t\|\end{aligned}$$

where eq (A2b) follows from eq (A2a) since, from the hypothesis, H has center $\frac{1}{2}(b+a)$ and radius $\frac{1}{2}(b-a)$. It follows that $g(H)\leq\max(|a|, |b|)$. Q.E.D.

B. Proof of Theorem 2a

The proof is divided into three parts: (1) The transformation of Fig. 5 is carried out, giving a new relation E_2'; E_2' is shown to contain E_2. (2) The new gain product is shown to be less than one. (3) E_2' is shown to be bounded, by Theorem 1; the boundedness of E_2 and E_1 follows.

Let $c=\frac{1}{2}(b+a)$ and $r=\frac{1}{2}(b-a)$.

B.1 Transformation of Eqs. (1)-(2)

The proof will be worked backwards from the end; the equations of the transformed system of Fig. 5 are,

$$e_1' = w_1' + a_1'x + y_2' \quad \text{(A3a)}$$

$$e_2 = w_2 + a_2x + y_1 \quad \text{(A3b)}$$

$$y_2' = H_2'e_2 \quad \text{(A4a)}$$

$$y_1 = H_1'e_1' \quad \text{(A4b)}$$

where

$$H_2' = (H_2 + cI) \quad \text{(A5a)}$$

$$H_1' = (H_1^{-1} + cI)^{-1}. \quad \text{(A5b)}$$

(It may be observed that these equations have the same form as eqs. (1)–(2), but H_1 is replaced by H_1' and H_2 is replaced by H_2'.) Let E_2' be the closed-loop relation that consists of all pairs (x, e_2) satisfying eqs. (A3)–(A4). It shall now be shown that E_2' contains E_2, that is, that any solution of eqs. (1)–(2) is also a solution of eqs. (A3)–(A4); thus boundedness of E_2' will imply boundedness of E_2.

In greater detail

(I) let (x, e_2) be any given element of E_2.

(II) Let e_1, y_1, y_2, H_1e_1, and H_2e_2 be fixed elements of X_e that satisfy eqs. (1)–(2) simultaneously with x and e_2.

(III) (Using Fig. 5 as a guide,) define two new elements of X_e,

$$y_2' = y_2 + ce_2 \quad \text{(A6a)}$$

$$e_1' = e_1 + cy_1. \quad \text{(A6b)}$$

It shall now be shown that there are elements $H_1'e_1'$ and $H_2'e_2'$ in X_e that satisfy eqs. (A3)–(A4) simultaneously with the elements defined in (I)–(III). Taking eqs. (A3)–(A4) one at a time:

Equation (A3a). Substituting eq. (1a) for e_1 in eq. (A6b), and eq. (1b) for y_1,

$$e_1' = (w_1 - cw_2) + (a_1 - ca_2)x + (y_2 + ce_2). \quad \text{(A7)}$$

If $w_1'=w_1-cw_2$ and $a_1'=a_1-ca_2$, then, with the aid of eq. (A6a), eq. (A7) reduces to eq. (A3a).

Equation (A3b): This is merely eq. (1b), repeated.

Equation (A4a): Recalling that $H_2'=H_2+cI$, it follows, from eqs. (A6a) and (2a), that there is an $H_2'e_2$ in X_e for which eq. (A4a) holds.

Equation (A4b): If eq. (A6b) is substituted for e_1 in eq. (2b), it is found that there exists $H_1(e_1'-cy_1)$ in X_e such that $y_1=H_1(e_1'-cy_1)$. Therefore,

(after inversion) $H_1^{-1}y_1 = e_1' - cy_1$

(after rearrangement) $(H_1^{-1} + cI)y_1 = e_1'$

(after inversion) $y_1 = (H_1^{-1} + cI)^{-1}e_1'$.

That is, there exists $H_1'e_1'$ in X_e for which eq. (A4b) holds. Since eqs. (A3)–(A4) are all satisfied, (x, e_2) is in E_2'. Since (x, e_2) is an arbitrary element of E_2, E_2' contains E_2.

B.2 Boundedness of E_2'

It will be shown that $g(H_1')\cdot g(H_2')<1$.

The Case $\Delta>0$, $\delta=0$: $g(H_2')$ will be bounded first. Since H_2 is in $\{-b+\Delta, -a-\Delta\}$ by hypothesis, (H_2+cI) is in $\{-b+\Delta+c, -a-\Delta+c\}$ by the Sum Rule of Section 4.2. Observing that $(H_2+cI)=H_2'$, that $(-b+c)=-r$, and that $(-a+c)=r$, it is concluded that H_2' is in $\{-r+\Delta, r-\Delta\}$. Therefore $g(H_2')\leq r-\Delta$.

Next, $g(H_1')$ will be bounded. In Case 1a, where $a>0$ and H_1 is outside

$$\left\{-\frac{1}{a}, -\frac{1}{b}\right\},$$

the Inverse Rule of Section 4.2 implies that H_1^{-1} is outside $\{-b, -a\}$; the same result is obtained in Cases 1b and 2. In all cases, therefore, the Sum Rule implies that $(H_1^{-1}+cI)$ is outside $\{-r, r\}$. By the Inverse Rule again, $(H_1^{-1}+cI)^{-1}$ is in

$$\left\{-\frac{1}{r}, \frac{1}{r}\right\}.$$

Therefore $g(H_1')\leq 1/r$.

Finally,

$$g(H_1')\cdot g(H_2') \leq \frac{r-\Delta}{r} < 1.$$

The Case $\Delta=0$, $\delta>0$: It shall be shown that this is a special case of the case $\Delta>0$, $\delta=0$. In other words, it will be shown that there are real constants a^*, b^*, and Δ^* for which the conditions of the case $\Delta>0$, $\delta=0$ are fulfilled, but with a replaced by a^*, b by b^*, and Δ by Δ^*.

Consider Case 1a, in which $a>0$. (Cases 1b and 2 have similar proofs, which will be omitted.) It must be shown that: (1) $-\boldsymbol{H}_2$ is in $\{a^*+\Delta, b^*-\Delta\}$. (2) $\boldsymbol{H}_1$ is outside

$$\left\{-\frac{1}{a^*}, \frac{1}{b^*}\right\}.$$

Without loss of generality it can be assumed that δ is smaller than either $1/a$ or $1/b$. Choose a^* and b^* in the ranges

$$\frac{a}{1+a\delta} < a^* < a \quad \text{and} \quad b < b^* < \frac{b}{1-b\delta}\cdot$$

Since $-\boldsymbol{H}_2$ is in $\{a, b\}$ by hypothesis, and since $a^*<a$ and $b^*>b$ by construction, there must be a $\Delta^*>0$ such that $\boldsymbol{H}_2$ satisfies condition (1). Since $\boldsymbol{H}_1$ is outside

$$\left\{-\frac{1}{a}-\delta, -\frac{1}{b}+\delta\right\}$$

by hypothesis, and since by construction

$$-\frac{1}{a^*} > -\frac{1}{a}-\delta \quad \text{and} \quad -\frac{1}{b^*} < -\frac{1}{b}+\delta,$$

condition (2) is satisfied. Hence this is, indeed, a special case of the previous one.

B.3 Conclusion of the Proof

Since $g(\boldsymbol{H}_1')\cdot g(\boldsymbol{H}_2')<1$, $\boldsymbol{E}_2'$ is bounded by Theorem 1, and so is $\boldsymbol{E}_2$, which is contained in $\boldsymbol{E}_2'$. Moreover, the boundedness of $\boldsymbol{E}_2$ implies the boundedness of $\boldsymbol{E}_1$; for, if (x, e_1) is in $\boldsymbol{E}_1$ and (x, e_2) is in $\boldsymbol{E}_2$, then

$$\|e_1\| \leq \|w_1\| + |a_1|\cdot\|x\| + g(\boldsymbol{H}_2)\|e_2\|. \quad \text{(A8)}$$

Thus, if $\|x\| \leq$const. and $\|e_2\| \leq$const., then $\|e_1\| \leq$const. (Inequality (A8) was obtained by applying the Triangle Inequality and Inequality (4) to eq. (1a), and taking the limit as $t\to\infty$. It may be noted that $g(\boldsymbol{H}_2)<\infty$, since $-\boldsymbol{H}_2$ is in $\{a, b\}$ by hypothesis.) Q.E.D.

C. Proof of Theorem 2

This shall be reduced to a special case of Theorem 2 [Case 2 with $\delta=0$]. In particular, it shall be shown that there are constants $b>0$ and $\Delta>0$ for which (I) $-\boldsymbol{H}_2$ is inside $\{\Delta, b-\Delta\}$, and, (II) the relation $[\boldsymbol{H}_1+(1/b)\boldsymbol{I}]$ is positive.

$[\boldsymbol{H}_1+(1/b)\boldsymbol{I}]$ is clearly positive for any $b>0$, since by hypothesis $\boldsymbol{H}_2$ is positive; the second condition is therefore satisfied. To prove the first condition it is enough to show that $\boldsymbol{H}_2$ is conic with center $-r$ and radius $r-\Delta$, where $r=b/2$. This is shown as follows: The hypothesis implies that, for some constant $\sigma>0$ and for any constant $\lambda>g(\boldsymbol{H}_2)$, the following inequalities are true

$$-\langle x_t, (\boldsymbol{H}_2x)_t\rangle \geq \sigma\|x_t\|^2 \quad \text{(A9)}$$

$$\|(\boldsymbol{H}_2x)_t\|^2 \leq \lambda^2\|x_t\|^2 \quad \text{(A10)}$$

for any x in X_e and for any t in T. Hence, for any $r>0$,

$$\|(\boldsymbol{H}_2x)_t + rx_t\|^2 \leq (\lambda^2 - 2r\sigma + r^2)\|x_t\|^2. \quad \text{(A11)}$$

Equation (A11) was obtained by expanding the square on its l.h.s., and applying eqs. (A9) and (A10). Constants λ, r, and Δ, are selected so that $\lambda>\sigma$, $r=\lambda^2/\sigma$, and $\Delta=r[1-\sqrt{1-(\sigma/\lambda)^2}]$. Now it can be verified that, for this choice of constants, the term $(\lambda^2-2r\sigma+r^2)$ in eq. (A11) equals $(r-\Delta)^2$; also, $0<\Delta<r$ since $(\sigma/\lambda)<1$); therefore eq. (A11) implies that $\boldsymbol{H}_2$ is conic with center $-r$ and radius $r-\Delta$. Q.E.D.

Acknowledgment

The author thanks Dr. P. Falb for carefully reading the draft of this paper, and for making a number of valuable suggestions concerning its arrangement and concerning the mathematical formulation.

References

[1] V. M. Popov, "Absolute stability of nonlinear systems of automatic control," *Automation and Remote Control*, pp. 857–875, March 1962. (Russian original in August 1961.)

[2] (a) G. Zames, "Conservation of bandwidth in nonlinear operations," M.I.T. Res. Lab. of Electronics, Cambridge, Mass., Quarterly Progress Rept. 55, pp. 98–109, October 15, 1959.
(b) ——, "Nonlinear operators for system analysis," M.I.T. Res. Lab. of Electronics, Tech. Rept. 370, September 1960.
(c) ——, "Functional analysis applied to nonlinear feedback systems," *IEEE Trans. on Circuit Theory*, vol. CT-10, pp. 392–404, September 1963.
(d) ——, "On the stability of nonlinear, time-varying feedback systems," *Proc. NEC*, vol. 20, pp. 725–730, October 1964.
(e) ——, "Contracting transformations—A theory of stability and iteration for nonlinear, time-varying systems," *Summaries, 1964 Internat'l Conf. on Microwaves, Circuit Theory, and Information Theory*, pp. 121–122.
(f) ——, "Nonlinear time varying feedback systems—Conditions for L∞-boundedness derived using conic operators on exponentially weighted spaces," *Proc. 1965 Allerton Conf.*, pp. 460–471.

[3] K. S. Narendra and R. M. Goldwyn, "A geometrical criterion for the stability of certain nonlinear nonautonomous systems," *IEEE Trans. on Circuit Theory (Correspondence)*, vol. CT-11, pp. 406–408, September 1964.

[4] R. W. Brockett and J. W. Willems, "Frequency domain stability criteria," pts. I and II, *1965 Proc. Joint Automatic Control Conf.*, pp. 735–747.

[5] (a) I. W. Sandberg, "On the properties of some systems that distort signals," *Bell Sys. Tech. J.*, vol. 42, p. 2033, September 1963, and vol. 43, pp. 91–112, January 1964.
(b) ——,"On the L_2-boundedness of solutions of nonlinear functional equations," *Bell. Sys. Tech. J.*, vol. 43, pt. II, pp. 1581–1599, July 1964.

[6] J. Kudrewicz, "Stability of nonlinear feedback systems," *Automatika i Telemechanika*, vol. 25, no. 8, 1964 (and other papers).

[7] E. H. Zarantonello, "Solving functional equations by contractive averaging," U. S. Army Math. Res. Ctr., Madison, Wis. Tech. Summary Rept. 160, 1960.

[8] I. I. Kolodner, "Contractive methods for the Hammerstein equation in Hilbert spaces," University of New Mexico, Albuquerque, Tech. Rept. 35, July 1963.

[9] G. J. Minty, "On nonlinear integral equations of the Hammerstein type," survey appearing in *Nonlinear Integral Equations*, P. M. Anselone, Ed. Madison, Wis.: University Press, 1964, pp. 99–154.

[10] F. E. Browder, "The solvability of nonlinear functional equations," *Duke Math. J.*, vol. 30, pp. 557–566, 1963.

[11] J. J. Bongiorno, Jr., "An extension of the Nyquist-Barkhausen stability criterion to linear lumped-parameter systems with time-varying elements," *IEEE Trans. on Automatic Control (Correspondence)*, vol. AC-8, pp. 166–170, April 1963.

[12] A. N. Kolmogorov and S. V. Fomin, *Functional Analysis*, vols. I and II. New York: Graylock Press, 1957.

On the Input-Output Stability of Time-Varying Nonlinear Feedback Systems–Part II: Conditions Involving Circles in the Frequency Plane and Sector Nonlinearities

G. ZAMES, MEMBER, IEEE

Abstract—**The object of this paper is to outline a stability theory based on functional methods. Part I of the paper was devoted to a general feedback configuration. Part II is devoted to a feedback system consisting of two elements, one of which is linear time-invariant, and the other nonlinear.**

An attempt is made to unify several stability conditions, including Popov's condition, into a single principle. This principle is based on the concepts of conicity and positivity, and provides a link with the notions of gain and phase shift of the linear theory.

Part II draws on the (generalized) notion of a "sector nonlinearity." A nonlinearity N is said to be INSIDE THE SECTOR $\{\alpha, \beta\}$ if it satisfies an inequality of the type $\langle (N\mathbf{x}-\alpha \mathbf{x})_t, (N\mathbf{x}-\beta\mathbf{x})_t\rangle \leq 0$. If N is memoryless and is characterized by a graph in the plane, then this simply means that the graph lies inside a sector of the plane. However, the preceding definition extends the concept to include nonlinearities with memory.

There are two main results. The first result, the CIRCLE THEOREM, asserts in part that: ***If the nonlinearity is inside a sector $\{\alpha, \beta\}$, and if the frequency response of the linear element avoids a "critical region" in the complex plane, then the closed loop is bounded; if $\alpha>0$ then the critical region is a disk whose center is halfway between the points $-1/\alpha$ and $-1/\beta$, and whose diameter is greater than the distance between these points.***

The second result is a method for taking into account the detailed properties of the nonlinearity to get improved stability conditions. This method involves the removal of a "multiplier" from the linear element. The frequency response of the linear element is modified by the removal, and, in effect, the size of the critical region is reduced. Several conditions, including Popov's condition, are derived by this method, under various restrictions on the nonlinearity N; the following cases are treated:

(i) N is instantaneously inside a sector $\{\alpha, \beta\}$.
(ii) N satisfies (i) and is memoryless and time-invariant.
(iii) N satisfies (ii) and has a restricted slope.

1. Introduction

THE feedback system of Fig. 1 consists[1] of a linear time-invariant element H and a (not necessarily linear or time-invariant) element N. It will be supposed, for the moment, that N has no memory. These assumptions are among, the simplest which ensure that the system is both

(i) general enough to have many applications
(ii) complicated enough to exhibit such characteristic nonlinear phenomena as jump resonances, subharmonics, etc.

The object here is to find stability conditions for the closed-loop system. For practical reasons, it is desirable to express these conditions in terms of quantities that can be measured experimentally, such as frequency responses, transfer characteristics, etc. In particular, the following question is of interest: Imagine that the graph of N lies inside a sector of the plane, as shown in Fig. 2(a), and that the frequency response of H is plotted in the complex plane; can the complex plane be divided

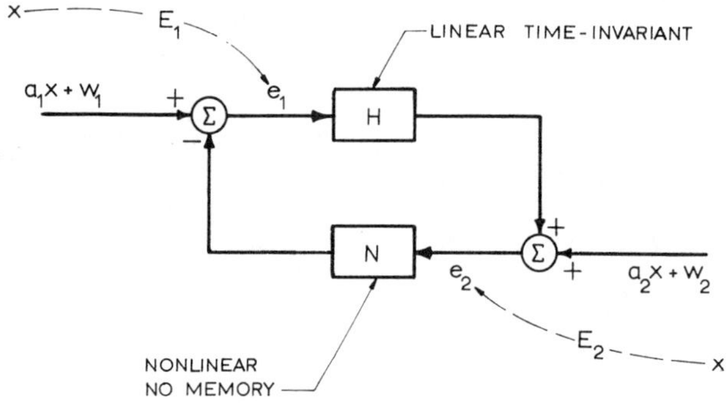

Fig. 1. A feedback system.

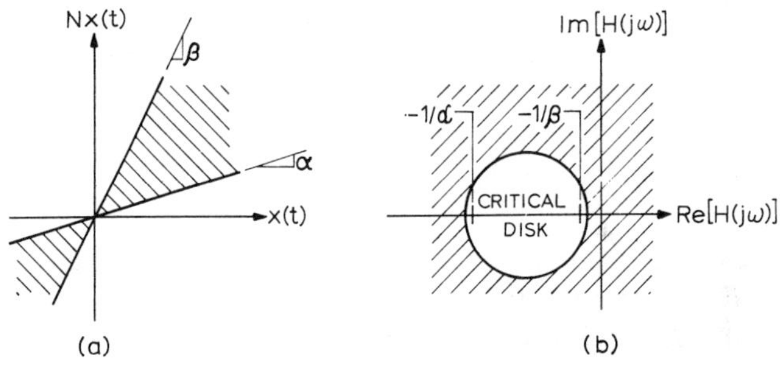

Fig. 2. If $Nx(t)$ vs. $x(t)$ and $H(j\omega)$ lie in the shaded regions, and if the Nyquist diagram of $H(j\omega)$ does not encircle the critical disk, then the closed loop is bounded.

Manuscript received December 29, 1964; revised October 1, 1965, and May 10, 1966. Parts of this paper were presented at the 1964 National Electronics Conference [1a], Chicago, Ill. This work was carried out in part under support extended by the National Aeronautics and Space Administration under Contract NsG-496 with the M.I.T. Center for Space Research.

The author is with the Department of Electrical Engineering, Massachusetts Institute of Technology, Cambridge, Mass.

[1] A single input x, multiplied by real constants a_1 and a_2, is added in at *two* points. By setting a_1 or a_2 to zero, it is possible to obtain a single-input system, in which the element closest to the input is either the linear element or the nonlinearity. The terms w_1 and w_2 are fixed bias functions, which will be used to account for the effects of initial conditions. The variables e_1 and e_2 are outputs.

Reprinted from *IEEE Trans. Automat. Contr.*, vol. AC-11, pp. 465–476, Jul. 1966.

into regions that are "safe" or "unsafe" as far as stability is concerned?

It will be shown that, with certain qualifications, such a division is possible. In fact it has already been shown in Part I that such regions, called "conic sectors," exist in a quite general sense. Here these general results will be applied to some concrete situations, involving frequency responses, etc. (Fig. 2, which illustrates the simplest of the results to be obtained here, gives some idea of what is being sought.)

2. Statement of the Problem

The purpose of this section is to define $\boldsymbol{H}$ and $\boldsymbol{N}$, and to write feedback equations. $\boldsymbol{H}$ and $\boldsymbol{N}$ will be represented by input-output relations or by operators, in keeping with the theory outlined in Part I.

Definition: *$R[0, \infty)$ is the space of real-valued functions on the interval $[0, \infty)$.*

L_p, where $p=1, 2, \cdots$, is the space consisting of those x in $R[0, \infty)$ for which the integral $\int_0^\infty |x(t)|^p dt$ is finite. In addition, for the case $p=2$, it is assumed that L_2 is an inner-product space, with inner-product

$$\langle x, y\rangle = \int_0^\infty x(t)y(t)dt$$

and norm $\|x\|_2$. The symbol $\|x\|$, without subscript, will often be used instead of $\|x\|_2$.

L_∞ is the space consisting of those functions x in $R[0, \infty)$ that are measurable and essentially bounded. L_∞ is assumed to be a normed linear space, with norm

$$\|x\|_\infty = \operatorname*{ess\,sup}_{t\geq 0} |x(t)|.$$

No distinction will be made between functions differing over sets of zero measure.

Those definitions which were introduced in Part I will only be summarized here. Following the convention of Part I, the subscripted symbol x_t denotes a function in $R[0, \infty)$ *truncated* after $[0, t)$. The space L_{pe}, where $p=1, 2, \cdots, \infty$, is the *extension* of L_p, i.e.,

$$L_{pe} = \{x \mid x \in R[0, \infty) \text{ and } x_t \in L_p \text{ for all } t \geq 0\}.$$

An *extended norm* $\|x\|_{pe}$ is defined on L_{pe}, where $\|x\|_{pe} = \|x\|_p$ if $x \in L_p$ and $\|x\|_{pe} = \infty$ if $x \notin L_p$. The symbol $\|x\|_{2e}$ will usually be abbreviated to $\|x\|_e$.

The concept of a *relation $\boldsymbol{H}$ on L_{pe}*, with *domain $Do(\boldsymbol{H})$* and *range $Ra(\boldsymbol{H})$* was introduced in Part I. A relation $\boldsymbol{H}$ on L_{pe} is *L_p-bounded* if $\boldsymbol{H}$ maps bounded subsets of L_{pe} into bounded subsets of L_{pe}. $\boldsymbol{H}$ is *L_p-continuous* if, given any x in $Do(\boldsymbol{H})$ and any $\Delta>0$, there is a $\delta>0$ such that, for any y in $Do(\boldsymbol{H})$, if $\|x-y\|_{pe}<\delta$ then $\|\boldsymbol{H}x-\boldsymbol{H}y\|_{pe}<\Delta$.

Part II will be devoted entirely to finding L_2 conditions (for boundedness and continuity), since these are easier to derive than the other L_p conditions. However, most of the results of this paper have been extended to the L_∞ norm, in [1b]. It has been found that, in most cases, the L_2 conditions imply L_∞-boundedness or continuity. For physical applications the most appropriate definitions of boundedness and continuity are, of course, obtained in the L_∞ norm.

Definition: *Let $\mathcal{R}_0$ be the class of relations on L_{2e} having the property that the zero element, denoted o, is in $Do(\boldsymbol{H})$, and $\boldsymbol{H}o=o$.* An operator $\boldsymbol{H}$ on L_{2e} is any function of the type $\boldsymbol{H}$: $L_{2e}\rightarrow L_{2e}$.

Definition: *An operator $\boldsymbol{H}$ on L_{2e} is* time-invariant *if it commutes with all delays. That is, for $t\geq 0$ let $\boldsymbol{T}_\tau$ be the operator on L_{2e} given by: $\boldsymbol{T}_\tau x(t)=x(t-\tau)$ for $t\geq\tau$, and $\boldsymbol{T}_\tau x(t)=0$ for $t<\tau$. Then $\boldsymbol{H}\boldsymbol{T}_\tau=\boldsymbol{T}_\tau\boldsymbol{H}$ for all $\tau\geq 0$.*

$\boldsymbol{H}$ is memoryless *if $\boldsymbol{H}x(t)$ is a function of $x(t)$ (i.e., only of $x(t)$) for all x in L_{2e} and for all $t\geq 0$.*

2.1. The Operator Classes $\mathfrak{N}$ and $\mathfrak{L}$

Definition: *$\mathfrak{N}$ is the class of operators on L_{2e} having the following property: If $\boldsymbol{N}$ is in $\mathfrak{N}$ then there s a function, N: Reals→Reals, satisfying[2]*

$$\boldsymbol{N}x(t) = N(x(t)) \qquad (x \in L_{2e};\, t \geq 0) \tag{1}$$

and having the following properties: (i) $N(0)=0$, (ii) $|N(x)| \leq$ const. $|x|$, and (iii) for any real x, $\int_0^x N(x')dx'$ is finite.

An operator in $\mathfrak{N}$ is memoryless, time-invariant, not necessarily linear, and can be characterized by a graph in the plane. The letter N will indicate the graph of $\boldsymbol{N}$.

Definition. *$\mathfrak{L}$ is the class of those operators $\boldsymbol{H}$ on L_{2e} satisfying an equation of the type[2]*

$$\boldsymbol{H}x(t) = h_\infty x(t) + \int_0^t h(t-\tau)x(\tau)d\tau \quad (x \in L_{2e};\, t \geq 0) \tag{2}$$

in which h_∞ is a real constant, and the impulse response h is a function in L_1 with the property that, for some $\sigma_0<0$, $h(t)\exp(-\sigma_0 t)$ is also in L_1.

Operators in $\mathfrak{L}$ are linear and time-invariant.

2.2. Feedback Equations

Consider the feedback system of Fig. 1, but with two modifications: (i) $\boldsymbol{N}$ is not necessarily memoryless; (ii) a_1 and a_2 are operators on L_{2e}, multiplying x. (This amount of generality will be needed for some of the intermediate results; ultimately, the interesting case is that in which $\boldsymbol{N}$ has *no* memory, and a_1 and a_2 are *real* constants.) The equations of this system are

$$e_1 = a_1 x + w_1 - \boldsymbol{N}e_2 \tag{3a}$$

$$e_2 = a_2 x + w_2 + \boldsymbol{H}e_1 \tag{3b}$$

in which it is assumed that:

$\boldsymbol{H}$ is an operator in $\mathfrak{L}$
$\boldsymbol{N}$ is a relation in $\mathcal{R}_0$

[2] It can be verified that every mapping of the type $\boldsymbol{N}$: $L_{2e}\rightarrow R[0, \infty)$ satisfying (1) is in fact an operator on L_{2e}. Similarly, every mapping $\boldsymbol{H}$: $L_{2e}\rightarrow R[0, \infty)$ satisfying (2) is an operator on L_{2e} [see (B1) of Appendix B].

x in L_{2e} is an input
e_1 and e_2 in L_{2e} are outputs
w_1 and w_2 in L_2 are fixed biases
either a_1 and a_2 are real constants, or, more generally,[3] *a_1 is a relation on L_{2e} having the property that $\|a_1x\|_e \leq$ const. $\|x\|_e$, and similarly for a_2.*

REMARK: If, to begin with, the linear element satisfies a state equation, then He_1 is set equal to the "zero-initial-condition response" of the state equation, and w_2 is set equal to the "zero-input response."

The closed-loop relations which map x into e_1 and e_2 will be denoted E_1 and E_2. The objective here is: *Find conditions on N and H which ensure that E_1 and E_2 are L_2-bounded and L_2-continuous.*

3. Conditions for Conicity and Positivity

This section has some preliminary results, which will be needed later in the analysis of stability. The following questions are fundamental to this analysis. Under what conditions is an operator conic or positive? Under what conditions is the composition product of two operators conic or positive?

The definitions of conicity and positivity were introduced in Part I. They are repeated here, for the special case of relations on L_{2e}.

DEFINITION: *Let H be a relation in $\mathcal{R}_0$. H is* INTERIOR CONIC *if c and $r \geq 0$ are real constants and the inequality*

$$\|(Hx)_t - cx_t\| \leq r\|x_t\| \qquad (x \in Do(H); t \geq 0) \qquad (4)$$

holds. H is exterior conic if (4) holds with the inequality sign reversed. c will be called the center parameter of H, and r will be called the radius parameter of H.

H is INSIDE (OUTSIDE) THE SECTOR $\{a, \beta\}$ *if $a \leq \beta$ and if the inequality*

$$\langle (Hx - \alpha x)_t, (Hx - \beta x)_t \rangle \leq 0 \quad (x \in Do(H); t \geq 0) \quad (5)$$

holds (with the inequality sign reversed).

H is POSITIVE *if it satisfies the inequality $\langle x_t, (Hx)_t \rangle \geq 0$ for all x in $Do(H)$ and all $t \geq 0$.*

In Part I, the concepts of conicity and positivity were subdivided into categories such as "instantaneous" conicity, "incremental" conicity, etc. The definitions of these terms are listed in Appendix A.

REMARK: The following conditions are equivalent: (i) H is interior conic with parameters c and r. (ii) H is inside $\{c-r, c+r\}$.

3.1. Memoryless, Time-Invariant Nonlinearities

Consider the operator class $\mathfrak{N}$; the conditions for N in $\mathfrak{N}$ to be conic, positive, etc., are simply the "instantaneous" conditions of Appendix A. Some of these conditions are illustrated in Fig. 3. In particular, N is inside the sector $\{\alpha, \beta\}$ if its graph lies in a sector of the plane bounded by lines of slopes α and β; N is incrementally inside $\{\alpha, \beta\}$ if, *in addition*, N satisfies the slope restrictions $\alpha \leq [N(x)-N(y)]/(x-y) \leq \beta$. N is positive if its graph lies in fhe first and third quadrants; N is incrementally positive if, *in addition*, N is nondecreasing.

[3] The more general assumption will be needed in Section 5 only.

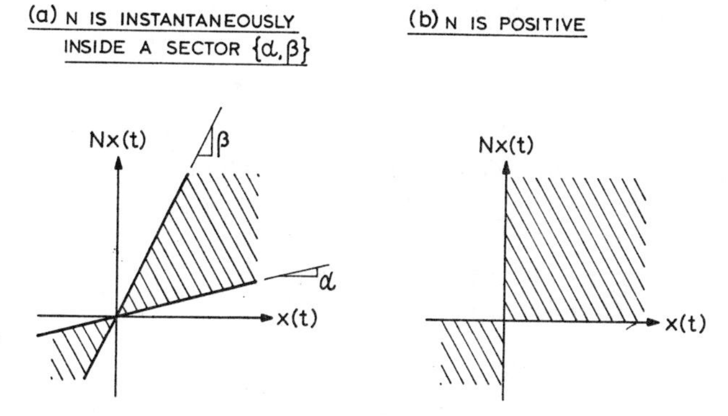

Fig. 3. Permissible regions (shaded) for instantaneously confined nonlinearities.

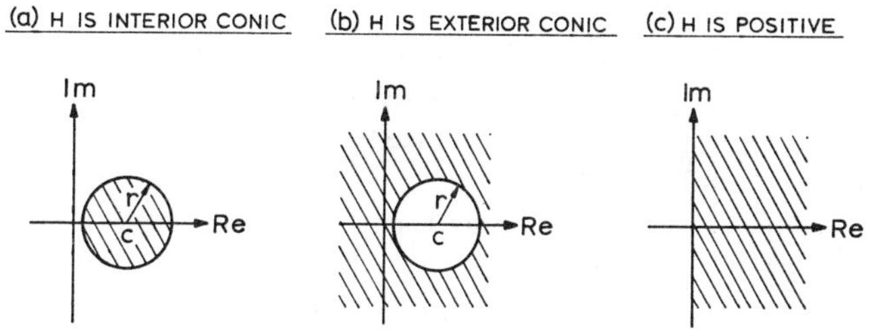

Fig. 4. Permissible regions (shaded) for the frequency response $H(j\omega)$.

3.2. Linear Time-Invariant Operators

Consider the operator class $\mathcal{L}$; it will be shown, roughly speaking, that a conic sector has a counterpart in the frequency plane, in the form of a circular disk (see Fig. 4). This disk degenerates into a half-plane in the case of a positive operator.

DEFINITION: *Let $s = \sigma + j\omega$ denote a point in the complex plane. The* LAPLACE TRANSFORM *$H(s)$ of H in $\mathcal{L}$ is*

$$H(s) = h_\infty + \int_0^\infty h(t) \exp(-st)dt \qquad (\sigma \geq 0) \qquad (6)$$

(The integral on the right-hand side of (6) exists and is analytic for $\sigma \geq 0$ [See (B1) of Appendix B].)

DEFINITION: *The* NYQUIST DIAGRAM *of $H(s)$ is a curve in the complex plane consisting of*: (i) *the image of the $j\omega$-axis under the mapping $H(s)$, and* (ii) *the point h_∞.*

LEMMA 1. *Let H be an operator in $\mathcal{L}$, and let c and $r \geq 0$ be real constants.*

(a) *If $H(s)$ satisfies the inequality*

$$|H(j\omega) - c| \leq r \qquad (\omega \in (-\infty, \infty)) \qquad (7)$$

then H is incrementally interior conic with center parameter c and radius parameter r.

(b) *If $H(s)$ satisfies the inequality*

$$|H(j\omega) - c| \geq r \qquad (\omega \in (-\infty, \infty)) \tag{8}$$

and if the Nyquist diagram of $H(s)$ does not encircle the point $(c, 0)$, then ***H*** *is incrementally exterior conic with center parameter c and radius parameter r.*

(c) *If* $\mathrm{Re}\{H(j\omega)\} \geq 0$ *for* $\omega \in (-\infty, \infty)$ *then* ***H*** *is incrementally positive.*

The Proof of Lemma 1 is in Appendix B.

REMARK. The gains $g(\boldsymbol{H})$ and $\tilde{g}(\boldsymbol{H})$ were defined in Part I. It follows from Lemma 1(a) that if $|H(j\omega)| \leq c$, then $\tilde{g}(\boldsymbol{H}) = g(\boldsymbol{H}) \leq c$.

3.3. Composition Products and Sector Products

The composition product of two positive operators need not be positive. Those special cases in which the product is positive are of interest because they give a tighter bound on the composite behavior than would be obtained in general. (They form the basis of the factorization method of Section 5.2.)

Similarly, those special cases in which the product of two sector operators lies inside the "product sector" are of interest.

DEFINITION: *The* PRODUCT SECTOR $\{\alpha_1, \beta_1\} \times \{\alpha_2, \beta_2\}$ *is the sector* $\{\alpha, \beta\}$, *where* $[\alpha, \beta]$ *is the interval of the reals defined by* $[\alpha, \beta] = \{xy \mid x \in [\alpha_1, \beta_1]$ *and* $y \in [\alpha_2, \beta_2]\}$.

In other words, product sectors behave like pointwise products of the corresponding real intervals (see Fig. 5).

It is easy to show that if both operators are memoryless, say if both operators are in $\mathfrak{N}$, then their product has the above mentioned properties. [This can be shown by expressing the ratio $N_1(N_2(x))/x$ as the product $(N_1(y)/y) \times (N_2(x)/x)$, where $y \triangleq N_2(x)$.] More difficult are cases in which one operator is in $\mathfrak{N}$ and the other is in $\mathfrak{L}$, as in Lemmas 2 and 3.

3.4. A Memoryless Nonlinearity and a First-Order Multiplier

The following lemma is the basis for Popov's condition (Section 5.1).

LEMMA 2. *Let* ***N*** *be an operator in* $\mathfrak{N}$, ***K*** *be an operator in* $\mathfrak{L}$, *and let the Laplace transform of* ***K*** *be* $K(s) = k\lambda/s + \lambda$ *where* $k > 0$ *and* $\lambda > 0$.

(a) *If* ***N*** *is positive*[4] *then* ***NK*** *is positive.*

(b) *If* ***N*** *is inside*[5] *a sector* $\{\alpha, \beta\}$ *then* ***NK*** *is inside the product sector* $\{\alpha, \beta\} \times \{0, k\}$.

The proof of Lemma 2 is in Appendix C. (Note that ***K*** itself is positive and inside $\{0, k\}$, since $K(j\omega)$ lies entirely in the right-half plane and since $|K(j\omega) - \frac{1}{2}k| = \frac{1}{2}k$.)

[4] i.e., $xN(x) \geq 0$.

[5] i.e., $\alpha \leq N(x)/x \leq \beta$.

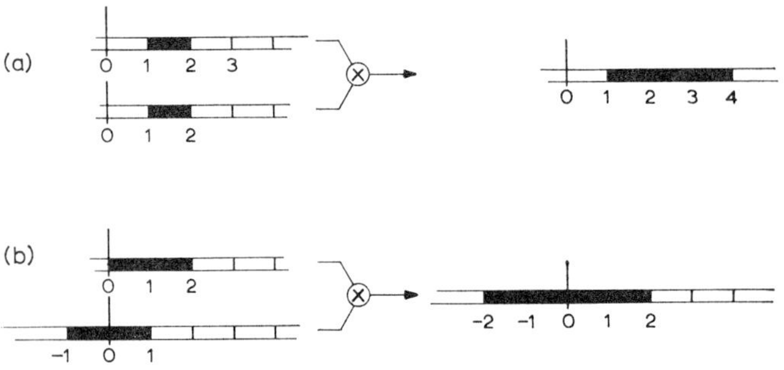

Fig. 5. Products of intervals.

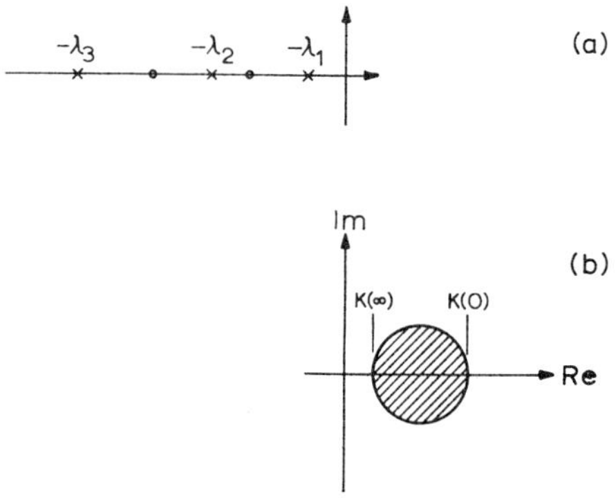

Fig. 6. $\mathfrak{RC}$ operators. (a) Typical pole-zero pattern. (b) Circle of confinement of $K(j\omega)$.

3.5. A Memoryless Nonlinearity and an $\mathfrak{RC}$ Multiplier

A situation resembling Lemma 2, but with ***N*** more restricted and ***K*** more general, is considered next. ***K*** is taken to be a sum of first-order terms, of a type that can be realized as the driving-point impedance of an *RC* network (see Guillemin [2], ch. 4).

DEFINITION: *Let* $\mathfrak{RC}$ *be the class of those operators* ***K*** *in* $\mathfrak{L}$ *having Laplace transforms of the form*

$$K(s) = \sum_{i=1}^{n} \frac{k_i \lambda_i}{s + \lambda_i} + K(\infty) \tag{9}$$

where $k_i \geq 0$, $\lambda_i > 0$, *and* $K(\infty) \geq 0$ *are real constants.*

An operator ***K*** in $\mathfrak{RC}$ has poles and zeros alternating on the negative-real axis, with a pole nearest but not at the origin. The frequency response of ***K*** lies inside a circle in the right-half plane, located as shown in Fig. 6(b); it follows that ***K*** is positive and inside the sector $\{K(\infty), K(0)\}$. (Observe that

$$K(0) = K(\infty) + \sum_{i=1}^{n} k_i \geq K(\infty).)$$

LEMMA 3. *Let* ***N*** *be an operator in* $\mathfrak{N}$, *and* ***K*** *be an operator in* $\mathfrak{RC}$.

(a) *If* ***N*** *is incrementally positive then* ***NK*** *is positive.*

(b) *If* ***N*** *is incrementally inside the sector* $\{\alpha, \beta\}$ *then* ***NK*** *is inside the product sector* $\{\alpha, \beta\} \times \{K(\infty), K(0)\}$.

In other words, multiplication by ***K*** affects the composite sector as if ***K*** had no memory. The proof of Lemma 3 is in Appendix D.

4. Circle Conditions for Stability

Consider now the main problem of this paper, namely, the problem of stability for the loop of Fig. 1. Suppose that $\boldsymbol{N}$ is a relation (which may or may not be memoryless) inside a sector $\{\alpha, \beta\}$. What conditions on the frequency response $H(j\omega)$ are sufficient to ensure boundedness of the closed loop? It will appear that the following "circle conditions" are sufficient:

Definition: *$H(j\omega)$ will be said to* satisfy the circle conditions for the sector $\{\alpha, \beta\}$, with offset δ, *where $\alpha \leq \beta$, $\beta > 0$, and $\delta \geq 0$ are real constants, if the following conditions hold:*

Case 1a. *If $\alpha > 0$, then*

$$\left| H(j\omega) + \frac{1}{2}\left(\frac{1}{\alpha} + \frac{1}{\beta}\right) \right| \geq \frac{1}{2}\left(\frac{1}{\alpha} - \frac{1}{\beta}\right) + \delta \qquad (\omega \in (-\infty, \infty)) \qquad (10)$$

and the Nyquist diagram of $H(j\omega)$ does not encircle the point $-\frac{1}{2}(1/\alpha + 1/\beta)$.

Case 1b. *If $\alpha < 0$, then*

$$\left| H(j\omega) + \frac{1}{2}\left(\frac{1}{\alpha} + \frac{1}{\beta}\right) \right| \leq \frac{1}{2}\left(\frac{1}{\beta} - \frac{1}{\alpha}\right) - \delta \qquad (\omega \in (-\infty, \infty)). \qquad (11)$$

Case 2. *If $\alpha = 0$, then* $\mathrm{Re}\{H(j\omega)\} \geq -(1/\beta) + \delta$ *for* $\omega \in (-\infty, \infty)$.

In other words, the complex plane is divided into two regions, shaped either like a circular disk and its complement, or like two half-planes. (The case $\alpha > 0$ is illustrated in Fig. 2.) One of the regions will be called "permissible" and the other will be called "critical." If $H(j\omega)$ does not enter or encircle the critical region, then the closed loop is bounded. If, in addition, $\boldsymbol{N}$ is *incrementally* inside $\{\alpha, \beta\}$, then the closed loop is continuous. These results are formalized in the following theorem:

A Circle Theorem. *Suppose that*

(I) *$\boldsymbol{N}$ is a relation in $\mathcal{R}_0$, (incrementally) inside the sector $\{\alpha + \Delta, \beta - \Delta\}$, where $\beta > 0$.*

(II) *$\boldsymbol{H}$ is an operator in $\mathcal{L}$, which satisfies the circle conditions for the sector $\{\alpha, \beta\}$ with offset δ.*

(III) *δ and Δ are non-negative constants, at least one of which is greater than zero.*

Then the closed-loop operators $\boldsymbol{E}_1$ and $\boldsymbol{E}_2$ are L_2-bounded (L_2-continuous).

The Circle Theorem is based on Theorem 2 of Part I. It was assumed in Theorem 2 that a_1 and a_2 were real constants. However, with only minor changes in the proof, it can be shown that Theorem 2 holds more generally if a_1 and a_2 are relations on L_{2e}, provided a_1 and a_2 satisfy inequalities of the type $\|a_1 x\|_e \leq \text{const.} \|x\|_e$. The Circle Theorem then follows immediately with the aid of Lemma 1 of Part II.

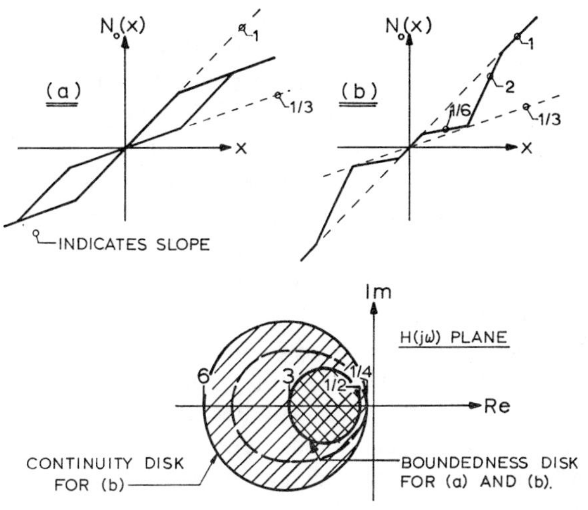

Fig. 7. Critical disks for Example 1. (Broken curve indicates edges of jump region in $H(j\omega)$ plane.)

The Circle Theorem can be viewed as a generalization of Nyquist's criterion,[6] in which a critical region replaces the critical point. For a given $\boldsymbol{N}$ there are two critical regions, one for boundedness and one for continuity. It can be shown that the continuity region always contains the boundedness region (see Example 1 and Fig. 7).

The Circle Theorem will serve as the generating theorem for the rest of this paper; i.e., the remaining results will be obtained as corollaries to the Circle Theorem by variously constraining the form of $\boldsymbol{N}$. In particular, the following corollary is obvious.

4.1. *A Circle Condition for Instantaneous Nonlinearities*[7]

Corollary 1. *If* (I) *$\boldsymbol{N}$ in $\mathcal{R}_0$ is instantaneously (incrementally) inside the sector $\{\alpha + \Delta, \beta - \Delta\}$ where $\beta > 0$, and if conditions* (II) *and* (III) *of the Circle Theorem hold, then $\boldsymbol{E}_1$ and $\boldsymbol{E}_2$ are L_2-bounded (L_2-continuous).*

Example 1. (a) Let N_0 be the relation shown in Fig. 7(a), and $\boldsymbol{N}$ be the relation in $\mathcal{R}_0$ defined by the equation $\boldsymbol{N}x(t) = [1 + \sin^2(t)] \cdot N_0(x(t))$. Find the critical regions for boundedness and continuity. (b) Repeat for the function shown in Fig. 7(b).

(a) Observe that N_0 is inside the sector $\{1/3, 1\}$ and that the time-varying gain $[1 + \sin^2(t)]$ is inside the sector $\{1, 2\}$. It follows that $\boldsymbol{N}$ is inside the product sector, $\{1/3, 1\} \times \{1, 2\} = \{1/3, 2\}$. Corollary 1 therefore implies that the critical region for boundedness is a disk, as shown in Fig. 7. However, since $\boldsymbol{N}$ is multivalued, and therefore not incrementally in any sector, Corollary 1 provides no information about continuity.

(b) The same results as in (a) are obtained for boundedness. In addition, $\boldsymbol{N}$ is incrementally inside $\{1/6, 4\}$, and a continuity disk is obtained, as shown in Fig. 7.

[6] More accurately, of the sufficient part of Nyquist's criterion.

[7] Similar or closely related circle conditions were found independently by the author [1a], Sandberg [5], Narendra and Goldwyn [6], and Kudrewicz [7].

Observe that the nonlinearity N in Corollary 1 *can* be time-varying and *can* have memory. In fact, very little has been assumed about the detailed character of N. The price paid for this is that Corollary 1 is often conservative, i.e., the critical region is too large. This is especially true of the boundedness condition (see Example 2). The continuity condition probably gives a quite fair estimate of what to expect. In fact, an approximate analysis, based on the harmonic balance method (cf. Hatanaka [3]), suggests that continuity breaks down in the following way: There is a zone, inside the critical continuity disk, in which jump-resonance phenomena occur. The zone is not much smaller than the continuity disk. Furthermore, the magnitudes of jump resonances depend on the Nyquist diagram behavior inside the continuity disk.

5. Conditions with Transferred Multipliers

The next two corollaries can be viewed as attempts to reduce the size of the critical region, at the cost of added restrictions on N. In certain cases, it will be possible to remove a "multiplier" K from the linear element, *before* applying the Circle Theorem. The removal of K will shift the frequency response of the remainder, $H_1(j\omega)$, away from the critical region. Thus the effective size of the critical region will be reduced.

5.1. *Popov's Condition*

Consider the feedback system of Fig. 1, under the same conditions as in Corollary 1, but with the added constraint that N is a memoryless, time-invariant operator. The following condition for boundedness (*not* continuity) involves the removal of a first-order multiplier from H.

Corollary 2. *If*

(I) *N is an operator in $\mathfrak{N}$, inside the sector $\{\alpha, \beta\}$ where $\beta>0$.*

(II) *H is an operator in $\mathcal{L}$ that can be factored into a product $H=KH_1$, where H_1 and K are in $\mathcal{L}$, and $K(s)=\lambda/(s+\lambda)$ where $\lambda>0$.*

(III) *H_1 satisfies the circle conditions for the product sector $\{\alpha, \beta\}\times\{0, 1\}$ with offset δ, where $\delta>0$.*

(IV) *$a_2=0$ and $\dot{w}_2$ is in L_2, where $\dot{w}_2$ denotes the derivative on $[0, \infty)$.*

Then E_1 and E_2 are L_2-bounded.

Remarks: (i) For $\alpha>0$, Condition III simply means that $\mathrm{Re}\{(j\omega+\lambda)H(j\omega)\}\geq-\lambda/\beta+\delta$. (ii) Condition IV limits the result to that configuration in which the directions of flow is from the input to H to N.

Proof of Corollary 2. The feedback equations will be transformed, as illustrated in Fig. 8; i.e., H will be split into a product, $H=KH_1$, and the multiplier K will be transferred into a composition with N. It will then be shown, in Step 1, that the transformed equations are bounded, and, in Step 2, that they are equivalent to the original equations as far as stability is concerned.

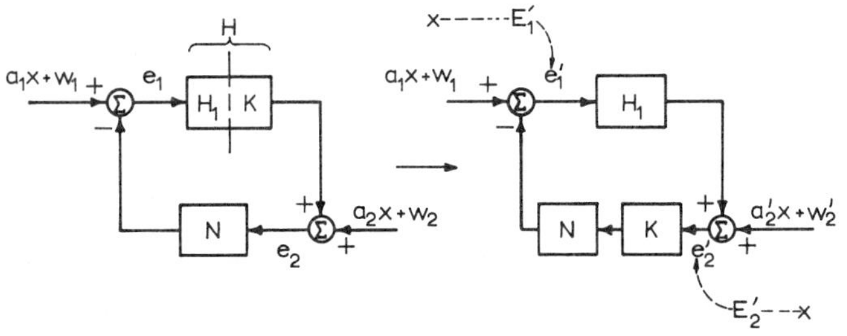

Fig. 8. A transformation.

Letting $w_2'=w_2+\lambda^{-1}\dot{w}_2$, and recalling that $a_2=0$, consider the equations of the transformed system of Fig. 8,

$$e_1' = w_1 + a_1x - NKe_2' \tag{12a}$$

$$e_2' = w_2' + H_1e_1' \tag{12b}$$

Let E_1' and E_2' be the closed-loop relations for (12a)–(12b).

Step 1. E_1' and E_2' are L_2-bounded. This follows from the Circle Theorem whose hypotheses are satisfied because: w_2' is in L_2 by assumption IV; NK is in the product sector $\{\alpha, \beta\}\times\{0, 1\}$ by Lemma 2; and NK satisfies the appropriate circle conditions.

Step 2. It will be shown (below) that

$$E_1 = E_1' \tag{13a}$$

$$E_2 = KE_2' \tag{13b}$$

Since E_1' and E_2' have been proved L_2-bounded, and since K is certainly L_2-bounded, it follows that E_1 and E_2 are L_2-bounded.

To prove (13b), recall that E_2 and E_2' are subsets (of a product space), so that it is enough to establish that each contains the other. Suppose that (x, e_2) is an element of E_2; by definition of E_2, there is an e_1 in L_{2e} satisfying (3a)–(3b); let $e_1'=e_1$ and $e_2'=w_2'+H_1e_1$. Direct substitution shows that (x, e_1', e_2') satisfies (12a)–(12b), so that (x, e_2') belongs to E_2'. Substitution also shows that $e_2=Ke_2'$, so that (x, e_2) is in KE_2'. Since (x, e_2) is an arbitrary element of E_2, it follows that KE_2' contains E_2. It can similarly be shown that E_2 contains KE_2', so that (13b) holds. The proof of (13a) is similar. Q.E.D.

Example 2. Let N be the operator in $\mathfrak{N}$ whose graph is shown in Fig. 9(a), and let $H(s)=k/(s+\lambda)(s+\mu)$. For what values of k is the closed-loop L_2-bounded? Compare Corollaries 1 and 2.

Here N is inside $\{0, 1\}$, so the critical region is a half-plane, $\mathrm{Re}\{\cdot\}\leq-1+\delta$, in both corollaries. In Corollary 2 let $K(s)=\lambda/(s+\lambda)$ and $H_1(s)=k/\lambda(s+\mu)$; the following estimates are obtained:

Corollary 1: $-\lambda\mu<k<(\lambda+\mu)(\lambda+\mu+2\sqrt{\lambda\mu})$
Corollary 2: $-\lambda\mu<k$

Corollary 2 is less conservative than Corollary 1, as it shows the closed loop to be bounded for *all* positive k.

Figure 10 also illustrates the following point: For $a\leq0$, both corollaries predict the same critical region; however, in many cases of interest, $H_1(j\omega)$ is further from the critical region than $H(j\omega)$.

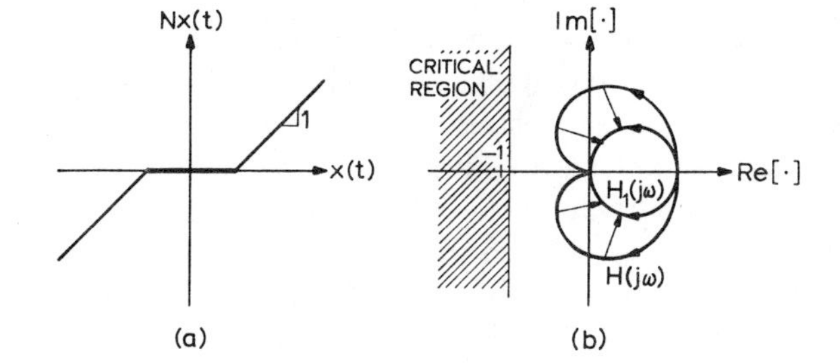

Fig. 9. An example of Popov's Condition. Arrows indicate shift away from critical region.

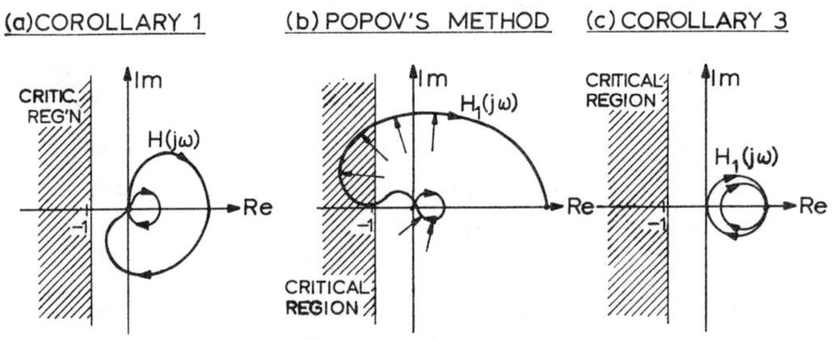

Fig. 10. Nyquist diagrams for Corollaries 1–3.

5.2. The Factorization Method

The proof of Corollary 2 suggests a method for generating a class of Popov-like conditions. The method consists of a factorization of H into $H=KH_1$, followed by the transformation of (3a)–(3b) into (12a)–(12b) followed by an application of the Circle Theorem. Various stability conditions are produced by variously choosing the multiplier K.

The method has two preconditions:

(Ia) Either K^{-1} exists or $a_2=0$.
(Ib) There is a w_2' in L_2 such that $K(w_2')=w_2$.

These preconditions ensure that (3) are transformable into (12). Note that if K^{-1} exists, then a_2 need not be zero; however, in that case, (12b) must be modified by the addition of a term $a_2'x$ where $a_2'x=K^{-1}a_2x$ (that is, a_2' is a *relation* on L_{2e}).

The method is worthwhile only if it gives a smaller effective critical region than Corollary 1. This happens if:

(IIa) NK lies in a sector not greater than the product of the sectors of N and K.
(IIb) KH_1 lies in a sector greater than the product of the sectors of K and H_1.

If Requirements (IIa)–(IIb) are satisfied, then it is advantageous to transfer K from a composition with H_1 into a composition with N. Requirement (IIa) usually means that the multiplier K has a very special form, and the difficulty in finding suitable multipliers is the main problem in applying this method. Once K is fixed, Requirement (IIb) defines a (limited) class of operators H for which this method is useful.

As an illustration of this method, a condition resembling Popov's is derived next.

5.3. A Slope-Restricted Nonlinearity and an $\mathcal{RC}$ Multiplier

Consider the feedback system of Fig. 1, under the conditions of Corollary 2, but with an added slope restriction on N, and a more general type of multiplier K.

COROLLARY 3.[8] *If:*

(I) N *is an operator in* $\mathfrak{N}$, *incrementally inside*[9] $\{\alpha, \beta\}$ *where* $\beta>0$.
(II) H *is an operator in* $\mathcal{L}$, *which can be factored into a product* $H=KH_1$, *where* K *is in* $\mathcal{RC}$ *and* H_1 *is in* $\mathcal{L}$.
(III) H_1 *satisfies the circle conditions for the product sector* $\{\alpha, \beta\}\times\{K(\infty), K(0)\}$ *with offset* δ, *where* $\delta>0$.
(IV) *There is*[10] *a* w_2' *such that* $K(w_2')=w_2$.
(V) *Either* $K(\infty)>0$ *or* $a_2=0$.

Then E_1 *and* E_2 *are* L_2*-bounded.*

Corollary 3 is obtained immediately by the factorization method, with the help of Lemma 3.

REMARK: For suitably restricted N, Corollary 3 has several advantages over Popov's method:

(i) The shift away from the critical region, which depends on $K(j\omega)$, can be controlled more flexibly as a function of ω. This is likely to be useful where a negative magnitude slope $d/d\omega|H(j\omega)|$ is followed by a positive slope at a larger ω.
(ii) a_2 need not be zero if $K(\infty)>0$.
(iii) If $\alpha>0$, the critical region predicted by Corollary 3 (a disk) is sometimes smaller than by Popov's method (which always gives a half-plane for $\alpha>0$).

EXAMPLE 3. Let N be the operator in $\mathfrak{N}$ whose graph is shown in Fig. 9(a) (the same as in Example 2), and let H have the Laplace transform

$$H(s) = kr^{-1}\left\{\frac{s+1}{s+r^{-1}}\right\} \cdot\left\{\frac{r^{-1}s}{(s+r^{-2})(s+r^{-1})}+\frac{r^2s}{(s+r)(s+r^2)}\right\}$$

where $r\gg1$. For what values of k is the closed loop bounded? Compare Corollaries 1, 2, and 3.

Figure 10(a) illustrates the significant features of the Nyquist diagram of $H(j\omega)$ (not drawn to scale). Observe that $H(j\omega)$ has two "pass bands," one for $r^{-2}<\omega<r^{-1}$ and the other for $r<\omega<r^2$; these "pass bands" produce the two loops in Fig. 10(a). Note that the critical region is the same half-plane in all corollaries, namely, $\mathrm{Re}\{\cdot\}\geq-1+\delta$.

[8] Corollary 3 and the factorization method, in a functional setting, were introduced by the author in Reference [1a]. A related method in a Liapunov setting has been exploited by Brockett, Willems, and Forys [4a]–[4b].

[9] i.e., $\alpha\leq\frac{N(x)-N(y)}{x-y}\leq\beta$.

[10] This condition is satisfied automatically if $K(\infty)>0$. If $K(\infty)=0$, then it is satisfied if $\dot{w}_2$ is in L_2.

Corollary 1 predicts boundedness for $-1<k<8$ approximately.

Popov's method is useless here. A comparison of Figs. 10(a) and 10(b) shows the effect of removing the multiplier $\lambda/s+\lambda$: $H_1(j\omega)$ is moved away from the critical region in the lower left half-plane (in the decaying edge of the lower pass band, $r^{-1}<\omega<1$); however, this improvement is more than offset by the bulge introduced in the upper left half-plane (in the rising edge of the upper pass band, $1<\omega<r$).

What is obviously needed here is a multiplier that acts like Popov's in the lower pass band, but has no effect in the upper pass band. The $\mathcal{RC}$ multiplier $K(s) = r^{-1}(s+1)(s+r^{-1})$ accomplishes just this. Its removal shifts $H_1(j\omega)$ entirely into the right half-plane [Fig. 10(c)]. Corollary 3 therefore implies that the closed loop is bounded for all positive k, in fact, for $k>-1$.

6. Comments and Conclusions

6.1. *Circle Conditions*

The main result here is the Circle Theorem. The Circle Theorem is a sufficient condition for closed-loop stability, which requires the nonlinearity $\boldsymbol{N}$ to lie inside a sector, but which leaves $\boldsymbol{N}$ free otherwise. The other conditions are all corollaries of the Circle Theorem.

Corollary 1 is probably the most useful result, since it roughs out the region of stability, with a minimum of restrictions on $\boldsymbol{N}$. However, it is often conservative.

Corollaries 2 and 3 provide a tradeoff between limitations on $\boldsymbol{N}$ and limitations on $H(j\omega)$. Probably more significant than the actual conditions is the fact that there is a method of generating them, namely, the factorization method.

The results derived in Part II hold for nonzero initial conditions in the linear element, provided the "zero-input response" w_2 satisfies the indicated restrictions.

6.2. *Extensions of the Theory*

The theory has been extended in several directions (see [1b]), notably,

1) to L_∞,
2) to systems with a limited rate of time variation.

The extension to L_∞ involves the use of exponential weighting factors, which transform L_∞ functions into L_2 functions. The extension to time-varying systems involves the use of a shifted Nyquist diagram, $H(\sigma+j\omega)$, in which σ depends on the rate of time variation.

6.3. *Gain and Phase Shift in Relation to Nonlinear Time-Varying Systems*

The stability of a linear time-invariant feedback system depends on the amounts of gain and phase shift introduced by the open loop. Are similar considerations involved in nonlinear, time-varying problems? Of course the classical definitions of gain and phase shift, in terms of frequency response, have no strict meaning in nonlinear or time-varying systems. However, stability does seem to depend on certain measures of signal amplification and signal shift. Thus the norm ratio $\|\boldsymbol{H}x\|/\|x\|$ plays a role similar to the role of gain. Furthermore, the inner product $\langle x, \boldsymbol{H}x\rangle$, a measure of input-output cross-correlation, is closely related to the notion of phase shift. For example, for linear time-invariant operators in $\mathcal{L}$ the condition of positivity, $\langle x, \boldsymbol{H}x\rangle \geq 0$, is equivalent (by Lemma 1) to the phase condition,

$$|\operatorname{Arg}\{H(j\omega)\}| \leq 90°.$$

It may be worthwhile to see what the theorems of Part I mean in terms of gain and phase shift. This can be done with the help of Lemma 1. Theorem 1 of Part I can be viewed as a generalization to nonlinear time-varying systems of the rule that, "if the open-loop gain is less than one, then the closed loop is stable." Theorem 3 can be viewed as the generalization of, "if the open-loop absolute phase shift is less than 180° then[11] the closed loop is stable." Theorem 2 places gain and phase shift in competition, permitting large gains at small phase shifts, etc.

6.4. *Conclusions*

Some of the salient features of the functional theory are:

(i) It provides an alternative to the method of Liapunov, an alternative resembling the classical Nyquist-Bode theory.

(ii) It is well suited to input-output problems.

(iii) It is free of state-space restrictions, and is therefore useful for distributed systems, hysteritic systems, etc. It also lends itself well to multivariable systems.

(iv) It unifies several results in stability theory. In particular, it is noteworthy that Popov's condition, the slope-restricted-$\boldsymbol{N}$ result, etc., can all be derived from the Circle Theorem.

(v) It has led to some new results, notably Corollary 3 and [1b].

The theory outlined here is probably still far from its definitive form. Nevertheless, it provides enough insight to make possible a reasonably systematic design of stabilizers.

Appendix A

Definitions of Conicity and Positivity

It will be assumed that $\boldsymbol{H}$ is a relation in $\mathcal{R}_0$ and that c, $r\geq 0$, and $\alpha\leq\beta$ are real constants.

Group I. *"Incremental" Conditions*

$\boldsymbol{H}$ is incrementally interior conic if

$$\|(\boldsymbol{H}x - \boldsymbol{H}y)_t - c(x-y)_t\| \leq r\|(x-y)_t\|;$$

[11] There are two positive elements in the open loop; each contributes an absolute phase shift of less than 90°; the open-loop absolute phase shift is therefore less than 180°.

H is incrementally inside the sector $\{\alpha, \beta\}$ if

$$\langle (Hx - Hy)_t - \alpha(x-y)_t, (Hx - Hy)_t - \beta(x-y)_t \rangle \leq 0;$$

H is incrementally positive if

$$\langle (x-y)_t, (Hx - Hy)_t \rangle \geq 0;$$

(where the inequalities of Group I hold for all x and y in $Do(H)$ and all $t \geq 0$).

The definitions of an operator that is "exterior" conic or "outside" a sector, are identical to the preceding ones except for a reversal of the inequality sign, and will therefore be omitted.

REMARK: If H is incrementally inside $\{\alpha, \beta\}$ then H is inside $\{\alpha, \beta\}$. Similarly, each inequality in Group I implies a corresponding inequality in Section 3.

GROUP II. *"Instantaneous" Conditions*

H is instantaneously inside the sector $\{\alpha, \beta\}$ if

$$\alpha \leq Hx(t)/x(t) \leq \beta \qquad (x \in L_{2e};\ t \geq 0;\ x(t) \neq 0);$$

H is instantaneously positive if

$$x(t) \cdot Hx(t) \geq 0 \qquad (x \in L_{2e};\ t \geq 0).$$

GROUP III. *"Instantaneous Incremental" Conditions*

H is instantaneously incrementally inside the sector $\{\alpha, \beta\}$ if

$$\alpha \leq \frac{Hx(t) - Hy(t)}{x(t) - y(t)} \leq \beta$$
$$(x \in L_{2e};\ t \geq 0;\ x(t) - y(t) \neq 0).$$

H is instantaneously incrementally positive if

$$[Hx(t) - Hy(t)] \cdot [x(t) - y(t)] \geq 0 \qquad (x \in L_{2e};\ t \geq 0).$$

REMARK: If H is instantaneously inside $\{\alpha, \beta\}$, then H is inside $\{\alpha, \beta\}$. Similarly, each inequality in Group II implies a corresponding inequality in Section 3. Also each inequality in Group III implies a corresponding inequality in Group II.

APPENDIX B

LEMMA 1

The proof of Lemma 1(b) will be based on the Principle of the Argument, a theorem of Paley and Wiener, and Parseval's theorem. The proofs of Lemmas 1(a) and 1(c), being straightforward applications of Parseval's theorem, will be omitted.

Some preliminary lemmas and properties will now be introduced.

DEFINITION: *If x is a function in L_2 then its* L.I.M. TRANSFORM *is*

$$X(s) = \underset{T\to\infty}{\text{l.i.m.}} \int_0^T x(t) \exp(-st)dt. \qquad (\sigma \geq 0) \qquad \text{(B1)}$$

The l.i.m. transform of $X(s)$ is

$$x_1(\tau) = \frac{1}{2\pi} \underset{W\to\infty}{\text{l.i.m.}} \int_{-W}^{W} X(j\omega) \exp(j\omega\tau)d\omega. \quad (\tau \text{ real}) \quad \text{(B2)}$$

The limits in the mean in (B1)–(B2) exist, and $x_1(\tau) = x(\tau)$.[12]

B.1. Properties of Transforms

In the following properties, H is an operator in $\mathcal{L}$ having a Laplace transform $H(s)$.

(A) The integral defining $H(s)$ [see (6)] converges and is bounded for $\sigma > \sigma_0$, since

$$\int_0^\infty h(t) \exp(-st)dt$$
$$\leq \int_0^\infty |h(t)| \exp(-\sigma_0 t)dt = \text{const.}$$

(B) $H(s)$ is analytic for $\sigma > \sigma_0$.[13]

(C) For $\sigma \geqq 0$, $\lim_{|s|\to\infty} H(s) = h_\infty$.[14]

(D) If x is in L_2 then Hx is in L_2.[15]

(E) If the l.i.m. transforms of $x \in L_2$ and $Hx \in L_2$ are $X(s)$ and $Y(s)$ respectively, then[15]

$$Y(s) = H(s)X(s) \qquad \text{(B3)}$$

One consequence of Property D is that every mapping of the type defined by the right-hand side of (2) is an operator[16] on L_{2e}, and belongs to $\mathcal{R}_0$.

B.2. Some Consequences of Nonencirclement

A contour in the complex plane will be said to have Property N if it does not pass through or encircle the origin.

LEMMA 4. If the Nyquist diagram of $H(s)$ has Property N then: (a) $1/H(s)$ is analytic for $\sigma \geq 0$. (b) If the inequality $1/|H(\sigma + j\omega)| \leq M$ holds for $\sigma = 0$ then it holds for all $\sigma \geq 0$.

PROOF: (a) Since $H(s)$ is analytic for $\sigma \geq 0$, it is enough to show that $H(s) \neq 0$ for $\sigma \geq 0$ to prove (a). For this purpose several contours are defined: Let Γ_ω denote the $j\omega$-axis (as shown in Fig. 11); for $R \geq 0$ a constant, let Γ_R denote the clockwise contour bounding the semicircular region $|\sigma + j\omega| \leq R$ where $\sigma \geq 0$; let $\Gamma_\omega - \Gamma_R$ denote the difference contour; and let $H(\Gamma_\omega)$ and $H(\Gamma_\omega - \Gamma_R)$ denote images of the respective contours, each augmented with the point h_∞.

It will be shown that $H(\Gamma_R)$ has Property N for $R \geq R_0$; since by hypothesis $H(s)$ is analytic for $\sigma \geq 0$, and has no zeros on the $j\omega$-axis, Lemma 4(a) follows by the Principle of the Argument.

[12] See Widder [8], ch. II, Theorem 10.

[13] *Ibid.*, Theorem 5a.

[14] The special case $s = j\omega$ is implied by the Rieman-Lebesgue theorem (Titchmarsh [9a], Theorem 1). The general case follows from the special case and from Properties A and B by a theorem of Phragmén-Lindelöf (Titchmarsh [9b], sec. 5.64).

[15] This follows from Theorem 65 of Titchmarsh [9a], which implies that the convolution of an L_2 function with an L_1 function is in L_2, and has a transform of the type (B3).

[16] Suppose that x is in L_2; x_t is certainly in L_2, and $H(x_t)$ is in L_2 by Property D; since $[H(x_t)]_t = [Hx]_t$, it follows that $[Hx]_t$ is in L_2; i.e., Hx is in L_{2e}. Thus H maps L_{2e} into L_{2e}; since H also maps o into o, it follows that H is an operator on L_{2e} and in $\mathcal{R}_0$.

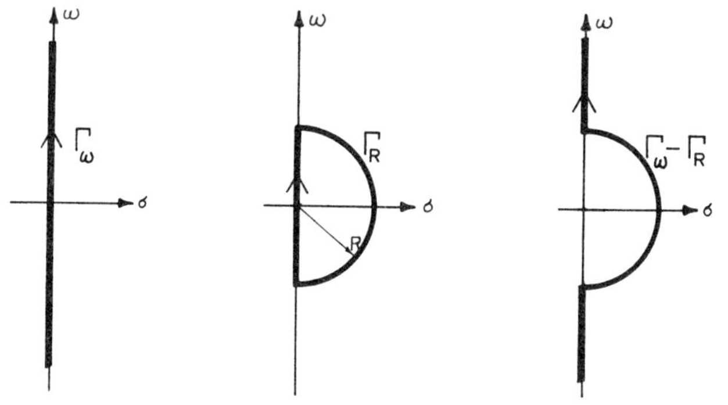

Fig. 11. Contours.

To prove that $H(\Gamma_R)$ has Property N observe that $H(\Gamma_R)=H(\Gamma_\omega)+H(\Gamma_R-\Gamma_\omega)$; since $H(\Gamma_\omega)$ has Property N by hypothesis, it is enough now to show that $H(\Gamma_R-\Gamma_\omega)$ has Property N. This can be accomplished by showing that $H(\Gamma_R-\Gamma_\omega)$ lies in a circle centered at h_∞ and not including the origin. The last assertion is a consequence of two facts.

(i) There is an $R_0>0$ for which, for $R\geq R_0$ and s in $(\Gamma_R-\Gamma_\omega)$, $|H(s)-h_\infty|\leq\frac{1}{2}|h_\infty|$.
(ii) $h_\infty\neq 0$.

(i) is obtained from Property C of Appendix B.1 for $|s|\geq R_0$, and therefore certainly holds for s in $(\Gamma_R-\Gamma_\omega)$.
(ii) holds since

$$h_\infty = \lim_{\omega\to\infty} H(j\omega),$$

and since $H(j\omega)\neq 0$ by Property N.

(b) This is a special case of the Maximum Modulus Theorem of Phragmén-Lindelof.[17] The theorem implies that a function analytic in a half-plane, and bounded on the boundary, is bounded throughout the half-plane.

B.3. A Paley-Wiener Lemma

A complex-valued function $W(s)$ will be said to satisfy the Paley-Wiener conditions if

(PW1) $W(s)$ is analytic for $\sigma>0$, and

(PW2) $\int_{-\infty}^{\infty}|W(\sigma+j\omega)|^2d\omega\leq\text{const.}\qquad(\sigma>0).$

The following lemma is a modification of Theorem 5 of Paley-Wiener [10], and is stated without proof.

LEMMA 5. (a) If w is in L_2, $w_t=0$, and $W(s)$ is the l.i.m. transform of $w(\tau)$, then $W(s)\exp(st)$ satisfies the Paley-Wiener conditions. (b) Conversely, if $t\geq 0$ and $W(s)\exp(st)$ satisfies the Paley-Wiener conditions, then there is a function w in L_2 having the properties that $w_t=0$ and that $W(s)$ is the l.i.m. transform of w.

B.4. Proof of Lemma 1(b)

Let x in L_{2e} and $t\geq 0$ be given. Since $\boldsymbol{H}$ is linear, it is enough to show that $\boldsymbol{H}$ is conic with parameters c and r; that is,

$$\|(\boldsymbol{H}x-cx)_t\|\geq r\|x_t\|. \tag{B4}$$

For this purpose, let $y\triangleq(\boldsymbol{H}x-cx)$ and $\delta\triangleq\boldsymbol{H}(x_t)-[\boldsymbol{H}x]_t$. Hence

$$y_t=(\boldsymbol{H}x-cx)_t=\boldsymbol{H}(x_t)-cx_t-\delta. \tag{B5}$$

Now x_t is in L_2. Hence $\boldsymbol{H}(x_t)$ is in L_2 by Property D of Appendix B.1. Since $[\boldsymbol{H}(x_t)]_t=(\boldsymbol{H}x)_t$, it follows that $(\boldsymbol{H}x)_t$ is in L_2. Thus δ is in L_2, all terms in (B5) are in L_2, and by Property E,

$$Y_t(s)=H(s)X_t(s)-cX_t(s)-\Delta(s) \tag{B6}$$

where $Y_t(s)$, $X_t(s)$, and $\Delta(s)$ are the l.i.m. transforms of y_t, x_t, and δ. Hence

$$\{X_t(s)\}-\left\{\frac{\Delta(s)}{H(s)-c}\right\}=\left\{\frac{Y_t(s)}{H(s)-c}\right\}. \tag{B7}$$

Now the braced terms in (B7) are l.i.m. transforms of functions in L_2; for $X_t(s)$ this is true by definition; for the remaining terms, this can be proved by the reasoning given below in Assertion 1. Suppose that $\Delta(s)/H(s)-c$ is the l.i.m. transform of a function $q(\tau)$; it follows that

$$\|x_t-q\|^2=\frac{1}{2\pi}\int_{-\infty}^{\infty}\left|x_t(j\omega)-\frac{\Delta(j\omega)}{H(j\omega)-c}\right|^2d\omega$$

(Parseval's Theorem)

$$=\frac{1}{2\pi}\int_{-\infty}^{\infty}\left|\frac{Y_t(j\omega)}{H(j\omega)-c}\right|^2d\omega\quad\text{[by (B7)]}$$

$$\leq\frac{1}{2\pi r^2}\int_{-\infty}^{\infty}|Y_t(j\omega)|^2d\omega$$

[by inequality (8) of Section 3.2]

$$=\frac{1}{r}\|y_t\|^2\quad\text{(Parseval's Theorem)} \tag{B8}$$

It will be shown, in Assertion 1, that $q(\tau)=0$ for almost all $\tau<t$. Therefore

$$\|x_t-q\|^2=\|x_t\|^2+\|q\|^2\geq\|x_t\|^2. \tag{B9}$$

(B8) and (B9) imply (B4).

ASSERTION 1. The expression $\Delta(s)/[H(s)-c]$ is the l.i.m. transform of a function q in L_2; furthermore $q(\tau)=0$ for almost all $\tau<t$.

PROOF OF ASSERTION 1. By Lemma 5b, it is enough to show that $[\Delta(s)\exp(st)]/[H(s)-c]$ satisfies the Paley-Wiener conditions.

To prove (PW1), observe that the following three terms are analytic for $\sigma>0$: $\Delta(s)$, because it is the l.i.m. transform of an L_2 function; $\exp(st)$, because it is analytic throughout the plane; $[H(s)-c]^{-1}$, by Lemma 4 and the hypothesis on the Nyquist diagram. The product of these terms must therefore also be analytic for $\sigma>0$.

To prove (PW2), observe that

[17] Titchmarsh [9b], sec. 5.61.

$$\int_{-\infty}^{\infty}\left|\frac{\Delta(s)\exp(st)}{H(s)-c}\right|^2 d\omega \le \frac{1}{r^2}\int_{-\infty}^{\infty}|\Delta(s)\exp(st)|\,d\omega$$
$$\le \text{const.} \quad (\sigma > 0) \text{ [by inequality (8)]}$$

(Since $\delta \in L_2$ and $\delta_t = 0$ by construction, the last inequality is implied by Lemma 5(a).) Q.E.D.

Appendix C

Lemma 2

A preliminary assertion will be proved first.

Assertion 2. If $\boldsymbol{N}$ in $\mathfrak{N}$ is positive, $\boldsymbol{K}$ is in $\mathfrak{L}$, and $y = \boldsymbol{K}x$, then

$$\int_0^t \frac{dy}{d\tau}\cdot N(y(\tau))d\tau \ge 0. \tag{C1}$$

Proof of Assertion 2.

$$\int_0^t \frac{dy}{d\tau}\cdot N(y(\tau))d\tau = \int_{y(0)}^{y(t)} N(y')dy'. \tag{C2}$$

Since $\boldsymbol{K}$ is in $\mathfrak{L}$, $y(t)$ is given by a convolution integral, whose kernel is fixed for a fixed x, and whose limits of integration are 0 and t; therefore $y(0) = 0$. Furthermore, since $\boldsymbol{N}$ is positive, its graph lies in the first and third quadrants. It follows that the right-hand side of (C2) is non-negative. Q.E.D.

C.1. Proof of Lemma 2

Part a) It is required to show that, for any given x in L_{2e} and any given $t \ge 0$, the inequality

$$\int_0^t x(\tau)\cdot[\boldsymbol{NK}x(\tau)]d\tau \ge 0 \tag{C3}$$

holds. For this purpose, make the following substitutions: Write $y \triangleq \boldsymbol{K}x$, and observe that, since $K(s) = k\lambda/(s+\lambda)$, y is differentiable and

$$x(\tau) = \frac{1}{k\lambda}\frac{dy}{d\tau} + \frac{1}{k}y(\tau). \tag{C4}$$

(C3) is therefore equivalent to

$$\int_0^t \left\{\frac{1}{k\lambda}\frac{dy}{d\tau} + \frac{1}{k}y(\tau)\right\}\cdot N(y(\tau))d\tau \ge 0 \text{ or}$$

$$\frac{1}{k\lambda}\int_0^t \frac{dy}{d\tau}\cdot N(y(\tau))d\tau + \frac{1}{k}\int_0^t y(\tau)\cdot N(y(\tau))d\tau \ge 0. \tag{C5}$$

Now k and λ are positive by hypothesis; the first integral in (C5) is non-negative by Assertion 2; the second integral is non-negative, since $\boldsymbol{N}$ is a positive operator; therefore (C5) is true. Q.E.D.

Part b) It will be assumed, for simplicity, that $\beta > 0$.

Case A. Suppose $\alpha \ge 0$. It must be shown that $\boldsymbol{NK}$ is inside $\{\alpha, \beta\} \times \{0, k\}$. This is equivalent to saying that $\boldsymbol{NK}$ is inside $\{0, k\beta\}$, or that

$$\langle(\boldsymbol{NK}x)_t), (\boldsymbol{NK}x - k\beta x)_t\rangle \le 0. \tag{C6}$$

(C6) is equivalent to the inequality

$$k\beta\langle x_t, (\boldsymbol{N}y)_t\rangle \ge \|(\boldsymbol{N}y)_t\|^2 \tag{C7}$$

where $y = \boldsymbol{K}x$. Now recalling that $\langle x_t, (\boldsymbol{N}y)_t\rangle$ equals the left-hand side of (C5), we get

$$k\beta\langle x_t, (\boldsymbol{N}y)_t\rangle \ge \beta\int_0^t y(\tau)\cdot N(y(\tau))d\tau.$$

Observing that, for $\alpha \ge 0$, N satisfies the inequality $\beta y(\tau)\cdot N(y(\tau)) \ge [N(y(\tau))]^2$, we get

$$k\beta\langle x_t, (\boldsymbol{N}y)_t\rangle \ge \int_0^t [N(y(\tau))]^2 d\tau,$$

which implies (C7). Q.E.D.

Case B. Suppose $\alpha < 0$. Decompose $N(x)$ into two parts, $N(x) = N_+(x) + N_-(x)$; let $N_+(x) = N(x)$ for $N(x) \ge 0$ and $N_+(x) = 0$ elsewhere, and let $N_-(x)$ be similarly defined.

Since $\boldsymbol{N}_+$ is clearly inside $\{0, \beta\}$, Case A implies that $\boldsymbol{N}_+\boldsymbol{K}$ is inside $\{0, k\beta\}$. Similarly $\boldsymbol{N}_-\boldsymbol{K}$ is inside $\{k\alpha, 0\}$. On summing the sectors of $\boldsymbol{N}_+\boldsymbol{K}$ and $\boldsymbol{N}_-\boldsymbol{K}$ (by the Sum Rule of Part I) it is found that $\boldsymbol{NK}$ is inside $\{k\alpha, k\beta\}$; that is, inside $\{\alpha, \beta\} \times \{0, k\}$. Q.E.D.

Appendix D

Lemma 3

Before proving Lemma 3, a few related assertions will be introduced.

Assertion 3. Let $\boldsymbol{K}$ be an operator in $\mathfrak{RC}$, x a fixed element of L_{2e}, and $y \triangleq \boldsymbol{K}x$. Then x has a "Foster expansion" in y;[18] that is, x can be expressed as a finite sum,

$$x = \sum_{i=0}^{m} \boldsymbol{F}_i y,$$

in which $\boldsymbol{F}_i$ are operators mapping the image under $\boldsymbol{K}$ of L_{2e} into $R[0, \infty)$, as follows:

Case 1. $\boldsymbol{F}_0 y = K^{-1}(0)\cdot y$.

Case 2. If $i = 1, 2, \cdots, (m-1)$, then $\boldsymbol{F}_i$ is in $\mathfrak{L}$ and has a Laplace Transform,

$$F_i(s) = h_i s/(s+\theta_i), \quad (h_i > 0, \quad \theta_i > 0).$$

Case 3. $\boldsymbol{F}_m y = h_m \dot{y}$ if $K(\infty) = 0$ and $\boldsymbol{F}_m y = 0$ otherwise, where $h_m \ge 0$.

Assertion 4. If $\boldsymbol{N}$ is incrementally positive, and $\langle x_t, [\boldsymbol{N}y]_t\rangle \ge 0$ then $\langle x_t, [\boldsymbol{N}(x+y)]_t\rangle \ge 0$.

Proof of Assertion 4. It is enough to show that

$$\langle x_t, [\boldsymbol{N}(x+y)_t]\rangle - \langle x_t, [\boldsymbol{N}y]_t\rangle \ge 0 \tag{D1}$$

But the left-hand side of (D1) can be expressed as

$$\langle(x+y)_t - y_t, [\boldsymbol{N}(x+y)]_t - (\boldsymbol{N}y)_t\rangle$$

which has the form $\langle x_{1t} - x_{2t}, \boldsymbol{N}x_{1t} - \boldsymbol{N}x_{2t}\rangle$, and is non-negative, since $\boldsymbol{N}$ is an incrementally positive operator. Therefore (D1) holds. Q.E.D.

[18] See Guillemin [2], p. 115.

ASSERTION 5. If N is an operator in $\mathfrak{N}$, incrementally inside a sector $\{\alpha, \beta\}$ where $\alpha<0$ and $\beta>0$, then N can be decomposed into $N=N_{+}+N_{-}$, where N_{-} is inside $\{\alpha, 0\}$, and N_{+} is inside $\{0, \beta\}$.

PROOF OF ASSERTION 5. Since N is incrementally inside a sector, its graph N is continuous and has bounded variation on every finite interval. Consequently N can be expressed as an integral, $N(x)=\int_0^x n(x')dx'$. Let $n_{+}(x)=n(x)$ if $n(x)\geq 0$, and $n_{+}(x)=0$ if $n(x)<0$; let $N_{+}(x)=\int_0^x n_{+}(x')dx'$. Clearly N_{+} has the desired property. N_{-} is constructed similarly. Q.E.D.

D.1. Proof of Lemma 3

Part a) Let x be any given element of L_{2e}, and t any given point in $[0, \infty)$; it is required to show that

$$\langle x_t, (NKx)_t\rangle \geq 0. \tag{D2}$$

Letting $y \triangleq Kx$, and recalling that x can be expressed by the Foster expansion

$$x = \sum_{i=0}^{m} F_i y$$

(see Assertion 3), (D2) is equivalent to

$$\sum_{i=0}^{m} \langle (F_i y)_t, (Ny)_t\rangle \geq 0. \tag{D3}$$

It will be shown that each component on the left-hand side of (D3) is non-negative.

CASE 1. Here $F_0 y = K^{-1}(0)\cdot y$. Hence $\langle (F_0 y)_t, (Ny)_t\rangle = [K^{-1}(0)]\cdot\langle y_t, (Ny)_t\rangle$; this is non-negative since N is a positive operator, and since $K(0)$ is necessarily positive.

CASE 2. Here $F_i(s)=h_i s/(s+\theta_i)$. Let

$$z(t) = h_i^{-1}\int_0^t F_i y(\tau)d\tau.$$

It follows that $y=\dot{z}+\theta_i z$ almost everywhere, and that $F_i y = h_i \dot{z}$ almost everywhere. Hence

$$\langle (F_i y)_t, (Ny)_t\rangle = h_i\langle \dot{z}_t, [N(\dot{z}+\theta_i z)]_t\rangle. \tag{D4}$$

Now, observing that $\theta_i>0$, Assertion 2 implies that $\langle \dot{z}, [N(\theta_i z)]_t\rangle$ is non-negative. Observing that h_i is positive, the right-hand side of (D4) is non-negative by Assertion 4. Thus Case 2 is proved.

CASE 3. Here $F_m y = h_m \dot{y}$ if $K(\infty)=0$. Hence $\langle (F_m y)_t, (Ny)_t\rangle = h_m\langle \dot{y}_t, (Ny)_t\rangle$. Case 3 follows by Assertion 2.

Since the inner product is non-negative in all three cases, (D3) holds. Q.E.D.

Part b) Assume, for simplicity, that $\beta>0$.

CASE A. If $\alpha=0$ then, by reasoning similar to that used in Lemma 2(b), (C5)–(C7), the following inequality is obtained:

$$\langle x_t, (NKx)_t\rangle \geq [\beta K(0)]^{-1}\|(Ny)_t\|^2.$$

Hence NK is inside $\{0, \beta K(0)\}$, which equals $\{0, \beta\}\times\{0, K(0)\}$.

CASE B. If $\alpha>0$ then NK is decomposed into three parts

$$NK = \{[N-\alpha I]K\} + \{\alpha[K - K(\infty)\cdot I]\} + \{\alpha K(\infty)\cdot I\}. \tag{D5}$$

Now the three parts lie in the sectors $\{0, (\beta-\alpha)K(0)\}$, $\{0, \alpha[K(0)-K(\infty)]\}$, and $\{\alpha K(\infty), \alpha K(\infty)\}$, respectively. (The first two of these sectors are determined by the rule formed in Case A, after observing that $[N-\alpha I]$ is inside $\{0, \beta-\alpha\}$, and that $[K-K(\infty)\cdot I]$ is inside $\{0, [K(0)-K(\infty)]\}$; the third sector is simply the sector of a constant times the identity.) On summing the three sectors (by the Sum Rule of Part I), it is found that NK is inside $\{\alpha K(\infty), \beta K(0)\}$; that is, inside $\{\alpha, \beta\}\times\{K(\infty), K(0)\}$.

CASE C. If $\alpha<0$, N is decomposed into N_{+} and N_{-}, as in Assertion 5. This case then follows by the reasoning used in Case B of Lemma 2. Q.E.D.

ACKNOWLEDGMENT

The author thanks Dr. P. Falb for correcting the manuscript, and for offering many valuable suggestions. He also thanks Dr. G. Kovatch and NASA's Electronic Research Center, Cambridge, Mass., for supporting the completion of the paper, and Mrs. Iris McDonald for typing it.

REFERENCES

[1a] G. Zames, "On the stability of nonlinear, time-varying feedback systems," *Proc. 1964 NEC*, vol. 20, pp. 725–730.

[1b] ——, "Nonlinear, time-varying feedback systems—Conditions for L_∞-boundedness derived using conic operators on exponentially weighted spaces," *Proc. 1965 Allerton Conf.*, pp. 460–471.

[1c] ——, "On the input-output stability of time-varying nonlinear feedback systems—Part I. Conditions derived using concepts of loop gain, conicity, and positivity," *IEEE Trans. on Automatic Control*, vol. AC-11, pp. 228–239, April 1966.

[2] E. A. Guillemin, *Synthesis of Passive Networks.* New York: Wiley, 1957.

[3] H. Hatanaka, "The frequency responses and jump-resonance phenomena of nonlinear feedback control systems," *Trans. ASME*, pp. 236–242, June 1963.

[4a] R. W. Brockett and J. W. Willems, "Frequency domain stability criteria, Parts I and II," *Proc. JACC*, pp. 735–747, 1965.

[4b] R. W. Brockett and L. J. Forys, "On the stability of systems containing a time-varying gain," *Proc. 1964 Allerton Conf.*, pp. 413–430.

[5] I. W. Sandberg, "A frequency domain condition for the stability of systems containing a single time-varying nonlinear element," *Bell Sys. Tech. J.*, vol. 43, p. 1601, 1964.

[6] K. S. Narendra, and R. M. Goldwyn, "A geometrical criterion for the stability of certain nonlinear, nonautonomous systems," *IEEE Trans. on Circuit Theory*, vol. CT-11, pp. 406–408, September 1964.

[7] J. Kudrewicz, "Stability of nonlinear feedback systems," *Automatika i Telemechanika*, vol. 25, no. 8, 1964.

[8] D. V. Widder, *The Laplace Transform.* Princeton, N. J.: Princeton University Press, 1946.

[9a] E. C. Titchmarsh, *Introduction to the Theory of Fourier Integrals*, 2nd ed. Oxford, England: University Press, 1962.

[9b] ——, *The Theory of Functions*, 2nd ed. Oxford, England: University Press, 1964.

[10] R. Paley and N. Wiener, *Fourier Transforms in the Complex Domain.* New York: Am. Math. Soc. Colloquium Publications, 1934.

Frequency-Domain Instability Criteria for Time-Varying and Nonlinear Systems

R. W. BROCKETT, MEMBER, IEEE, AND H. B. LEE, MEMBER, IEEE

Abstract—**Recent research has produced a number of frequency-domain stability criteria applicable to linear systems having nonlinear and/or time-varying feedback. One of the more interesting of these stability criteria is the so-called Circle Criterion which represents a generalization of the familiar result of Nyquist.**

The present paper provides a basis for generating instability counterparts of most of the available frequency-domain stability criteria. The procedure is described in detail for the Circle Criterion. Once the general pattern is established, it becomes a simple matter to generate instability counterparts of other similar stability criteria. Several worked examples are included to illustrate the theory.

The paper has been written with both the general reader and the specialist in mind; it is hoped that both will find something of interest.

I. Introduction

THE average PROCEEDINGS reader might feel that the scope and limitations of frequency-domain methods in system analysis were completely defined by the early workers. Recent research in control theory has indicated that this definitely is not the case, however. Impressive new results have been obtained in stability, optimization, passive network characterization, and even sensitivity, by using frequency-domain ideas in entirely new ways. Outstanding examples of such work can be found in the paper of Popov [1] which describes a completely rigorous frequency-domain stability criterion for nonlinear feedback systems, and that of Kalman [2] which links least-square optimization with classical sensitivity results.

In the relatively short time since Popov's work appeared, at least one hundred papers on generalizations and extensions of his stability results have been published. To the best of the present authors' knowledge, however, no corresponding instability results have been reported. The purpose of this paper is to provide a basis for generating instability counterparts for many of the recent stability criteria. Our exposition consists of thoroughly developing the instability counterpart of one particularly interesting stability criterion, and then indicating how others can be derived.

Like all of the recent stability results, our results depend heavily upon frequency-domain ideas. In large part the paper represents a fusion of elementary notions from Lyapunov stability theory, network synthesis, and optimal control.

Manuscript received December 19, 1966; revised March 15, 1967. This invited paper is one of a series planned on topics of general interest. —*The Editor*.

R. W. Brockett was supported in part by NASA Contract NGR-22-009(124). H. B. Lee was supported in part by the Joint Services Electronics Program under Contract DA 36-039-AMC-03200(E).

The authors are with the Department of Electrical Engineering, Massachusetts Institute of Technology, Cambridge, Mass.

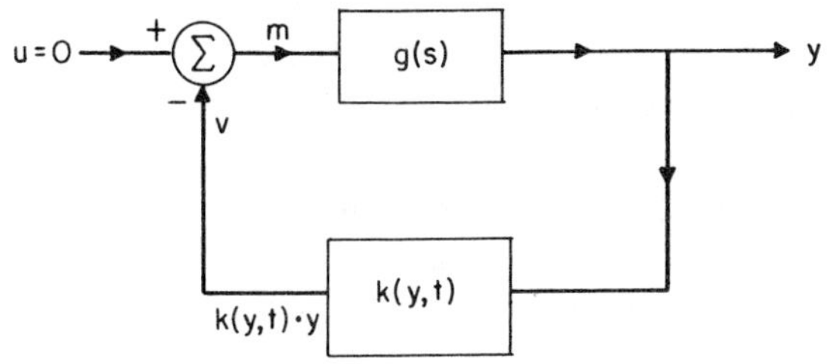

Fig. 1. The basic feedback configuration.

II. The Circle Criteria

The feedback configuration around which much of the recent stability research centers is shown in Fig. 1. The upper box represents a linear time-invariant system characterized by a transfer function $g(s)=q(s)/p(s)$, while the lower box corresponds to a gain unit that may be time-varying and/or nonlinear. For ease of reference we shall designate the aggregate system as S.

When the gain function $k(t, y)$ is linear and time-invariant, the stability of S can be preducted by Nyquist's classical result [3]. Specifically, if $g(s)$ has ρ poles in the half-plane Re $[s]>0$, then S is stable if and only if the Nyquist locus Γ of $g(j\omega)$ makes ρ counterclockwise encirclements[1] of the critical point $g=-1/k$ in the g-plane.[2]

Perhaps the most attractive of the recent stability criteria are the so-called circle criteria [4]–[12].[3] The Circle Criteria are generalizations of the conventional Nyquist result that are useful for predicting the *stability* of S when the function $k(t, y)$ satisfies a gain limitation of the form

$$\alpha \leq k(t, y) \leq \beta \tag{1}$$

where α and β denote positive constants. Note that (1) permits the gain function $k(t, y)$ to be both nonlinear and time-varying. Whereas the conventional Nyquist result involves a "critical point," the circle criteria involve two "critical disks" that shrink to the conventional critical point

[1] There are several equivalent ways of defining the notions of "clockwise encirclement" of a point. The one that we use here is as follows. *The number of times Γ encircles the $g=-1/k$ point in the clockwise sense is $1/2\pi i$ times the net change in argument of $[1/k+g(j\omega)]$ as ω is increased from minus infinity to plus infinity.*

The number of times Γ encircles the $g=-1/k$ point in the counterclockwise sense is the negative of the above.

[2] In most applications the open-loop system is stable so that $\rho=0$. In such cases Nyquist's result asserts that S is stable if and only if Γ does not encircle the $-1/k$ point.

[3] Of the original research papers we particularly recommend those of Sandberg [11] and Zames [12] as being somewhat more general with respect to assumptions on $g(s)$.

Reprinted from *Proc. IEEE*, vol. 55, pp. 604–619, May 1967.

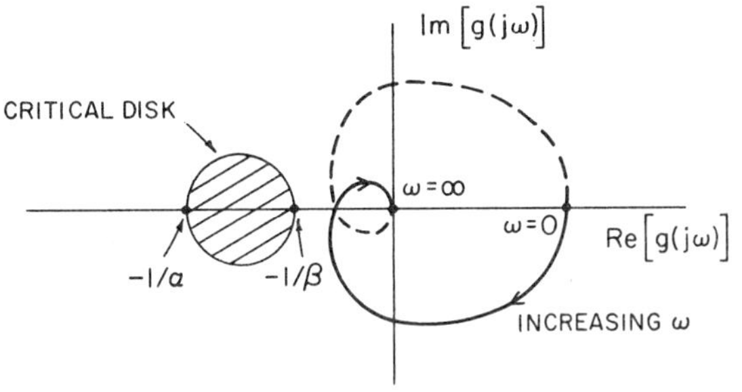

Fig. 2. Illustrating the circle criterion.

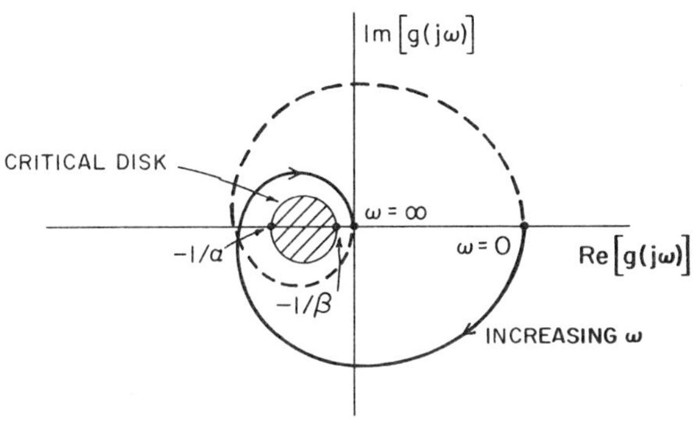

Fig. 3. An encirclement of the "critical disk."

as the gain limits α and β approach each other. These disks which we shall designate as $D(\alpha, \beta)$ and $D[\alpha, \beta]$ are, respectively, open and closed disks[4] in the g-plane, centered at the point $g = -(\alpha+\beta)/2\alpha\beta$ and having radius $|\alpha-\beta|/2\alpha\beta$ (see Fig. 2). Specifically, the circle criteria are as follows.

1) If Γ does not intersect the disk $D(\alpha, \beta)$ and encircles it ρ times in the counterclockwise direction,[5] then S is stable in the sense that all sets of initial conditions lead to outputs (y) that are bounded as $t \to \infty$.[6]
2) If Γ does not intersect the disk $D[\alpha, \beta]$ and encircles it ρ times in the counterclockwise direction, then S is stable in the sense that all sets of initial conditions lead to outputs that approach zero as $t \to \infty$.

Notice that criteria 1) and 2) predict stability for a system having a stable $g(s)$ with the Nyquist locus shown in Fig. 2.

In the present paper we devote a large part of our attention to deriving instability counterparts of the circle criteria. Once this has been accomplished, we indicate how the results can be used to generate instability counterparts of other recent stability criteria.

In essence the instability counterparts of the circle criteria that we obtain are as follows.

3) If Γ does not intersect the disk $D(\alpha, \beta)$ and encircles it fewer than ρ times in the counterclockwise direction, then S is unstable in the sense that one or more sets of initial conditions lead to outputs that do not approach zero as $t \to \infty$.
4) If Γ does not intersect the disk $D[\alpha, \beta]$ and encircles it fewer than ρ times in the counterclockwise direction, then S is unstable in the sense that one or more sets of initial conditions lead to outputs that grow without bound as $t \to \infty$.[7,8]

Note that the above criteria predict instability for a system having a stable $g(s)$ with the Nyquist locus shown in Fig. 3.

III. Preliminaries and Basic Assumptions

We will use boldface lower-case letters to denote (column) vectors; boldface capitals denote square matrices. We use a prime for the transpose, so that $\mathbf{c}'\mathbf{x}(t)$, for example, is a scalar quantity. If m is a function of time, then $\hat{m}$ denotes its (single-sided) Laplace transform; its time derivatives are denoted by $d^i m/dt^i = m^{(i)}$ or $d^i m/dt = D^i m$ with the additional option $dm/dt = \dot{m}$.

We will make use of several concepts that have become standard in control theory. Thus, for example, we freely employ the notions of state, observability, etc. The nonspecialist can find explanations of these ideas in any one of several recent books on system theory (e.g., Zadeh and Desoer [13]).

With regard to the linear time-invariant unit of S, it is assumed that

A1) *the degree of $p(s)$ exceeds that of $q(s)$.*

Thus this unit can be described by a pair of equations of the form

$$\begin{bmatrix} \dot{x}_1(t) \\ \dot{x}_2(t) \\ \vdots \\ \dot{x}_{n-1}(t) \\ \dot{x}_n(t) \end{bmatrix} = \begin{bmatrix} 0 & 1 & 0 & \cdots & 0 \\ 0 & 0 & 1 & \cdots & 0 \\ \cdots & \cdots & \cdots & \cdots & \cdots \\ 0 & 0 & 0 & \cdots & 1 \\ -p_0 & -p_1 & -p_2 & \cdots & p_{n-1} \end{bmatrix} \begin{bmatrix} x_1(t) \\ x_2(t) \\ \vdots \\ x_{n-1}(t) \\ x_n(t) \end{bmatrix} + \begin{bmatrix} 0 \\ 0 \\ \vdots \\ 1 \end{bmatrix} m(t) \tag{2a}$$

$$y(t) = [q_0, q_1, \cdots, q_{n-1}][x_1(t), x_2(t), \cdots, x_n(t)]' \tag{2b}$$

where the column vector $[x_1, x_2, \cdots, x_n]'$ summarizes the unit's state, the p_i and q_j are real constants, and the scalar functions $m(t)$ and $y(t)$ are the input and output variables indicated in Fig. 1.

For the sake of easy reference, (2a) and (2b) are abbreviated

[4] Recall that an open disk does not include its boundary whereas a closed disk does.

[5] With regard to the notions of clockwise and counterclockwise encirclements of a disk, we adhere to the following. Γ is said to encircle a disk D if it does not interesect D. In such cases the number of encirclements of the disk is the number of times that Γ encircles any point within D.

[6] Note that if $\rho = 0$ this result asserts that S is stable provided Γ makes no encirclements of $D(\alpha, \beta)$.

Note that if $\rho = 0$ then this result asserts that S is unstable if Γ encircles $D[\alpha, \beta]$ one or more times in the clockwise sense.

[8] It can be shown that Γ cannot encircle $D(\alpha, \beta)$ or $D[\alpha, \beta]$ more than ρ times in the counterclockwise sense. Thus results 1)–4) account for all possibilities of encirclement.

$$\dot{x}(t) = Ax(t) + bm(t); \qquad y(t) = c'x(t). \tag{3a, b}$$

An elementary calculation shows that (2a) and (2b) imply the following relationship between the transforms of m and y, the input and output variables:

$$\frac{\hat{y}}{\hat{m}} = \frac{q(s)}{p(s)} = \frac{q_{n-1}s^{n-1} \cdots + q_1 s + q_0}{s^n + p_{n-1}s^{n-1} \cdots + p_1 s + p_0}. \tag{4}$$

It further is assumed that

A2) *the polynomials $p(s)$ and $q(s)$ do not have common factors.*

We note in passing that (2a) is controllable. In this case assumption A2) is both necessary and sufficient to insure observability.

Finally, to avoid any possible ambiguity about the Nyquist locus, we will assume that

A3) *$g(s)=q(s)/p(s)$ is analytic on the axis* Re $[s]=0$, *and has ρ poles in the half-plane* Re $[s]>0$.

With regard to the gain unit of S, it is assumed that $k(t, y)$ satisfies a condition of the form (1).

Moreover, since for our purposes a nonlinear time-varying gain function can always be replaced by an equivalent linear time-varying gain, it is assumed that

A4) *the gain unit is characterized by a linear time-varying gain $k(t)$ that satisfies either*

$$0 < \alpha \le k(t) \le \beta < \infty \tag{5a}$$

with $\alpha<\beta$ (positive gain) or

$$-\infty < \alpha \le k(t) \le \beta < 0 \tag{5b}$$

with $\alpha<\beta$ (negative gain).

Equations (2a, b) and (5a, b) together with the relationships

$$m = u - v \text{ and } u = 0 \tag{6a, b}$$

completely characterize S. Elimination of the variables u, v, and y from (2a, b), (5a, b), and (6a, b) leads to the following equivalent characterization of S:

$$\begin{bmatrix} \dot{x}_1(t) \\ \dot{x}_2(t) \\ \vdots \\ \dot{x}_{n-1}(t) \\ \dot{x}_n(t) \end{bmatrix} = \begin{bmatrix} 0 & 1 & 0 & \cdots & 0 \\ 0 & 0 & 1 & \cdots & 0 \\ \cdots & \cdots & \cdots & \cdots & \cdots \\ 0 & 0 & 0 & \cdots & 1 \\ -p_0 & -p_1 & -p_2 & \cdots & -p_{n-1} \end{bmatrix} \begin{bmatrix} x_1(t) \\ x_2(t) \\ \vdots \\ x_{n-1}(t) \\ x_n(t) \end{bmatrix} - k(t) \begin{bmatrix} 0 & 0 & \cdots & 0 \\ 0 & 0 & \cdots & 0 \\ \cdots & \cdots & \cdots & \cdots \\ 0 & 0 & \cdots & 0 \\ q_0 & q_1 & \cdots & q_{n-1} \end{bmatrix} \begin{bmatrix} x_1(t) \\ x_2(t) \\ \vdots \\ x_{n-1}(t) \\ x_n(t) \end{bmatrix}; \tag{7a}$$

$$y(t) = [q_0, q_1, \cdots, q_{n-1}][x_1(t), x_2(t), \cdots, x_n(t)]'. \tag{7b}$$

To ensure that (7a) admits of a well-defined solution passing through every initial state $x(0)$, it is assumed that

A5) *$k(t)$ is integrable in the sense of Lebesgue over every finite interval.*

Under this assumption, given any initial state $x(0)$ there exists a unique absolutely continuous $x(t)$ that satisfies (7a) almost everywhere. (See Sansone and Conti [14], page 15.)

Elimination of the variables $x_2, x_3, \cdots, x_n$ from the set of n scalar equations implied by (7a) leads to the following useful scalar equation for $x_1(t)$:

$$[D^n + p_{n-1}D^{n-1} \cdots + p_1 D + p_0]x_1(t) + k(t)[q_{n-1}D^{n-1} \cdots + q_1 D + q_0]x_1(t) = 0. \tag{8}$$

The use of the abbreviations

$$p(D) = D^n + p_{n-1}D^{n-1} \cdots + p_1 D + p_0;$$

$$q(D) = q_{n-1}D^{n-1} \cdots + q_1 D + q_0$$

yields the equivalent equation

$$p(D)x_1(t) + k(t)q(D)x_1(t) = 0. \tag{9}$$

At this point we can make the following more precise statements of our results.

Theorem 1

Let assumptions A1)–A5) be satisfied. Moreover, suppose the Nyquist locus of $g(j\omega)=q(j\omega)/p(j\omega)$ does not intersect $D(\alpha, \beta)$ and encircles it fewer than ρ times in the counterclockwise sense. Then for at least one initial state $x(0)$, the solution of (7a, b) is unstable in the sense that:

a) there exists a positive constant a such that for all $t>0$

$$\|x(t)\|^2 \ge a; \; \|x(t)\|^2 = [x_1^2(t) + x_2^2(t) \cdots + x_n^2(t)] \tag{10}$$

b) there exists a positive constant b such that

$$|y(t)| \ge b \tag{11}$$

at least once in every unit interval $t' \le t \le t'+1$, $t'>0$.

Theorem 2

Let assumptions A1)–A5) be satisfied. Moreover, assume that the Nyquist locus of $g(j\omega)=q(j\omega)/p(j\omega)$ does not intersect $D[\alpha, \beta]$ and encircles it fewer than ρ times in the counterclockwise sense. Then for at least one initial state $x(0)$, the solution of (7a, b) is unstable in the sense that:

a) $\|x(t)\|^2 \to \infty$ as $t \to \infty$ (12)

b) given *any* positive constant c, there exists a t_0 such that

$$|y(t)| \ge c \tag{13}$$

at least once in every interval $t' \le t \le t'+1$, $t'>t_0$.

Notice that the implication of Theorem 1 is that the origin is not asymptotically stable in the sense of Lyapunov [15] and that the implication of Theorem 2 is that the origin is not even stable in the sense of Lyapunov.

IV. The Lemmas

Our proofs of Theorems 1 and 2 are of the Lyapunov type [15]. The reader will recall that such proofs involve the generation of an "energy-like" function of the state variables called a *Lyapunov function*. Stability is proven by showing that the Lyapunov function either is bounded or tends to zero at $t \to \infty$, so that the state variables do likewise.

Instability is proven by establishing that, for suitable initial conditions, the Lyapunov function either is bounded away from zero or approaches infinity as $t \to \infty$.

The present section is concerned with the generation of Lyapunov functions that can be used to prove Theorems 1 and 2. For the sake of easy reference, the results are stated as lemmas. The content of the lemmas can be summarized as follows. Lemmas 1–3 serve as background for Lemma 4 which relates the Nyquist loci and the critical disks of Section II to functions $q_0(s)/p_0(s)$ that possess the property

$$0 \leq \operatorname{Re}\left[q_0(j\omega)/p_0(j\omega)\right] = \frac{p_0(j\omega)q_0(-j\omega) + p_0(-j\omega)q_0(j\omega)}{2|p_0(j\omega)|^2} \tag{14}$$

for all real ω. Lemmas 5, 6, and 7 link functions that satisfy inequality (14) to a particular quadratic form. Lemmas 5*, 6*, and 7* relate the functions that satisfy the stronger condition

$$0 < \operatorname{Re}\left[q_0(j\omega)/p_0(j\omega)\right]$$

for all real ω, to a second quadratic form. The quadratic forms of Lemmas 5, 6, 7 and 5*, 6*, 7* eventually serve as our Lyapunov functions.

Lemmas 1 through 7a) have all been used elsewhere in one form or another. The new results of this section are Lemmas 7b), 5*, 6*, and 7*.

Lemma 1

Let $p_0(s)$ and $q_0(s)$ be relatively prime polynomials having real coefficients. The quantity $q_0(s)/p_0(s)$ is a positive real function[9] if and only if

a) $$\operatorname{Re}\left[q_0(j\omega)/p_0(j\omega)\right] = \frac{p_0(j\omega)q_0(-j\omega) + p_0(-j\omega)q_0(j\omega)}{2|p_0(j\omega)|^2} \geq 0$$

for all real ω, and

b) the zeros of the polynomial $p_0(s)+q_0(s)$ are confined to the half-plane $\operatorname{Re}[s]<0$.

The above result stems from the fact that a wave reflected from a passive impedance cannot be stronger than the incident wave. A proof can be found in a paper by Weinberg and Slepian [16].[10]

Lemma 2

If $p(s)$ and $q(s)$ are relatively prime polynomials, then the related polynomials

$$p_0(s) = q(s) + \frac{1}{\alpha}\, p(s)$$

$$q_0(s) = q(s) + \frac{1}{\beta}\, p(s)$$

with $\alpha \neq 0$, $\beta \neq 0$, and $\alpha \neq \beta$ also are relatively prime.

Proof: Any common factor of $p_0(s)$ and $q_0(s)$ is a factor of both $p(s)$ and $q(s)$ since $p(s) = \alpha\beta/(\beta-\alpha)[p_0(s) - q_0(s)]$ and $q(s) = 1/(\alpha-\beta)[\alpha p_0(s) - \beta q_0(s)]$. Thus if $p(s)$ and $q(s)$ have no common factors, then $p_0(s)$ and $q_0(s)$ have no common factors.

Q.E.D.

Lemma 3

Let $p_0(s)$ and $q_0(s)$ be the polynomials of Lemma 2.

a) If the Nyquist locus Γ of $g(j\omega) = q(j\omega)/p(j\omega)$ does not intersect the disk $D(\alpha, \beta)$, then for all real ω

$$p_0(j\omega)q_0(-j\omega) + p_0(-j\omega)q_0(j\omega) \geq 0. \tag{15}$$

b) If Γ does not intersect the disk $D[\alpha, \beta]$, then for all real ω

$$p_0(j\omega)q_0(-j\omega) + p_0(-j\omega)q_0(j\omega) > 0. \tag{16}$$

Proof: a) The mapping

$$z(s) = \frac{g(s) + 1/\alpha}{g(s) + 1/\beta} \tag{17}$$

takes the exterior of the disk $D(\alpha, \beta)$ in the g-plane into the half-plane $\operatorname{Re}[z] \geq 0$. Hence, if $g(j\omega)$ is exterior to $D(\alpha, \beta)$ for all real ω, then for all real ω

$$0 \leq \operatorname{Re}\left[z(j\omega)\right] = \operatorname{Re}\left[\frac{g(j\omega) + 1/\alpha}{g(j\omega) + 1/\beta}\right] = \frac{p_0(j\omega)q_0(-j\omega) + p_0(-j\omega)q_0(j\omega)}{2|p_0(j\omega)|^2}. \tag{18}$$

Inequality (15) follows at once from (18).

b) The same argument applies here with $D(\alpha, \beta)$ replaced by $D[\alpha, \beta]$ and the weak inequality (15) replaced by the inequality (16).

Q.E.D.

Lemma 4

Let $p(s)$ and $q(s)$ be real coefficient polynomials which satisfy assumptions A1)–A3) given in Section III. Let $p_0(s)$ and $q_0(s)$ be the polynomials of Lemma 2, with α and β real.

a) If the Nyquist locus Γ of $g(j\omega) = q(j\omega)/p(j\omega)$ does not intersect the disk $D(\alpha, \beta)$ and encircles it ρ times in the counterclockwise sense, then

$$z(s) = \frac{g(s) + 1/\alpha}{g(s) + 1/\beta} = \frac{q_0(s)}{p_0(s)} \tag{19}$$

is a positive real function.

b) If Γ does not intersect $D(\alpha, \beta)$ and encircles it fewer than ρ times in the counterclockwise sense, then (19) is not positive real.

[9] The reader will recall that a function $z(s)$ is said to be a positive real function if 1) $z(s)$ is real for real s and 2) $\operatorname{Re}[z(s)] \geq 0$ for $\operatorname{Re}[s] \geq 0$. Positive real functions are of interest in circuit and system theory because they characterize *passive* systems (see, for example, Guillemin [39]).

[10] Weinberg and Slepian do not explicitly state that $q(s)$ and $p(s)$ do not have common factors, but it is clear that one must somehow avoid common factors in $\operatorname{Re}[s] \geq 0$.

Proof: Assumptions A1)–A3) together with Lemmas 2 and 3 ensure that $z(s)$ satisfies all conditions of Lemma 1 except possibly condition b). Thus it suffices to show that condition b) is satisfied under the hypothesis of Lemma 4a), and is not satisfied under the hypothesis of Lemma 4b).

The polynomial $p_0(s)+q_0(s)$ takes the form

$$p_0(s) + q_0(s) = 2\left[q(s) + \frac{1}{2}\left(\frac{1}{\alpha} + \frac{1}{\beta}\right)p(s)\right]. \tag{20}$$

The hypotheses of Lemma 4a) and b) both prevent Γ from passing through the point $g=-\frac{1}{2}(1/\alpha+1/\beta)$ (i.e., the center of the disk). Thus (20) has no j-axis zeros. According to Nyquist's theorem, (20) has $\rho-n_c$ zeros in the half-plane Re $[s]>0$, where n_c denotes the number of times Γ encircles the point $g=-\frac{1}{2}(1/\alpha+1/\beta)$ in the counterclockwise direction. Thus (20) has

$$z = \rho - n_c$$

zeros in the closed half-plane Re $[s]\geq 0$.

When the hypothesis of Lemma 4a) is satisfied, $n_c=\rho$ so that $z=0$. Thus condition b) of Lemma 1 is satisfied in this case, and (19) is positive real.

When the hypothesis of Lemma 4b) is satisfied, $n_c<\rho$ so that $z>0$. Condition b) of Lemma 1 is not satisfied in this case. Hence (19) is not positive real.

Q.E.D.

Lemma 5

Let $p_0(D)$ and $q_0(D)$ be polynomials in the differential operator $D=d/dt$. If

a) the coefficients of $p_0(D)$ and $q_0(D)$ are real, and
b) $p_0(D)$ and $q_0(D)$ are such that

$$p_0(j\omega)q_0(-j\omega) + p_0(-j\omega)q_0(j\omega) \geq 0 \tag{21}$$

for all real ω,

then there exists at least one polynomial $r_0(D)$ with real coefficients such that

$$2r_0(D)r_0(-D) = p_0(D)q_0(-D) + p_0(-D)q_0(D). \tag{22}$$

This result is well known [17] and is basic in network synthesis and least-squares optimization. Accordingly, we do not give a proof here.

Lemma 6

Let $r_0(D)$ be any polynomial with real coefficients that solves (22). Then the function

$$[p_0(D)x(t)][q_0(D)x(t)] - [r_0(D)x(t)]^2 \tag{23}$$

is the time derivative of a quadratic form in the variables $x(t), x^{(1)}(t), \cdots, x^{(n-1)}(t)$. That is, there exists a constant, real, symmetric matrix $\boldsymbol{K}_0$ such that

$$d/dt[\boldsymbol{x}'\boldsymbol{K}_0\boldsymbol{x}] = [p_0(D)x(t)][q_0(D)x(t)] - [r_0(D)x(t)]^2 \tag{24}$$

where $\boldsymbol{x}$ denotes a column vector having $x(t), x^{(1)}, \cdots, x^{(n-1)}(t)$ as its elements.

For a proof of this result see Brockett [18], [19].

We now come to the main results of the section.

Lemma 7

If the polynomials $p_0(D)$ and $q_0(D)$ are relatively prime, then the matrix $\boldsymbol{K}_0$ of Lemma 6

a) is positive definite if the function $q_0(s)/p_0(s)$ is positive real
b) is neither positive definite nor positive semidefinite if $q_0(s)/p_0(s)$ is not positive real.

Proof:[11] a) If $q_0(s)/p_0(s)$ is positive real, then $p_0(s)+q_0(s)$ has all of its zeros in the half-plane Re $[s]<0$ (see Lemma 1). Consequently, the general solution of the differential equation

$$p_0(D)x(t) + q_0(D)x(t) = 0 \tag{25}$$

takes the form

$$x(t) = \sum_i c_i t^{d_i} e^{-a_i t}\cos(b_i t + \phi_i) \tag{26}$$

with the $a_i>0$. Let $\boldsymbol{x}$ be an arbitrary real, nonzero, column matrix having elements $x_1, x_2, \cdots, x_n$, and let $x_0(t)$ denote the solution to (25) that satisfies the inital conditions $[x_0(0), x_0^{(1)}(0), \cdots, x_0^{(n-1)}(0)]'=\boldsymbol{x}_0$. According to (24) and (25)

$$\boldsymbol{x}_0'\boldsymbol{K}_0\boldsymbol{x}_0\Big|_0^\infty = \int_0^\infty [p_0(D)x_0(t)][q_0(D)x_0(t)] - [r_0(D)x_0(t)]^2dt$$

$$= -\int_0^\infty [q_0(D)x_0(t)]^2 + [r_0(D)x_0(t)]^2dt. \tag{27}$$

The form (26) of the general solution to (25) requires that $\boldsymbol{x}_0'(\infty)\boldsymbol{K}_0\boldsymbol{x}_0(\infty)=0$. Thus (27) reduces to

$$x_0'K_0x_0 = \int_0^\infty [q_0(D)x_0(t)]^2 + [r_0(D)x_0(t)]^2dt. \tag{28}$$

The quantity $q_0(D)x_0(t)\not\equiv 0$ if $\boldsymbol{x}_0\neq 0$, for otherwise $q_0(s)$ and $p_0(s)$ would have common zeros, contradicting the hypothesis that $q_0(s)$ and $p_0(s)$ are relatively prime. In addition, $q_0(D)x_0(t)$ is continuous. Hence it follows from (28) that $\boldsymbol{x}_0'\boldsymbol{K}_0\boldsymbol{x}_0>0$ for $\boldsymbol{x}_0\neq 0$.

b) Here it suffices to give a real column vector $\boldsymbol{x}$ for which $\boldsymbol{x}_0'\boldsymbol{K}_0\boldsymbol{x}_0<0$.

If $q_0(s)/p_0(s)$ is not positive real, then $p_0(s)+q_0(s)$ has one or more roots in the half-plane Re $[s]\geq 0$ (Lemma 1). But $q_0(s)+p_0(s)$ cannot have j-axis zeros since

$$\text{Re}\left[\frac{q_0(j\omega)+p_0(j\omega)}{p_0(j\omega)}\right] = \frac{p_0(j\omega)q_0(-j\omega)+p_0(-j\omega)q_0(j\omega)}{2|p_0(j\omega)|^2} + 1 \geq 1$$

for all real ω. Hence $p_0(s)+q_0(s)$ has one or more roots in the half-plane Re $[s]>0$. If $a+jb$ denotes one such zero, then

[11] A somewhat shorter version of part a) of this proof, using standard results from Lyapunov theory, has already appeared [18], [20]. It is also possible to shorten the proof of part b) by using known properties of $\boldsymbol{KA}+\boldsymbol{A}'\boldsymbol{K}'=-\boldsymbol{C}$. Appendix II considers additional aspects of Lemma 7.

$$x_0(t) = e^{at}\cos\{bt - \operatorname{Arg}[q_0(a+jb)]\}$$

is a solution of (25), According to (24) and (25)

$$\boldsymbol{x}_0'(t)\boldsymbol{K}_0\boldsymbol{x}_0(t)\Big|_0^T = -\int_0^T [q_0(D)x_0(t)]^2 + [r_0(D)x_0(t)]^2 dt$$

so that

$$\begin{aligned}\boldsymbol{x}_0'(T)&\boldsymbol{K}_0\boldsymbol{x}_0(T)\\ &= \boldsymbol{x}_0'(0)\boldsymbol{K}_0\boldsymbol{x}_0(0) - \int_0^T [q_0(D)x_0(t)]^2 + [r_0(D)x_0(t)]^2 dt\\ &\le \boldsymbol{x}_0'(0)\boldsymbol{K}_0\boldsymbol{x}_0(0) - |q_0(a+jb)|^2\int_0^T e^{2at}\cos^2 bt\,dt\\ &\le \boldsymbol{x}_0'(0)\boldsymbol{K}_0\boldsymbol{x}_0(0) - |q_0(a+jb)|^2 T/4 \end{aligned} \tag{29}$$

for $T \ge 0$. The quantity $q_0(a+jb) \ne 0$ because $q_0(s)$ and $p_0(s)$ are relatively prime. Hence

$$\boldsymbol{x}_0'(T)\boldsymbol{K}_0\boldsymbol{x}_0(T) < 0 \tag{30}$$

for $T > |4\boldsymbol{x}_0'(0)\boldsymbol{K}_0\boldsymbol{x}_0(0)/q_0^2(a+jb)|$.

Q.E.D.

*Lemma 5**

Let $p_0(D)$ and $q_0(D)$ be polynomials in $D = d/dt$. If

a) the coefficients of $p_0(D)$ and $q_0(D)$ are real
b) the degrees of $p_0(D)$ and $q_0(D)$ are equal, and
c) $p_0(D)$ and $q_0(D)$ are such that for all real ω

$$p_0(j\omega)q_0(-j\omega) + p_0(-j\omega)q_0(j\omega) > 0 \tag{31}$$

then for real ε of sufficiently small absolute value, the equation

$$\begin{aligned}2r_0(D)r_0(-D) = p_0(D+\varepsilon)&q_0(-D+\varepsilon)\\ &+ p_0(-D+\varepsilon)q_0(D+\varepsilon)\end{aligned} \tag{32}$$

possesses a real coefficient solution, $r_0(D)$.

Proof: It is well known that (32) has a real coefficient solution for $r_0(D)$, provided

$$p_0(j\omega+\varepsilon)q_0(-j\omega+\varepsilon) + p_0(-j\omega+\varepsilon)q_0(j\omega+\varepsilon) \ge 0 \tag{33}$$

for all ω. Thus it suffices to show that inequality (33) is satisfied for small ε.

Let m denote the minimum value of the quantity

$$\operatorname{Re}\left[\frac{q_0(j\omega)}{p_0(j\omega)}\right] = \frac{p_0(j\omega)q_0(-j\omega) + p_0(-j\omega)q_0(j\omega)}{2|p_0(j\omega)|^2} \tag{34}$$

over the closed interval $-\infty \le \omega \le \infty$. Condition (31) and hypothesis b) of Lemma 5* ensure that $m > 0$.

The polynomial $p_0(s)$ cannot have a zero on the imaginary axis in view of (31). Thus $d/ds[q_0(s)/p_0(s)] = [p_0(s)q_0'(s) - p_0'(s)q_0(s)]/p_0^2(s)$ can be bounded by a positive constant M within a strip $-|d| \le \operatorname{Re}[s] \le |d|$ with $|d| > 0$. It follows that

$$\begin{aligned}\frac{p_0(j\omega+\varepsilon)q_0(-j\omega+\varepsilon) + p_0(-j\omega+\varepsilon)q_0(j\omega+\varepsilon)}{2|p_0(j\omega+\varepsilon)|^2}\\ = \operatorname{Re}\left[\frac{q_0(j\omega+\varepsilon)}{p_0(j\omega+\varepsilon)}\right]\\ \ge \operatorname{Re}\left[\frac{q_0(j\omega)}{p_0(j\omega)}\right] - |\varepsilon|M\\ \ge m - |\varepsilon|M\end{aligned} \tag{35}$$

for $|\varepsilon| \le |d|$. Inequality (35) shows that (33) follows for $|\varepsilon| \le \min[|d|, m/M]$.

Q.E.D.

*Lemma 6**

If (33) has a real coefficient solution $r_0(D)$, then there exists a constant real symmetric matrix $\boldsymbol{K}_1$ such that

$$\begin{aligned}d/dt[\boldsymbol{x}'(t)\boldsymbol{K}_1\boldsymbol{x}(t)] \equiv 2\varepsilon \boldsymbol{x}'(t)\boldsymbol{K}_1\boldsymbol{x}(t)\\ + [p_0(D)x(t)][q_0(D)x(t)] - [r_0(D-\varepsilon)x(t)]^2\end{aligned} \tag{36}$$

where $\boldsymbol{x}(t)$ denotes a column matrix having $x(t), x^{(1)}(t), \cdots, x^{(n-1)}(t)$ as its elements.

Proof: Inequality (33) must be satisfied, for otherwise (32) does not have a real coefficient solution. Thus according to Lemma 6, there exists a quadratic form $\boldsymbol{z}'(t)\boldsymbol{K}_0\boldsymbol{z}(t)$ such that

$$\begin{aligned}d/dt[\boldsymbol{z}'(t)\boldsymbol{K}_0\boldsymbol{z}(t)]\\ = [p_0(D+\varepsilon)z(t)][q_0(D+\varepsilon)z(t)] - [r_0(D)z(t)]^2\end{aligned} \tag{37}$$

where $\boldsymbol{z}(t)$ is a column vector having $z(t), z^{(1)}(t), \cdots, z^{(n-1)}(t)$ as its elements. Let

$$z(t) = e^{-\varepsilon t}x(t). \tag{38}$$

Making this substitution in the quadratic form $\boldsymbol{z}'(t)\boldsymbol{K}_1\boldsymbol{z}(t)$ leads to a quadratic form in the $x^{(i)}(t)$, multiplied by $e^{-2\varepsilon t}$. Thus there exists a constant real symmetric matrix $\boldsymbol{K}_1$ such that

$$\boldsymbol{z}'(t)\boldsymbol{K}_0\boldsymbol{z}(t) = e^{-2\varepsilon t}\boldsymbol{x}'(t)\boldsymbol{K}_1\boldsymbol{x}(t) \tag{39}$$

where $\boldsymbol{x}(t)$ is a column vector having $x(t), x^{(1)}, \cdots, x^{(n-1)}(t)$ as its components. Substitution of (39) and (38) in (37), followed by use of the identities $m(D+\varepsilon)[e^{-\varepsilon t}x(t)] \equiv e^{-\varepsilon t}m(D)x(t)$ and $m(D)[e^{-\varepsilon t}x(t)] \equiv e^{-\varepsilon t}m(D-\varepsilon)x(t)$, and cancellation of the factor $e^{-2\varepsilon t}$ yields (36).

Q.E.D.

*Lemma 7**

Let the polynomials $p_0(D)$ and $q_0(D)$ be relatively prime. Then for real ε of sufficiently small absolute value the matrix $\boldsymbol{K}_1$ of Lemma 6*

a) is positive definite if the function $q_0(s)/p_0(s)$ is positive real
b) is neither positive definite nor positive semi-definite if $q_0(s)/p_0(s)$ is not positive real.

Proof: a) Equation (36) can be rewritten as

$$d/dt[e^{-2\varepsilon t}\boldsymbol{x}'(t)\boldsymbol{K}_1\boldsymbol{x}(t)] = e^{-2\varepsilon t}[p_0(D)x(t)][q_0(D)x(t)] - e^{-2\varepsilon t}[r_0(D-\varepsilon)x(t)]^2. \quad (40)$$

Along the solution $x_0(t)$ considered in the proof of Lemma 7a), (40) takes the form

$$d/dt[e^{-2\varepsilon t}\boldsymbol{x}_0'(t)\boldsymbol{K}_1\boldsymbol{x}_0(t)] = -e^{-2\varepsilon t}\{[q_0(D)x_0(t)]^2 + [r_0(D-\varepsilon)x_0(t)]^2\}. \quad (41)$$

Integration of (41) on the interval $[0, \infty]$ yields

$$\boldsymbol{x}_0'\boldsymbol{K}_1\boldsymbol{x}_0 = \int_0^\infty e^{-2\varepsilon t}\{[q_0(D)x_0(t)]^2 + [r_0(D-\varepsilon]x_0(t)]^2\}\,dt \quad (42)$$

for

$$-\min_i [a_i] < \varepsilon. \quad (43)$$

The right-hand member of (42) is positive according to the argument given in the proof of Lemma 7b). Thus $\boldsymbol{x}'\boldsymbol{K}_1\boldsymbol{x}>0$ for $\boldsymbol{x}\neq 0$ provided (43) is satisfied.

b) Equation (40) takes the following form along the solution $x_0(t)$ considered in the proof of Lemma 7b):

$$d/dt[e^{-2\varepsilon t}\boldsymbol{x}_0'(t)\boldsymbol{K}_1\boldsymbol{x}_0(t)] = -e^{2(a-\varepsilon)t}\{|q_0(a+jb)|^2\cos^2 + |r_0(a-\varepsilon+jb)|^2\cos^2[bt + \operatorname{Arg} r_0(a+jb) - \operatorname{Arg} q_0(a+b)]\}. \quad (44)$$

Integration of (44) over the interval $[0, T]$ and use of the argument given in Lemma 7b) shows that $\boldsymbol{x}_0'(T)\boldsymbol{K}_1\boldsymbol{x}_0(T)<0$ for sufficiently large T, provided $0\leq a-\varepsilon$. Thus $\boldsymbol{K}_1$ is neither positive definite nor positive semidefinite for $\varepsilon\leq a$.

Q.E.D.

V. Proofs of Theorems 1 and 2

We prove Theorem 1a) by showing that, for a suitable choice of initial conditions, the quantity $\boldsymbol{x}'(t)\boldsymbol{K}_0\boldsymbol{x}(t)$ (i.e., our first Lyapunov function) is bounded away from zero as $t\to\infty$. Theorem 1b) then follows with the aid of an elementary result from the Theory of Optimal Control. Theorem 2a) is proved by showing that, for a suitable choice of initial conditions, the quantity $\boldsymbol{x}'(t)\boldsymbol{K}_1\boldsymbol{x}(t)$ (i.e., our second Lyapunov function) approaches minus infinity as $t\to\infty$. Theorem 2b) then follows easily.

The proofs of both theorems rely heavily on an alternative expression of (9) which takes the form

$$\{[1/k(t)] - [1/\beta]\}p_0(D)x_1(t) + \{[1/\alpha] - [1/k(t)]\}q_0(D)x_1(t) = 0 \quad (45)$$

where

$$p_0(D) = q(D) + [1/\alpha]p(D) \quad (46a)$$
$$q_0(D) = q(D) + [1/\beta]p(D). \quad (46b)$$

To see that (45) is equivalent to (9), one merely needs to substitute these expressions into (45).

Proof of Theorem 1

a) Lemmas 1–7 have established that, when assumptions A1)–A5) given in Section III are satisfied, and Γ encircles $D(\alpha, \beta)$ fewer than ρ times, the following conditions obtain: 1) inequality (15) is satisfied (Lemma 3), 2) the quantity $q_0(s)/p_0(s)$ is not positive real (Lemma 4), 3) (22) admits a real coefficient solution for $r_0(D)$ (Lemma 5), 4) there exists a real symmetric matrix $\boldsymbol{K}_0$ that satisfies (24) (Lemma 6), and 5) the matrix $\boldsymbol{K}_0$ is neither positive definite nor positive semidefinite (Lemma 7).

Thus there exist column vectors $\boldsymbol{x}$ such that $\boldsymbol{x}'\boldsymbol{K}_0\boldsymbol{x}<0$. Let $\boldsymbol{n}=[n_1, n_2, \cdots, n_n]'$ be one such vector. In addition let $\boldsymbol{x}(t)$ denote the solution of (7a) that satisfies the initial conditions

$$\boldsymbol{x}(0) = \boldsymbol{n}. \quad (47)$$

Consider the quadratic form $\boldsymbol{x}'(t)\boldsymbol{K}_0\boldsymbol{x}(t)$. Evidently

$$\boldsymbol{x}'(0)\boldsymbol{K}_0\boldsymbol{x}(0) = \boldsymbol{n}\boldsymbol{K}_0\boldsymbol{n} < 0. \quad (48)$$

Use of (5a) or (5b) in (24) for the derivative of $\boldsymbol{x}(t)\boldsymbol{K}_0\boldsymbol{x}(t)$ yields

$$d/dt[\boldsymbol{x}'(t)\boldsymbol{K}_0\boldsymbol{x}(t)] = \begin{cases} \dfrac{[1/\alpha]-[1/k(t)]}{[1/\beta]-[1/k(t)]}[q_0(D)x_1(t)]^2 - [r_0(D)x_1(t)]^2 \\ \dfrac{[1/\beta]-[1/k(t)]}{[1/\alpha]-[1/k(t)]}[p_0(D)x_1(t)]^2 - [r_0(D)x_1(t)]^2 \end{cases} \quad (49)$$

where the first expression is valid if $k(t)\neq\beta$, the second is valid if $k(t)\neq\alpha$ and either is correct otherwise. Clearly all terms in (49) are nonpositive if $\alpha\leq k(t)\leq\beta$. Thus $\boldsymbol{x}'(t)\boldsymbol{K}_0\boldsymbol{x}(t)$ is nonincreasing. That is,

$$\boldsymbol{x}'(t)\boldsymbol{K}_0\boldsymbol{x}(t) \leq \boldsymbol{x}'(0)\boldsymbol{K}_0\boldsymbol{x}(0) = -|\boldsymbol{n}\boldsymbol{K}_0\boldsymbol{n}| \quad (50)$$

for $t>0$. The quadratic form $\boldsymbol{x}'(t)\boldsymbol{K}_0\boldsymbol{x}(t)$ can be bounded in terms of $\|\boldsymbol{x}(t)\|^2=\boldsymbol{x}'(t)\boldsymbol{x}(t)$ using the standard inequality (Bellman, [21], page 113)

$$-|\lambda_k|\boldsymbol{x}'\boldsymbol{x} \leq \boldsymbol{x}'\boldsymbol{K}_0\boldsymbol{x} \quad (51)$$

where λ_k denotes the most negative eigenvalue of K. Use of (51) in (50) yields

$$\|\boldsymbol{x}(t)\|^2 \geq \frac{1}{|\lambda_k|}|\boldsymbol{n}\boldsymbol{K}_0\boldsymbol{n}| \quad (52)$$

for $t\geq 0$. Thus (10) follows with $a=|\boldsymbol{n}\boldsymbol{K}_0\boldsymbol{n}|/|\lambda_k|$ for the choice of initial conditions (47).

Q.E.D.

b) According to a result well known in the Theory of Optimal Control (see Athans and Falb [22], page 782) there exists for (2a) and (2b) a function $m(t)$ that minimizes the integral

$$J = \int_{t'}^{t'+1} [m^2(t) + y^2(t)]dt$$
$$= \int_{t'}^{t'+1} [m^2(t) + \boldsymbol{x}(t)\boldsymbol{c}\boldsymbol{c}'\boldsymbol{x}(t)]dt \tag{53}$$

when the state vector $\boldsymbol{x}(t)$ is subject to an initial condition of of the form

$$\boldsymbol{x}(t') = \boldsymbol{\chi} = [\chi_1, \chi_2, \cdots, \chi_n]'.$$

Moreover, the minimum value of J can be expressed as a quadratic form in $\boldsymbol{\chi}$. That is, there exists a real, constant, symmetric matrix $\boldsymbol{Q}$ (independent of χ) such that

$$\boldsymbol{\chi}'\boldsymbol{Q}\boldsymbol{\chi} = \underset{\substack{m(t)\\ \boldsymbol{x}(t')=\boldsymbol{\chi}}}{\text{Min}} \int_{t'}^{t'+1} [m^2(t) + y^2(t)]dt. \tag{54}$$

The matrix $\boldsymbol{Q}$ is obviously non-negative definite. In the present case where $m(t)$, $\boldsymbol{x}(t)$, and $y(t)$ are related by the observable description (2a, b), the quadratic form is positive definite. To see this, note that

$$m(t) = p(D)x_1(t) \quad \text{and} \quad y(t) = q(D)x_1(t). \tag{55}$$

For (54) to be zero $x_1(t)$ must simultaneously satisfy

$$p(D)x_1(t) = 0 \quad \text{and} \quad q(D)x_1(t) = 0. \tag{56a, b}$$

But (56a) and (56b) admit only the zero solution since $p(D)$ and $q(D)$ have no common factors [assumption A2]. Thus (54) is zero only when $\boldsymbol{\chi} = [x_1(t'), x_1^1(t'), \cdots, x_1^{n-1}(t')]' = \mathbf{0}$.

If $m(t)$ is taken to be the input variable associated with the solution of part a) of Theorem 1 [i.e., $m(t) = k(t)y(t)$], it follows that

$$\int_{t'}^{t'+1} [k^2(t) + 1]y^2(t)\, dt \equiv \int_{t'}^{t'+1} [m^2(t) + y^2(t)]dt$$
$$\geq \underset{m(t)}{\text{Min}} \int_{t'}^{t'+1} [m^2(t) + y^2(t)]dt$$
$$\geq \boldsymbol{x}(t')\boldsymbol{Q}\boldsymbol{x}(t'). \tag{57}$$

Use of the inequality

$$\boldsymbol{x}'\boldsymbol{Q}\boldsymbol{x} \geq \lambda_q \boldsymbol{x}'\boldsymbol{x} \tag{58}$$

in (57), where λ_q denotes the smallest eigenvalue of $\boldsymbol{Q}$, indicates

$$\int_{t'}^{t'+1} [k^2(t) + 1]y^2(t)\, dt \geq \lambda_q \|\boldsymbol{x}(t')\|^2. \tag{59}$$

Since $\boldsymbol{Q}$ is positive definite we have

$$\lambda_q > 0. \tag{60}$$

Use of conditions (5a, b) and (52) in (59) leads to the self-explanatory sequence of inequalities:

$$\int_{t'}^{t'+1} y^2(t)\, dt \geq \frac{\lambda_q \|\boldsymbol{x}(t')\|^2}{\beta^2 + 1} \tag{61}$$

$$\underset{t' \leq t \leq t'+1}{\text{Max}} [y^2(t)] \geq \int_{t'}^{t'+1} y^2(t)\, dt \geq \frac{\lambda_q \|\boldsymbol{x}(t')\|^2}{\beta^2 + 1} \tag{62}$$

$$\underset{t' \leq t \leq t'+1}{\text{Max}} [|y(t)|] \geq \left[\frac{\lambda_q \|x(t')\|^2}{\beta^2 + 1}\right]^{1/2} \geq \left[\frac{\lambda_q |\boldsymbol{n}'\boldsymbol{K}_0\boldsymbol{n}|}{(\beta^2 + 1)|\lambda_k|}\right]^{1/2} \tag{63}$$

valid for $t' > 0$.

Inequality (63) shows that (11) obtains with

$$b = \left[\frac{\lambda_g |\boldsymbol{n}\boldsymbol{K}_0\boldsymbol{n}|}{|\lambda_k|(\beta^2 + 1)}\right]^{1/2}$$

for the initial conditions (47).

Q.E.D.

Proof of Theorem 2

a) The proof here parallels that of Theorem 1a), the main difference being the use of the quadratic form of Lemma 6* in place of that of Lemma 6. Specifically Lemmas 3b), 4b), 5*, 6*, and 7* ensure that for small $\varepsilon > 0$

1) There exists a quadratic form $\boldsymbol{x}_0(t)\boldsymbol{K}_1\boldsymbol{x}_0(t)$ that satisfies (36)
2) there exists a real column vector $\boldsymbol{n}$ such that $\boldsymbol{n}'\boldsymbol{K}_1\boldsymbol{n} < 0$.

Thus the following counterpart of (49) is satisfied along the solution of (7a) that satisfies the initial condition $\boldsymbol{x}(0) = \boldsymbol{n}$:

$$d/dt[\boldsymbol{x}'(t)\boldsymbol{K}_1\boldsymbol{x}(t)] = 2\varepsilon \boldsymbol{x}'(t)\boldsymbol{K}_1\boldsymbol{x}(t)$$
$$+ \frac{[1/\alpha] - [1/k(t)]}{[1/\beta] - [1/k(t)]} [q_0(D)x_1(t)]^2 - [r_0(D - \varepsilon)x_1(t)]^2$$
$$\leq 2\varepsilon \boldsymbol{x}'(t)\boldsymbol{K}_1\boldsymbol{x}(t). \tag{64}$$

Multiplication of (64) by $e^{-2\varepsilon t}$, followed by integration over the interval $[0, T]$, leads to

$$e^{-2\varepsilon T}\boldsymbol{x}'(T)K_1\boldsymbol{x}(T) - \boldsymbol{x}'(0)K_1\boldsymbol{x}(0) \leq 0$$

or

$$|\boldsymbol{n}'\boldsymbol{K}_1\boldsymbol{n}|e^{2\varepsilon T} \leq -\boldsymbol{x}'(T)\boldsymbol{K}_1\boldsymbol{x}(T). \tag{65}$$

The use in (65) of the inequality $-\boldsymbol{x}'\boldsymbol{K}_1\boldsymbol{x} \leq |\lambda_k| \|\boldsymbol{x}\|^2$ where λ_k denotes the most negative eigenvalue of $\boldsymbol{K}_1$ yields

$$\frac{|\boldsymbol{n}'\boldsymbol{K}_1\boldsymbol{n}|}{|\lambda_k|} e^{2\varepsilon T} \leq \|\boldsymbol{x}(T)\|^2. \tag{66}$$

Clearly $\|\boldsymbol{x}\|^2 \to \infty$ as $T \to \infty$. Thus (12) is satisfied for the choice of initial condition

$$\boldsymbol{x}(0) = \boldsymbol{n}. \tag{67}$$

Q.E.D.

b) Inequality (62) continues to apply. The substitution of (66) into (62) followed by square root extraction indicates

$$\max_{t' \leq t \leq t'+1} |y(t)| \geq e^{\varepsilon t} \left[\frac{\lambda_q |\boldsymbol{n}'\boldsymbol{K}_1 \boldsymbol{n}|}{|\lambda_k|(\beta^2 + 1)} \right]^{1/2} \tag{68}$$

Thus condition (13) follows with

$$t_0 = \frac{1}{2\varepsilon} \ln \frac{c^2 |\lambda_k| (\beta^2 + 1)}{\lambda_k |\boldsymbol{n}'\boldsymbol{K}_1 \boldsymbol{n}|} \tag{69}$$

and the choice of initial conditions given by (67).

Q.E.D.

VI. Discussion

Between them, the stability and instability versions of the Circle Criteria resolve the question of stability for a large class of practical systems. Moreover, the criteria are attractive because of the ease with which they can be applied. Thus before passing to a discussion of other instability results, we first briefly point out some interesting features of the circle criteria in general, and of the instability versions of these criteria in particular.

The following example illustrates the kind of conclusions that can be drawn from the Circle Criteria.

Example 1

Consider the system shown in Fig. 4. The Nyquist locus Γ for $g(j\omega)$ is shown in Fig. 5. Note that $\rho = 0$.

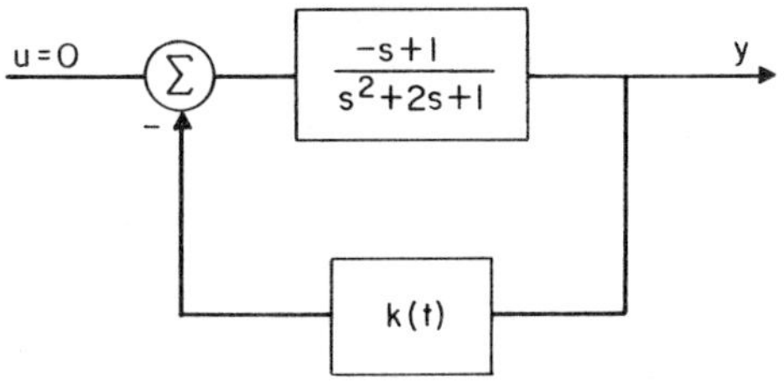

Fig. 4. The block diagram for Example 1.

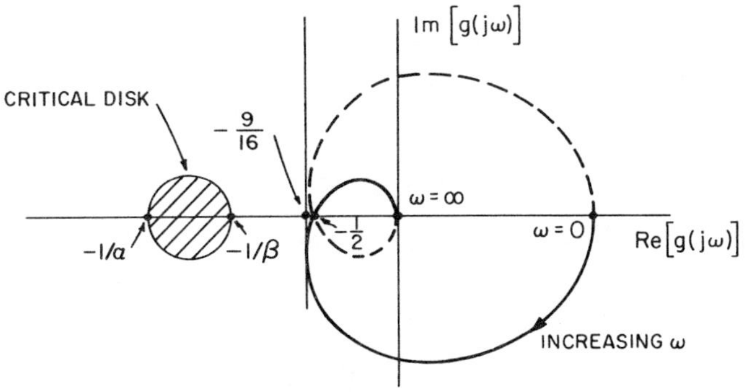

Fig. 5. The Nyquist locus of Example 1.

A side calculation[12] shows that for $1/\beta$ in the interval $1/2 > 1/\beta > 0$, Γ encircles the critical disk $D[\alpha, \beta]$ without touching it provided $\alpha > F_1(\beta)$, where

$$F_1(\beta) = \frac{9\beta^2 - 16\beta}{3\beta^2 - 9\beta + 8 + 4(\beta - 2)\sqrt{\beta + 1}}$$

while the same situation occurs for $D(\alpha, \beta)$ provided $\alpha \geq F_1(\beta)$. Thus the system is unstable

[12] Notice that Lemma 3 can be used here. Specifically, one determines the smallest value of α such that inequality (15) is satisfied.

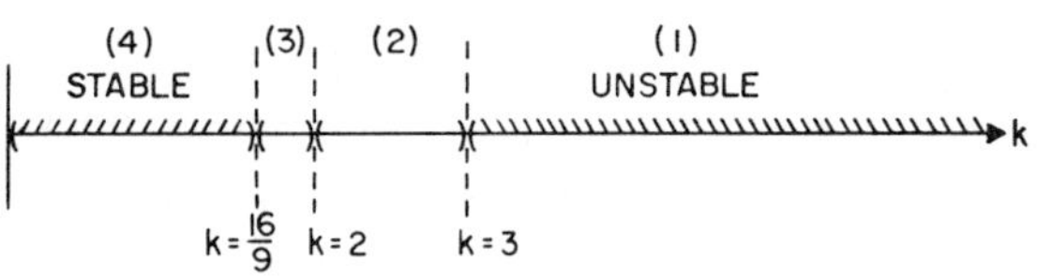

Fig. 6. The ranges of stability and instability for Example 1.

a) in the sense of Theorem 1 for any time-varying gain that satisfies

$$\alpha \leq k(t) \leq \beta \tag{70}$$

with $\beta > 0$ and $\alpha > F_1(\beta)$

b) in the sense of Theorem 2 for any time-varying gain that satisfies (70) with $\beta > 0$ and $\alpha \geq F_1(\beta)$.

It can be shown that $3 > F_1(\beta)$ for $\beta > 2$. Thus the system is unstable in both senses for $\alpha \geq 3$ and $\infty > \beta > \alpha$.

An additional calculation shows that the critical disk $D[\alpha, \beta]$ remains outside of Γ and does not touch it provided either of the following conditions is satisfied:

a) $16/9 > \beta$ and $\alpha > 0$ (71)

b) $2 > \beta > 16/9$ and $\alpha > F_2(\beta)$ (72)

where

$$F_2(\beta) = \frac{9\beta^2 - 16\beta}{3\beta^2 - 9\beta + 8 - 4(\beta - 2)\sqrt{\beta + 1}}.$$

Thus according to the stability results cited previously [4]–[12], the system is asymptotically stable in the large for any time-varying gain $k(t)$ that satisfies (70) provided either (71) or (72) is satisfied.

The above conclusions are summarized in Fig. 6. The system

a) is unstable in the sense of Theorem 2 provided α and β are restricted to interval (1) of the gain axis

b) is unstable in the sense of Theorem 2 for β in interval (2) provided $\alpha > F_1(\beta)$.

c) is asymptotically stable in the large for β in interval (3) provided $\alpha > F_2(\beta)$.

d) is asymptotically stable in the large provided α and β are restricted to interval (4).

Note that $k = 2$ corresponds to the instability borderline for the time-invariant case (i.e., k = constant).

(End of Example 1.)

As with the conventional Nyquist criteria, cases where

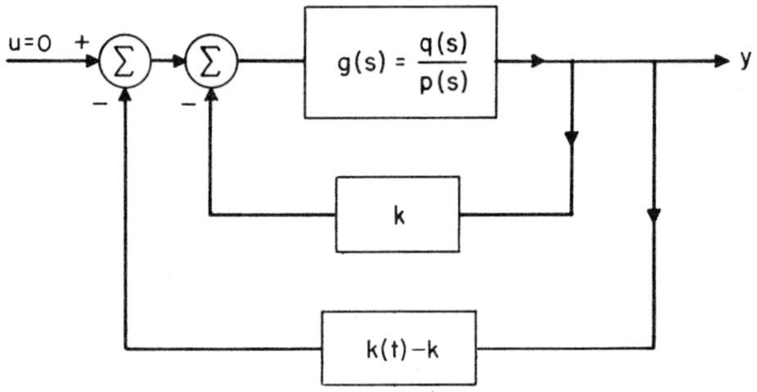

Fig. 7. Illustrating the removal of imaginary axis zeros.

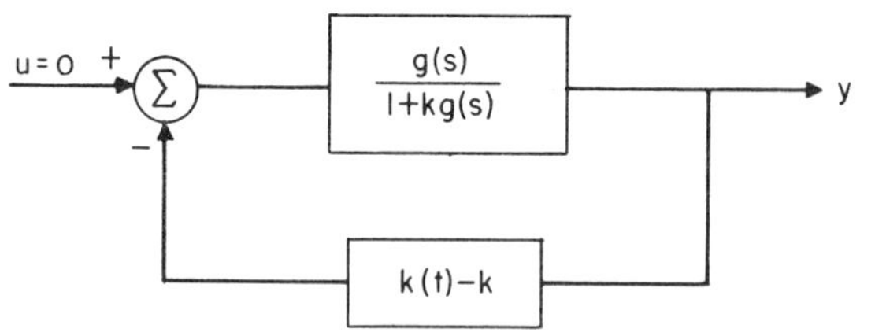

Fig. 8. System equivalent to that of Fig. 7.

$g(s)$ has j-axis poles require special treatment. A simple procedure [12] for handling such cases is to transform the system into the equivalent system shown in Fig. 7, and thence into that shown in Fig. 8. The constant k is chosen so that $p_0(s)+kq_0(s)$ has no j-axis zeros. Conditions that ensure instability or stability then are deduced by applying the available criteria to the system of Fig. 8. The following example illustrates the procedure.

Example 2

Consider the system S having

$$g(s) = \frac{-s+1}{s(s+3)}. \tag{73}$$

Because of the pole of $g(s)$ at $s=0$, the stability and instability criteria cannot directly be applied. The criteria can be applied to the equivalent system shown in Fig. 8, however, provided $p(s)+kq(s)=s^2+(3-k)s+k$ has no j-axis zeros, or $k\neq 3$. The choice $k=1$ leads to

$$g'(s) = \frac{1-s}{(s+1)^2}. \tag{74}$$

It will be recognized that $g'(s)$ is the function considered in Example 1. Thus the conclusions of Example 1 are applicable to S. Specifically, with reference to Fig. 9, the system S

a) is unstable in the sense of Theorem 2 provided α and β are restricted to interval (1)
b) is unstable in the sense of Theorem 2 for β in interval (2) provided $\alpha>1+F_1(\beta-1)$
c) is asymptotically stable in the large for β in interval (3) provided $\alpha>1+F_2(\beta-1)$
d) is asymptotically stable in the large provided α and β are restricted to interval (4).

(End of Example 2.)

Theorems 1 and 2 are useful for predicting instability when $k(t)$ is either positive for all t, or negative for all t [see assumption A4)]. By slightly modifying the arguments of the preceding sections, one can deduce criteria that are

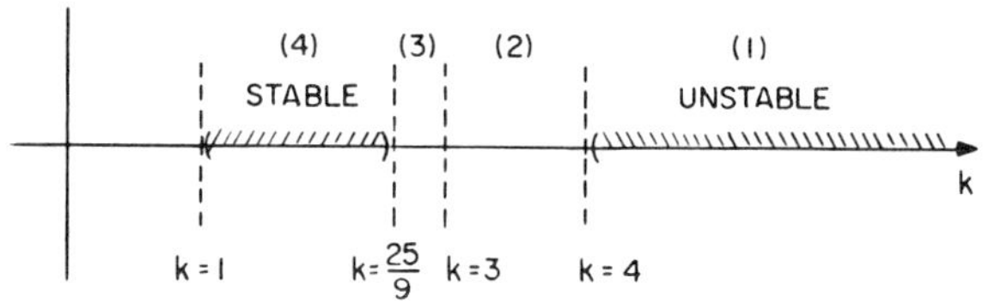

Fig. 9. Ranges of stability and instability for Example 2.

applicable when $k(t)$ takes on both signs. The criteria are given in the following theorems; proofs are outlined in Appendix I.

Theorem 3

If

a) assumptions A1)–A3), A5) given in Section III are satisfied
b) $k(t)$ satisfies $\alpha\leq k(t)\leq\beta$ with $-\infty<\alpha<0$ and $0<\beta<+\infty$
c) the Nyquist locus of $g(j\omega)$ is contained within the disk $D[\alpha,\beta]$
d) $\rho\geq 1$

then S is unstable in the sense of Theorem 1.

Theorem 4

If

a) assumptions A1)–A3), A5) are satified
b) $k(t)$ satisfies $\alpha\leq k(t)\leq\beta$ with $-\infty<\alpha<0$ and $0<\beta<+\infty$
c) the Nyquist locus of $g(j\omega)$ is contained within the disk $D(\alpha,\beta)$
d) $\rho\geq 1$

then S is unstable in the sense of Theorem 2.

The above theorems represent instability counterparts of stability theorems given by Sandberg [11] and Zames [12]. Although interesting from an academic point of view, Theorems 3 and 4 may not be as useful in applications as Theorems 1 and 2, since Theorems 3 and 4 require the open-loop system to be unstable, while Theorems 1 and 2 do not.

Theorems 1–4 all require that S be unstable for all fixed (i.e., time-invariant) gains that satisfy the condition

$$\alpha\leq k\leq\beta. \tag{75}$$

Therefore the question naturally arises: does instability for all fixed gains that satisfy (75) in itself imply instability for

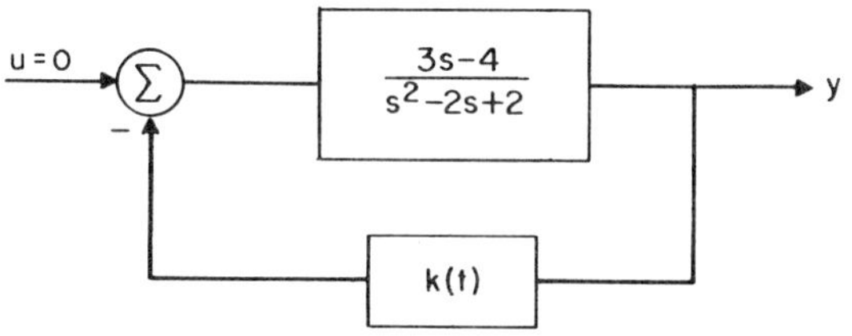

Fig. 10. The block diagram for Example 3.

all time-varying gains that satisfy (75)? The following example shows that the answer to the question is "no."

Example 3

Consider the system S shown in Fig. 10. For fixed gain in the interval

$$0\leq k\leq 1 \tag{76}$$

the poles of the closed-loop transfer function lie on the root locus shown in Fig. 11. For this range of gain the closed-loop transfer function has one or more poles in the half-

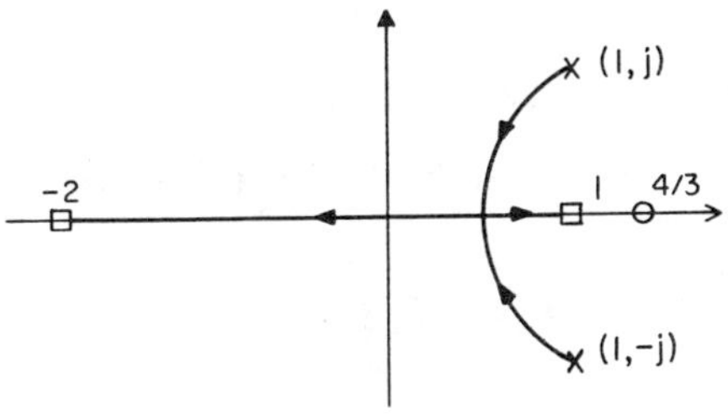

Fig. 11. Showing the pole locations for the example of Fig. 10 for $0 \leq k \leq 1$.

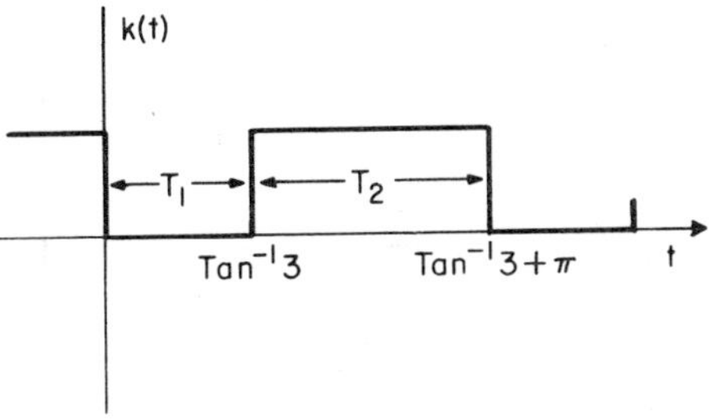

Fig. 12. The time-varying gain $k(t)$ of Example 3.

plane Re $[s]>0$. Thus S is unstable for all fixed gain in the interval (76).

Let $k(t)$ vary periodically between the limits $k=0$ and $k=1$ according to the relationship

$$k(t) = \begin{cases} 0 & \text{for } 0 \leq t - nT < T_1 \quad n = 0, 1, 2, \cdots \\ 1 & \text{for } T_1 \leq t - nT < T \quad n = 0, 1, 2, \cdots \end{cases} \tag{77}$$

where $T_1 = \tan^{-1} 3$, $T_2 = \pi$, $T = T_1 + T_2$ (see Fig. 12).

For $k(t)$ given by (77), solutions of (7a) [or equivalently of (8)] takes the form [23]:[13]

$$x(t) = p_1(t)e^{\lambda_1 t} + p_2(t)^{\lambda_2 t} \tag{78}$$

where $p_1(t)$ and $p_2(t)$ are bounded periodic functions dependent on the initial state having period T, and the λ_i are the so-called characteristic exponents. A straightforward but lengthy calculation shows that the quantities $e^{\lambda_i} = z_i$ satisfy

$$z_i^2 + [e^{T_1 - 2T_2} \cos T_1] z_i + e^{2T_1 - T_2} = 0. \tag{79}$$

Use of the quadratic formula shows that $|z_1| < 1$ and $|z_2| < 1$. Thus regardless of the initial state, $\|x(t)\|^2$ approaches zero at an exponential rate at $t \to \infty$. In view of (7b), $y(t)$ does likewise.

Accordingly, the system of Fig. 10 is one that is unstable for all fixed gain satisfying (76) but which is stable for at least one time-varying gain that satifies (76) [namely, (77)]. (End of Example 3.)

Example 3 shows that the matter of predicting instability for a time-varying feedback control system is a nontrivial one. Specifically, one cannot conclude instability of a system merely by verifying instability for all fixed gain in the range covered by the time-varying gain.[14]

VII. Other Instability Criteria

As we have indicated previously, the Circle Criteria are typical of a large class of recently developed frequency-domain stability criteria. By using the same approach that has been used to prove Theorems 1–4, one can deduce instability counterparts for most of the other criteria as well. The basic idea is to find a scalar (Lyapunov) function $v[\mathbf{x}(t)]$ that satisfies the following conditions.

1) There exists an initial state $\mathbf{x}(0)$ for which $v[\mathbf{x}(0)]$ is negative. (80)
2) Along solutions of the system equations, $d/dt v[\mathbf{x}(t)]$ or $d/dt\{e^{-2\epsilon t} v[\mathbf{x}(t)]\}$ is nonpositive. (81)
3) The condition $\|\mathbf{x}\|^2 \geq \lambda |v| [\mathbf{x}]|$ is valid for all $\mathbf{x}$, where λ denotes a positive constant. (82)

In most cases Lemma 7 or 7* provides the key for finding a suitable $v[\mathbf{x}]$.

The problem of finding instability counterparts of Popov's stability criteria [1] is an excellent case in point. Popov's results apply to the *time-invariant* nonlinear system S' shown in Fig. 13, rather than the time-varying one shown in Fig. 1. Specifically, assumptions A4) and A5) given in Section III are replaced by the following assumption.

A6) *The gain unit is characterized by a continuous nonlinear function $f(\ )$ that satisfies a sector limitation of the form*

$$0 \leq f(y)/y \leq \beta$$

for all $y \neq 0$.

Thus (7a, b) are replaced by the following equation of motion:

$$\begin{bmatrix} \dot{x}_1(t) \\ \dot{x}_2(t) \\ \vdots \\ \dot{x}_{n-1}(t) \\ \dot{x}_n(t) \end{bmatrix} = \begin{bmatrix} 0 & 1 & 0 & \cdots & 0 \\ 0 & 0 & 1 & \cdots & 0 \\ \vdots & \vdots & \vdots & & \vdots \\ 0 & 0 & 0 & \cdots & 1 \\ -p_0 & -p_1 & -p_2 & \cdots & -p_{n-1} \end{bmatrix} \begin{bmatrix} x_1(t) \\ x_2(t) \\ \vdots \\ x_{n-1}(t) \\ x_n(t) \end{bmatrix} + \begin{bmatrix} 0 \\ 0 \\ \vdots \\ 0 \\ 1 \end{bmatrix} f[q_0 x_1(t) \cdots q_{n-1} x_n(t)] \tag{83a}$$

$$y = [q_0, q_1, \cdots, q_{n-1}][x_1(t), x_2(t), \cdots, x_n(t)]' \tag{83b}$$

or in terms of the variable x_1 alone

$$p(D)x_1(t) + f[q(D)x_1(t)] = 0; \quad y(t) = q(D)x_1(t). \tag{84a, b}$$

In essence Popov's results are as follows.

1) If for some real γ the Nyquist locus of the auxiliary function $z(s) = (1 + \gamma s)g(s) + 1/\beta$ lies in the half-plane

[13] Because the differential equation is linear with periodic coefficients, Floquet theory can be used. In this case the equation is piecewise constant and so may be solved by joining together the solutions found for the linear-constant pieces.

[14] Thus the situation is analogous to that which occurs when one attempts to predict stability. It is well known that a system need not be stable for a time-varying gain that satisfies a relationship of the type (75), even though it is stable for all fixed gain that satisfy (75) (see, for example, Brockett [30]).

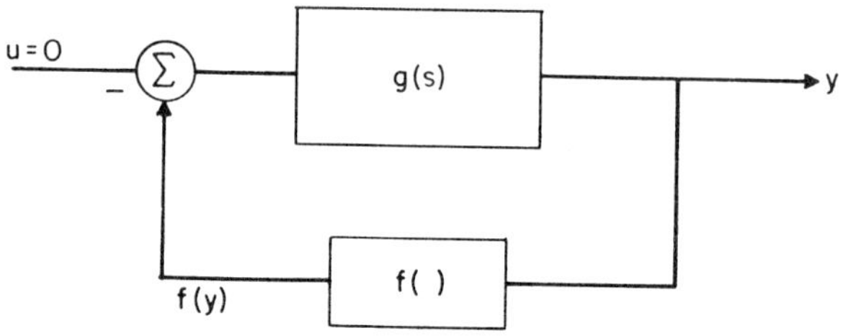

Fig. 13. The block diagram for Popov's theorem.

Re $[z]\geq 0$, and if the zeros of $p(s)$ are restricted to the half-plane Re $[s]<0$, then S' is stable in the sense that all initial conditions lead to solutions $y(t)$ of (83a, b) that are bounded.

2) If for some real γ the Nyquist locus of $z(s)$ lies in the plane Re $[z]>0$, and if the zeros of $p(s)$ are restricted to the half-plane Re $[s]>0$, then S' is stable in the sense that all sets of initial conditions lead to solutions $y(t)$ of (83a, b) that tend to zero as $t\to\infty$.

Although the Circle Criteria predict stability for time-invariant systems, Popov's criteria are of interest because they predict stability for a wider class of such systems.

The instability counterparts of Popov's criteria that one obtains using Lemmas 7 and 7* are as follows.

Theorem 5[15]

Let assumptions A1)–A3) and A6) be satisfied. Moreover, suppose that for some real γ the Nyquist locus of the auxiliary function

$$z(s) = (1+\gamma s)g(s) + 1/\beta$$

lies in the half-plane Re $[z]\geq 0$, and that $p(s)$ has one or more zeros in the half-plane Re $[s]>0$. Then for at least one initial state $\boldsymbol{x}(0)$, the solution of (83a, b) is unstable in the sense that

a) there exists a positive constant a such that

$$\|\boldsymbol{x}(t)\|^2 \geq a$$

for $t\geq 0$

b) there exists a positive constant b such that

$$|y(t)| \geq b$$

at least once in every interval $t_1\leq t\leq t_1+1$; $t_1\geq 0$.

Theorem 6

Let assumptions A1)–A3) and A6) be satisfied. Moreover, suppose that for some real γ the Nyquist locus of $z(s)$ lies in the half-plane Re $[z]>0$, and that $p(s)$ has one or more zeros in the half-plane Re $[s]>0$. Then for at least one initial state $\boldsymbol{x}(0)$, the solution of (83a, b) is unstable in the sense that

a) $\|\boldsymbol{x}(t)\|^2\to\infty$ as $t\to\infty$

b) given *any* positive constant c, there exists a time t_0 such that

$$|y(t)| > c$$

at least once in every interval $t_1\leq t\leq t_1+1$; $t_1>t_0$.

Theorem 5 can be established by taking the quantity

$$v(\boldsymbol{x}) = \boldsymbol{x}'\boldsymbol{K}_0\boldsymbol{x} + \beta\gamma\int_0^{[q_0,q_1,\cdots,q_{n-1}]\boldsymbol{x}} f(\sigma)\,d\sigma \tag{85}$$

as a Lyapunov function, where $\boldsymbol{K}_0$ denotes the matrix of Lemma 6 obtained for the choices

$$p_0(D)=p(D),\quad q_0(D)=\beta(1+\gamma D)q(D)+p(D) \tag{86a, b}$$

$r_0(D)=$ any real coefficient solution of (22) that has no factors in common with either $p_0(D)$ or $q_0(D)$. (87)

That (85) satisfies condition (80) can be seen by examining its behavior along a solution of the differential equation

$$q_0(D)x(t) = 0. \tag{88}$$

A little reflection shows that the hypotheses require $q_0(s)$ to have one or more zeros in the half-plane Re $[s]\geq 0$. Thus (88) admits of a solution of the form

$$x_0(t) = e^{at}\cos bt \tag{89}$$

with $a\geq 0$, $b\geq 0$. Along the solution (89)

$$d/dt\; v[\boldsymbol{x}_0(t)] = -\,|r_0(a+jb)|^2 e^{2at}\cos^2 bt \neq 0. \tag{90}$$

It follows from (90) that, regardless of the value of $v[\boldsymbol{x}_0(0)]$, $v[\boldsymbol{x}_0(t)]$ eventually becomes negative. Thus there exist vectors $\boldsymbol{n}$ such that $v(\boldsymbol{n})<0$.

That (85) satisfies (81) can be seen by differentiation and use of (84a) to obtain

$$d/dt[v(\boldsymbol{x})] = -\,[r_0(D)x]^2 - f[q(D)x]\{\beta q(D)x - f[q(D)x]\}. \tag{91}$$

Reference to assumption A6) shows that $f(\xi)[\beta\xi - f(\xi)]\geq 0$. Hence $d/dt\; v[\boldsymbol{x}(t)]\leq 0$.

Finally, satisfaction of (82) is ensured by the inequalities

$$v(\boldsymbol{x}) \leq \boldsymbol{x}'\boldsymbol{K}_0\boldsymbol{x} + \frac{\beta^2}{2}\boldsymbol{x}'\boldsymbol{c}'\boldsymbol{c}\boldsymbol{x} \leq \lambda_1\|\boldsymbol{x}\|^2 \tag{92}$$

$$v(\boldsymbol{x}) \geq \boldsymbol{x}'\boldsymbol{K}_0\boldsymbol{x} - \frac{\beta^2}{2}\boldsymbol{x}'\boldsymbol{c}'\boldsymbol{c}\boldsymbol{x} \geq -\,|\lambda_2|\,\|\boldsymbol{x}\|^2 \tag{93}$$

where λ_1 denotes the most positive eigenvalue of the quadratic form $\boldsymbol{x}'\boldsymbol{K}_0\boldsymbol{x}+(\beta^2/2)x'\boldsymbol{c}'\boldsymbol{c}\boldsymbol{x}$, and λ_2 denotes the most negative eigenvalue of the quadratic for $\boldsymbol{x}'\boldsymbol{K}_0\boldsymbol{x}-(\beta^2/2)\boldsymbol{x}'\boldsymbol{c}'\boldsymbol{x}$.

Thus the proof of Theorem 5 proceeds without difficulty.

The proof of Theorem 6 proceeds in a parallel fashion. The main difference is that the matrix $\boldsymbol{K}_0$ which appears in (85) is replaced by the matrix K_1 of Lemma 6* so that along solutions of (83a)

$$d/dt[v(x)] = 2\varepsilon v(\boldsymbol{x}) - [r_0(D-\varepsilon)x]^2 - f[q(D)x]\{\beta q(D)x - f[q(D)x]\} \tag{94}$$

with $\varepsilon>0$.

[15] Note that Theorem 5 is a somewhat stronger result than the absence of asymptotic stability which one would infer from a linearization argument.

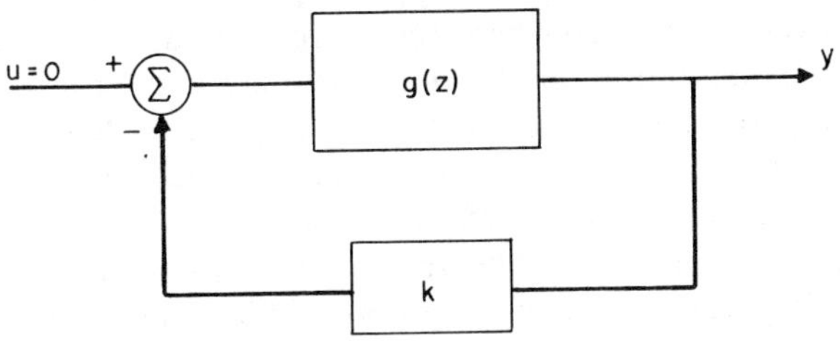

Fig. 14. A linear, constant, discrete time feedback system.

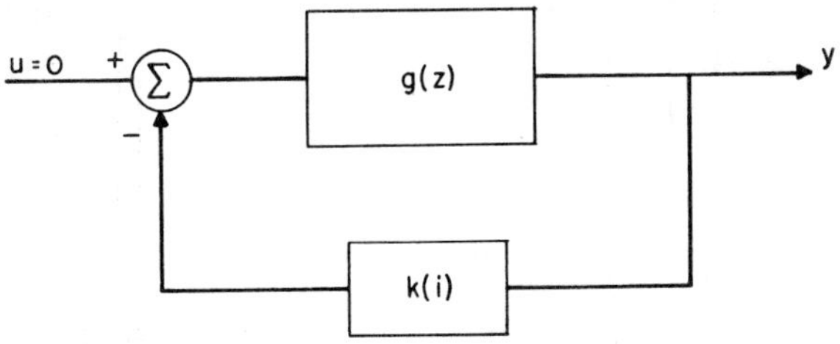

Fig. 15. A linear discrete time system with time-varying feedback; the model for the discrete version of the circle criterion.

VIII. Discrete Time Systems

Iterative processes, digital simulations, control systems with samplers, as well as many other systems of interest are characterized by difference equations. To what extent can the above results be duplicated for difference equations? It turns out that as much can be said about difference equations as we have said about the continuous case. Here we only have room to outline the discrete analog of the circle criterion, however.

The analogs of D and s in the study of difference equations are E and z which we use as the shift operator

$$Ex(i) = x(i+1) \tag{95}$$

and the z-transform variable

$$\tilde{x}(z) = \sum_{i=0}^{\infty} z^{-i}x(i). \tag{96}$$

From these definitions it follows that, if $u(k)$ and $y(k)$ related by

$$[E^n + p_{n-1}E^{n-1} + \cdots p_0]y(k) = [q_{n-1}E^{n-1} + \cdots q_0]u(k) \tag{97}$$

or more simply

$$p(E)y(k) = q(E)u(k), \tag{98}$$

then the transforms of y and u are related by

$$\tilde{y}(z)/\tilde{u}(z) = q(z)/p(z) = g(z) \tag{99}$$

provided all initial conditions are zero. We will call $g(z)$ the *pulse transfer function* to distinguish it from $g(s)$ as used before.

It is well known [24] that stability for linear time-invariant discrete time systems depends on where the zeros of $p(z)$ lie relative to the unit circle $|z|=1$ rather than the line Re $[s]=0$ as in the continuous case. For this reason the relevant Nyquist locus is the image of the unit circle under the mapping $g(z)$. If $g(z)$ has ρ poles outside the unit disk, then a linear constant feedback system of the type shown in Fig. 14 is stable if and only if the Nyquist locus of the pulse transfer function makes ρ counterclockwise encirclements of the critical point $g=-1/k$.

Apparently Tsypkin [25] was the first to state a stability result generalizing this to the case where the feedback gain is variable. With the above definition of the Nyquist locus, statements 1 and 2 of our Introduction remain true for discrete time systems of the form shown in Fig. 15, provided $\alpha \le k(i) \le \beta$. Tsypkin's proof follows that due to Popov. Szego [26] has given an alternate proof based on Liapunov theory, and Sandberg has extended these results giving functional-analysis-type proofs [27].

By discretizing the arguments of the foregoing sections one can establish instability counterparts of Tsypkin's stability criteria. To make precise statements of the instability results we require the following assumptions.

B1) *The degree of $p(z)$ exceeds that of $q(z)$.*

Thus the linear time-invariant part can be described by a pair of equations of the form.

$$\begin{bmatrix} x_1(k+1) \\ x_2(k+1) \\ \vdots \\ x_{n-1}(k+1) \\ x_n(k+1) \end{bmatrix} = \begin{bmatrix} 0 & 1 & 0 & \cdots & 0 \\ 0 & 0 & 1 & \cdots & 0 \\ \cdots & \cdots & \cdots & \cdots & \cdots \\ 0 & 0 & 0 & \cdots & 1 \\ -p_0 & -p_1 & -p_2 & \cdots & -p_{n-1} \end{bmatrix} \begin{bmatrix} x_1(k) \\ x_2(k) \\ \vdots \\ x_{n-1}(k) \\ x_n(k) \end{bmatrix} + \begin{bmatrix} 0 \\ 0 \\ \vdots \\ 0 \\ 1 \end{bmatrix} m(k) \tag{100a}$$

$$y(k) = [q_0, q_1, \cdots, q_{n-1}][x_1(k), x_2(k), \cdots, x_n(k)]' \tag{100b}$$

which we abbreviate as

$$\boldsymbol{x}(k+1) = \boldsymbol{Ax} + \boldsymbol{b}u(k); \qquad y(k) = \boldsymbol{c}'\boldsymbol{x}(k). \tag{101}$$

B2) *The polynomials $p(z)$ and $q(z)$ do not have common factors.*

B3) *$g(z)=q(z)/p(z)$ is analytic on the circle $|z|=1$ and has ρ poles in the set $|z|>1$.*

B4) *The gain unit is characterized by a linear time-varying gain that satisfies $\alpha \le k(i) \le \beta$.*

Combining (100a, b) and (6a, b) leads to the following equations for the closed loop system:

$$\begin{bmatrix} x_1(i+1) \\ x_2(i+1) \\ \vdots \\ x_{n-1}(i+1) \\ x_n(i+1) \end{bmatrix} = \begin{bmatrix} 0 & 1 & 0 & \cdots & 0 \\ 0 & 0 & 1 & \cdots & 0 \\ \cdots & \cdots & \cdots & \cdots & \cdots \\ 0 & 0 & 0 & \cdots & 1 \\ -p_0 & -p_1 & -p_2 & \cdots & -p_{n-1} \end{bmatrix} \begin{bmatrix} x_1(i) \\ x_2(i) \\ \vdots \\ x_{n-1}(i) \\ x_n(i) \end{bmatrix}$$

$$+ k(i) \begin{bmatrix} 0 & 0 & 0 & \cdots & 0 \\ 0 & 0 & 0 & \cdots & 0 \\ \cdots & \cdots & \cdots & \cdots & \cdots \\ 0 & 0 & 0 & \cdots & 0 \\ -q_0 & -q_1 & -q_2 & \cdots & -q_{n-1} \end{bmatrix} \begin{bmatrix} x_1(i) \\ x_2(i) \\ \vdots \\ x_{n-1}(i) \\ x_n(i) \end{bmatrix} \quad (102a)$$

$$y(i) = [q_0, q_1, \cdots, q_{n-1}]x(i). \quad (102b)$$

In terms of these definitions we can state the following instability counterparts of Tsypkin's stability criteria.

Theorem 7

Let assumptions B1)–B4) be satisfied. Moreover, suppose that the pulse transfer function $g(z)$ has a Nyquist locus which does not intersect $D(\alpha, \beta)$ and encircles it fewer than ρ times in the counterclockwise sense. Then for at least one initial state $x(0)$, the solution of (93a, b) is unstable in that

a) there exists a positive constant a such that for all $i=1, 2, 3, \cdots$

$$x'(i)x(i) = \|x(i)\|^2 > a$$

b) there exists a positive constant b such that

$$|y(i)| > b$$

at least once in every interval $j \leq i \leq j+n; j>0$, where n is the dimension of the state vector.

Theorem 8

Let assumptions B1)–B4) be satisfied. Moreover, assume that the pulse transfer function $g(z)$ has a Nyquist locus which does not intersect $D[\alpha, \beta]$ and encircles it fewer than ρ times in the counterclockwise sense. Then for at least one initial state $x(0)$, the solution of (93a, b) is unstable in the sense that

a) $\|x(i)\|^2 \to \infty$ as $i \to \infty$
b) given *any* positive constant c, there exists an integer i_0 such that

$$|y(i)| > c$$

at least once in every interval $i_1 \leq i \leq i_1+n;\ i_1 \geq i_0$.

The key to proving Theorems 7 and 8 is the establishment of a discrete counterpart of Lemma 6. Specifically it is necessary to show that whenever the equation

$$2r(z)r(z^{-1}) = p(z)q(z^{-1}) + p(z^{-1})q(z) \quad (103)$$

admits a real coefficient solution $r(z)$, there exists a quadratic form $v[x(i)]$ in the variables $x(v), x(v+1), \cdots, x(v-n+1)$ that has the difference

$$v[x(i+1)] - v[x(i)] = [p(E)x(i)][q(E)x(i)] - [r(E)x(i)]^2. \quad (104)$$

This can be done by taking the approach described by Brockett [18], everywhere replacing integration by parts with summation by parts. Once the quadratic form $v[x(i)]$ is available, it is a simple matter to show that $v[x(i)]$ is positive definite if $p(z)+q(z)$ has its zeros inside the unit disk and is neither positive definite nor positive semidefinite if this is not the case. The remaining steps in the proofs closely parallel those of the proofs of Theorems 1 and 2.

IX. Conclusion

The effective fusion of time- and frequency-domain ideas for the analysis of stability in time-varying and nonlinear feedback problems has only been accomplished in the last few years. In the present paper we have extended some of the main results in this area by showing how instability theorems of similar type can be obtained. Our proofs are based on Lyapunov ideas but the key new result is Lemma 7b) which relates a frequency-domain condition to the indefiniteness of a certain quadratic form. Lemma 7b) complements an important result of Yacubovich and Kalman, and with it one can prove instability counterparts of a number of stability statements, including some which have been excluded here for lack of space.

Outstanding questions which remain include the following.

1) Can other types of stability proofs such as the ones offered by Popov [1], Sandberg [28], and Zames [29] be modified so as to give instability results? If so, it is probably possible to weaken our hypotheses so that systems can be treated in terms of their impulse responses instead of requiring the existence of a finite dimensional vector differential representation.

2) Are the given results in any sense necessary as well as being sufficient? It has been shown [30] that the stability part of the Circle Criterion gives results which are too conservative. Probably the same is true of the instability criteria but this requires investigation.

3) A number of authors [31]–[35] have extended the stability results to systems with n nonlinear or time-varying feedback gains. It remains to state and prove a matrix analog of Lemma 7b).

Appendix I

Outline of the Proof of Theorem 3

The function $z_1(s) = -[g(s)+1/\alpha]/[g(s)+1/\beta]$ maps the disk $D[\alpha, \beta]$ in the g-plane into the closed right half of the z_1-plane. Hence reasoning analogous to that used in Lemma 3 shows

$$p_1(j\omega)q_1(-j\omega) + p_1(-j\omega)q_1(j\omega) \geq 0$$

for all ω, where $p_1(s)=q(s)+(1/\alpha)p(s)$ and $q_1(s)=-[g(s)+(1/\beta)p(s)]$. The polynomials $p_1(s)$ and $q_1(s)$ are relatively prime according to Lemma 2. The sum of the numerator and denominator polynomials of $z_1(s)$ is $p_1(s)+q_1(s) = [(1/\alpha)-(1/\beta)]p_1(s)$ which, by hypothesis, has $\rho \geq 1$ zeros in the half-plane Re $[s]>0$. Thus, according to Lemma 1, $z_1(s)$ is not positive real. Lemma 5 ensures that the equation

$$2r_1(D)r_1(-D) = p_1(D)q_1(-D) + p_1(-D)q_1(D)$$

admits of a real coefficient solution for $r_1(D)$. Lemma 6 in turn ensures the existence of a real constant symmetric matrix $\boldsymbol{K}_0$ such that

$$d/dt[\boldsymbol{x}_1'(t)\boldsymbol{K}_0\boldsymbol{x}_1(t)] = [p_1(D)x_1(t)][q_1(D)x_1(t)] - [r_1(D)x_1(t)]^2.$$

According to Lemma 7 there exists a real column matrix $\boldsymbol{n}$ such that $\boldsymbol{n}'\boldsymbol{K}_0\boldsymbol{n}<0$. Equation (49) is replaced by

$$\frac{d}{dt}[\boldsymbol{x}'(t)\boldsymbol{K}_0\boldsymbol{x}(t)] = \left\{\begin{array}{l} \dfrac{k(t)/\alpha-1}{k(t)/\beta-1}[q_1(D)x_1(t)]^2-[r_1(D)x_1(t)]^2 \text{ for } k(t)\neq\beta \\ \dfrac{k(t)/\beta-1}{k(t)/\alpha-1}[p_1(D)x_1(t)]^2-[r_1(D)x_1(t)]^2 \text{ for } k(t)\neq\alpha \end{array}\right\} \leq 0.$$

The inequality follows from the assumption $\alpha \leq k(t) \leq \beta$. Hence the argument used to prove Theorem 1 also establishes Theorem 3.

Outline of the Proof of Theorem 4

Use of Lemmas 5*, 6*, 7* (with $\varepsilon>0$) in place of Lemmas 5, 6, 7 in the foregoing argument establishes Theorem 4.

Appendix II

In an appendix of Popov's paper [1] it is shown that his result cannot be *improved* upon by using a Lyapunov function consisting of a quadratic form plus an integral of the nonlinear term with a specific upper limit. Popov focused attention on the problem of determining whether or not his results could be derived using Lyapunov methods but did not resolve it. In order to resolve this question it was necessary to relate the existence of the solution of a pair of simultaneous equations (in our notation)

$$\boldsymbol{KA} + \boldsymbol{A}'\boldsymbol{K} = -\boldsymbol{dd}' \qquad (105)$$

$$(\boldsymbol{Kb} - \boldsymbol{c}) = \boldsymbol{d}(1/2k) \qquad (106)$$

to a frequency-domain condition on

$$z(s) = \boldsymbol{c}'(\boldsymbol{I}s - \boldsymbol{A})^{-1}\boldsymbol{b} + 1/k.$$

The specific question was: when does there exist a real symmetric positive definite matrix $\boldsymbol{K}$ and a real column vector $\boldsymbol{d}$ such that (105) and (106) are satisfied for a given $\boldsymbol{A}$, $\boldsymbol{b}$, and $\boldsymbol{c}$? Yacubovich [36] and Kalman [37] resolved this problem shortly after Popov's paper appeared. (See Meyer [38] for complete proofs in the appropriate generality.)

Our Lemma 7 provides additional information regarding the existence of solutions of (105) and (106) for the case $k=\infty$. This fact becomes evident if it is noted that Lemma 7 can be restated as follows.

Lemma 8

If Re $[\boldsymbol{c}'(\boldsymbol{I}j\omega - \boldsymbol{A})^{-1}\boldsymbol{b}]$ is non-negative for all real ω, and if det $(\boldsymbol{I}s-\boldsymbol{A})$ and det $(\boldsymbol{I}s - \boldsymbol{A} + \boldsymbol{bc}')$ have no common factors, then there exists a real solution pair $\boldsymbol{K}$, $\boldsymbol{d}$ for the equations $(\boldsymbol{K}'=\boldsymbol{K})$

$$\boldsymbol{KA} + \boldsymbol{A}'\boldsymbol{K} = -\boldsymbol{dd}'$$

$$\boldsymbol{Kb} = \boldsymbol{c}.$$

Moreover, $\boldsymbol{K}$ is positive definite if $\boldsymbol{c}'(\boldsymbol{I}s-\boldsymbol{A})^{-1}\boldsymbol{b}$ is positive real and neither positive definite nor positive semidefinite if $\boldsymbol{c}'(\boldsymbol{I}s-\boldsymbol{K})^{-1}\boldsymbol{b}$ is not positive real.

References

[1] V. M. Popov, "Absolute stability of nonlinear systems of automatic control," *Automation and Remote Control*, vol. 22, pp. 857–875, March 1962. (For Russian original see *Avtomatika i Telemekhanika*, August 1961.)
[2] R. E. Kalman, "When is a linear control system optimal?" *Trans. ASME (J. Basic Engrg.)*, pt. D, pp. 51–60, March 1964.
[3] H. Nyquist, "Regeneration theory," *Bell Sys. Tech. J.*, vol. 11, pp. 126–147, 1932.
[4] J. J. Bongiorno, Jr., and D. Graham, "An extension of the Nyquist-Barkhausen stability criterion to linear lumped-parameter systems with time-varying elements," *IEEE Trans. on Automatic Control (Correspondence)*, vol. AC-8, pp. 166–170, April 1963.
[5] E. N. Rosenvasser, "The absolute stability of nonlinear systems," *Automation and Remote Control*, vol. 24, no. 3, 1963 (English translation, pp. 283–291).
[6] K. S. Narendra and R. M. Goldwyn, "A geometrical criterion for the stability of certain nonlinear, nonautonomous systems," *IEEE Trans. on Circuit Theory (Correspondence)*, vol. CT-11, pp. 406–408, September 1964.
[7] J. J. Bongiorno, Jr., "Real-frequency stability criteria for linear time-varying systems," *Proc. IEEE*, vol. 52, pp. 832–841, July, 1964.
[8] B. N. Naumov and Y. Z. Tsypkin, "A frequency criterion for absolute process stability in nonlinear automatic control systems," *Automation and Remote Control*, vol. 25, June 1964. (English translation, pp. 765–778).
[9] J. Kudrewicz, "Stability of nonlinear systems with feedback," *Automation and Remote Control*, vol. 25, August 1964 (English translation, pp. 1027–1037).
[10] I. W. Sandberg, "On the stability of solutions of linear differential equations with periodic coefficients," *J. SIAM*, vol. 12, no. 2, pp. 487–496, 1964.
[11] ——, "A frequency domain condition for the stability of systems containing a single time-varying nonlinear element," *Bell Sys. Tech. J.*, vol. 43, pp. 1601–1638, 1964.
[12] G. Zames, "The input-output stability of nonlinear and time-varying feedback systems," *Proc. NEC*, pp. 725–730, 1964.
[13] L. Zadeh and C. A. Desoer, *Linear System Theory*. New York: McGraw-Hill, 1963.
[14] G. Sansone and R. Conti, *Non-Linear Differential Equations*. New York: Macmillan, 1964.
[15] J. P. LaSalle and S. Lefschetz, *Stability by Liapunov's Direct Method*. New York: Academic, 1961.
[16] L. Weinberg and P. Slepian, "Positive real matrices," *J. Math. and Mech.*, vol. 9, no. 1, pp. 71–83, 1960.
[17] Y. W. Lee, *Statistical Theory of Communication*. New York: Wiley, 1960.
[18] R. W. Brockett, "On the stability of nonlinear feedback systems," *IEEE Trans. on Applications and Industry*, vol. 83, pp. 443–449, November 1964.
[19] ——, "Path integrals, Liapunov functions and quadratic minimization," *Proc. 4th Annual Allerton Conf. on Circuit and Systems Theory*. Urbana, Ill.: University of Illinois, 1966.
[20] R. W. Brockett and J. L. Willems, "Frequency domain stability criteria—Parts I and II," *IEEE Trans. on Automatic Control*, vol. AC-10, pp. 255–261, July 1965 and pp. 407–413, October 1965.
[21] R. Bellman, *Introduction to Matrix Analysis*. New York: McGraw-Hill, 1960.
[22] M. Athans and P. Falb, *Optimal Control*. New York: McGraw-Hill, 1966.
[23] W. Kaplan, *Operational Methods for Linear Systems*. Reading, Mass.: Addison-Wesley, 1962.
[24] H. Freeman, *Discrete-Time Systems*. New York: Wiley, 1965.
[25] Y. Z. Tsypkin, "On the stability in the large of nonlinear sampled-data systems," *Dokl. Akad. Nauk SSSR*, vol. 145, pp. 52–55, 1962.
[26] G. Szego, "On the absolute stability of sampled-data control systems," *Proc. Nat'l Acad. Sci.*, vol. 49, no. 9, pp. 558–560, 1963.
[27] I. W. Sandberg, "On the boundedness of solutions of nonlinear integral equations," *Bell Sys. Tech. J.*, vol. 44, pp. 439–453, 1965.

[28] ——, "Some results on the theory of physical systems governed by nonlinear integral equations," *Bell Sys. Tech. J.*, vol. 44, pp. 871–894, 1965.

[29] G. Zames, "On the input-output stability of time-varying nonlinear feedback systems—Parts I and II," *IEEE Trans. on Automatic Control*, vol. AC-11, pp. 228–238, April 1966 and pp. 465–476, July 1966.

[30] R. W. Brockett, "Optimization and the converse of the circle criterion," *Proc. NEC*, pp. 697–701, 1965.

[31] V. M. Popov, "Criterio de stabilitate pentru sistemele neliniare de regiare automata, bazate pe utilizarea transformatei laplace," *Studii si cercetari de energetico*, Acad. RPR, vol. IX, 1959. (English translations available as TR 64-267, Bell Telephone Labs., Inc.)

[32] Li Xun-Jing, "On the absolute stability of systems with time lags," *Acta. Math. Sinica*, vol. 13, no. 4, 1963.

[33] E. I. Jury and B. W. Lee, "The absolute stability of systems with many nonlinearities," *Automation and Remote Control*, vol. 25, pp. 945–965, June 1965.

[34] B. D. O. Anderson, "Stability of control systems with multiple nonlinearities," *J. Franklin Inst.*, September 1966.

[35] I. W. Sandberg, "On the boundedness of solutions of nonlinear integral equations," *Bell Sys. Tech. J.*, vol. 44, pp. 239–453, 1965.

[36] V. A. Yacubovich, "The solution of certain matrix inequalities in automatic control theory," *Dokl. Akad. Nauk SSSR*, vol. 143, pp. 1304–1307, 1962.

[37] R. E. Kalman, "Liapunov functions for the problem of Luré in automatic control," *Proc. Nat'l Acad. Sci.*, vol. 49, pp. 201–205, 1963.

[38] K. Meyer, "On the existence of Lyapunov functions for the problem of Luré," *SIAM J. on Control*, vol. 3, no. 3, pp. 373–383, 1966.

[39] E. A. Guillemin, *Synthesis of Passive Networks*. New York: Wiley, 1957.

The Parabola Test for Absolute Stability

A. R. BERGEN, MEMBER, IEEE, AND M. A. SAPIRO, STUDENT MEMBER, IEEE

Abstract—**In applying the Popov stability test, a certain straight line is drawn; the Popov locus must lie on one side of this line. Thus geometric considerations alone indicate that the interesting sectors of absolute stability for conditionally stable systems cannot be found directly. However, the straight line of the Popov test may be replaced by a certain parabola and the conditionally stable sectors of absolute stability may then be discovered. The test has its best application for conditionally stable systems but can be used whenever the Popov test can be used. In fact, the Popov straight line may be obtained as a limiting form of the parabola.**

The test is ordinarily weaker than the Popov test, but nonlinear sectors having a nonzero lower bound may be found more directly

I. Introduction

If the nonlinear system shown in Fig. 1 is conditionally stable, it is not possible to find all the sectors of abolute stability by the direct application of the Popov test [1], [2]. In principle, there is no real difficulty in finding the sectors. It is only necessary to make the transformation shown in Fig. 2 and apply the Popov test to the system $T_h(\sum)$; the use of a transformation of this type is quite common [3]–[5]. The constant h should be chosen so that G' is strictly stable. Then if the Popov test establishes that $T_h(\sum)$ is absolutely stable in the sector $[0, k]$, it follows that $\sum$ is absolutely stable in the sector $[h, h+k]$.

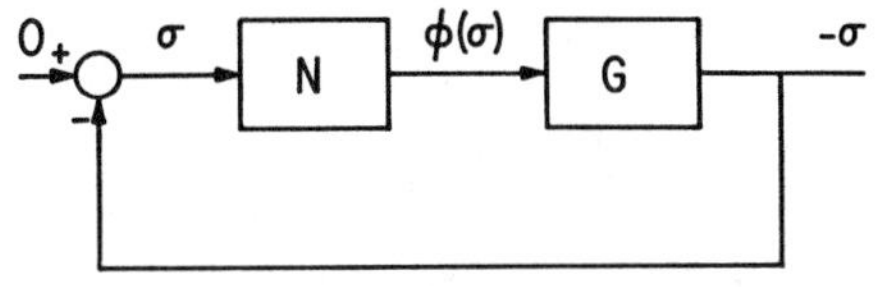

Fig. 1. The system Σ.

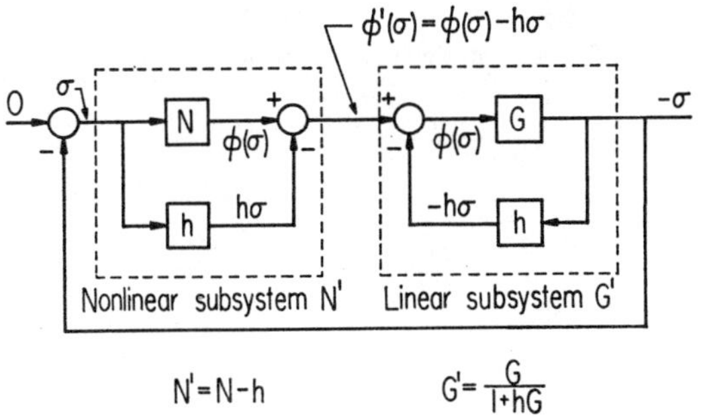

Fig. 2. The system $T_h(\Sigma)$.

The question of how to choose h to maximize the sector $[h, h+k]$ is unanswered and is one of the difficulties with the procedure. A process of trial and error seems indicated.

There is also difficulty if adjustments of the sector by compensation is desired. It is not at all clear how compensation of the system $\sum$ will affect the Popov plot of $T_h(\sum)$, and again a time-consuming process of trial and error may be necessary.

It would thus be helpful if sectors of absolute stability for the conditionally stable system $\sum$ could be determined directly, without transformations. The parabola test serves just this purpose.

Manuscript received February 8, 1966; revised August 25, 1966, and February 7, 1967. This work was supported in part by the Air Force Office of Scientific Research under Grant AF-AFOSR-230-66 and by an NSF Traineeship.

The authors are with the Dept. of Elec. Engrg., University of California, Berkeley, Calif.

II. The Parabola Test

If there exist real constants $k>0$, $h\neq 0$, and q such that

1) G', the linear part of the system $T_h(\sum)$, is strictly stable[1] and has more poles than zeros,[2] and
2) the parabola in the X^*, Y^* plane

$$X^{*2}+\frac{k+2h}{h(h+k)}X^*-\frac{kqY^*}{h(h+k)}+\frac{1}{h(h+k)}=0$$

does not contain[3] either the origin or any part of the Popov locus $G^*(j\omega)=X^*(j\omega)+jY^*(j\omega)$,

then the system $\sum$ is absolutely stable in the sector $[h, h+k]$.

The parabola is easy to draw. It passes through the two points $(-1/h, 0)$ and $(-1/(h+k), 0)$, and the slope of the tangents at these points is $-1/q$ and $1/q$, respectively. It is a property of parabolas that if, from the intersection of these two tangents, a perpendicular is constructed to the X^* axis, the parabola intersects this perpendicular at its midpoint and has slope zero at this point. See Fig. 3 for the construction and application of a typical parabola. It should be noted that the parabola drawn is not unique; different choices of q, h, and k result in different parabolas.

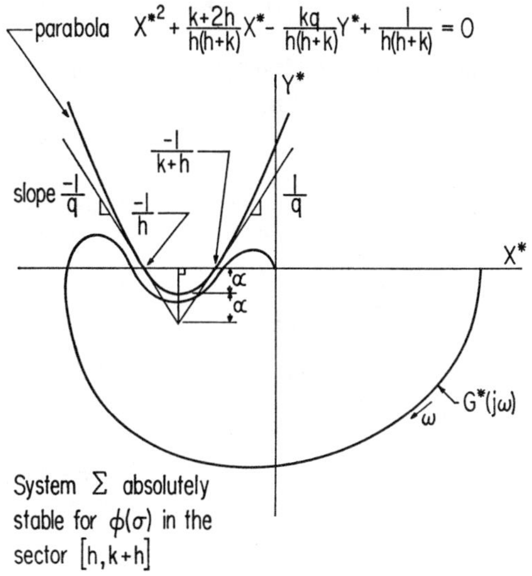

Fig. 3. Application of the parabola test.

III. Proof of Parabola Test

First, some notation is needed. Let X^* and Y^* be the real and imaginary parts of the modified frequency response $G^*(j\omega)$ (which is plotted as the Popov locus) corresponding to $G(j\omega)$, and X and Y be the real and imaginary parts of $G(j\omega)$. Then

$$X^*(j\omega)\triangleq X(j\omega)=\operatorname{Re}G(j\omega)$$
$$Y^*(j\omega)\triangleq \omega Y(j\omega)=\omega\operatorname{Im}G(j\omega).$$

Also, from Fig. 2

$$G'(j\omega)=\frac{G(j\omega)}{1+hG(j\omega)}. \tag{1}$$

Now let

$$U(j\omega)\triangleq \operatorname{Re}G'(j\omega)$$
$$V(j\omega)\triangleq \operatorname{Im}G'(j\omega).$$

[1] The Popov diagram for G has the same crossings of the real axis as the Nyquist diagram and can be used to investigate the stability of G'.

[2] If G has more poles than zeros, so does G'.

[3] Contain is used in the sense that the parabola contains both itself and the convex set of which it is the boundary.

Reprinted from *IEEE Trans. Automat. Contr.*, vol. AC-12, pp. 312–314, June 1967.

Next, apply the Popov stability criterion to the transformed system $T_h(\sum)$. Since, by assumption, G' is strictly stable (a principal case), the sufficient condition for the absolute stability of the origin in the sector $[0, k]$ is that for some q

$$U(j\omega) - \omega q V(j\omega) + \frac{1}{k} > 0, \qquad \text{for all } \omega \geq 0. \tag{2}$$

This condition may be stated equivalently in terms of the primary quantities $X(j\omega)$ and $Y(j\omega)$. Using (1),

$$G' = U + jV = \frac{X + jY}{1 + hX + jhY} = \frac{(X + jY)(1 + hX - jhY)}{(1 + hX)^2 + (hY)^2}$$

$$= \frac{X(1 + hX) + hY^2 + jY}{(1 + hX)^2 + (hY)^2} \tag{3}$$

hence

$$U = \frac{X(1 + hX) + hY^2}{(1 + hX)^2 + (hY)^2}, \qquad V = \frac{}{(1 + hX)^2 + (hY)^2}, \tag{4}$$

and (2) may be replaced by

$$\frac{X(1 + hX) + hY^2}{(1 + hX)^2 + (hY)^2} - \frac{\omega q Y}{(1 + hX)^2 + (hY)^2} + \frac{1}{k} > 0, \quad \text{for all } \omega \geq 0. \tag{5}$$

Equivalently, by multiplying through by the positive demoninator and collecting like terms,

$$h(h + k)X^2(j\omega) + (k + 2h)X(j\omega) + h(h + k)Y^2(j\omega) - k\omega q Y(j\omega) + 1 > 0 \tag{6}$$

for all $\omega \geq 0$. As a check it may be noted that setting $h = 0$ in (6) gives the Popov criterion for the system $\sum$.

It will next be shown that satisfaction of the parabola test implies the satisfaction of the condition in (6). By assumption, the parabola

$$X^* + \frac{k + 2h}{h(h + k)} X^* - \frac{kq}{h(h + k)} Y^* + \frac{1}{h(h + k)} = 0 \tag{7}$$

does not contain either the origin or any part of the Popov locus. Thus it is clear that $(1/h(h+k)) > 0$ and for all $\omega \geq 0$

$$X^{*^2}(j\omega) + \frac{k + 2h}{h(h + k)} X^*(j\omega) - \frac{kq}{h(h + k)} Y^*(j\omega) + \frac{1}{h(h + k)} > 0. \tag{8}$$

Substituting $X(j\omega)$ for $X^*(j\omega)$ and $\omega Y(j\omega)$ for $Y^*(j\omega)$ and multiplying by the positive quantity $h(h+k)$

$$h(h + k)X^2(j\omega) + (k + 2h)X(j\omega) - k\omega q Y(j\omega) + 1 > 0 \tag{9}$$

for all $\omega \geq 0$. Comparing (6) and (9) it is clear that the left side of (9) is more positive than the left side of (6), since it is augmented by the non-negative quantity $h(h+k)Y^2(j\omega)$. The parabola test, therefore, is sufficient to establish absolute stability of the origin of system $T_h(\sum)$ in the sector $[0, k]$ and, equivalently, that of the system $\sum$ in the sector $[h, h+k]$.

IV. Remarks

1) While the parabola test is very simple to apply, it should be noted that it imposes somewhat stricter conditions than does the Popov test.

2) Nothing has been said which precludes the use of this test for a system which is not conditionally stable. In some cases, as compared with the usual Popov test, a better upper bound to the sector of absolute stability may be found at the cost of a worse lower bound. The test usually gives better results than the circle test [6], [7] but does not, of course, establish results for time-varying nonlinearities.

3) In the limit as $h \to 0$, the parabola reduces to the Popov line.

V. Conclusions

A new "parabola" stability test has been developed. This test is easily applied and may be of use in determining sectors of absolute stability for conditionally stable systems, without preliminary transformations.

Acknowledgment

The authors wish to acknowledge a reviewer's comment which led to a more direct proof of the parabola test.

References

[1] M. A. Aizerman and F. R. Gantmacher, *Absolute Stability of Regulator Systems.* San Francisco, Calif.: Holden Day, 1964.

[2] C. A. Desoer, "A generalization of the Popov criterion," *IEEE Trans. on Automatic Control*, vol. AC-10, pp. 182–185, April 1965.

[3] Z. V. Rekasius and J. E. Gibson, "Stability analysis of nonlinear control systems by the second method of Liapunov," *IRE Trans. on Automatic Control*, vol. AC-7, pp. 3–14, January 1962.

[4] A. R. Bergen and I. J. Williams, "Verification of Aizerman's conjecture for a class of third-order systems," *IRE Trans. on Automatic Control*, vol. AC-7, pp. 42–46, April 1962.

[5] G. Zames, "Functional analysis applied to nonlinear feedback systems," *IEEE Trans. on Circuit Theory*, vol. CT-10, pp. 392–404, September 1963.

[6] K. S. Narendra and R. M. Goldwyn, "A geometrical criterion for the stability of certain nonlinear nonautonomous systems," *IEEE Trans. on Circuit Theory*, vol. CT-11, pp. 406–408, September 1964.

[7] I. W. Sandberg, "Some results on the theory of physical systems governed by nonlinear functional equations," *Bell Sys. Tech. J.*, vol. 44, pp. 871–898, May–June 1965.

An Off-Axis Circle Criterion for the Stability of Feedback Systems with a Monotonic Nonlinearity

YO-SUNG CHO AND KUMPATI S. NARENDRA,
SENIOR MEMBER, IEEE

Abstract—**An off-axis circle criterion is stated in this paper as a sufficient condition for the stability of a nonlinear feedback system with a single monotonic nonlinearity. The criterion provides a geometric method for determining a sector ($K_1 < [F(y_1) - F(y_2)]/(y_1 - y_2) < K_2$) within which the nonlinearity may lie for asymptotic stability. The relation between the criterion stated and the well-known Popov criterion and the circle criterion for time-varying systems is also discussed. Two examples are included to clarify various aspects of the criterion and its relation to existing results.**

I. Introduction

Ever since Popov [1] stated the conditions for the stability of a nonlinear feedback system in the frequency domain, there has been considerable interest in deriving similar frequency domain conditions for systems with other types of nonlinearities. At the present time, frequency conditions for determining the stability of systems with monotonic and odd monotonic nonlinearities are well established—see Zames [2], [3], Brockett and Willems [4], Narendra and Neuman [5]. These conditions are expressed in terms of the transfer function $G(s)$ of the linear part of the system and a multiplier $Z(s)$ having a specific form so that $G(s)Z(s)$ is positive real. However, it is seldom apparent how such a multiplier can be found. In this paper a geometric condition is derived for the existence of an RL or an RC multiplier for the stability of feedback systems with monotonic nonlinearities. It is shown that if any circle can be drawn to intersect the negative real axis at $-1/K_1$ and $-1/K_2$ on the Nyquist plane so that the Nyquist plot of $G(i\omega)$ lies outside the circle and does not completely encircle it, then the nonlinear feedback system is asymptotically stable for all real valued functions $F(\cdot)$ satisfying $K_1 < [F(y_1) - F(y_2)]/(y_1 - y_2) < K_2$, where K_1 and K_2 are positive constants. The center of such a circle need not lie on the real axis.

II. Definitions

The general formulation of Zames [2], [3] will be adopted here. L_{2e} which is an extension of the L_2 space of square integrable functions is defined as follows.

L_2: A function $x(t)$ defined in the interval $t \in [0, \infty]$ belongs to L_2 if $\int_0^\infty x^2(t)dt < \infty$. The norm of $x(t)$ in L_2 is denoted by $\|x\|_2 = \{\int_0^\infty x^2(t)dt\}^{1/2}$.

L_{2e}: A function $x(t)$ belongs to L_{2e} if every finite time truncation of $x(t)$ belongs to L_2. If $x_\tau(t)$ denotes the truncated function, then $x_\tau(t) = x(t)$ for $t < \tau$ and $\tau \in T$, where T is the subinterval of the reals $[0, \infty)$, and $x_\tau(t) = 0$ elsewhere. An extended norm denoted by $\|x\|_{2e}$ is assigned to each $x(t)$ in L_{2e} as follows.

$$\|x\|_{2e} = \left\{\int_0^\infty x^2 dt\right\}^{1/2} = \|x\|_2, \quad \text{if } x \in L_2$$

$$\|x\|_{2e} = \infty, \quad \text{if } x \notin L_2.$$

The feedback system whose stability is considered in this paper has the form shown in Fig. 1. If the operators G and F map L_{2e} into itself, then the feedback equations for the system for $t \geq 0$ may be formulated as

Manuscript received December 2, 1966; revised May 1, 1967, November 28, 1967, and April 18, 1968.
Y. S. Cho is with Honeywell Inc., Waltham, Mass.
K. S. Narendra is with the Dept. of Engineering and Applied Science, Yale University, New Haven, Conn.

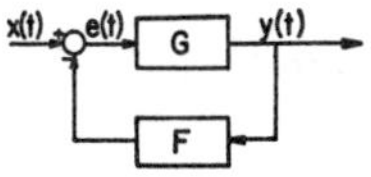

Fig. 1. Nonlinear feedback system.

$$\begin{aligned} FGe(t) + e(t) &= x(t) \\ Ge(t) &= y(t). \end{aligned} \tag{1}$$

Here G is assumed to be a linear time-invariant operator and $F(\cdot)$ a nonlinear operator. The operators are assumed to satisfy the following conditions.

G: The operator G is linear and time invariant and is defined by

$$Ge(t) = \int_0^t g(t - \tau)e(\tau)d\tau + g_1(t)$$

where the impulse response function $g(t)$ is in $L_1 \cap L_2$ and the function $g_1(t)$, representing the effect of initial conditions, is in L_2. The Laplace transform of $g(t)$ is

$$G(s) = \int_0^\infty g(t)e^{-st}dt \qquad \text{for Re } [s] > 0.$$

F: The operator $F(\cdot)$ is nonlinear and time invariant and satisfies the following conditions.

1) $F(y) = 0$, if $y = 0$.
2) $K_1 \leq [F(y_1) - F(y_2)]/(y_1 - y_2) \leq K_2$ for all real numbers y_1 and y_2 such that $y_1 \neq y_2$, and K_1 and K_2 are real constants satisfying the condition $-\infty < K_1 < K_2 < \infty$. Note that if $K_1 \geq 0$, then $F(\cdot)$ is a monotonically increasing function.

Assuming that the solution to (1) exists and belongs to L_{2e}, the problem of interest may now be stated as follows. If the input to the feedback system $x(t)$ belongs to L_2, determine the conditions on the linear part G of the system so that

1) $y(t) \in L_2$
2) $\lim_{t \to \infty} |y(t)| \to 0$.

III. Preliminary Results

Let RL be the class of complex valued functions $Z(s)$ having the form

$$Z(s) = \prod_{n=0}^{N} \frac{s + \alpha_n}{s + \beta_n}$$

where s is a complex variable and $0 < \alpha_0 < \beta_0 < \alpha_1 < \beta_1 \cdots$, and let RC be the class of functions $Z(s)$ for which $Z^{-1}(s)$ is in RL.

Theorem 1 and Lemma 1 stated in this section are used for deriving the circle criterion. Theorem 1 is a minor extension of a multiplier theorem originally presented in Zames [2], and later proved using a Liapunov approach in Brockett and Willems [4] and Narendra and Neuman [5]. While all the methods essentially lead to the same conditions for proving the stability of systems with monotonic nonlinearities, Brockett and Willems [4] and Narendra and Neuman [5] use a differential equation framework which is distinctly different from the approach used in Zames [2]. The approach used in this paper is similar to that used in Zames [2], [3].

Lemma 1 provides the specific form of the multiplier $Z(s)$ in RL or RC that is needed for the proof of the geometric criterion.

Theorem 1 (Skeleton Theorem)

In the feedback system of Fig. 1, let G and F satisfy the conditions stated in Section II. Then if there exists a multiplier $Z(s)$ in RL

Reprinted from *IEEE Trans. Automat. Contr.*, vol. AC-13, pp. 413–416, Aug. 1968.

or RC with the property

$$\text{Re}\left\{\frac{K_2G(i\omega)+1}{K_1G(i\omega)+1}Z(i\omega)\right\} \geq \delta > 0, \qquad \text{for all } -\infty < \omega < \infty$$

the system is stable in the following sense:

1) $x(t) \in L_2$ implies $y(t) \in L_2$

2) $\lim_{t\to\infty} |y(t)| \to 0.$

Lemma 1 (Construction of Multipliers)

Let $[a, b]$ be any subinterval of $(0, \infty)$, θ any constant in $(-\pi/2, \pi/2)$, and $\epsilon>0$ a constant.

1) If $\theta\geq 0$, then there exists a function $Z(i\omega)$ in RL such that

$$|\arg\{Z(i\omega)\} - \theta| < \epsilon, \qquad \text{for all } \omega \text{ in } [a, b].$$

2) If $\theta<0$, then there exists a function $Z(i\omega)$ in RC with the property that

$$|\arg\{Z(i\omega)\} - \theta| < \epsilon, \qquad \text{for all } \omega \text{ in } [a, b].$$

A heuristic explanation of the method of proof may be outlined as follows. The multiplier $Z(i\omega)$ will be defined by a function having alternating poles and zeros on the negative real axis. It will then be shown that arg $\{Z(i\omega)\}$ can be expressed as a convolution of a "step function" and a "smoothing kernel," and this fact will be used to obtain a bound on $|\arg\{Z(i\omega)\}-\theta|$ using Holders inequality.

Proof of Lemma 1: Let $c=\theta/(\pi/2)$. Let $\alpha>0$ and $\rho>1$ be constants and N a positive integer with the property $\alpha<a$ and $\alpha\rho^{N+C}>b$. Let the multiplier $Z(i\omega)$ be defined by

$$Z(i\omega) = \prod_{n=0}^{N} \frac{(i\omega+\alpha\rho^n)}{(i\omega+\alpha\rho^{n+c})}.$$

Then

$$\arg\{Z(i\omega)\} = \sum_{n=0}^{N}\left\{\tan^{-1}\left(\frac{\omega}{\alpha\rho^n}\right) - \tan^{-1}\left(\frac{\omega}{\alpha\rho^{n+c}}\right)\right\}.$$

Let Ω be the variable defined by $\Omega=\log\omega$; let $\Omega_n=\log\omega_n$, where $\omega_n=\alpha\rho^n$ for $n=1, 2, \cdots, N$; let $f(\Omega)$ be the function of Ω defined by

$$f(\Omega) = \tan^{-1}\{\exp(\Omega)\}.$$

Then arg $\{Z(i\omega)\}$ can be written in the form

$$\arg\{Z(i\omega)\} = \sum_{n=0}^{N}\{f(\Omega-\Omega_n) - f(\Omega-\Omega_{n+c})\}.$$

Let $u(\Omega)$ and $g(\Omega)$ be functions of Ω defined by

$$\underset{[\Omega_n,\Omega_{n+c}]}{u(\Omega)} = \begin{cases}1, & \text{for } \Omega \text{ in } [\Omega_n, \Omega_{n+c}]\\ 0, & \Omega \text{ elsewhere}\end{cases}$$

and

$$g(\Omega) = \sum_{n=0}^{N} \underset{[\Omega_n,\Omega_{n+c}]}{u(\Omega)}.$$

Then arg $\{Z(i\omega)\}$ can be expressed as a convolution

$$\arg\{Z(i\omega)\} = \int_{\Omega_c}^{\Omega_{N+c}} g(\lambda)f'(\Omega-\lambda)d\lambda' \equiv g(\Omega)\otimes f'(\Omega).$$

Hence

$$\begin{aligned}\arg\{Z(i\omega)\} &= c\underset{[\Omega_0,\Omega_{N+c}]}{u(\Omega)}\otimes f'(\Omega)\\ &\quad + \{g(\Omega) - c\underset{[\Omega_0,\Omega_{N+c}]}{u(\Omega)}\}\otimes f'(\Omega)\\ &= c\{f(\Omega-\Omega_c) - f(\Omega-\Omega_{N+c})\}\\ &\quad + \left\{\int_{\Omega_0}^{\Omega}[g(\Omega')-c]d\Omega'\right\}\otimes f''(\Omega).\end{aligned}$$

Hence the following bound is obtained on arg $\{Z(i\omega)\}-\theta$.

$$\begin{aligned}|\arg\{Z(i\omega)\}-\theta| &\leq c\left|f(\Omega-\Omega_0) - f(\Omega-\Omega_{N+c}) - \frac{\theta}{c}\right|\\ &\quad + \left\|\int_{\Omega_0}^{\Omega}[g(\Omega')-c]d\Omega'\right\|_\infty \cdot \|f''(\Omega)\|_1\end{aligned}$$

where $\|\ \|_\infty$ and $\|\ \|_1$ denote the norms in L_∞ and L_1, respectively. Since

$$\left\|\int_{\Omega}^{\Omega}[g(\Omega')-c]d\Omega'\right\|_\infty = c(1-c)\log\rho$$

and

$$\|f''(\Omega)\|_1 = \int_{-\infty}^{\infty}|f''(\Omega)|d\Omega \leq 2$$

it follows that

$$\begin{aligned}|\arg\{Z(i\omega)\}-\theta| &\leq c\left|\tan^{-1}\left(\frac{\omega}{\omega_0}\right) - \tan^{-1}\left(\frac{\omega}{\omega_{N+c}}\right) - \frac{\pi}{2}\right|\\ &\quad + 2c(1-c)\log\rho.\end{aligned}$$

Now α and ρ can be chosen small enough and N large enough so that for any ω in $[a, b]$, $\tan^{-1}(\omega/\omega_0)-\pi/2<\epsilon/3$, $\tan^{-1}(\omega/\omega_{N+c})<\epsilon/3$, and $2c(1-c)\log\rho<\epsilon/3$. Thereupon, the inequality $|\arg\{Z(i\omega)\}-\theta| <\epsilon$ is satisfied, and consequently Lemma 1 is true.

IV. Main Results

The following three theorems are direct consequences of Theorem 1 and Lemma 1 and constitute the main results of this paper.

Theorem 2

Consider the feedback equations (1) (see Fig. 1). If 1) the Nyquist plot of the linear part of the system $G(i\omega)$ lies entirely to the right of a straight line passing through the point $(-(1/K_2)+\delta, 0)$ where $\delta>0$ and if 2) $0\leq[F(y_1)-F(y_2)]/(y_1-y_2)\leq K_2$ for all $y_1\neq y_2$, then the system is asymptotically stable, i.e., $\lim_{t\to\infty}|y(t)|=0$.

Theorem 3

If 1) the Nyquist plot of $G(i\omega)$ lies outside a circle passing through $(-(1/K_2)+\delta_1, 0)$ and $(-(1/K_1)-\delta_1, 0)$ where $\delta_1>0$ without completely encircling it and if 2) $K_1\leq[F(y_1)-F(y_2)]/(y_1-y_2)\leq K_2$ for all $y_1\neq y_2$, then the system is asymptotically stable.

Theorem 4

If 1) the Nyquist plot of $G(i\omega)$ lies entirely inside a circle passing through $(-(1/K_2)+\delta_1, 0)$ and $((1/K_1)-\delta_1, 0)$ where $\delta_1>0$ and if 2) $-K_1\leq[F(y_1)-F(y_2)]/(y_1-y_2)\leq K_2$ for all $y_1\neq y_2$, the system is asymptotically stable.

Only Theorem 2 is proved here since it can be shown that Theorems 3 and 4 can be derived using simple transformations from Theorem 2 [6], [8].

Proof of Theorem 2 (Fig. 2):

1) Case A:

$$\frac{\pi}{2} > \theta > 0.$$

Let the transfer function be defined as $G_1(i\omega)=G(i\omega)+(1/K_2)$ and let the locus of $G(i\omega)$ lie to the right of a straight line passing through $(-(1/K_2)+\delta, 0)$ and making an angle θ with the imaginary axis. The argument of $G_1(i\omega)$ lies in the range

$$-\frac{\pi}{2}-\theta < \arg\{G_1(i\omega)\} < \frac{\pi}{2}-\theta.$$

Hence positive constants ϵ_1 and ϵ_2 exist such that

$$-\frac{\pi}{2}+\epsilon_1 \leq \arg\{G_1(i\omega)\}+\theta \leq \frac{\pi}{2}-\epsilon_2$$

where the left and right equalities hold for frequencies $\omega=a$ and $\omega=b$. Let ϵ be a positive constant such that $\epsilon<\epsilon_1$ and ϵ_2. By Lemma 1 there exists a multiplier $Z(i\omega)$ in RL such that

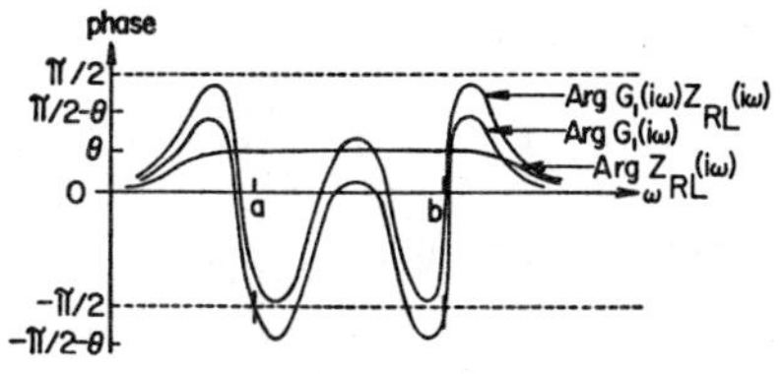

Fig. 2. Proof of Theorem 2.

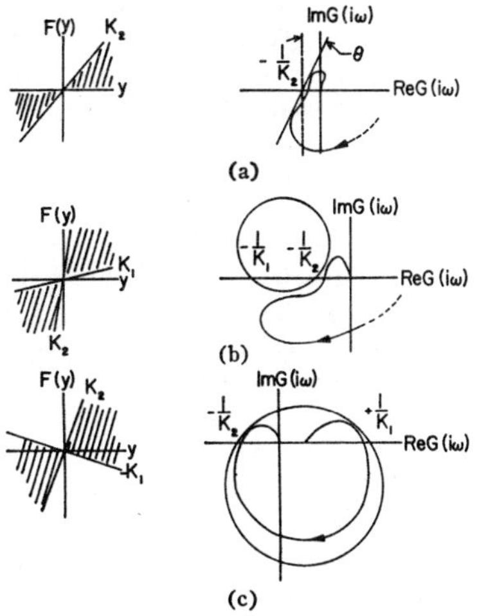

Fig. 3. Admissible regions for $F(\cdot)$ for given $G(i\omega)$. (a) Theorem 2. (b) Theorem 3. (c) Theorem 4.

$$|\arg\{Z(i\omega)\} - \theta| \leq \epsilon, \quad \text{for } a \leq \omega \leq b.$$

Hence the argument of $Z(i\omega)G_1(i\omega)$ lies in the range

$$-\frac{\pi}{2} + \epsilon_1 - \epsilon \leq \arg\{Z(i\omega)G_1(i\omega)\} < \frac{\pi}{2} - \epsilon_2 + \epsilon$$

or

$$|\arg\{Z(i\omega)G_1(i\omega)\}| < \frac{\pi}{2} - \epsilon_3.$$

Hence Re $G_1(i\omega)Z(i\omega \geq \delta > 0$ and by Theorem 1 the system is asymptotically stable.

2) Case B: $0 > \theta > -\pi/2$.

Using similar arguments as in case A one can construct, again by Theorem 1, a multiplier $Z(i\omega)$ in RC such that

$$|\arg\{Z(i\omega)G_1(i\omega)\}| < \frac{\pi}{2} - \epsilon_3.$$

Since Re $\{G_1(i\omega)Z(i\omega)\} \geq \delta > 0$, the system is asymptotically stable.

While a proof for Theorem 3 is not given here the approach may be outlined as follows. If the Nyquist plot of $G(i\omega)$ lies outside a circle passing through $(-1/K_1, 0)$ and $(-1/K_2, 0)$ (Fig. 3(c)), it can be shown [6], [8] using simple transformations that the Nyquist plot of $K_2/[1+K_2G(i\omega)]$ lies entirely to the right of a straight line through $(-K_1K_2/(K_2-K_1), 0)$. Hence by Theorem 2 the feedback system can be shown to be asymptotically stable for all monotonic nonlinear functions $F(\cdot)$ in the sector

$$K_1 \leq \frac{F(y_1) - F(y_2)}{y_1 - y_2} \leq K_2.$$

V. Some Comments on the Circle Criterion

Some comments can now be made regarding the applicability of the criterion in practical situations as well as its relation to well-known existing criteria.

1) The circle criterion stated in Theorems 3 and 4 may be applied in a practical situation in many ways. In particular, the maximum range of stability given by the criterion may be determined as follows. If the lower limit of the monotonic gain K_1 is specified, the upper limit K_2 of the gain defined by $K_1 < F(y)/y < K_2$ within which the nonlinear feedback system is asymptotically stable may be obtained by drawing the circle, which passing through $(-1/K_1, 0)$ touches $G(i\omega)$ at two points. The second intersection of the circle with the negative real axis yields $-1/K_2$.

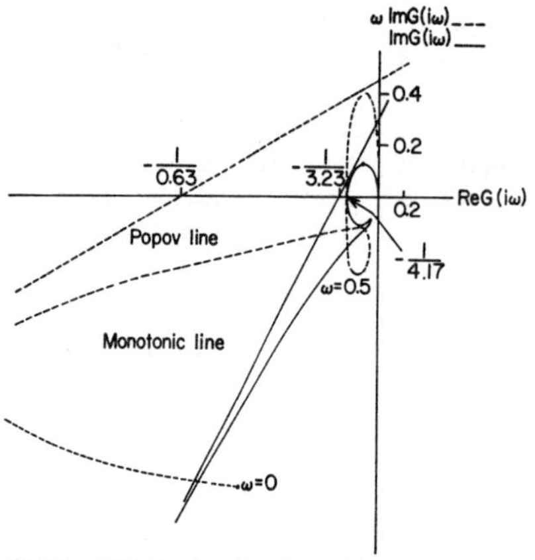

Modified Nyquist Plot (----) and Nyquist Plot (——) of

$$G(s) = \frac{(s+1)}{s(s+0.1)(s^2+0.5s+9)}$$

Fig. 4. Example 1.

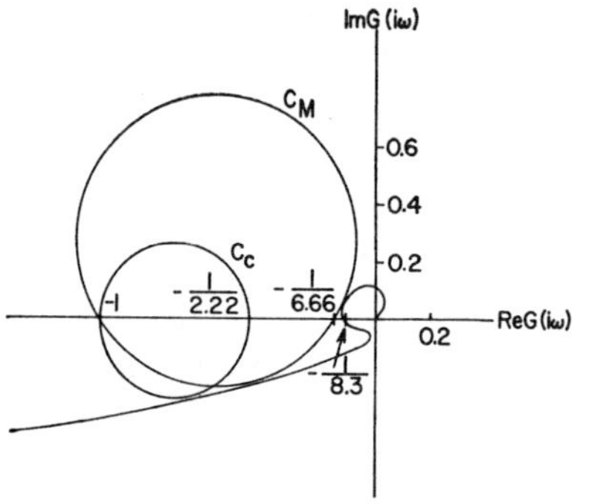

Nyquist Plot of $G(s) = \frac{3(s+1)}{s^2(s^2+s+25)}$

Fig. 5. Example 2.

2) The criterion given by Theorem 3 is a sufficient condition and by no means necessary for the stability of the nonlinear feedback system. Since the theorem is proved for the most stringent case, the actual stability range for a specific $G(s)$ may be $K_1 \leq F(y)/y \leq \overline{K}_2$, where $K_2 < \overline{K}_2$. In such cases a multiplier Z_{RL} may exist so that $G(s)Z_{RL}(s)$ is positive real even when $G(i\omega)$ does not lie to the right of a straight line, or outside a circle.

3) If the lower limit $K_1 = 0$, for a given linear system $G(i\omega)$, gains K_N, K_M, K_P, and K_C represent the gains for which the feedback system is asymptotically stable with 1) constant gains, K_N = Nyquist gain; 2) monotonic gains K_M obtained by the criterion stated in this paper; 3) first and third quadrant nonlinearities, K_P = Popov gain, and 4) nonlinear time-varying gain K_C obtained by the circle criterion [6]–[8].

The methods for obtaining these values in practical situations are illustrated in Figs. 4 and 5 for Examples 1 and 2. It is well known that $K_C \leq K_P \leq K_N$. In most situations the gain K_M is found to lie between the Nyquist gain and the Popov gain, i.e., $K_P \leq K_M \leq K_N$.

4) The circle criterion for time-varying systems calls for a circle with its center on the negative real axis while the circle criterion for monotonic nonlinearities calls for any circle touching $G(i\omega)$ at two points. The two are identical only in the particular case where $G(i\omega)$ is symmetrical about the real axis. In general the monotonic circle (C_M) criterion yields a much larger sector of stability for monotonic

nonlinearities than the circle (C_C) criterion does for time-varying nonlinearities. The sectors for a specific example are shown in Fig. 5.

VI. Examples

Two examples are given here to demonstrate the applicability of the criterion derived in Section V and to compare it with Popov's criterion and the circle criterion for time-varying systems.

Example 1

The transfer function of the linear part of the feedback system in Fig. 1 is given by

$$G(s) = \frac{s+1}{s(s+0.1)(s^2+0.5s+9)}.$$

The Nyquist plot $G(i\omega)$ as well as the modified Nyquist plot (Re G versus ω Im G) are shown in Fig. 4. The Nyquist gain for the system is $K_N=4.17$ while the Popov gain $K_P=0.63$ is obtained by drawing a straight line tangential at two points to the modified Nyquist plot. The straight line tangential to $G(i\omega)$ at two points intersects the real axis at $(-1/3.23, 0)$ yielding a $K_M=3.23$. Hence the system is asymptotically stable for all monotonic increasing nonlinear functions in the sector

$$0 < \frac{F(y_1) - F(y_2)}{y_1 - y_2} < 3.23.$$

Example 2

In this case

$$G(s) = \frac{3(s+1)}{s^2(s^2+s+25)}.$$

It is required to find a sector $1 < [F(y_1) - F(y_2)]/(y_1 - y_2) < K_2$ within which the system is asymptotically stable. The Nyquist plot $G(i\omega)$ is shown in Fig. 5.

1) The Nyquist gain $K_N=8.30$. Hence for all constant gains K in the feedback path $0<K<8.3$, the system is asymptotically stable.

2) A circle C_C with its center on the negative real axis, passing through $(-1, 0)$ and touching $G(i\omega)$, intersects the real axis a second time at $-1/2.22$. Hence for all nonlinear time-varying gain functions in the feedback path satisfying $1 < F(y, t)/y < 2.22$, the system is asymptotically stable.

3) A circle C_M, passing through $(-1, 0)$ and touching the Nyquist plot at two points, intersects the real axis at $-1/6.66$. Hence by the circle criterion developed in this paper, the feedback system with monotonic increasing nonlinear functions in the feedback path is stable for all $F(\cdot)$ satisfying

$$1 < \frac{F(y_1) - F(y_2)}{y_1 - y_2} < 6.66.$$

VII. Conclusion

A simple geometric criterion is derived in this paper as a sufficient condition for determining the asymptotic stability of a feedback system with a single monotonic increasing nonlinear gain function in the feedback path.

Using the fundamental lemma derived, it is shown that if the Nyquist plot $G(i\omega)$ lies entirely to the right of a straight line, an RL or RC multiplier $Z(s)$ can always be found such that $G(s)Z(s)$ is positive real. This in turn insures the stability of the system for all monotonic feedback gains in some range

$$0 < \frac{F(y_1) - F(y_2)}{y_1 - y_2} < \overline{K}.$$

By suitable transformations, it can also be shown that if the Nyquist plot $G(i\omega)$ of the linear part lies entirely outside a circle intersecting the negative real axis at $(-1/K_1, 0)$ and $(-1/K_2, 0)$, then the nonlinear system is asymptotically stable in the sector

$$K_1 < \frac{F(y_1) - F(y_2)}{y_1 - y_2} < K_2.$$

Acknowledgment

The authors would like to thank the reviewer for suggesting the form of the multiplier used in the main lemma.

References

[1] V. M. Popov, "Absolute stability of nonlinear systems of automatic control," *Automation and Remote Control*, vol. 22, pp. 857–875, March 1962.
[2] G. Zames, "On the stability of nonlinear, time-varying feedback systems," *Proc. Nat'l Electronics Conf.*, vol. 20, pp. 725–730, October 1964.
[3] ——, "On the input-output stability of time-varying nonlinear feedback systems," pts. I and II, *IEEE Trans. Automatic Control*, vol. AC-11, pp. 228–238, April 1966, and pp. 465–476, July 1966.
[4] R. W. Brockett and J. W. Willems, "Frequency domain stability criteria," pts. I and II, *IEEE Trans. Automatic Control*, vol. AC-10, pp. 255–261, July 1965, and pp. 407–413, October 1965.
[5] K. S. Narendra and C. P. Neumann, "Stability of a class of differential equations with a single monotone nonlinearity," *SIAM J. Control*, vol. 4, pp. 295–308, May 1966.
[6] K. S. Narendra and R. M. Goldwyn, "A geometrical criterion for the stability of certain nonlinear nonautonomous systems," *IEEE Trans. Circuit Theory (Correspondence)*, vol. CT-11, pp. 406–408, September 1964.
[7] I. W. Sandberg, "On the L_2-boundedness of solutions of nonlinear functional equations," *Bell Sys. Tech. J.*, vol. 43, pp. 1581–1599, July 1964.
[8] ——, "A frequency-domain condition for the stability of feedback systems containing a single time-varying nonlinear element," *Bell Sys. Tech. J.*, vol. 43, pp. 1601–1608, July 1964.
[9] M. A. Aizerman and F. R. Gantmacher, *Absolute Stability of Regulator Systems.* San Francisco, Calif.: Holden-Day, 1964.
[10] C. T. Lee and C. A. Desoer, "Stability of single-loop nonlinear feedback systems," Electronic Research Laboratory, University of California, Berkeley, Calif., Rept. ERL 66-13, May 1966.

Frequency Domain Stability Criteria for Stochastic Systems

JAN C. WILLEMS, MEMBER, IEEE, AND GILMER L. BLANKENSHIP, STUDENT MEMBER, IEEE

***Abstract*—The stability of a class of dynamical systems containing random parameters is investigated. An input-output stability concept is formulated for stochastic systems. The specific class of systems considered consists of those feedback systems whose open loop consists of the cascade of a white noise multiplicative gain and a linear deterministic dynamical system. Necessary and sufficient frequency domain conditions for stability are derived and it is shown that the uncertainty has a destabilizing effect. The resulting stability conditions depend on the open-loop stability, the rms value of the stochastic gain element, and the effective bandwidth of the linear element.**

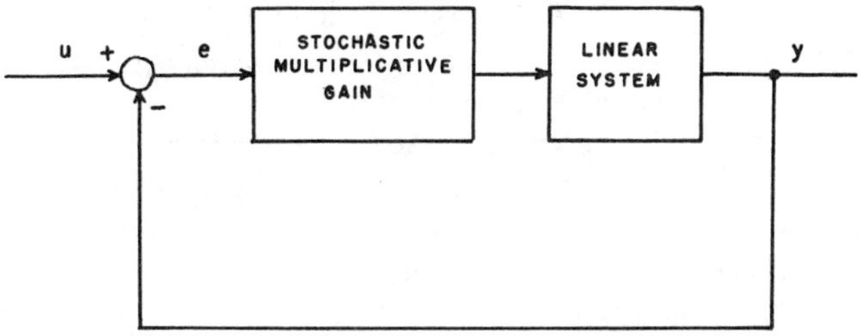

Fig. 1. Feedback system under consideration.

I. Introduction

THOUGH it is customary in modern control theory to study systems in which disturbances enter additively, many control problems encountered in practice include disturbances that may be modeled more accurately as uncertain multiplicative gains. Such systems are usually represented as featuring multiplicative gains that are random processes with known statistics. A number of papers treating the control [1], [2] of such systems have recently appeared in the literature. A great deal of work on the stability of such systems has also appeared, especially in the Russian literature (see [3] for a survey).

The logical first step in the study of problems of this nature is to consider the system to be linear and the gain to be a white noise random process. (The nonwhite noise multiplicative gain case is in a very real sense a nonlinear problem.)

The most prominent examples of systems featuring such a white-noise multiplicative gain are the following.

1) Models for the human operator whose error in observation and/or control is proportional (with a random proportionality factor) to the observed signal or the desired control action [4].

2) Models for the round-off error in floating point arithmetic numerical calculations.

The present paper is concerned with the stability of such systems. More so than for deterministic systems there appears to be a great deal of uncertainty as to which type of stability is to be preferred in such studies (see [3] for a discussion on this point). The present paper proposes an input-output stability concept that should serve as a useful type of stability in this context. The stability obtained is by and large a mean square stability, however, and will thus have the usual disadvantages that result from this type of convergence.

The discussion will be concerned with both discrete and continuous systems, but the proofs will be carried out for the discrete case only. This keeps the analysis elementary since it avoids the technical subtleties of methods based on the Itô calculus. The proofs presented here reduce the stochastic stability problem to a deterministic one to which well-known techniques may then be applied. Since the results hold for time-varying systems as well as for stationary systems, and for nonstationary stochastic processes as well as for stationary ones, the general case will be presented.

To keep the notation simple, the discussion will be restricted to scalar input-scalar output feedback systems as the one shown in Fig. 1.

II. Mathematical Formulation of the Problem

A. Discrete Systems

Consider the input-output relation determined by the implicit functional equations

$$e_n = u_n - y_n$$

$$y_n = \sum_{l=0}^{n-1} w_{nl} f_l e_l, \qquad n \in I^+ \triangleq \text{nonnegative integers.} \quad (1)$$

In terms of the feedback system shown in Fig. 1, $\{w_{kl}\}$, $k > l \in I^+$ represents the weighting pattern of the linear system in the forward loop whereas $\{f_n\}, n \in I^+$ represents the values of the memoryless gain. The sequences $\{u_n\}$, $\{y_n\}$, and $\{e_n\}$ represent, respectively, the input, the output, and the error of this feedback system.

It is assumed that $w_{kl}, k > l \in I^+$ is a given real number and that the sequence $\{f_n\}, n \in I^+$ is a real-valued discrete stochastic process with given second-order statistics:

Manuscript received June 10, 1970; revised March 19, 1971. Paper recommended by E. F. Infante, Chairman of the IEEE S-CS Stability Theory and Nonlinear Systems Committee. This research was supported by the National Aeronautic and Space Administration under Contract NGL-22-009-124 and by the National Science Foundation under Grant GK-14152, both with the Electronic Systems Laboratory of the Massachusetts Institute of Technology.

The authors are with the Decision and Control Sciences Group, Electronic Systems Laboratory, Massachusetts Institute of Technology, Cambridge, Mass. 02139.

Reprinted from *IEEE Trans. Automat. Contr.*, vol. AC-16, pp. 292-299, Aug. 1971.

$$E\{f_n\} = 0 \qquad E\{f_n f_m\} = \begin{cases} 0, & m \neq n \\ q_n^2, & m = n, \end{cases} \qquad n \in I^+.$$

The input $\{u_n\}, n \in I^+$ is assumed to be a real-valued stochastic process that is independent of the process $\{f_n\}, n \in I^+$. It is clear from the equations that under these circumstances there exists a unique solution $\{e_n\}$, $\{y_n\}, n \in I^+$ to the feedback equations for all processes $\{f_n\}$ and $\{u_n\}, n \in I^+$. These will in turn be real-valued stochastic processes and the boundedness properties of these processes in terms of the boundedness properties of $\{u_n\}, n \in I^+$ is the aim of stability studies. Note that in general neither e nor y will be a Markov process and that the state of the open-loop and thus of the closed-loop system may well be infinite dimensional.

A large number of stability concepts for stochastic systems have been proposed. However, even if one decides to work in the usual Lyapunov setting there are two choices that must be made at the outset.

1) What is the basic random variable whose properties are to be studied?

2) What type of probabilistic convergence will be employed in the analysis?

One possibility, for example, is to consider

$$a_T = \sup_{t_0 \leq t \leq T} ||x(t;x_0,t_0)||, \qquad x = \text{the state of the system}$$

as the basic random variable whose convergence is at question, whereas another possibility is to consider $||x(t)||$ as the basic random variable to be studied.

In considering 2) it should be realized that there are no compelling reasons for preferring one type of probabilistic convergence to another. The apparent difficulty in identifying the natural mode of convergence is characteristic of studies of systems with distributed parameters. In stochastic systems the distributed effect arises from the fact that the instantaneous probability distribution of the signals is the system state, and its evolution (at least in the Markov case) is governed by a partial differential equation (the Fokker–Planck equation). Thus, one is forced naturally into a situation where the choice of a distance function is crucial and rather subtle. For a survey of the properties of stochastic equations from this point of view using Lyapunov theory see [5], [6], and [7], and the references therein. See also [8] for an alternate approach that considers properties of the distributions.

Another way of considering stability is to permit disturbances of the system at the input and to determine stability by examining properties of the resulting output. An input–output stability concept for deterministic systems has been formulated by Sandberg [9] and Zames [10], and it has enjoyed wide application in the literature. The following definition is a natural analog of this concept in a stochastic setting.

Definition: The system under consideration is said to be second-order stochastic input–output stable if every input process $\{u_n\}, n \in I^+$, whose second-order statistics satisfy the boundedness condition $E\{u_n^2\} \in l_\infty(I^+)$ (i.e., $E\{u_n^2\} \leq M < \infty$, for all $n \in I^+$), generates error and output processes $\{e_n\},\{y_n\}, n \in I^+$, whose second-order statistics similarly satisfy $E\{e_n^2\}, E\{y_n^2\} \in l_\infty(I^+)$.

B. Continuous Systems

Consider the input–output relation determined (informally) by the implicit stochastic integral equation

$$e(t) = u(t) - y(t)$$

$$y(t) = \int_0^t w(t,\tau)e(\tau)f(\tau)d\tau, \qquad t \in R^+ \triangleq \text{the nonnegative real line} \quad (2)$$

where $f(t)$ denotes a white noise process with $E\{f(t)\} = 0$ and $E\{f(t)f(t-\tau)\} = q^2(t)\delta(\tau), t \in R^+$, ($\delta$ denotes the Dirac delta function).

The above equations are to be interpreted rigorously as the Itô integral equation

$$e(t) = u(t) - \int_0^t w(t,s)e(s)d\beta(s)$$

with $y(t) = u(t) - e(t)$ where β is a generalized Wiener process with independent increments and statistics

$$E\{\beta(t)\} = 0$$

$$E\{[\beta(t) - \beta(t-s)]^2\} = \begin{cases} \int_{t-s}^{t} q^2(\sigma)d\sigma, & s \geq 0 \\ \int_{t}^{t-s} q^2(\sigma)d\sigma, & s \leq 0. \end{cases}$$

The analogous definition of input–output stability follows.

Definition: The stochastic system (2) is said to be second-order stochastic input–output stable if every input process $\{u(t)\}, t \in R^+$, whose second-order statistics satisfy the boundedness conditions $E\{u^2(t)\} \in L_\infty(R^+)$ (i.e., $E\{u^2(t)\} \leq M < \infty$, for almost all $t \in R^+$), generates well-defined error and output processes $\{e(t)\},\{y(t)\}, t \in R^+$, whose second-order statistics similarly satisfy $E\{e^2(t)\}, E\{y^2(t)\} \in L_\infty(R^+)$.

Contrary to the discrete case it is of course not clear *a priori* whether every process $\{u(t)\}$ and $\{\beta(t)\}, t \in R^+$, satisfying the above conditions, generates well-defined processes $\{e(t)\}$ and $\{y(t)\}, t \in R^+$, with finite first and second moments. Some additional conditions are in fact necessary to ensure this. Although the paper is not concerned with this question, let it just be mentioned that if

$$\sup_{0 \leq t \leq T} \int_0^t |w(t,\tau)| d\tau < \infty$$

and

$$\sup_{0 \leq t \leq T} \int_0^t |w(t,\tau)|^2 q^2(\tau) d\tau < \infty$$

for all $T \in R^+$, then unique solution processes e,y exist that are bounded (L^2) on every (finite) interval $[0,T]$. Note again that neither e nor y will in general have the Markov property.

C. Main Results

The following theorems and corollaries constitute the main results of this paper.

Theorem 1: The discrete stochastic system described by (1) is second-order stochastic input–output stable if

$$\sum_{l=0}^{n-1} |w_{nl}|^2 q_l^2 \leq \alpha < 1, \qquad n \in I^+.$$

Theorem 2: The continuous stochastic system described by (2) is second-order stochastic input–output stable if

$$\int_0^t |w(t,\tau)|^2 q^2(\tau) d\tau \leq \alpha < 1, \qquad t \in R^+.$$

The case in which the linear system is time invariant and the gain is a stationary stochastic process is of particular interest. Theorems 1 and 2 then specialize to the following corollaries, which become necessary and sufficient conditions.

Corollary 1: Assume that the weighting pattern describing the stochastic system 1 is time invariant, i.e., that $w_{kl} = w_{k-l}$ for $k > l \in I^+$, and that the stochastic process $\{f_n\}, n \in I^+$ is wide-sense stationary, i.e., $q_n^2 = q^2$ for all $n \in I^+$, then the stochastic system (1) is second-order stochastic input–output stable if and only if

$$\{qw_k\} \in l_2(I^+)$$

and[1]

$$q^2 \sum_{k=1}^{\infty} w_k^2 = \frac{1}{2\pi} \oint_{|z|=1} q^2 |\hat{W}(z)|^2 dz < 1$$

where $\hat{W}(z) = \sum_{k=1}^{\infty} w_k z^{-k}$ is the z transform of the impulse response $\{w_k\}$.

Corollary 2: Assume that the kernel describing the stochastic system (2) is time invariant, i.e., that $w(t,\tau) = w(t-\tau, 0)$ for $t \geq \tau \in R^+$, and that the stochastic process $\{\beta(t)\}, t \in R^+$ is wide-sense stationary, i.e., $q^2(t) = q^2$ for all $t \in R^+$ then the stochastic system CSS is second-order stochastic input–output stable if and only if $qw(t) \in L_2(R^+)$ and

$$q^2 \int_0^{\infty} w^2(t) dt = q^2 \frac{1}{2\pi} \int_{-\infty}^{+\infty} |\hat{W}(j\omega)|^2 d\omega < 1$$

where $\hat{W}(j\omega) = \int_0^{\infty} w(t) e^{-j\omega t} dt$ is the transform of the impulse response $w(t)$.

There are some generalizations of the results that pertain to the case in which the stochastic gain f_k or $f(t)$ is not a zero mean process. These will be stated only for the continuous stationary case. The system under consideration is thus

$$e(t) = u(t) - y(t)$$

$$y(t) = \int_0^t w(t-\tau) e(\tau) d\beta(\tau), \qquad t \in R^+ \qquad (2')$$

with $\beta(t)$ a Wiener process with stationary (independent) increments and statistics

$$E\{\beta(t)\} = f_0 t$$

and

$$E\{(d\beta(t) - f_0 dt)^2\} = q^2 dt, \qquad t \in R^+.$$

Theorem 3: Assume that the impulse response $w(t) \in L_1(R^+)$, then the continuous stochastic system described by the equations (2′) is second-order stochastic input–output stable if and only if

$$\inf_{\mathrm{Re}\, s \geq 0} |1 + f_0 \hat{W}(s)| > 0$$

and

$$q^2 \frac{1}{2\pi} \int_{-\infty}^{\infty} |\hat{W}(j\omega)/(1 + f_0 \hat{W}(x\omega))|^2 d\omega < 1.$$

The above theorem leads to the following two corollaries, which show more than a passing similarity to the circle criterion of deterministic stability theory (e.g. [9], [10]).

Corollary 3: Assume that the impulse response $w(t) \in L_1(R^+)$. Then the continuous stochastic system described by the equations (2′) is second-order stochastic input–output stable if there exists a $\gamma \in R$ such that

$$\frac{q^2 w(0)}{f_0 + \gamma} < 1$$

and one of the following conditions is satisfied.

Case 1: $f_0/\gamma > 0$, and the Nyquist locus $\hat{W}(j\omega)$ lies inside the disc centered on the real axis of the complex plane that passes through the origin and the point $\gamma^{-1} + 0j$.

Case 2: $-1 < f_0/\gamma < 0$, and the Nyquist locus $\hat{W}(j\omega)$ lies inside the disc centered on the real axis of the complex plane that passes through the origin and the point $\gamma^{-1} + 0j$.

Case 3: $f_0/\gamma < -1$, and the Nyquist locus $\hat{W}(j\omega)$ does not encircle or intersect the disc centered on the real axis of the complex plane that passes through the origin and the point $\gamma^{-1} + 0j$ (see Fig. 2).

Corollary 4: Assume that the impulse response $w(t) \in L_1(R^+)$. Then the continuous stochastic system described by the equations (2′) is second-order stochastic input–output stable if

$$f_0 > q^2 w(0)$$

and

$$\mathrm{Re}\, \hat{W}(j\omega) \geq 0, \qquad \forall \omega \geq 0.$$

The proofs of the theorems and corollaries are given in the Appendix.

D. Discussion of Results

1) Theorems 1 and 2 are based on the fact that the stochastic stability of the system under consideration is

[1] The explicit statement $\{qw_k\} \in l_2(I^+)$ may be somewhat confusing since it is implied by the second condition of the Corollary. However, it serves to draw attention to the fact that the frequency domain conditions of the second condition should be supplemented by this requirement. This remark also holds for Corollary 2.

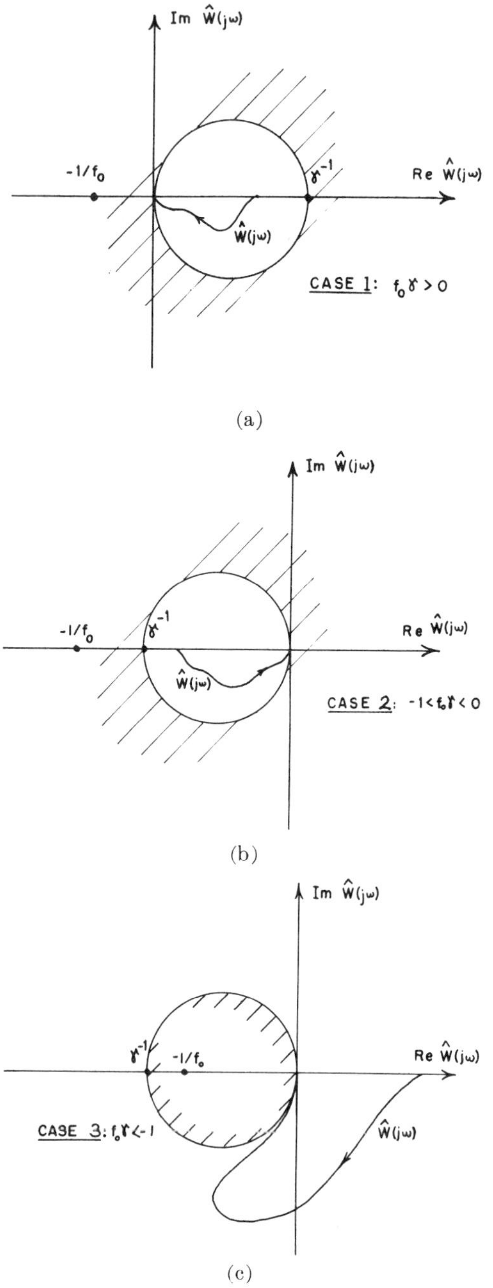

Fig. 2. Stability regions derived from Corollary 3.

equivalent to the (deterministic) $l_\infty(I^+)$ stability[2] of the feedback system described by

$$e_n' = u_n' - y_n'$$

$$y_n' = -\sum_{l=0}^{n-1} m_{nl}e_l', \qquad n \in I^+$$

and

$$e'(t) = u'(t) - y'(t)$$

$$y'(t) = -\int_0^t m(t,\tau)e'(t)d\tau, \qquad t \in R^+,$$

[2] A deterministic system is said to be $l_\infty(I^+)$ input–output stable if input sequences $\{u_k\} \in l_\infty(I^+)$ yield $\{e_k\},\{y_k\} \in l_\infty(I^+)$. See [11] for a discussion of this concept.

respectively, where

$$m_{nl} = w_{nl}^2 q_l^2$$

and

$$m(t,\tau) = w^2(t,\tau)q^2(\tau).$$

This observation has as an intermediate consequence that, in the time-varying case, it makes the deterministic frequency domain stability criteria directly applicable to the stochastic stability problem. In particular, letting, for instance, $w(t,\sigma) = w(t - \sigma,0)$ and $q^2(t)$ be time-varying leads to the sufficient condition for stochastic stability à la circle criterion requring that $w \in L_2(R^+)$ and

$$\sup_{t\geq 0} q^2(t) \int_0^\infty w^2(s)ds = \sup_{t\geq 0} q^2(t) \cdot \frac{1}{2\pi}\int_{-\infty}^{+\infty} |\hat{W}(j\omega)|^2 d\omega \leq \alpha < 1.$$

It also follows from this discussion that the stability results have somewhat stronger boundedness implications than those suggested by the definitions of stability. In particular, they imply finite gain stability in the sense that there exists a number $K < \infty$, $(K = (1 - \alpha)^{-1})$ such that $||E\{e_k^2\}||_{l_\infty(I^+)} \leqq ||E\{u_k^2\}||_{l_\infty(I^+)}$, and similarly for the continuous case. Secondly, it shows that precisely the same results hold in the context of l_p stability $(1 \leqq p \leqq \infty)$.

Note finally that the results of Section C show that the presence of the stochastic gain always has a destabilizing effect on the closed-loop system. While it is difficult to convince oneself intuitively that this is the case, the mathematics reveal this clearly. This has as a consequence that the often conjectured and observed "stabilization by introducing random vibrations" will not work for the class of linear systems considered here. See also [12] in this regard.

2) The necessary and sufficient conditions obtained in Corollaries 1 and 2 require minimal knowledge of the system and may quite easily be obtained experimentally. Corollary 2, for instance, requires that the rms. value of the output of the linear system, when driven by zero-mean wide sense stationary white noise with rms. value $|q|$, be less than unity. Notice also that these corollaries do not require the systems to be finite dimensional. They may hence be used to study with systems with delays. Thus, these results are applicable to systems with a human operator in the control loop, since any reasonable model of a human operator invariably involves a delay. This appears to be a significant result since the human operator is also the most prominent example of a system commonly modeled by a multiplicative stochastic gain.

Corollary 2 reveals clearly the relevant parameters for stochastic stability of open-loop stable feedback systems with a zero-mean white stationary multiplicative feedback gain in cascade with a time-invariant dynamical system: these are the variance of the gain, and a parameter that could be termed the effective bandwidth of the system. The dependence on the variance was to be expected. Here it plays the role that the gain plays in the analogous deterministic results. The effective bandwidth $1/2\pi \int_{-\infty}^{+\infty} |\hat{W}(j\omega)|^2 d\omega$ is a measure of the bandwidth of the system. If $|\hat{W}(j\omega)|$ is of the order of the resonant peak at many frequencies (i.e., if the system is broad band) then this term will be large and the stability question becomes critical. If, however, the frequency response is spiked around its resonant frequency (i.e., if the system is narrow band) then this term will be small and the uncertainty of the stochastic gain will not critically affect the closed-loop stability.

The design dilemmas that result from this criterion are very familiar in classical control theory where the trade-off between accuracy (high open-loop gain) versus stability (low open-loop gain) and speed of response (high bandwidth) versus noise immunity (low bandwidth) is by and large the basis of design procedures. The stochastic stability criterion stated in Corollary 2 reaffirms that the bandwidth and the gain should be sufficiently small for satisfactory stability performance in the presence of noise.

3) The results of Corollary 2 have appeared in a somewhat different context for finite-dimensional systems, i.e., when the transform $\hat{W}(s)$ is a rational function of s. The verification of the condition

$$q^2 \int_0^\infty w^2(t)dt = q^2 \frac{1}{2\pi} \int_{-\infty}^{\infty} |\hat{W}(j\omega)|^2 d\omega < 1$$

may then be carried out in terms of the coefficients of the numerator and the denominator of the transfer function

$$\hat{W}(s) = \frac{q_{n-1}s^{n-1} + q_{n-2}s^{n-2} + \cdots + q_0}{p_n s^n + p_{n-1}s^{n-1} + \cdots + p_0}, \qquad p_n \neq 0.$$

The condition $w(t) \in L_2(R^+)$ is indeed equivalent to the Hurwitz conditions [13, p. 55]

$$\Delta_1 = p_{n-1} > 0, \qquad \Delta_2 = \det \begin{bmatrix} p_{n-1} & p_n \\ p_{n-3} & p_{n-2} \end{bmatrix} > 0$$

$$\Delta_3 = \det \begin{bmatrix} p_{n-1} & p_n & 0 \\ p_{n-3} & p_{n-2} & p_{n-1} \\ p_{n-5} & p_{n-4} & p_{n-3} \end{bmatrix} > 0,$$

$$\cdots, \Delta_n = \det \begin{bmatrix} p_{n-1} & p_n & 0 & 0 \cdots 0 \\ p_{n-3} & p_{n-2} & p_{n-1} & p_n \cdots 0 \\ \cdot & \cdot & \cdot & \cdot \quad \cdot \\ \cdot & \cdot & \cdot & \cdot \quad \cdot \\ \cdot & \cdot & \cdot & \cdot \quad \cdot \\ 0 & 0 & 0 & 0 \cdots p_0 \end{bmatrix} > 0$$

whereas the second condition requires [14], [15, p. 372]

$$q^2 \left| \det \begin{bmatrix} r_{2n-2} & p_n & 0 & 0 \cdots 0 \\ r_{2n-4} & p_{n-2} & p_{n-1} & p_n \cdots p \\ \cdot & \cdot & \cdot & \cdot \quad \cdot \\ \cdot & \cdot & \cdot & \cdot \quad \cdot \\ \cdot & \cdot & \cdot & \cdot \quad \cdot \\ r_0 & 0 & 0 & 0 \quad p_0 \end{bmatrix} \right| < \Delta_n$$

where

$$r_m = \begin{cases} \sum_{j=0}^{m} (-1)^j q_j q_{m-j}, & 0 \le m \le n-1 \\ \sum_{j=m-n+1}^{n-1} (-1)^j q_j q_{m-j}, & n \le m \le 2n-2. \end{cases}$$

Note that values of the integrals $1/2\pi \int_{-\infty}^{\infty} |\hat{W}(j\omega)|^2 d\omega$ terms of the coefficients $\{p_i, q_i\}$ are tabulated in [15, pp. 371–381] for up to tenth-order systems.

4) Kleinman [16] has recently obtained a less explicit condition equivalent to the one stated in Corollary 2. His condition requires solving the linear equation

$$XA + A'X + q^2 b'Xbcc' = -Q$$

for the $(n \times n)$ matrix X when $Q = Q' > 0$ and $\{A, b, c'\}$ is a minimal realization [13, p. 91–101] of the transfer function $\hat{W}(s) = c'(Is - A)^{-1}b$. Stability then results if and only if $X = X' > 0$. This condition leads to Corollary 2 as follows. Since A is asymptotically stable, there exists a unique symmetric positive definite solution to $PA + A'P = -cc'$. In fact, $P = \int_0^\infty e^{A't}cc'e^{At}dt$. It then follows that

$$XA + A'X + q^2 b'Xbcc' = -cc'$$

has a positive definite symmetric solution if and only if

$$q^2 \int_0^\infty w^2(t)dt < 1.$$

In fact,

$$X = \left[1 - q^2 \int_0^\infty w^2(t)dt\right]^{-1} P$$

and this is also the unique solution. The result then follows by continuity and letting $Q = cc' + \epsilon I$ with $\epsilon > 0$ in the original equation.

These considerations show also that if the system is finite dimensional and stationary, then the stability considered above is equivalent to Lyapunov stability with probability one, mean-square Lyapunov stability, and almost sure Lyapunov stability.

5) Although Corollaries 3 and 4 are only sufficient conditions that follow from Theorem 3, it should be noted that they are extremely simple to apply. These corollaries provide a systematic method for designing the admissible mean value of the feedback gains without requiring evaluation of the effective bandwidth of the closed-loop system. The parameter γ appearing in the statement of Corollary 3 is merely an auxillary constant whose value may be read off from the Nyquist locus. Theorem 3 and Corollary 3 allow, moreover, an interpretation in terms of gain and phase margins.

Note also that there are several alternate expressions for the term $w(0)$. Specifically, if $w \in L_1(R^+)$, then

$$w(0) = \lim_{s \to \infty} s\hat{W}(s) = \frac{1}{2\pi} \int_{-\infty}^{+\infty} \hat{W}(j\omega)d\omega$$

$$= \frac{1}{\pi} \int_0^\infty \mathrm{Re}\, \hat{W}(j\omega)d\omega$$

and in the finite dimensional case $w(0) = q_{n-1}/p_n$.

The criterion in Corollary 4 shows a striking similarity to the passive operator theorem of deterministic stability theory. It guarantees stability provided the linear part of the open-loop system is passive ($\text{Re}\,\hat{W}(j\omega) \geqq 0$) and provided the time-varying part is "on the average" sufficiently passive ($f_0 > q^2w(0)$). One obviously is interested in generalizations of this result. Notice, however, that the stochastic gain will never be passive in the usual sense since this would require pointwise positivity of $f(t)$. A result similar to Corollary 4 has been announced in [17].

E. Example

Consider the feedback system shown in Fig. 3 with e^{-sT} a delay of length $T > 0$. Let $E\{f(t)\} = 0$ and $E\{f(t)f(t-\tau)\} = q^2\delta(\tau)$. Then stability results if and only if $\zeta\omega_n > 0$ and

$$q^2I = q^2\frac{1}{2\pi j}\int_{-j\infty}^{j\infty}\frac{K^2}{(s^2+2\zeta\omega_n s+\omega_n^2)(s^2-2\zeta\omega_n s+\omega_n^2)}\cdot ds < 1.$$

From Newton, Gould, and Kaiser [15, p. 372]

$$I = \frac{K^2}{4\zeta\omega_n^3}.$$

Thus the necessary and sufficient condition for stability is

$$\frac{q^2K^2}{\zeta\omega_n^3} < 4.$$

F. Generalizations

Consider now the continuous multiple input–multiple output stationary feedback system in which the error is described by the equation

$$\boldsymbol{e}(t) = \boldsymbol{u}(t) - \int_0^t \boldsymbol{W}(t-s)d\boldsymbol{K}(s)\boldsymbol{e}(s), \qquad t \in R^+$$

where $d\boldsymbol{K}$ is a $(p \times r)$ matrix of zero-mean stationary white noise multiplications and $\boldsymbol{W}$ is a time-invariant $(r \times p)$ matrix convolution kernel. Calculations similar to those for the scalar case lead to the following equation determining the $(r \times r)$ matrix $E\{\boldsymbol{e}(t)\boldsymbol{e}'(t)\} = [\sigma_{ij}(t)]$ in terms of $E\{\boldsymbol{u}(t)\boldsymbol{u}'(t)\} = [\rho_{ij}(t)]$, $i,j = 1,2,\cdots,r$:

$$\sigma_{ij}(t) = \rho_{ij}(t) + \int_0^t \sum_{k,m=1}^{p}\sum_{l,n=1}^{r} q_{klmn}{}^2 w_{ik}(t-s)$$
$$\cdot w_{jm}(t-s)\,\sigma_{ln}(s)ds, \qquad t \in R^+, \qquad i,j, = 1,2,\cdots,q$$

where

$$E\{dK_{kl}(s)dK_{mn}(t)\} = \begin{cases}0, & s \neq t\\ q_{klmn}{}^2ds, & s = t\end{cases}$$
$$k,m = 1,2,\cdots,p \qquad l,n = 1,2,\cdots,r.$$

The above equation is linear in the σ_{ij} and although the use of higher order tensors would greatly condense the notation, their introduction is hardly warranted. This equation will hence be written in augmented matrix form.

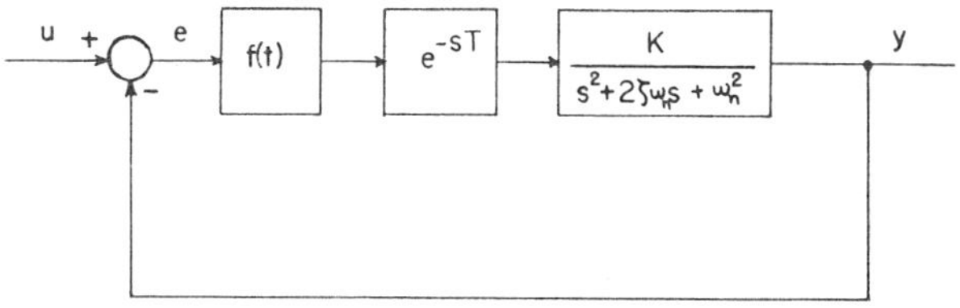

Fig. 3. Example including delay.

The stochastic stability is again equivalent to a deterministic stability problem. The deterministic system is a multiple input–multiple output system with r^2 inputs and outputs and may be represented as $\boldsymbol{\Sigma}(t) = \boldsymbol{R}(t) + \int_0^t \boldsymbol{G}(t-s)\boldsymbol{\Sigma}(s)ds$ with $\boldsymbol{\Sigma}$ the r^2-dimensional vector with entries σ_{ij} and $\boldsymbol{G}$ the appropriate (known) $(r^2 \times r^2)$ matrix. It is well known [20] that a necessary and sufficient condition for the stability of this system is that

$$\inf_{\text{Re}\, s \geq 0} |\det [\boldsymbol{I} - \hat{\boldsymbol{G}}(s)]| > 0$$

with $\hat{\boldsymbol{G}}(s)$ the Laplace transform of $\boldsymbol{G}(t)$. Particular cases of interest follow.

1) $r = 1$. The necessary and sufficient condition then becomes

$$\int_0^\infty \boldsymbol{W}(t)\boldsymbol{Q}\boldsymbol{W}^T(t)dt = \frac{1}{2\pi}\int_{-\infty}^{\infty}\hat{\boldsymbol{W}}(j\omega)\boldsymbol{Q}\hat{\boldsymbol{W}}^T(-j\omega)d\omega < 1$$

where

$$E\{dK_i(s)dK_j(t)\} = \begin{cases}0, & s \neq t,\\ (\boldsymbol{Q})_{ij}ds, & s = t,\end{cases} \qquad i,j = 1,2,\cdots,p.$$

2) $p = 1$. The necessary and sufficient condition then becomes, after some manipulations,

$$\int_0^\infty \boldsymbol{W}(t)^T\boldsymbol{Q}\boldsymbol{W}(t)dt = \frac{1}{2\pi}\int_{-\infty}^{\infty}\hat{\boldsymbol{W}}^T(j\omega)\boldsymbol{Q}\hat{\boldsymbol{W}}(-j\omega)d\omega < 1$$

where $\boldsymbol{Q}$ is as in 1).

Nakamiro [21] has recently obtained a special case of this result.

3) It can always be assumed without loss of generality that the r^2 white noise gains in $d\boldsymbol{K}$ are mutually uncorrelated, i.e., that $E\{dK_{kl}(s)dK_{mn}(t)\} = 0$ unless $k = m$ and $l = n$. If this is the case, then the necessary and sufficient condition becomes

$$\inf_{\text{Re}\, s \geq 0} |\det [\boldsymbol{I} - \hat{\boldsymbol{Z}}(s)]| > 0$$

where $\hat{\boldsymbol{Z}}(s) = \hat{\boldsymbol{R}}(s)\boldsymbol{Q}$ with

$$E\{dK_{ij}(s)dK_{ij}(t)\} = \begin{cases}0, & s \neq t,\\ (Q)_{ij}ds, & s = t,\end{cases}$$
$$i = 1,2,\cdots,p, \qquad j = 1,2,\cdots,r$$

and $\hat{\boldsymbol{R}}(s)$ the transform of $\boldsymbol{R}(t) \triangleq \boldsymbol{W}(t) \circledS \boldsymbol{W}(t)$ where $\circledS$ denotes Schur product (i.e., $(\boldsymbol{A} \circledS \boldsymbol{B})_{ij} = a_{ij}b_{ij}$). Although every element of $\hat{\boldsymbol{Z}}(s)$ is the transform of a nonnegative time function, it appears that this determinant condition can nevertheless not be made more explicit.

G. Further Remarks and Conclusions

The criteria of Theorems 1 and 2 strongly suggest that the stability results obtained here may be in fact based on a stochastic version of the small loop gain theorem of Zames [10]. Indeed, this is the case and moment bounds of the kind given here may be determined in a far more general setting in a way conceptually identical to the procedure in [9] and [10], though in specific instances the evaluation of operator gains is more involved. However, the implications of these criteria are far deeper than we have indicated here and one can use them to make rather precise statements about the properties of the probability distributions involved. This work is contained in [8] and will appear elsewhere.

In summary we have presented here a series of stability criteria for feedback systems whose open loop consists of a linear deterministic system in cascade with a white noise gain. The stability concept used is a stochastic version of the familiar concept of bounded-input–bounded-output stability.

The results give both time and frequency domain conditions for stability, and a number of sufficient conditions involving simple graphical frequency domain tests are given. The latter provide fast and explicit tests that may be used to help the designer in estimating the performance of a control system containing uncertain parameters. The results of the paper essentially dispense with the stability question in linear systems with white noise stochastic parameters by reducing the problem to an equivalent deterministic one. Unfortunately, the methods do not appear to be applicable to any other related classes of systems. In particular the treatment of the case of linear stochastic systems with Gauss–Markov multiplicative parameters requires a different approach since the problem is in essence nonlinear.

Appendix

Proof of Theorem 1: The equations governing $\{e_n\}$ and $\{y_n\}$ are

$$e_n + \sum_{l=0}^{n-1} w_{nl} e_l f_l = u_n, \qquad n \in I^+$$

$$y_n = u_n - e_n,$$

which shows that e_n is independent of f_l for $l \geq n$. Hence $E\{e_n\} = E\{u_n\}$, $E\{y_n\} = 0$, and $E\{e_n e_m\} = E\{u_n u_m\}$, for $n \neq m$. Also,

$$E\{e_n^2\} = E\left\{\left(u_n - \sum_{l=0}^{n-1} w_{nl} e_l f_l\right)^2\right\}$$

$$= E\{u_n^2\} + E\left(\sum_{l=0}^{n-1} w_{nl} e_l f_l\right)^2$$

$$= E\{u_n^2\} + \sum_{l=0}^{n-1} w_{nl}^2 E\{e_l^2\} q_l^2.$$

Thus,

$$E\{e_n^2\} - \sum_{l=0}^{n-1} w_{nl}^2 q_l^2 E\{e_l^2\} = E\{u_n^2\}$$

and if the conditions of Theorem 1 are satisfied then

$$\sup_{0 \leq l \leq N} E\{e_l^2\} \leq \frac{1}{1-\alpha} \sup_{0 \leq l \leq N} E\{u_l^2\}$$

so that $E\{u_n^2\} \in l_\infty(I^+)$ implies $E\{e_n^2\} \in l_\infty(I^+)$ and, since $y_n = u_n - e_n$, stability. Q.E.D.

Proof of Theorem 2: Since the mechanics of the proof of Theorem 2 are exactly the same as those of Theorem 1, but since the analytical details are much more intricate due to the subtleties of Itô calculus, the proof will be deleted. These intricacies are, moreover, only peripherally related to the topic of this paper. See [8] for a complete treatment.

Proof of Corollary 1: By the proof of Theorem 1 it thus suffices to prove that if $\sum_{n=1}^{\infty} q^2 w_n^2 \geq 1$, then there exists an $l_\infty(I^+)$ sequence $\{v_n\}$ with $v_n \geq 0$ such that the solution $\{r_n\}$ to the equation $r_n - q^2 \sum_{l=0}^{n-1} w_{n-l}^2 r_l = v_n$, $n \in I^+$, is unbounded. Let G denote the operator that maps the sequence $\{r_n\}$ into the sequence $\{q^2 \sum_{l=0}^{n-1} w_{n-l}^2 r_l\}$. Clearly $(I - G)^{-1}$ exists and can be represented by a lower triangular infinite matrix with all its entries nonnegative since the entries of the infinite matrix corresponding to G are also nonnegative. It is well known (e.g., the work by Desoer and Wu [18]) that the operator $(I - G)^{-1}$ maps $l_\infty(I^+)$ sequences into $l_\infty(I^+)$ sequences if and only if

$$\inf_{|z| \geq 1} \left| 1 - \sum_{n=0}^{\infty} q^2 w_n^2 z^{-n} \right| > 0.$$

Clearly if $\sum_{n=1}^{\infty} q^2 w_n^2 \geq 1$ there exists a real number $\alpha \geq 1$ such that $1 = \sum_{n=1}^{\infty} q^2 w_n^2 \alpha^{-n}$, which shows that there exists a sequence $\{v_n\} \in l_\infty(I^+)$ such that the sequence $\{r_n\}, n \in I^+$ is unbounded. It remains to be shown that the sequence $\{v_n\} \in l_\infty(I^+)$ may be chosen with $v_n \geq 0$. This, however, is an immediate consequence of the nonnegativity of the entries in the matrix corresponding to $(I - G)^{-1}$ and the Perron–Frobenius theorem (e.g., [19, p. 278]).

Proof of Corollary 2: The remarks made on occasion of the proof of Theorem 2 apply also here. The details of the proof are left to the reader.

Proof of Theorem 3: The equation governing $e(t)$ is

$$e(t) + \int_0^t w(t-\tau) e(\tau) d\beta(\tau) = u(t), \qquad t \in R^+$$

or

$$e(t) + f_0 \int_0^t w(t-\tau) e(\tau) d\tau + \int_0^t w(t-\tau) \cdot e(\tau)[d\beta(\tau) - f_0 d\tau] = u(t), \qquad t \in R^+.$$

Letting W denote the operator that maps $e(t)$ into $\int_0^t w(t - \tau) e(\tau) d\tau$, it follows that $[(I + f_0 W)e](t) + (Wm)(t) = u(t)$ where $m(t) = \int_0^t e(\tau)[d\beta(\tau) - f_0 d\tau]$ and hence $z = (I + f_0 W)e$ is governed by $z(t) + [W(I + f_0 W)^{-1} n](t) = u(t)$, $t \in R^+$, where $n(t) = \int_0^t z(\tau) \cdot [d\beta(\tau) - f_0 d\tau]$. The invertibility of $I + f_0 W$ follows from the results of [18] and [20] and uses the condition

$w \in L_1(R^+)$. The result of Theorem 3 then follows from Corollary 2.

Proof of Corollary 3: By Theorem 3 it suffices to show that

$$q^2 \frac{1}{2\pi} \int_{-\infty}^{+\infty} |\hat{W}(j\omega)/[1 + f_0\hat{W}(j\omega)]|^2 d\omega < 1.$$

By the restrictions on the graph of $\hat{W}(j\omega)$ it follows that

$$\left|\frac{f_0\hat{W}(j\omega)}{1 + f_0\hat{W}(j\omega)}\right|^2 \leq \frac{1}{1 + \dfrac{\gamma}{f_0}} \operatorname{Re} \frac{f_0\hat{W}(j\omega)}{1 + f_0\hat{W}(j\omega)}.$$

Hence

$$q^2 \frac{1}{2\pi} \int_{-\infty}^{+\infty} |\hat{W}(j\omega)/[1 + f_0\hat{W}(j\omega)]|^2 d\omega$$

$$\leq \frac{q^2}{f_0 + \gamma} \frac{1}{2\pi} \int_{-\infty}^{+\infty} \frac{\hat{W}(j\omega)}{1 + f_0\hat{W}(j\omega)} d\omega$$

$$= \frac{q^2 w(0)}{f_0 + \gamma},$$

which yields the result. The last step uses the fact that $w \in L_1(R^+)$.

Proof of Corollary 4: Corollary 4 is a limiting case of Corollary 3 for $\gamma \to 0$.

References

[1] W. M. Wonham, "Optimal stationary control of linear systems with state-dependent noise," *SIAM J. Contr.*, vol. 5, Aug. 1967, pp. 486–500.

[2] D. L. Kleinman, "Optimal stationary control of linear system with control-dependent noise," *IEEE Trans. Automat. Contr.*, vol. AC-14, Dec. 1969, pp. 673–677.

[3] F. Kozin, "A survey of stability of stochastic systems," *Automatica*, vol. 5, 1969, pp. 95–112.

[4] W. L. Levison, D. L. Kleinman, and S. Baron, "A model for human operator remnant," Bolt, Beranek, and Newman, Inc., Cambridge, Mass., Tech. Rep. 1731, Oct. 1968.

[5] R. Khas'minskii, "Ergodic properties of recurrent diffusion processes and stabilization of the solution to the Cauchy problem for parabolic equations," *Theory Prob. Appl.*, vol. 5, 1960, pp. 179–196.

[6] A. Il'in and R. Khas'minskii, "Asymptotic behavior of solutions of parabolic equations and an ergodic property of inhomogeneous diffusion processes," *Amer. Math. Soc. Transl.*, ser. 2, vol. 49, 1966, pp. 241–268.

[7] H. Kushner, "The Cauchy problem for a class of degenerate parabolic equations and asymptotic properties of the related diffusion processes," *J. Differential Equations*, 6, 1969, pp. 209–231.

[8] G. Blankenship, "Stability of uncertain systems," Ph.D. dissertation, Dep. Elec. Eng., M.I.T., Cambridge, June 1971.

[9] I. W. Sandberg, "Some results on the theory of physical systems governed by nonlinear functional equations," *Bell Syst. Tech. J.*, vol. 44, 1965, pp. 871–898.

[10] G. Zames, "On the input-output stability of time-varying nonlinear feedback systems. Part I: Conditions derived using concepts of loop gain, conicity, and positivity," *IEEE Trans. Automat. Contr.*, vol. AC-11, Apr. 1966, pp. 228–239.

——, "On the input-output stability of time-varying nonlinear feedback systems. Part II: Conditions involving circles in the frequency plane and sector nonlinearities," *ibid.*, vol. AC-11, July 1966, pp. 465–476.

[11] G. Zames, "Nonlinear time varying feedback systems—Conditions for L_∞-boundedness derived using conic operators on exponentially weighted spaces," *Proc. 3rd Allerton Conf. Circuit and System Theory*, 1965, pp. 460–471.

[12] I. Rabotnikov, "On the impossibility of stabilizing a system in the mean square by a random perturbation of its parameters," *Appl. Math. Mech.*, vol. 28, 1964, pp. 1131–1136.

[13] R. W. Brockett, *Finite Dimensional Linear Systems.* New York: Wiley, 1970.

[14] M. B. Nevelson and R. Z. Khas'minskii, "Stability of a linear system with random disturbances of its parameters," *Prikl. Mat. Mekh.*, vol. 30, 1966, p. 487.

[15] G. Newton, L. Gould, and J. Kaiser, *Analytical Design of Linear Feedback Controls.* New York: Wiley, 1957.

[16] D. L. Kleinman, "On the stability of linear stochastic systems," *IEEE Trans. Automat. Contr.* (Corresp.), vol. AC-14, Aug. 1969, pp. 429–430.

[17] J. E. Brandeberry and S. H. Wu, "On the stability of a class of continuous stochastic systems," *Proc. 7th Allerton Conf. Circuit and System Theory*, 1969, pp. 730–731.

[18] C. A. Desoer and M. Y. Wu, "Stability of linear time-invariant systems," *IEEE Trans. Circuit Theory*, vol. CT-15, 1968, pp. 245–250.

[19] R. Bellman, *Introduction to Matrix Analysis.* New York: McGraw-Hill, 1960.

[20] C. A. Desoer and M. Y. Wu, "Stability of multiple-loop feedback linear time-invariant systems," *J. Math. Anal. Appl.*, vol. 23, 1968, pp. 121–129.

[21] T. Nakamizo, "A simpler mean-square stability criterion for a class of linear stochastic systems," *IEEE Trans. Automat. Contr.* (Corresp.), vol. AC-14, 1969, pp. 584–585.

The Describing Function Matrix

A. I. MEES

Department of Applied Mathematics and Theoretical Physics,
Cambridge University

[Received 7 September 1971 and in revised form 5 November 1971]

The Describing Function method (or method of harmonic balance) is a means of finding approximations to periodic solutions of non-linear O.D.E.'s by replacing the nonlinear terms by a pseudo-linear representation of their effect on a single harmonic. This paper generalizes that representation to a matrix which gives the effect of the nonlinear terms on any desired finite number of harmonics; contrary to what has been the case in previous generalizations of this kind, there is an algorithm for calculation of the matrix. Bounds on the error of a solution of given order are obtained using a contraction mapping theorem, and the paper also studies the problem of when such a finite order approximation method is capable of predicting a specific periodic solution of a particular system of O.D.E.'s. A number of examples show how the method is applied to autonomous systems, both critical and non-critical, and demonstrate that discontinuities and memory in the nonlinear terms do not preclude either the finding of solutions or the testing of their validity.

1. Introduction

THE DESCRIBING FUNCTION (DF) method is a form of quasilinearization much used by engineers in studying systems which can be described by ordinary differential equations, usually of fairly high order and containing non-linear elements which are often rather badly-behaved: they may fail to satisfy Lipschitz conditions, they may be frequency-dependent, and they may have energy storage elements such as those involved in backlash or hysteresis. In spite of the power of the method, it has somewhat fallen out of favour—at least with theoreticians—because of the difficulty of providing a rigorous justification (Bass, 1960; Holtzman, 1970) and, more pertinently, because the method as normally applied has been shown to fail in certain cases (Holtzman, 1970; Willems, 1966).

The usual DF method (Holtzman, 1970; Gelb, 1968; Grensted, 1962) replaces a nonlinear element n by a quasi-linear one N which correctly gives the transfer function for the first Fourier component of the output produced by a pure sinusoidal input; one can then attempt to balance the first harmonic components in the system. If the linear part of the system is such as to attenuate higher harmonics, it seems plausible that any balance found (in frequency and amplitude) will be "near" to an actual periodic solution of the system of equations. The main attraction of the method lies in its simplicity of application: for example, there exists a graphical technique (Gelb, 1968; Grensted, 1962) for solving the balance equations which immediately determines whether or not there are solutions. In addition, the system designer can easily change the linear part of the system and observe the effect without having to recalculate the

Reprinted with permission from *J. Inst. Math. Its Appl.*, vol. 10, pp. 49–67, 1972.

DF. Obvious generalizations (in particular, the retention of more harmonic elements in the trial input (Gelb, 1968)) are usually difficult to apply and there is no straightforward method of proceeding from a DF of given order to one of higher order. This paper deals with a generalization of the DF to a DF matrix in which the inclusion of another harmonic only entails the calculation of another row and column of the matrix, and, while it does not provide anything comparable to the graphical solution method (one must resort to purely numerical solution of the balance equations), it provides a means of stepping from a solution with a given number of harmonics to one with a higher order balance. It is possible to test whether there are higher—perhaps infinite—order solutions close to that already known.

The representation of a high order DF by a matrix is not new (Fitts, 1966) but the nonuniqueness of the elements allows many different choices of the ways in which the matrix is constructed. In this case, the matrix can be found directly, in a way which allows it to be calculated analytically if this is possible (e.g. for the cubic nonlinearity as in Example 4.1) or else numerically (e.g. for a relay as in Example 4.2). Although the paper is concerned only with exactly periodic oscillation in autonomous systems, the DF matrix can also be used in other fields (Gelb, 1968) where the conventional DF has application.

Previous studies of the DF—notably by Bass—have tended to work mainly in terms of the properties of the nonlinearity itself rather than those of its DF. It has usually been necessary (Bass, 1960) to ask that n be smooth which, of course, excludes many of the functions of interest to the control engineer. The conditions on nonlinearities derived here are in terms of their DFs for two reasons: first, N may be expected to be a better-behaved function of the vector $\mathbf{a}$ of Fourier components of the input x than n is of x (e.g. N for a memoryless relay is a continuous function), and secondly, an *a posteriori* check may be made: one actually does some calculations and then attempts to verify the conditions which say if the results are reliable. However, this approach does leave open the questions of existence and properties of N for classes of n.

In all, the paper is closer to the work of Urabe (1965) than to that of Bass; Urabe dealt with the high order DF problem for noncritical, nonautonomous systems of O.D.E.s, although he did not use the DF concept in the usual sense. In a recent paper, Bergen & Franks (1971) answer similar questions to those of Section 3 of this paper, except that they concentrate mainly on the first order DF whereas the methods introduced here are explicitly concerned with higher order solutions.

2. The DF Matrix

Consider a nonlinear element n which gives output $y = n(x)$ for an input x. Here and elsewhere in the paper, the notation used will be such as to suggest that x and n are scalar, but the generalization to vectors requires no changes in principle.

We are interested in the behaviour of n under an input which is exactly periodic. Let

$$x = \mathrm{Re}\left\{\sum_{r=0}^{\infty} a_r e^{ir\omega t}\right\}$$

and write

$$\mathbf{a} = (a_0, a_1, a_2, \ldots)^T$$
$$\mathbf{a}^m = (a_0, a_1, a_2, \ldots, a_m)^T$$

where T signifies transposition.

Let $\mathbf{c}$ be the analogous vector of complex Fourier coefficients of the output y. Then an infinite matrix N, called the describing function matrix, may be defined as follows: The 0th column is given by

$$N_{k0} = c_k(\mathbf{a}^0)/a_0$$

The 1st column is given by

$$N_{k1} = \{c_k(\mathbf{a}^1) - c_k(\mathbf{a}^0)\}/a_1$$

e.g. the (3, 1) element is the amplitude of the 3rd output harmonic divided by that of the 1st input harmonic.
The 2nd column is given by

$$N_{k2} = \{c_k(\mathbf{a}^2) - c_k(\mathbf{a}^1)\}/a_2$$

i.e. we find the output for an input $\mathbf{a}^2$ consisting only of a constant and 1st and 2nd harmonics, subtract off the part $\mathbf{c}(\mathbf{a}^1)$ which would have been generated by input $\mathbf{a}^1$ and divide the result by the amplitude of the second input harmonic. In general,

$$N_{kj} = \{c_k(\mathbf{a}^j) - c_k(\mathbf{a}^{j-1})\}/a_j \tag{2.1}$$

N has thus been defined so that

$$N\mathbf{a} = \mathbf{c}. \tag{2.2}$$

Note that column 1 is a function only of (a_0, a_1) and perhaps ω, and so on, so if we write

$$N^m = \{N_{kj} | k \leqslant m \quad \text{and} \quad j \leqslant m\}$$

(viz. the first $m+1$ rows and columns of N) then N^m is a function only of $a_0, a_1, \ldots, a_m$ and ω.

The following properties of the DF matrix are worth pointing out:

(i) Partition N^{m+p} as follows:

$$N^{m+p} = \begin{pmatrix} N^m & W^{mp} \\ V^{pm} & U^p \end{pmatrix}$$

and correspondingly partition

$$\mathbf{a}^{m+p} = \begin{pmatrix} \mathbf{a}^m \\ \boldsymbol{\alpha}^p \end{pmatrix}, \qquad \mathbf{c}^{m+p} = \begin{pmatrix} \mathbf{c}^m \\ \boldsymbol{\gamma}^p \end{pmatrix}.$$

Then N^m and V^{pm} are clearly independent of $\boldsymbol{\alpha}^p$. The point is that there is no back-tracking in calculating the matrix: the first column is completely known once a one-harmonic input has been tried, the second is known when a two-harmonic input has been tried, and so on. This is the key to the theory proved later.

(ii) With the above partitioning,

$$V^{\infty m}\mathbf{a}^m = \boldsymbol{\gamma}^\infty(\mathbf{a}^m)$$

so $V\mathbf{a}$ is the residual, i.e. that part neglected in balancing harmonics up to the mth.

(iii) In spite of the division by a_j in expression (2.1), it will not normally be the case that N has infinite elements when a_j is zero, since clearly

$$c_k(\mathbf{a}^j) - c_k(\mathbf{a}^{j-1}) = 0$$

if $a_j = 0$. We may define N_{kj} to be zero when $a_j = 0$ since all that is required of N is that it should make the equation

$$N^m\mathbf{a}^m = \mathbf{c}^m(\mathbf{a}^m)$$

true for all m. In fact, if $\mathbf{c}$ satisfies a Lipschitz condition as a function of $\mathbf{a}$ in some domain, it is clear that the elements of N will be bounded in that domain. A fuller investigation is actually required of when N exists for a given n; this is a point which is usually glossed over in DF theory, and it will simply be assumed throughout this paper that $N_{kj}(\mathbf{a})$ exists and is unique everywhere—except perhaps at isolated points—in the domains under examination.

(iv) As is the case with the conventional DF, the DF matrix for the nonlinearity

$$k_1 n_1 + k_2 n_2,$$

is

$$k_1 N_1 + k_2 N_2.$$

Whether or not one can represent series connection of nonlinearities by taking the product of their DF matrices N_1 and N_2, however, (Gelb, 1968) depends on to what extent $W_1 V_2$ may be neglected, since the output from N_2 for an $\mathbf{a}^m$ is actually

$$\mathbf{c}_2 = \begin{pmatrix} N_2^m \\ V_2^{\infty m} \end{pmatrix} \mathbf{a}^m$$

which produces a truncated output from N_1 of

$$\mathbf{c}^m = (N_1^m \;\; W_1^{m\infty}) \begin{pmatrix} N_2^m \\ V_2^{\infty m} \end{pmatrix} \mathbf{a}^m = (N_1 N_2 + W_1 V_2)\mathbf{a}^m.$$

(Note that W_1 is a function of $\mathbf{c}_2$ etc.)

3. Oscillations in Autonomous Feedback Systems

Consider the system shown in Fig. 3.1, where n is, as before, a nonlinearity and g is a linear feedback. Under what conditions can this system support an exactly periodic oscillation?

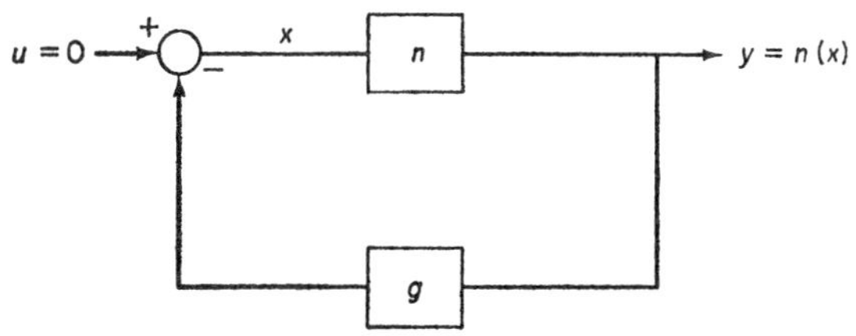

FIG. 3.1. The nonlinear feedback system of Section 3.

To answer this question, let

$$G = \operatorname{diag}(g(0), g(i\omega), g(2i\omega), \ldots)$$

so that, with the notation used earlier and writing, with an obvious meaning, $G^{m+p} = \operatorname{diag}(G^m, H^p)$, the condition for the existence of an x with period $2\pi/\omega$ is that

$$(GN+1)\mathbf{a} = 0 \tag{3.1}$$

should have a solution $\Psi = \begin{pmatrix} \omega \\ \mathbf{a} \end{pmatrix}$.

The describing function method tries to find a solution $\Psi_m = \begin{pmatrix} \omega \\ \mathbf{a}^m \end{pmatrix}$ to the equation

$$(G^m N^m + 1)\mathbf{a}^m = 0 \tag{3.2}$$

and, if one is found, assumes it is close to Ψ. It is shown in Appendix 1.1, using the implicit function theorem, that if there is a unique* solution to (3.1) then provided $\mathbf{c}$ satisfies a local Lipschitz condition as a function of Ψ, there is a solution to (3.2) for some finite value of m. In other words, if there really is an oscillatory solution, a describing function method of some order will predict it. It is *not*, however, claimed that the first order DF method ($m = 1$) will necessarily predict the oscillation and in fact it is possible to show that this is not the case; an example of the breakdown of the first order DF method is given in Section 4. Fitts (1966) points out that, given any nonlinearity and some value of m, there exists a feedback g which will cause oscillation but for which the equations (3.2) have no solution. Unfortunately, the theorem of A1.1 does not lend itself to a straightforward determination of the value of m which guarantees a solution for some given problem.

Appendix 1.2 proves a converse result, giving conditions under which a solution to (3.2) of some order implies solutions of some or all higher orders. Before this is discussed, a digression into certain problems connected with the solution of (3.2) is necessary.

If we temporarily neglect the (real) variable a_0, (3.2) is m complex equations in m complex unknowns $\mathbf{a}^m$ and one real unknown ω. A solution which is unique in some neighbourhood (i.e. isolated) is desired. However, the solution need only be unique up to time translation since it does not matter from what point of the solution cycle time is measured. Thus only the relative phases of $a_1, ..., a_m$ are important, and one therefore has the additional constraint that the solution be invariant under the transformation

$$\mathbf{a} := (a_0, a_1 e^{i\phi}, a_2 e^{2i\phi}, ...) \tag{3.3}$$

for arbitrary real ϕ. In practice, the easiest way to incorporate the constraint (3.3) is to fix the phase of some a_j in advance, e.g. to make a_1 purely real. This tends to mask the fact that the Jacobian with respect to Ψ^m of the left hand side of (3.2) is really an $m \times (m+1)$ matrix (or, in terms of real variables and taking a_0 into account, $(2m+1) \times (2m+2)$). Because a_1 is partially determined, it is only necessary that the Jacobian should have rank m (or $(2m+1)$) for questions of uniqueness etc. to be settled; it can be shown that (3.3) implies that the Jacobian of (3.2) *wrt* $\mathbf{a}^m$ is singular, so the $\partial/\partial\omega$ column must appear in any $m \times m$ submatrix used in iterative solution methods. Partly because of the additional complications which this introduces into the notation, the result in A1.2 assumes that a convergent (Newton-Raphson or similar) iteration exists for the starting solution Ψ^m rather than stating conditions under which this is the case. In any particular problem, conditions for the convergence of, say, the Newton-Raphson method (Saaty, 1967) may be checked, if desired, once the form of the Jacobian is known.

The line of argument leading to the connection between solutions of different orders will now be outlined; Appendix 1.2 gives the full statement in theorem form.

Suppose, then, that a solution $\hat{\Psi}^m$ to (3.2) is known, and that there is some ball centred on $\hat{\Psi}^m$ within which there is defined a contractive iteration

$$\Psi^m_{k+1} = \Psi^m_k - \{\Gamma(G^m N^m + 1)\mathbf{a}^m\}_k \tag{3.4}$$

* In the sense to be defined shortly.

which has $\hat{\Psi}^m$ as its limit, Γ being some linear operator such as the inverse Jacobian. (It is understood that some nonzero harmonic has been fixed in phase as explained above.) Is there a solution Ψ^{m+p} to equation (3.2) with m replaced by $m+p$ where Ψ^{m+p} is close to $(\hat{\Psi}, \alpha = 0)$?

The $(m+p)$ equations which Ψ^{m+p} would have to satisfy are

$$(G^m N^m + 1)\mathbf{a}^m + G^m W^{mp}\alpha^p = 0 \tag{3.5}$$

$$H^p V^{pm}\mathbf{a}^m + (H^p U^p + 1)\alpha^p = 0 \tag{3.6}$$

or, suppressing the superfixes but emphasizing the functional dependence,

$$(G(\omega)N(\omega, \mathbf{a}) + 1)\mathbf{a} + G(\omega)W(\omega, \mathbf{a}, \alpha)\alpha = 0 \tag{3.5$'$}$$

$$H(\omega)V(\omega, \mathbf{a})\mathbf{a} + (H(\omega)U(\omega, \mathbf{a}, \alpha) + 1)\alpha = 0. \tag{3.6$'$}$$

It can be seen from (3.6) that for α to be "small", as would be hoped, it is sufficient that $H(\omega)$ should also be small—in other words, g should be a low-pass filter. Specifically, either if $\|HU\|$ is small enough or if $\|HU\alpha\|$ satisfies a Lipschitz condition with small enough constant, then by rewriting (3.6) we obtain a convergent iteration

$$\alpha_{k+1} = -H(V\mathbf{a} + \{U\alpha\}_k) \tag{3.7}$$

which defines α as a function of Ψ^m; α will be small if the previous residual $V\mathbf{a}$ is not too large. Assuming reasonable behaviour of G, H, N, U, V, W, therefore, (3.5) with α found from (3.7) will have a solution Ψ^m which is close to $\hat{\Psi}^m$ because the $GW\alpha$ term is a small perturbation on the original equation (3.2).

The condition found in A1.2 for (3.5) and (3.6) to have a solution Ψ^{m+p} is that

$$k_1\|GW\alpha\| \leqslant (1-\theta)\varepsilon \tag{3.8}$$

where $\|\Gamma\| \leqslant k_1$, θ is the contraction constant of (3.4) and ε the radius of a closed ball Ω^m centred on $\hat{\Psi}^m$ within which the norms are measured, together with conditions to ensure that (3.7) converges.

However, the satisfaction of the conditions implies neither that the solution is unique nor that it may be reached by the iteration (3.4) with $-\{\Gamma GW\alpha\}_k$ added to the right hand side.

While it is comforting to know that there is an existence theorem for solutions of higher order than one already known, it must be confessed that in practice the work involved in testing that the above conditions are satisfied is more than that involved in actually finding the higher order solutions as is done in Section 4. What is more interesting is whether one can say that there are solutions of infinite order and for this reason a corollary to the theorem is given. This requires the boundedness of the elements of N for $\mathbf{a}$ contained in some region which, as already mentioned, is the case if $\mathbf{c}$ satisfies a Lipschitz condition in $\mathbf{a}$. Even for a relay, $\mathbf{c}$ will be Lipschitzian in a domain in which, as $\mathbf{a}$ varies, no new relay output pulses appear or disappear completely, while for a function n which itself satisfies a Lipschitz condition there is no difficulty.

The corollary is given in two forms: one where a bound B on the elements of N is known and one where a Lipschitz constant L for $\mathbf{c}$ is known. Other things being equal, the second version gives rather tighter bounds on the distance between the finite and infinite order solutions, but it is often easier to find B than to find L. The reader is referred to Appendix 1.2 for the details of the conditions, which are basically tests of the size of the residual and the extent to which the filter is low-pass. Since $\|H\|$ can be made arbitrarily small by increasing m, it will usually be possible to satisfy the conditions provided a starting solution of high enough order is used.

The corollary also ensures that the infinite order solution to equation (3.1) does indeed correspond to a solution for the feedback system in Fig. 3.1, since it ensures that

$$\sum |a_k| < \infty$$

so x and all of its time derivations exist in the sense of generalized functions and the operator equation

$$(gn+1)x = 0$$

is therefore satisfied in the sense of generalized functions.

4. Examples

A number of examples will now be given to illustrate how higher order solutions are found from those of lower order and how the corollary to Theorem 2 is applied. Appendix 2 gives details of how the DF matrix is calculated in each case.

The nonlinearities dealt with will be the function x^3, a relay with deadband and hysteresis, and the function $x+x^{\frac{1}{3}}$. Although these are all odd functions, it is not intended to imply that only odd functions can be dealt with. Further, although for the sake of simplicity only solutions made up of odd harmonics are considered, it would be incorrect to suggest that a system with an odd nonlinearity cannot support an oscillation containing even harmonics.

The method of solution is that suggested by Theorem 2; except in 4.1(b) the iterative scheme was modified Newton, i.e. Γ of (3.4) is the inverse Jacobian evaluated at the starting point ($\hat{\Psi}, \boldsymbol{\alpha} = 0$) and $\boldsymbol{\alpha}$ calculated as the limit of (3.7) at each value of $\hat{\Psi}^m$ was used by adding $-\{\Gamma G W \boldsymbol{\alpha}\}_k$ to the right-hand side of (3.4). The contraction constant θ was estimated as the largest value of the ratio of successive corrections, using various starting points.

Application of the corollary is limited mainly by the radius within which the iteration is known to be contractive and for this reason a higher order starting solution than would be expected is often needed. A quick estimate of ε and $\boldsymbol{\delta}$ may be obtained by calculating $\|G\|_\infty$ etc. at the solution point rather than in a ball around the solution, then using these values to estimate ε and $\boldsymbol{\delta}$ using C(v) and C(vi) of A1. Allowing some safety margin, since the values found are probably optimistic, one may now choose radii for Ω^m and X and evaluate k_3 etc in this domain; tests C(v) and C(vi) can then be carried out.

4.1. *The Cubic Nonlinearity*

(a) The system $n(x) = x^3$

$$g(s) = \frac{s+1}{s^3+2s^2+s+3}.$$

The Nyquist locus for this feedback is shown in Fig. 4.1. It intersects the negative real axis—along which lies the locus of $-1/N_{11}$—when $\omega = \sqrt{2}$, giving a first order solution

$$\Psi^1: \quad \omega = 1{\cdot}414$$
$$a_1 = 1{\cdot}155.$$

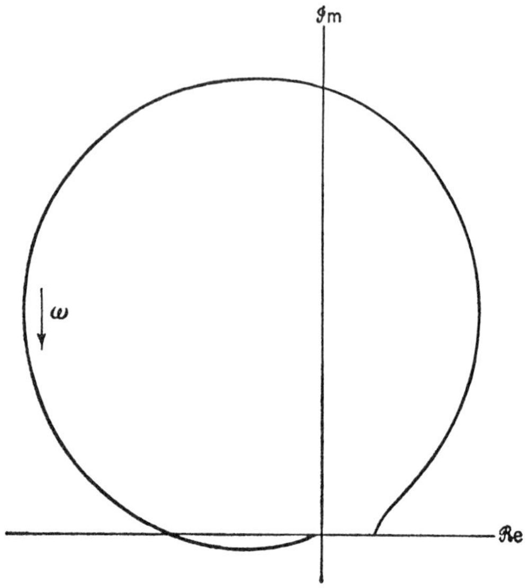

FIG. 4.1. Nyquist locus of g in Example 4.1(a).

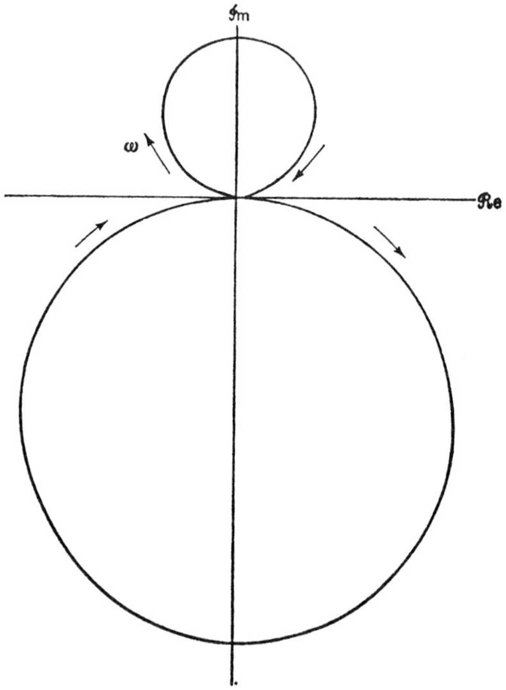

FIG. 4.2. Nyquist locus of g in Example 4.1(b).

A third order solution found as explained above is

$$\Psi^3\colon\ \omega = 1{\cdot}411 \qquad a_1 = 1{\cdot}136 \qquad a_3 = 0{\cdot}022 + i0{\cdot}005.$$

A fifth order solution is found to give a_5 of order 0·0005 and to produce changes to ω, a_1, a_3 only in the 5th decimal place. The convergence is very rapid in each case, the contraction constant even with $-\Gamma G W\alpha$ added being less than 0·1.

If the corollary to Theorem 2 is applied to the first solution, the value of ε estimated as suggested above is about 0·6, whereas the radius of contraction of the iteration is less than 0·1, so instead take Ψ^3 as the starting point. The estimated ε is 0·05, and in Ω^3 with this radius and X defined by

$$\delta_{2r+1} = \frac{0.03}{(2r+1)^2}$$

the relevant quantities are found to satisfy

$$B < 2{\cdot}5 \qquad \theta < 0{\cdot}1$$

$$k_1 = 3{\cdot}9 \qquad k_3 < 0{\cdot}025 \qquad k_4 < 1{\cdot}72 \qquad k_5 < 0{\cdot}07$$

so

$$B\mu k_1 k_4 k_5 < 0{\cdot}036 < (1-\theta)\varepsilon$$

and

$$\mu |H_{2r+1}| < \frac{0{\cdot}04}{\omega_{\min}^2 (2r+1)^2} < \frac{0{\cdot}03}{(2r+1)^2}\,.$$

Thus the required conditions are satisfied and there is a solution to the infinite set of equations for which

$$|\omega - 1{\cdot}41|,\quad |a_1 - 1{\cdot}14|,\quad |a_3 - 0{\cdot}02 - i0{\cdot}01|$$

are all less than 0·05, and $|a_{2r+1}| \leqslant \delta_{2r+1}$ for $r > 1$.

(b) The system

$$n(x) = \varepsilon x^3$$

$$g(s) = \frac{s^2}{(s^2+1)(s^2+9) + (\varepsilon/16)(3s^3 + 29s^2 + 15s + 117)}\,.$$

The feedback has been chosen so that with $\varepsilon = 0$, there are periodic solutions but for sufficiently small ε, the system *appears* to be stable according to the usual DF criterion. However, the 3rd order DF method predicts a solution (Holtzman, 1971; Willems, 1966) close to

$$\omega = 1 \qquad a_1 = 1 \qquad a_3 = i.$$

If $\varepsilon = 0{\cdot}1$ then the system is equivalent for present purposes to

$$n(x) = x^3$$

$$g(s) = \frac{1{\cdot}6s^2}{16s^4 + 0{\cdot}3s^3 + 162{\cdot}9s^2 + 1{\cdot}5s + 155{\cdot}7}$$

and numerical solution of the 3rd order balance equations (i.e. (3.2) with $m = 3$), starting from the above values, leads to

$$\Psi_1^3\colon\ \omega = 1{\cdot}0200 \qquad a_1 = 1{\cdot}0096 \qquad a_3 = -0{\cdot}0324 + i0{\cdot}9613.$$

There also appears to be a solution not mentioned by Holtzman or Willems, viz.:

$$\Psi_2^3:\quad \omega = 1{\cdot}0206$$
$$a_1 = 1{\cdot}0569$$
$$a_3 = -0{\cdot}4114 + i0{\cdot}9174.$$

This is interesting, because the two solutions are very close in frequency and amplitude, differing mainly in the phase of the 3rd harmonic. Now ω is really an eigenvalue in this type of problem, so perhaps there is some connection with other cases where solutions of eigenvalue equations are at first degenerate but split up in certain circumstances, as with energy levels in atomic physics. It is also possible that these are different third order approximations to the same infinite order solution, so further investigation is necessary. Both the ordinary and modified Newton iterative methods have very small radii of contraction around the above solutions, and it would appear that one might have to go to solutions of order 30 or so to allow the conditions of the corollary to be satisfied. However, comparison of 3rd, 5th, 7th and 9th order solutions gives every encouragement to believe that Ψ_1^∞ and Ψ_2^∞ exist and are distinct: in each case, by the time the 9th order solution is reached, corrections to previous values are of magnitude 10^{-4}, and $|a_5|$, $|a_7|$ and $|a_9|$ are all small. There is no obvious reason in principle why the conditions of the Corollary should not be satisfied if a high enough order starting solution is used, but let us take the above evidence as being convincing enough on its own.

4.2. *Relay*

For this example, n will be taken to be a relay with deadband and hysteresis, having output sign(x) when on and zero when off, and switching on at $\pm 1{\cdot}8$ and off at $\pm 0{\cdot}2$.

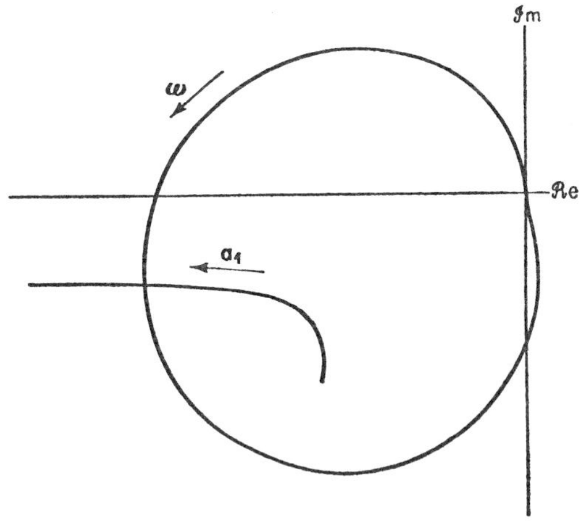

FIG. 4.3. Loci of g as ω varies and of $-1/N_{11}$ as a_1 varies, in Example 4.2.

The feedback used will be

$$g(s) = \frac{-4s}{s^4+s^3-s^2+2s-1}$$

the Nyquist plot of which is shown in Fig. 4.3 with the locus of $-1/N_{11}$ for $a_1 > 1{\cdot}8$ shown superimposed. The loci intersect at

$$\Psi^1:\ \omega = 0{\cdot}851$$
$$a_1 = 3{\cdot}742$$

which is the solution to the first order balance equation. The 3rd order solution derived from this is

$$\Psi^3:\ \omega = 0{\cdot}848$$
$$a_1 = 3{\cdot}733$$
$$a_3 = -0{\cdot}023+i0{\cdot}054.$$

To ensure that **c** is Lipschitzian in **a**, and hence that $|N_{kj}|$ is bounded, it is necessary to choose ε and $\boldsymbol{\delta}$ small enough that no maxima or minima of x move to the other side of a switching line as **a** varies. With $\varepsilon = 0{\cdot}05$ and $\delta_{2r+1} = 1/(2r+1)^3$ for $r \geqslant 2$, B is found to be less than 0·5 and if the Ψ^3 solution is taken as the basis, the conditions of Corollary 1 are satisfied.

4.3. *Cube Root Nonlinearity*

This example is given to show that the method does not break down if there is an exact solution of finite order. Let

$$n(x) = x+x^{\frac{1}{3}}$$

$$g(s) = \frac{12s^2-27s}{s^4+4{\cdot}5s^3+67{\cdot}5s+27}.$$

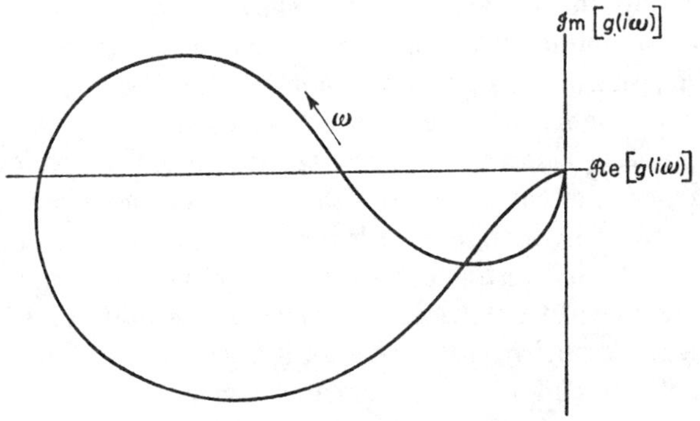

FIG. 4.4. Locus of the feedback used in Example 4.3.

The Nyquist locus is shown in Fig. 4.4; it intersects the real axis at $-3/7$ and -1. (The choice of coefficients for $g(s)$ is arbitrary here except for the requirement that the filter be low-pass and that $g(i) = -3/7$ and $g(i3) = -1$.) The locus of $-1/N_{11}$ lies on the real axis between -1 and 0, so there is a first order DF solution

$$\Psi^1:\ \omega = 1$$
$$a_1 = 0{\cdot}811.$$

Not surprisingly, considering that $|g(i3)| > |g(i)|$, the iteration (3·7) fails to converge. However, Newton-Raphson iteration for the 3rd order balance equations (i.e. (3.2) with $m = 3$) with starting point $\omega = 1$, $a_1 = 0{\cdot}811$, $a_3 = 0$ arrives at a solution

$$\Psi^3:\quad \omega = 1$$
$$a_1 = 0{\cdot}750$$
$$a_3 = 0{\cdot}250$$

and further attempts to increase the solution order predict that a_{2r+1} for $r > 1$ is zero and ω, a_1, and a_3 are unchanged. The reason that all of the a_{2r+1} are zero can only be that $V\mathbf{a}$ is zero, and this is indeed the case—the solution is exact, since

$$\tfrac{1}{4}(3\cos\theta+\cos 3\theta) = \cos^3\theta$$

so the output from the nonlinearity is

$$\tfrac{1}{4}(7\cos\theta+\cos 3\theta)$$

and no higher harmonics are generated.

The method presented is probably most useful in improving the accuracy of already-known DF solutions, and in providing a format for the study of high order DFs. Testing the validity of solutions using Theorem 2 or its corollary usually involves more labour than the easily mechanized process of increasing the solution order until corrections to values found earlier are acceptably small (being on guard, of course, for large values of high order coefficients). However, there may be cases when the type of analysis done in Example 4.1(a) is necessary: perhaps a reliable bound on the error is required, or there may be some reason to doubt the solution's validity—though in the latter case the theorem is somewhat devalued by the sort of difficulty which occurred in Example 4.1(b), viz. the need to go to a very high order solution before the tests can be carried out.

5. Conclusion

This paper has shown how to represent the behaviour of a nonlinear element under a periodic input by an infinite matrix, finite partitions of which may be used in finding approximations to periodic signals in autonomous feedback systems containing the element in question. The matrix is so defined that it may be progressively enlarged as the approximation order is increased, terms already found remaining unchanged.

Two theorems were presented, the first showing that under certain conditions an approximate method of high enough order will succeed in predicting oscillations if they occur, and the second investigating when the existence of an approximate solution implies that there is a nearby exact solution. The main assumption was that the vector $\mathbf{c}$ of output harmonic coefficients satisfied a local Lipschitz condition in the analogous input vector $\mathbf{a}$. Different conditions could no doubt give more powerful results, but the one used allowed a simple development valid for a large class of nonlinearities met in practice, and examples were given showing the application of the method to a few common nonlinearities.

I am very grateful to Professor Sir James Lighthill for his guidance and help, and to Professor Jan Willems of MIT for innumerable discussions. The method of Appendix 2.2 is a result of conversations with Mr J. Huthnance.

I should also like to thank the Carnegie Trust for the Universities of Scotland, who supported this research.

References

BASS, R. W. 1960 *Proc IFAC Moscow* 1960. p. 895.
BERGEN, A. R. & FRANKS, R. L. 1971 *SIAM J. Control*, **9**, 568.
FITTS, R. E. 1966 *Linearization of nonlinear feedback systems*, PhD. thesis M.I.T.
GELB, A. & VANDER VELDE, W. E. 1968 *Multiple input describing functions*. New York: McGraw-Hill.
GRENSTED, P. E. W. 1962 *Progress in control engineering* **1**, 105.
HOLTZMAN, J. M. 1970 *Nonlinear system theory*, New York: Prentice-Hall.
LANG, S. 1969 *Analysis II*, p. 125. New York: Addison-Wesley.
SAATY, T. L. 1967 *Modern nonlinear equations*. New York: McGraw-Hill.
URABE, M. 1965 *Arch. ration Mech. Analysis* **20**, 120.
WILLEMS, J. C. 1966 *Proc. 4th Allerton Conference on Circuit and System Theory*, p. 836. Urbana: Illinois University.

Appendix 1

In this appendix the theorems mentioned in Section 3 are proved. First, the notation will be summarized.

$$\text{Nonlinearity input} = x = \text{Re} \sum_{r=0}^{\infty} a_r e^{ir\omega t}.$$

$$\text{Nonlinearity output} = y = \text{Re} \sum_{r=0}^{\infty} c_r e^{ir\omega t}.$$

$$\mathbf{a} = (a_0, a_1, \ldots)^T, \qquad \mathbf{a}^m = (a_0, a_1, \ldots, a_m)^T, \qquad \mathbf{a}^{m+p} = \begin{pmatrix} \mathbf{a}^m \\ \alpha^p \end{pmatrix}$$

and similarly for **c**.
Also

$$\Psi^m = \begin{pmatrix} \omega \\ \mathbf{a}^m \end{pmatrix}.$$

The DF matrix N is defined such that

$$\mathbf{c} = N\mathbf{a}$$
$$\mathbf{c}^m(\mathbf{a}^m) = N^m \mathbf{a}^m$$

where

$$N^m = \{[N_{kj}] \| \; k \leqslant m \quad \text{and} \quad j \leqslant m\},$$

and N^m and V^{pm} are independent of α, where

$$N^{m+p} = \left(\begin{array}{c|c} N^m & W^{mp} \\ \hline V^{pm} & U^p \end{array}\right).$$

g is a linear feedback and

$$G = \text{diag}(g(0), g(i\omega), g(2i\omega), \ldots)$$
$$G^{m+p} = \text{diag}(G^m, H^p).$$

The closed ball Ω^m centred on $\hat{\Psi}^m$ is defined by

$$\Omega^m = \{\Psi^m \| \|\Psi^m - \hat{\Psi}^m\| \leqslant \varepsilon\}$$

where the phase of some specified nonzero a_k is fixed equal to that of $\hat{a}_k$.

Unless otherwise stated, norms may be either $\|.\|_1$ or $\| \|_\infty$ where

$$\|\Psi^m\|_1 = \omega + \sum_{r \leqslant m} |a_r|$$

and

$$\|\Psi^m\|_\infty = \max(\omega, \max_{r \leqslant m} |a_r|).$$

Matrix norms are defined subordinate to these vector norms so that for a matrix A,

$$\|A\|_\infty = \max_k \sum_j |A_{kj}|$$

$$\|A\|_1 = \max_j \sum_k |A_{kj}|.$$

For a function defined on a domain, the norm is taken to be the supremum of the norms evaluated at the points of the domain.

A1.1. Theorem 1

Suppose:

(i) The infinite matrix equations

$$(GN+1)\mathbf{a} = 0 \tag{3.1}$$

have a locally unique, bounded solution $\hat{\Psi}$ for which $\|\hat{\boldsymbol{\alpha}}\| \to 0$ as $m \to \infty$.

(ii) $N\mathbf{a}$ and each of its partitions (e.g. $U\boldsymbol{\alpha}$) satisfies a Lipschitz condition as a function of $\mathbf{a}$ in Ω^∞, with constant $\leqslant L$.

(iii) There exists $m_0 > 0$ such that in Ω^∞, for all $m \geqslant m_0$ and for all p,

$$\|H^p\| < \frac{1}{L}(1-\lambda)$$

for some $0 < \lambda \leqslant 1$; and $\lambda \to 1$ uniformly in Ω^∞ as $m \to \infty$.

(iv) The Jacobian matrix with respect to Ψ of the modified set of equations (3.1)′, to be defined below, exists and is continuous in Ω^∞ and has full rank when evaluated at $\hat{\Psi}$.

Then: There exists $m_1 \geqslant m_0$ and $p_0 \geqslant 0$ such that if $m \geqslant m_1 + p_0$, there is a solution $\Psi^m \in \Omega^m$ to the equations

$$(G^m N^m + 1)\mathbf{a}^m = 0 \tag{3.2}$$

Notes:

(i) Uniqueness is used in the sense of Section 3. $\|\hat{\boldsymbol{\alpha}}\| \to 0$ is meant in the sense that as m increases, $\mathbf{a}^m$ removes more and more terms from $\boldsymbol{\alpha}^\infty$.

(ii) Condition (ii) means that $\mathbf{c}$ satisfies a local Lipschitz condition, which is much less restrictive than the requirement that n should do so.

(iii) Condition (iii) is the low-pass hypothesis.

(iv) Condition (iv) is of a technical nature to allow the implicit function theorem to be applied. This, or some equivalent, is necessary but makes it difficult to check that the conditions are satisfied in practice.

Proof: The first $m_1 + p$ equations are

$$(G^{m_1} N^{m_1} + 1)\mathbf{a}^{m_1} + G^{m_1} W^{m_1 p} \boldsymbol{\alpha}^p = 0 \tag{A1.1}$$

$$H^p V^{p m_1} \mathbf{a}^{m_1} + (H^p U^p + 1)\boldsymbol{\alpha}^p = 0. \tag{A1.2}$$

From (A1.2) using (ii) and (iii), the mapping

$$M(\boldsymbol{\alpha}_k) \equiv \boldsymbol{\alpha}_{k+1} = -H(V\mathbf{a}+\{U\boldsymbol{\alpha}\}_k) \tag{A1.3}$$

defines a convergent iteration which gives $\boldsymbol{\alpha}^p$ as a function of Ψ^m since for any $\boldsymbol{\alpha}'$ and $\boldsymbol{\alpha}''$ in Ω^{m_1+p},

$$\begin{aligned}\|M(\boldsymbol{\alpha}')-M(\boldsymbol{\alpha}'')\| &\leqslant \|H\|\,\|U\boldsymbol{\alpha}'-U\boldsymbol{\alpha}''\| \\ &< \frac{1}{L}(1-\lambda)L\,\|\boldsymbol{\alpha}'-\boldsymbol{\alpha}''\| \\ &= (1-\lambda)\|\boldsymbol{\alpha}'-\boldsymbol{\alpha}''\|\end{aligned}$$

i.e. M is a contraction map. And

$$\|\boldsymbol{\alpha}\| \leqslant \frac{\|H\|\,\|V\mathbf{a}\|}{1-L\|H\|} < \frac{\|V\mathbf{a}\|}{L}\left(\frac{1}{\lambda}-1\right)$$

so $\|\boldsymbol{\alpha}^p\|\to 0$ as $m\to\infty$ (because $\lambda\to 1$). But $\|\hat{\boldsymbol{\alpha}}^p\|\to 0$ as $m\to\infty$, so $\exists m_1 \geqslant m_0$ such that

$$\|\boldsymbol{\alpha}^p-\hat{\boldsymbol{\alpha}}^p\| \leqslant \varepsilon$$

i.e. $\Psi^{m_1}\in\Omega^{m_1}$ implies $\Psi^{m_1+p}\in\Omega^{m_1+p}$.
Thus if (A1.1) with $\boldsymbol{\alpha}^p$ defined by (A1.2) can be shown to have a solution Ψ^{m_1} in Ω^{m_1}, the complete solution Ψ^m will be in Ω^m, where

$$m = m_1+p.$$

We now show that this is the case.
First, use the iteration (A1.3) to rewrite all of the equations up to the m_1th in such a way that they only depend on Ψ^{m_1}; this gives equations (3·1)′. Since the Jacobian wrt Ψ of (3.1)′ has full rank at $\hat{\Psi}$, the first m_1 rows have rank m_1 and so the Jacobian wrt Ψ^{m_1} of (A1.1) has rank m_1 at $\hat{\Psi}^{m_1}$.
Although $\|\boldsymbol{\alpha}^p\|\to 0$ as $m\to\infty$, we can't apply the implicit function theorem at once as the number of equations being considered changes with p.
However:

Let $\quad \mathbf{a}^\infty = \begin{pmatrix}\mathbf{a}^{m_1}\\ \boldsymbol{\alpha}^p\\ \boldsymbol{\beta}^\infty\end{pmatrix} \qquad N^\infty = \left(\begin{array}{c|c|c} N^{m_1} & W_1 & W_2 \\ \hline V & U^p & W_3 \\ \hline \cdots & \cdots & \cdots\end{array}\right)$

and let $G = \text{diag}(G^{m_1}, H^p, J^\infty)$
so

$$(GN+1)\mathbf{a}+GW_1\boldsymbol{\alpha}+GW_2\boldsymbol{\beta} = 0, \tag{A1.4}$$
$$HV\mathbf{a}+(HU+1)\boldsymbol{\alpha}+HW_3\boldsymbol{\beta} = 0. \tag{A1.5}$$

For given $\boldsymbol{\beta}$ (A1.5) defines $\boldsymbol{\alpha}^p$ as a function of Ψ^{m_1}. We wish to show that, keeping m_1 fixed, there is a p_0 such that if $p \geqslant p_0$, (A1.4) with $\boldsymbol{\beta} = 0$ may be satisfied by a $\Psi^{m_1}\in\Omega^{m_1}$, i.e. that

$$E(p) = \|G\|\,\|W_1\boldsymbol{\alpha}_0-W_1\hat{\boldsymbol{\alpha}}-W_2\hat{\boldsymbol{\beta}}\|$$

(where $\boldsymbol{\alpha}_0$ means $\boldsymbol{\alpha}(\boldsymbol{\beta} = 0)$) may be made arbitrarily small by taking p large enough.

$$\begin{aligned}E(p) &\leqslant \|G\|\{\|W_1\boldsymbol{\alpha}_0-W_1\hat{\boldsymbol{\alpha}}\|+\|W_2\hat{\boldsymbol{\beta}}\|\} \\ &\leqslant L\|G\|\{\|\boldsymbol{\alpha}_0-\hat{\boldsymbol{\alpha}}\|+\|\hat{\boldsymbol{\beta}}\|\}.\end{aligned}$$

But

$$\|\boldsymbol{\alpha}_0-\hat{\boldsymbol{\alpha}}\| \leqslant \|H\| \, \|U\boldsymbol{\alpha}_0-U\hat{\boldsymbol{\alpha}}-W_3\hat{\boldsymbol{\beta}}\| \qquad \text{by (A1.5)}$$

$$\leqslant \|H\|L\{\|\boldsymbol{\alpha}_0-\hat{\boldsymbol{\alpha}}\|+\|\hat{\boldsymbol{\beta}}\|\}$$

$$\|\boldsymbol{\alpha}_0-\hat{\boldsymbol{\alpha}}\| \leqslant \frac{L\|H\| \, \|\hat{\boldsymbol{\beta}}\|}{1-L\|H\|},$$

since

$$\|H\| < \frac{1}{L},$$

so

$$E(p) \leqslant \|\hat{\boldsymbol{\beta}}\| \, L\|G\|\left\{1+\frac{\|H\|}{1-L\|H\|}\right\}$$

$$\to 0 \qquad \text{as } p\to\infty \qquad \text{by (i).}$$

Thus the conditions of an implicit function theorem (Lang, 1969) may be satisfied for equations (A1.1.4) provided only p is taken large enough.

A1.2. Theorem 2

Let $\mathscr{A}^m$ be the space $\{\mathbf{a}^m|a_k$ is an arbitrary complex number$\}$, and note that the dimensions of $\mathscr{A}^m$ and Ω^m are the same.

Suppose:

(i) The equations

$$(G^mN^m+1)\mathbf{a}^m = 0 \tag{3.2}$$

have a locally unique solution $\hat{\Psi}^m$ and there exists a bounded invertible linear operator Γ from $\mathscr{A}^m$ to Ω^m with

$$\|\Gamma\| \leqslant k_1$$

and such that

$$\Psi^m_{k+1} = \Psi^m_k-\{\Gamma[(G^mN^m+1)\boldsymbol{\alpha}^m]\}_k$$

is a contraction map in Ω^m with contraction constant $\theta < 1$ and (therefore) unique fixed point $\hat{\Psi}^m$.

(ii) $N^{m+p}\mathbf{a}^{m+p}$ and all of its partitions are continuous in Ω^{m+p}, as is G^{m+p}.

(iii) (a) either: $\|H(U\boldsymbol{\alpha}'-U\boldsymbol{\alpha}'')\| \leqslant k_2\|\boldsymbol{\alpha}'-\boldsymbol{\alpha}''\|$ in $\Omega^m_{\cup}X^p$ where $X^p = \{\boldsymbol{\alpha}^p|\|\boldsymbol{\alpha}^p\| \leqslant \delta\}$ with $\delta > 0$ and $k_2 < 1$

or: $\|HU\| \leqslant k_2 < 1$ in $\Omega^m_{\cup}X^p$.

(b) $\dfrac{\|H\| \, \|V\mathbf{a}\|}{1-k_2} \leqslant \delta$ in Ω^m.

(c) $k_1\|GW\boldsymbol{\alpha}\| \leqslant (1-\theta)\varepsilon$ in $\Omega^m_{\cup}X^p$.

Then: There is at least one solution Ψ^{m+p} in $\Omega^m_{\cup}X^p$ to the simultaneous equations

$$(G^mN^m+1)\mathbf{a}^m+G^mW^{mp}\boldsymbol{\alpha}^p = 0, \tag{3.5}$$

$$H^pV^{pm}\mathbf{a}^m+(H^pU^p+1)\boldsymbol{\alpha}^p = 0. \tag{3.6}$$

Proof: By (iii) (a) and (b), as in Theorem 1,

$$\boldsymbol{\alpha}_{k+1} = -H(V\mathbf{a}+\{U\boldsymbol{\alpha}\}_k) \qquad \text{(A1.3)}$$

defines a convergent iteration which gives $\boldsymbol{\alpha}^p$ as a function of Ψ^m for all Ψ^m in Ω^m. Define the mappings M_1 and M_2 by

$$M_1\Psi^m = \Psi^m - \Gamma(G^m N^m + 1)\mathbf{a}^m$$
$$M_2\Psi^m = -\Gamma G^m W^{mp}\boldsymbol{\alpha}^p.$$

Then for all Ψ^m in Ω^m,

$$\begin{aligned}\|M_1\Psi^m + M_2\Psi^m - \hat{\Psi}^m\| &\leqslant \|M_1\Psi^m - M_1\hat{\Psi}^m\| + \|M_2\Psi^m\| \\ &\quad \text{since } M_1\hat{\Psi}^m = \hat{\Psi}^m \\ &\leqslant \theta\|\Psi^m - \hat{\Psi}^m\| + \|M_2\Psi^m\| \\ &\leqslant \theta\varepsilon + (1-\theta)\varepsilon = \varepsilon \\ &\quad \text{by (iii) (c)}\end{aligned}$$

i.e. $M_1 + M_2$ maps Ω^m into itself, and is continuous by (ii), so by the Schauder theorem it has a fixed point in Ω^m.

Note: If $\Gamma G W \boldsymbol{\alpha}$ satisfies a Lipschitz condition as a function of Ψ^m with constant L_1 then the map $M_1 + M_2$ is contractive, with unique fixed point, if $L_1 < 1-\theta$.

Corollary 1

Define

$$X = \{\boldsymbol{\alpha} \mid |\alpha_k| \leqslant \delta_k\}$$

where $\boldsymbol{\delta}$ is a constant vector with positive real components and $\sum_{k=0}^{\infty} \delta_k < \infty$.

Suppose:

C(i) Condition (i) of Theorem 2 holds with respect to $\|.\|_\infty$.

C(ii) $|N_{kj}| \leqslant B \quad \forall k, j \quad$ and $\quad \forall \mathbf{a} \in \Omega^m_\cup X$.

C(iii) $\sum_{r=1}^{\infty} |g((m+r)i\omega)| \leqslant k_5 \quad$ for $\quad \omega \in \Omega^m$, and $\quad Bk_5 < 1$.

C(iv) $\|V\mathbf{a}\|_\infty \leqslant k_3 \quad \forall \mathbf{a}^m \in \Omega^m$.
and $\|G\|_\infty \leqslant k_4 \quad \forall \omega \in \Omega^m$.

C(v) $\mu|g((m+r)i\omega)| \leqslant \delta_{m+r} \quad \forall \omega \in \Omega^m, \quad r = 1, 2, \ldots$
where

$$\mu = \frac{k_3}{1-Bk_5}.$$

C(vi) $B\mu k_1 k_4 k_5 \leqslant (1-\theta)\varepsilon$.

Then: There is at least one solution Ψ in $\Omega^m_\cup X$ to the equations (3.1).

Proof:

$$\begin{aligned}|\boldsymbol{\alpha}_k| &\leqslant |H_k|\{\|U\boldsymbol{\alpha}\|_\infty + \|V\mathbf{a}\|_\infty\} \\ &\leqslant |H_k|\{B\|\boldsymbol{\alpha}\|_1 + \|V\mathbf{a}\|_\infty\}\end{aligned}$$

by C(ii), so by C(iii) the iteration (A1.3) converges and

$$\|\boldsymbol{\alpha}\|_1 \leqslant \frac{k_3 k_5}{1-Bk_5}$$

and

$$|\alpha_k| \leqslant |H_k| \left\{ \frac{k_3 B k_5}{1 - B k_5} + k_3 \right\} \leqslant \delta_k$$

by C(v). So $\boldsymbol{\alpha} \in X$ where $\boldsymbol{\alpha}$ is a function of Ψ^m by (A1.3), and by C(i) and C(vi) $\exists \mathbf{a}^m \in \Omega^m$ which satisfies (3·5) with $p = \infty$.

Corollary 2

Corollary 1 holds if

$$\|N^q \mathbf{a}^q\| \leqslant L \|\mathbf{a}^q\| \qquad \forall q$$

if B is replaced throughout by L and if k_5 is redefined as $\|H\|_\infty$. The proof is straightforward.

Appendix 2. Calculation of N

The sections of this appendix are numbered to correspond with the examples of Section 4. Note that the methods of A2.2 and A2.3 may be combined to deal with general piecewise continuous nonlinearities, with or without memory and frequency dependence.

In the cases of A2.2 and A2.3, of course, N must be recalculated for every new value of **a**.

A2.1

For polynomials and for functions which have been fitted by polynomials, the matrix N may be found in a closed form. Some sort of automatic algebra manipulation system with selection facilities becomes very useful for high values of m and here the CAMAL and HUMP systems at Cambridge have proved invaluable. As an example, the DF matrix of x_3 for odd harmonics up to 5 is given below, using * to mean complex conjugate.

$$N^5_{[\text{odd}]} = \tfrac{3}{4} \begin{bmatrix} a_1 a_1^* & 2a_1 a_3^* + a_1^{*2} & 2(a_1 a_5^* + a_1^* a_3^*) + a_3^2 \dfrac{a_5^*}{a_5} \\ \tfrac{1}{3} a_1^2 & 2a_1 a_1^* + a_3 a_3^* & 2(a_1 a_3^* + a_3 a_5^*) + a_1^{*2} \\ 0 & a_1^* a_3 + a_1^2 & 2(a_1 a_1^* + a_3 a_3^*) + a_5 a_5^* \end{bmatrix}$$

A2.2. Treatment of Discontinuities

In the case of a relay as in Example 4.2, the problem in calculating N is not really one of integration but of finding, to some desired accuracy, *every* point where the input x crosses the switching lines. Fortunately, this can be done by a fast method which is a modification of the Newton-Raphson process.

The method depends on the observation that both the first and the second derivatives of the trial input x are bounded. Thus if, for example,

$$x(\theta) = \text{Re}(a_1 e^{i\theta} + a_3 e^{i3\theta})$$

then

$$|x| \leqslant |a_1| + |a_3| = d_0$$
$$|x'| \leqslant |a_1| + 3|a_3| = d_1$$
$$|x''| \leqslant |a_1| + 9|a_3| = d_2.$$

The iteration

$$\theta_{k+1} = \theta_k - \frac{x - s_1}{d_1}$$

will, therefore, find the first value above θ_0 for which the input crosses the line $x = s_1$. Having found this point, we can take it as a new θ_0 and find a turning point by using

$$\theta_{k+1} = \theta_k + \frac{x'}{d_2}$$

and then proceed to find the switch-off point where x crosses s_2 by

$$\theta_{k+1} = \theta_k + \frac{x - s_2}{d_1}$$

This process may be repeated until θ has increased by 2π from its initial value, when all the points will have been found where s_1 was crossed while x was increasing and s_2 was crossed while x was decreasing. (It is not difficult to convince oneself by drawing a few diagrams that if a stationary point is found immediately after a switching point, certain difficulties arising from limitations on the accuracy of the calculation will be overcome.)

In Example 4.2, x contains only odd harmonics so it is sufficient to find the positive-going crossing points θ^{2r} of $s_1 = 1.8$ and the negative-going crossing points θ^{2r+1} of $s_2 = 0{\cdot}2$ for $0 \leqslant \theta < 2\pi$. Then

$$c_k = \frac{2i}{\pi k} \sum_r (e^{-ik\theta^{2r+1}} - e^{-ik\theta^{2r}}).$$

A2.3

For general continuous functions the most obvious way to find N is to find $\mathbf{c}^{m+p}$ by numerical integration. Thus for an odd, single valued, frequency-independent function n,

$$c_k(\mathbf{a}^j) = \frac{2}{\pi} \int_0^{\pi} d\theta \, e^{-ik\theta} \, n\left(\mathrm{Re}\left\{\sum_{\substack{r=1 \\ r \text{ odd}}}^{j} e^{ir\theta}\right\}\right)$$

which can be calculated numerically. This is, naturally, comparatively slow for functions with large slopes, but will often be the only way to proceed, especially if n depends on frequency.

Describing Functions Revisited

ALISTAIR I. MEES AND ARTHUR R. BERGEN, SENIOR MEMBER, IEEE

***Abstract*—The well-known graphical describing function procedure can be simply modified to provide a completely reliable method for predicting whether or not certain kinds of nonlinear feedback system can oscillate. The modified method is easy to use and quantifies, in a natural way, the usual intuitive ideas about describing function reliability. In addition to the usual graphs, the user has to draw a band which measures the amount of uncertainty introduced by the approximations inherent in the method; in return for this extra work, the method gives error bounds for oscillation predictions, as well as ranges of frequency and amplitude over which oscillation is impossible. The main restriction is that the nonlinear element must be single valued and have bounded slope.**

I. Introduction

In the past few years, substantial progress has been made in justifying and improving the describing function (DF) method [1]–[4]. However, although the method is now rather well understood, the results obtained by theoreticians are not much used in practice: the user relies almost entirely on intuition and experience to decide whether he can trust DF predictions of the behavior of a nonlinear feedback system. There are good reasons for this. First, previous studies have said nothing about the most popular use of the method, which is in designing systems that do not oscillate. Second, although there is material on finding error bounds for predictions of the amplitude and frequency of oscillations, much work is needed to find the bounds and one cannot use the powerful graphical representation which makes the DF method attractive in the first place. In addition, the error bounds are often unduly pessimistic.

The purpose of this paper is to show how one can, with relatively little effort, make some definite statements about whether a single-loop nonlinear feedback system will oscillate. We will only deal here with cases where the nonlinear element is single valued and has bounded slope, because in this case it is possible to produce a simple graphical method. If, say, a relay is being considered, it is often still possible to use the general principles of this paper, but error bounds are more conservative and difficult to find, and the graphical interpretation is less straightforward.

The present paper is based on earlier work by the authors and others [1]–[4]. The inspiration for the graphical approach comes from the work of Rosenbrock [5] and indeed the new method has already been described in an incomplete form [6], [7]. Freeman [8], in a review paper covering the work of Bergen and Franks [2], suggests one of the ideas used in this paper (viz., the condition for inequality (23) to hold). The paper is oriented toward applications. We hope the graphical procedure will be useful to practicing engineers, many of whom may not wish to follow the details of the proof.

We begin therefore with a description of the method, followed by some examples. The basic theorem is proved later by methods similar to [2], and the paper ends with a brief discussion of refinements and limitations of the technique.

Manuscript received March 13, 1974; revised August 30, 1974. Paper recommended by R.A. Skoog, Past Chairman of the IEEE S-CS Stability, Nonlinear, and Distributed Systems Committee. The work of A. R. Bergen was sponsored by the Joint Electronics Program under Contract F44620-71-C-0087. The work of A.I. Mees was sponsored by the Commonwealth Fund of the Harkness Foundation.

The authors are with the Department of Electrical Engineering and Computer Sciences and the Electronics Research Laboratory, University of California, Berkeley, Calif. 94720.

II. Main Results

An autonomous feedback system is shown in Fig. 1. We will denote the system by S and assume that it can be split into a linear, time-invariant part g and a nonlinear part n whose characteristic has odd symmetry, is single valued and has slope between α and β, i.e.,

$$\alpha(x_1-x_2)\leqslant(nx_1-nx_2)\leqslant \beta(x_1-x_2) \tag{1}$$

for all real numbers x_1 and $x_2<x_1$.

The question is whether the system will oscillate. The DF approach to answering this question (see, e.g., [9]) proceeds as follows. Let $G(j\omega)$ be the frequency response function of the linear part and let the describing function be

$$N(a)=\frac{1}{\pi a}\int_0^{2\pi} e^{-j\theta}n(a\cos\theta)\,d\theta \qquad (a\geqslant 0). \tag{2}$$

In our case it is easy to show that $N(a)$ is a real-valued function for which

$$\alpha\leqslant N(a)\leqslant \beta. \tag{3}$$

The DF method states [9] that if

$$[G(j\omega)N(a)+1]a=0 \tag{4}$$

has a solution (ω,a), there is "probably" a π-symmetric oscillation[1] in the system with frequency and amplitude, at the input to the nonlinearity, close to ω and a. Conversely, if (4) has no solutions, the system "probably" cannot sustain a π-symmetric oscillation. It is the purpose of this paper to show how to replace the word "probably" with "certainly."

One way to solve (4) is to plot the loci in the complex

[1]A π-symmetric oscillation is one with the property $x(t+\pi/\omega)=-x(t)$, i.e., it only has odd harmonics.

Reprinted from *IEEE Trans. Automat. Contr.*, vol. AC-20, pp. 473–478, Aug. 1975.

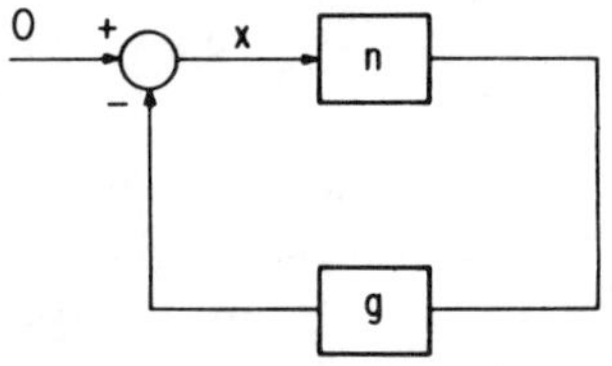

Fig. 1. Nonlinear feedback system studied.

plane of $N(a)$ as a varies and of $-1/G(j\omega)$ as ω varies.[2] Since the distance between a point on one locus and a point on the other is $|N(a)+1/G(j\omega)|$, every intersection of the loci corresponds to

$$N(a)+\frac{1}{G(j\omega)}=0 \tag{5}$$

and therefore to a solution of (4). Conversely, every solution of (4) except $a=0$ is represented by an intersection.

In Section IV it is shown that (4) is an approximate version of an exact equation

$$[G(j\omega)N(a)+1]a=E(\omega,a) \tag{6}$$

and similarly, (5) corresponds to

$$N(a)+\frac{1}{G(j\omega)}=F(\omega,a). \tag{7}$$

Note that $E(\omega,a)=aG(j\omega)\,F(\omega,a)$. The functions $E(\cdot,\cdot)$ and $F(\cdot,\cdot)$ cannot be found exactly but can often be bounded. If the errors introduced by neglecting these functions are small enough, then solutions of (4) and (5) should be close to those of (6) and (7). As will be shown, the bound on F can be used to define an uncertainty band around the $-1/G$ locus in such a way that the presence or absence of intersections between this band and the $N(a)$ locus guarantees the presence or absence of corresponding oscillations in S.

We need first to specify the uncertainty band. First we define a quantity $\rho(\omega)$ which (as will be shown later) measures the effect of the system's response to higher harmonics. Call the point on the $-1/G$ locus corresponding to ω, P_1, that corresponding to 3ω, P_3, and so on. Draw a circle with the interval $[\alpha,\beta]$ on the real axis as diameter; the $N(a)$ locus lies inside this circle by (3). Now consider an ω such that every $P_k (k\neq 1,\ k \text{ odd})$ lies outside this critical circle, as in Fig. 2, and let P_{k_0} be the point closest to the circle. Then $\rho(\omega)$ is the distance from P_{k_0} to the center of this critical circle, i.e.,

$$\rho(\omega)=\min_{\substack{k>1\\ k\,\text{odd}}}\left|\frac{\beta+\alpha}{2}+\frac{1}{G(jk\omega)}\right|. \tag{8}$$

Note that we have only defined $\rho(\omega)$ for certain values of ω, namely those in the set $\Gamma \triangleq \{\omega\colon \rho(\omega)>(\beta-\alpha)/2\}$.

[2]It is usual to plot loci of $G(j\omega)$ and $-1/N(a)$, but this is much less convenient here.

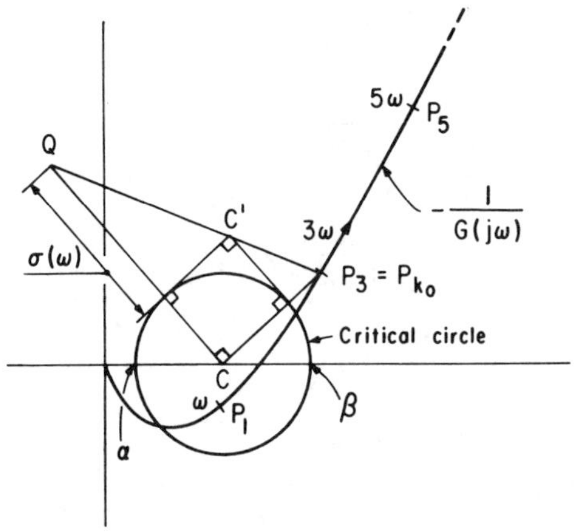

Fig. 2. Finding $\rho(\omega)$ and $\sigma(\omega)$. Here P_3 is the closest point to the circle, so $k_0=3$ and ρ in (8) is CP_3.

It is now possible to define a positive function $\sigma(\omega)$ on any subset of Γ.

$$\sigma(\omega)=\left(\frac{\beta-\alpha}{2}\right)^2\Big/\left(\rho(\omega)-\frac{\beta-\alpha}{2}\right). \tag{9}$$

This can be calculated directly, but also has a geometrical interpretation which is useful when one is drawing the diagrams by hand. Referring to Fig. 2, draw the line segment from P_{k_0} to C [the length$=\rho(\omega)$], and erect a perpendicular at C. Draw a square which determines the point C'. The point Q is defined in the figure as is the positive quantity $\sigma(\omega)$. In our case we note that as ω increases $\sigma(\omega)$ decreases, while as ω decreases $\sigma(\omega)$ increases until it diverges as P_{k_0} approaches the critical circle.

Now draw an error circle centered on $-1/G(j\omega)$ with radius $\sigma(\omega)$. The envelope of all such circles over a connected subset Γ' of Γ is an uncertainty band. The reason for choosing a subset of Γ is that as P_{k_0} approaches the critical circle, the error circles become arbitrarily large and cease to give any useful information. The choice of subset Γ' is best made while the band is being drawn and is chosen with the objective of drawing a narrow band. If $G(j\omega)$ is low pass, the band can be quite narrow over Γ'. In any case let us assume that we have fixed Γ' and drawn the corresponding band.

The two most important cases for which we can make definite statements regarding the solution of (7) are as follows.

Case 1: No part of the band intersects the $N(a)$ locus.

Case 2: The band intersects the locus completely as in Fig. 3.

Roughly speaking, in Case 1 there is no solution of (7) while in Case 2 there is. This is in accord with practical experience in using the DF method since only a complete (nonglancing) intersection or nonintersection is treated with confidence, and then only when there is good reason to believe that high harmonics are unimportant. The latter requirement is satisfied when the band is narrow, so all we are really doing is quantifying the low-pass hypothesis.

In Case 2 we can find error bounds by examining the

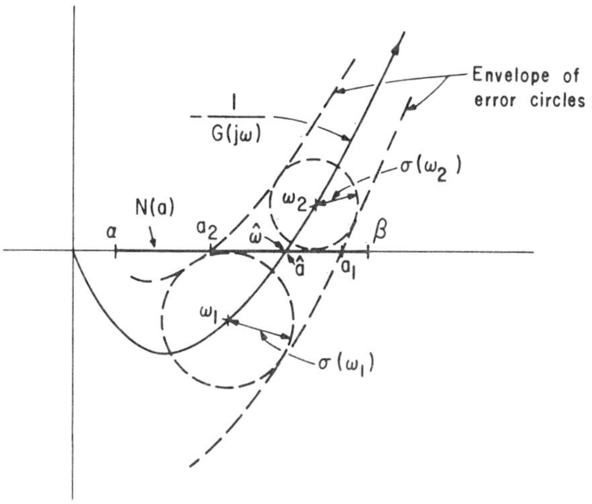

Fig. 3. How Ω is found.

intersection (Fig. 3) and reading off 1) the amplitudes a_1 and a_2 corresponding to the intersections of the boundary of the uncertainty band with the $N(a)$ locus, and 2) the frequencies ω_1 and ω_2 corresponding to the error circles [of radii $\sigma(\omega_1)$ and $\sigma(\omega_2)$] which are tangent to the $N(a)$ locus on either side of it.

On the basis of these numbers we can define a rectangle Ω in the (ω, a) plane, containing the point $(\hat{\omega}, \hat{a})$ for which the two loci intersect.

$$\Omega = \{(\omega, a) : \omega_1 < \omega < \omega_2,\ a_1 < a < a_2\}. \tag{10}$$

Next we have to define a condition of regularity as follows: $N(a)$ is regular in Ω if $d/da\,N(a) \neq 0$ for all $a \in \Omega$, and $G(j\omega)$ is regular in Ω if $d/d\omega\,G(j\omega) \neq 0$ for all $\omega \in \Omega$. These conditions are easy to check by examining the parameterization of the loci, and are nearly always satisfied.

A *complete intersection* between the uncertainty band and the $N(a)$ locus can now be precisely defined as taking place when the $-1/G(j\omega)$ locus itself intersects the $N(a)$ locus and a finite Ω can be defined as above, on which $N(a)$ and $G(j\omega)$ are regular and the loci are never parallel.

Finally, recall that Γ was the set on which $\rho(\omega)$ could be defined and Γ' was that subset of Γ for which we chose to draw the uncertainty band. Let Γ'' be the subset of Γ for which all harmonics (including the first) have the corresponding $-1/G$ point outside the critical circle, i.e.,

$$\Gamma'' = \left\{ \omega : \left| \frac{\beta+\alpha}{2} + \frac{1}{G(jk\omega)} \right| > \frac{\beta-\alpha}{2}, k = 1,3,5,\cdots \right\}$$

We can now state the basic theorem.

Theorem

Case 1: The system S can have no π-symmetric oscillation of any fundamental frequency $\omega \in \Gamma''$.

Case 2: The system S can have no π-symmetric oscillation of any fundamental frequency $\omega \in \Gamma'$ if there is no intersection of any part of the uncertainty band with the $N(a)$ locus.

Case 3: There can be no π-symmetric oscillation in S with fundamental frequency $\omega \in \Gamma$ and fundamental amplitude a if the corresponding error circle does not contain the point $N(a)$.

Case 4: For each complete intersection of the uncertainty band with the $N(a)$ locus, there is at least one π-symmetric oscillation with (ω, a) contained in the corresponding $\bar{\Omega}$.

Note that Case 1 saves us the trouble of drawing the band at high frequencies. Case 2 concerns a complete nonintersection, Case 4 a complete intersection, but neither of these is required by Case 3. In all four cases we only make statements regarding π-symmetric oscillations of frequency $\omega \in \Gamma$, or Γ', or Γ''.

III. Examples

Before proving the theorem we present some examples of its use. First, take

$$nx = (\operatorname{sgn} x)\left(\sqrt{1+|x|} - 1\right).$$

This is two parabolic segments joined to give a smooth odd function. The values of α and β are 0 and $\frac{1}{2}$ and the locus of $N(a)$ must be on the real axis between these limits. The diagram for the case where

$$G(s) = \frac{3}{2}\,\frac{s-1}{s^3(s+1)}$$

is shown in Fig. 4; Γ is $\{\omega : \omega > 0.30\}$ but Γ' is chosen to be $\{\omega : \omega > 0.48\}$ and so by Case 2 this system cannot oscillate with an angular frequency greater than 0.48.

Incidentally, the incremental circle criterion [10] cannot say anything about this system because the Nyquist locus passes inside the critical circle.

As an illustration of Case 4, take n to be the limiter (saturation nonlinearity)

$$nx = \begin{cases} x, & |x| \leqslant 1 \\ \operatorname{sgn} x, & |x| > 1 \end{cases}$$

so that $\alpha = 0$, $\beta = 1$. With

$$G(s) = \frac{2(s-1)}{s^3(s+1)}$$

the situation is as shown in Fig. 5, with $[\omega_1, \omega_2] = [0.94, 1.03]$ and $[a_1, a_2] = [2.25, 2.90]$. The regularity conditions and the nonparallel requirement are satisfied in this region, so by Case 4 there is an oscillation in the system whose frequency and first harmonic amplitude are within the above ranges.

There may be other oscillations too, but Cases 3 and 1 assure us that no π-symmetric oscillation of frequency $0.72 < \omega < 0.94$ or $1.03 < \omega < \infty$ can occur.

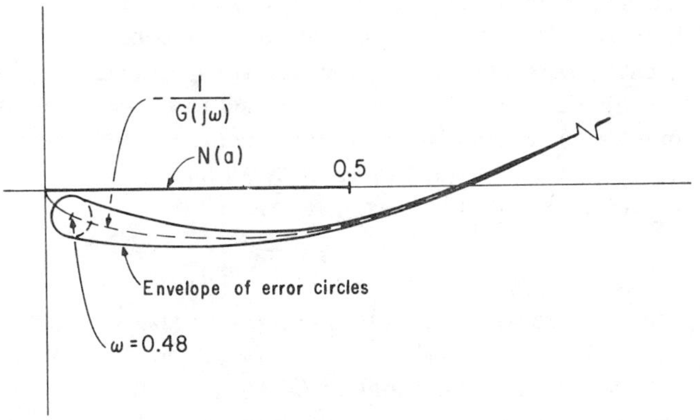

Fig. 4. Band and locus for first example.

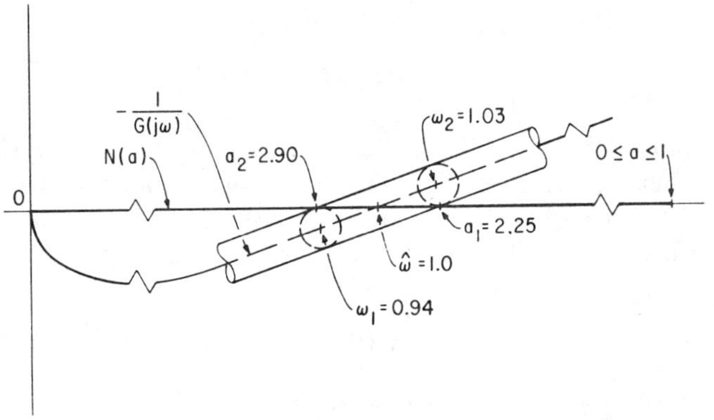

Fig. 5. Band and locus for second example. Area near intersection is enlarged.

IV. Proof of Theorem

From Fig. 1 the system must satisfy

$$x = -gnx. \tag{11}$$

Assume a steady-state π-symmetric periodic oscillation of the form

$$x(t) = \operatorname{Re} \sum_{\substack{k=1 \\ k\,\text{odd}}}^{\infty} a_k e^{jk\omega t}. \tag{12}$$

Because g is linear and time-invariant and n is odd, the assumption is consistent. In order to separate the effect of the higher harmonics from that of the first harmonic, define a projection operator P by

$$Px(t) = x_1(t) \triangleq \operatorname{Re} a_1 e^{j\omega t} \tag{13}$$

and its orthogonal complement operator P^* by

$$P^*x = x^* \triangleq x - x_1. \tag{14}$$

Without loss of generality we may assume $a = a_1$ is real, thereby fixing the time origin.

Solving (11) is equivalent to solving both (15) and (16)

$$x^* = -P^*gn(x_1 + x^*) \tag{15}$$

$$x_1 = -Pgn(x_1 + x^*). \tag{16}$$

We shall not solve (15) but obtain a bound on its solution. To do so, we introduce the norm $\|\cdot\|$ defined on the space of 2π-periodic functions $y(t)$ by

$$\|y\|^2 = \frac{1}{\pi}\int_0^{2\pi} y^2(\theta)\,d\theta \qquad \theta = \omega t.$$

Rather than deal with (15) directly, we obtain a better result by pole shifting:

$$\left(I + P^*g\frac{\beta+\alpha}{2}\right)x^* = -P^*g\left[n(x_1+x^*) - \frac{\beta+\alpha}{2}x^*\right]. \tag{17}$$

It can be shown [10, p. 57] that the linear operator on the left side of (17) has an inverse if

$$\inf_{\substack{k>1 \\ k\,\text{odd}}} \left|1 + G(jk\omega)\frac{\beta+\alpha}{2}\right| \neq 0. \tag{18}$$

This condition is always satisfied if $\omega \in \Gamma$ because the left side of (18) can vanish only if $\rho(\omega) = 0$, i.e., P_{k_0} in Fig. 2 lies at the center of the critical circle, whereas we have defined Γ by the requirement that $\rho(\omega) > (\beta-\alpha)/2$, i.e., P_{k_0} lies completely outside the circle.

Because the inverse exists, we can write (17) as

$$x^* = Fx^* \triangleq -\left(I + \frac{\beta+\alpha}{2}P^*g\right)^{-1} \cdot P^*g\left[n(x_1+x^*) - \frac{\beta+\alpha}{2}(x_1+x^*)\right] \tag{19}$$

where we have used the fact that $P^*gx_1 = 0$. The nonlinear operator F has a Lipschitz norm on the space of π-symmetric functions of fundamental frequency ω.

$$\|F\| = \lambda(\omega) = \sup_{\substack{k>1 \\ k\,\text{odd}}} \left|\frac{G(jk\omega)}{1 + \frac{\beta+\alpha}{2}G(jk\omega)}\right| \frac{\beta-\alpha}{2} \tag{20}$$

$$= \frac{1}{\inf\limits_{\substack{k>1 \\ k\,\text{odd}}} \left|\frac{\beta+\alpha}{2} + \frac{1}{G(jk\omega)}\right|}\,\frac{\beta-\alpha}{2} \tag{21}$$

$$= \frac{1}{\rho(\omega)}\,\frac{\beta-\alpha}{2} < 1, \qquad \forall \omega \in \Gamma. \tag{22}$$

In (22) we have used (8) and the comment just following it.

Thus as long as $\omega \in \Gamma$, F is a contraction map and (18) has a unique fixed point $x^* = m(\omega, a)$ which satisfies

$$\|x^*\| \leqslant \frac{1}{1-\lambda(\omega)} \left\|\left(I + \frac{\beta+\alpha}{2}P^*g\right)^{-1} P^*g\right\| \frac{\beta-\alpha}{2}\|x_1\|$$

$$= \frac{\lambda(\omega)a}{1-\lambda(\omega)} = \frac{2\sigma(\omega)a}{\beta-\alpha} \tag{23}$$

using (22) and (9). This bound on $\|x^*\|$ will be used later.

If we had defined $P=0$ and $P^*=I$ then F would still be a contraction map if $\omega\in\Gamma''$, so that $x\equiv x^*=0$ would be the unique solution of (11). This proves Case 1 of the theorem.

We turn next to (16). Adding $Pgnx_1$ to both sides gives

$$x_1+Pgnx_1=Pg[nx_1-n(x_1+x^*)] \tag{24}$$

or, using the phasor representation of both sides,

$$[1+G(j\omega)N(a)]a=E(\omega,a) \tag{6}$$

where $E(\omega,a)$ reflects the effect of the higher harmonics contained in x^*. We now examine the solution (ω,a) of (6).

Taking norms on both sides of (24) gives

$$|1+G(j\omega)N(a)|a\leqslant|G(j\omega)|\frac{\beta-\alpha}{2}\|x^*\|\leqslant|G(j\omega)|\sigma(\omega)a \tag{25}$$

by (23). Thus, using (6),

$$|E(\omega,a)|\leqslant|G(j\omega)|\sigma(\omega)a. \tag{26}$$

Dividing (6) by $G(j\omega)a$ we get

$$N(a)+\frac{1}{G(j\omega)}=\frac{E(\omega,a)}{G(j\omega)a}\triangleq F(\omega,a) \tag{7}$$

and using (26) in (7),

$$\left|N(a)+\frac{1}{G(j\omega)}\right|\leqslant\sigma(\omega) \tag{27}$$

is a necessary condition for the assumed oscillation. Geometrically, this states that the point $N(a)$ is contained in a circle with center $-1/G(j\omega)$ and radius $\sigma(\omega)$; Case 3 of the theorem denies this for a specific (ω,a) while Case 2 denies it for any $\omega\in\Gamma'$ and all amplitudes a. Hence in either case the assumed oscillation is impossible, as claimed.

Case 4 is easiest to prove if we direct attention to the complex plane containing the loci rather than to the (ω,a) plane. The uncertainty area around the intersection has been defined so that a fixed-point theorem may be applied to it and we now formalize this. Let

$$z=N(a)+\frac{1}{G(j\omega)} \tag{28}$$

and call Z the image of Ω under this mapping. Thus Z is defined by the area of uncertainty around the intersection point and consists of all vectors joining points on the two loci for which $(\omega,a)\in\Omega$. The boundary ∂Z of Z (corresponding to $\partial\Omega$) is made up of vectors one of whose end points is an extreme point $N(a_1)$, $N(a_2)$, $-1/G(j\omega_1)$ or $-1/G(j\omega_2)$; the opposite end lies anywhere on that part of the other locus for which $(\omega,a)\in\Omega$ (reference to Fig. 3 will clarify this). Thus for all points on ∂Z,

$$|z|\geqslant\sigma(\omega). \tag{29}$$

The regularity and nonparallel conditions allow (ω,a) to be found as a continuous function of z on Z by inverting the map (28), so that in turn $F(\omega,a)$ can be written as a function $H(z)$ of z. The function $H(z)$ is continuous in z because F is continuous in ω and $\boldsymbol{a}$ (by continuity of g and n) while (ω,a) has just been stated to be a continuous function of z. The continuity arguments parallel those in [2] and hence are not treated in detail here.

The net result is that we can write (7) as

$$z=Hz \tag{30}$$

which would—if it could be solved—describe the effect of the neglected harmonics x^* in terms of the separation z between the loci. Solutions of (7) within Ω are in one-to-one correspondence with fixed points of (30), so we can now use a fixed-point theorem on (30) to prove Case 4 of the theorem.

By (29), if $z\in\partial Z$ and $\lambda>1$ then

$$|\lambda z|>\sigma(\omega)$$

and so by (27), $Hz=\lambda z$ cannot have a solution on ∂Z whenever $\lambda>1$. By the Leray–Schauder theorem stated in the Appendix, H must therefore have a fixed point in $\bar{Z}$. Correspondingly, (ω,a) has a fixed point in $\bar{\Omega}$ as required. This (ω,a) is a solution of (7) and therefore of (16), so

$$x(\cdot)=\mathrm{Re}\,ae^{j\omega(\cdot)}+(m(\omega,a))(\cdot) \tag{31}$$

is a solution to (11), where $m(\omega,a)$ was defined just before (23).

V. Further Comments

The theorem we have proven gives a sufficient condition for oscillation and a sufficient condition for nonoscillation. This is not, of course, the same as a necessary and sufficient condition for either case. When high harmonics are not well enough attenuated (see, e.g., [3]) the theorem is unlikely to give useful information: either the band will be so wide as to embrace all or most of the DF locus, without a complete intersection, or else it will be impossible to define the band at all for some significant frequency range. What the theorem *does* do is to quantify the well-known low-pass assumption[3] and show where it does not hold: if the band is very wide then the assumption that only one harmonic matters is false and a higher order approximation is needed [3].

One slightly disappointing feature is that nonoscillation predictions can never be made for all frequencies: there is always a lower limit below which the band cannot be defined. The reason for this is that the low-pass hypothesis does not hold for very low-frequency oscillations, so the DF method cannot be used. A certain amount of improvement on our earlier results is possible by supposing that the sinusoid predicted by the DF method is not the first harmonic of an unknown

[3]But notice that we do not require $|G(s)|\to 0$ as $|s|\to\infty$, only that the high-frequency tail of the $-1/G$ locus be outside the critical circle.

oscillation but the qth harmonic. Unfortunately, one has to test each value of q separately and q cannot exceed a certain upper limit. Consequently, one still cannot reach zero frequency.

Finally, it might be added that the band and the locus can be plotted in the more conventional way [a band surrounding the $G(j\omega)$ locus and a locus $-1/N(a)$] but that one has to take care to correctly map the error circles forming the band into the new representation.

Appendix

Leray–Schauder Theorem

Let C be an open, bounded set in R^n containing the origin and $H: C \subset R^n \rightarrow R^n$ a continuous mapping. If $Hz \neq \lambda z$ whenever $\lambda > 1$ and $z \in \partial C$, then H has a fixed point in $\overline{C}$.

Acknowledgment

The authors wish to thank the reviewers for their corrections and helpful comments, particularly with reference to the construction of $\sigma(\omega)$ shown in Fig. 2.

References

[1] J. Kudrewicz, "Theorems on the existence of periodic vibrations based upon the describing function method," in *Proc. Int. Fed. Automat. Contr.*, Warsaw, Poland, 1969.
[2] A. R. Bergen and R. L. Franks, "Justification of the describing function method," *SIAM J. Contr.*, vol. 9, no. 4, pp. 568–589, 1971.
[3] A. I. Mees, "The describing function matrix," *J. Inst. Math. Appl.*, vol. 10, pp. 49–67, 1972.
[4] T. Frey, J. Somio, and N. Van Quy, "The use of operators with degenerated kernel for nonlinear system investigation," in *Proc. Int. Fed. Automat. Contr.*, Paris, France, 1972, Paper 32.5.
[5] H. H. Rosenbrock, *State Space and Multivariable Theory*. London, England: Nelson, 1970.
[6] M. J. Lighthill and A. I. Mees, "Stability of nonlinear feedback systems," in *Recent Mathematical Developments in Control*, D. J. Bell, Ed. London, England: Academic, 1973, pp. 1–20.
[7] A. I. Mees, "Describing functions, circle criteria and multiple-loop feedback systems," *Proc. Inst. Elec. Eng.* (London), vol. 120, no. 1, pp. 126–130, 1973.
[8] E. A. Freeman, "Some control system stability and optimality results obtained via functional analysis," in *Recent Mathematical Developments in Control*, D. J. Bell, Ed. London, England: Academic, 1973, pp. 45–68.
[9] J. C. Hsu and A. U. Meyer, *Modern Control Principles and Applications*. New York: McGraw-Hill, 1970.
[10] J. M. Holtzman, *Nonlinear System Theory*. Englewood Cliffs, N. J.: Prentice-Hall, 1970, pp. 53–58.
[11] J. M. Ortega and W. C. Rheinboldt, *Iterative Solution of Nonlinear Equations in Several Variables*. New York: Academic, 1970, p. 162.

Part IV
Multivariable Systems

A systematic attack on the problem of developing a frequency-response theory for multivariable systems was begun in a pioneering paper by Rosenbrock [62], which ushered in a decade of increasing interest in a revitalized frequency-response approach. The definition and study of the poles and zeros of a rational transfer-function matrix is an essential first step in such an undertaking, and Rosenbrock [64] put forward the required extension in his important study of algebraic system theory. This approach to the definition of multivariable poles and zeros was based on McMillan's work on a canonical form for rational matrices [47]. The McMillan form of a rational matrix had previously played an important role in Kalman's study of the realization problem [27].

I. Poles and Zeros of Multivariable Systems

If the dynamical system associated with a transfer function matrix $G(s)$ has at least as many outputs as inputs, and if the complex number v is neither a pole nor a zero of $G(s)$, then it can be shown [13] that, for all nonzero vectors

$$k \in \mathbf{C}^l$$

where $\mathbf{C}^l$ denotes the space of l-dimensional complex vectors, there is a polynomial

$$m(s) = m_0 + m_1 s + m_2 s^2 + \cdots$$

such that the input

$$u(t) = k \exp(vt)\, 1(t) + \sum_{\alpha} m_\alpha \delta^{(\alpha)}(t) \tag{4.1}$$

produces the zero-state response with the exponential form

$$y(t) = G(v) k \exp(vt) \neq 0, \qquad \text{for all } t > 0.$$

Here $1(t)$ denotes a Heaviside unit step function and $\delta^{(\alpha)}(t)$ denotes a Dirac impulse function of order α. (The role of the generalized impulse functions in the input specified in (4.1) is to kick the dynamical system into an appropriate initial condition at the time $t = 0+$.) This shows that, assuming we have an appropriate set of initial conditions, the response to a vector exponential input of the form

$$u(t) = k \exp(vt)$$

can be made to be of the form

$$y(t) = G(v) k \exp(vt)$$

and is thus associated with a complex constant transmittance matrix found by substituting $s = v$ in the system transfer-function matrix $G(s)$. Hence, the transfer-function matrix $G(s)$ may be regarded as defining the system's response to a vector of exponential inputs of exponent s, and thus the complex variable s can be regarded as a complex frequency variable as is familiar in the single-input single-output case. Poles are associated with specific values of complex frequency at which a transmittance becomes unbounded, and zeros with specific values of complex frequency at which a transmittance vanishes. Roughly speaking, a pole is associated with a characteristic frequency of a dynamical system. The set of system poles is a subset of the eigenvalues of the matrix A which appears in a state-space realization $\{A, B, C, D\}$ for $G(s)$ and the poles are related to characteristic modes which are both controllable and observable. Poles are thus characteristic of the "internal dynamical machinery" of a system. Zeros are characteristic of the ways in which this dynamical machinery is coupled to the environment in which the system is embedded. A survey of the various roles played by poles and zeros in linear multivariable systems has been given by MacFarlane and Karcanias [39].

The generalization of the concepts of the poles and zeros of a scalar transfer function to the general matrix transfer-function case is done using the standard form for transfer function matrices of McMillan [47]; this is usually called the Smith-McMillan form since it is a direct consequence of the Smith form for polynomial matrices [2].

Smith Form: If all the elements of a real-coefficient rational-function matrix $G(s)$ are polynomials in s, it is called a polynomial matrix. Such an $m \times l$ matrix of normal rank r can be put into a standard form called the Smith form $S(s)$ by a series of elementary row and column operations:

$$S(s) = \begin{bmatrix} S^*(s)_{r,r} & 0_{r,l-r} \\ 0_{m-r,r} & 0_{m-r,l-r} \end{bmatrix}$$

where

$$S^*(s) = \operatorname{diag}\{s_1(s), s_2(s), \cdots, s_r(s)\}$$

and

$$s_1(s) | s_2(s) | s_3(s) | \cdots | s_r(s)$$

where the notation $s_i(s) | s_j(s)$ denotes that the polynomial $s_i(s)$ divides the polynomial $s_j(s)$ without remainder.

Smith-McMillan Form: Any rational function matrix $G(s)$ of order $m \times l$ and normal rank r can be written in the form

$$G(s) = \frac{1}{d(s)} N(s)$$

where $N(s)$ is a polynomial matrix and $d(s)$ is the least common denominator of all the elements of $G(s)$. If $N(s)$ has a Smith form $S(s)$, then

$$N(s) = L^{-1}(s)\, S(s)\, R^{-1}(s)$$

where $L^{-1}(s)$ and $R^{-1}(s)$ are appropriate unimodular matrices (a unimodular matrix is one having a determinant independent of s). The Smith-McMillan form of $G(s)$ is then defined as

$$M(s) = \frac{1}{d(s)} S(s) = L(s)\, G(s)\, R(s)$$

where $M(s)$ has the form

$$M(s) = \begin{bmatrix} M^*(s)_{r,r} & 0_{r,l-r} \\ 0_{m-r,r} & 0_{m-r,l-r} \end{bmatrix}$$

with

$$M^*(s) = \text{diag}\left[\frac{\epsilon_1(s)}{\psi_1(s)}, \frac{\epsilon_2(s)}{\psi_2(s)}, \cdots, \frac{\epsilon_r(s)}{\psi_r(s)}\right]$$

where each $\epsilon_i(s)$ divides all $\epsilon_{i+j}(s)$, and each $\psi_i(s)$ divides all $\psi_{i-j}(s)$.

If

$$y(s) = G(s)\, u(s)$$

then it can be shown that, when $G(s)$ has a zero kernel (as a rational matrix):

1) $y(s)$ vanishes for $u(s) \neq 0$ and s finite if and only if some $\epsilon_i(s)$ is zero,
2) $||y(s)|| \to \infty$ for $||u(s)|| < \infty$ and s finite if and only if some $\psi_i(s) \to 0$.

These considerations led Rosenbrock [64], [65] to the following definitions.

Poles of G(s): The poles of $G(s)$ are defined to be the set of all zeros of the set of polynomials $\{\psi_i(s): i = 1, 2, \cdots, r\}$.

Zeros of G(s): The zeros of $G(s)$ are defined to be the set of all zeros of the set of polynomials $\{\epsilon_i(s): i = 1, 2, \cdots, r\}$.

It is not necessary to carry out a transformation to Smith-McMillan form in order to calculate the zero polynomial $z(s)$ and the pole polynomial $p(s)$ given by

$$z(s) = \prod_{i=1}^{r} \epsilon_i(s) \qquad p(s) = \prod_{i=1}^{r} \psi_i(s).$$

Simple rules have been given for finding these polynomials (Kontakos [29], MacFarlane and Karcanias [39]). The order $\delta[p(s)]$ of the pole polynomial $p(s)$ is the same as that of a minimal realization for $G(s)$ (Kalman [27]); thus a completely controllable and completely observable realization for $G(s)$ will be stable if and only if none of the zeros of the pole polynomial $p(s)$ lie in the right-half complex plane.

The zeros defined above are what are usually called the transmission zeros for the system. There are many other definitions; the interested reader should consult Rosenbrock [64]-[68], MacFarlane and Karcanias [39], [43], Davison and Wang [10], Desoer and Schulman [13], and Wolovich [72].

Hsu and Chen [22] derived an important relationship between open-loop and closed-loop characteristic polynomials for a multivariable feedback system which is the point of departure for many studies of multivariable feedback system stability.

II. Characteristic Frequencies and Characteristic Gains

The classical approaches to single-loop feedback systems analysis involve:

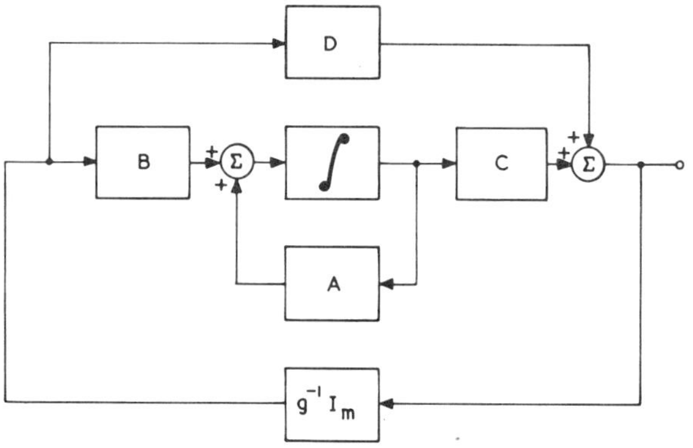

Fig. 1

1) studying open-loop gain as a function of imposed frequency—the Nyquist-Bode approach; or
2) studying closed-loop characteristic frequency as a function of imposed gain—the Evans' root-locus approach.

Both of these may be extended to the multivariable case; furthermore, such an extension may be done in a way which shows that there is a fundamental duality between open-loop characteristic gain and closed-loop characteristic frequency. Consider first the determination of closed-loop characteristic frequency as a function of a gain parameter. The closed-loop characteristic frequencies for the feedback configuration shown in Fig. 1 are the eigenvalues of the matrix

$$S(g) = A + B(gI_m - D)^{-1} C$$

and are thus found via the equation

$$\nabla(s, g) = \det\, [sI_n - S(g)] = 0$$

where $S(g)$ may be called the closed-loop frequency matrix for a system $\mathcal{S}$ (A, B, C, D) having the same number of inputs and outputs. $S(g)$ has a strikingly symmetrical relationship with the open-loop gain matrix

$$G(s) = D + C(sI - A)^{-1} B$$

and this leads one to seek an open-loop concept which is dual to the concept of closed-loop characteristic frequency. An obvious candidate is one associated with the eigenvalues of $G(s)$. These open-loop characteristic gains are found via the equation

$$\Delta(g, s) = \det\, [gI_m - G(s)] = 0$$

and it can be shown that (MacFarlane and Karcanias [43])

$$\det\, [sI_n - A]\; \Delta(g, s) = \det\, [gI_m - D]\; \nabla(s, g)$$

which implies that, for values of $s \notin \sigma(A)$ and values of $g \notin \sigma(D)$ where $\sigma(A)$ denotes the set of eigenvalues (spectrum) of A:

$$\Delta(g, s) = 0 \Leftrightarrow \nabla(s, g) = 0$$

This shows that a knowledge of characteristic gain as a function of frequency for $G(s)$ is equivalent to a knowledge of characteristic frequency as a function of gain for $S(g)$ and vice versa. These ideas can be used to extend classical Nyquist-Bode and root-locus techniques to the multivariable case. The use of the frequency-dependent eigenvalues of a matrix transfer function to discuss the stability and performance of a multivariable feedback system in generalized Nyquist terms was discussed in an early paper by Bohn and Kasvand [6]. The systematic use of "gain spectra" (the frequency-dependent eigenvalues of the gain matrix $G(s)$) and "frequency spectra" (the gain-dependent eigenvalues of the frequency matrix $S(g)$) for the analysis and design of linear multivariable feedback systems was developed in a series of papers by MacFarlane and his collaborators (MacFarlane [36], MacFarlane and Belletrutti [37], MacFarlane and Postlethwaite [41], [42], MacFarlane and Kouvaritakis [40], MacFarlane, Kouvaritakis and Edmunds [44]). In these studies there is no essential loss of generality involved in the fact that one needs "square" operators (having the same number of inputs and outputs) to have a spectrum. A crucial part of such investigations is concerned with how the state-space parameters of a general linear dynamical system enter into a design procedure when forming the "square" operators involved from the "nonsquare" systems around which feedback loops are being closed.

The equations

$$\Delta(g,s) = 0 \quad \text{and} \quad \nabla(s,g) = 0$$

are algebraic equations relating a pair of complex variables s and g. They are used for any dynamical system having the same number of inputs and outputs (such as will arise in considering vector loop transmittances in a multivariable feedback configuration) to define a pair of algebraic functions:

1) a characteristic gain function $g(s)$ which gives open-loop characteristic gain as a function of frequency, and
2) a characteristic frequency function $s(g)$ which gives closed-loop characteristic frequency as a function of gain (MacFarlane and Postlethwaite [42]).

A. Characteristic Gain Function

The characteristic gain function $g(s)$ is defined via the equation

$$\Delta(g,s) = \det\,[gI_m - G(s)] = 0$$

For transfer function matrices arising from practical situations, $\Delta(g,s)$ can be taken to be irreducible over the field of rational functions in s. $\Delta(g,s)$ will have the form

$$\Delta(g,s) = g^m + a_1(s)\,g^{m-1} + \cdots + a_m(s) \tag{4.2}$$

where $\{a_i(s): i = 1, 2, \cdots, m\}$ are rational functions in s. If $b_0(s)$ is the least common denominator of the $\{a_i(s)\}$, then (4.2) can be put in the form

$$b_0(s)g^m + b_1(s)g^{m-1} + \cdots + b_m(s) = 0 \tag{4.3}$$

where the coefficients $\{b_i(s): i = 1, 2, \cdots, m\}$ are now polynomials in s.

A function of a complex variable $g(s)$ defined by an equation of the form (4.3) is called an algebraic function, and is a generalization of the basic concept of a function of a complex variable. There is a well-established theory of such functions (Bliss [5]), and its use lies at the heart of the generalization of the classical single-variable feedback system techniques to the multivariable case (MacFarlane and Postlethwaite [41]). An algebraic function is said to have a branch point whenever its defining algebraic equation has repeated roots. In every simply-connected region of the complex plane which does not contain any branch points, the theory of algebraic functions shows that the m values of the characteristic gain function, obtained as the m roots of the defining algebraic equation, form a set of analytic functions $\{g_i(s): i = 1, 2, \cdots, m\}$; each of these analytic functions is called a branch of $g(s)$ and each branch may be analytically continued into any other branch. A single domain on which $g(s)$ is a single-valued function of position may be constructed out of m copies of the complex plane, suitably joined together along arbitrary cuts between the branch points at which the various branches of $g(s)$ take common values. Such a domain is called a Riemann surface for $g(s)$; the theory underlying the Riemann surface for $g(s)$ and a systematic method for its construction have been described by MacFarlane and Postlethwaite [41], [42]. The poles of $g(s)$ are defined as the roots of

$$b_0(s) = 0$$

and the zeros of $g(s)$ are defined as the roots of

$$b_m(s) = 0.$$

If the Smith–McMillan-form-defined poles and zeros of $G(s)$ are the roots of

$$p(s) = 0 \quad \text{and} \quad z(s) = 0,$$

respectively, then it can be shown that these algebraically defined poles and zeros are related to those defined in terms of the polynomials $b_0(s)$ and $b_m(s)$ via

$$p(s) = e(s)b_0(s) \quad \text{and} \quad z(s) = e(s)b_m(s)$$

where $e(s)$ is the least common denominator of all nonzero nonprincipal minors with all factors common to $b_0(s)$ removed.

The poles and zeros of the characteristic gain function $g(s)$ are located on the Riemann surface for $g(s)$. This surface can be thought of as an organized set of all possible closed-loop characteristic frequencies associated with all possible values of the gain parameter g. It is useful to exhibit the nature of $g(s)$ by drawing constant-amplitude and constant-phase contours of $g(s)$ on the Riemann surface. In his classic paper, Nyquist [50] briefly discusses the significance of a Riemann surface of this sort.

B. Characteristic Frequency Function

The characteristic frequency function $s(g)$ is defined via the equation

$$\nabla(s,g) = \det\,[sI_n - S(g)] = 0.$$

It is also an algebraic function, and exactly the same considerations apply as for the characteristic gain function, with the roles of s and g suitably interchanged. It has as domain a Riemann surface formed out of n copies of the complex plane since there are n values of closed-loop characteristic frequency for every given value of g. This Riemann surface can be thought of as the set of all possible open-loop characteristic gains of the open-loop transfer-function matrix $G(s)$ associated with all possible values of open-loop-forcing-frequency variable s. Its nature may be exhibited by overlaying it with constant-real-part and constant-imaginary-part or with constant-amplitude and constant-phase contours of $s(g)$. The complex function $s(g)$, of course, has poles and zeros, but their significance is quite different from those of $g(s)$.

C. Multivariable Nyquist Diagrams: Characteristic Gain Loci and the Multivariable Nyquist Stability Criterion

In what follows it is convenient to refer to the Riemann surface for the characteristic gain function $g(s)$ as the frequency-surface (since it is built out of m copies of the frequency-plane or s-plane) and to the Riemann surface for the characteristic frequency function $s(g)$ as the gain-surface (since it is built out of n copies of the gain-plane or g-plane).

Associated with any open-loop $m \times m$ transfer-function matrix $G(s)$ is (assuming that $\Delta(g, s)$ of (4.2) is irreducible) a characteristic gain function $g(s)$ having an appropriate frequency surface as domain. Let D be the standard Nyquist contour in the complex plane, and suppose that a copy of D is placed on each of the m copies of the s-plane out of which the frequency-surface is constructed. Let N be the image set under $g(s)$ on the gain surface of this set of copies of D on the frequency-surface: then this set of complex numbers N is called the characteristic gain locus for $g(s)$ (and hence for $G(s)$). In practice, the characteristic gain locus is usually generated as the set of loci in a single copy of the gain plane traced out by the set of m eigenvalues of $G(s)$ as s traverses the Nyquist contour in the s-plane. This set of complex numbers N on the gain-surface corresponds to the $\pm 90°$ constant-phase contours of $s(g)$ on the gain surface. When viewed on the gain-surface (a Riemann surface) the closed image curve N never intersects itself; when represented as a set of loci in a single copy of the complex plane, however, these loci usually do intersect. These characteristic gain loci are generalizations of the classical single-loop Nyquist diagram and may accordingly be called multivariable Nyquist diagrams (MacFarlane and Postlethwaite [41], [42]).

Multivariable Nyquist Stability Criterion: The multivariable Nyquist stability criterion relates the closed-loop stability of the configuration of Fig. 2 to the characteristic gain loci for the loop-gain matrix $G(s)H(s)$. Let the system of Fig. 2 have no uncontrollable and/or unobservable modes whose corresponding characteristic frequencies lie in the right-half plane. Then this feedback configuration will be closed-loop stable if and only if the net sum of anticlockwise encirclements of the critical point $(-1 + j0)$ by the set of characteristic gain loci of $G(s)H(s)$ is equal to the total number of right-half-plane poles of $G(s)$ and $H(s)$.

Proofs of multivariable versions of the Nyquist stability criterion were given by Barman and Katzenelson [1] and MacFarlane and Postlethwaite [41], following earlier heuristic approaches by Bohn and Kasvand [6] and MacFarlane [36]. The use of the frequency-dependent eigenvalue spectrum of a transfer function matrix played a key role in the important paper by Freedman, Falb, and Zames [19] which generalized the circle criterion for nonlinear feedback system stability to a wide class of systems.

D. Multivariable Root Loci

The loci of open-loop characteristic gain with frequency are generalizations of classical Nyquist diagrams in the gain-plane.

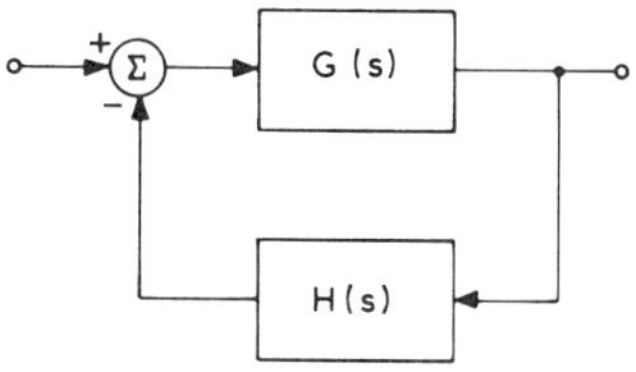

Fig. 2

There is a corresponding generalization of the classical Evans' root locus diagrams in the frequency-plane. These are the characteristic frequency loci, which are the 180° phase contours of $g(s)$ on the frequency surface. Let R^- denote the negative real axis in the complex plane, and suppose that a copy of R^- is placed on each of the n copies of the g-plane out of which the gain surface is constructed. Let E be the image set under $s(g)$ on the frequency surface of this set of copies of R^- on the gain surface; then this set of complex numbers E is called the characteristic frequency locus for $s(g)$ (and hence for $S(g)$). In practice the characteristic frequency locus is generated as the set of loci in a single copy of the complex frequency plane traced out by the eigenvalues of $s(g)$ as g traverses the negative real axis in the gain plane. These characteristic frequency loci are generalizations of the classical single-loop root-locus diagram and may accordingly be called multivariable root-locus diagrams. In common with the classical root-locus approach, these multivariable root-locus diagrams are usually calibrated in terms of a direct feedback gain parameter $k = g^{-1}$.

The use of such multivariable root loci is discussed in papers by Retallack [60], Kouvaritakis and Shaked [30], MacFarlane, Kouvaritakis, and Edmunds [44], Kouvaritakis and Edmunds [31], Kouvaritakis [32], [33] and in the book by Owens [56].

III. Diagonal Dominance

A natural approach to the problem of multivariable feedback control system design is to seek to reduce it to a set of classical single-loop design problems. The first such proposal, by Boksenbom and Hood [78], is usually called the Noninteractive Control Method. This consists simply of first choosing a $K(s)$ for a given plant transfer function matrix $G(s)$ such that the compensated system $G(s)K(s)$ has a diagonal transfer-function matrix, thus making the resulting overall system completely noninteractive. Subsequent to such a choice of $K(s)$, a set of single-loop controllers $k_1(s)$, $k_2(s)$, $\cdots$ could be designed using standard single-loop techniques. The required compensating matrix $K(s)$ in such a procedure will necessarily be complicated for all except the very simplest forms of $G(s)$, and the most succinct objection to this approach is that it is unnecessary to go to such lengths simply to reduce closed-loop interaction. Rosenbrock put forward a new approach to the deployment of classical ideas in a multivariable context when he introduced his Inverse Nyquist Array Method.

A. Inverse Nyquist Array Method

The Inverse Nyquist Array Method, proposed and developed by Rosenbrock [63], [67], [69], seeks to *reduce* interaction to an amount which will enable single-loop techniques to be deployed, rather than to eliminate it completely. Unlike the

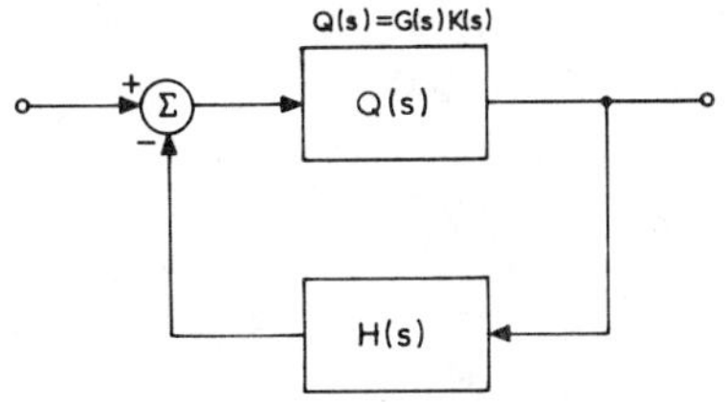

Fig. 3.

naive noninteractive procedure, the Rosenbrock approach is based upon a careful use of a specific criterion of partial interaction—the diagonal-dominance concept. The Inverse Nyquist Array (subsequently abbreviated to INA where appropriate) Method uses inverse transfer-function representations for a number of reasons, among which is the fact that the relatively complicated relationship for the standard feedback configuration between closed-loop and open-loop transfer-function matrices for the configuration of Fig. 3:

$$R(s) = [I_m + Q(s)H(s)]^{-1}Q(s)$$

becomes the much simpler relationship

$$R^{-1}(s) = Q^{-1}(s) + H(s)$$

between their inverses. In the INA method this is used to give a quick and neat way of converting between open-loop and closed-loop quantities. The main concept exploited is that of diagonal-dominant matrices (and thus, by a mild abuse of language, of diagonal-dominant systems). The advantages of using an inverse matrix are listed in [67, p. 155].

Diagonal Dominance: An $m \times m$ matrix $Z(s)$ is said to be row-diagonal-dominant on a stipulated contour Γ in the s-plane if

$$|z_{ii}(s)| > \sum_{\substack{j=1 \\ j \neq i}}^{m} |z_{ij}(s)|$$

everywhere on Γ. It is said to be column-diagonal-dominant on Γ if

$$|z_{ii}(s)| > \sum_{\substack{j=1 \\ j \neq i}}^{m} |z_{ji}(s)|$$

everywhere on Γ. If *either* of these conditions is satisfied at all points of Γ, $Z(s)$ is said to be diagonal-dominant on Γ.

If the open-loop inverse transfer-function matrix $Q^{-1}(s)$ is diagonal-dominant everywhere on the Nyquist contour, then the stability of the closed-loop system can be inferred from a set of extended inverse-Nyquist-type criteria applied to bands of circles of known radius (usually called Gershgorin bands) which are swept out by the diagonal elements as s traverses the Nyquist contour. Hence, stability is inferred from the frequency-response behavior of these diagonal elements. Since in this method one is faced with the notational difficulty of distinguishing between the elements of an inverse matrix and the inverses of the elements of the original matrix (which are, of course, usually different) the inverses Q^{-1} and R^{-1} are usually denoted by $\hat{Q}$ and $\hat{R}$, respectively. Thus the inverse of the ith diagonal elements of Q and $Q^{-1} = \hat{Q}$ are respectively denoted by q_{ii}^{-1} and $\hat{q}_{ii}$, and $q_{ii}^{-1} \neq \hat{q}_{ii}$, in general.

Diagonal-dominance is achieved by means of a precompensator, usually chosen to be real, and the design process is then finished off via a set of single-loop controllers. In these latter stages a further use is made of bands of circles swept out by the diagonal elements of an inverse matrix. These Gershgorin bands (or a new set the Ostrowski bands) are used to locate the inverse transmittances seen when all feedback loops except one are connected. This enables the partially uncoupled loops to be accurately handled one at a time on a single-loop basis.

Gershgorin Circles and Bands: Gershgorin's theorem (Marcus and Minc [45]) states that all the eigenvalues of a matrix A over the complex field are located in the union of circular disks defined by

$$|\lambda - a_{ii}| \leqslant r_i, \qquad i = 1, 2, \cdots, m$$

where the radii r_i are given by

$$r_i = \sum_{\substack{j=1 \\ j \neq i}}^{n} |a_{ij}|.$$

Since the eigenvalues of A^t are the same as those of A, a similar result holds for radii ρ_i given by

$$\rho_i = \sum_{\substack{i=1 \\ i \neq j}}^{m} |a_{ij}|.$$

The circles with centers a_{ii} and radii r_i or ρ_i are called Gershgorin circles for the matrix A. If the elements of A are functions of the complex frequency s, then the bands swept out by the Gershgorin circles as s traverses a stipulated contour in the s-plane (usually the Nyquist contour) are called Gershgorin bands.

Graphical Test for Dominance: Let H be a diagonal matrix of frequency-independent gains h_i. Then from

$$\hat{R}(s) = \hat{Q}(s) + H$$

we have that

$$\hat{r}_{ii}(s) = \hat{q}_{ii}(s) + h_i, \qquad i = 1, 2, \cdots, m$$

$$\hat{r}_{ij}(s) = \hat{q}_{ij}(s), \qquad i, j = 1, 2, \cdots, m \quad i \neq j$$

The Gershgorin circles thus have the same radii for both $\hat{Q}$ and $\hat{R}$, and the centers of the Gershgorin circles for $\hat{R}$ are simply those of $\hat{Q}$ horizontally shifted by the gain h_i. This leads to the following simple graphical tests for dominance.

1) If the set of Gershgorin bands swept out by the diagonal elements of $\hat{Q}(s)$ excludes the origin of the complex plane, then $\hat{Q}(s)$ is diagonally-dominant on the contour involved.

2) If the set of Gershgorin bands swept out by the diagonal elements of $\hat{Q}(s)$ excludes the points $(-h_i, 0)$, then $\hat{R}(s)$ is diagonally-dominant on the contour involved.

Rosenbrock's Stability Theorems: Let D be the usual Nyquist contour and let $\det Q(s)$ map D into a locus Γ_Q in the complex plane, while $\det R(s)$ maps D into a locus Γ_R in the complex plane. As the complex-variable point s moves once round D in a clockwise direction, let Γ_Q encircle the origin of the complex plane N_Q times clockwise, and let Γ_R

encircle the origin N_R times clockwise. Now suppose that the open-loop system characteristic polynomial has p_0 zeros in the closed right-half complex plane, and that the closed-loop characteristic polynomial has p_c zeros in the closed right-half plane. Then it can be shown that (Rosenbrock [67])

$$N_R - N_Q = p_0 - p_c.$$

Thus since $p_c = 0$ for asymptotic stability of the closed-loop system, it follows that a necessary and sufficient condition for closed-loop system stability is that

$$N_R - N_Q = p_0.$$

If the map of D under $\det \hat{Q}$ is $\Gamma_{\hat{Q}}$ and encircles the origin $N_{\hat{Q}}$ times clockwise, while that of $\det \hat{R}$ is $\Gamma_{\hat{R}}$ and encircles the origin $N_{\hat{Q}}$ times (all encirclements being counted positive when clockwise) then

$$N_{\hat{Q}} - N_{\hat{R}} = p_0 + p_c$$

since inverse polar plots are now being used. Suppose that $\hat{Q}(s)$ is row (or column) diagonal-dominant on the Nyquist contour D, having no zero of $\det \hat{Q}(s)$ on D and no pole of $\{\hat{q}_{ii}(s): i = 1, 2, \cdots, m\}$ on D. Let the diagonal elements $\{\hat{q}_{ii}(s): i = 1, 2, \cdots, m\}$ map D into the set of loci $\{\Gamma_{\hat{q}i}\}$ and $\det \hat{Q}(s)$ map D into $\Gamma_{\hat{Q}}$. Then, if $\Gamma_{\hat{q}i}$ encircles the origin of the complex plane $N_{\hat{q}i}$ times and $\Gamma_{\hat{Q}}$ encircles the origin $N_{\hat{Q}}$ times (all encirclements being counted positive when clockwise), it can be shown that

$$N_{\hat{Q}} = \sum_{i=1}^{m} N_{\hat{q}i}.$$

Now suppose that $\hat{R}(s)$ is also dominant on D and that $\hat{r}_{ii}(s)$ maps D into $\Gamma_{\hat{r}i}$ encircling the origin $N_{\hat{r}i}$ times clockwise. Then, with p_0 defined as above, the closed-loop system will be stable if and only if

$$\sum_{i=1}^{m} N_{\hat{q}i} - \sum_{i=1}^{m} N_{\hat{r}i} = p_0.$$

Ostrowski's Theorem and Ostrowski Bands: Let a rational $m \times m$ matrix $Z(s)$ be row dominant on any closed elementary contour C having on it no pole of $\{z_{ii}(s): i = 1, 2, \cdots, m\}$. Then if s_0 is a point on C, $Z(s_0)$ has an inverse $\hat{Z}(s_0)$ such that

$$|\hat{z}_{ii}^{-1}(s_0) - z_{ii}(s_0)| < \phi_i d_i(s_0) < d_i(s_0), \qquad i = 1, 2, \cdots, m$$

where

$$d_i(s_0) = \sum_{\substack{j=1 \\ j \neq i}}^{m} |z_{ij}(s_0)|$$

are the radii of a set of Gershgorin circles centered on $\{z_{ii}(s_0)\}$ and ϕ_i are a set of "shrinking factors" defined by

$$\phi_i(s_0) = \max_{\substack{j \\ j \neq i}} \frac{d_j(s_0)}{|z_{jj}(s_0)|}.$$

If $Z(s)$ is column-dominant on C, then an equivalent relationship holds with $d_i(s_0)$ replaced by

$$d_i'(s_0) = \sum_{\substack{j=1 \\ j \neq i}}^{m} |z_{ji}(s_0)|$$

and $\phi_i(s_0)$ replaced by

$$\phi_i'(s_0) = \max_{\substack{j \\ j \neq i}} \frac{d_j'(s_0)}{|z_{jj}(s_0)|}.$$

The importance of Ostrowski's theorem in the context of the INA method is that it enables one to locate the diagonal elements of an inverse matrix within the Gershgorin bands swept out by the diagonal elements of the original matrix. Further, it locates them within a narrower band of circles (naturally called the Ostrowski band); these smaller circles are obtained by applying the shrinking factors ϕ_i to the radii of the Gershgorin circles.

The INA Design Technique: The essence of the INA approach is that, by means of a suitably chosen compensation matrix, a multivariable feedback problem is turned into a succession of classical single-loop problems. Let $R(s)$ be the closed-loop transfer-function matrix of the standard multivariable feedback configuration shown in Fig. 3 so that, when H is again a diagonal matrix, $r_{ii}(s)$ = transmittance between ith reference input and ith controlled output when all feedback paths are closed, that is, when $h_i \neq 0, i = 1, 2, \cdots, m$. Define a quantity $l_i(s)$, where $l_i(s)$ = transmittance between ith reference input and ith controlled output when the feedback loops 1, 2, $\cdots$, $(i-1)$, $(i+1)$, $\cdots$, m are closed and the ith feedback loop is open, that is, when $h_i = 0$ and $h_j \neq 0, j \neq i$. Then

$$r_{ii}^{-1}(s) = l_i^{-1}(s) + h_i, \qquad i = 1, 2, \cdots, m.$$

When one wishes to carry out a succession of single-loop designs, opening one feedback path at a time and keeping all the other feedback loops closed, it is the quantity $l_i(s)$ which has to be handled.

If the Gershgorin bands swept out by $\{q_{ii}(j\omega)\}$ exclude the origin (so that $\hat{Q}$ is diagonal dominant), encircle the origin $\{N_{\hat{q}i}\}$ times, also exclude the critical points $(-h_i, 0)$ (so that $\hat{R}$ is diagonal-dominant), and encircle these critical points $\{N_{\hat{r}i}\}$ times for $i = 1, 2, \cdots, m$, then closed-loop stability is ensured if and only if

$$\sum_{i=1}^{m} N_{\hat{q}i} - \sum_{i=1}^{m} N_{\hat{r}i} = p_0.$$

Thus the Gershgorin bands for $\hat{Q}$ can be used to check closed-loop stability. An application of the Ostrowski theorem, however, enables one to also locate the frequency-response loci of the terms $l_i^{-1}(s)$ which one is handling in the latter stages of the INA design technique. If we put

$$Z(s) = \hat{R}(s) = \hat{Q}(s) + H$$

then the Ostrowski theorem tells us that, for each s on the Nyquist contour D, the diagonal elements of the closed-loop transfer-function matrix $R(s)$ will satisfy

$$|r_{ii}^{-1}(s) - [h_i + \hat{q}_{ii}(s)]| < \phi_i(s)\, d_i(s) < d_i(s) \tag{4.4}$$

for row-dominance or

$$|r_{ii}^{-1}(s) - [h_i + \hat{q}_{ii}(s)]| < \phi_i'(s)\, d_i'(s) < d_i'(s) \tag{4.5}$$

for column-dominance. In terms of the quantities h_i and $\hat{q}_{ii}(s)$, the shrinking factors are given by

$$\phi_i(s) = \max_{\substack{j \\ j \neq i}} \frac{d_j(s)}{|h_j + \hat{q}_{jj}(s)|}$$

$$\phi_i'(s) = \max_{\substack{j \\ j \neq i}} \frac{d_j'(s)}{|h_j + \hat{q}_{jj}(s)|}.$$

Now since

$$l_i^{-1}(s) = r_{ii}^{-1}(s) - h_i,$$

one may re-write (4.4) and (4.5) as

$$|l_i^{-1}(s) - \hat{q}_{ii}(s)| < \phi_i(s)\, d_i(s) < d_i(s)$$

for a row-dominant $\hat{R}(s)$, or

$$|l_i^{-1}(s) - \hat{q}_{ii}(s)| < \phi_i'(s)\, d_i'(s) < d_i'(s)$$

for a column-dominant $\hat{R}(s)$.

These results have the following obvious graphical interpretation. For each s on the Nyquist contour D, $l_i^{-1}(s)$ lies within a circle centered on $\hat{q}_{ii}(s)$ and having a radius $\phi_i(s)\, d_i(s) < d_i(s)$ if $\hat{R}$ is row-dominant at s (or having radius $\phi_i'(s)\, d_i'(s) < d_i'(s)$ if $\hat{R}$ is column-dominant at s). As s traverses D, these circles will sweep out a set of Ostrowski bands which will lie inside the Gershgorin bands for $\hat{Q}(s)$. In the INA approach these Ostrowski bands fulfill two functions.

1) They locate the frequency response of the inverse transfer functions $l_i^{-1}(s)$. If one wishes to design a single-loop compensator for the ith loop, then the transfer function for which it must be designed is $l_i(s)$. As the other feedback gains $h_1, h_2, \cdots, h_{i-1}, h_{i+1}, \cdots, h_m$ vary, the observed transmittance $l_i(s)$ will change. However, so long as dominance of R is maintained, $l_i^{-1}(s)$ will lie within the appropriate Ostrowski bounds, evaluated for $\{h_i: i = 1, 2, \cdots, m\}$. It is important to notice that the shrinking factors $\phi_i(s)$ and $\phi_i'(s)$ will depend on the gains in the other loops so that the width of the ith Ostrowski band will depend on these gains. The Gershgorin band, however, is independent of the loop gains and so always gives an outer bound for the Ostrowski bands.

2) The Ostrowski bands may be used to determine the stability margins of the loops being designed. When only one of the feedback gains h_i is being varied, a single-loop situation essentially exists, and if the Ostrowski band is narrow enough it may in practice be treated as though it were a single-loop inverse Nyquist plot.

B. Use of Diagonal Dominance in the Stability Analysis of Nonlinear Multivariable Systems

Rosenbrock [66] gave a generalization of the circle criterion to multivariable systems which applies to the case where a diagonally-dominant linear multivariable system has a diagonal nonlinear or time-varying feedback around it. This requires that appropriately defined bands drawn around the Nyquist plots for the diagonal elements of the open-loop transfer function matrix or its inverse must avoid certain disks in the complex plane. These disks differ in radius from those appropriate to the use of the single-loop circle criterion for the corresponding diagonal nonlinear or time-varying element. Cook [8] subsequently derived an alternative generalization of the circle criterion to the multivariable case in which the radii of the disks remain the same as for the single-loop case by using a different definition of diagonal dominance.

In a study of conditions for the absence of limit cycles in a class of nonlinear feedback systems, Cook [9] made a further extension of these multivariable circle criteria which is of an "off-axis circle" type. The usefulness of this particular extension depends on the presence of some degree of diagonal dominance in the linear part of the feedback arrangement being considered.

IV. Frequency-Response Design Techniques for Multivariable Feedback Control Systems

Work on the analysis, synthesis, and design of multivariable control systems was transformed by the introduction of state-space-based approaches. The Riccati equation solution of the optimal linear regulator problem (Kalman [23], [25], Kalman and Englar [28]) was the first true synthesis procedure for control-system design. Together with the fundamentally important work done on Kalman–Bucy filtering (Kalman and Bucy [24]), observers (Luenberger [34], [35]), pole-shifting (Rosenbrock [61], Simon and Mitter [71], Wonham [73], the separation theorem (Joseph and Tou [21], Wonham [74]) and the duality between optimal control and optimal filtering (Kalman and Bucy [24]) this supplied a solid basis for the analysis and design of multivariable control systems (see the IEEE Special Issue on the Linear-Quadratic-Gaussian Problem, Vol. AC-16, Number 6, December 1971). The use of these state-space methods solved many important control problems in the aerospace field and aroused great interest in the possibility of their wider application. Such techniques, however, tended to require fairly accurate plant models as a necessary point of departure and were thus not immediately suitable for certain kinds of industrial plant for which only very sketchy experimentally derived descriptions were available. From the point of view of many practicing industrial engineers, they also lacked the physical immediacy and familiarity of the classical frequency-response approaches. This, together with a naturally growing curiousity among some research workers about the great blank on the control map where multivariable frequency-response methods should be found, led to work on developing suitable frequency-response approaches to multivariable control.

In surveying the various approaches which have developed it is useful to classify them as follows.

1) Methods which seek to reduce a multivariable control problem to a set or sequence of single-loop problems. In this category we have the noninteractive method, the in-

verse Nyquist array method, the sequential return difference method, and to a certain extent, the dyadic decomposition method.

2) Approaches which try to make a direct use of accurate generalizations of classical results like Nyquist's stability theorem to the multivariable case. These include the characteristic locus method, generalized Nyquist-Bode methods, and generalized root-locus methods. The dyadic decomposition method also comes under this category to some degree.

3) Frequency-response approaches to optimal multivariable controller design under constraint such as the multivariable Wiener-Hopf technique.

4) Approaches which seek to extend into the frequency domain the powerful general results which have emerged from the huge effort expended on controller analysis and design since the 1960's. In contrast to the extended classical techniques, which are usually concerned with design methods which allow and require a great deal of intuitive judgment, these approaches are more concerned with the establishment of exact synthesis methods. They also seek to use general results such as Wonham's internal model principle (Wonham [75], Francis and Wonham [17]).

A. The Inverse Nyquist Array Method

The basic results on which this method is based have already been outlined in Section IV-A above. Descriptions of the method and its applications are given in Rosenbrock [67], Munro [48], and Rosenbrock and Munro [69].

B. The Sequential Return Difference Method

The sequential return difference method was proposed by Mayne [46]; like the Rosenbrock inverse Nyquist array method it attempts to reduce a multivariable feedback design to a set of conventional single-loop problems. Its main feature is a simple procedure for calculating the effect on an overall system transfer function matrix of closing a set of loops one at a time. Like the INA method, it uses a precompensator to modify a given plant transmittance matrix to an appropriate form from which the design process may be completed via a set of single loops. The situation considered is shown in Fig. 4; the given plant transfer function matrix $G(s)$ is assumed square and of order $m \times m$; $K_c(s)$ is a precompensator matrix which will normally be chosen such that $\det K_c(s) = 1$; and

$$K(s) = \operatorname{diag}\,[k_1(s), k_2(s), \cdots, k_m(s)]$$

is a diagonal matrix of single-loop controllers. The break point A is chosen as a convenient place to which to refer the calculation of return-difference matrices. Let

$$K^i(s) = \operatorname{diag}\,[k_1(s), k_2(s), \cdots, k_i(s), 0, 0 \cdots, 0]$$

and

$$Q(s) = G(s)K_c(s)$$

so that $Q(s)$ represents the compensated plant. Let the sequence of return-difference matrices calculated at the break point A which are obtained as the various loops denoted by the diagonal elements of $K(s)$ are switched in one at a time be

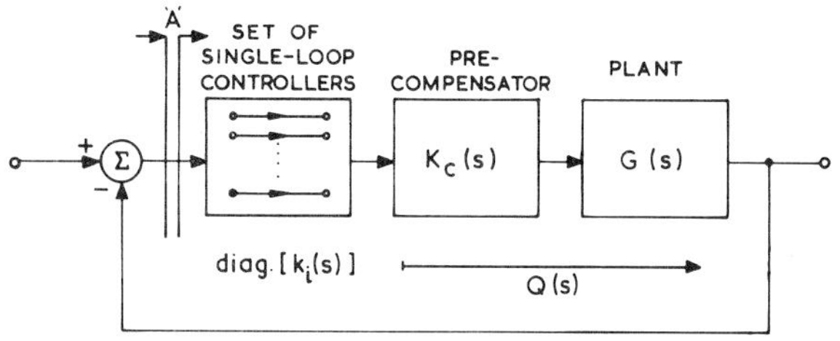

Fig. 4

denoted by

$$F_i = I_m + QK^i$$

and let

$$Q^i = F_i^{-1}Q.$$

Let q_{ij}^k denote the element of the matrix Q^k at the intersection of the ith row and jth column. Now suppose that the first $(i-1)$ loops of $K(s)$ are closed. Then the scalar return-difference observed at A for injection of signals into the ith loop will be given by

$$f_i(s) = 1 + k_i(s)q_{ii}^{i-1}(s), \tag{4.6}$$

and it can be shown that

$$\det F_i(s) = \prod_{j=1}^{i} f_j(s)$$

which leads to the following result.

Mayne's Stability Theorem: Let $\{f_i(s): i = 1, 2, \cdots, m\}$ be the scalar return-difference set defined in (4.6), and let them map the usual Nyquist contour D into a set of loci $\{\gamma_i: i = 1, 2, \cdots, m\}$ in the complex plane. Then if each of the loci satisfy the usual Nyquist stability criterion for return differences (that is to say for an open-loop stable system that each γ_i does not encircle or pass through the origin in the complex plane), then the set of systems obtained by the successive closing of the various loops as the $\{k_i: i = 1, 2, \cdots, m\}$ are inserted into the feedback arrangement are all stable.

For the implementation of the SRD method, formulae are required to recursively compute Q^i and f_i, and these are given in Mayne [46]. This approach assumes that a satisfactory sequence of single-loop designs can be carried out one at a time. As each single-loop design is satisfactorily completed, the corresponding loop gain k_j is increased to a suitably high value. What is thus needed to enable the final design steps to be carried out is a formula which gives the transmittance seen by the ith controller when the gains of all the previously designed loops are increased to appropriately high values. If $\{\Delta_k(s)\}$ is the set of principal minors of $Q(s)$, then Mayne, following a result of Rosenbrock, showed that as all previous loop gains are increased to high values,

$$q_{ii}^{i-1}(s) \rightarrow \frac{\Delta_i(s)}{\Delta_{i-1}(s)}.$$

Hence, the transmittances seen when designing the individual loop controllers in the SRD method are defined by the ratios of principal minors of $Q(s) = G(s)K_c(s)$. The SRD design pro-

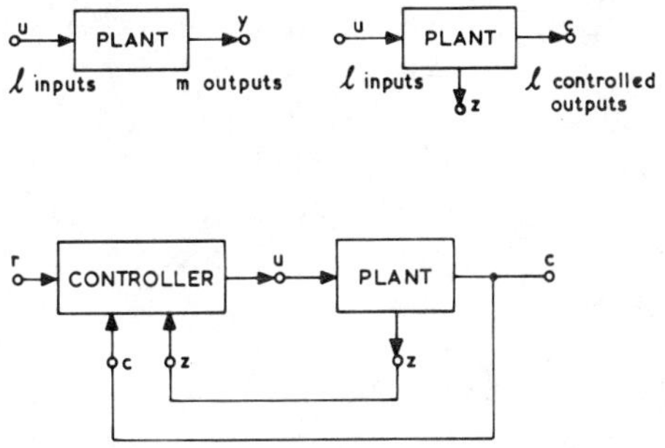

Fig. 5.

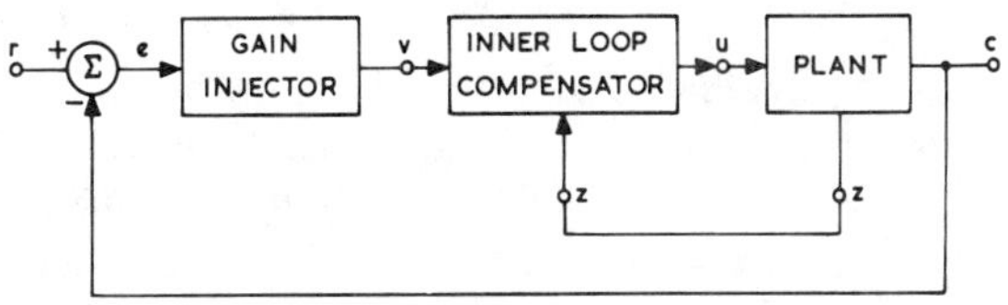

Fig. 6.

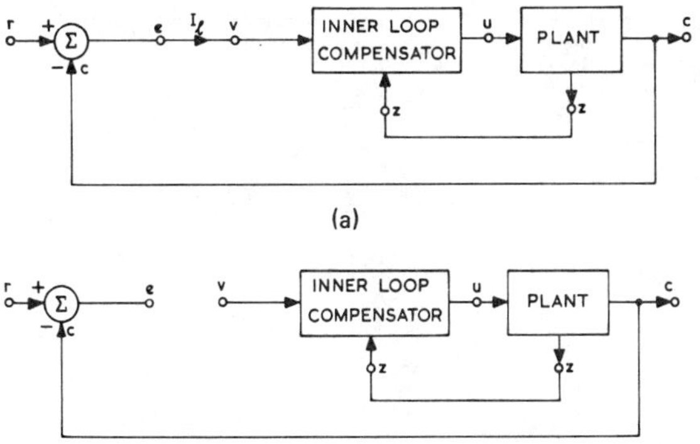

(a)

(b)

Fig. 7.

cedure is thus to simply choose the precompensator $K_c(s)$ so that Δ_1 (which is just q_{11}), $\Delta_2, \cdots$, are of a satisfactory form and then design the single-loop controllers $k_1(s)$, $k_2(s), \cdots$, one at a time by classical methods increasing each gain to an acceptably high value before proceeding to the next stage.

C. A Two-Stage Design Technique Based on Generalizations of the Classical Nyquist-Bode and Root-Locus Approaches

Both the inverse Nyquist array and the sequential return difference design approaches seek to deploy, in the multivariable context, the basic tools of classical single-input single-output design. In the INA approach this is done by first partially decoupling the system, and in the SRD approach by designing one loop at a time in a suitable sequential fashion. By contrast, MacFarlane and his collaborators have developed an approach to multivariable feedback system design which makes a direct use of generalized Nyquist diagrams and generalized root-locus diagrams (MacFarlane and Kouvaritakis [40], MacFarlane, Kouvaritakis, and Edmunds [44], Kouvaritakis and Edmunds [31]).

The configuration considered is shown in Fig. 5. A given plant has l inputs and m outputs, and it is assumed that $m > l$. The plant output vector y consists of two subvectors c and z:

$$y = \begin{bmatrix} c \\ z \end{bmatrix}$$

where c is an l-dimensional vector of variables whose behavior is to be controlled and z is an $(m - l)$-dimensional vector of extra available measurements. The design process is carried out in two main stages, corresponding to the arrangement shown in Fig. 6.

Stage 1—Compensator Design: The purpose of the compensator is to make use of the extra information contained in the vector z to create a new l-dimensional input vector v which gives a suitable form of transmittance from v to the set of controlled outputs c. A suitable form of this transmittance is taken to be one which allows acceptably large amounts of feedback gain to be applied around this modified plant.

Stage 2—Gain Injector Design: Having used all of the available measurements to the best advantage in arranging for a suitable transmission characteristic between v and c, the design is completed by choosing a gain injector block which will inject the suitably high feedback gains required to meet the closed-loop performance specification over the operating bandwidth. The gain injector block will normally contain both integral action terms to remove low-frequency errors and phase-compensating terms to improve closed-loop damping. Early treatments of this part of the approach are often called the characteristic locus method because it is essentially based on the manipulation of characteristic gain loci (generalized Nyquist diagrams).

The basic idea behind the compensator design is best seen from a consideration of the arrangement shown in Fig. 7(a) where the gain-injector block has been replaced by a unit transmittance operator. In this arrangement the compensator is designed in such a way that a suitable set of closed-loop characteristic frequencies is obtained. How the suitability of such a set is judged is suggested from a study of the implications of Fig. 7. The set of closed-loop characteristic frequencies associated with Fig. 7(a) depends on the nature of the characteristic gain loci for the transmittance between v and c in Fig. 7(b). Hence, the manipulation of the closed-loop frequencies for the arrangement of Fig. 7(a) is equivalent to the manipulation of the characteristic gain loci for the compensated plant of Fig. 8.

Design of Gain Injector: Assume that the first stage of the design procedure has been carried out; one is then considering the second-stage situation shown in Fig. 9 where $K(s)$ is the transfer-function matrix of the gain injector and $G_c(s)$ is the transfer-function matrix of the compensated plant.

Let

$$Q(s) = G_c(s)\,K(s)$$

so that the closed-loop transfer-function matrix for this arrangement is

$$R(s) = [I_m + Q(s)]^{-1} Q(s).$$

It follows from standard relationships in matrix algebra that every eigenvector $w_i(s)$ of $Q(s)$ is also an eigenvector of $R(s)$,

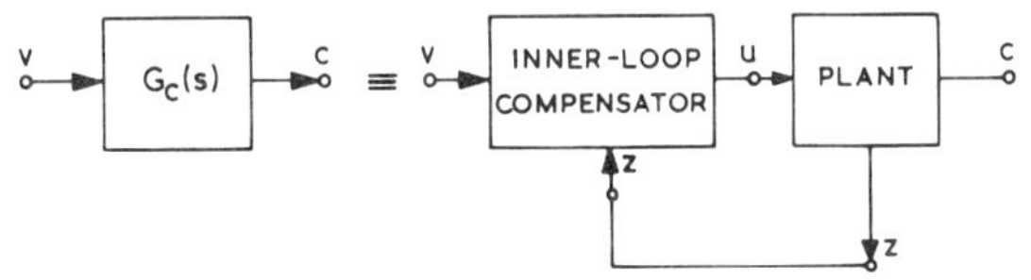

Fig. 8.

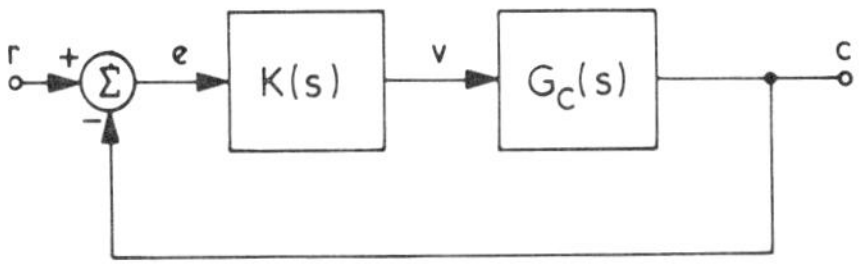

Fig. 9.

and that for every eigenvalue $q_i(s)$ of $Q(s)$ there is a corresponding eigenvalue $q_i(s)/[1+q_i(s)]$ of $R(s)$. Since the set of complex numbers $\{q_i(1+q_i)^{-1}: i=1,2,\cdots,m\}$ will have two or more members with the same value if and only if the set of complex numbers $\{q_i: i=1,2,\cdots,m\}$ has two or more members with the same value, it follows that the set of branch points associated with the matrices $R(s)$ and $Q(s)$ are identical. The characteristic gain algebraic functions associated with the open-loop matrix $Q(s)$ and the closed-loop matrix $R(s)$ thus share the same Riemann surface, and these matrices also share the same set of eigenvectors. Therefore, if the open-loop matrix $Q(s)$ has a dyadic expansion of the form

$$Q(s)=\sum_{i=1}^{m} q_i(s)\, w_i(s)\, v_i^t(s)$$

valid for almost all values of s (that is, except at the branch points), then $R(s)$ will have a corresponding dyadic expansion of the form

$$R(s)=\sum_{i=1}^{m}\left[\frac{q_i(s)}{1+q_i(s)}\right] w_i(s)\, v_i^t(s) \tag{4.7}$$

valid in the same punctured plane as $Q(s)$ (that is, the complex plane with the set of branch points deleted).

Equation (4.7) can be made the basis of a design technique for systems having the same number of inputs and outputs. The closed-loop frequency response is given by

$$R(j\omega)=\sum_{i=1}^{m}\left[\frac{q_i(j\omega)}{1+q_i(j\omega)}\right] w_i(j\omega)\, v_i^t(j\omega)$$

If

$$q_i(j\omega)\to\infty,\qquad i=1,2,\cdots,m,$$

then

$$R(j\omega)\to\sum_{i=1}^{m} w(j\omega)\, v_i^t(j\omega)=I_m,$$

where I_m is a unit matrix of order m, so that good closed-loop performance may be achieved by making all the characteristic gains of $Q(s)$ sufficiently high over a required operating frequency range. The amounts of characteristic gain required for a given quality of closed-loop performance, and the amount of closed-loop interaction which will result, depend on the behavior with frequency of the eigenvectors of $Q(s)$. The desired properties of the characteristic gain loci and characteristic gain directions (eigenvectors) of $G_c(s)\,K(s)$ are therefore determined by the following considerations.

1) The characteristic gain loci (generalized Nyquist diagrams) of $G_c(s)\,K(s)$ must satisfy the generalized Nyquist stability criterion.

2) For high tracking performance, and therefore low interaction, at any stipulated frequency, the gains of all the characteristic loci must be suitably large. This is particularly relevant to the low-frequency situation in which it is feasible to have high characteristic gains.

3) At high frequencies, however, it is not generally feasible, because of the excessive power requirements involved, to have large gains in the characteristic loci. Such high gains at high frequencies would, in many cases, also tend to violate the generalized Nyquist stability criterion. To reduce interaction at high frequencies, therefore, one cannot in general deploy high gains for this purpose and so must instead make the characteristic direction set of the open-loop transference align with the standard basis vector set at high frequencies.

The principal components of a design approach exploiting these ideas are, therefore,

a) a method of manipulating characteristic gain loci, and
b) a method of manipulating characteristic gain directions.

Manipulation of Characteristic Gains and Directions: From the spectral analysis point of view the essential difficulty in choosing an appropriate form of controller matrix $K(s)$ lies in the fact that very little is known of the way in which the eigenvalues and eigenvectors of the product of two matrices $G_c(s)$ and $K(s)$ are related to the individual eigenvalues and eigenvectors of $G_c(s)$ and $K(s)$. There is one exception to this situation, however, and this is that in which the matrices concerned commute, that is, when

$$G_c(s)\,K(s)=K(s)\,G_c(s).$$

This happens if and only if $G_c(s)$ and $K(s)$ have a common set of eigenvectors. In such a situation the eigenvalues of the product $G_c(s)\,K(s)$ are simply appropriate products of the individual eigenvalues of the matrices $G_c(s)$ and $K(s)$; the eigenvalues which are multiplied together are those associated with a common eigenvector.

Since the equation

$$\det\,[g\,I_m - G_c(s)]=0$$

will normally be irreducible, the eigenvalues and eigenvectors of the matrix $G_c(s)$ will not be expressible in terms of rational functions. It will therefore not normally be feasible to construct a realizable controller $K(s)$ which will exactly commute with $G_c(s)$ for all values of s. Even in the rare cases when this might be possible, such a controller could be unnecessarily complicated. A more practical and rewarding approach is to investigate the possibility of using controllers which are approximately commutative with the plant at appropriately chosen values of frequency. In one approach of this sort (MacFarlane and Kouvaritakis [40]) the controller matrix is chosen to have the specific form

$$K(s) = H\Lambda_k(s) J$$

where H and J are matrices with real elements and $\Lambda_k(s)$ is a diagonal matrix of rational functions in s. The matrix $K(s)$ can therefore be expressed in the dyadic form

$$K(s) = \sum_{j=1}^{m} k_i(s)\, h_i j_i^t$$

where the vector sets

$$\{h_i: i = 1, 2, \cdots, m\} \quad \text{and} \quad \{j_i^t: i = 1, 2, \cdots, m\}$$

are both real. An approximately-commutative controller is one whose constituent real matrices H and J are chosen in such a way that $K(s)$ is approximately commutative with $G_c(s)$ at some specific value of complex frequency $\bar{s}$. At such a frequency one has that

$$q_i(\bar{s}) \simeq g_i(\bar{s})\, k_i(\bar{s}), \qquad i = 1, 2, \cdots, m$$

where $q_i(\bar{s}), g_i(\bar{s})$ are eigenvalues of $Q(\bar{s})$ and $G_c(\bar{s})$, respectively, and $k_i(\bar{s})$ are appropriate diagonal elements of $\Lambda_k(\bar{s})$. This set of relationships gives an obvious basis for manipulating the characteristic gain loci of $Q(s)$ in a systematic manner; it also turns out that this approximately commutative technique can be used to manipulate the eigenvectors of $Q(s)$. Such manipulation techniques have been described by MacFarlane and Kouvaritakis [40].

Design of the Inner-Loop Compensator: The ideas behind the design of the inner-loop compensator are illustrated by Figs. 10-12. The form of the characteristic gain loci for the compensated plant $G_c(s)$, that is, for the transmittance between v and c in Fig. 7(b), is directly related to the nature of the closed-loop characteristic frequencies for the arrangement of Fig. 7(a), which in turn is equivalent to Figs. 10 and 11. Thus the problem of choosing the component blocks F_c and F_z of Fig. 10 for the compensator is essentially the problem of choosing the feedback matrix F in the configuration of Fig. 11 in such a way that a suitable set of closed-loop characteristic frequencies is obtained. Since F has m inputs and l outputs, where $l < m$, the choice of F is often referred to as a "squaring-down" procedure. The choice of F is essentially based on generalized root-locus ideas and involves the placement of finite zeros and the manipulation of root-locus asymptotes (MacFarlane, Kouvaritakis, and Edmunds [44]). The final objective of the "inner-loop compensator" design is to get suitable locations for the closed-loop poles seen by the gain injector $K(s)$ in Fig. 12. A satisfactory achievement of this objective requires some dynamical insight and engineering judgment since, in the usual case when all the plant states are not directly accessible, it will not normally be possible to place finite zeros in arbitrarily specified locations in the complex plane. Nevertheless, the basic ideas underlying the technique of inner-loop compensator design are quite straightforward: one places finite zeros and manipulates root-locus asymptote patterns in such a way that, by setting a gain parameter at a suitable value, the closed-loop poles of the system "seen by" the gain-injector $K(s)$ are pulled into suitable locations in the

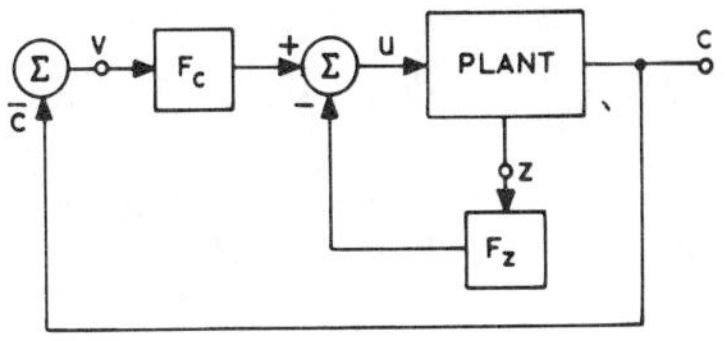

Fig. 10.

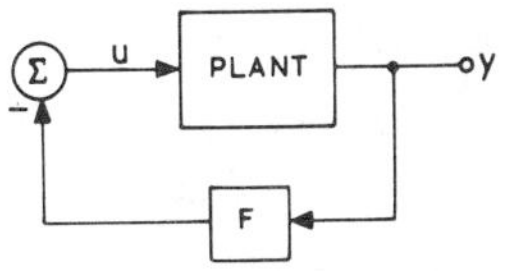

Fig. 11.

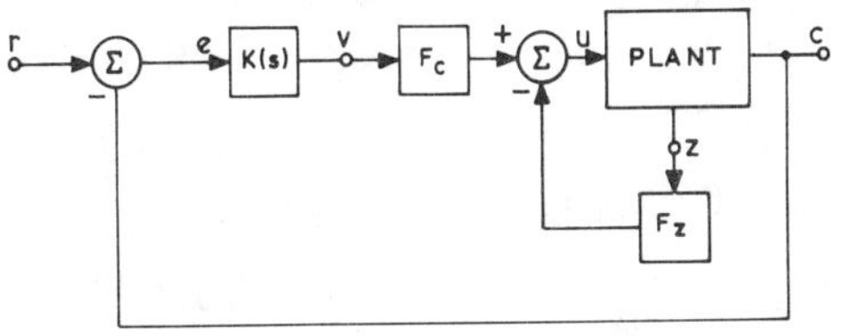

Fig. 12.

complex plane. In some circumstances one may wish to pull such closed-loop poles well over into the left-half complex plane in order to speed up closed-loop response and to allow $K(s)$ to inject a desired amount of gain before the overall (inner plus outer loops) system has its closed-loop characteristic frequencies driven into unacceptable regions of the complex plane. In other circumstances one may wish to "freeze" the location of major poles associated with certain open-loop plant characteristic frequencies by placing finite zeros near them. Often a judicious mixture of both approaches will be required.

D. Gain and Phase Margin for Optimal Multivariable Regulators and Robustness Against Gain Variation

Kalman [26] first studied the frequency-response characterization of optimal feedback controllers, and his results were extended to the multivariable case by MacFarlane [36].

Safanov and Athans [70] have discussed the gain and phase margins of multivariable linear-quadratic (LQ) regulators. They show that such designs are robust against a variety of nonlinear and time-varying changes in open-loop dynamics, and give an illuminating discussion of the reasons underlying these useful properties. However, as shown by Fuller [20] and Doyle [14], these desirable properties do not extend to the full linear-quadratic-Gaussian (LQG) case. Fuller [20] discussed the effect of measurement noise when low-frequency stochastic disturbances are present, and Doyle [14] considered the incorporation of a Kalman-Bucy filter in the control loop.

E. Dyadic Decomposition Method

Owens has formulated an interesting approach to the design of linear multivariable feedback systems based on what he terms a dyadic transfer function matrix (Owens [51]-[56].

Dyadic Transfer Function Matrix: An $m \times m$ transfer-function matrix is said to be dyadic if and only if det $G(s)$ is not identically zero and there exist constant $m \times m$ matrices P_1, P_2 and a set of scalar transfer functions $\{g_1(s), \cdots, g_m(s)\}$ such that

$$G(s) = P_1 \text{ diag } \{g_1(s), \cdots, g_m(s)\} P_2$$

$$= \sum_{j=1}^{m} g_j(s)\, \alpha_j \beta_j^t$$

where $\{\alpha_j: j = 1, \cdots, m\}$ and $\{\beta_j^t: j = 1, 2, \cdots, m\}$ are the columns of P_1 and the rows of P_2, respectively.

If a controller of the form

$$K(s) = P_2^{-1} \text{ diag } \{k_1(s), \cdots, k_m(s)\} P_1^{-1}$$

is used in the standard multivariable feedback configuration, one then gets a closed-loop transfer-function matrix of the form

$$R(s) = [I_m + G(s)\, K(s)]^{-1} G(s)\, K(s)$$

$$= P_1 P_1^{-1} [I_m + G(s)\, K(s)]^{-1} G(s)\, K(s)\, P_1 P_1^{-1}$$

$$= P_1 \text{ diag} \left\{ \frac{g_i(s)\, k_i(s)}{1 + g_i(s)\, k_i(s)} \right\} P_1^{-1}.$$

This shows that the design of the feedback controller may accordingly be reduced to a set of m noninteracting single-loop designs. Since the design of a controller becomes such a straightforward process when the plant is of dyadic form, Owens has naturally been led to consider the approximation of arbitrary transfer-function matrices by dyadic ones. A useful feature of this approach is the comprehensive way in which stability under failure conditions may be studied. Owens has also extended the scope of this approach to the design problem by using it to derive a systematic way of dealing with the manipulation and compensation of the characteristic loci (generalized Nyquist diagrams) of a system described by a transfer-function matrix, using rational function approximations to the characteristic loci (Owens [56]).

F. Multivariable Wiener–Hopf Method

Youla, Jabr, and Bongiorno [77] have extended the frequency-response treatment of designing optimal control systems to the multivariable case. This approach is based on a least squares Wiener–Hopf minimization of an appropriately chosen cost functional using spectral factorization techniques. Their treatment imposes no restrictions on the plant transfer-function matrix and deals with input noise, load disturbances, and measurement noise specified in terms of spectral densities. Feedforward compensation is also considered. An optimal controller is derived which is proper (having a finite frequency response at arbitrarily high frequencies). Such a treatment establishes illuminating links between state-space approaches to the controller synthesis problem and frequency-response design techniques. It offers the possibility of developing powerful synthesis methods in the frequency domain which are well adapted to handle the constraints imposed by practical engineering considerations.

G. Algebraic Synthesis Methods and General Studies of the Multivariable Control Problem

The desire to develop synthesis (as opposed to design) solutions to multivariable control problems has naturally led to a deeper study of the mathematical aspects of regulator and control problems. Wonham's work on a geometric approach (Wonham [75]) had a profound influence in defining certain key problems in an appropriate mathematical setting and led to an important series of investigations in the time domain (Francis and Wonham [16], [17], Davison [11], Davison and Goldenberg [12], Wonham and Pearson [76], Pearson and Staats [57], Francis [15], Pearson, Shields, and Staats [58]). During the course of his investigations Wonham and his collaborators developed a new and valuable principle—the internal model principle—which roughly states that any good regulator must contain a model of the dynamic structure of the environment in the closed-loop system (Wonham [75], Francis and Wonham [17]). Wonham also focused attention on a sharply defined problem—the regulator problem with internal stability (Wonham [75]), which was subsequently investigated in a state-space setting in considerable generality.

These general approaches have also been studied in a frequency-response context. Wolovich [72] gave a synthesis procedure for systems described by rational transfer-function matrices which achieves closed-loop stability and the rejection of step disturbances. His synthesis procedure combines integral feedforward compensation with asymptotic state estimation treated via frequency-response techniques. Bengtsson [4] has given a frequency-response treatment of the internal model principle and shown how to use it to construct compensators which give output regulation with internal stability. An input–output treatment of the multivariable servomechanism problem has been given by Francis [18]. He examines the effects of model uncertainty and gives qualitative characterizations of closed-loop stability and tracking and their sensitivity to model errors. A comparison of his results in an input–output setting is made with those obtained using a state-space approach. The problems studied by Bengtsson and Francis have been treated from a slightly more general point of view by Cheng and Pearson [7]. They give a frequency-domain treatment of the regulator problem with internal stability, and obtain necessary and sufficient conditions which guarantee output regulation with internal stability.

V. Comparison and Review of the Various Design Approaches

Two different trends are clearly discernable in the currently developing literature on multivariable feedback control. One trend is towards a better mathematical formulation of the problems involved, to the development of fundamental principles, to the establishment of appropriate necessary and sufficient conditions for the solution of specific control problems, and to the development of synthesis techniques. Good examples of this approach are Wonham's work on a unified geometric approach to multivariable control (Wonham [75]) and the work of Wolovich [72], Bengtsson [3], [4], Francis

[15], [18], Davison [11], and Pernebo [59]. The other trend is towards a more pragmatic and practical engineering approach in which a design problem is formulated in a way which may make good sense to an experienced engineer but which may appear distinctly vague and ill-defined from a more mathematical viewpoint. Such approaches to design problems tend to use a few key physically based concepts and to be critically dependent on the amount of physical insight which they can generate. Frequency-response techniques have always featured prominently in such approaches because of their direct link with experimental measurements. This particular trend has received a considerable boost from rapid developments in interactive computing (Rosenbrock [67]). When such engineering design approaches are used with an interactive computer graphic display, techniques which lend themselves to graphical interpretation have a built-in advantage, and so it is natural that generalized Nyquist diagrams and generalized root-locus diagrams should emerge as useful design tools.

It is useful in this context to distinguish between the concepts of design and synthesis. Given an appropriately agreed meaning, these terms become useful labels when classifying and discussing various trends and developments. In developing a synthesis technique one strives to formulate a sharply defined problem with a well-founded mathematical solution, preferably expressible in the form of a workable and robust computer algorithm. In developing a design technique one strives to give a practising and experienced engineer a set of manipulative and interpretive tools which will enable him to build up, modify, and assess a design put together on the basis of physical reasoning within the guidelines laid down by his engineering experience. The optimal control problem and its solution is a good example of a synthesis procedure. It nevertheless cannot avoid placing some burden on the engineering designer in the form of having to choose the performance index to be optimized.

The inverse Nyquist array method is clearly conceived as a design approach. Indeed its appearance marked the resurgence of interest in design rather than synthesis. In its current form it is only adapted to deal with a situation in which a plant has equal numbers of inputs and outputs. It has the great advantage that the procedure which a designer has to adopt is clear-cut and straightforward, and the further excellent point that it has good integrity properties. The term "high integrity" refers to the maintenance of closed-loop stability in the face of sensor (and also possibly actuator) failures and is an important aspect of many design problems. The price paid for these advantages, which stem from the reduction of a multivariable problem to a set of single-loop problems, is that the decoupling carried out at low frequencies may result in poor root-locus asymptote patterns and hence reduced gains and reduced closed-loop bandwidth for a given degree of closed-loop damping (Kouvaritakis [32]). Its use can also require the exercise of considerable skill to find an appropriate precompensator which will achieve diagonal dominance. If diagonal dominance is, on the other hand, to be attained by the use of automatic computer procedures, then the design rather than synthesis aspects of the method start to disappear.

The sequential return difference method does not seem to have been used on many practical problems, so there is less evidence available on which to base an assessment than for some other design approaches. It is very much a loop-at-a-time technique and might be difficult to use for a plant with many inputs and outputs. There is no in-built measure of interaction, and so little feel is available for the vector-input vector-output aspects of a multivariable design.

A generalized two-stage classical approach using characteristic locus diagrams and multivariable root-locus diagrams has a strong appeal to designers with a background of using classical frequency-response techniques. Its use requires a considerable amount of design insight, and further development work needs to be done on the manipulation of frequency-conscious eigenvalues and eigenvectors. The use of generalized Nyquist diagrams and generalized root-locus diagrams does, however, give an experienced designer a great deal of insight into the general aspects of the multivariable feedback problem, and the importance of using such diagrams thus probably transcends their attachment to any specific design technique. There therefore appears to be considerable scope for amalgamating this approach with various forms of compensation synthesis techniques to get a fairer sharing of the investigational burden between computer and designer.

The dyadic decomposition approach shows that a certain class of multivariable systems—those which can be represented by dyadic transfer matrices—are very tractable from a frequency-response design point of view. Furthermore, this approach affords the possibility of "cataloguing" design solutions according to an appropriate cataloguing of dyadic transfer matrices (Owens [56]). Its wider utility depends on the difficulty and feasibility of approximating arbitrary transfer function matrices by simpler dyadic forms which will give an approximation which may be sensibly valid over only a small frequency interval around a chosen frequency point.

A multivariable Wiener–Hopf approach offers the possibility of a valuable synthesis technique which is well adapted to handle engineering descriptions and constraints. The treatment given by Youla and his collaborators is impressive in its breadth, its lack of restrictions on plant, and in its incorporation of input noise, load disturbance, and feedforward compensation. The characterization of noise and disturbances in spectral density terms is particularly useful. Much work on the development of robust algorithms for the factorization and manipulation of rational matrices would need to be done before it could be made a routine approach for complex industrial plant use. Nevertheless, it has great promise, not least in its ability to handle constraints imposed by plant saturation and measurement noise. It also gives a solution to the standard optimal control problem in certain cases when the LQG approach in the time domain breaks down.

In the long run, controller system development and design will become increasingly computer-based. There will therefore be very great incentives for the creation of powerful automatic synthesis techniques, and thus for ever sharper and more comprehensive mathematical formulations of key design problems. A range of general principles—such as the internal model principle—will emerge to take their place alongside the feedback principle, feedforward principle, duality principle, and separation principle (MacFarlane [38]). One would therefore expect designers to work increasingly with a variety of synthesis techniques deployed within the guidance available from a framework of general principles. Design approaches will always be required, however, for problems which remain ill-defined from a mathematical point of view, since engineering practice invariably runs ahead of the theory required for a comprehensive treatment. One would thus hope and expect the continued development of flexible, imaginative, and innovative design techniques, many of which will probably retain a strong affinity to frequency-response ideas. Although the discussion of design techniques given here has been confined to the continuous-time case, similar approaches can be used for multivariable discrete-time systems [49].

REFERENCES

[1] J. F. Barman and J. Katzenelson, "A generalized Nyquist-type stability criterion for multivariable feedback systems," *Int. J. Control*, 20, 593–622, 1974.

[2] S. Barnett, *Matrices in Control Theory*. London: Van Nostrand Reinhold, 1971.

[3] G. Bengtsson, "A theory for control of linear multivariable systems," Report No. 7341, Lund Institute of Technology, Lund, 1973.

[4] —, "Output regulation and internal models—a frequency domain approach," *Automatica*, 13, 333–345, 1977.

[5] G. A. Bliss, *Algebraic Functions*. Providence, RI: American Mathematical Society, 1933.

[6] E. V. Bohn and T. Kasvand, "Use of matrix transformations and system eigenvalues in the design of linear multivariable control systems," *Proc. IEE*, 110, 989–997, 1963.

[7] L. Cheng and J. B. Pearson, "Frequency domain synthesis of multivariable linear regulators," *IEEE Trans. Automat. Control*, AC-23, 3–15, 1978.

[8] P. A. Cook, "Modified multivariable circle theorems," in *Recent Mathematical Developments in Control*, D. J. Bell, Ed. London: Academic Press, 367–372, 1973.

[9] —, "Conditions for the absence of limit cycles," *IEEE Trans. Automat. Control*, AC-21, 339–345, 1976.

[10] E. J. Davison and S. H. Wang, "Properties and calculation of transmission zeros of linear multivariable systems," *Automatica*, 10, 643–658, 1974.

[11] E. J. Davison, "A generalization of the output control of linear multivariable systems with unmeasurable arbitrary disturbances," *IEEE Trans. Automat. Control*, AC-20, 788–795, 1975.

[12] E. J. Davison and A. Goldenberg, "Robust control of a general servomechanism problem: The servocompensator," *Automatica*, 11(5), 461–472, 1975.

[13] C. A. Desoer and J. D. Schulman, "Zeros and poles of matrix transfer functions and their dynamical interpretation," *IEEE Trans. Circuits Syst.*, CAS-21, 3–8, 1974.

[14] J. C. Doyle, "Guaranteed margins for LQG regulators," *IEEE Trans. Automat. Control*, AC-23(4), 756–757, 1978.

[15] B. A. Francis, "The linear multivariable regulator problem," Electron. Res. Lab. Memo. ERL-M560, Univ. California, Berkeley, 1975.

[16] B. A. Francis and W. M. Wonham, "The role of transmission zeros in linear multivariable regulators," *Int. J. Control*, 22, 657–681, 1975.

[17] —, "The internal model principle for linear multivariable regulators," *J. Appl. Math. Optimiz.*, 2, 1975.

[18] B. A. Francis, "The multivariable servomechanism problem from the input-output viewpoint," *IEEE Trans. Automat. Control*, AC-22, 322–328, 1977.

[19] M. I. Freedman, P. L. Falb, and G. Zames, "A Hilbert space stability theory over locally compact Abelian groups," *SIAM J. Control*, 7, 479–495, 1969.

[20] A. T. Fuller, "Feedback control systems with low-frequency stochastic disturbances," *Int. J. Control*, 24, 165–207, 1976.

[21] P. D. Joseph and J. Tou, "On linear control theory," *Trans. AIEE*, 80, 193–196, 1961.

[22] C. H. Hsu and C. T. Chen, "A proof of the stability of multivariable feedback systems," *Proc. IEEE*, 56, 2061–2062, 1968.

[23] R. E. Kalman, "Contributions to the theory of optimal control," *Bol. Soc. Mat. Mex.*, Second Series, 5, 102–119, 1960.

[24] R. E. Kalman and R. S. Bucy, "New results in linear filtering and prediction theory," *Trans. ASME J. Basic Engrg.* 83D, 95–108, 1961.

[25] R. E. Kalman, "The theory of optimal control and the calculus of variations," in R. Bellman, Ed., *Mathematical Optimization Techniques*. Berkeley: University of California Press, 1963.

[26] —, "When is a linear control system optimal?" *Trans. ASME J. Basic Eng.*, Ser. D. 86, 51–60, 1964.

[27] —, "Irreducible realizations and the degree of a rational matrix," *SIAM J. Control*, 13, 520–544, 1965.

[28] R. E. Kalman and T. Englar, "ASP—The automatic synthesis program (program C), NASA Contractor Report CR-475, 1966.

[29] T. Kontakos, Ph.D. Thesis, University of Manchester, 1973.

[30] B. Kouvaritakis and U. Shaked, "Asymptotic behaviour of root-loci of linear multivariable systems," *Int. J. Control*, 23, 297–340, 1976.

[31] B. Kouvaritakis and J. Edmunds, "The characteristic frequency and characteristic gain design method for multivariable feedback systems," *Alternatives for Linear Multivariable Control*, National Engineering Consortium, Chicago, 229–246, 1977.

[32] B. Kouvaritakis, "Gain margins and root locus asymptotic behaviour in multivariable design," *Int. J. Control*, 27, 705–724 and 725–751, 1978.

[33] —, "The optimal root loci of linear multivariable systems," *Int. J. Control*, 28, 33–62, 1978.

[34] D. G. Luenberger, "Observing the state of a linear system," *IEEE Trans. Military Electronics*, MIL-8, 74–80, 1964.

[35] —, "Observers for multivariable systems," *IEEE Trans. Automat. Control*, AC-11, 190–197, 1966.

[36] A. G. J. MacFarlane, "The return-difference and return-ratio matrices and their use in the analysis and design of multivariable feedback control systems," *Proc. IEE*, 117, 2037–2049, 1970.

[37] A. G. J. MacFarlane and J. J. Belletrutti, "The characteristic locus design method," *Automatica*, 9, 575–588, 1973.

[38] A. G. J. MacFarlane, "Feedback," *J. Inst. Meas. Control*, 449–462, 1976.

[39] A. G. J. MacFarlane and N. Karcanias, "Poles and zeros of linear multivariable systems: A survey of the algebraic, geometric and complex-variable theory," *Int. J. Control*, 24, 33–74, 1976.

[40] A. G. J. MacFarlane and B. Kouvaritakis, "A design technique for linear multivariable feedback systems," *Int. J. Control*, 25, 837–874, 1977.

[41] A. G. J. MacFarlane and I. Postlethwaite, "The generalized Nyquist stability criterion and multivariable root loci," *Int. J. Control*, 25, 81–127, 1977.

[42] —, "Characteristic frequency functions and characteristic gain functions," *Int. J. Control*, 26, 265–278, 1977.

[43] A. G. J. MacFarlane and N. Karcanias, "Relationships between state-space and frequency-response concepts," *Proc. Seventh IFAC World Congress*, Preprints, 3, 1771–1779, 1978.

[44] A. G. J. MacFarlane, B. Kouvaritakis, and J. M. Edmunds, "Complex variable methods for multivariable feedback systems analysis and design," *Alternatives for Linear Multivariable Control*, National Engineering Consortium, Chicago, 189–228, 1978.

[45] M. Marcus and H. Minc, *A Survey of Matrix Theory and Matrix Inequalities*. Boston: Allyn and Bacon.

[46] D. Q. Mayne, "The design of linear multivariable systems," *Automatica*, 9, 201–207, 1973.

[47] B. McMillan, "Introduction to formal realizability theory," *Bell Syst. Tech. J.*, 31, 217–279 and 541–600, 1952.

[48] N. Munro, "Design of controllers for open-loop unstable multivariable system using inverse Nyquist array," *Proc. IEE*, 119, 1377–1382, 1972.

[49] N. Munro and A. Ibrahim, "Computer aided design and multivariable sampled-data systems," *IEE Conf. Computer Aided Control System Design*, Cambridge, 133–148, 1973.

[50] H. Nyquist, "Regeneration theory," *Bell Syst. Tech. J.*, 11, 126–147, 1932.

[51] D. H. Owens, "Dyadic approximation method for multivariable-control systems analysis with a nuclear-reactor application," *Proc. IEE.*, 120, 801–809, 1973.

[52] ——, "Multivariable-control-system design concepts in failure analysis of a class of nuclear-reactor spatial-control systems," *Proc. IEE*, 120, 119–125, 1973.
[53] ——, "Dyadic expansion for the analysis of linear multivariable systems," *Proc. IEE*, 121, 713–716, 1974.
[54] ——, "Dyadic expansion, characteristic loci and multivariable-control-systems design," *Proc. IEE*, 122, 315–320, 1975.
[55] ——, "First and second-order-like structures in linear multivariable-control-systems design," *Proc. IEE*, 122, 935–941, 1975.
[56] ——, "Feedback and multivariable systems," *IEE Control Engineering Series No. 7*. Stevenage: Peter Peregrinus, 1978.
[57] J. B. Pearson and P. W. Staats, "Robust controllers for linear regulators," *IEEE Trans. Automat. Control*, AC-19, 231–234, 1974.
[58] J. B. Pearson, R. W. Shields, and P. W. Staats, "Robust solutions to linear multivariable control problems," *IEEE Trans. Automat. Control*, AC-19, 508–517, 1974.
[59] L. Pernebo, "Algebraic control theory for linear multivariable systems," Report No. LUTFD2/TFRT-1016/1-307, Lund Institute of Technology, Lund, 1978.
[60] D. G. Retallack, "Extended root-locus technique for design of linear multivariable feedback systems," *Proc. IEE*, 117, 618–622, 1970.
[61] H. H. Rosenbrock, "Distinctive problems of process control," *Chem. Eng. Progress*, 58, 43–50, 1962.
[62] ——, "On the design of linear multivariable control systems," *Proc. Third IFAC World Cong.* London, 1A1–1A16, 1966.
[63] ——, "Design of multivariable control systems using the inverse Nyquist array," *Proc. IEE*, 116, 1929–1936, 1969.
[64] ——, "State space and multivariable theory." London: Nelson, 1970.
[65] ——, "The zeros of a system," *Int. J. Control*, 18, 297–299, 1973.
[66] ——, "Multivariable circle theorems," in *Recent Mathematical Developments in Control*, D. B. Bell, Ed. London: Academic Press, 1973.
[67] ——, *Computer-Aided Control System Design*. London: Academic Press, 1974.
[68] ——, "Correction to 'The zeros of a system'," *Int. J. Control*, 20, 525–527, 1974.
[69] H. H. Rosenbrock and N. Munro, "The inverse Nyquist array method," *Alternatives for Linear Multivariable Control*. Chicago: National Engineering Consortium, 101–137, 1978.
[70] M. G. Safanov and M. Athans, "Gain and phase margin for multiloop LQG regulators," *IEEE Trans. Automat. Control*, AC-22, 173–179, 1977.
[71] J. D. Simon and S. K. Mitter, "A theory of modal control," *Inform. Control*, 13, 316–353, 1968.
[72] W. A. Wolovich, *Linear Multivariable Systems*. New York: Springer-Verlag, 1974.
[73] W. M. Wonham, "On pole assignment in multi-input controllable linear systems," *IEEE Trans. Automat. Control*, AC-12, 660–665, 1967.
[74] ——, "On the separation theorem of stochastic control," *SIAM J. Control*, 6, 312–326, 1968.
[75] ——, *Linear Multivariable Control: A Geometric Approach*. Berlin: Springer, 1974.
[76] W. M. Wonham and J. B. Pearson, "Regulation and internal stabilization in linear multivariable systems," *SIAM J. Control*, 12, 5–18, 1974.
[77] D. C. Youla, H. A. Jabr, and J. J. Bongiorno, Jr., "Modern Wiener–Hopf design of optimal controllers—Part II: The multivariable case," *IEEE Trans. Automat. Control*, AC-21, 319–338, 1976.
[78] A. S. Boksenbom and R. Hood, "General algebraic method applied to control analysis of complex engine types," National Advisory Committee for Aeronautics, Report NCA-TR-980, Washington, DC, 1949.

Design of multivariable control systems using the inverse Nyquist array

Prof. H. H. Rosenbrock, D.Sc., C.Eng., M.I.Chem.E., F.I.E.E.

Abstract

The inverse Nyquist array is a set of diagrams corresponding to the elements of the inverse of the open-loop transfer function of a control system. A number of theorems are proved which show how this array can be used to investigate the stability of multivariable control systems. The application of the array to the design of such systems is illustrated.

1 Introduction

Though increasing attention is being given to the design of multivariable systems, this has been a relatively neglected subject. Many methods have been suggested, and a survey is being compiled by MacFarlane.[1] Most of them, however, suffer from three defects.

First, if they are specialised to single-loop systems, they are generally less useful than the traditional methods. Secondly, they usually make it difficult to include engineering constraints such as a restriction on the phase advance produced by the controller. Thirdly, they tend to produce complicated control schemes where simpler schemes would be equally satisfactory.

For these reasons, there is room for alternative methods such as the one presented here. It allows engineering constraints to be imposed, and in the single-loop case reduces to the traditional methods. Its scope has yet to be determined, but in examples it gives rise to simple and satisfactory control systems. Work is actively proceeding to develop the method further.

2 Inverse Nyquist array

The system which will be considered first is shown in Fig. 1: a more general system is suggested in Section 4. The

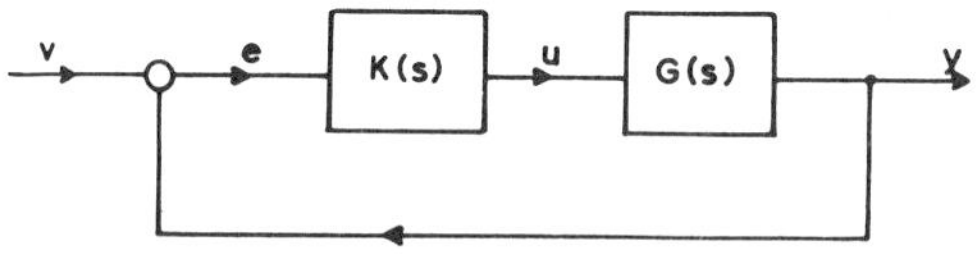

Fig. 1
Multivariable control system
Vectors v, e, u and y all have m components

plant has the $m \times m$ transfer function matrix $G(s)$, and the controller is represented by an $m \times m$ matrix $K(s)$. The object is to find a suitable matrix $K(s)$ which will ensure that the closed-loop system meets certain performance specifications.

It will be assumed that the elements of $G(s)$ and $K(s)$ are rational polynomial functions of s, and that neither $|G(s)|$ nor $|K(s)|$ is identically zero. It will also be assumed that all the zeros of $|K(s)|$ are in the open left halfplane; it has previously been shown[2] that right halfplane zeros in $|G(s)K(s)|$ give rise to control difficulties, so that there will be no incentive to introduce them in $|K(s)|$. Finally, it is assumed that the plant from which $G(s)$ arises is asymptotically stable before control is applied, and that $K(s)$ has all its poles in the open left halfplane. These assumptions are valid in many situations of practical interest.

Paper 5955 C, first received 21st March and in revised form 1st July 1969
Prof. Rosenbrock is Professor of Control Engineering at the University of Manchester Institute of Science & Technology, PO Box 88, Sackville Street, Manchester M60 1QD, England

The open-loop transfer function is

$$Q(s) = G(s)K(s) \quad \ldots \ldots \quad (1)$$

A notation for the elements of the inverse matrices G^{-1}, K^{-1}, Q^{-1} etc. will be required; these matrices will be written

$$G^{-1} = \hat{G} \quad K^{-1} = \hat{K} \quad Q^{-1} = \hat{Q} \text{ etc.} \quad \ldots \quad (2)$$

The elements of the matrices will be represented, in the usual way, by q_{ij}, $\hat{q}_{ij}$ etc. The cofactor of q_{ij} will be denoted by Q_{ij}, and similarly for the other matrices. Notice that

$$\hat{q}_{ij} = Q_{ji}/|Q| \quad \ldots \ldots \quad (3)$$

$$\neq q_{ij}^{-1} \quad \ldots \ldots \quad (4)$$

in general. From Fig. 1,

$$y = GKe = Q(v - y) \quad \ldots \ldots \quad (5)$$

so that the closed-loop transfer function which relates $y(s)$ to $v(s)$ is

$$H = (I_m + Q)^{-1}Q \quad \ldots \ldots \quad (6)$$

and $$H^{-1} = \hat{H} = I_m + \hat{Q} \quad \ldots \ldots \quad (7)$$

For the purposes of design a more general result than eqn. 7 is desirable. Let only p of the feedback loops from y be closed, and let F be a matrix having all its entries zero except for unit entries on the principal diagonal corresponding to those loops which are closed. For example if $m = 3$, $p = 2$ and the first and third loops are closed,

$$F = \begin{bmatrix} 1 & 0 & 0 \\ 0 & 0 & 0 \\ 0 & 0 & 1 \end{bmatrix} \quad \ldots \ldots \quad (8)$$

Then from Fig. 1,

$$y = GKe = Q(v - Fy) \quad \ldots \ldots \quad (9)$$

Reprinted with permission from *Proc. Inst. Elec. Eng.*, vol. 116, pp. 1929–1936, Nov. 1969.

so that the transfer function relating $y(s)$ to $v(s)$ becomes

$$R = (I_m + QF)^{-1}Q \quad . \quad . \quad . \quad . \quad . \quad . \quad . \quad . \quad (10)$$

and $$R^{-1} = \hat{R} = F + \hat{Q} \quad . \quad . \quad . \quad . \quad . \quad . \quad . \quad . \quad . \quad (11)$$

When $F = 0$, $\hat{R} = \hat{Q}$, while $F = I_m$, $\hat{R} = \hat{H}$.

The inverse Nyquist array (I.N.A.) is the set of m^2 diagrams representing the elements $\hat{q}_{ij}(j\omega)$ of $\hat{Q}(j\omega)$. The I.N.A. allows the elements of $\hat{R}(j\omega)$ to be obtained in an elementary way, because $\hat{r}_{ij} = \hat{q}_{ij}$ when $i \neq j$, $\hat{r}_{ii} = \hat{q}_{ii}$ if the ith loop is open and $\hat{r}_{jj} = 1 + \hat{q}_{jj}$ if the jth loop is closed. In the last case, all that is needed is to shift the origin in the diagram for $\hat{q}_{jj}$ to the point $(-1, 0)$, when the new diagram represents $\hat{r}_{jj}$.

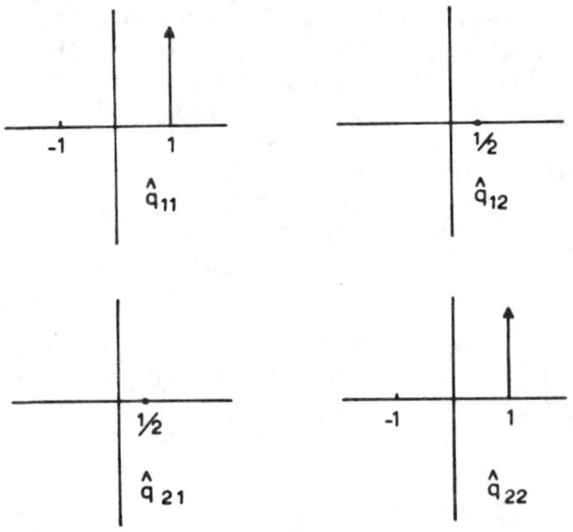

Fig. 2
Inverse Nyquist array corresponding to eqn. 13

As an example, let

$$G(s) = \begin{bmatrix} \dfrac{4(1+s)}{(1+2s)(3+2s)} & \dfrac{-2}{(1+2s)(3+2s)} \\ \dfrac{-2}{(1+2s)(3+2s)} & \dfrac{4(1+s)}{(1+2s)(3+2s)} \end{bmatrix} \quad (12)$$

which can arise from a second-order system, and let $K = I_2$. Then

$$\hat{Q}(s) = \begin{bmatrix} 1+s & \frac{1}{2} \\ \frac{1}{2} & 1+s \end{bmatrix} \quad . \quad . \quad . \quad . \quad . \quad . \quad . \quad (13)$$

and the I.N.A. is shown in Fig. 2.

2.1 Structure of controller

Since the objective is to design a suitable controller $K(s)$, it is desirable to know what structure is adequate to describe a general $K(s)$. It will be assumed that $K(s)$ is a rational polynomial matrix, with all its poles in the open left halfplane, and that $|K(s)| \neq 0$ and has all its zeros in the open left halfplane. It is shown, in theorem 1 of Appendix 7, that any such $K(s)$ can be written as a product

$$K(s) = K_a K_b(s) K_c(s) \quad . \quad . \quad . \quad . \quad . \quad . \quad . \quad . \quad . \quad (14)$$

where the three matrices K_a, $K_b(s)$ and $K_c(s)$ have the following properties:

(*a*) The matrix K_a is a permutation matrix. It therefore represents a preliminary renumbering of the inputs to G, which usually will be done so that the new input i affects chiefly the output i. The inverse $\hat{K}_a$ of K_a is another permutation matrix.

(*b*) The matrix $K_b(s)$ has determinant $|K_b(s)| = 1$ and represents a sequence of elementary column operations. Each such operation consists of adding, to column j of the matrix Q operated on, a multiple of $\alpha_{ij}(s)$ by column i. Here α_{ij} is a rational polynomial function having as its denominator either 1 or a polynomial with all its zeros in the open left halfplane. The inverse $\hat{K}_b$ of K_b can be expressed as a corresponding sequence of row operations. For example when $m = 3$ the matrix

$$K_{b1} = \begin{bmatrix} 1 & 0 & 1/(1+s) \\ 0 & 1 & 0 \\ 0 & 0 & 1 \end{bmatrix} \quad . \quad . \quad . \quad . \quad . \quad . \quad (15)$$

represents the addition of $1/(1+s)$ times column 1 of Q to column 3 of Q. Its inverse is

$$\hat{K}_{b1} = \begin{bmatrix} 1 & 0 & -1/(1+s) \\ 0 & 1 & 0 \\ 0 & 0 & 1 \end{bmatrix} \quad . \quad . \quad . \quad . \quad . \quad (16)$$

which represents the subtraction, from row 1 of $\hat{Q}$, of $1/(1+s)$ times row 3 of $\hat{Q}$.

(*c*) The matrix $K_c(s)$ is diagonal, and its nonzero entries have all their poles and zeros in the open left halfplane. If K_c is written

$$K_c(s) = \mathrm{diag}\{k_i(s)\} \quad . \quad . \quad . \quad . \quad . \quad . \quad . \quad . \quad . \quad (17)$$

the inverse $\hat{K}_c$ is

$$\hat{K}_c(s) = \mathrm{diag}\{\hat{k}_i(s)\} \quad . \quad . \quad . \quad . \quad . \quad . \quad . \quad . \quad (18)$$

where $\hat{k}_i(s) = k_i^{-1}(s)$ and has all its poles and zeros in the open left halfplane. Note that if $|k_i(s_0)|$ is large for some s_0, then $|\hat{k}_i(s_0)|$ is small.

The structure which corresponds to eqn. 14 is illustrated for $m = 3$ in Fig. 3. The matrix $K_b(s)$ accomplishes a modification of the interaction in the plant, while $K_c(s)$ represents m independent controllers. The m loops which contain the $k_i(s)$ will be called the m principal loops. The importance of the decomposition of K into K_a, K_b and K_c is that the successive application of K_a, K_b and K_c is sufficient to generate the most general K satisfying the conditions on K stated above. This is not immediately obvious; e.g., if

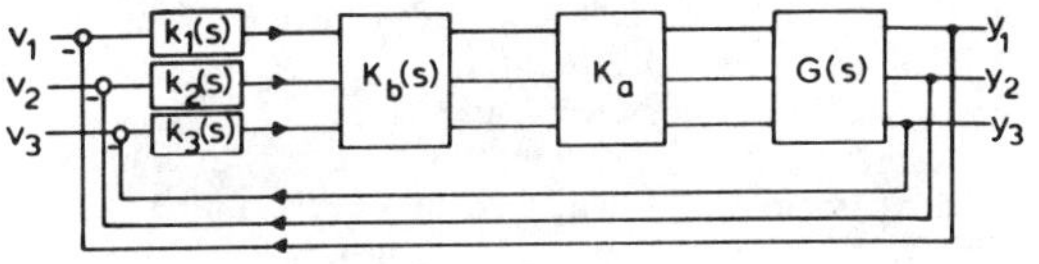

Fig. 3
Structure of multivariable control system resulting from eqn. 14

$$K(s) = \begin{bmatrix} \dfrac{(1-s)}{(1+s)^2} & \dfrac{-s}{1+s} \\ \dfrac{1}{1+s} & 1 \end{bmatrix} \quad . \quad . \quad . \quad . \quad . \quad . \quad (19)$$

the ordinary process of Gauss reduction[3] leads to

$$K(s) = \left\{ \begin{bmatrix} 1 & 0 \\ \dfrac{1+s}{1-s} & 1 \end{bmatrix} \begin{bmatrix} 1 & \dfrac{-s(1-s)}{1+s} \\ 0 & 1 \end{bmatrix} \right\} \begin{bmatrix} \dfrac{1-s}{(1+s)^2} & 0 \\ 0 & \dfrac{1}{1-s} \end{bmatrix} \quad . \quad . \quad . \quad . \quad (20)$$

$$= \{K_b'(s)\}K_c'(s) \quad . \quad . \quad . \quad . \quad . \quad . \quad . \quad . \quad . \quad . \quad (21)$$

but here both K_b' and K_c' have right halfplane poles. By the procedure used in the proof of theorem 1, K can be put in the alternative form

$$K(s) = \left\{ \begin{bmatrix} 1 & -1 \\ 0 & 1 \end{bmatrix} \begin{bmatrix} 1 & 0 \\ \dfrac{1+s}{2} & 1 \end{bmatrix} \begin{bmatrix} 1 & \dfrac{2}{1+s} \\ 0 & 1 \end{bmatrix} \right\} \begin{bmatrix} \dfrac{2}{(1+s)^2} & 0 \\ 0 & \frac{1}{2} \end{bmatrix} \quad . \quad . \quad . \quad . \quad (22)$$

There is, of course, no need to generate K in the form shown in eqn. 14 if some other form commends itself. For example it may be profitable to make the real part of Q diagonal at some particular frequency ω_0, which can be done by a matrix

$$K = \{\mathrm{Re}\, Q(j\omega_0)\}^{-1} \quad . \quad . \quad . \quad . \quad . \quad . \quad . \quad . \quad . \quad (23)$$

if this exists. No matter how K is generated, however, it can be put in the form of eqn. 14 provided that K satisfies the initial assumptions. Subject to these assumptions, therefore, there is no loss of generality in obtaining K by successive choice of K_a, K_b and K_c.

The aim of the method to be presented is to find such K_a and $K_b(s)$ that the final stage, of finding $K_c(s)$, can be done by the single-loop theory. If $|G(s)|$ has all its zeros in the open left halfplane, theorem 2 shows that K_a and $K_b(s)$ can be found so that $G(s)K_aK_b(s)$ is diagonal. This has been proposed[4] as a possible design method, but it has two defects.

First, it often leads to relatively complicated controllers. Secondly, when $|G(s)|$ has a zero in the right halfplane, it is shown in theorem 3 that generally no K_a and $K_b(s)$ exist (subject to the conditions imposed earlier) which will make $G(s)K_aK_b(s)$ diagonal; if $K_e(s)$ is such that $G(s)K_e(s)$ is diagonal, theorem 4 shows that in general $|K_e(s)|$ has a zero in the right halfplane. This is known[2] to be undesirable. This second difficulty can be avoided by asking only that $G(s)K_aK_b(s)$ should be triangular, when the single-loop theory can again be used. The first difficulty, that of unnecessary complication, persists. We therefore wish to find a less severe preliminary transformation [represented by K_a and $K_b(s)$] which still allows the single-loop theory to be applied.

The procedure for generating K_a and $K_b(s)$ will be developed in terms of the inverse matrices $\hat{K}_a$ and $\hat{K}_b(s)$. These have a simple interpretation in terms of their effect on the I.N.A. The final stage is then to design controllers $k_i(s)$ for each of the principal loops. If $\hat{Q}$ (and therefore Q) had previously been made diagonal or triangular, this final stage would also have a simple representation in the I.N.A., as the diagonal elements $\hat{q}_{ii}$ of $\hat{Q}$ would then give conventional inverse Nyquist diagrams for the m loops, and the corresponding design methods are well known. If $\hat{Q}$ is not first brought to diagonal (or triangular) form, this design procedure is not immediately available. This problem is therefore considered in Sections 2.2 and 2.3.

2.2 Loop transfer functions

When some of the principal loops are open and some are closed, the transfer function between input v_i and output y_i is

$$r_{ii}(s) = \hat{R}_{ii}(s)/|\hat{R}(s)| \quad . \quad . \quad . \quad . \quad . \quad . \quad . \quad . \quad (24)$$

The inverse Nyquist diagram for this path is obtained from

$$r_{ii}^{-1}(s) = |\hat{R}(s)|/\hat{R}_{ii}(s) \quad . \quad . \quad . \quad . \quad . \quad . \quad . \quad . \quad (25)$$

which can be expanded to give

$$r_{ii}^{-1}(s) = \hat{r}_{ii}(s) + \sum_{\substack{j=1 \\ j \neq i}}^{m} \hat{r}_{ij}(s)\hat{R}_{ij}(s)/\hat{R}_{ii}(s) \quad . \quad . \quad . \quad (26)$$

or alternatively

$$r_{ii}^{-1}(s) = \hat{r}_{ii}(s) + \sum_{\substack{j=1 \\ j \neq i}}^{m} \hat{r}_{ji}(s)\hat{R}_{ji}(s)/\hat{R}_{ii}(s) \quad . \quad . \quad . \quad (27)$$

Eqns. 26 and 27 are valid whether the ith principal loop is open or closed.

If $\hat{R}$ is diagonal, eqns. 26 and 27 show, as expected, that $r_{ii}^{-1} = \hat{r}_{ii}$. The same is true when $\hat{R}$ is triangular. In both cases, as is otherwise evident, the diagrams on the principal diagonal of the I.N.A. can be used as conventional inverse Nyquist diagrams to design the controllers in the principal loops. In the general case, eqns. 26 and 27 can be used to compute the correction to $\hat{r}_{ii}$ which gives r_{ii}^{-1}. This will entail the use of a computer, and will usually not permit much insight into the nature of the $\hat{K}_a$ and $\hat{K}_b$ which will bring the system to the desired form.

On the other hand, if the sum in eqns. 26 or 27 is sufficiently small, we shall expect to be able to work with $\hat{r}_{ii}$ alone as an approximation to r_{ii}^{-1}. Section 2.3 gives a result of this type. With its aid, the system can first be modified until the sum in eqns. 26 or 27 is small enough to be safely neglected. Then the design can be carried on using the $\hat{r}_{ii}$ as though they were inverse Nyquist diagrams for separate loops. The remaining effect of interaction can be found if desired from eqns. 26 or 27, or we may revert to simulation to finalise the design. It should be noted[2] that, at any frequency ω_0, a high enough gain in all other loops except the ith will make the sum in eqns. 26 or 27 negligible.

2.3 A multivariable stability theorem

Let S_0 be the open-loop system consisting of a controller with transfer-function matrix $K(s)$ cascaded with the given plant. Because the plant is asymptotically stable and $K(s)$ has all its poles in the open left halfplane we may assume that S_0 is asymptotically stable. Let S_c be the closed-loop system which results from feedback according to eqn. 9. Define

$$d_i(s) = \sum_{\substack{j=1 \\ j \neq i}}^{m} |\hat{q}_{ij}(s)| \quad . \quad . \quad . \quad . \quad . \quad . \quad . \quad . \quad . \quad (28)$$

and let D be a contour in the complex plane consisting of the imaginary axis from $-j\alpha$ to $+j\alpha$ and a semicircle of radius α in the right halfplane. Here α is sufficiently large to ensure that all finite poles and zeros of the functions of interest ($|Q|$, $|R|$, q_{ij}, $\hat{q}_{ij}$, r_{ij}, $\hat{r}_{ij}$) lying in the open right halfplane are inside D, and all such poles and zeros on the imaginary axis lie on D.

From theorem 6 of Appendix 7, the following sufficient condition for the asymptotic stability of S_c is immediately deduced. Suppose that $\hat{q}_{ii}(s)$ maps D into $\hat{\Gamma}_{0i}$; i.e. $\hat{\Gamma}_{0i}$ is the inverse Nyquist diagram (completed in the usual way) obtained from $\hat{q}_{ii}(s)$. S_c is asymptotically stable if the three following conditions are fulfilled:

(*a*) For each loop j which is closed in S_c, $\hat{\Gamma}_{0j}$ encircles the point $(-1, 0)$ the same number of times (in the same direction) as it encircles the origin.

(*b*) For $i = 1, 2, \ldots, m$ and for all s on D,

$$|\hat{q}_{ii}(a)| - d_i(s) \geqslant \epsilon > 0 \quad . \quad . \quad . \quad . \quad . \quad . \quad (29)$$

(*c*) For each loop j which is closed in S_c and for all s on D,

$$|\hat{r}_{jj}(s)| - d_j(s) \geqslant \epsilon > 0 \quad . \quad . \quad . \quad . \quad . \quad . \quad (30)$$

The first of these conditions resembles the usual Nyquist criterion for a single loop around a plant with transfer function $\hat{q}_{jj}^{-1}$. The remaining conditions ensure that the interactions are sufficiently small to allow stability to be deduced from the diagonal elements $\hat{q}_{jj}$ alone. As the criterion is sufficient but not necessary, instability cannot be inferred from the failure of the conditions. In conditions (*b*) and (*c*) d_i can be replaced throughout by

$$\delta_i = \sum_{\substack{j=1 \\ j \neq i}}^{m} |\hat{q}_{ji}(s)| \quad . \quad . \quad . \quad . \quad . \quad . \quad . \quad . \quad . \quad . \quad (31)$$

3 Examples

The design procedures to which the I.N.A. lends itself will now be illustrated by two examples. The first is the system having a transfer-function matrix G given by eqn. 12. The I.N.A. is shown for $k_1 = k_2 = 1$ in Fig. 2, and it is easily verified that conditions (*a*), (*b*) and (*c*) of Section 2.3 are already fulfilled for any $k_1 \geqslant 0$ and $k_2 \geqslant 0$. Arbitrarily high gains k_1 and k_2 can therefore be applied in each of the two principal loops without instability.

The effect of applying a gain k_1 is to multiply $\hat{q}_{11}$ and $\hat{q}_{12}$ by $\hat{k}_1 = k_1^{-1}$, and similarly for k_2. Consequently, as k_1 and k_2 are increased, the system becomes more and more nearly noninteracting. Eqn. 26 shows that the transfer function seen between input v_1 and output y_1, when the second loop is closed with gain k_2 and the first is open, is

$$r_{11}^{-1}(s) = \hat{q}_{11}(s) - \frac{\hat{k}_2\hat{q}_{12}(s)\hat{q}_{21}(s)}{1 + \hat{k}_2\hat{q}_{22}(s)} \quad . \quad . \quad . \quad . \quad . \quad (32)$$

so that

$$r_{11}^{-1}(j\omega) = 1 + j\omega - \frac{1}{4(k_2 + 1 + j\omega)} \quad . \quad . \quad . \quad (33)$$

When k_2 becomes large, this is approximately $1 + j\omega$, which is $\hat{q}_{11}(j\omega)$. A similar result holds for the second loop when it is open and the first loop is closed with k_1 large. In other words, no attempt need be made to reduce the interaction by elementary row operations on the I.N.A.; large gains k_1 and k_2 can be used without instability; and when high gains are used the system behaves effectively as though it were noninteracting, with each loop having transfer function $1/(1 + s)$.

This example is exceptional because there is no difficulty in exerting control. Nevertheless, it illustrates the ability of the I.N.A. to suggest simple control schemes. Current alternative methods for designing multivariable controllers are the use of a state observer and either modal analysis[5] or optimal-control theory.[6] Those methods would give a simple answer for this example, but it would be easy to devise systems of higher order, having similar $G(j\omega)$, for which the I.N.A. would suggest the same control scheme whereas the alternatives would suggest much more complicated schemes.

The second example is

$$G(s) = \begin{bmatrix} \dfrac{1-s}{(1+s)^2} & \dfrac{2-s}{(1+s)^2} \\ \dfrac{1-3s}{3(1+s)^2} & \dfrac{1-s}{(1+s)^2} \end{bmatrix} \quad . \quad . \quad . \quad . \quad (34)$$

which has been considered previously.[2] The inverse of G is

$$\hat{G}(s) = (1+s)\begin{bmatrix} 3(1-s) & -3(2-s) \\ -(1-3s) & 3(1-s) \end{bmatrix} \quad . \quad . \quad (35)$$

from which the I.N.A. shown in Fig. 4 is obtained.

An obvious first step in the design procedure is to bring

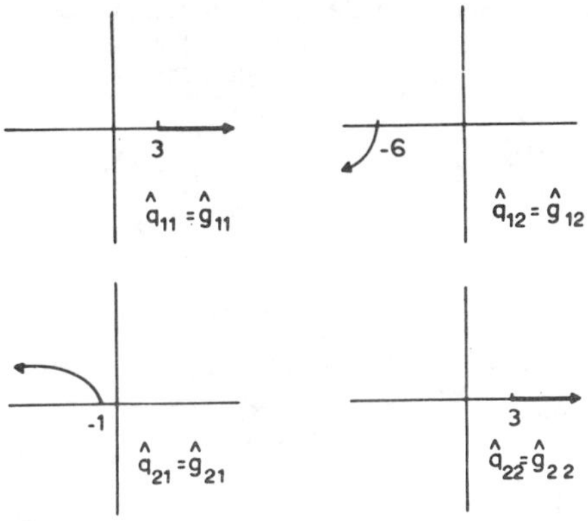

Fig. 4
Inverse Nyquist array for eqn. 35

$\hat{Q}(0)$ to diagonal form by premultiplying $\hat{G}(s)$ by the constant matrix $\hat{G}^{-1}(0) = G(0)$, which is nonsingular. [If $G(0)$ were singular, this would indicate that the inputs were badly chosen for the given outputs, since it would then be impossible to find inputs which would achieve arbitrarily chosen steady-state outputs.] The result is

$$\hat{Q}(s) = (1+s)\begin{bmatrix} 1 & 2 \\ 1/3 & 1 \end{bmatrix}\begin{bmatrix} 3(1-s) & -3(2-s) \\ -(1-3s) & 3(1-s) \end{bmatrix} \quad . \quad (16)$$

$$= (1+s)\begin{bmatrix} 1+3s & -3s \\ 2s & 1-2s \end{bmatrix} \quad . \quad . \quad . \quad . \quad (37)$$

from which the I.N.A. of Fig. 5 is obtained. This shows that

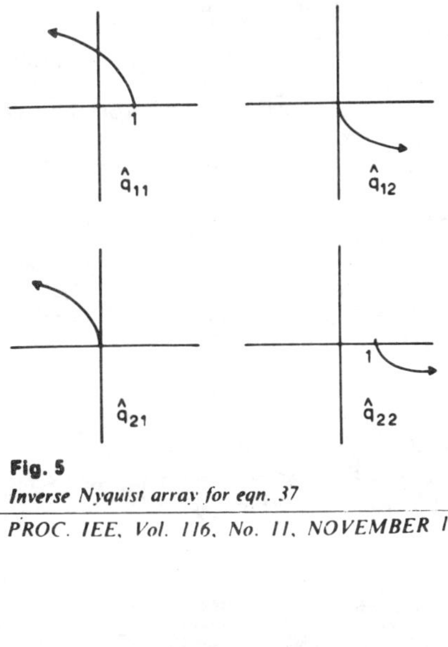

Fig. 5
Inverse Nyquist array for eqn. 37

$\hat{q}_{11}$ satisfies condition (*a*) of Section 2.3 for all $k_1 \geqslant 0$. Moreover, the d_1 calculated from eqn. 28 shows that conditions (*b*) and (*c*) will be fulfilled, so far as the first principal loop is concerned, for $k_1 \geqslant 0$.

On the other hand, $\hat{q}_{22}$ has a zero at $s = \frac{1}{2}$, and so at the point $(\alpha, 0)$ on D,

$$\left|\frac{\hat{q}_{22}(s)}{1+s}\right| = |1 - 2\alpha| = 2\alpha - 1 < 2\alpha = \left|\frac{\hat{q}_{21}(s)}{1+s}\right| \quad (38)$$

showing that condition (*b*) is not fulfilled for the second loop. To correct this, we may subtract a multiple of row 1 from row 2. To achieve the desired effect, the multiplier must exceed $\frac{2}{3}$, but must not exceed 1. Accordingly we choose $\frac{5}{6}$, giving a new $\hat{Q}$:

$$\hat{Q}(s) = (1+s)\begin{bmatrix} 1 & 0 \\ -\frac{5}{6} & 1 \end{bmatrix}\begin{bmatrix} 1+3s & -3s \\ 2s & 1-2s \end{bmatrix} \quad . \quad (39)$$

$$= (1+s)\begin{bmatrix} 1+3s & -3s \\ -\frac{5}{6}-\frac{1}{2}s & 1+\frac{1}{2}s \end{bmatrix} \quad . \quad . \quad . \quad . \quad (40)$$

The I.N.A. is shown in Fig. 6, and it follows from Section 2.3

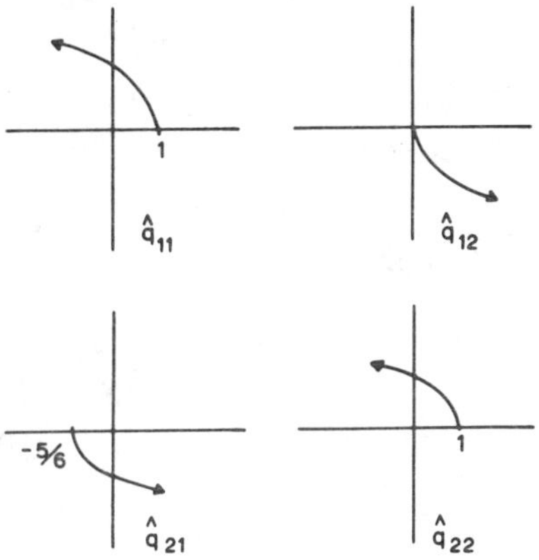

Fig. 6
Inverse Nyquist array for eqn. 40

that the closed-loop system is stable for all $k_1 \geqslant 0$ and $k_2 \geqslant 0$.

As k_1 and k_2 are increased, the system now approximates over an increasingly wide frequency band to a diagonal system. At high enough frequencies interaction remains important, and eqn. 26 gives, with the first loop open,

$$r_{11}{}^1(s) = (1+s)(1+3s) - \frac{3s(1+s)^2(\frac{5}{6}+\frac{1}{2}s)}{k_2 + (1+s)(1+\frac{1}{2}s)} \quad . \quad (41)$$

and with the second loop open,

$$r_{22}{}^1(s) = (1+s)(1+\frac{1}{2}s) - \frac{3s(1+s)^2(\frac{5}{6}+\frac{1}{2}s)}{k_1 + (1+s)(1+3s)} \quad . \quad (42)$$

The design may therefore proceed on this basis, and compensating networks may be used if desired in the two loops to improve their response. The importance of the stability theorem of Section 2.3 in permitting us to proceed in this way will be clear. In a previously suggested method,[2] resembling this in some respects, the assurance of stability was absent.

The final matrix $\hat{K}$ is

$$\hat{K} = \begin{bmatrix} 1 & 0 \\ -\frac{5}{6} & 1 \end{bmatrix}\begin{bmatrix} 1 & 2 \\ \frac{1}{3} & 1 \end{bmatrix} = \begin{bmatrix} 1 & 2 \\ -\frac{1}{2} & -\frac{2}{3} \end{bmatrix} \quad . \quad . \quad . \quad (43)$$

from which

$$K = \begin{bmatrix} -2 & 6 \\ \frac{3}{2} & 3 \end{bmatrix} \quad . \quad . \quad . \quad . \quad . \quad . \quad . \quad . \quad . \quad (44)$$

$$Q(s) = G(s)K = \frac{1}{(1+s)^2}\begin{bmatrix} 1+\frac{1}{2}s & 3s \\ \frac{5}{6}+\frac{1}{2}s & 1+3s \end{bmatrix} \quad . \quad (45)$$

and (with a slight rearrangement) the system appears as in Fig. 7. This system was simulated on an analogue computer.

and the step responses for $k_1 = 50$ and $k_2 = 50$ are shown in Fig. 8.

An interesting point arises from the above procedure. If

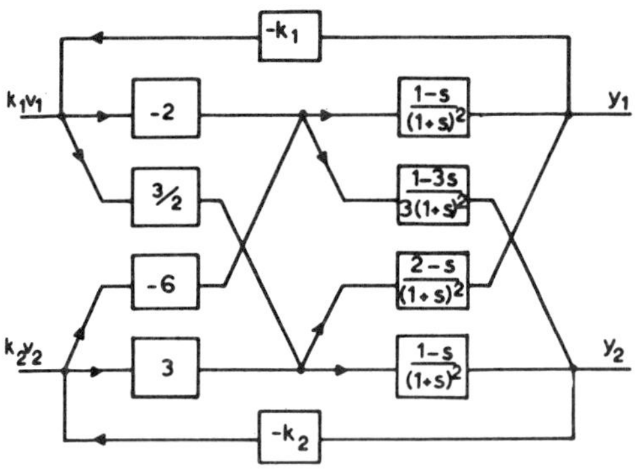

Fig. 7
System corresponding to eqn. 45 as simulated

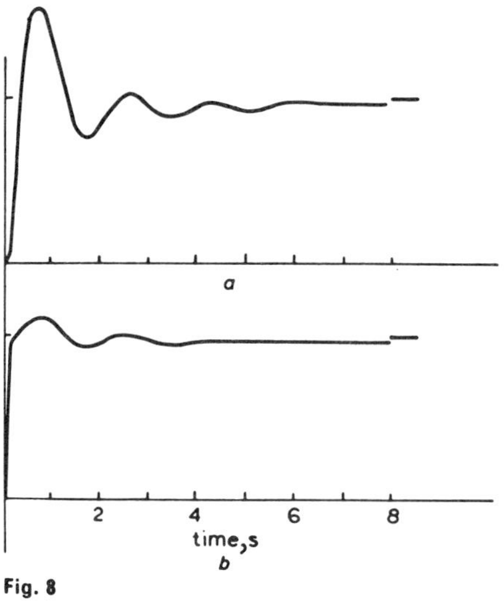

Fig. 8
Closed-loop responses of system in Fig. 7 with $k_1 = k_2 = 50$
a y_1 for unit step in v_1
b y_2 for unit step in v_2

the multiplier in eqn. 39 is reduced from $\frac{5}{6}$ towards $\frac{2}{3}$, the second time constant occurring in $\hat{q}_{22}{}^1$ is reduced, becoming zero when the multiplier is $\frac{2}{3}$. The temptation to exploit this should probably be resisted, because it clearly makes the system more sensitive to variations in the form of G. Moreover, the response of the system can always be improved by the use of compensating networks in the two principal loops. Such considerations are easily incorporated in the present method.

This second example is not a trivial one. The original system, eqn. 34, allows four different single control loops to be set up. All of these have nonminimum phase, and they all present considerably more difficulty than either of the two loops in Fig. 7. Attempts to set up two loops simultaneously around the original system are equally unpromising. Yet only a matrix of constant interconnections is needed, as in Fig. 7, to allow two simultaneous loops of relatively good, and easily improved, performance. The method described allows this matrix to be obtained by a systematic procedure, which can take account of engineering constraints.

4 Generalisations and further work

So far it has been assumed that the control action will be exerted by the controller K preceding the plant. It has been pointed out elsewhere[2] that there is sometimes an advantage in using the more general system illustrated in Fig. 9. This is particularly true when $|G(s)|$ has right half-plane zeros, because the more general system may confine the resulting difficulties to fewer loops.

There are two contexts in which Fig. 9 may apply. In many

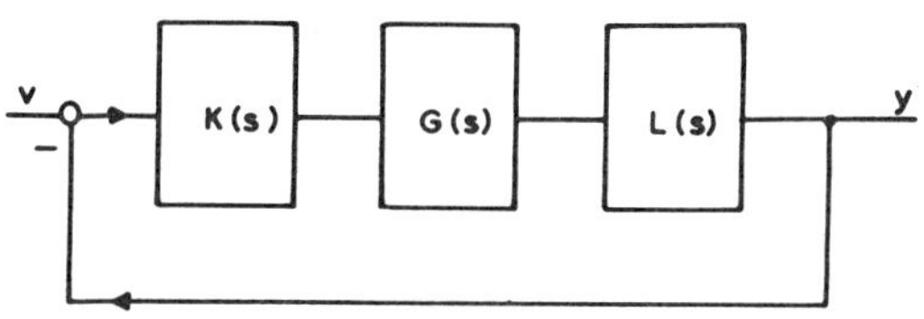

Fig. 9
More general multivariable control scheme

industrial regulator problems, the matrix L may actually be implemented; it will then most probably be restricted to be independent of s. For example, if two temperatures are to be controlled, it may be equally satisfactory to implement a scheme which controls the sum and the difference of the two temperatures. This may allow better control than a scheme in which the two temperatures are themselves treated as the controlled variables.

The matrix L may also be useful as a conceptual device, even when it is not implemented physically. The transformation of Fig. 10 shows that the dynamic behaviour of the

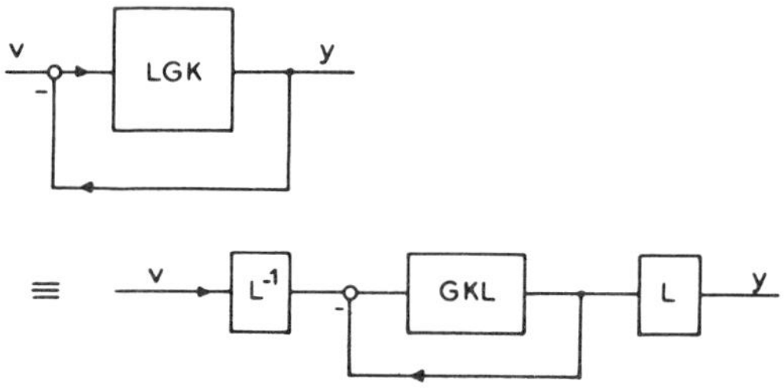

Fig. 10
Illustrating the matrix identity

multivariable closed-loop system can be analysed in terms of LGK, even when the system which is implemented uses GKL. Suppose, for example, that in the previous illustration the difference $(\theta_1 - \theta_2)$ between the two temperatures could be well controlled, while $\theta_1 + \theta_2$ could only be poorly controlled. Then both θ_1 and θ_2 will in general contain some component of $\theta_1 + \theta_2$, and so will show poor response. However, if the system is designed with K alone, θ_1, θ_2 and also $\theta_1 - \theta_2$ might all show poor response. Then the component of any disturbance affecting $\theta_1 - \theta_2$ would be less well controlled than before. By designing in terms of LGK, and implementing GKL, this possibility may be avoided.

It seems possible that the method illustrated by the examples in Section 3 may allow the describing function to be applied to multivariable systems. It may also be possible to adapt root-locus techniques as an alternative to the inverse Nyquist array. These are subjects for further study.

In the simple examples treated in Section 3, the modification of $\hat{Q}$ was carried out algebraically. If $G(j\omega)$ is obtained by measurement, it will be necessary to compute $\hat{Q}(j\omega)$ numerically, frequency by frequency. This may also be the simplest thing to do in more complicated examples when a computer is used, even when G is given algebraically, because the manipulation of polynomials in a computer is not easy to organise.

It seems, therefore, that for practical applications it will be desirable to have computer facilities which will allow the I.N.A. to be visually displayed. The effect of any proposed operation on the I.N.A. could then be computed by the machine and displayed, allowing the designer to assess its effect. Without such facilities, the labour of implementing the method would in many cases become excessive.

5 Acknowledgments

The assistance of P. D. McMorran in simulating the system shown in Fig. 7 is acknowledged.

6 References

1 MACFARLANE, A. G. J.: 'Survey of multivariable regulator theory', University of Manchester Institute of Science & Technology report, in preparation
2 ROSENBROCK, H. H.: 'On the design of linear multivariable control systems'. Proceedings of the 3rd international IFAC congress, London, 1966
3 ROSENBROCK, H. H., and STOREY, C.: 'Mathematics of dynamical systems' (Nelson, 1969)
4 CHATTERJEE, H. K.: 'Multivariable process control'. Proceedings of the 1st international IFAC congress, Moscow, Vol. 2, 1960, pp. 132–141
5 SIMON, J. D., and MITTER, S. K.: 'A theory of modal control', *Information and Control*, 1968, 13, pp. 316–353
6 ATHANS, M., and FALB, P. L.: 'Optimal control' (McGraw-Hill, 1966), chap. 9
7 GANTMACHER, F. R.: 'The theory of matrices—Vol. 1' (Chelsea, 1959), chap. 6
8 GANTMACHER, F. R.: *ibid.*, p. 21
9 ROSENBROCK, H. H.: 'Transformation of linear constant system equations', *Proc. IEE*, 1967, 114, (4), pp. 541–544

7 Appendix

Theorem 1

Let $K(s)$ be a nonsingular rational polynomial matrix. Let all the poles of $K(s)$, and all the zeros of $|K(s)|$, lie in the open left halfplane. Then $K(s)$ can be written as a product $K_aK_b(s)K_c(s)$ where

(*a*) K_a is a permutation matrix
(*b*) $K_b(s)$ is the product of elementary column operations, each consisting of the addition of a multiple $\alpha_{ij}(s)$ of column i to column j; α_{ij} is a rational polynomial function having all its poles in the open left halfplane
(*c*) $K_c(s)$ is a nonsingular diagonal matrix. All the poles and all the zeros of the principal diagonal elements of $K_c(s)$ lie in the open left halfplane.

Proof

Let $p_i(s)$ be the least common multiple of the denominators of the ith column of $K(s)$. Clearly each $p_i(s)$ has its zeros in the open left halfplane. In the polynomial matrix $K(s)$ diag$\{_ip(s)\}$, let $D_1(s)$ be the greatest common factor of elements in the first column. Let $D_2(s)$ be the greatest common factor of all 2×2 minors formed from the first two columns. In general, let $D_i(s)$ be the greatest common factor of all $i \times i$ minors formed from the first i columns. It follows from the Laplace expansion of a determinant that $D_i(s)$ divides D_{i+1}, $i = 1, 2, \ldots, m-1$. Then because a zero of $D_m(s)$ is a zero of $|K(s)|$ or of a $p_i(s)$, it follows that each $D_i(s)$ has all its zeros in the open left halfplane.

Multiply the first column of $K(s)$ by $p_1(s)/D_1(s)$. The resulting column will have polynomial entries with no common factor. Using a known procedure,[7] the first column can therefore be reduced to the form $(a_1, 0, 0, \ldots, 0)^T$, where a_1 is a nonzero constant, by successive operations of the following types

(i) transpose two rows
(ii) add to row i a multiple by $\alpha_{ij}(s)$ of row j, where $\alpha_{ij}(s)$ is a polynomial in s.

These operations do not change the greatest common factor $D_2(s)$ of 2×2 minors formed from the first two columns. It follows that if the second column is multiplied by $p_2(s)$ the elements in positions (2, 2), (3, 2), ..., (m, 2) are then polynomials with highest common factor $D_2(s)/D_1(s)$. Divide the resulting second column by $D_2(s)/D_1(s)$ to give $m-1$ polynomial elements with no common factor other than 1. As before, reduce this $(m-1)$-vector to the form $(a_2, 0, 0, \ldots, 0)^T$ by row operations of the two types applied to the last $m-1$ rows. The element in position (1, 2) is a rational polynomial function. Add a suitable multiple of row 2 to row 1 to reduce the element (1, 2) to zero. This does not affect the element (1, 1), so that the matrix now has the form

$$\left[\begin{array}{cc:c} a_1 & 0 & \\ 0 & a_2 & T_1(s) \\ \hdashline & 0 & T_2(s) \end{array}\right]$$

where T_1 is $2 \times (m-2)$, and T_2 is $(m-2) \times (m-2)$.

Proceeding in this way, the matrix can be reduced to the form diag (a_i). Write $D_0(s) = 1$, and put

$$K_c(s) = \text{diag}\left\{\frac{a_iD_i(s)}{p_i(s)D_{i-1}(s)}\right\} \quad . \quad . \quad . \quad . \quad . \quad . \quad (46)$$

The above argument shows that

$$K_d(s)K(s)K_c^{-1}(s) = I_m \quad . \quad . \quad . \quad . \quad . \quad . \quad . \quad . \quad . \quad (47)$$

where $K_d(s)$ is a matrix generated by row operations of the types

(*a*) transpose two rows
(*b*) add to row i a multiple by $\alpha_{ij}(s)$ of row j, where $\alpha_{ij}(s)$ is a rational function of s having as denominator either 1, or one of the polynomials $D_1/D_0, D_2/D_1, \ldots, D_m/D_{m-1}$.

Each of these two types of operation has an inverse which is of the same type. Moreover if K_e represents a transposition of two rows, and K_f a row operation described by (*b*) above, it is easy to see that $K_fK_e = K_eK_f'$, where K_f' is a (different) matrix of the same type as K_f. For example

$$\begin{bmatrix} 1 & 0 & \alpha_{12} \\ 0 & 1 & 0 \\ 0 & 0 & 1 \end{bmatrix}\begin{bmatrix} 0 & 0 & 1 \\ 1 & 0 & 0 \\ 0 & 1 & 0 \end{bmatrix} = \begin{bmatrix} 0 & \alpha_{12} & 1 \\ 1 & 0 & 0 \\ 0 & 1 & 0 \end{bmatrix} = \begin{bmatrix} 0 & 0 & 1 \\ 1 & 0 & 0 \\ 0 & 1 & 0 \end{bmatrix}\begin{bmatrix} 1 & 0 & 0 \\ 0 & 1 & 0 \\ 0 & \alpha_{12} & 1 \end{bmatrix} \quad . \quad . \quad . \quad (48)$$

Further, a row operation of type (*b*) above is represented by a matrix such as the last matrix in eqn. 48. When operating on the right of another matrix this represents a column operation of the type used to define $K_b(s)$. By virtue of these remarks $K_d^{-1}(s)$ can be written as a product $K_aK_b(s)$, where K_a, $K_b(s)$ have the properties stated in the theorem. Eqn. 47 then gives

$$K(s) = K_aK_b(s)K_c(s) \quad . \quad . \quad . \quad . \quad . \quad . \quad . \quad . \quad . \quad (49)$$

which completes the proof.

Theorem 2

Let $G(s)$ be a nonsingular rational polynomial matrix. Let all the poles of $G(s)$, and all the zeros of $|G(s)|$, lie in the open left halfplane. Then K_a and $K_b(s)$ can be found, defined as in theorem 1, such that $G(s)K_aK_b(s)$ is nonsingular, diagonal, and has all the poles and zeros of its principal diagonal elements in the open left halfplane.

Proof

Interchanging the roles of rows and columns in the proof of theorem 1, it follows that $G(s)$ can be written

$$G(s) = G_c(s)G_b(s)G_a \quad . \quad . \quad . \quad . \quad . \quad . \quad . \quad . \quad (50)$$

Here G_a is a permutation matrix; $G_b(s)$ represents the product of elementary row operations each consisting of the addition of a multiple of row j by $\alpha_{ij}(s)$ to row i, where α_{ij} is a rational polynomial function having all its poles in the open left halfplane; and $G_c(s)$ is nonsingular, diagonal, and with all the poles and zeros of its principal diagonal elements in the open left halfplane. The choice

$$K_a = G_a^{-1} \quad . \quad . \quad . \quad . \quad . \quad . \quad . \quad . \quad . \quad . \quad (51)$$

$$K_b(s) = G_b^{-1}(s) \quad . \quad . \quad . \quad . \quad . \quad . \quad . \quad . \quad . \quad (52)$$

gives the desired result.

Theorem 3

Let $G(s)$ satisfy the conditions in theorem 2, except that $|G(s)|$ has one or more zeros in the closed right halfplane. Then K_a and $K_b(s)$ can be found, defined as in theorem 1, such that $G(s)K_aK_b(s)$ is triangular (upper or lower as desired). In general $G(s)K_aK_b(s)$ cannot be made diagonal.

Proof

Let $p_i(s)$ be the least common multiple of the denominators of the ith row of $G(s)$. Each $p_i(s)$ has its zeros in the open left halfplane. In the polynomial matrix diag $[p_i(s)]G(s)$, let $D_i(s)$ be the greatest common factor of all $i \times i$ minors formed from the first i rows and put $D_0(s) = 1$. Let

$$D_i(s) = D_{il}(s)D_{ir}(s) \quad . \quad . \quad . \quad . \quad . \quad . \quad . \quad . \quad (53)$$

where $D_{il}(s)$ has all its zeros in the open left halfplane and $D_{ir}(s)$ has all its zeros in the closed right halfplane. It follows, from the Laplace expansion of a determinant, that $D_{il}(s)$ [resp. $D_{ir}(s)$] divides $D_{i+1,l}(s)$ [resp. $D_{i+1,r}(s)$], $i = 1, 2, \ldots, m-1$.

Multiply the first row of $G(s)$ by $p_1(s)$. The resulting row has polynomial entries with greatest common factor $D_1(s)$. Using a known procedure,[7] the first row can therefore be brought to the form $\{a_1D_1(s), 0, 0, \ldots, 0\}$, where a_1 is a nonzero constant, by successive operations of the types

(*a*) transpose two columns
(*b*) add to column j a multiple by $\alpha_{ij}(s)$ of column i, where $\alpha_{ij}(s)$ is a polynomial in s.

These operations do not change the greatest common factor $D_2(s)$ of the 2×2 minors formed from the first two rows. Multiply the second row by $p_2(s)$. The elements in positions (2, 2), (2, 3), ..., (2, m) are then divisible by $D_2(s)/D_1(s)$. By operations of the two types described above the last $m-1$ elements in the second row can be brought to the form $\{a_2D_2(s)/D_1(s), 0, 0, \ldots, 0\}$. Now

$$\frac{D_2(s)}{D_1(s)} = \frac{D_{2l}(s)}{D_{1l}(s)}\frac{D_{2r}(s)}{D_{1r}(s)} \quad . \quad . \quad . \quad . \quad . \quad . \quad . \quad . \quad (54)$$

so that a multiple [by a rational polynomial expression having as denominator the polynomial $D_{2l}(s)/D_{1l}(s)$] of column 2 can be subtracted from column 1 in such a way that the degree of the elements in position (2, 1) is less than the degree of the polynomial $D_{2r}(s)/D_{1r}(s)$.

Proceeding in this way we generate a lower triangular polynomial matrix $T_1(s)$. As in the proof of theorem 1, it follows that

$$G(s) = \text{diag}\{1/p_i(s)\}T_1(s)G_b(s)G_a \quad . \quad . \quad . \quad . \quad . \quad (55)$$

where G_a is a permutation matrix; $G_b(s)$ is a product of column operations, each consisting of adding a multiple (by a rational polynomial expression having its poles, if any, in the open left halfplane) of one column to another; and $T_1(s) = [\tau_{ij}(s)]$ is a lower triangular polynomial matrix in which the degree of $\tau_{ij}(s)$ when $i > j$ is less than the degree of $D_{ir}(s)/D_{i-1,r}(s)$. Setting $K_a = G_a^{-1}$ and $K_b(s) = G_b^{-1}(s)$, it follows that

$$G(s)K_aK_b(s) = T(s) \quad . \quad . \quad . \quad . \quad . \quad . \quad . \quad . \quad (56)$$

where $T(s)$ is a lower triangular matrix. With minor changes in the proof, an upper triangular matrix can be generated.

That reduction to diagonal form is not generally possible when K_a and $K_b(s)$ are as defined in theorem 1 is shown by the example

$$G(s) = \begin{bmatrix} \dfrac{1-s}{(1+s)^2} & \dfrac{1}{1+2s} \\ 0 & \dfrac{1}{1+s} \end{bmatrix} \quad . \quad . \quad . \quad . \quad . \quad . \quad (57)$$

Attempt to find $K(s)$ such that

$$G(s)K(s) = \begin{bmatrix} \dfrac{1-s}{(1+s)^2} & \dfrac{1}{1+2s} \\ 0 & \dfrac{1}{1+s} \end{bmatrix} \begin{bmatrix} k_{11}(s) & k_{12}(s) \\ k_{21}(s) & k_{22}(s) \end{bmatrix} \quad (58)$$

is diagonal. Then it follows that $k_{21}(s) = 0$, and

$$\frac{1-s}{(1+s)^2}k_{12}(s) + \frac{1}{1+2s}k_{22}(s) = 0 \quad . \quad . \quad . \quad . \quad (59)$$

Consequently

$$|K(s)| = k_{11}(s)k_{22}(s) = -k_{11}(s)k_{12}(s)\frac{(1+2s)(1-s)}{(1+s)^2} \quad . \quad (60)$$

No choice of $k_{11}(s)$ and $k_{12}(s)$ with left halfplane poles can avoid a factor $1 - s$ in $|K(s)|$. But with the definition of theorem 1, $|K_a| = \pm 1$ and $|K_b(s)| = 1$, so that $K(s)$ cannot be represented by $K_aK_b(s)$.

Theorem 4

Let $G(s)$ be as in theorem 3. Find K_a and $K_b(s)$ as in that theorem so that eqn. 56 is true. Then $T(s)$ may be diagonal. If not, let $K_e(s)$ be any nonsingular rational polynomial matrix having all its poles in the open left halfplane and such that $G(s)K_e(s)$ is diagonal. Then $|K_e(s)|$ has at least one zero in the closed right halfplane.

Proof

Assume $T(s)$ is lower triangular. We have

$$G(s)K_aK_b(s)\{K_b^{-1}(s)K_a^{-1}K_e(s)\}$$
$$= T(s)K_f(s) = D(s) \quad . \quad . \quad . \quad (61)$$

where $D(s) = [d_{ij}(s)]$ and $K_f(s) = [\kappa_{ij}(s)]$. Hence

$$K_f(s) = T^{-1}(s)D(s) \quad . \quad . \quad . \quad . \quad . \quad . \quad . \quad . \quad (62)$$

and so $K_f(s)$ is lower triangular. It is also nonsingular, and has all its poles in the open left halfplane.

If $T(s)$ is not diagonal, there is a $t_{ii}(s)$ having a zero in the closed right halfplane, and a $t_{ij}(s) \neq 0$ with $i > j$ such that

$$t_{i,j+1}(s) = t_{i,j+2}(s) = \ldots = t_{i,i-1}(s) = 0 \quad . \quad (63)$$

Then in eqn. 61

$$0 = d_{ij}(s) = t_{ij}(s)\kappa_{jj}(s) + t_{ii}(s)\kappa_{ij}(s) \quad . \quad . \quad . \quad . \quad (64)$$

and so

$$\kappa_{jj}(s) = -\frac{\kappa_{ij}(s)t_{ii}(s)}{t_{ij}(s)} \quad . \quad . \quad . \quad . \quad . \quad . \quad . \quad . \quad (65)$$

It follows from the proof of theorem 3 that

$$t_{ii}(s) = \frac{a}{p_i(s)}\{D_{il}(s)/D_{i-1,l}(s)\}\{D_{ir}(s)/D_{i-1,r}(s)\} \quad . \quad (66)$$

and $$t_{ij}(s) = \frac{\tau_{ij}(s)}{p_i(s)} \quad . \quad . \quad . \quad . \quad . \quad . \quad . \quad . \quad . \quad (67)$$

where $\tau_{ij}(s)$ is an element of $T_1(s)$. Because the polynomial $D_{ir}(s)/D_{i-1,r}(s)$ has all its zeros in the closed right halfplane and exceeds $\tau_{ij}(s)$ in degree, it follows from eqn. 65 and the properties of $\kappa_{ij}(s)$ and the $D_{il}(s)$ that $\kappa_{jj}(s)$ has a zero in the closed right halfplane. Consequently $|K_f(s)|$ has a zero there, and by eqn. 61 and the properties of K_a and $K_b(s)$, so does $|K_e(s)|$. The proof holds, with minor changes, if $T(s)$ is upper triangular, and it is exemplified by eqn. 60.

Theorem 5

Let a system S_0 be described by a set of linear ordinary differential equations with constant coefficients, and after Laplace transformation with zero initial conditions let its equations be

$$T(s)z(s) = U(s)e(s) \quad . \quad . \quad . \quad . \quad . \quad . \quad . \quad . \quad . \quad (68)$$

$$y(s) = V(s)z(s) + W(s)e(s) \quad . \quad . \quad . \quad . \quad . \quad (69)$$

where $T(s)$, $U(s)$, $V(s)$ and $W(s)$ are polynomial matrices, respectively $r \times r$, $r \times m$, $m \times r$, and $m \times m$, let $|T(s)| \neq 0$. Let S_0 be asymptotically stable and let its transfer function matrix be $Q(s) = V(s)T^{-1}(s)U(s) + W(s)$, where $|Q(s)|$ has no zero on any finite part of the imaginary axis. Let feedback be applied to S_0 according to the equation

$$e(s) = v(s) - Fy(s) \quad . \quad . \quad . \quad . \quad . \quad . \quad . \quad . \quad . \quad (70)$$

where F is as defined in Section 2, so that the transfer function matrix of the resulting system S_c is $R(s) = \{I_m + Q(s)F\}^{-1}Q(s)$. Let D be a contour consisting of the imaginary axis from $-i\alpha$ to $+i\alpha$ and a semicircle of radius α in the right halfplane. Here α is large enough to ensure that every finite pole or zero of $|Q|$, $|R|$, q_{ij}, $\hat{q}_{ij}$, r_{ij} and $\hat{r}_{ij}$ $(i, j = 1, 2, \ldots, m)$, which is in the open right halfplane lies within D, and every finite imaginary pole or zero of these functions lies on D. Let $|Q(s)|$ (resp. $|\hat{Q}(s)|$) map D into Γ_0 (resp. $\hat{\Gamma}_0$) and let $|R(s)|$ (resp. $|\hat{R}(s)|$) map D into Γ_c (resp. $\hat{\Gamma}_c$). Then S_c is asymptotically stable if and only if $|R(s)|$ (resp. $|\hat{R}(s)|$) has no pole (resp. zero) on any finite part of the imaginary axis and Γ_c (resp. $\hat{\Gamma}_c$) encircles the origin as often in a clockwise (resp. counterclockwise) direction as Γ_0 (resp. $\hat{\Gamma}_0$).

Proof

The system of eqns. 68–70 can be written

$$\begin{bmatrix} T(s) & U(s) & 0 \\ -V(s) & W(s) & -I_m \\ 0 & I_m & F \end{bmatrix} \begin{bmatrix} -z(s) \\ e(s) \\ y(s) \end{bmatrix} = \begin{bmatrix} 0 \\ 0 \\ v(s) \end{bmatrix} \quad . \quad (71)$$

so that S_c is asymptotically stable if and only if the roots of

$$|P_c(s)| = \begin{vmatrix} T(s) & U(s) & 0 \\ -V(s) & W(s) & -I_m \\ 0 & I_m & F \end{vmatrix} = 0 \quad . \quad . \quad . \quad (72)$$

are all in the open left halfplane. Similarly, on putting $F = 0$ in eqn. 72, it follows from the known asymptotic stability of S_0 that all the roots of

$$\begin{vmatrix} T(s) & U(s) & 0 \\ -V(s) & W(s) & -I_m \\ 0 & I_m & 0 \end{vmatrix} = |T(s)| = 0 \quad . \quad . \quad . \quad (73)$$

lie in the open left halfplane.

From eqn. 71

$$\begin{bmatrix} -z(s) \\ e(s) \\ y(s) \end{bmatrix} = P_c^{-1}(s) \begin{bmatrix} 0 \\ 0 \\ v(s) \end{bmatrix} \quad . \quad . \quad . \quad . \quad . \quad . \quad . \quad (74)$$

and because

$$y(s) = R(s)v(s) \quad . \quad . \quad . \quad . \quad . \quad . \quad . \quad . \quad . \quad . \quad (75)$$

it follows that $|R(s)|$ is the minor, formed from the elements of $P_c^{-1}(s)$ in rows $r + m + 1, r + m + 2, \ldots, r + 2m$ and columns $r + m + 1, r + m + 2, \ldots, r + 2m$. By a known result,[8] this is

$$|R(s)| = \begin{vmatrix} T(s) & U(s) \\ -V(s) & W(s) \end{vmatrix} \div \begin{vmatrix} T(s) & U(s) & 0 \\ -V(s) & W(s) & -I_m \\ 0 & I_m & F \end{vmatrix} \quad (76)$$

The corresponding formula for $|Q(s)|$, which has been given previously,[9] is obtained by putting $F = 0$ in eqn. 76 and after simplification is

$$|Q(s)| = \begin{vmatrix} T(s) & U(s) \\ -V(s) & W(s) \end{vmatrix} \div |T(s)| \quad . \quad . \quad . \quad . \quad (77)$$

Let $|R(s)|$ have z_c finite zeros and p_c finite poles in the closed right halfplane, and let $|Q(s)|$ have z_0 finite zeros and p_0 finite poles there. Since $|T(s)|$ has all its zeros in the open left halfplane, it follows that $p_0 = 0$, and z_0 is the number of zeros of

$$\begin{vmatrix} T(s) & U(s) \\ -V(s) & W(s) \end{vmatrix} \quad . \quad . \quad . \quad . \quad . \quad . \quad . \quad . \quad . \quad . \quad (78)$$

in the open right halfplane. This expression has no imaginary zeros because $|Q(s)|$ has no finite imaginary zeros. Comparison of eqns. 72 and 76 now shows that S_c is asymptotically stable if and only if

$$z_c - p_c = z_0 = z_0 - p_0 \quad . \quad . \quad . \quad . \quad . \quad . \quad . \quad (79)$$

By eqn. 76, $|R(s)|$ has no finite zero on the imaginary axis. If it also has no finite pole on the imaginary axis, it follows that $z_c - p_c$ is the number of clockwise circuits of Γ_c about the origin. Also $z_0 - p_0$ is the number of clockwise circuits of Γ_0 about the origin. The system S_c is therefore asymptotically stable if and only if $|R(s)|$ has no finite pole on the imaginary axis and Γ_c, Γ_0 make the same number of clockwise circuits of the origin. The corresponding statements in terms of $|\hat{R}(s)|$, $\hat{\Gamma}_c$ and $\hat{\Gamma}_0$, follow at once.

Theorem 6

Let the contour D be as defined in theorem 5, and let the element $\hat{q}_{ii}(s)$ of $\hat{Q}(s)$ map D into $\hat{\Gamma}_{0i}$. Similarly let $\hat{r}_{ii}(s)$ map D into $\hat{\Gamma}_{ci}$. Let $\hat{\Gamma}_{0i}$ and $\hat{\Gamma}_{ci}$ encircle the origin n_{0i} times and n_{ci} times respectively (the counterclockwise direction being taken as positive). Define $d_i(s)$ [resp. $\delta_i(s)$] by

$$d_i(s) = \sum_{\substack{j=1 \\ j \neq i}}^{m} |\hat{q}_{ij}(s)| \quad . \quad . \quad . \quad . \quad . \quad . \quad . \quad . \quad . \quad . \quad (80)$$

$$\delta_i(s) = \sum_{\substack{j=1 \\ j \neq i}}^{m} |\hat{q}_{ji}(s)| \quad . \quad . \quad . \quad . \quad . \quad . \quad . \quad . \quad . \quad . \quad (81)$$

Then if S_0, S_c are as defined in theorem 5, a sufficient condition for the asymptotic stability of S_c is that the following conditions are fulfilled

(*a*) $\sum_{i=1}^{m} n_{0i} = \sum_{i=1}^{m} n_{ci}$

(*b*) For all s on D and for $i = 1, 2, \ldots, m$,

$|\hat{q}_{ii}(s)| - d_i(s) \geqslant \epsilon > 0$ {resp. $|\hat{q}_{ii}(s)| - \delta_i(s) \geqslant \epsilon > 0$}

(*c*) For all s on D and for $i = 1, 2, \ldots, m$,

$|\hat{r}_{ii}(s)| - d_i(s) \geqslant \epsilon > 0$ {resp. $|\hat{r}_{ii}(s)| - \delta_i(s) \geqslant \epsilon > 0$}

Proof

Because $\hat{q}_{ii}(s) = Q_{ii}(s)/|Q(s)|$, it follows from the properties of $Q(s)$ that $\hat{q}_{ii}(s)$ has no finite imaginary pole. Also by condition (*b*), $\hat{q}_{ii}(s)$ has no finite imaginary zero. Let $\hat{Q}(\theta, s)$ be the matrix having elements

$$\left. \begin{aligned} \hat{q}_{ii}(\theta, s) &= \hat{q}_{ii}(s) \\ \hat{q}_{ij}(\theta, s) &= \theta \hat{q}_{ij}(s), \ i \neq j \end{aligned} \right\} \quad . \quad . \quad . \quad . \quad . \quad . \quad . \quad (82)$$

where $\hat{Q}(s) = [\hat{q}_{ij}(s)]$ is the matrix defined in theorem 5, and $0 \leqslant \theta \leqslant 1$. The function $|\hat{Q}(0, s)| = \prod_{i=1}^{m} |\hat{q}_{ii}(s)|$ has no finite pole or zero on the imaginary axis; let it map D into $\hat{\Gamma}_p$. Also $|\hat{Q}(1, s)| = |Q(s)|^{-1}$ has no finite pole or zero on the imaginary axis, by the properties of $Q(s)$. It maps D into $\hat{\Gamma}_0$. If s_0 is a point on D, the function $|\hat{Q}(\theta, s_0)|$ of θ defines a continuous curve γ joining a point on $\hat{\Gamma}_p$ to a point on $\hat{\Gamma}_0$. As s_0 traces out D, starting from $s_0 = 0$, so γ sweeps out a region of the complex plane, and returns at last to its initial position.

Assume, contrary to what is to be proved, that $\hat{\Gamma}_p$ and $\hat{\Gamma}_0$ do not encircle the origin the same number of times. Then the region swept out by γ includes the origin; i.e. there is some θ and some s on D for which $|\hat{Q}(\theta, s)| = 0$. This implies that $\hat{Q}(\theta, s)$ has a zero eigenvalue, which is impossible by Gershgorin's theorem[3] and condition (*b*) of the theorem. Therefore $\hat{\Gamma}_0$ makes the same number of circuits of the origin as $\hat{\Gamma}_p$, which is $\sum_{i=1}^{m} n_{0i}$ because $\hat{Q}(0, s)$ is diagonal.

In the same way, $\hat{r}_{ii}(s)$, which is either $\hat{q}_{ii}(s)$ or $1 + \hat{q}_{ii}(s)$, has no finite pole on the imaginary axis. Also by condition (*c*), $\hat{r}_{ii}(s)$ has no finite zero on the imaginary axis. Therefore $\prod_{i=1}^{m} |\hat{r}_{ii}(s)|$ has no finite imaginary pole or zero. Further, $|\hat{R}(s)| = |F + \hat{Q}(s)|$ has no finite imaginary pole by the properties of $\hat{Q}(s)$: it has no finite imaginary zero by condition (*c*) and Gershgorin's theorem. Hence, as before, the number of circuits of the origin by $\hat{\Gamma}_c$ is $\sum_{i=1}^{m} n_{ci}$. It follows from condition (*a*) of the theorem, that $\hat{\Gamma}_0$ and $\hat{\Gamma}_c$ make the same number of circuits about the origin, and it has already been seen that $|\hat{R}(s)|$ has no finite imaginary zero. By theorem 5, S_c is therefore asymptotically stable.

A corresponding theorem with Q, R etc., in place of $\hat{Q}$, $\hat{R}$ etc., can be stated, but it seems to be less useful.

Multivariable Circle Theorems*

H. H. Rosenbrock

Control Systems Centre, University of Manchester Institute of Science and Technology, Manchester, England

1. Introduction

Let a linear, time-invariant system have the equations

$$\dot{x} = Ax + Bu$$
$$y = Cx \tag{1}$$

where x, u, y are real vectors, of dimension n, m, m respectively. We do not assume in general that this system has least order. The resulting $m \times m$ transfer function matrix is

$$G(s) = C(sI_n - A)^{-1}B \tag{2}$$

Now let feedback be applied to the system (1) according to the equation

$$u = -Fy \tag{3}$$

where

$$F = \text{diag}\,[f_i(t, y)] \tag{4}$$

and

$$0 < \alpha_i \leqslant f_i(t, y) \leqslant \beta_i, \qquad \alpha_i < \beta_i, \qquad i = 1, 2, \ldots, m \tag{5}$$

The resulting closed-loop system obeys the nonlinear time-dependent equation

$$\dot{x} = (A - BFC)\,x \tag{6}$$

We assume F to be such that this equation has a unique solution, passing through any $x(t_0) = c$, which can be extended to all times t. Our problem is to find conditions for the stability of (6).

When $m = 1$ and $F(t, y) = F(y)$, the above problem is a form of the extensively-studied Lur'e problem [1, 2], for which Popov's criterion [3, 4] and the circle theorem [4] are available: the latter permits F to depend

* This paper was presented by the editor of these proceedings.

Reprinted with permission from *Proc. IMA Conf. on Recent Mathematical Developments in Control*, Bath, 1972, D. J. Bell, Ed. London: Academic Press, 1973, pp. 345–365.

explicitly on t. When $m > 1$, no simple result corresponding to the circle criterion has previously been known. In this paper such a result will be obtained by placing further restrictions on $G(s)$.

2. Stability

We start from the following theorem, which we regard as known. It does not appear in precisely this form in the literature, but can readily be constructed from known results. The outline of a proof is given in the Appendix.

THEOREM 1. *Let* (1) *have least order, and let*

$$[\beta^{-1} + G(s)]^{-1}[\alpha^{-1} + G(s)] \tag{7}$$

$$\left[\text{resp}\,[\alpha^{-1} + G(s)][\beta^{-1} + G(s)]^{-1}\right] \tag{8}$$

$$\left[\text{resp}\,[I_m + G(s)\alpha]^{-1}[I_m + G(s)\beta]\right] \tag{9}$$

$$\left[\text{resp}\,[I_m + \beta G(s)][I_m + \alpha G(s)]^{-1}\right] \tag{10}$$

exist and be positive real [5], *where* $\alpha = \text{diag}\,(\alpha_i)$ *and* $\beta = \text{diag}\,(\beta_i)$. *Then the system* (6) *is stable in the sense of Liapunov.*

The desired results are obtained from Theorem 1 by a sequence of further theorems. Of these 2 is the key result and is believed to be new, while 3 and 4 are slightly adapted from standard results [5].

THEOREM 2. *Let* $\hat{Z}$ *be a complex* $m \times m$ *matrix, and let real constants* $\theta_i > 0$ *exist such that*

$$|\hat{z}_{ii}|\theta_i^{-1} - \sum_{j=1,\, j\neq i}^{m} |\hat{z}_{ij}|\theta_j^{-1} > 1, \qquad i = 1, 2, \ldots, m \tag{11}$$

$$\left[\text{resp}\ \theta_i^{-1}|\hat{z}_{ii}| - \sum_{j=1, j\neq i}^{m} \theta_j^{-1}|\hat{z}_{ji}| > 1, i = 1, 2, \ldots, m\right] \tag{12}$$

Then $\hat{Z}$ *has an inverse* Z *satisfying*

$$\|Z\| = \|Z^*\| < \sqrt{\left(\sum_i \theta_i^{-2}\right)} \tag{13}$$

where the norm is subordinate to the Euclidean vector norm, and the star denotes the complex conjugate transpose.

Proof. Write $\theta = \text{diag}\,(\theta_i)$, which is non-singular. The inverse of $\hat{Z}\theta^{-1}$ [resp $\theta^{-1}\hat{Z}$] exists by Gershgorin's theorem, and so therefore does the inverse of $\hat{Z}$. Because $\|Z\|^2$ is the largest eigenvalue of Z^*Z, which has the same eigenvalues as ZZ^*, it follows that $\|Z\| = \|Z^*\|$. If a is a complex m-vector we also have

$$\|Z\| = \max_a \frac{\|Za\|}{\|a\|} \tag{14}$$

where $\|Za\|$, $\|a\|$ are the Euclidean norms. Write $Za = \theta^{-1}b$, so that

$$\|Z\| = \max_b \frac{\|\theta^{-1}b\|}{\|\hat{Z}\theta^{-1}b\|} \tag{15}$$

$$= 1 \Bigg/ \left\{ \min_b \frac{\|\hat{Z}\theta^{-1}b\|}{\|\theta^{-1}b\|} \right\} \tag{16}$$

If
$$\|b\|_c = \max_i |b_i|$$

is the cubic norm of b, we have

$$\min_b \frac{\|\hat{Z}\theta^{-1}b\|}{\|\theta^{-1}b\|} = \min_b \left\{ \frac{\|\hat{Z}\theta^{-1}b\|}{\|b\|_c} \cdot \frac{\|b\|_c}{\|\theta^{-1}b\|} \right\} \tag{17}$$

$$\geqslant \left\{ \min_b \frac{\|\hat{Z}\theta^{-1}b\|}{\|b\|_c} \right\} \left\{ \min_b \frac{\|b\|_c}{\|\theta^{-1}b\|} \right\} \tag{18}$$

$$\geqslant \left\{ \min_b \frac{\|\hat{Z}\theta^{-1}b\|_c}{\|b\|_c} \right\} \Bigg/ \left\{ \max_b \frac{\|\theta^{-1}b\|}{\|b\|_c} \right\} \tag{19}$$

Here (18) follows from (17) by relaxing the constraint that b should be the same in both factors within braces in (17), and (19) uses the fact that for any complex m-vector v, the Euclidean norm $\|v\|$ and the cubic norm $\|v\|_c$ satisfy $\|v\| \geqslant \|v\|_c$.

Now we have

$$\|\hat{Z}\theta^{-1}b\|_c = \max_i \left| \sum_{j=1}^{m} \hat{z}_{ij}\theta_j^{-1}b_j \right| \tag{20}$$

$$= \max_i \left| \hat{z}_{ii}\theta_i^{-1}b_i + \sum_{j=1, j\neq i}^{m} \hat{z}_{ij}\theta_j^{-1}b_j \right| \tag{21}$$

$$\geqslant \max_i \left\{ |\hat{z}_{ii}\theta_i^{-1}b_i| - \sum_{j=1, j\neq i}^{m} |\hat{z}_{ij}\theta_j^{-1}b_j| \right\} \tag{22}$$

$$> \max_i \left\{ |b_i| + \sum_{j=1, j\neq i}^{m} |\hat{z}_{ij}\theta_j^{-1}b_i| - \sum_{j=1, j\neq i}^{m} |\hat{z}_{ij}\theta_j^{-1}b_j| \right\} \tag{23}$$

on using (11). Because $\|\mu b\| = \mu\|b\|$ for any norm and any real $\mu > 0$, we may put $\|b\|_c = 1$ in (19) without affecting the result. In (23), we then have some k for which $|b_k| = 1$, and $|b_j| \leqslant 1$ for $j \neq k$. Evaluating the quantity within braces for $i = k$, we obtain

$$1 + \sum_{j=1, j\neq k}^{m} |\hat{z}_{kj}\theta_j^{-1}| - \sum_{j=1, j\neq k}^{m} |\hat{z}_{kj}\theta_j^{-1}|\,|b_j| \geqslant 1 \tag{24}$$

whence the maximum over i is certainly not less than 1. That is, $\|\hat{Z}\theta^{-1}b\|_c > 1$ when $\|b\|_c = 1$.

Similarly,

$$\|\theta^{-1}b\|^2 = \sum_{i=1}^{m} |\theta_i^{-1}b_i|^2 \tag{25}$$

and if $\|b\|_c = 1$, the maximum of this expression is clearly achieved when $|b_i| = 1, i = 1, 2, \ldots, m$, and is

$$\sum_{i=1}^{m} \theta_i^{-2}.$$

On comparing (16) and (19), the results thus established give the first part of the theorem. For the second part of the theorem, we notice that if (12) is true for $\hat{Z}$, then (11) is true for $Q = \hat{Z}^*$, because

$$\begin{aligned}\theta_i^{-1}|\hat{z}_{ii}| - \sum_{j=1, j\neq i}^{m} \theta_j^{-1}|\hat{z}_{ji}| &= \theta_i^{-1}|q_{ii}| - \sum_{j=1, j\neq i}^{m} \theta_j^{-1}|\bar{q}_{ij}| \\ &= |q_{ii}|\theta_i^{-1} - \sum_{j=1, j\neq i}^{m} |q_{ij}|\theta_j^{-1}\end{aligned} \tag{26}$$

THEOREM 3. *With the same norm as in Theorem* 2, *let* $\|Z\| < 1$. *Then*

$$Y = (I_m + Z)(I_m - Z)^{-1} = (I_m - Z)^{-1}(I_m + Z)$$

is finite, and $Y + Y^*$ *is positive definite.*

Proof. The two expressions for Y are equal whenever they exist because $(I_m + Z)$ and $(I_m - Z)^{-1}$ commute. Because $\|Z\| < 1$, it follows that Z is finite. If $I_m - Z$ were singular, then $\lambda = 1$ would be an eigenvalue of Z. There would then be an eigenvector v such that $Zv = v$, giving $\|Zv\| = \|v\|$, and so contradicting the assumption that $\|Z\| < 1$. Hence $I_m - Z$ is non-singular and Y is finite. Now we have to show that if a is any complex m-vector,

$$a^*(Y + Y^*)a > 0, \qquad a \neq 0. \tag{27}$$

From the definition of Y we obtain

$$a^*(Y + Y^*)a$$

$$= a^*[(I_m + Z)(I_m - Z)^{-1} + (I_m - Z^*)^{-1}(I_m + Z^*)]\, a \tag{28}$$

$$= b^*[(I_m - Z^*)(I_m + Z) + (I_m + Z^*)(I_m - Z)]\, b \tag{29}$$

$$= 2b^*[I_m - Z^*Z]\, b \tag{30}$$

$$= 2[\|b\|^2 - \|Zb\|^2] \tag{31}$$

$$\geqslant 2\|b\|^2\,[1 - \|Z\|^2] > 0 \qquad \text{if } b \neq 0 \tag{32}$$

where

$$b = (I_m - Z)^{-1}a \tag{33}$$

and is non-zero if a is non-zero. This completes the proof.

THEOREM 4. *Let the rational $m \times m$ matrix $Y(s)$ have no pole inside or on a closed contour C. Let $Y(s) + Y^*(s)$ be positive definite for all s on C. Then $Y(s) + Y^*(s)$ is positive definite for all s inside or on C.*

Proof. Let a be any non-zero complex m-vector. Then

$$\phi(s) = a^*Y(s)\,a = \sum_{i,j=1}^{m} \bar{a}_i y_{ij}(s)\, a_j \tag{34}$$

is a rational function of s which has no pole inside or on C. By the maximum-modulus theorem, $|e^{-\phi(s)}|$ therefore achieves its greatest value on C. But on C,

$$|e^{-\phi(s)}| = \exp\{-\tfrac{1}{2}a^*[Y(s) + Y^*(s)]\, a\} < 1 \tag{35}$$

whence it follows that for any s_0 inside C,

$$|e^{-\phi(s_0)}| < 1 \tag{36}$$

$$\operatorname{Re}\phi(s_0) > 0 \tag{37}$$

$$a^*[Y(s_0) + Y^*(s_0)]\, a > 0 \tag{38}$$

This is true for any non-zero a, whence $Y(s_0) + Y^*(s_0)$ is positive definite. Since s_0 is any point inside C, this completes the proof.

Now define matrices ζ, η by

$$\zeta = \operatorname{diag}(1/2\alpha_i + 1/2\beta_i), \qquad \eta = \operatorname{diag}(1/2\alpha_i - 1/2\beta_i) \tag{39}$$

where α_i, β_i are defined by (5). Also let D be a contour consisting of the imaginary axis from $s = -iR$ to $s = iR$, together with a semi-circle of radius R in the right half-plane. The contour D is indented into the left half-plane to avoid any imaginary poles of $g_{ii}(s)$, and R is chosen large enough to ensure that all poles of $g_{ii}(s)$ lying in the closed right half-plane are inside D, $i = 1, 2, \ldots, m$.

THEOREM 5. *Let there exist real constants* $\theta_i > 0$, *satisfying*

$$\sum_{i=1}^{m} \theta_i^{-2} \leqslant 1,$$

such that for each s *on* D' *having* $R' \geqslant R$

$$|\zeta_i + g_{ii}(s)| - \sum_{j=1, j\neq i}^{m} |g_{ij}(s)| > \theta_i \eta_i, \qquad i = 1, 2, \ldots, m \tag{40}$$

$$\left[\text{resp } |\zeta_i + g_{ii}(s)| - \sum_{j=1, j\neq i}^{m} |g_{ji}(s)| > \theta_i \eta_i, \qquad i = 1, 2, \ldots, m\right]. \tag{41}$$

Let (1) *have least order, and let the linear time-invariant closed-loop system defined by* (1) *and*

$$u = -\beta y \tag{42}$$

be asymptotically stable. Then the nonlinear time-dependent closed-loop system defined by (1), (3) *is stable in the sense of Liapunov.*

Proof. By the choice of D, $g_{ii}(s)$ is finite for all s on D' having $R' \geqslant R$, and by (40) [resp (41)] so also is $g_{ij}(s), i, j = 1, 2, \ldots, m$. Make the substitutions $u_1 = \theta^{-1}u, y_1 = \theta^{-1}y$ in (1) and (3), where $\theta = \text{diag}(\theta_i)$. This replaces G by $Q = \theta^{-1}G\theta$ and F by $\theta F \theta^{-1} = F$. Now (40) gives

$$1 < |\eta_i^{-1}\theta_i^{-1}[\zeta_i + g_{ii}(s)]| - \sum_{j=1, j\neq i}^{m} |\eta_i^{-1}\theta_i^{-1}g_{ij}(s)|$$

$$= |\eta_i^{-1}[\zeta_i + q_{ii}(s)]\,\theta_i^{-1}| - \sum_{j=1, j\neq i}^{m} |\eta_i^{-1}q_{ij}\theta_j^{-1}| \tag{43}$$

and by Theorem 2

$$\|[\zeta + Q(s)]^{-1}\eta\| < 1. \tag{44}$$

Then by Theorem 3

$$Y(s) = \{I_m - [\zeta + Q(s)]^{-1}\eta\}^{-1}\{I_m + [\zeta + Q(s)]^{-1}\eta\} \tag{45}$$

$$= [\zeta + Q(s) - \eta]^{-1}[\zeta + Q(s) + \eta] \tag{46}$$

$$= [\beta^{-1} + Q(s)]^{-1}[\alpha^{-1} + Q(s)] \tag{47}$$

is finite and $Y + Y^*$ is positive definite. This is true for all s on D. Moreover, Y has no pole in the closed right half-plane, for if it did (47) shows that $\theta^{-1}[I_m + \beta G(s)]^{-1}\beta\alpha^{-1}\theta$ or $\theta^{-1}[I_m + \beta G(s)]^{-1}\beta G(s)\theta$ would have a pole there. In either case the system defined by (1) and (42) could not be asymptotically stable. Provided that the indentations of D into the left half-plane are sufficiently small, Y therefore has no pole inside or on D. By Theorem 4, $Y + Y^*$ is positive definite for all s inside or on D. As R can be increased indefinitely, $Y + Y^*$ is positive definite everywhere in the closed right half-plane.

We have now established that Y satisfies the following conditions:

(i) Y is a rational function of s with real coefficients

(ii) Y has no pole in the closed right half-plane

(iii) $Y + Y^*$ is positive definite everywhere in the closed right half-plane.

It therefore follows that Y is positive real, and so the condition relating to (7) in Theorem 1 is satisfied for the system giving $Q(s)$. But apart from a change in notation, this is the system (1), (3), and the first part of the theorem is proved.

For the second part, make the substitutions $u_1 = \theta u$, $y_1 = \theta y$ in (1) and (3), which replaces G by $Q = \theta G\theta^{-1}$ and F by $\theta^{-1}F\theta = F$. Then (41) gives

$$1 < |[\zeta_i + g_{ii}(s)]\,\theta_i^{-1}\eta_i^{-1}| - \sum_{j=1, j\neq i}^{m} |g_{ji}(s)\theta_i^{-1}\eta_i^{-1}|$$

$$= |\theta_i^{-1}[\zeta_i + q_{ii}(s)]\eta_i^{-1}| - \sum_{j=1, j\neq i}^{m} |\theta_j^{-1}\hat{q}_{ji}(s)\eta_i^{-1}| \tag{48}$$

and as above we obtain

$$\|\eta[\zeta + Q(s)]^{-1}\| < 1 \tag{49}$$

$$Y(s) = \{I_m + \eta[\zeta + Q(s)]^{-1}\}\{I_m - \eta[\zeta + Q(s)]^{-1}\}^{-1} \tag{50}$$

$$= [\zeta + Q(s) + \eta]\,[\zeta + Q(s) - \eta]^{-1} \tag{51}$$

$$= [\alpha^{-1} + Q(s)]\,[\beta^{-1} + Q(s)]^{-1} \tag{52}$$

which has the same properties as before. The result then follows on verifying the conditions of Theorem 1, using (8).

We now assume that the $m \times m$ matrix $G(s)$ has an inverse $G^{-1}(s) = \hat{G}(s)$. This condition ensures that the system is controllable(f), and will normally be satisfied. Use of the inverse transfer function matrix G is convenient because [6] when all loops except loop i, in a linear time-invariant closed-loop system, are tightly controlled, the transfer function seen in loop i approximates $\hat{g}_{ii}$. We also define matrices γ, δ by

$$\gamma = \mathrm{diag}\left(\frac{\beta_i}{2} + \frac{\alpha_i}{2}\right), \qquad \delta = \mathrm{diag}\left(\frac{\beta_i}{2} - \frac{\alpha_i}{2}\right). \tag{53}$$

The contour D consists as before of the imaginary axis from $s = -iR$ to $s = iR$, and of a semi-circle of radius R in the right half-plane. The contour is indented into the left half-plane to avoid any imaginary pole of $\hat{g}_{ii}(s)$, while R is chosen large enough to ensure that every pole of $\hat{g}_{ii}(s)$ lying in the closed right half-plane is inside D, $i = 1, 2, \ldots, m$.

THEOREM 6. *Let there exist real constants* $\theta_i > 0$, *satisfying*

$$\sum_{i=1}^{m} \theta_i^{-2} \leqslant 1,$$

such that for each s *on* D' *having* $R' \geqslant R$

$$|\gamma_i + \hat{g}_{ii}(s)| - \sum_{j=1, j \neq i}^{m} |\hat{g}_{ij}(s)| > \theta_i \delta_i, \qquad i = 1, 2, \ldots, m \tag{54}$$

$$\left[\mathrm{resp}\ |\gamma_i + \hat{g}_{ii}(s)| - \sum_{j=1, j \neq i}^{m} |\hat{g}_{ji}(s)| > \theta_i \delta_i, \qquad i = 1, 2, \ldots, m\right] \tag{55}$$

Let (1) *have least order, and let the linear time-invariant system defined by* (1) *and*

$$u = -\alpha y \tag{56}$$

by asymptotically stable. Then the nonlinear time-dependent closed-loop system defined by (1), (3) *is stable in the sense of Liapunov.*

Proof. By the choice of D, $\hat{g}_{ii}(s)$ is finite for all s on D' having $R' \geqslant R$, and by (54) [resp (55)] so also is $\hat{g}_{ij}(s)$, $i, j = 1, 2, \ldots, m$. Make the substitutions $u_1 = \theta^{-1} u, y_1 = \theta^{-1} y$ in (1) and (3). Then $\hat{G}$ is replaced by $\hat{Q} = \theta^{-1} \hat{G} \theta$ and F by $\theta F \theta^{-1} = F$. Then rearrange (54) to give

$$1 > |\delta_i^{-1} \theta_i^{-1} [\gamma_i + \hat{g}_{ii}(s)]| - \sum_{j=1, j \neq i}^{m} |\delta_i^{-1} \theta_i^{-1} \hat{g}_{ij}(s)|$$

$$= |\delta_i^{-1} [\gamma_i + \hat{q}_{ii}(s)] \theta_i^{-1}| - \sum_{j=1, j \neq i}^{m} |\delta_i^{-1} \hat{q}_{ij}(s) \theta_j^{-1}| \tag{57}$$

and from Theorem 2 obtain

$$\|[\gamma + Q(s)]^{-1} \delta\| < 1. \tag{58}$$

Then

$$Y(s) = \{I_m - [\gamma + \hat{Q}(s)]^{-1}\delta\}^{-1}\{I_m + [\gamma + \hat{Q}(s)]^{-1}\delta\} \quad (59)$$

$$= [\gamma + \hat{Q}(s) - \delta]^{-1}[\gamma + \hat{Q}(s) + \delta] \quad (60)$$

$$= [\hat{Q}(s) + \alpha]^{-1}[\hat{Q}(s) + \beta] \quad (61)$$

$$= [I_m + Q(s)\alpha]^{-1}[I_m + Q(s)\beta] \quad (62)$$

which agrees with (9) and by Theorem 3 is finite, while $Y + Y^*$ is positive definite. Moreover, Y has no pole in the closed right half-plane, for if it did, (62) shows that

$$\theta^{-1}[I_m + G(s)\alpha]^{-1}\theta \quad \text{or} \quad \theta^{-1}[I_m + G(s)\alpha]^{-1}G(s)\alpha(\alpha^{-1}\beta\theta)$$

would have a pole there. In either case the system defined by (1) and (56) could not be asymptotically stable. Provided that the indentations of D into the left half-plane are sufficiently small, Y therefore has no pole inside or on D. By Theorem 4, $Y + Y^*$ is positive definite for all s inside or on D, and so for all s in the closed right half-plane. As in Theorem 5, this establishes that Y is positive real. All the conditions of Theorem 1 are satisfied, and the first part of the theorem is proved.

For the second part, substitute $u_1 = \theta u, y_1 = \theta y$ in (1) and (3), so replacing $\hat{G}$ by $\hat{Q} = \theta\hat{G}\theta^{-1}$ and F by $\theta^{-1}F\theta = F$. From (55) obtain

$$1 > |\gamma_i + \hat{g}_{ii}]\theta_i^{-1}\delta^{-1}| - \sum_{j=1, j\neq i}^{m} |\hat{g}_{ji}\theta_i^{-1}\delta_i^{-1}|$$

$$= |\theta_i^{-1}[\gamma_i + \hat{q}_{ii}]\delta_i^{-1}| - \sum_{j=1, j\neq i}^{m} |\theta_j^{-1}\hat{q}_{ji}\delta_i^{-1}| \quad (63)$$

and from Theorems 2 and 3

$$\|\delta[\gamma + \hat{Q}(s)]^{-1}\| < 1 \quad (64)$$

$$Y(s) = \{I_m + \delta[\gamma + \hat{Q}(s)]^{-1}\}\{I_m - \delta[\gamma + \hat{Q}(s)]^{-1}\}^{-1} \quad (65)$$

$$= [\gamma + \hat{Q}(s) + \delta][\gamma + \hat{Q}(s) - \delta]^{-1} \quad (66)$$

$$= [\hat{Q}(s) + \beta][\hat{Q}(s) + \alpha]^{-1} \quad (67)$$

$$= [I_m + \beta Q(s)][I_m + \alpha Q(s)]^{-1} \quad (68)$$

which is finite and positive definite everywhere on D. The result then follows as before, using (10) in Theorem 1.

3. Graphical Interpretation

Theorems 5 and 6 have a simple graphical interpretation, which we now state. First we give some preliminary definitions. Let the system (1) have p_0 poles in the closed right half-plane (that is, let A have p_0 eigenvalues there). Let the contour D be indented into the left half-plane to avoid any imaginary poles of $g_{ii}(s)$, and let R be chosen so that all poles of $g_{ii}(s)$ lying in the closed right half-plane are inside $D, i = 1, 2, \ldots, m$. For each s on D write

$$d_i(s) = \sum_{j=1, j\neq i}^{m} |g_{ij}(s)|, \qquad i = 1, 2, \ldots, m \tag{69}$$

$$d_i'(s) = \sum_{j=1, j\neq i}^{m} |g_{ji}(s)|, \qquad i = 1, 2, \ldots, m \tag{70}$$

Call a disc with centre $g_{ii}(s)$ and radius $d_i(s)$ [resp $d'_i(s)$] an ith Gershgorin row [resp column] disc. Call the band swept out by the ith Gershgorin row [resp column] disc, as s goes round D, the ith Gershgorin row [resp column] band. Let a disc be constructed with centre at $[-(1/2\alpha_i + 1/2\beta_i), 0]$ and radius $\theta_i(1/2\alpha_i - 1/2\beta_i)$; call this the ith critical disc (see Figure 1). The θ_i are any real positive numbers satisfying

$$\sum_{i=1}^{m} \theta_i^{-2} \leqslant 1$$

so that there is freedom to reduce one critical disc at the expense of another.

THEOREM 5a. *Let* (1) *have least order, and let the ith Gershgorin row [resp column] band have no point in common with the ith critical disc. Let this band go* N_{ci} *times clockwise around the ith critical disc,* $i = 1, 2, \ldots, m$, *as s goes once clockwise round D. Let these conditions remain satisfied for all* D' *having* $R' \geqslant R$. *If*

$$\sum_{i=1}^{m} N_{ci} = -p_0 \tag{71}$$

the closed-loop system defined by (1), (3) *is stable in the sense of Liapunov.*

Proof. Consider the system defined by (1) and (42). Because $(-1/\beta_i, 0)$ is in the ith critical disc, the conditions of the theorem show that for all s on D

$$|1/\beta_i + g_{ii}(s)| - \sum_{j=1, j\neq i}^{m} |g_{ij}(s)| > 0, \qquad i = 1, 2, \ldots, m \tag{72}$$

$$\left[\text{resp } |1/\beta_i + g_{ii}(s)| - \sum_{j=1, j\neq i}^{m} |g_{ji}(s)| > 0, \qquad i = 1, 2, \ldots, m\right]. \tag{73}$$

By (72) [resp (73)] and the definition of D, no $g_{ij}(s)$ has a pole on D, and so $|\beta^{-1} + G(s)|$ has no pole there. Also by (72) [resp (73)] no $1/\beta_i + g_{ii}(s)$ has a zero on D, and by Gershgorin's theorem $|\beta^{-1} + G(s)|$ has no zero there. As R may be increased indefinitely, it follows that every finite pole and zero of $|\beta^{-1} + G(s)|$ lying in the closed right half-plane is inside D. Let $1/\beta_i + g_{ii}(s)$ map D into Γ_i, which encircles the origin n_i times clockwise as s goes once clockwise around D. Let $|\beta^{-1} + G(s)|$ map D into Γ, which goes n times clockwise round the origin as s goes once clockwise round D, Then by a known theorem [6] we find

$$n = \sum_{i=1}^{m} n_i. \tag{74}$$

But the number n_i of encirclements of the origin by Γ_i is the number of encirclements of $(-1/\beta_i, 0)$ by the map of D under $g_{ii}(s)$, and this is N_{ci}. It is known that the system defined by (1), (42) is asymptotically stable if $n = -p_0$, and by what has been proved this is ensured by (71).

Moreover, the centre of the ith critical disc is $\zeta_i = 1/2\alpha_i + 1/2\beta_i$ and its radius is $\theta_i\eta_i = \theta_i(1/2\alpha_i - 1/2\beta_i)$. The conditions of the theorem ensure that (40) [resp (41)] is true, and remains true as R is increased. All the conditions of Theorem 5 are satisfied, and the proof is complete.

For the corresponding generalisation of Theorem 6, we suppose D to be suitably indented, and R suitably chosen, so that every pole of $\hat{g}_{ii}(s)$ lying in the closed right half-plane is inside D, $i = 1, 2, \ldots, m$. The radii of the Gershgorin row and column discs are now respectively

$$\hat{d}_i(s) = \sum_{j=1, j \neq i}^{m} |\hat{g}_{ij}(s)| \tag{75}$$

$$\hat{d}_i'(s) = \sum_{j=1, j \neq i}^{m} |\hat{g}_{ji}(s)| \tag{76}$$

The Gershgorin row and column bands are defined in the corresponding way. The ith critical disc now has its centre at $[-\frac{1}{2}(\beta_i + \alpha_i), 0]$ and has radius $\frac{1}{2}\theta_i(\beta_i - \alpha_i)$. The θ_i again satisfy

$$\sum_{i=1}^{m} \theta_i^{-2} \leqslant 1.$$

THEOREM 6a. *Let* (1) *have least order, and let the ith Gershgorin row [resp column] band have no point in common with the origin or with the ith critical disc,* $i = 1, 2, \ldots, m$. *Let this band go* $\hat{N}_{0i}$ *times clockwise round the origin, and* $\hat{N}_{ci}$ *times clockwise round the ith critical disc,* $i = 1, 2, \ldots, m$, *as s goes once clockwise round D. Let these conditions remain satisfied for all D' having $R' \geqslant R$. Then if*

$$\sum_{i=1}^{m}\left(\hat{N}_{0i} - \hat{N}_{ci}\right) = p_0 \tag{77}$$

the system defined by (1), (3) *is stable in the sense of Liapunov.*

Proof. Consider the system (1), (56). By the conditions of the theorem, for all s on D,

$$|\hat{g}_{ii}(s)| - \sum_{j=1, j\neq i}^{m} |\hat{g}_{ij}(s)| > 0, \qquad i = 1, 2, \ldots, m \tag{78}$$

$$\left[\text{resp } |\hat{g}_{ii}(s)| - \sum_{j=1, j\neq i}^{m} |\hat{g}_{ji}(s)| > 0, \qquad i = 1, 2, \ldots, m\right]. \tag{79}$$

Hence, by the definition of D, no $\hat{g}_{ii}(s)$ nor $|\hat{G}(s)|$ has a pole on D. Also no $\hat{g}_{ii}(s)$ nor (by Gershgorin's Theorem) $|\hat{G}(s)|$ has a zero on D. As R can be increased indefinitely, every finite pole and zero of $|\hat{G}(s)|$ lying in the closed right half-plane is inside D. Let the map of D under $\hat{g}_{ii}(s)$ go $\hat{n}_{0i}$ times clockwise round the origin, and the map under $|\hat{G}(s)|$ go $\hat{n}_0$ times clockwise round the origin, as s goes once clockwise round D. Then [6]

$$\hat{n}_0 = \sum_{i=1}^{m} \hat{n}_{0i}. \tag{80}$$

In a similar way every finite pole and zero of $|\alpha + G(s)|$ lying in the closed right half-plane is inside D. Let the map of D under $\alpha_i + \hat{g}_{ii}(s)$ go $\hat{n}_{ci}$ times clockwise round the origin, and the map under $|\alpha + \hat{G}(s)|$ go $\hat{n}_c$ times clockwise round the origin, as s goes once clockwise round D. Then [6]

$$\hat{n}_c = \sum_{i=1}^{m} \hat{n}_{ci}. \tag{81}$$

Also $\hat{n}_{0i} = \hat{N}_{0i}$, $\hat{n}_{ci} = \hat{N}_{ci}$, and the system (1), (56) is asymptotically stable because

$$\hat{n}_0 - \hat{n}_c = \sum_{i=1}^{m} \hat{N}_{0i} - \sum_{i=1}^{m} \hat{N}_{ci} = p_0. \tag{82}$$

Moreover, the centre of the ith critical disc is at $\gamma_i = \frac{1}{2}(\beta_i + \alpha_i)$ and its radius is $\theta_i\delta_i = \frac{1}{2}\theta_i(\beta_i - \alpha_i)$. The conditions of the theorem verify (54) [resp (55)], and this is true for all D' having $R' \geqslant R$. All the conditions of Theorem 6 are satisfied and the proof is complete.

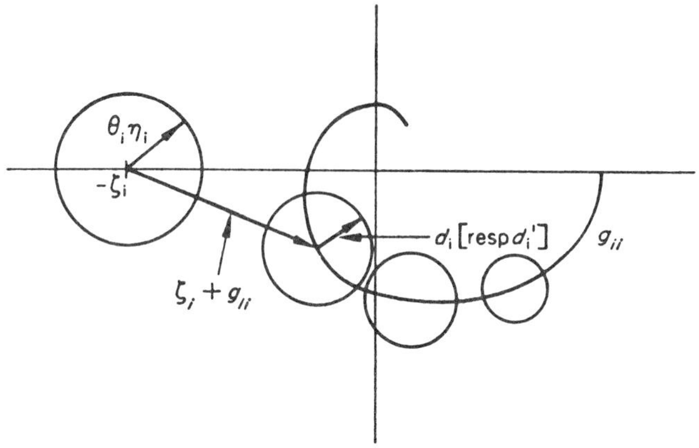

FIG. 1. The Gershgorin band is swept out by circles with radius $d_i(s)$ [resp $d_i'(s)$] as s goes round D. As usual, only the part corresponding to the positive imaginary segment of D is shown. The critical disc has centre at $-\zeta_i$ and radius $\theta_i\eta_i$. If the Gershgorin band does not have any point in common with the critical disc then (40) [resp (41)] is satisfied. Stability is then ensured by (71). A stronger result is obtained from Theorem 5b when the distance between the Gershgorin band and the critical disc is always greater than ε.

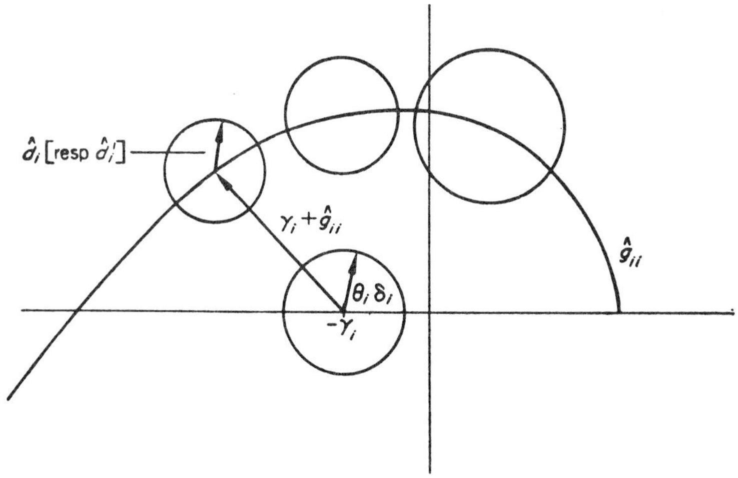

FIG. 2. The interpretation of Theorems 6a, 6b is similar to that of Theorems 5a, 5b. If the Gershgorin bands avoid the origin and the critical discs, and if (77) is satisfied, then Theorem 5a gives stability.

The results in Theorems 5a and 6a are illustrated in Figs 1 and 2 respectively. They are direct generalisations of the circle theorem and of results given earlier [7] for dominant linear time-invariant systems. The values of θ_i are subject to choice, and whenever θ_i exist, satisfying

$$\sum_{i=1}^{m} \theta_i^{-2} \leqslant 1$$

and verifying the conditions of either theorem, then the system (1), (3) is stable.

4. Stronger Theorems

The above theorems can now be strengthened to give asymptotic stability, and also to cover systems not having least order. An alternative procedure would be to seek a stronger form of Theorem 1, and obtain the following theorems directly in place of 5a and 6a.

THEOREM 5b. *Suppose that* (1) *does not necessarily have least order and let the least distance, between the Gershgorin row [resp column] discs centred on* g_{ii} *and the ith critical disc, be greater than* $\varepsilon > 0$, $i = 1, 2, \ldots, m$. *Let this be true for all* D' *having* $R' \geqslant R$. *If* (71) *is true, then the system* (1), (3) *is uniformly asymptotically stable in the large.*

Proof. For $\sigma > 0$ define

$$\left.\begin{aligned} x' &= xe^{\sigma t}, \qquad u' = ue^{\sigma t}, \qquad y' = ye^{\sigma t} \\ A' &= A + \sigma I, \qquad F'(t, y') = F(t, y) \end{aligned}\right\} \tag{83}$$

Then a direct calculation shows that

$$\left.\begin{aligned} \dot{x}' &= A'x' + Bu' \\ y' &= Cx' \end{aligned}\right\} \tag{84}$$

which gives

$$G'(s) = G(s - \sigma). \tag{85}$$

The eigenvalues $\lambda_i(A')$ are related to the eigenvalues $\lambda_i(A)$ by $\lambda_i(A') = \sigma + \lambda_i(A)$. There is therefore some $\sigma_1 > 0$ such that for all $\sigma < \sigma_1$, A' has the same number p_0 of eigenvalues in the closed right half-plane as A. Further, as in the proof of Theorem 5a, no $g_{ij}(s)$ has a pole on any D' having $R' \geqslant R$, and so every $g_{ij}(s)$ is a continuous function of s in some neighbourhood of every point on such D'. Since $G(s) \to 0$

as $s \to \infty$, it follows that there is some $\sigma_2 > 0$ such that for all $\sigma < \sigma_2$, and all s on D' having $R' \geqslant R$, and for $i, j = 1, 2, \ldots, m$,

$$|g_{ij}(s) - g_{ij}(s - \sigma)| < \varepsilon/m \tag{86}$$

Choose $0 < \sigma < \min(\sigma_1, \sigma_2)$. Then A' has p_0 eigenvalues in the closed right half-plane, and for all s on D' having $R' \geqslant R$,

$$|\zeta_i + g_{ii}'(s)| - \sum_{j=1, j \neq i}^{m} |g_{ij}'(s)| > \theta_i \eta_i, \qquad i = 1, 2, \ldots, m \tag{87}$$

$$\left[\text{resp } |\zeta_i + g_{ii}'(s)| - \sum_{j=1, j \neq i}^{m} |g_{ji}'(s)| > \theta_i \eta_i, \qquad i = 1, 2, \ldots, m\right]. \tag{88}$$

Now carry out a canonical decomposition [8] of (84) to give

$$\left.\begin{aligned}
\dot{x}_1 &= A_{11}x_1 \\
\dot{x}_2 &= A_{21}x_1 + A_{22}x_2 \\
\dot{x}_3 &= A_{31}x_1 \qquad\qquad + A_{33}x_3 \qquad\qquad + B_3u' \\
\dot{x}_4 &= A_{41}x_1 + A_{42}x_2 + A_{43}x_3 + A_{44}x_4 + B_4u' \\
y' &= C_1x_1 \qquad\qquad + C_3x_3
\end{aligned}\right\} \tag{89}$$

where $(x')^T = (x_1^T, x_2^T, x_3^T, x_4^T)$. As in the proof of Theorem 5a, we can show that the closed-loop system defined by (1) and (42) is asymptotically stable, the proof being valid for systems not having least order*. But the decoupling zeros z_i of the system (1), (42) are those of (1), which consequently lie in the open left half-plane. By the choice of σ_1, the decoupling zeros $z_i - \sigma$ of (89) also lie in the open left half-plane: these decoupling zeros are the eigenvalues of A_{11}, A_{22}, A_{44}, taken all together.

Choose some arbitrary initial condition $x_i(0) = c_i, i = 1, 2, 3, 4$ for (89). Then there is some $\mu_1(c_1, c_2)$ and some $\sigma_4 > 0$ such that $\|x_1(t)\| + \|x_2(t)\| < \mu_1 e^{-\sigma_4 t}$ for all $t \geqslant 0$. The system

$$\left.\begin{aligned}
\dot{x}_3 &= A_{33}x_3 + B_3u' \\
y' &= C_3x_3
\end{aligned}\right\} \tag{90}$$

has least order and gives $G'(s)$ satisfying (87) [resp (88)]. From (83) it follows that

$$0 < \alpha_i \leqslant f_i'(t, y') \leqslant \beta_i \tag{91}$$

and so the system defined by (9)) and

$$u' = -F'y' \tag{92}$$

* This point is considered in more detail in "Computer-aided Control System Design" by H. H. Rosenbrock (to be published).

obeys the conditions of Theorem 5, and is stable. A Liapunov function for this system is given in (122) of the Appendix [resp a similar result obtained from (126)]. The derivative of this Liapunov function, when $\dot{x}_3$ is given by (89), is

$$\frac{d}{dt} x_3{}^T P x_3 \leqslant 2x_3{}^T P(A_{31} - B_3 F' C_1) x_1 \tag{93}$$

If H is the positive definite square-root of P, (93) gives

$$\frac{d}{dt} \|Hx_3\|^2 \leqslant \|Hx_3\| \, \|2H(A_{31} - BF'C_1) x_1\| \tag{94}$$

$$\leqslant \|Hx_3\| \, \mu_2 e^{-\sigma_4 t} \tag{95}$$

by (91) and what was proved about $\|x_1\|$. Hence

$$\|x_3(t)\| \leqslant \mu_3 \tag{96}$$

for all $t \geqslant 0$.

Because the eigenvalues of A_{44} lie in the open left half-plane, there is a positive definite P_1 such that

$$A_{44}{}^T P_1 + P_1 A_{44} \tag{97}$$

is negative definite. Then when $\dot{x}_4$ is given by (89) we have

$$\frac{d}{dt} x_4{}^T P_1 x_4 \leqslant 2x_4{}^T P_1[(A_{41} - B_4 F' C_1) x_1 + A_{42} x_2 + (A_{43} - B_4 F' C_3) x_3]. \tag{98}$$

If H_1 is the positive definite square root of P_1, we obtain from what has been proved above

$$\frac{d}{dt} \|H_1 x_4\|^2 \leqslant \|H_1 x_4\| \, (\mu_4 e^{-\sigma_4 t} + \mu_5) \tag{99}$$

$$\|x_4\| \leqslant \mu_6 + \mu_7 t \tag{100}$$

for all $t \geqslant 0$. Consequently, by (83) and what has been proved about $\|x_1\|$, $\|x_2\|$, $\|x_3\|$ and $\|x_4\|$,

$$\|x\| \leqslant (\mu_8 + \mu_9 t)\, e^{-\sigma t} \tag{101}$$

As the origin of time can be shifted without affecting the proof, this establishes the theorem.

THEOREM 6b. *Suppose that* (1) *does not necessarily have least order. Let the Gershgorin row [resp column] band based on* $\hat{g}_{ii}(s)$ *exclude the origin. Let the least distance, between the Gershgorin disc centred on* $\hat{g}_{ii}(s)$ *and the critical disc centred on* γ_i, *be not less than* $\varepsilon|\gamma_i + \hat{g}_{ii}(s)|$. *Let this be true for* $i = 1, 2, \ldots, m$ *and for all s on D' having* $R' \geqslant R$. *If* (77) *is true, then the system* (1), (3) *is uniformly asymptotically stable in the large.*

Proof. From (83), (84) and (85) we obtain

$$\hat{G}(s) = \hat{G}(s - \sigma) \tag{102}$$

By the definition of D, no $\hat{g}_{ii}(s)$ has a pole on D. The conditions of the theorem give, for row dominance,

$$|\gamma_i + \hat{g}_{ii}(s)| - \sum_{j=1, j\neq i}^{m} |\hat{g}_{ij}(s)| > \theta_i\eta_i + \varepsilon|\gamma_i + \hat{g}_{ii}(s)| \tag{103}$$

$$1 - \sum_{j=1, j\neq i}^{m} \left|\frac{\hat{g}_{ij}(s)}{\gamma_i + \hat{g}_{ii}(s)}\right| > \frac{\theta_i\eta_i}{|\gamma_i + \hat{g}_{ii}(s)|} + \varepsilon. \tag{104}$$

We may therefore write

$$\frac{\hat{g}_{ij}(s)}{\gamma_i + \hat{g}_{ii}(s)} = \mu_{ij} + \phi_{ij}(s) \tag{105}$$

where μ_{ij} is a constant and $\phi_{ij}(s)$ is a proper rational function. Then from (103), no $\hat{g}_{ij}(s)$ has a pole on D, and $\gamma_i + \hat{g}_{ii}(s)$ has no zero on D. Hence $\phi_{ij}(s)$ is a continuous function of s in some neighbourhood of every point on D, and moreover on every D' having $R' \geqslant R$. There is therefore some $\sigma_2 > 0$ such that for all $\sigma < \sigma_2$,

$$|[\mu_{ij} + \phi_{ij}(s)] - [\mu_{ij} + \phi_{ij}(s - \sigma)]| < \varepsilon/m, \qquad i, j = 1, 2, \ldots, m. \tag{106}$$

In a similar way there is a $\sigma_3 > 0$ such that for all $\sigma < \sigma_3$,

$$\left|\frac{\theta_i\eta_i}{\gamma_i + \hat{g}_{ii}(s)} - \frac{\theta_i\eta_i}{\gamma_i + \hat{g}_{ii}(s - \sigma)}\right| < \frac{\varepsilon}{m}, \qquad i, j = 1, 2, \ldots, m. \tag{107}$$

If we choose $\sigma < \min(\sigma_1, \sigma_2, \sigma_3)$, it follows that

$$1 - \sum_{j=1, j\neq i}^{m} \left|\frac{\hat{g}_{ij}(s - \sigma)}{\gamma_i + \hat{g}_{ii}(s - \sigma)}\right| > \frac{\theta_i\eta_i}{|\gamma_i + \hat{g}_{ii}(s - \sigma)|} \tag{108}$$

$$|\gamma_i + \hat{g}_{ii}(s - \sigma)| - \sum_{j=1, j\neq i}^{m} |\hat{g}_{ij}(s - \sigma)| > \theta_i\eta_i \tag{109}$$

and a similar result can be obtained for column dominance.

The remaining part of the proof follows similar lines to the proof of Theorem 5b, and is omitted.

5. Discussion

The results given have an obvious application to the design of multivariable systems, as will be clear from Figures 1 and 2. Mathematically, the chief interest probably lies in the demonstration that algebraic results of the type of Theorem 2 have direct applications to the analysis of stability. The passage from (17) to (19) involves two weak steps, and it is therefore likely that better results can be obtained. These would improve Theorems 5b and 6b by permitting values of θ_i not allowed by Theorem 2. In this connection it can be shown [11] that if (11) and (12) are true simultaneously, with $\theta_i = 1, i = 1, 2, \ldots, m$, then $\|Z\| = \|Z^*\| < 1$. Simultaneous achievement of (11) and (12), however, will usually be difficult to achieve, and for this reason Theorem 2 in the form given is preferred.

6. Acknowledgement

I am grateful to Professor R. W. Brockett for a number of helpful suggestions: also to Dr. P. A. Cook for a counterexample which exposed an error in a previous (incorrect) version of Theorem 2. This error was also pointed out by Professor B. D. O. Anderson.

References

1. Lur'e, A. I., "Some Non-linear Problems in the Theory of Automatic Control", H.M.S.O., London (1957) (translation of 1951 monograph).
2. Aizerman, M. A. and Gantmacher, F. R., "Absolute Stability of Regulator Systems". Holden-Day (1964).
3. Popov, V. M., Absolute stability of nonlinear control systems of automatic control. *Automation and Remote Control* **22** (1962), 857–875.
4. Willems, J. L., "Stability Theory of Dynamical Systems. Nelson (1970).
5. Newcomb, R. W., "Linear Multiport Synthesis". McGraw-Hill (1966).
6. Rosenbrock, H. H., "State-space and Multivariable Theory". Nelson (1970).
7. Rosenbrock, H. H., Progress in the design of multivariable control systems. *Measurement and Control* **4** (1971), 9–11.
8. Kalman, R. E., Canonical structure of linear dynamical systems. *Proc. Nat. Acad. Sci.* **48** (1962), 596–600.
9. Bodewig, E., "Matrix Calculus". Interscience (1956).
10. Anderson, B. D. O., A system theory criterion for positive real matrices. *SIAM J. Control* **5** (1967), 171–182.
11. Cook, P. A. Private Communication: also independently J. C. Willems.

7. Appendix

As in the conditions of Theorem 1, let the system (1) have least order. Associate with (1) the system

$$\left.\begin{aligned} \dot{x}_1 &= A_1 x_1 + B_1 u_1 = (A - B\beta C) x_1 - B(\beta\alpha^{-1} - I_m) u_1 \\ y_1 &= C_1 x_1 + D_1 u_1 = \beta C x_1 + \beta\alpha^{-1} u_1 \end{aligned}\right\} \tag{110}$$

Then we have

$$[sI_n - A + B\beta C, -B(\beta\alpha^{-1} - I_m)] = (sI_n - A, B)\begin{pmatrix} I_n & 0 \\ \beta C & I_m - \beta\alpha^{-1} \end{pmatrix} \tag{111}$$

and the last matrix in (111) is non-singular by (5), while

$$\begin{pmatrix} sI_n - A + B\beta C \\ -\beta C \end{pmatrix} = \begin{pmatrix} I_n & -B\beta \\ 0 & \beta \end{pmatrix}\begin{pmatrix} sI_n - A \\ -C \end{pmatrix} \tag{112}$$

and the first matrix on the right-hand side of (112) is again non-singular by (5). Hence the decoupling zeros of (110) are those of (1): that is (110) also has least order.

Now the transfer function corresponding to (110) is

$$G_1(s) = -\beta C(sI_n - A + B\beta C)^{-1} B(\beta\alpha^{-1} - I_m) + \beta\alpha^{-1} \tag{113}$$

$$= I_m + [I_m - \beta C(sI_n - A + B\beta C)^{-1}B]\,(\beta\alpha^{-1} - I_m) \tag{114}$$

$$= I_m + [I_m + \beta C(sI_n - A)^{-1}B]^{-1}\,(\beta\alpha^{-1} - I_m) \tag{115}$$

$$= [I_m + \beta G(s)]^{-1}\,[I_m + \beta G(s) + \beta\alpha^{-1} - I_m] \tag{116}$$

$$= [I_m + \beta G(s)]^{-1}\,[\beta\alpha^{-1} + \beta G(s)] \tag{117}$$

$$= [\beta^{-1} + G(s)]^{-1}\,[\alpha^{-1} + G(s)] \tag{118}$$

where $G(s) = C(sI_n - A)^{-1}B$ and (115) follows from (114) by a matrix identity attributed by Bodewig [9] to Frobenius. By assumption in Theorem 1, $G_1(s)$ is positive real, and Anderson's generalisation [10] of the Kalman–Yacubovich lemma shows that there exists a symmetric positive definite matrix P such that

$$\begin{pmatrix} A_1^T P + P A_1 & P B_1 - C_1^T \\ B_1^T P - C_1 & -2D_1 \end{pmatrix} = \begin{pmatrix} A_1^T P + P A_1 & P B_1 \\ B_1^T P & 0 \end{pmatrix} - \begin{pmatrix} 0 & C_1^T \\ C_1 & 2D_1 \end{pmatrix} \tag{119}$$

is negative semidefinite.

Equation (6) can be written

$$\dot{x} = \{A_1 + B_1[(\beta\alpha^{-1} - I_m)^{-1}(F - \beta)\beta^{-1}]\,C_1\}\,x \tag{120}$$

or

$$\left.\begin{aligned} \dot{x} &= A_1 x + B_1 u_2 \\ u_2 &= -(\beta\alpha^{-1} - I_m)^{-1}\beta^{-1}(\beta - F)\, C_1 x \triangleq -\mu(\beta - F)\, C_1 x \end{aligned}\right\} \tag{121}$$

on commuting diagonal matrices. Hence, using (119),

$$\frac{d}{dt} x^T P x = x^T(A_1{}^T P + P A_1)\, x + 2x^T P B_1 u_2 \tag{122}$$

$$\leqslant 2u_2{}^T C_1 x + 2u_2{}^T D_1 u_2 \tag{123}$$

$$= -2x^T C_1{}^T \mu(\beta - F)\, \{\mu^{-1} - \beta\alpha^{-1}(\beta - F)\}\, \mu C_1 x \tag{124}$$

$$= -2x^T C_1{}^T \mu(\beta - F)\, \{\beta\alpha^{-1}(F - \alpha)\}\, \mu C_1 x \tag{125}$$

and it is easy to see that this quadratic form is negative semi-definite. It follows that the system (6) is stable in the sense of Liapunov. This proves the first part of the theorem.

The second part is proved in a similar way by using instead of (110)

$$\left.\begin{aligned} \dot{x}_1 &= A_1 x_1 + B_1 u_1 = (A - B\beta C)\, x_1 - B\beta u_1 \\ y_1 &= C_1 x_1 + D_1 u_1 = (\beta\alpha^{-1} - I_m)\, C x_1 + \beta\alpha^{-1} u_1 \end{aligned}\right\} \tag{126}$$

giving as in (113) to (118)

$$G_1(s) = [\alpha^{-1} + G(s)]\, [\beta^{-1} + G(s)]^{-1} \tag{127}$$

Similarly the third part uses

$$\left.\begin{aligned} \dot{x}_1 &= A_1 x_1 + B_1 u_1 = (A - B\alpha C)\, x_1 + B(\beta - \alpha)\, u_1 \\ y_1 &= C_1 x_1 + D_1 u_1 = C x_1 + u_1 \end{aligned}\right\} \tag{128}$$

which gives

$$G_1(s) = C(sI_n - A + B\alpha C)^{-1} B(\beta - \alpha) + I_m \tag{129}$$

$$= \beta\alpha^{-1} + [I_m - C(sI_n - A + B\alpha C)^{-1}\beta\alpha]\, (I_m - \beta\alpha^{-1}) \tag{130}$$

$$= \beta\alpha^{-1} + [I_m + C(sI_n - A)^{-1}\beta\alpha]^{-1}\, (I_m - \beta\alpha^{-1}) \tag{131}$$

$$= \beta\alpha^{-1} + [I_m + G(s)\alpha]^{-1}\, (\alpha\beta^{-1} - I_m)\, \beta\alpha^{-1} \tag{132}$$

$$= \beta\alpha^{-1} + [I_m + G(s)\alpha]^{-1}\, [-I_m - G(s)\alpha + \alpha\beta^{-1} + G(s)\alpha]\, \beta\alpha^{-1} \tag{133}$$

$$= [I_m + G(s)\alpha]^{-1}\, [I_m + G(s)\beta] \tag{134}$$

Finally, the fourth part uses

$$\left.\begin{aligned} \dot{x}_1 &= A_1 x_1 + B_1 u_1 = (A - B\alpha C)\, x_1 + B u_1 \\ y_1 &= C_1 x_1 + D_1 u_1 = (\beta - \alpha)\, C x_1 + u_1 \end{aligned}\right\} \tag{135}$$

giving as in (129) to (134)

$$G_1(s) = [I_m + \beta G(s)]\,[I_m + \alpha G(s)]^{-1} \tag{136}$$

Discussion

COOK (*University of Loughborough*). Perhaps I can clarify the situation about this matrix theorem. The previous version of Theorem 2, the matrix theorem by Rosenbrock, is certainly wrong. What may be correct is the stability criterion which he attempted to base upon it without the θ_i. Several people have claimed that this can be proved although I'm not yet convinced.

BELL. Thank you for raising that. In fact, I believe Willems has hinted that he has a proof.†

COOK. Yes, he has but I haven't seen it.

MEES (University of Cambridge). You remember that Professor Lighthill and I presented a theorem for multivariable systems which was a generalization of the circle criterion. This said that the eigenvalues, the spectrum if you like, of the linear part had to avoid a disc. This disc was much the same as your disc except that yours had a different α and β for each principal loop. This theorem is restricted to the case in which the operators are normal in the linear part. However, it turns out in this case that by applying a few transformations one can prove that Rosenbrock's conjectured stronger theorem, at least for the inverse Nyquist diagrams, reduces to sufficient conditions for this other generalized circle criterion. So presumably it gives sufficient conditions for stability. I don't think it's quite so easy doing it the right way up but it is certainly true for the inverse Nyquist diagrams.

† *Editor's Note.* Several attempts have been made to obtain a proof. The only new result to date is due to Dr. Cook and is given in the paper immediately following the above discussion.

Modified Multivariable Circle Theorems†

P. A. Cook

Department of Mathematics
Loughborough University of Technology,
Leicestershire, England

1. Introduction

In the above paper by Rosenbrock, (reference [1] of this paper), a generalisation of the circle criterion for stability is obtained which applies to diagonally-dominant multivariable linear systems with diagonal (nonlinear and/or time-varying) feedback. The generalised criterion requires that certain bands drawn around the Nyquist plots of diagonal elements of the open-loop transfer function matrix (or its inverse) should avoid certain discs in the complex plane. Unfortunately, these discs are not, as might be expected, those which would be associated with the corresponding feedback elements by the single loop circle criterion; although concentric with them, they have their radii expanded by certain factors (called θ_i by Rosenbrock) which, though to some extent adjustable, are always greater than unity. In this paper, we shall derive an alternative criterion which removes the θ_i-factors by employing a different definition of diagonal dominance.

We shall follow Rosenbrock's notation, and number our theorems consecutively with his paper, to avoid confusion. In Section 2, we prove a matrix theorem to be used in place of Rosenbrock's Theorem 2, and then use it to deduce counterparts of his Theorems 5 and 6. Finally, in Section 3, we state and discuss the graphical interpretation of these results.

2. Stability Criteria

We first prove the following theorem, which appears to be new, although related to known regularity theorems [2].

† December 1972. This work was supported by the Science Research Council under grant No. B/SR/8561.

THEOREM 7. *Let $\hat{Z}$ be a complex $m \times m$ matrix and let there be real numbers $\lambda_i > 0$ such that*

$$|\hat{z}_{ii}| - \sum_{j=1, j \neq i}^{m} \frac{\lambda_j}{\lambda_i} \left[\frac{|\hat{z}_{ij}| + |\hat{z}_{ji}|}{2} \right] > 1 \ (i = 1, 2, \ldots . m). \tag{1}$$

Then $\hat{Z}$ has an inverse Z with spectral norm

$$\|Z\| < 1.$$

Proof. Introduce the diagonal unitary matrix

$$\Phi = \text{diag}(\hat{z}_{ii}/|\hat{z}_{ii}|)$$

and define the Hermitian matrix

$$X = \tfrac{1}{2}(\Phi^* \hat{Z} + \hat{Z}^* \Phi).$$

Then the diagonal elements of X are real and, by (1),

$$x_{ii} - \sum_{j=1, j \neq i}^{m} \frac{\lambda_j}{\lambda_i} |x_{ij}| > 1 \ (i = 1, 2, \ldots m).$$

Hence, by Gershgorin's Theorem, all the eigenvalues of X are greater than unity, and so, with v denoting a complex m-vector,

$$\inf_{v \neq 0} \frac{v^* X v}{\|v\|^2} > 1. \tag{2}$$

Also, using Schwartz's inequality,

$$\begin{aligned} \|\hat{Z}v\| \, \|v\| &= \|\hat{Z}v\| \, \|\Phi v\| \\ &\geqslant |v^* \Phi^* \hat{Z} v| \\ &\geqslant \text{Re}(v^* \Phi^* \hat{Z} v) = v^* X v \end{aligned}$$

and then (2) gives

$$\inf_{v \neq 0} \frac{\|\hat{Z}v\|}{\|v\|} > 1. \tag{3}$$

Thus $\hat{Z}$ is nonsingular and the quantity on the L.H.S. of (3) is $\|Z\|^{-1}$, so that

$$\|Z\| < 1.$$

Now we use Theorem 7 to establish the next two results, which we state in terms of quantities defined in Rosenbrock's paper [1], assuming the conditions stated in his Section 1 to hold.

THEOREM 8. *Suppose that, for each s on D′ having $R' \geqslant R$,*

$$|\zeta_i + g_{ii}(s)| - \sum_{j=1, j\neq i}^{m} \frac{|g_{ij}(s)| + |g_{ji}(s)|}{2} > \eta_i \quad (i = 1, 2, \ldots m) \tag{4}$$

Let (A, B, C) be a least-order realization of G(s), and let the linear time-invariant system

$$\dot{x} = (A - B\beta C)x \tag{5}$$

be asymptotically stable.

Then the nonlinear time-dependent system

$$\dot{x} = (A - BFC)x \tag{6}$$

is stable in the sense of Liapunov.

Proof. By Theorem 7, identifying λ_i with $\sqrt{\eta_i}$, (4) gives

$$\|\sqrt{\eta}[\zeta + G(s)]^{-1}\sqrt{\eta}\| < 1 \tag{7}$$

where

$$\sqrt{\eta} \equiv \text{diag}(+ \sqrt{\eta_i})$$

and (7) can be written as

$$\|[\zeta + G_1(s)]^{-1}\eta\| < 1 \tag{8}$$

where

$$G_1(s) \equiv \sqrt{\eta}G(s)\sqrt{\eta}^{-1}$$

so that a least-order realization of $G_1(s)$ is given by

$$(A_1, B_1, C_1) = (A, B\sqrt{\eta}^{-1}, \sqrt{\eta}C).$$

But then, since (A, B, C) can be replaced in (5) and (6) by (A_1, B_1, C_1), the result follows from (8) exactly as in the proof of Rosenbrock's Theorem 5.

THEOREM 9. *Suppose that G(s) has an inverse $\hat{G}(s)$ such that, for each s on D′ having $R' \geqslant R$,*

$$|\gamma_i + \hat{g}_{ii}(s)| - \sum_{j=1, j\neq i}^{m} \frac{|\hat{g}_{ij}(s)| + |\hat{g}_{ji}(s)|}{2} > \delta_i \qquad (i = 1, 2, \ldots m). \tag{9}$$

Let (A, B, C) be a least order-realization of G(s), and let the linear time-invariant system

$$\dot{x} = (A - B\alpha C)x \tag{10}$$

be asymptotically stable.

Then the nonlinear time-dependent system (6) *is stable in the sense of Liapunov.*

Proof. By Theorem 7, identifying λ_i with $\sqrt{\delta_i}$, (9) gives

$$\|\sqrt{\delta}[\gamma + \hat{G}(s)]^{-1}\sqrt{\delta}\| < 1 \tag{11}$$

where

$$\sqrt{\delta} \equiv \text{diag}(+ \sqrt{\delta_i})$$

and we can rewrite (11) as

$$\|[\gamma + \hat{G}_2(s)]^{-1}\delta\| < 1 \tag{12}$$

where $\hat{G}_2(s)$ is the inverse of

$$G_2(s) \equiv \sqrt{\delta}\, G(s)\sqrt{\delta}^{-1}$$

which has the least-order realization

$$(A_2, B_2, C_2) = (A, B\sqrt{\delta}^{-1}, \sqrt{\delta}\, C).$$

Then, since (A, B, C) can be replaced by (A_2, B_2, C_2) in (6) and (10), the result follows from (12) as in the proof of Rosenbrock's Theorem 6.

3. Graphical Interpretation

We now consider the graphical interpretation of Theorems 8 and 9, stating the results in terms of quantities defined in Section 3 of [1]. We call the band swept out as s goes round D by the disc with centre $g_{ii}(s)$ and radius $[d_i(s) + d_i'(s)]/2$ the ith Gershgorin mean band, and the disc on $(-1/\alpha_i, -1/\beta_i)$ as diameter the ith critical disc.

THEOREM 8a. *Let (A, B, C) be a least-order realization of $G(s)$, with A having p_0 eigenvalues in the closed right half-plane. For $i = 1, 2, \ldots m$, let the ith Gershgorin mean band have no point in common with the ith critical disc and encircle it N_{ci} times clockwise as s goes once clockwise round D, these conditions remaining satisfied for all D' with $R' \geqslant R$, and suppose*

$$\sum_{i=1}^{m} N_{ci} = - p_0. \tag{13}$$

Then the system (6) *is stable in the sense of Liapunov.*

Proof. Since (4) is satisfied, we have, for each s on D',

$$\left|\frac{1}{\beta_i} + g_{ii}(s)\right| > \frac{d_i(s) + d'_i(s)}{2} \qquad (i = 1, 2, \ldots m)$$

and it follows, by arguments analogous to those in [3], that $|G(s) + \beta^{-1}|$ encircles the origin $\sum_{i=1}^{m} N_{ci}$ times clockwise as s goes once clockwise round D', and that (13) then guarantees that the system (5) is asymptotically stable. Thus the conditions of Theorem 8 are satisfied and the result follows.

Assuming next that $G(s)$ has an inverse $\hat{G}(s)$, we call the band swept out as s goes round D by the disc with centre $\hat{g}_{ii}(s)$ and radius $[\hat{d}_i(s) + \hat{d}'_i(s)]/2$ the ith inverse Gershgorin mean band and the disc on $(-\beta_i, -\alpha_i)$ as diameter the ith inverse critical disc.

THEOREM 9a. *Let (A, B, C) be a least-order realization of $G(s)$, with A having p_0 eigenvalues in the closed right half-plane. For $i = 1, 2, \ldots m$, let the ith inverse Gershgorin mean band have no point in common with the origin or with the ith inverse critical disc, let it encircle them $\hat{N}_{0i}$ and $\hat{N}_{ci}$ times respectively, clockwise as s goes once clockwise round D, these conditions remaining satisfied for all D′ with $R' \geqslant R$, and suppose*

$$\sum_{i=1}^{m} (\hat{N}_{0i} - \hat{N}_{ci}) = p_0. \tag{14}$$

Then the system (6) *is stable in the sense of Liapunov.*

Proof. Since (9) is satisfied, we have, for each s on D',

$$|\alpha_i + \hat{g}_{ii}(s)| > \frac{\hat{d}_i(s) + \hat{d}'_i(s)}{2} \qquad (i = 1, 2, \ldots m)$$

and also, since each inverse Gerschgorin mean band avoids the origin,

$$|\hat{g}_{ii}(s)| > \frac{\hat{d}_i(s) + \hat{d}'_i(s)}{2} \qquad (i = 1, 2, \ldots m)$$

whence, by procedures analogous to those of [3], it follows that $|\hat{G}(s) + \alpha|$ and $|\hat{G}(s)|$ encircle the origin $\sum_{i=1}^{m} \hat{N}_{ci}$ and $\sum_{i=1}^{m} \hat{N}_{0i}$ times, respectively, clockwise, as s goes once clockwise round D', and that (14) then guarantees that the system (10) is asymptotically stable. Hence the conditions of Theorem 9 are satisfied and the result follows.

Theorems 8a and 9a are evidently counterparts of Theorems 5a and 6a of [1], their advantage being that the critical discs here are those of the single-loop circle criterion, while in [1] the *i*th disc has its radius magnified by a factor θ_i, for $i = 1, 2, \ldots m$, where the restriction

$$\sum_{i=1}^{m} \theta_i^{-2} \leqslant 1$$

must be satisfied. The Gershgorin discs in our case are also different, of course, their radii being the arithmetic means of those of the corresponding row and column discs used in [1].

By strengthening the assumptions, we can also derive counterparts of Theorems 5b and 6b of [1], which we state without proof, since they are obtained in essentially the same way as in [1].

THEOREM 8b. *Let the conditions of Theorem 8a be satisfied and let the least distance between the ith Gershgorin mean band and the ith critical disc be greater than* $\varepsilon > 0$, *for* $i = 1, 2, \ldots m$, *and for all* D' *with* $R' \geqslant R$.

Then the system (6) *is uniformly asymptotically stable in the large.*

THEOREM 9b. *Let the conditions of Theorem 9a be satisfied and let there be some* $\varepsilon > 0$ *such that*

$$(1 - \varepsilon)\,|\alpha_i + \hat{g}_{ii}(s)| > \frac{\hat{d}_i(s) + \hat{d}_i'(s)}{2} \qquad (i = 1, 2, \ldots m)$$

for each s on D' *with* $R' \geqslant R$.

Then the system (6) *is uniformly asymptotically stable in the large.*

Note. The assumption of least-order in the above theorems can be relaxed just as in [1].

Acknowledgement

The extent of the author's indebtedness to Professor H. H. Rosenbrock will be manifest to anyone who has read this paper.

References

1. Rosenbrock, H. H., Multivariable circle theorems. This Volume, pp. 345–365.
2. Marcus, M. and Minc, H., "A Survey of Matrix Theory and Matrix Inequalities". Allyn and Bacon (1964), pp 150–151.
3. Rosenbrock, H. H., "State-space and Multivariable Theory". Nelson (1970), Chapter 5, Section 6.

The Design of Linear Multivariable Systems*

La Conception de Systèmes Linéaires Multivariables

Der Entwurf linearer multivariabler Systeme

Конструкция линейных многовариантных систем

DAVID Q. MAYNE†

A satisfactory closed-loop linear system may be obtained via a sequence of single-loop designs, in which classical techniques such as Nyquist diagrams, root-loci etc. are employed.

Summary—This paper describes a computer-aided procedure whereby a succession of single-loop designs, using Nyquist loci, yields a multivariable design which is stable and attenuates disturbances. The procedure permits more freedom than previously available for the selection of the compensating matrix. It is shown how a simple modification of the procedure enables security against component failure to be obtained.

1. INTRODUCTION

THE classical frequency methods for designing single-loop control systems have proved to be so useful that it is surprising that so little effort has been devoted to extending these techniques to multivariable systems. This may be due to the development of modern control theory, which though originally motivated by open-loop trajectory optimisation problems, yielded useful and elegant results for linear multivariable control and filtering problems. The resultant controllers are complex, however, requiring a dynamic filter or observer of almost the same order of complexity as the plant or process being controlled. In order to reduce complexity of the controller, CUMMING [1] developed a useful algorithm for optimising the parameters of a given control structure.

ROSENBROCK, in a pioneering paper [2], redirected attention to the problem of extending classical procedures to multivariable problems. Besides providing a useful theoretical basis, Rosenbrock describes a useful technique, based on the inverse Nyquist array, for designing multivariable systems, and a similar technique using the Nyquist array, and these methods are extended by MACFARLANE [3]. A series compensator $G_c(s)$ is chosen to transform the transfer function $G_p(s)$, which is the $m\times m$ matrix transfer function of the system being controlled to $G(s)\underline{\Delta}G_p(s)G_c(s)$ where $G(s)$ is "diagonally dominant" [2]. Then, m single-loop control problems are considered, choosing $k_i(s)$, $i=1\ldots m$ so that $|1+g_{ii}(j\omega)k_i(j\omega)|$ is large for $\omega\leq\omega_c^i$ where ω_c^i is the desired bandwidth for the ith loop and the Nyquist "set" consisting of the union of circles with centre $1+g_{ii}(j\omega)k_i(j\omega)$ and radius

$$\sum_{\substack{j=1\\ j\neq i}} |g_{ij}(j\omega)k_i(j\omega)|)$$

does not encircle the origin. Satisfaction of the latter condition is a sufficient condition of asymptotic stability, and necessary and sufficient if the system is diagonally dominant in the sense that if the Nyquist set encircles the origin, completely, the system is unstable.

The design criteria [3] are assumed to be: (i) performance, e.g. elements of $T^{-1}(j\omega)$ have small magnitude for specified range of ω—see below, (ii) stability, (iii) security, or integrity, the maintenance of stability in face of component failure, and (iv) low interaction. Stability and performance are basic criteria. Security is achieved in practice by a variety of means, e.g. switching to alternative controllers should any component fail, and may have to be achieved at the expense of performance. Hence a design method, which ensures stability in

* Received 27 March 1972; revised 18 September 1972. The original version of this paper was presented at the 5th IFAC Congress which was held in Paris, France during June 1972. It was recommended for publication in revised form by Associate Editor H. Kwakernaak.

† Department of Computing and Control, Imperial College of Science and Technology, Exhibition Road, London, S.W.7.

the event of the failure of any specified combinations of N components, should also be flexible enough to include the case $N=0$. Interaction at low frequencies is automatically reduced in high performance systems, and may not be important at high frequencies, so that, like security, it may not be an important factor in some designs. Hence, in the sequel, a basic design algorithm, consisting of a sequence of single-loop designs, for achieving good performance and stability is first described. It is then shown how the algorithm may be modified to achieve security and, high-frequency, low interaction. Diagonal dominance is not necessarily required, though it can be employed if desired; so that increased flexibility in the choice of the compensating matrix $G_c(s)$ is available. Diagonal dominance, however, automatically provides security against arbitrary, output transducer failure and also limits interaction.

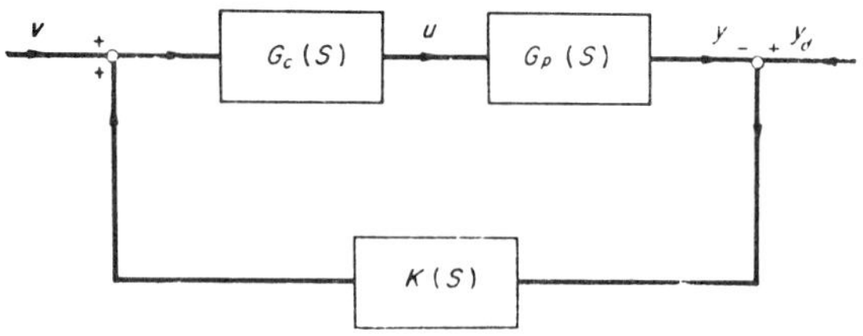

FIG. 1. Multivariable control system.

The system considered is shown in Fig. 1. The process to be controlled has the $m \times m$ transfer function $G_p(s)$. $G_c(s)$ is a $m \times m$ compensator matrix and:

$$G(s) \triangleq G_p(s)G_c(s) \tag{1}$$

$G(s)$ is $m \times m$. $K(s)$ is a $m \times m$ diagonal matrix. It is assumed that:

(A1) Neither $|G(s)|$ nor $|K(s)|$ are identically zero.

The matrix return difference $T(s)$ is defined to be:

$$T(s) \triangleq I_m + G(s)K(s). \tag{2}$$

The system has a state space representation:

$$\dot{x}(t) = Ax(t) + Be(t) \tag{3}$$

$$y(t) = Cx(t) \tag{4}$$

$$e(t) = y_d(t) - y(t) \tag{5}$$

i.e.

$$\dot{x}(t) = (A - BC)x(t) + By_d(t). \tag{6}$$

The expressions

$$\rho_o(s) \triangleq |sI - A| \tag{7}$$

$$\rho_c(s) \triangleq |sI - A + BC| \tag{8}$$

are, respectively, the open- and closed-loop characteristic polynomials. Let $\bar{G}(s) \triangleq G(s)K(s)$, the loop transfer function, and let $R(s)$ denote the closed-loop transfer function relating $y(s)$ to $y_d(s)$. Clearly $\bar{G}(s) = C(sI - A)^{-1}B$. Since:

$$T(s)\bar{G}(s) = \bar{G}(s)T(s)$$

we have

$$R(s) = T^{-1}(s)\bar{G}(s) = \bar{G}(s)T^{-1}(s). \tag{9}$$

If an external disturbance $n(s)$ is present, so that, now:

$$y(s) = \bar{G}(s)e(s) + n(s) \tag{10}$$

then:

$$y(s) = R(s)y_d(s) + T^{-1}(s)n(s) \tag{11}$$

$\rho_c(s)$ and $\rho_o(s)$ are related by the following well known result, for which a simple derivation, due to CUMMING [1, 4], is given in the Appendix.

Theorem 1

$$|T(s)| = \rho_c(s)/\rho_c(s). \tag{12}$$

If we make the further assumptions:

(A2) The process, with transfer function $G_p(s)$, is open-loop asymptotically stable. Note that the assumption of asymptotic stability is made for simplicity in presentation.

(A3) $G_c(s)$ and $K(s)$ have poles and zeros in the open left-half plane only and $|G_c(s)| = 1$.

then $\rho_o(s)$ has zeros in the open left-half plane only. From Theorem 1 it follows that the closed loop system is asymptotically stable if and only if the locus Γ_m of $|T(j\omega)|$ does not encircle or pass through the origin. To illustrate this, let D be a closed contour consisting of the imaginary axis from $-j\alpha$ to $j\alpha$ and a semicircle of radius α in the right half plane. α is large enough to enclose every pole or zero of $t_i(s)$, $i = 1 \ldots m\rho_c(s)$ and $\rho_o(s)$ lying in the right half plane—see (15) for definition of $t_i(s)$. $|T|$ maps D into Γ_m, and Γ_m is called the locus of $|T|$. Hence, from equation (11) and Theorem 1, the closed loop system will be assymptotically stable and will reduce the effect of disturbances, for $\omega \xi \Omega$, if:

(a) Γ_m, the locus of $|T|$, does not encircle or pass through the origin

(b) $\|T^{-1}(j\omega)\| < 1$ for $\omega \varepsilon \Omega$,

i.e. elements of $T^{-1}(j\omega)$ are small, where

$\|A\| \triangleq \sup \|Ax\|$ subject to $\|x\| = 1$ for $A \varepsilon R^{m \times m}$, $x \varepsilon R^m$.

To achieve (a) a single-loop design is often satisfactory. To achieve (b) m "tight", or high gain, loops are required. These can be designed sequentially. For convenience some extra terms, appropriate to the condition when the first i loops are closed and the remaining open, i.e. $k_j(s)\equiv 0$, $j=i+1 \dots m$, are defined:

$$K_i(s) \triangleq \mathrm{diag}(k_1(s), \dots k_i(s), 0 \dots 0) \quad (13)$$

$$T_i(s) \triangleq I_m + G(s)K^i(s) \quad (14)$$

$$G^i(s) \triangleq T_i^{-1}(s)G(s) \quad (15)$$

for $i=0 \dots m$. Clearly $T_o(s)=I_m$, $G^o(s)=G(s)$. $G^i(s)$ is the transfer function relating y to v (Fig. 1) when loops $i+1 \dots m$ are open. We also define, for $i=1 \dots m$, the scalar return difference:

$$t_i(s) \triangleq 1 + k_i(s) g_{ii}^{i-1}(s) \quad (16)$$

where $g_{ij}^k(s)$ is the ijth element of $G^k(s)$.

It is shown below that if the scalar return differences $t_i(s)$, where t_i maps D into γ_i, the locus of t_i, $i=1 \dots m$ can be chosen to satisfy the usual criteria, i.e. magnitude of $t_i(j\omega)$ is large for $\omega\varepsilon\Omega$ and γ_i does not encircle or pass through the origin, then the resultant closed loop system is satisfactory in the sense of satisfying (a) and (b) above. Hence a naive design procedure, currently used in practice, would be to choose k_1 so that $t_1 = 1 + k_1 g_{11}$ is satisfactory, calculate G^1, choose k_2 so that $t_2 = 1 + k_2 g_{22}^1$ is satisfactory, calculate G^2 etc. However this procedure ignores the fact that even if $|G_p(s)|$ has no right-half plane zeros, so that m tight loops are possible [5], g_{ii}^{i-1}, $i=1 \dots m$, as obtained above, may have right-half plane zeroes. The role of G_c, where $|G_c(s)|=1$, in the *basic* algorithm, which has the objectives: performance and asymptotic stability, is to ensure that, if possible, g_{ii}^{i-1}, $i=1 \dots m$ have no right half plane zeroes and to apportion "design difficulty" appropriately to the various loops.

As shown below the above procedure achieves security for the following fault conditions: *simultaneous* failure of, output, transducers $j, j+1 \dots m$ (or, $k_j = k_{j+1} = \dots k_m = 0$) for $j=1 \dots m$. Note that if $G=G_cG_p$ rather than $G=G_pG_c$, the system is secure against simultaneous failure of input, actuators, $j, j+1 \dots m$ (or $k_j = k_{j+1} = \dots k_m = 0$) for $j=1 \dots m$. In other cases the transfer functions $G_p^\alpha(s)$, $\alpha=2 \dots N$ corresponding to each fault, i.e. $G_p^1(s) \triangleq G_p(s)$, must be calculated. For $\alpha=1 \dots N$, $i=0 \dots m$ we define:

$$G^{o,\alpha}(s) \triangleq G_p^\alpha(s) G_c(s) \quad (17)$$

$$T_i^\alpha(s) \triangleq I_m + G^{o\,\alpha}(s) K^i(s) \quad (18)$$

$$G^{i,\alpha}(s) \triangleq [T_i^\alpha(s)]^{-1} G^{o,\alpha}(s) \quad (19)$$

$$t_i^\alpha(s) \triangleq 1 + k_i(s) g_{ii}^{i-1,\alpha}(s). \quad (20)$$

Note:

$$G^{o,1}(s) = G^o(s) = G(s).$$

For $i=1 \dots m$, k^i is chosen so that the N loci γ_i^α, $\alpha=1 \dots N$, where t_i^α maps D into γ_i^α, are satisfactory. This achieves security, but places an extra requirement on k_i, possibly leading to a reduction in performance, *unless* these loci are close together. For the case of arbitrary transducer failure, i.e. actuator failure if $G=G_cG_p$, this can be achieved by choosing G_c so that G is diagonally dominant *or* so that G is approximately upper or lower triangular, i.e. $g_{ij} \doteqdot 0$ for all $j<i$ or for all $j>i$. For mixed transducer, actuator failure, there does not necessarily exist a G_c such that the loci γ_i^α, $\alpha=1 \dots N$ are close together, so that a reduction in performance may result.

It is shown below that if the loop gains are high for $\omega\varepsilon\Omega$, the closed loop transfer function $R(j\omega) \to I$, so that interaction is low. At high frequencies, $R(j\omega) \to \bar{G}(j\omega)$, so that low interaction at high frequencies, if considered important, can be achieved by choosing G_c so that $\bar{G}(j\omega)$ is approximately diagonal as $\omega \to \infty$.

The design procedure commences by relabelling inputs and outputs, which corresponds to pre- and post-multiplication by permutation matrices, so that the resultant G_p is preferable, i.e. if possible, $[G_p(0)]_{ii} > [G_p(0)]_{ij}$ for all $j \neq i$.

Justification for the above comments and for the design algorithm follow from the results given in §2. The algorithm is specified in §3.

2. BASIC RESULTS

Let $g_{i\cdot}$, $g_{\cdot i}$ denote, respectively, the ith row and the ith column of G. Let S_o denote the open-loop state space representation (A, B, C) of

$$G_p(s)G_c(s)K(s)$$

given in equations (3) and (4). Let S_m denote the closed-loop state space representation $(A\text{–}BC, B, C)$ given in equations (3), (4) and (5). For $i=1 \dots m$, let S_i denote the state space representation $(A\text{–}B_iC, B_i, C)$ corresponding to the situation when the first i loops are closed and the remaining are open, i.e. $k_j(s)\equiv 0$, $j=i+1 \dots m$. Let $\rho_c^i(s) = |sI - A + B_iC|$ denote the characteristic polynomial of S_i. γ_i, resp. Γ_i, is the locus of t_i, resp. $|T_i|$, i.e. t_i maps D into γ_i etc.

The first result, also proven independently by ROSENBROCK [6], is:

Theorem 2

For $i=1\ldots m$

$$|T_i(s)|=\prod_{j=1}^{i} t_j(s). \tag{21}$$

Proof

$$|T_o(s)|=1$$

$$\begin{aligned}|T_i(s)|&=|T_{i-1}(s)+k_i(s)g_{ii}(s)e_i^T|\\&=|T_{i-1}(s)||I_m+k_i(s)g^{i-1}_{\cdot i}(s))e_i^T|\\&=|T_{i-1}(s)|(1+k_i(s)g_{ii}^{i-1}(s))\\&=|T_{i-1}(s)|t_i(s).\end{aligned} \tag{22}$$

The result follows by induction.

A direct corollary of this result is the following stability theorem, which also proves the assertion in §1 about security in face of simultaneous failure of, output, transducers $j+1\ldots m$, for $j=1\ldots m$.

Theorem 3

Let A_1–A_3 be satisfied. If $\gamma_1\ldots\gamma_m$ each satisfy the Nyquist criterion, i.e. γ_i does not encircle or pass through the origin, $i=1\ldots m$, then $S_1\ldots S_m$ are asymptotically stable.

Proof. Let $\rho_c^i(s)$ denote the characteristic polynomial of S_i, i.e. ρ_c^i has the same degree n as ρ_o, ρ_c. From Theorem 1:

$$|T_i(s)|=\rho_c^i(s)/\rho_o(s). \tag{23}$$

Let N_i, n_i denote, respectively, the number of net encirclements of the origin by Γ_i and γ_i. From Theorem 2:

$$N_i=\sum_{j=1}^{i} n_j. \tag{24}$$

Since $\rho_o(s)$ has no right half plane roots, N_i is equal to the number of roots of $\rho_c^i(s)$ in the right half plane. The result follows.

The next result gives a simple sequential method for calculating G^i and t_i, $i=1\ldots m$.

Theorem 4

The following algorithm generates G^i, t_i, $i=1\ldots m$:

(i) Set $G^i(s)=G(s)$.
Set $i=1$.

(ii) Set $t_i(s)=1+k_i(s)g_{ii}^{i-1}(s)$.

(iii) If $i=m$, stop. Otherwise:

Set $\bar{k}_i(s)=k_i(s)/t_i(s)$ (25)

Set $G^i(s)=G^{i-1}(s)-\bar{k}_i(s)g^{i-1}_{\cdot i}(s)g^{i-1}_{i\cdot}(s)$ (26)

Set $i=i+1$.

(iv) Go to (ii).

Proof.

$$\begin{aligned}T_i(s)&=T_{i-1}(s)+k_i(s)g_{\cdot i}(s)e_i^T\\&=T_{i-1}(s)[I_m+k_i(s)g^{i-1}_{\cdot i}(s)e_i^T].\end{aligned} \tag{27}$$

Hence, using a well known identity to invert the term in brackets:

$$T_i^{-1}(s)G(s)=[I_m-\bar{k}_i(s)g^{i-1}_{\cdot i}(s)e_i^T]G^{i-1}(s).$$

The result follows.

The next result shows how "tight" loops reduce

$G^i=T_i^{-1}G$, and hence, since $|G(s)|\not\equiv 0$, T_i^{-1}, $i=1\ldots m$.

Theorem 5

(a) Let $t_i(s)=\alpha_i(s)$, $i=1\ldots m$, where the coefficients of the rational function a_i are finite and $a_i(s)\not\equiv 0$. Then, for $i=1\ldots m$:

$$G^i(s)=\begin{bmatrix}\Lambda^i(s) & F^i(s)/\alpha\\ K^i(s)/\alpha & H^i(s)\end{bmatrix}+L^i(s) \tag{28}$$

where

$$\Lambda^i(s)=\mathrm{diag}(g^o_{11}(s)/t_1(s)\ldots g_{ii}^{i-1}(s)/t_i(s))$$

and the coefficients of the elements of L^i are of order $1/\alpha^2$ and $L_i^{pq}\equiv 0$ if $p\geqslant i$ and $q\geqslant i$.

(b) If $G^o(s)$ is lower, resp. upper, triangular, then $G^i(s)$ is lower, resp. upper, triangular, $i=1\ldots m$.

Proof. (a) From Theorem 4, $g^i_{\cdot i}$ and $g^i_{i\cdot}$ are give by:

$$\begin{aligned}g^i_{\cdot i}(s)&=g^{i-1}_{\cdot i}(s)(1-\bar{k}_i(s)g_{ii}^{i-1}(s))\\&=g^{i-1}_{\cdot i}(s)/t_i(s)\end{aligned} \tag{29}$$

$$\begin{aligned}g^i_{i\cdot}(s)&=g^{i-1}_{i\cdot}(s)(1-\bar{k}_i(s)g_{ii}^{i-1}(s))\\&=g^{i-1}_{i\cdot}(s)/t_i(s)\end{aligned} \tag{30}$$

i.e. the ith loop reduces the ith row and ith column of G^{i-1} by a factor $1/t_i$. Suppose $G^{i-1}(s)$ has the form given in equation (28), with i replaced by $i-1$. Application of equations (26), (29) and (30) show that G^i then has the form of equation (28). Since G has this form, using equations (29) and (30), the result follows.

(b) The result follows from equation (26).

Note that $G^m(s)\to 0$ as $\alpha\to\infty$, and $R(s)=G^mK(s)\to I$.

Result (b) merely states the well known fact that control loops for lower, or upper, triangular systems can be independently designed.

The final result gives an estimate for $g_{ii}^{i-1}(s)$ if loops $1 \dots i-1$ are "tight", i.e. $\alpha \to \infty$; see also, ROSENBROCK [5], where this result first appears. Let $[A]_k$ denote the $k \times k$ matrix whose pqth element is A_{pq}. Let $\Delta_k(s) \underline{\Delta} |[G(s)]_k|$.

Theorem 6

For $i = 1 \dots m$:

$$g_{ii}^{i-1}(s) = \Delta_i(s)/\Delta_{i-1}(s) + 0(1/\alpha)$$

where $\Delta_o(s)\underline{\Delta}1$, and $0(1/\alpha)$ denotes a rational polynomial function, whose coefficients are of order $1/\alpha$.

Proof. From equation (26), for $k \geq i$

$$[G^i(s)]_k = [I_m - \bar{k}_i(s) g_{.i}(s) e_i^T]_k [G^{i-1}(s)]_k .$$

Let $\Delta_k^i(s) \underline{\Delta} [G^i(s)]_k$.

Hence, for $k \geq i$; $i = 1 \dots m$:

$$\Delta_k^i(s) = \Delta_k^{i-1}(s)/t_i(s). \tag{31}$$

Hence

$$\Delta_j^{j-1}(s) = \Delta_j(s) \Big/ \prod_{i=1}^{j-1} t_i(s). \tag{32}$$

But from Theorem 5:

$$\Delta_j^{j-1}(s) = g_{jj}^{j-1}(s) \prod_{i=1}^{j-1} [g_{ii}^{i-1}(s) + 0(1/\alpha)]/t_i(s). \tag{33}$$

The result follows directly.

3. THE DESIGN ALGORITHM

For $i = 1 \dots m$, let $G_c^i(s)$ denote a compensating matrix, representing a sequence of elementary (column) operators, so that $|G_c^i(s)| = 1$, having the structure:

$$G_c^i(s) = \begin{bmatrix} I_{i-1} & 0 \\ 0 & X \end{bmatrix}.$$

Algorithm

(i) Recorder inputs and outputs as required

(ii) Choose $G_c^1(s)$.

Set $G^{0,\alpha}(s) = G_p^\alpha(s) G_c^1(s)$, $\alpha = 1 \dots N$.

Set $i = 1$.

(iii) Set $t_i^\alpha(s) = 1 + k_i(s) g_{ii}^{i-1,\alpha}(s)$, $\alpha = 1 \dots N$.

Choose $k_i(s)$.

(iv) If $i = m$, stop. Otherwise, for $\alpha = 1 \dots N$

Set $\bar{k}_i^\alpha(s) = k_i(s)/t_i^\alpha(s)$.

Set $G^{i,\alpha}(s) = G^{i-1,\alpha}(s) - \bar{k}_i^\alpha(s) g_{.i}^{i-1,\alpha}(s) g_{i.}^{i-1,\alpha}(s)$.

(v) Choose $G_c^{i+1}(s)$. $(G_c^m(s) = I_m)$:

Set $G^{i,\alpha}(s) = G^{i,\alpha}(s) G_c^{i+1}(s)$, $\alpha = 1 \dots N$.

Set $i = i + 1$.

(vi) Go to (ii).

Comment

1. The final compensation matrix is:

$$G_c(s) = G_c^1(s) . G_c^2(s) \dots G_c^m(s).$$

Because of the structure of G_c^i, $i = 1 \dots m$

$$T_i^\alpha(s) \underline{\Delta} I_m + G_p^\alpha(s) G_c(s) K_i(s)$$
$$= I_m + G_p^\alpha(s)[G_c^1(s) \dots G_c^i(s)] K_i(s)$$

so that T_i^α is unaffected by G_c^j, $j > i$. It is easily deduced that the theorems of §2 are unaffected by this sequential choice of G_c.

2. If an approximate lower triangular system is required, $G_c^{i,1}(s)$ must be chosen so that $g_{ij}^{i-1,1}(j\omega) \doteqdot 0$, $j = i+1, \dots m$, for all $\omega \varepsilon \Omega$. If an approximate diagonal system is required, in addition to the above, $G_c^1(s)$ must be chosen so that $G^{0,1}(j\omega)$ is approximately upper triangular.

3. In addition $G_c^i(s)$ must be chosen so that, if possible, $g_{ii}^{i-1,1}(s)$ is minimum phase, $i = 1 \dots m-1$.

4. Since $|G_c(s)| \equiv 1$, it follows from Theorem 6, that, if m high-gain loops are possible, i.e. $|G_p(s)|$ is minimum phase, then:

$$\prod_{i=1}^{m} g_{ii}^{i-1,1}(s) = |G_p(s)| + 0(1/\alpha)$$

so that G_c, in effect, shares the magnitude and phase characteristics of $G_p(j\omega)$ between the various loops.

Note that if $|G_p(s)|$ has right half zeros, these zeros will appear in one or more loops if the remaining loops are tight.

5. $k_i(s)$ is chosen so that the Nyquist loci γ_i^α, $\alpha = 1 \dots N$, do not encircle the origin, and, if possible, $|t_i^1(j\omega)| \gg 1$ for $\omega \varepsilon \Omega$.

6. If the resultant system is not satisfactory, $K(s)$ can be altered by repeating the design procedure with $G^{0,\alpha}(s)$ set equal to $G^{m,\alpha}(s)$ of the first iteration, $\alpha = 1 \dots N$, (which is approximately diagonal if m high loop gains were achieved in the first iteration) and $G_c(s)$ left unaltered. However the designer will now "see" $G^{m,\alpha}$ which differs appreciably from $G^{0,\alpha}$, the original system with compensation.

4. ILLUSTRATIVE EXAMPLES

Example 1, from [2].

$$(1+2s)(1+3s)G_p(s)=\begin{bmatrix}4(s+1) & -2\\ -2 & 4(s+1)\end{bmatrix}.$$

(a) Security in case of failure of loop 2 only required. Since

$$|G_p(s)|=16(s^2+2s+0{\cdot}75)/(1+2s)^2(1+3s)^2$$

two tight loops are possible. $g^{\circ}_{11}(s)$ is minimum phase with $G^1_c=G_c=I_2$. *Note that if $m=2$, it is only necessary to choose G_c so that $g^{\circ}_{11}(s)$ is minimum phase.* From Theorem 6, with the first loop tight

$$g^1_{22}(s)\doteqdot\Delta_2(s)/\Delta_1(s)$$
$$=4(s^2+2s+0{\cdot}75)/(1+2s)(1+3s)(1+s)$$

which is also easily controlled.

(b) Security for failure of either loop is required.

$$G^1_p(s)\triangleq G_p(s)$$
$$G^2_p(s)\triangleq\begin{bmatrix}0 & 0\\ -2 & 4(s+1)\end{bmatrix}.$$

It should be noted that $\alpha=2$ corresponds to failure of transducer 1. Failure of transducer 2 is already coped with by the procedure. To avoid too large a demand on k_2 choose $G^1_c=G_c$ so that $G^{0,1}$ is approximately lower triangular, e.g.

$$G_c=\begin{bmatrix}1 & 1/2\\ 0 & 1\end{bmatrix},\ \text{so that}$$

$$(1+2s)(1+3s)G^{0,1}(s)=\begin{bmatrix}4(s+1) & 2s\\ -2 & 4s+3\end{bmatrix}$$

which is lower triangular at $s=0$. Also:

$$(1+2s)(1+3s)G^{0,2}(s)=\begin{bmatrix}0 & 0\\ -2 & 4s+3\end{bmatrix}.$$

Hence:

$$g^{1,1}_{22}(s)\doteqdot4(s^2+2s+0{\cdot}75)/(1+2s)(1+3s)(1+s)$$
$$g^{1,2}_{22}(s)=(4s+3)/(1+2s)(1+3s)$$

$k_2(s)$ must be chosen so that $t^1_2(s)=1+k_1(s)g^{1,1}_{22}(s)$, $t^2_2(s)=1+k_1(s)g^{1,2}_{22}(s)$ are satisfactory. By virtue of the choice of G_c, $t^1_2(0)\doteqdot t^2_2(0)=1+3k_2(0)$ whereas with the previous choice of G_c:

$$g^{1,2}_{22}(s)=4(s+1)/(1+2s)(1+3s)$$

so that $t^1_2(0)\doteqdot1+3k_2(0)$, $t^2_2(0)=1+4k_2(0)$.

Example 2, from [2].

$$(1+s)^2G_p(s)=\begin{bmatrix}1-s & 1/3-s\\ 2-s & 1-s\end{bmatrix}.$$

Security in case of failure of loop 2 only is required.

$$|G_p(s)|=(1/3)(1+s)/(1+s)^4$$

so that two tight loops are possible, despite the right half plane zeros in G_p, and G_c can be chosen to make only g°_{11} satisfactory.

With:

$$G_c(s)=\begin{bmatrix}1 & 0\\ -2 & 1\end{bmatrix}$$

$$(1+s)^2G(s)=\begin{bmatrix}1/3+s & 1/3-s\\ s & 1-s\end{bmatrix}$$

and

$$g^{\circ}_{11}(s)=(1/3+s)/(1+s)^2$$

being minimum phase is easily controlled. With the first loop tight:

$$g^1_{22}(s)\doteqdot1/[3(1+s)(1/3+s)]$$

which is also easily controlled.

5. CONCLUSION

The above procedure is in the spirit of ROSENBROCK's proposals [2]. Its main feature is a simple procedure for calculating the effect on the transfer function, of closing each loop, and the effect of each component failure. The procedure provides some increased flexibility in the choice of G_c, since diagonal dominance is not required, although it can be incorporated if desired. Whether this increased flexibility offers significant advantages has yet to be assessed. In the basic algorithm, when security and interaction are not considered, G is not necessarily approximately diagonal or triangular. This has the following consequences:

(i) failure of loop j may cause instability if $j<m$.

(ii) it is not evident what is a good order of loop closings.

However if G_c is chosen so that G is approximately diagonal, or diagonally dominant, or approximately triangular the above difficulties disappear, since the loops are essentially independent. In fact, an advantage of the procedure is that the triangular structure is permitted. The effect of each component failure, in the general algorithm, is precisely calculated. This has the advantage of presenting precise information to the designer, but requires more calculation. This does not seem to be significant for $m=2,3$.

Acknowledgements—The basic algorithm given in (section 3) has been implemented, in a conversational mode, by I. S. Gordon, on a PDP-9 computer with visual display, using software developed by P. M. Newbold, as part of a project supported by the Science Research Council. The work described here has also been supported, in part, by the Joint Services Electronic Program NONR Contract N00014-67-A-029-0006 administered by Harvard University. The author's debt to Rosenbrock is obvious. The author is also grateful to A.G.J. MacFarlane for his comments and criticisms.

REFERENCES

[1] S. D. G. CUMMING: Ph.D. Thesis, Imperial College of Science and Technology (1969).

[2] H. H. ROSENBROCK: Design of multivariable control systems using the inverse Nyquist array. *Proc. IEE* **116**, 1929 (1969).

[3] A. G. J. MACFARLANE: Return-difference and return-ratio matrices and their use in the analysis and synthesis of multivariable control systems. *Proc. IEE* **117**, 2037 (1970)

[4] D. Q. MAYNE: A simple derivation of the relation $|T(s)=p_c(s)/p_o(s)$. Report 71/8, Department of Computing and Control, Imperial College of Science and Technology (1971).

[5] H. H. ROSENBROCK: On the Design of Linear Multivariable Control Systems, Proceedings of the 3rd IFAC Congress, London (1966).

[6] H. H. ROSENBROCK: The stability of multivariable systems. *Trans. IEEE Aut. Control* **16**, 105 (1971).

APPENDIX

A simple proof of Theorem I

Theorem 1:

$$|T(s)| = \rho_c(s)/\rho_o(s).$$

Proof

$$\begin{aligned}\rho_c(s) &= |sI - A + BC| \\ &= |sI - A||I + (sI - A)^{-1}BC| \\ &= \rho_o(s)|I + C(sI - A)^{-1}B|\end{aligned}$$

using the fact that if F is $n \times m$, G is $m \times n$, then:

$$|I_n + FG| = |I_m + GF|.$$

But:

$$G(s) = C(sI - A)^{-1}B$$

Hence:

$$\begin{aligned}\rho_c(s) &= \rho_o(s)|I + G(s)| \\ &= \rho_o(s)|T(s)|.\end{aligned}$$

Résumé—Cet exposé décrit une procédure utilisant un ordinateur, par laquelle une suite de conceptions à boucle simple avec lieux Nyquist, donne une conception multivariable stable et qui atténue les perturbations. La procédure permet une plus grande souplesse que jusqué là possible dans le choix de la matrice de la procédure compensatrice. Il est montré comment une simple modification de la procédure offre une assurance contre la défaillance des éléments.

Zusammenfassung—Beschrieben wird eine rechnergestützte Prozedur, wobei eine Folge von einschleifigen Entwürfen unter Benutzung von Nyquist-Kurven einen multivariablen Entwurf ergibt, der stabil ist und Störungen dämpft. Die Prozedur erlaubt mehr Freiheit als bisher bei der Wahl der Kompensationsmatrix. Gezeigt wird, wie eine einfache Modifikation der Prozedur Sicherheit gegen vorkommende Komponentenfehler ermöglicht.

Резюме—В этой работе описывается процедура, при которой с помощью счетно-вычислительной машины из ряда одноконтурных конструкций, пользуясь годографами Найквиста можно получить многовариантную устойчивую конструкцию, которая ослабляет нарушения. Процедура дает больше свободы, чем это было раньше, для вытора компенсирующей матрицы. Показано, как простое видоизменение процедуры может обеспечить ъезопасность при неисправностях компонентов.

Dyadic expansion, characteristic loci and multivariable-control-systems design

D.H. Owens, B.Sc., Ph.D., A.R.C.S.

Indexing terms: Control-system synthesis, Multivariable control systems

Abstract

Recent results in the dyadic representation of system interactions are used to derive a systematic approach to the manipulation and compensation of the characteristic loci of a system described by the $N \times N$ transfer-function matrix $G(s)$, using rational-transfer-function approximations to the characteristic loci. The approach is thought to strengthen the link between single-input and multivariable control-system design techniques by releasing well known classical compensation techniques for application to multivariable systems.

List of symbols

s = Laplace-transform variable
$G(s)$ = $N \times N$ matrix of plant transfer function
$K(s)$ = $N \times N$ matrix of controller transfer functions
$K(s,\omega_1)$ = $N \times N$ controller in the vicinity of $s = i\omega_1$
A^+ = adjoint or conjugate transpose of matrix A
A^T = transpose of matrix A
$|A|$ = determinant of matrix A
δ_{jl} = Kronecker delta function

diag $\{\lambda_1,\lambda_2,...,\lambda_N\}$ = diag $\{\lambda_j\}_{1<j<N}$ = diagonal matrix with $\lambda_1,\lambda_2,..$ along the diagonal

1 Introduction

In recent papers,[1,2] the dyadic description of the interaction structure of a plant described by an $N \times N$ transfer-function matrix $G(s)$ has been applied to the analysis of synthesis of feedback control systems for a class of nuclear-reactor spatial instabilities. In such cases, the approach has several important advantages:

(*a*) If $G(s)$ is a dyadic transfer-function matrix, a dyadic description of system-interaction structure makes possible the determination of a simple controller structure which decouples the output modes of the system. The N modal loops can then be designed independently using single-loop design concepts.

(*b*) The interpretation of the magnitude, form and frequency dependence of the plant dyadic structure is an important link between the physical insight available into process dynamics and the theoretical frequency-domain analysis. Such information can provide estimates of the effect of modelling errors on the final closed-loop design[3] and a technique for synthesising fail-safe feedback control systems[1,2].

It has been demonstrated[4] that similar considerations can alleviate difficulties arising in the application of sequential-return-difference (s.r.d.)[5] and inverse-Nyquist-array (i.n.a.)[6] design techniques.

Despite their relevance to reactor-control-system design, dyadic and approximately dyadic structures represent only a subclass of possible physical systems. This paper extends the previous results using a combination of the general principles of the characteristic-locus design method[8] and recent results[7] on the general dyadic representation of system interactions to propose a straightforward approach to the modification and compensation of general-system characteristic loci. The basic theoretical ideas are described in Section 2, where it is shown that an interplay between the concepts of modal decoupling[2,7] and characteristic loci[8] and the use of Gershgorin's theorem[9] permits the exact allocation of the characteristic loci at a particular frequency and the approximation of the loci in the vicinity of that point by rational polynomial transfer functions. An illustrative example is described in Section 3.

Finally, in Section 6, an analytic solution is obtained for a simple class of multivariable-feedback-control problems. This solution is used as a conceptual aid in Section 3.

2 Dyadic expansion, modal decoupling and characteristic loci

Consider a unity-negative-feedback configuration for the control of a system described by the $N \times N$ transfer-function matrix $G(s)$. Let $K(s)$ be the $N \times N$ forward path controller and D the usual Nyquist contour in the complex plane, traversed in the clockwise direction. It is well known[8] that the ratio of the system closed-loop characteristic polynomial to the system open-loop characteristic polynomial is given by the determinant of the return-difference matrix $T(s) = I + G(s)K(s)$. If $\{t_k(s)\}_{1<k<N}$ are the eigenvalues of $G(s)K(s)$,

$$|T(s)| = \prod_{k=1}^{N} \{1 + t_k(s)\} \tag{1}$$

If the image of D under $t_k(s)$ is defined as the kth characteristic locus,[8] and if p_0 is the number of right-half plane zeros of the open-loop characteristic polynomial, the closed-loop system is stable if, and only if,[8]

$$\sum_{k=1}^{N} n_k = -p_0 \tag{2}$$

where n_k is the number of clockwise encirclements of the kth characteristic locus about the $(-1,0)$ point of the complex plane.

The above result has been used to form the basis of the characteristic-locus method for multivariable-feedback-control-systems design.[8] The approach regards the design objective as the gain and phase compensation of the characteristic loci of the original plant $G(s)$ by the choice of a suitable controller $K(s)$. Unfortunately, as there is no general formula giving the eigenvalues of the product of two matrices as a function of the eigenvalues of the individual matrices, the systematic choice and modification of $K(s)$ to produce the required loci compensation is a major practical problem. The aim of this Section is to provide a framework for a systematic approach to the solution of this problem using recent results[7] on the dyadic representation of system interactions. The problem is regarded in three stages:

(i) The choice of a controller $K(s,\omega_1)$ such that the eigenvalues of $G(s)K(s,\omega_1)$ take specified values at $s = i\omega_1$. For practical purposes, both $G(s)$ and $K(s,\omega_1)$ are assumed to be analytic at $s = i\omega_1$ and non singular.

(ii) The systematic investigation of the effects of a particular choice of controller $K(s,\omega_1)$ on the characteristic loci in the vicinity of $s = i\omega_1$, and the use of such information in the choice of suitable compensation elements in $K(s,\omega_1)$.

(iii) By repeating (i) and (ii) at selected frequencies $\omega_1, \omega_2,...,\omega_l$, the controller matrix

$$K(s) = \sum_{j=1}^{l} K(s,\omega_j) \tag{3}$$

will produce the desired characteristic loci provided that each term $K(s,\omega_j)$ dominates the summation in the vicinity of $s = i\omega_j$.

2.1 Manipulation of characteristic loci at a given frequency

Consider the problem of the choice of a controller $K(s,\omega_1)$ such that the eigenvalues of $G(s)K(s,\omega_1)$ take specified values at $s = i\omega_1$. A solution is obtained below using the concepts of dyadic expansion and model decoupling.[7]

Consider the case when $|G(i\omega_1)| \neq 0$ and the matrix $G(-i\omega_1)G^{-1}(i\omega_1)$ has a complete set of eigenvectors $\{\alpha_k(\omega_1)\}_{1<k<N}$. Previous results[7] imply that

Paper 7378 C, first received 23rd August and in revised form 13th November 1974

Dr. Owens is with the Department of Control Engineering, University of Sheffield, Mappin Street, Sheffield S1 3JD, England

Reprinted with permission from *Proc. Inst. Elec. Eng.*, vol. 122, pp. 315–320, Mar. 1975.

$$G(i\omega_1) = \sum_{k=1}^{N} h_k(i\omega_1)\boldsymbol{\alpha}_k(\omega_1)\boldsymbol{\beta}_k^+(\omega_1) \qquad (4)$$

where $\{h_k(i\omega_1)\}_{1<k<N}$ are nonzero complex numbers and $\{\boldsymbol{\alpha}_k(\omega_1)\boldsymbol{\beta}_k^+(\omega_1)\}_{1<k<N}$ is a set of linearly independent dyads which are real or exist in complex conjugate pairs. In general, $\{\boldsymbol{\alpha}_k(\omega_1)\}_{1<k<N}$ are not the eigenvectors of $G(i\omega_1)$ and $\{h_k(i\omega_1)\}_{1<k<N}$ are not the eigenvalues.[7] However, defining

$$K_D(\omega_1) = \{\sum_{k=1}^{N}\boldsymbol{\alpha}_k(\omega_1)\boldsymbol{\beta}_k^+(\omega_1)\}^{-1} \qquad (5)$$

then[7] $K_D(\omega_1)$ is real and nonsingular and $(K_D(\omega_1))^{-1}K_D(\omega_1) = I$ implies that, for $1 \leqslant j$ and $k \leqslant N$,

$$\boldsymbol{\beta}_j^+(\omega_1)K_D(\omega_1)\boldsymbol{\alpha}_k(\omega_1) = \delta_{jk} \qquad (6)$$

and hence, for $1 \leqslant l \leqslant N$,

$$G(i\omega_1)K_D(\omega_1)\boldsymbol{\alpha}_l(\omega_1) = h_l(i\omega_1)\boldsymbol{\alpha}_l(\omega_1) \qquad (7)$$

i.e. $\{\boldsymbol{\alpha}_k(\omega_1)\}_{1<k<N}$ and $\{h_k(i\omega_1)\}_{1<k<N}$ are the eigenvectors and eigenvalues of $G(i\omega_1)K_D(\omega_1)$. In previous papers,[1,2] physical considerations have led to the term natural motions or modes for the vectors $\{\boldsymbol{\alpha}_k(\omega_1)\}$, and, in view of eqn. 7, the choice of controller $K_D(\omega_1)$ is termed modal decoupling and $K_D(\omega_1)$ is a decoupling matrix at the frequency ω_1.

Suppose that the desired values of the characteristic loci at $s = i\omega_1$ are $q_1, q_2, \ldots, q_N$. A suitable controller matrix $K(s,\omega_1)$ is obtained using modal decoupling to be the dyadic transfer-function matrix[2]

$$K(s,\omega_1) = K_D(\omega_1)\sum_{j=1}^{N} k_j(s,\omega_1)\boldsymbol{\alpha}_j(\omega_1)\boldsymbol{\gamma}_j^+(\omega_1) \qquad (8)$$

where $\{\boldsymbol{\gamma}_j^+(\omega_1)\}_{1<j<N}$ are vectors such that, $1 \leqslant j, l \leqslant N$,

$$\boldsymbol{\gamma}_j^+(\omega_1)\boldsymbol{\alpha}_l(\omega_1) = \delta_{jl} \qquad (9)$$

$\{k_j(s,\omega_1)\}_{1<j<N}$ are scalar rational polynomial transfer functions such that

$$k_j(i\omega_1,\omega_1) = q_j/h_j(i\omega_1) \qquad (10)$$

and, for $1 \leqslant j \leqslant N$, if $\overline{\boldsymbol{\alpha}_j(\omega_1)} = \boldsymbol{\alpha}_l(\omega_1)$,

$$k_j(\bar{s},\omega_1) = \overline{k_l(s,\omega_1)} \text{ for all } s \qquad (11)$$

Eqn. 11, together with the invariance of $\{\boldsymbol{\alpha}_k(\omega_1)\boldsymbol{\beta}_k^+(\omega_1)\}_{1<k<N}$ under complex conjugation, ensures that $K(\bar{s},\omega_1) = \overline{K(s,\omega_1)}$ everywhere in the complex plane. Eqns. 7–10 indicate that

$$\begin{aligned} G(i\omega_1)K(i\omega_1,\omega_1)\boldsymbol{\alpha}_l(\omega_1) &= G(i\omega_1)K_D(\omega_1)\sum_{j=1}^{N} k_j(i\omega_1,\omega_1)\boldsymbol{\alpha}_j(\omega_1) \\ &\quad \{\boldsymbol{\gamma}_j^+(\omega_1)\boldsymbol{\alpha}_l(\omega_1)\} \\ &= G(i\omega_1)K_D(\omega_1)\{q_l/h_l(i\omega_1)\}\boldsymbol{\alpha}_l(\omega_1) \\ &= q_l\boldsymbol{\alpha}_l(\omega_1) \quad \text{for} \quad 1 \leqslant l \leqslant N \end{aligned} \qquad (12)$$

so that $\{q_l\}_{1<l<N}$ are the eigenvalues of $G(i\omega_1)K(i\omega_1,\omega_1)$ as required and the modes $\{\boldsymbol{\alpha}_l(\omega_1)\}_{1<l<N}$ are the eigenvectors.

As the structure and orders of the compensation networks $\{k_j(s,\omega_1)\}_{1<j<N}$ are unspecified except for the constraints of eqns. 10 and 11, the matrix $K(s,\omega_1)$ is obviously nonunique. A technique for using these degrees of freedom in the compensation of the characteristic loci in the vicinity of $s = i\omega_1$ is described in the following Section.

2.2 Manipulation of characteristic loci in a frequency interval

It is convenient to manipulate $G(s)K(s,\omega_1)$ into a more amenable form by defining

$$T(\omega_1) = [\boldsymbol{\alpha}_1(\omega_1), \ldots, \boldsymbol{\alpha}_N(\omega_1)] \qquad (13)$$

and noting from eqns. 8 and 9 that

$$T^{-1}(\omega_1)G(s)K(s,\omega_1)T(\omega_1) = H(s,\omega_1)\operatorname{diag}\{k_1(s,\omega_1), \ldots, k_N(s,\omega_1)\} \qquad (14)$$

where

$$H(s,\omega_1) = T^{-1}(\omega_1)G(s)K_D(\omega_1)T(\omega_1) \qquad (15)$$

is a transfer-function matrix with rational polynomial elements. The common denominator of the elements of $H(s,\omega_1)$ is simply the common denominator of elements of $G(s)$. In general, the coefficients in the numerator polynomials of $H(s,\omega_1)$ are complex, but, if $\{\boldsymbol{\alpha}_j(\omega_1)\}_{1<j<N}$ are real vectors, all such coefficients are real numbers.

As eigenvalues are invariant under similarity transformation, the characteristic loci of $G(s)K(s,\omega_1)$ are identical to the characteristic loci of $H(s,\omega_1)\operatorname{diag}\{k_j(s,\omega_1)\}$. Also, the eigenvalues of $H(s,\omega_1)\operatorname{diag}\{k_j(s,\omega_1)\}$ are equal to the eigenvalues of $\operatorname{diag}\{k_j(s,\omega_1)\}H(s,\omega_1)$. Using this information, an estimate of the effect of a particular set of compensation elements $\{k_j(s,\omega_1)\}$ on the characteristic loci can be obtained by applying Gershgorin's theorem[9] to eqn. 14; i.e. the eigenvalues of $G(s)K(s,\omega_1)$ lie in the union of the closed discs $B_j(s,\omega_1)$ of centre $H_{jj}(s,\omega_1)k_j(s,\omega_1)$ and radius $d_j(s,\omega_1)$, where

$$d_j(s,\omega_1) = |k_j(s,\omega_1)|\sum_{i \neq j}|H_{ji}(s,\omega_1)| \text{ (row estimate)} \qquad (16)$$

or

$$d_j(s,\omega_1) = |k_j(s,\omega_1)|\sum_{i \neq j}|H_{ij}(s,\omega_1)| \text{ (column estimate)} \qquad (17)$$

Also, from eqns. 7 and 15, it follows that $H(s,\omega_1)$ is diagonal at $s = i\omega_1$ with eigenvalues $H_{jj}(i\omega_1,\omega_1) = h_j(i\omega_1)$. Hence, from eqns. 14, 16 and 17, $G(i\omega_1)K(i\omega_1,\omega_1)$ has eigenvalues $H_{jj}(i\omega_1,\omega_1)k_j(i\omega_1,\omega_1)$ and

$$d_j(i\omega_1,\omega_1) = 0 \quad \text{for} \quad 1 \leqslant j \leqslant N \qquad (18)$$

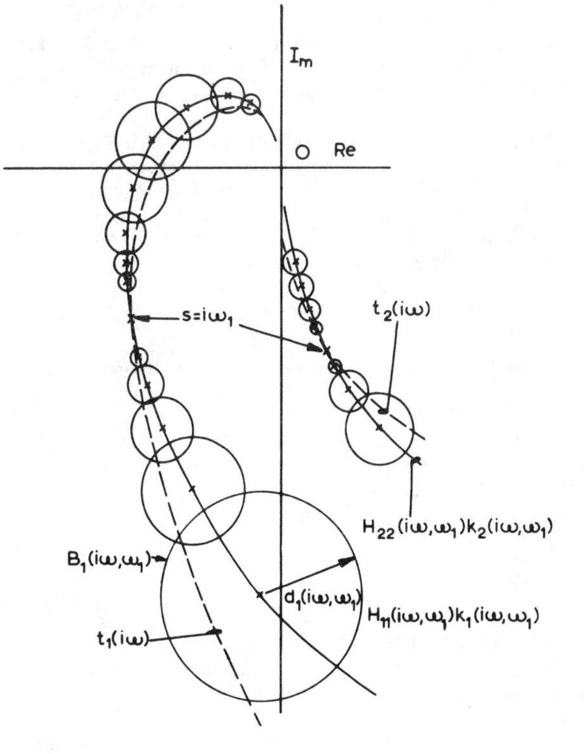

Fig. 1
Schematic representation of rational approximations

so that the Gershgorin circles at the point $s = i\omega_1$ have zero radius. A graphical representation of these ideas is given in Fig. 1 for $N = 2$.

The above analysis suggests intuitively that, in the vicinity of the point $s = i\omega_1$ where (eqn. 18) the Gershgorin circles are small, the diagonal terms $\{H_{jj}(s,\omega_1)k_j(s,\omega_1)\}_{1<j<N}$ will be reasonable approximations to the characteristic loci $\{t_j(s)\}_{1<j<N}$ of $G(s)K(s,\omega_1)$ in the sense that

$$t_j(s) \in B_j(s,\omega_1) \quad \text{for} \quad 1 \leqslant j \leqslant N \qquad (19)$$

and the fractional error, for $1 \leqslant j \leqslant N$,

$$\frac{|t_j(s) - H_{jj}(s,\omega_1)k_j(s,\omega_1)|}{|H_{jj}(s,\omega_1)k_j(s,\omega_1)|} \leqslant \frac{d_j(s,\omega_1)}{|H_{jj}(s,\omega_1)k_j(s,\omega_1)|} \qquad (20)$$

is small. With these assumptions, eqns. 16 and 17 indicate that the fractional error is independent of the chosen compensators $\{k_j(s,\omega_1)\}_{1<j<N}$ and hence that the validity of the loci approximations depends only on the extent to which $H(s,\omega_1)$ is diagonally dominant in the vicinity of $s = i\omega_1$.

The intuitive approach described above can be applied directly to the assessment of the effect of a particular choice of $\{k_j(s,\omega_1)\}$ on the characteristic loci of $G(s)K(s,\omega_1)$ in the vicinity of $s = i\omega_1$ by an analysis of the products $H_{jj}(s,\omega_1)k_j(s,\omega_1)$, $1 \leq j \leq N$. Also, bearing in mind that $H_{jj}(s,\omega_1)$, $1 \leq j \leq N$, are rational polynomials in s, the approach provides an intuitive but systematic approach to the choice of compensation elements $\{k_j(s,\omega_1)\}$ by the application of single-variable techniques (e.g. pole–zero analysis) to each approximation $H_{jj}(s,\omega_1)$ in turn. An example illustrating the approach is given in Section 3.

It is important to note that the characteristic loci of $G(s)K(s.\omega_1)$ do not, in general, satisfy expr. 19. For example, consider the matrix

$$\begin{bmatrix} 10 & 10i \\ i & 1 \end{bmatrix} \tag{21}$$

which has eigenvalues 8·7 and 2·3. This implies that the error bounds of eqn. 20 can be overoptimistic. However, if the process of compensation in the vicinity of $s = i\omega_1$ is regarded as an attempt to equalise the loci $H_{jj}(s,i\omega_1)k_j(s,i\omega_1)$ in that region, a consideration of perfect compensation, i.e. $H_{ll}(s,i\omega_1)k_l(s,i\omega_1) = H_{jj}(s,i\omega_1)k_j(s,i\omega_1)$, $1 \leq j$, $l \leq N$, and application of Gershgorin's theorem indicates that, for $1 \leq j \leq N$,

$$\frac{|t_j(s) - H_{jj}(s,\omega_1)k_j(s,\omega_1)|}{|H_{jj}(s,\omega_1)k_j(s,\omega_1)|} \leq \max_{1 \leq j \leq N} \frac{d_j(s,\omega_1)}{|H_{jj}(s,\omega_1)k(s,\omega_1)|} \tag{22}$$

i.e. the uncertainty in the position of the actual characteristic loci can be reduced by the very act of system compensation. In such cases, expr. 19 can be regarded as a feasible assumption for practical applications.

Finally, the size of the frequency interval over which the approximation is sensibly valid is an important consideration in practical applications. This will vary with the choice of ω_1 and the complexity of the interaction structure of the system under consideration. However, the example of Section 3 and previous experience with applications of the technique of dyadic approximation[1,2] imply that it can be large enough to make the approach a useful addition to already available multivariable-control-systems design aids.

2.3 Approach to multivariable-control-systems design

Based on the analysis of Sections 2.1 and . 2.2, the following procedure is suggested for the systematic manipulation and compensation of open-loop-system characteristic loci. The controller is based on the form

$$K(s) = \sum_{p=1}^{l} K(s,\omega_P) \tag{23}$$

where $\omega_1,...,\omega_l$ are distinct frequencies at which it is desired to manipulate the system characteristic loci. For theoretical purposes, it is assumed that the term $K(s,\omega_k)$ dominates the summation in the vicinity of $s = i\omega_k$ and hence that compensation achieved in this region is largely unaffected by subsequent design exercises in other frequency intervals. For practical purposes, the choice of $l = 2$, ω_1 and ω_2 as representative high and low frequencies, respectively, and $K(s,\omega_1)$, $K(s,\omega_2)$ as lead–lag and integral terms, respectively, should satisfy this assumption.

Step 1: Choose distinct frequencies $\omega_1 > \omega_2 > ... > \omega_l$ at which compensation of the characteristic loci is required. Set $j = 1$.

Step 2: Using the results of Sections 2.1 and 2.2, calculate the decoupling matrix $K_D(\omega_j)$ and transformation $T(\omega_j)$. Hence calculate the transfer-function matrix (eqn. 15) $H(s,\omega_j)$.

Step 3: Using the rational polynomials $\{H_{ll}(s,\omega_j)k_l(s,\omega_j)\}_{1 \leq l \leq N}$ as approximations to the system characteristic loci in the vicinity of $s = i\omega_j$, use single-loop design concepts to choose compensation networks $k_p(s,\omega_j)$, $1 \leq p \leq N$, so that the products $H_{pp}(s,\omega_j)k_p(s,\omega_j)$, $1 \leq p \leq N$, have the required properties in that region. Calculate $K(s,\omega_j)$ from eqn. 8.

Step 4: Compute the characteristic loci of $G(s) \sum_{p=1}^{j} K(s,\omega_p)$ to check that the desired loci characteristics have been obtained in the vicinity of $s = i\omega_j$ and also that compensation at the frequencies $\omega_1,\omega_2,...,\omega_{j-1}$ is unaffected.

Step 5: If $j = l$, set the controller to be as in eqn. 22. If $j < l$, replace j by $j + 1$ and go to step 2.

The application of the above procedure is illustrated in the following Section by an example.

3 Illustrative example

Consider a system with input-output relations defined by the transfer-function matrix

$$G(s) = \frac{1}{\Delta(s)} \begin{bmatrix} 32{\cdot}6 + 16s + 2{\cdot}15s^2 & 9{\cdot}4 + 4s + 1{\cdot}1s^2 \\ 6{\cdot}2 + 4s + 1{\cdot}05s^2 & 3 + 4s + s^2 \end{bmatrix} \tag{24}$$

where

$$\Delta(s) = (s+1)(s+2)(s+3) \tag{25}$$

As interactive effects in the system transient response are dominated by intermediate- to high-frequency-response characteristics of the system,[8] attention is initially focused on this region. Choosing $\omega_1 = 8{\cdot}0$, and applying the procedure of Section 2.3, the eigenvectors of $G(-i8)G^{-1}(i8)$ are

$$\alpha_1(8) = [1 \quad 0]^T \qquad \alpha_2(8) = [1 \quad 1]^T \tag{26}$$

The procedure of Section 2.1 yields the decoupling matrix

$$K_D(8) = \begin{bmatrix} -13{\cdot}4 & 13{\cdot}4 \\ 13{\cdot}4 & 20{\cdot}6 \end{bmatrix} \tag{27}$$

and hence, by eqns. 13 and 15,

$$H(s,8) = \frac{1}{\Delta(s)} \begin{bmatrix} -268 - 160{\cdot}8s - 13{\cdot}4s^2 & 153{\cdot}8 + 2{\cdot}4s^2 \\ -60{\cdot}7 - 0{\cdot}95s^2 & 102 + 136s + 34s^2 \end{bmatrix} \tag{28}$$

which is a matrix of rational polynomial transfer functions with real coefficients. Note that the off-diagonal terms are zero at $s = i8$, as expected.

The diagonal terms are

$$H_{11}(s,8) = \frac{-13{\cdot}4(s+10)}{(s+1)(s+3)} \tag{29}$$

and

$$H_{22}(s,8) = \frac{34{\cdot}0}{(s+2)} \tag{30}$$

Plots of the frequency responses of these transfer functions are shown in Fig. 2, together with the actual characteristic loci of $G(s)K_D(8)$. It is seen that the diagonal terms are good approximations to the loci at high frequencies and quite acceptable approximations at low frequencies. Typical Gershgorin circles (based on row estimates) are also plotted in the frequency interval $1 \leq \omega < +\infty$ and it can be seen that the characteristic loci of $G(s)K_D(8)$ are contained within the band defined by the circles. The fractional errors (eqn. 20) are less than 0·5 at all frequencies greater than 1·0, and hence we can have reasonable confidence in the effect of compensation elements in this frequency range.

Using the diagonal terms (eqns. 29 and 30) as rational-transfer-function approximations to the characteristic loci, elementary single-variable concepts indicate that, to ensure stability of the closed-loop system for arbitrarily high gains, the loci $H_{11}(i\omega,8)$ must be rotated 180°. Introducing some phase advance into $H_{11}(s,8)$, the above considerations suggest compensation networks of the form

$$k_1(s,8) = -k_1 \frac{(s+1)}{(s+10)} \tag{31}$$

$$\text{and} \quad k_2(s,8) = k_2 \tag{32}$$

where k_1 and k_2 are positive real numbers; i.e.

$$H_{11}(s,8)k_1(s,8) = \frac{13{\cdot}4k_1}{(s+3)} \tag{33}$$

$$H_{22}(s,8)k_2(s,8) = \frac{34{\cdot}0k_2}{(s+2)} \tag{34}$$

Comparison of these forms with the analysis of Section 6 indicates that, if responses of the approximate form $1 - e^{-kt}$ are required in each loop, then an intuitive estimate of the gains k_1,k_2 can be obtained by solving the linear simultaneous equations

$$3 + 13{\cdot}4k_1 = k \tag{35}$$

$$2 + 34{\cdot}0k_2 = k \tag{36}$$

Choosing $k = 20$, for example,

$$k_1 = 1{\cdot}3 \quad \text{and} \quad k_2 = 0{\cdot}53 \tag{37}$$

and hence the high-frequency controller factor (eqn. 8) is set equal to

$$K(s,8) = -1{\cdot}3\frac{(s+1)}{(s+10)}\begin{bmatrix}-13{\cdot}4\\ 13{\cdot}4\end{bmatrix}[1 \quad -1] + 0{\cdot}53\begin{bmatrix}0\\ 35{\cdot}0\end{bmatrix}[0 \quad 1] \tag{38}$$

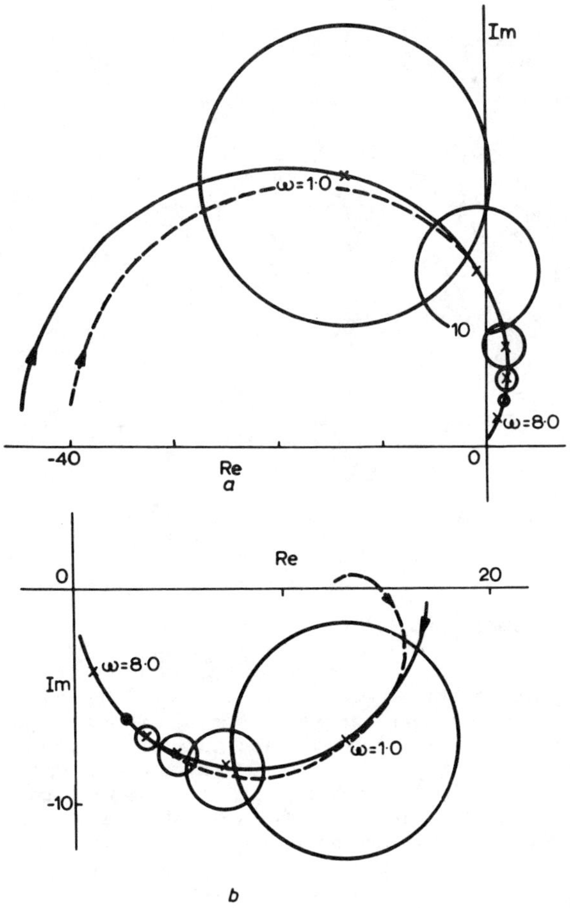

Fig. 2
Rational approximations and characteristic loci of $G(s)K_D(8)$

(a) $H_{11}(s,8)$ and $t_1(s)$
(b) $H_{22}(s,8)$ and $t_2(s)$
——— rational approximation
– – – – – characteristic loci

The characteristic loci of $G(s)K(s,8)$ are given in Fig. 3 together with the frequency responses $H_{jj}(s,8)k_j(s,8), j = 1,2$, for comparison. The desired compensation of the characteristic loci has been achieved with high accuracy at high frequencies, and with quite acceptable accuracy for intermediate frequencies ($\omega \geqslant 1{\cdot}0$). The closed-loop system is, in fact, asymptotically stable, and the design procedure could be terminated by the choice of controller $K(s) = K(s,8)$ (eqn. 38). However, the system responses to step inputs shown in Fig. 4 indicate that the steady-state errors and interaction effects are significant. Fig. 3 indicates that these could be reduced by increasing the overall gain of the system, or equivalently increasing the value of k in eqns. 35 and 36. For example, taking $k = 50$,

$$k_1 = 3{\cdot}5 \quad \text{and} \quad k_2 = 1{\cdot}4 \tag{39}$$

The svstem responses to step inputs for this case are shown in Fig. 5. The high-frequency controller factor $K(s,8)$ now becomes

$$K(s,8) = -3{\cdot}5\frac{(s+1)}{(s+10)}\begin{bmatrix}-13{\cdot}4\\ 13{\cdot}4\end{bmatrix}[1 \quad -1] + 1{\cdot}4\begin{bmatrix}0\\ 35{\cdot}0\end{bmatrix}[0 \quad 1] \tag{40}$$

The residual steady-state error and interaction effects can now be removed by the use of integral action. This can be achieved quite simply by applying the procedure of Section 2.3 in a frequency interval

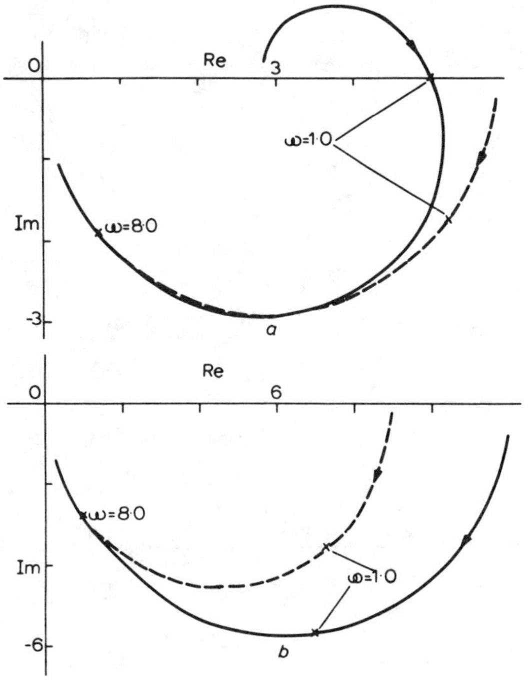

Fig. 3
Rational approximations and characteristic loci of $G(s)K(s,8)$

(a) $H_{11}(s,8)k_1(s,8)$ and $t_1(s)$
(b) $H_{22}(s,8)k_2(s,8)$ and $t_2(s)$
——— characteristic loci
– – – – – rational approximation

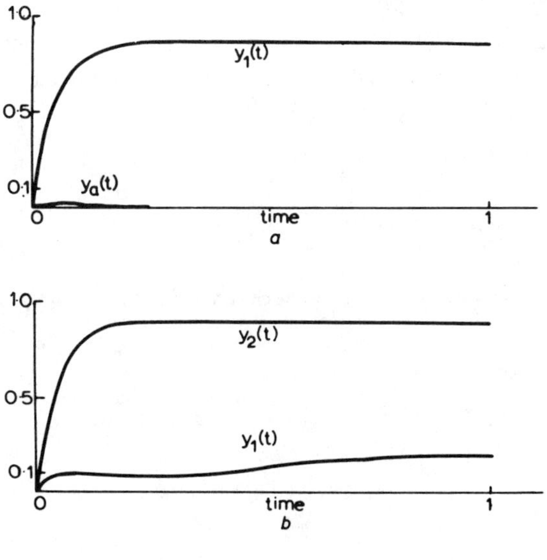

Fig. 4
System step responses

(a) Step input in channel 1
(b) Step input in channel 2

representative of low-frequency dynamics. However, low-frequency closed-loop dynamic responses are insensitive to the precise form of the compensation elements, provided that high controller gains are used and the system is closed-loop stable.[8] An adequate integral action can be obtained by using the technique of Section 2.1 to manipulate the characteristic loci at a representative low frequency. For example, taking $\omega_2 = 0{\cdot}5$ and applying the procedures of Section 2.1, the eigenvectors of $G(-i0{\cdot}5)G^{-1}(i0{\cdot}5)$ are

$$\alpha_1(0{\cdot}5) = \begin{bmatrix} -0{\cdot}23 \\ 0{\cdot}97 \end{bmatrix} \qquad \alpha_2(0{\cdot}5) = \begin{bmatrix} 0{\cdot}99 \\ 0{\cdot}17 \end{bmatrix} \tag{41}$$

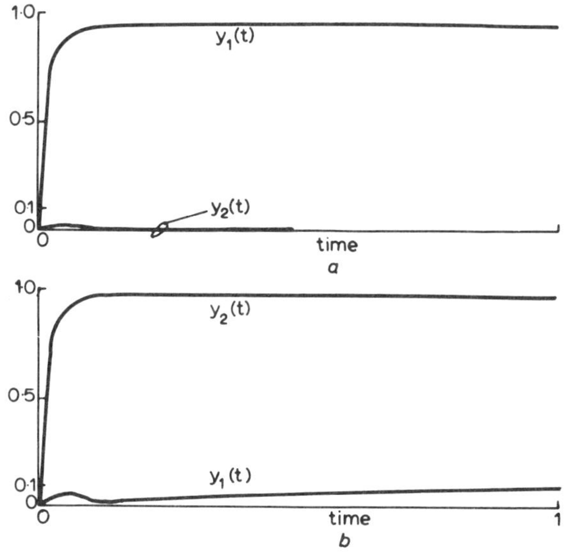

Fig. 5
System step responses

(*a*) Step input in channel 1
(*b*) Step input in channel 2

The decoupling matrix is

$$K_D(0{\cdot}5) = \begin{bmatrix} 0{\cdot}476 & -1{\cdot}06 \\ -0{\cdot}77 & 3{\cdot}85 \end{bmatrix} \tag{42}$$

and the eigenvalues of $G(i0{\cdot}5)K_D(0{\cdot}5)$ are

$$h_1(i0{\cdot}5) = 1{\cdot}0 + i0{\cdot}075$$
$$h_2(i0{\cdot}5) = 1{\cdot}0 - i0{\cdot}72 \tag{43}$$

Choosing $k_1(s,0{\cdot}5)$, $k_2(s,0{\cdot}5)$ to be pure integrators k_3/s, k_4/s, respectively, the gain of the eigenvalues of $G(s)K(s,0{\cdot}5)$ is equalised by setting,

$$|k_3h_1(i0{\cdot}5)| = |k_4h_2(i0{\cdot}5)| \tag{44}$$

i.e.

$$\left|\frac{k_3}{k_4}\right| = 1{\cdot}5 \tag{45}$$

The precise values of k_3, k_4 can now be chosen by a parametric analysis of the characteristic loci of $G(s)\{K(s,8) + K(s,0{\cdot}5)\}$. However, bearing in mind that the integral term will have only a small effect on the high-frequency loci of $G(s)K(s,8)$, the form of Fig. 3 and eqns. 43 indicate the desired low-frequency compensation can only be achieved by using positive values of k_4 and k_3. From eqns. 8 and 45, the controller integral becomes

$$K(s,0{\cdot}5) = \frac{k_4}{s}\begin{bmatrix} 0{\cdot}476 & -1{\cdot}06 \\ -0{\cdot}77 & 3{\cdot}85 \end{bmatrix}\begin{bmatrix} 1{\cdot}02 & -0{\cdot}11 \\ -0{\cdot}08 & 1{\cdot}48 \end{bmatrix}$$
$$= \frac{k_4}{s}\begin{bmatrix} 0{\cdot}57 & -1{\cdot}62 \\ -1{\cdot}09 & 5{\cdot}78 \end{bmatrix} \tag{46}$$

Trial-and-error simulation using a controller of the form (eqns. 46 and 40)

$$K(s) = K(s,8) + K(s,0{\cdot}5) \tag{47}$$

leads to a choice of $k_4 = 30{\cdot}0$. The transient responses for this final design are given in Fig. 6.

In summary, the use of dyadic expansions provides an approach to the synthesis of a feedback controller for the given system, by a systematic manipulation of the characteristic loci at high and low frequencies. System compensation is achieved very easily at high frequencies by approximating the system characteristic loci by the diagonal elements of the transfer function matrix $H(s,8)$ (eqn. 28) and applying well known single-input compensation procedures. Low-frequency control is obtained by using the method of Section 2.1 to balance the gains of the characteristic loci at a frequency of $\omega = 0{\cdot}5$. Fine tuning of the controller is then achieved by simulation studies.

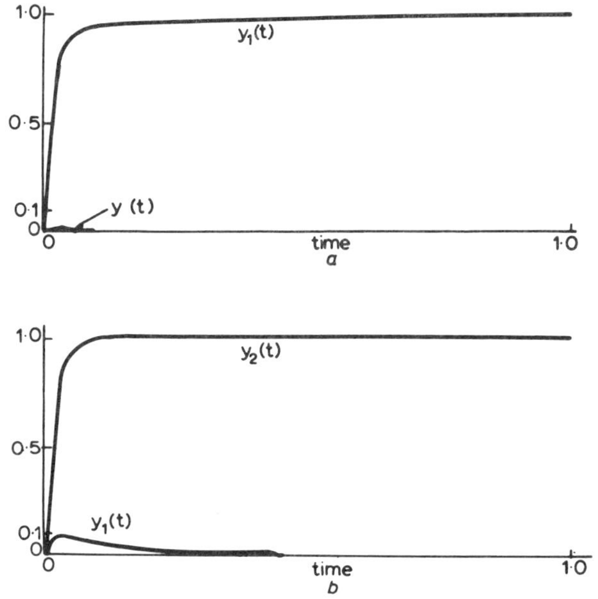

Fig. 6
System step responses

(*a*) Step input in channel 1
(*b*) Step input in channel 2

4 Conclusions

The paper presents a practical approach to the systematic manipulation of system characteristic loci for application to multivariable-feedback-control-systems design. The technique has the ability to manipulate exactly the loci at a given frequency point and to assess the effect of chosen compensation networks in the vicinity of that point. This is achieved by the use of rational transfer-function approximations to the system characteristic loci which are exact at the frequency of interest and in error at other frequencies to an extent defined by Gershgorin's theorem. This feature strengthens the link between single-input and multivariable-control design procedures by releasing well known single-variable compensation techniques for application to multivariable systems. The systematic nature of the approach is illustrated by an example, in which it is demonstrated that the use of rational approximations provides direct insight into suitable compensation networks.

As an aid to the analysis of Section 3, an analytical solution is obtained in Section 6 to a simple, but conceptually useful, class of multivariable-control problems.

5 References

1 OWENS, D.H.: 'Multivariable-control-system design concepts in failure analysis of a class of nuclear-reactor spatial-control systems', *Proc. IEE*, 1973, **120**, (1), pp. 119–125
2 OWENS, D.H.: 'Dyadic approximation method for multivariable control-systems analysis with a nuclear-reactor application', *ibid.*, 1973, **120**, (7), pp. 801–809
3 OWENS, D.H.: 'Multivariable control analysis of distributed parameter nuclear reactors'. Ph.D. thesis, London University, April 1973
4 OWENS, D.H.: 'Dyadic modification to sequential technique for multivariable-control-systems design', *Electron. Lett.*, 1974, **10**, pp. 25–26
5 MAYNE, D.Q.: 'The design of linear multivariable systems', *Automatica*, 1973, **9**, pp. 201–207
6 ROSENBROCK, H.H.: 'Design of multivariable control systems using the inverse Nyquist array', *Proc. IEE*, 1969, **116**, (11), pp. 1929–1936
7 OWENS' D.H.: 'Dyadic expansion for the analysis of linear multivariable systems', *ibid.*, 1974, **121**, (7), pp. 713–716
8 MACFARLANE, A'G'J. and BELLETRUTTI, J.J.: 'The characteristic locus design method', *Automatica*, 1973, **9**, pp. 575–588
9 ROSENBROCK, H.H. and STOREY, C.: 'Mathematics of dynamical systems' (Nelson, 1970), p. 105

6 Appendix

This appendix presents an approach to the design of a unity-feedback-control configuration for a system described by the $N \times N$ dyadic transfer-function matrix[7]

$$G(s) = \sum_{j=1}^{N} g_j(s)\boldsymbol{\alpha}_j\boldsymbol{\beta}_j^+ \tag{48}$$

where, for $1 \leqslant j \leqslant N$,

$$g_j(s) = \frac{a_j}{s + b_j} \tag{49}$$

$\{b_j\}_{1 \leqslant j \leqslant N}$ is a set of real poles, $\{a_j\}_{1 \leqslant j \leqslant N}$ is a set of nonzero real numbers and $\{\boldsymbol{\alpha}_j\boldsymbol{\beta}_j^+\}_{1 \leqslant j \leqslant N}$ is a set of linearly independent, real, frequency-independent dyads.

Applying the procedure of Section 2, suppose that $K_D(\omega_1)$ is a decoupling matrix for the system, then

$$G(s)K_D(\omega_1) = \sum_{j=1}^{N} \frac{a_j}{s + b_j}\boldsymbol{\alpha}_j\boldsymbol{\gamma}_j^+ \tag{50}$$

where $\{\boldsymbol{\gamma}_j\}_{1 \leqslant j \leqslant N}$ is a set of vectors such that

$$\boldsymbol{\gamma}_j^+\boldsymbol{\alpha}_k = \delta_{j,k} \qquad 1 \leqslant j, k \leqslant N \tag{51}$$

Noting[7] that $\boldsymbol{\alpha}_j(\omega_1) = \boldsymbol{\alpha}_j$ and $1 \leqslant j \leqslant N$, eqns. 14, 15, 50 and 51 give

$$T^{-1}(\omega_1)G(s)K(s,\omega_1)T(\omega_1) = \mathrm{diag}\{k_j(s,\omega_1)a_j/(s + b_j)\}_{1 \leqslant j \leqslant N} \tag{52}$$

Suppose that responses of the approximate form $1 - e^{-kt}$ are required from each channel, and choose $K(s,\omega_1)$ to be a proportional controller where $k_j(s,\omega_1) = k_j$, $1 \leqslant j \leqslant N$ and

$$b_j + k_j a_j = k \quad \text{for} \quad 1 \leqslant j \leqslant N \tag{53}$$

then the controller becomes (eqn. 8)

$$K(s,\omega_1) = K_D(\omega_1)\sum_{j=1}^{N} \frac{k - b_j}{a_j}\boldsymbol{\alpha}_j\boldsymbol{\gamma}_j^+ \tag{54}$$

and (eqns. 52 and 53) the system step responses are represented by

$$\{I + G(s)K(s,\omega_1)\}^{-1}G(s)K(s,\omega_1)\frac{1}{s} = \sum_{j=1}^{N} \frac{k - b_j}{s + k}\boldsymbol{\alpha}_j\boldsymbol{\gamma}_j^+\frac{1}{s}$$

$$= \left\{\frac{1}{s} - \frac{1}{s + k}\right\}\sum_{j=1}^{N} \frac{k - b_j}{k}\boldsymbol{\alpha}_j\boldsymbol{\gamma}_j^+ \tag{55}$$

i.e. the closed-loop system is represented by a single-scalar transfer function multiplying a constant matrix (dependent on the choice of k) which represents closed-loop interaction effects and steady-state error.

A suitable choice for k can be obtained by noting that

$$\lim_{k \to \infty} \sum_{j=1}^{N} \frac{k - b_j}{k}\boldsymbol{\alpha}_j\boldsymbol{\gamma}_j^+ = I \text{ (the unit matrix)} \tag{56}$$

so that interaction effects decrease as the desired speed of response increases. This implies that k should be much greater than the maximum of $|b_j|$, $1 \leqslant j \leqslant N$.

The physical relationship between $K(s,\omega_1)$ and the plant $G(s)$ can be obtained by noting that

$$K_D(\omega_1) = \left\{\sum_{j=1}^{N} \boldsymbol{\alpha}_j\boldsymbol{\beta}_j^+\right\}^{-1} = \sum_{j=1}^{N} \boldsymbol{\psi}_j\boldsymbol{\gamma}_j^+ \tag{57}$$

where $\{\boldsymbol{\psi}_j\}_{1 \leqslant j \leqslant N}$ are vectors such that $\boldsymbol{\beta}_j^+\boldsymbol{\psi}_l = \delta_{jl}$ ahd hence that (eqns. 54 and 51)

$$K(s,\omega_1) = \sum_{j=1}^{N} \frac{k - b_j}{a_j}\boldsymbol{\psi}_j\boldsymbol{\gamma}_j^+ \tag{58}$$

i.e.

$$K_\infty = \lim_{k \to \infty} k^{-1}K(s,\omega_1) = \sum_{j=1}^{N} a_j^{-1}\boldsymbol{\psi}_j\boldsymbol{\gamma}_j^+ \tag{59}$$

Also, defining

$$G_\infty = \lim_{s \to \infty} s\,G(s) = \sum_{j=1}^{N} a_j\boldsymbol{\alpha}_j\boldsymbol{\beta}_j^+ \tag{60}$$

then (eqn. 59)

$$G_\infty^{-1} = \sum_{j=1}^{N} a_j^{-1}\boldsymbol{\psi}_j\boldsymbol{\gamma}_j^+ = K_\infty \tag{61}$$

i.e., for large k, the designed controller tends to diagonalise the plant at high frequencies. Such a controller has previously been used intuitively.[8] The above analysis provides some theoretical justification for the approach.

In summary, a theoretical approach has been presented to the design of a simple, but conceptually useful, class of multivariable-feedback-control problems. As illustrated by the example in Section 3, the analysis can be an intiutive aid to the design of systems which approximate to this form at high frequencies. Finally, the form of the transfer functions (eqn. 49) and the ease with which a controller can be designed imply that the system can be regarded as a multivariable generalisation of the classical first-order system. The analysis of more general structures could be a useful aid in the practical application of multivariable-control theory.

Conditions for the Absence of Limit Cycles

PETER A. COOK

***Abstract*—Sufficient conditions are derived for the nonoccurrence of limit cycles in a class of nonlinear multivariable feedback systems, where the nonlinearities are single-valued, time-invariant, and slope-restricted. The conditions involve the transfer function matrix of the linear part of the system, and can be interpreted graphically in terms of Nyquist diagrams.**

I. Introduction

THIS paper is concerned with the behavior of nonlinear feedback systems of the form shown in Fig. 1, where the nonlinearities are memoryless, time-invariant devices for which the output is a Lipschitz-continuous function of the input, so that the derivative of output with respect to input is bounded. The aspect of system behavior studied here is the possibility of the existence of limit cycles, although it seems likely that a more complete analysis of stability properties could also be made using similar methods. The method actually adopted is to convert the restrictions on the nonlinear functions into relations between the Fourier transforms of their inputs and outputs, and then to use these, in conjunction with the frequency-domain description of the linear part of the system, to obtain conditions under which periodic motions cannot occur.

In Section II, some theorems are presented, which give sufficient conditions for the absence of limit cycles. In Section III, these are used to derive further conditions which have a useful graphical interpretation. The results are discussed and illustrated in Section IV, and the proofs are given in the Appendix.

The notation is mainly standard. An asterisk is used for the complex conjugate of a scalar and for the Hermitian conjugate of a vector or matrix, while a prime denotes the transpose of a matrix. The Euclidean spectral norm of a matrix is denoted by $\|\cdot\|$, i.e., for any matrix F,

$$\|F\| = \sqrt{\text{maximum eigenvalue of } F^*F}\ .$$

II. Exclusion of Limit Cycles

Suppose a multivariable feedback system consists of a linear and a nonlinear part, connected into a closed loop, as follows.

The linear part is a linear, time-invariant system, with finite-dimensional state-space, whose zero-state response is given by

$$\bar{y}(s) = H(s)\bar{z}(s) \tag{1}$$

Manuscript received June 5, 1975; revised December 4, 1975. Paper recommended by G. L. Blankenship, Chairman of the IEEE S-CS Stability, Nonlinear, and Distributed Systems Committee.

The author is with the Control Systems Centre, University of Manchester Institute of Science and Technology, Manchester, England.

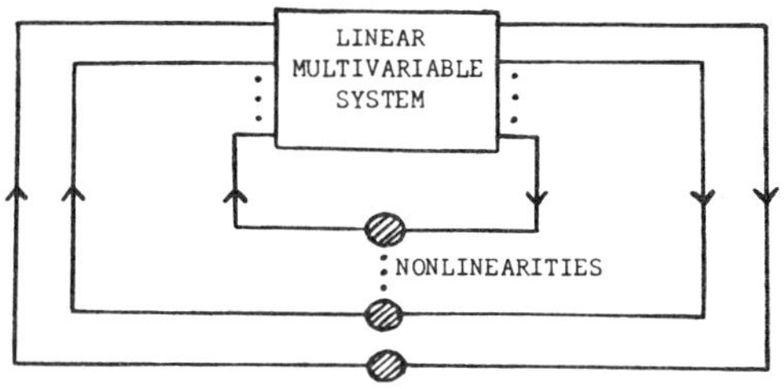

Fig. 1. A multivariable system with nonlinear feedback.

where $\bar{z}(s), \bar{y}(s)$ are the Laplace transforms of input $z(t)$ and output $y(t)$, respectively, both being m-vectors, and $H(s)$ is an $m \times m$ rational transfer function matrix which is strictly proper, i.e.,

$$H(s) \to 0 \quad \text{as} \quad s \to \infty. \tag{2}$$

The nonlinear part is composed of m independent memoryless nonlinearities, giving

$$z_j = -\rho_j(y_j), \qquad (j = 1, \cdots, m), \tag{3}$$

where the $\rho_j(\cdot)$ are nondecreasing functions satisfying Lipschitz conditions, i.e., there are real constants $\kappa_j(>0)$ such that

$$0 \leqslant (w-x)\left[\rho_j(w) - \rho_j(x)\right] \leqslant \kappa_j(w-x)^2, \qquad \forall (w,x), \qquad (j=1,\cdots,m). \tag{4}$$

It follows [1] that the components of $z(t)$ are absolutely continuous, and those of $y(t)$ are continuously differentiable, with respect to t. Hence, the components of $\dot{y}(t)$ are bounded on finite intervals, and therefore, so are those of $\dot{z}(t)$, by (3) and (4).

The next result concerns the possibility of the occurrence of limit cycles, i.e., nonconstant periodic oscillations.

Theorem 1: If there exists a diagonal matrix

$$D = \text{diag}(d_j)$$

with

$$\text{Re}\, d_j > 0, \qquad (j = 1, \cdots, m),$$

such that for every positive integer n, the matrix

$$M(n) = D\left(H\left(\frac{2\pi i n}{T}\right) + K^{-1}\right) + \left(H^*\left(\frac{2\pi i n}{T}\right) + K^{-1}\right)D^*$$

is positive-definite, where

$$K = \text{diag}(\kappa_j),$$

then the system described by (1)–(4) cannot support a limit cycle of period T.

Reprinted from *IEEE Trans. Automat. Contr.*, vol. AC-21, pp. 339–345, June 1976.

This result can be converted into other equivalent forms, adapted to cases where the nonlinearities satisfy restrictions different from (4). Thus, let the linear part of the system have input $\boldsymbol{u}(t)$ and output $\boldsymbol{y}(t)$, both m-vectors, with zero-state response

$$\bar{y}(s)=G(s)\bar{u}(s) \tag{5}$$

where $G(s)$ is a strictly proper $m\times m$ rational transfer function matrix

$$G(s)\to 0 \quad \text{as} \quad s\to\infty, \tag{6}$$

and let the nonlinearities be specified by

$$u_j=-\psi_j(y_j), \quad (j=1,\cdots,m) \tag{7}$$

where the $\psi_j(\cdot)$ are functions satisfying the Lipschitz sector bounds

$$\alpha_j(w-x)^2\leqslant(w-x)[\psi_j(w)-\psi_j(x)] \leqslant \beta_j(w-x)^2, \quad \forall(w,x), \quad (j=1,\cdots,m), \tag{8}$$

for some set of real constants $\alpha_j,\beta_j(>\alpha_j)$. Then, setting

$$z_j=u_j+\alpha_j y_j, \qquad (j=1,\cdots,m),$$

the system reduces to that defined by (1)–(4), with

$$H(s)=G(s)[I+AG(s)]^{-1} \tag{9}$$

and

$$K=B-A \tag{10}$$

where

$$A=\mathrm{diag}(\alpha_j), \quad B=\mathrm{diag}(\beta_j).$$

If $\det G(s)$ is not identically zero, so that $G(s)$ has an inverse $\hat{G}(s)$, for almost all s, the next result follows.

Theorem 2: Suppose there exist a real nonsingular diagonal matrix

$$P=\mathrm{diag}(p_j)$$

and a diagonal matrix

$$\Phi=\mathrm{diag}(\phi_j)$$

with

$$\phi_j=\exp(i\theta_j), \qquad (j=1,\cdots,m)$$

where the θ_j are real and satisfy

$$\frac{-\pi}{2}<\theta_j<\frac{\pi}{2}, \qquad (j=1,\cdots,m)$$

such that for every positive integer n, $\hat{G}(2\pi in/T)$ exists and

$$\left\|\Lambda Q^{-1}\left(\frac{2\pi in}{T}\right)\Lambda\right\|<1$$

where

$$Q(s)=P\hat{G}(s)P^{-1}+\left(\frac{B+A}{2}\right)+\left(\frac{B-A}{2}\right)(\Phi-\Phi^*)(\Phi+\Phi^*)^{-1},$$

and

$$\Lambda=\mathrm{diag}(\lambda_j)$$

with

$$\lambda_j=\sqrt{\frac{\beta_j-\alpha_j}{2\cos\theta_j}}, \qquad (j=1,\cdots,m).$$

Then, the system described by (5)–(8) cannot support a limit cycle of period T.

With some restrictions on the α_j and β_j, another similar result follows, whether $G(s)$ has an inverse or not.

Theorem 3: Suppose that

$$\alpha_j\beta_j>0, \qquad (j=1,\cdots,m),$$

and that there exist matrices P and Φ, with the same properties as in Theorem 2, such that, for every positive integer n,

$$\left\|\Delta R^{-1}\left(\frac{2\pi in}{T}\right)\Delta\right\|<1$$

where

$$R(s)=PG(s)P^{-1}+\left(\frac{A^{-1}+B^{-1}}{2}\right)+\left(\frac{A^{-1}-B^{-1}}{2}\right)(\Phi^*-\Phi)(\Phi+\Phi^*)^{-1},$$

and

$$\Delta=\mathrm{diag}(\delta_j)$$

with

$$\delta_j=\sqrt{\frac{\alpha_j^{-1}-\beta_j^{-1}}{2\cos\theta_j}}, \qquad (j=1,\cdots,m).$$

Then, the system described by (5)–(8) cannot support a limit cycle of period T.

III. Graphical Criteria

From the conditions, sufficient for the absence of limit cycles, which were given in the previous section, there may be deduced other conditions which, though less widely applicable, are easier to use and can be given a simple graphical significance.

Theorem 4: Let p_j be real positive constants, θ_j be real constants in $(-\pi/2,\pi/2)$, $\chi_j(n)$ be real positive numbers which may depend on the positive integer n, and $h_{jk}(s)$ be the elements of $H(s)$, $(j,k=1,\cdots,m)$.

Then, if for each positive integer n,

$$\mathrm{Re}\left\{\left(h_{jk}\left(\frac{2\pi in}{T}\right)+\kappa_j^{-1}\right)\exp(i\theta_j)\right\} > \xi_j(n), \quad (j=1,\cdots,m)$$

where

$$\xi_j(n)=\frac{1}{2}\sum_{\substack{k=1\\(k\neq j)}}^{m}\frac{\chi_k(n)}{\chi_j(n)} \cdot\left\{\frac{p_j}{p_k}\left|h_{jk}\left(\frac{2\pi in}{T}\right)\right|+\frac{p_k}{p_j}\left|h_{kj}\left(\frac{2\pi in}{T}\right)\right|\right\},$$

the system described by (1)–(4) cannot support a limit cycle of period T.

Corollary: If, for each positive integer n, the closed disc with center $h_{jj}(2\pi in/T)$ and radius $\xi_j(n)$ lies entirely to the right of a fixed nonhorizontal straight line passing through the point $-\kappa_j^{-1}$, $(j=1,\cdots,m)$, then the system described by (1)–(4) cannot support a limit cycle of period T.

Theorem 5: Let $p_j,\theta_j,\chi_j(n)$ be as in Theorem 4 and $\hat{g}_{jk}(s)$ be the elements of $\hat{G}(s)$, $(j,k=1,\cdots,m)$.

Then, if for each positive integer n

$$\left|\hat{g}_{jj}\left(\frac{2\pi in}{T}\right)+\left(\frac{\beta_j+\alpha_j}{2}\right)+i\left(\frac{\beta_j-\alpha_j}{2}\right)\tan\theta_j\right| > \eta_j(n)+\left(\frac{\beta_j-\alpha_j}{2\cos\theta_j}\right), \quad (j=1,\cdots,m),$$

where

$$\eta_j(n)=\frac{1}{2}\sum_{\substack{k=1\\(k\neq j)}}^{m}\frac{\chi_k(n)}{\chi_j(n)} \cdot\left\{\frac{p_j}{p_k}\left|\hat{g}_{jk}\left(\frac{2\pi in}{T}\right)\right|+\frac{p_k}{p_j}\left|\hat{g}_{kj}\left(\frac{2\pi in}{T}\right)\right|\right\},$$

the system described by (5)–(8) cannot support a limit cycle of period T.

Corollary: If, for each positive integer n, the closed disc with center $\hat{g}_{jj}(2\pi in/T)$ and radius $\eta_j(n)$ lies entirely outside a fixed circle passing through the points $-\alpha_j$ and $-\beta_j$, $(j=1,\cdots,m)$, then the system described by (5)–(8) cannot support a limit cycle of period T.

Theorem 6: Let $p_j,\theta_j,\chi_j(n)$ be as in Theorem 4, and $g_{jk}(s)$ be the elements of $G(s)$, $(j,k=1,\cdots,m)$.

Then, if

$$\alpha_j\beta_j>0, \qquad (j=1,\cdots,m),$$

and for each positive integer n,

$$\left|g_{jj}\left(\frac{2\pi in}{T}\right)+\left(\frac{\alpha_j^{-1}+\beta_j^{-1}}{2}\right)-i\left(\frac{\alpha_j^{-1}-\beta_j^{-1}}{2}\right)\tan\theta_j\right| > \zeta_j(n)+\left(\frac{\alpha_j^{-1}-\beta_j^{-1}}{2\cos\theta_j}\right), \quad (j=1,\cdots,m)$$

where

$$\zeta_j(n)=\frac{1}{2}\sum_{\substack{k=1\\(k\neq j)}}^{m}\frac{\chi_k(n)}{\chi_j(n)} \cdot\left\{\frac{p_j}{p_k}\left|g_{jk}\left(\frac{2\pi in}{T}\right)\right|+\frac{p_k}{p_j}\left|g_{kj}\left(\frac{2\pi in}{T}\right)\right|\right\},$$

the system described by (5)–(8) cannot support a limit cycle of period T.

Corollary: If for each positive integer n, the closed disc with center $g_{jj}(2\pi in/T)$ and radius $\zeta_j(n)$ lies entirely outside a fixed circle passing through the points $-\alpha_j^{-1}$ and $-\beta_j^{-1}$, where $\alpha_j\beta_j>0$, $(j=1,\cdots,m)$, then the system described by (5)–(8) cannot support a limit cycle of period T.

IV. Discussion of Results

The results of the preceding section give simple graphically interpretable conditions under which certain types of nonlinear feedback system can be guaranteed not to possess limit cycle behavior. In the case of a single nonlinearity ($m=1$) the conditions reduce to the requirement that certain points on the Nyquist plot of the linear part of the system, namely those corresponding to multiples of some fundamental frequency, should lie outside of a certain half-plane or circular region in the complex plane. Thus, if the entire positive-frequency part of the Nyquist plot has this property, then limit cycles are completely excluded, and this situation is exactly that which is required by the "off-axis circle criterion" [2] where it is already known that global asymptotic stability is ensured and hence, limit cycles cannot occur. The original motivation of the present work was, in fact, to extend the results of [2] to the multivariable case, but this has not yet been achieved, owing to technical difficulties in the proofs. The results actually obtained in the present paper may, however, be understood as a generalization, to the multinonlinear case, of the off-axis circle criterion, provided that this is regarded as a condition for the absence of limit cycles rather than for global asymptotic stability. Indeed, the present results are, in a sense, more general, since no assumption of stability is made for the linear part of the system in the open-loop situation, nor is any reference made to the existence of equilibria for the closed-loop system. Moreover, in practice, a knowledge of the behavior near equilibrium points, which can be obtained by linearization, together with information about the possibility or otherwise of limit cycles, will usually give a sufficiently complete picture of the stability properties of the system. It is also possible, of course, that there may be bounded sustained oscillations which are not limit cycles, being almost-periodic instead of periodic, and these are not necessarily excluded by the results of this paper. It seems unlikely, however, that such motions could occur under conditions which exclude the possibility of a limit cycle of any period whatever, since an almost-periodic function can be arbitrarily closely approximated by periodic functions.

In the multivariable case, the usefulness of the graphical form of the conditions depends on the presence of some degree of "diagonal dominance," in the sense that the radii of the discs, drawn around the diagonal element of the transfer function matrix or its inverse, depend on the moduli of the off-diagonal elements and should be as small as possible to give the sharpest results. This situation is the same as that obtained in earlier forms of multivariable circle criteria [3], which apply to more general nonlinearities but give less flexible results. The increased flexibility in the present case resides in the possibility of choosing the "forbidden regions" of the complex plane to be, for example, any circles through the pairs of points $-\alpha_j$, $-\beta_j$, instead of the particular ones whose centers lie on the real axis. It arises from the fact that the nonlinearities are required to be memoryless, time-independent, and slope-restricted, and the present results thus bear the same kind of relation to the earlier multivariable circle theorems as the off-axis circle criterion does to the original circle theorem [4] for the single input-single output case. The remaining arbitrariness in the size of the discs lies in the freedom to choose the numbers p_j and $\chi_j(n)$ in Theorems 4, 5, and 6, and is also implicit in the earlier multivariable circle criteria. The choice of the p_j corresponds to making a diagonal similarity transformation on the transfer function matrix and can be useful if this is nearly triangular, while the choice of the $\chi_j(n)$ enables one to exploit a certain amount of "tradeoff" between the sizes of the discs around the various diagonal elements.

The following example has been chosen so that the graphical conditions can be investigated analytically, without actually drawing the Nyquist diagrams.

Example: The system is as specified in (5)–(8), with the elements of the inverse transfer function matrix given by

$$\hat{g}_{jj}(s) = s(s + a_j)$$
$$\hat{g}_{jk}(s) = b_{jk}s, \qquad k \neq j$$

where the a_j and b_{jk}, $(j,k = 1,\cdots,m)$, are real constants, so that the differential equations governing the system are

$$\ddot{y}_j + a_j\dot{y}_j + \psi_j(y_j) + \sum_{\substack{k=1\\(k\neq j)}}^{m} b_{jk}\dot{y}_k = 0. \qquad (11)$$

The functions $\psi_j(\cdot)$ are assumed to be Lipschitz-continuous and nondecreasing, so that all the α_j of (8) can be taken to be zero and the β_j can be arbitrarily large.

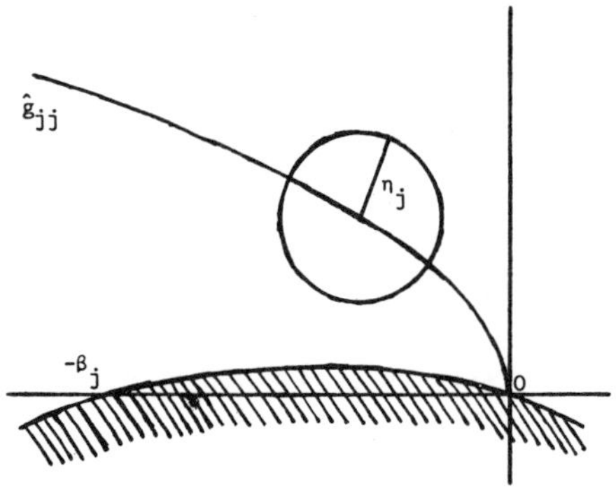

Fig. 2. Graphical investigation of the example in Section IV.

Now, defining a matrix W, with elements w_{jk}, by

$$w_{jj} = |a_j|$$
$$w_{jk} = -|b_{jk}|, \qquad k \neq j,$$

it will be shown that the conditions of Theorem 5 are satisfied provided that W is an M-matrix [5], i.e., a matrix whose off-diagonal elements are nonpositive and whose principal minors are positive.

For if W is an M-matrix, then [5] there exists a diagonal matrix P, with real positive diagonal elements, such that the matrix $X = PWP^{-1} + P^{-1}W'P$ is a positive-definite M-matrix, and consequently [5] there are real positive numbers χ_j such that the elements x_{jk} of X satisfy

$$\sum_{k=1}^{m} x_{jk}\chi_k > 0, \qquad (j = 1,\cdots,m).$$

Hence, the constants in Theorem 5 can be chosen so that

$$\eta_j(n) = \frac{\pi n}{T} \sum_{\substack{k=1\\(k\neq j)}}^{m} \frac{\chi_k}{\chi_j}(-x_{jk}) < \frac{2\pi n}{T}|a_j|, \qquad (j = 1,\cdots,m)$$

so the discs drawn around $\hat{g}_{jj}$ all lie entirely on the same side of the real axis, for each particular value of j. It follows that, for each j, a circle can be drawn through the points $-\alpha_j$ $(=0)$ and $-\beta_j$ such that all the discs centered on $\hat{g}_{jj}(2\pi in/T)$ lie entirely outside it, as required by Theorem 5.

Thus, if W is an M-matrix, the system described by (11), with nondecreasing, Lipschitz-continuous $\psi_j(\cdot)$, cannot support a limit cycle. To check whether or not W is an M-matrix, it is only necessary to examine the signs of its leading principal minors [5].

The Nyquist diagrams which would be drawn in the graphical investigation of this system are illustrated in Fig. 2.

Appendix

Here are collected the proofs of the theorems stated above, together with some auxiliary lemmas and their proofs.

Consider a memoryless nonlinearity which converts a real scalar input $v(t)$ into a real scalar output $z(t)$, related by

$$z=\sigma(v) \tag{A1}$$

where $\sigma(\cdot)$ is a nondecreasing function. It follows immediately [6] that, for any two inputs v, w

$$(v-w)\sigma(v) \geq \int_w^v \sigma(x)\,dx. \tag{A2}$$

Now, suppose the input is a periodic function of time, with period T, so that

$$v(t+T)=v(t), \qquad \forall t. \tag{A3}$$

The following lemma then holds.

Lemma 1: Subject to (A1)–(A3), with $v(t)$ and $z(t)$ in $L^2(0,T)$,

$$\int_0^T [v(t)-v(t+\tau)]z(t)\,dt \geq 0, \qquad \forall \tau.$$

Proof of Lemma 1: Define

$$f(t)=\int_0^{v(t)} \sigma(x)\,dx$$

so that

$$f(t+T)=f(t), \qquad \forall t.$$

Then, using (A2),

$$\begin{aligned}\int_0^T [v(t)-v(t+\tau)]z(t)\,dt &\geq \int_0^T [f(t)-f(t+\tau)]\,dt\\ &= \int_0^T f(t)\,dt - \int_\tau^{T+\tau} f(t)\,dt\\ &= \int_0^\tau f(t)\,dt - \int_T^{T+\tau} f(t)\,dt\\ &=0. \qquad \text{Q.E.D.}\end{aligned}$$

This result is exactly analogous to one in [6] for inputs and outputs in $L^2(-\infty,\infty)$. It can be reexpressed in the frequency domain by introducing Fourier coefficients $\tilde{v}(n), \tilde{z}(n)$, and writing

$$v(t)=\sum_{n=-\infty}^{\infty} \tilde{v}(n)\exp(2\pi i n t/T) \tag{A4}$$

with a similar expression for $z(t)$ in terms of $\tilde{z}(n)$.

Since $v(t)$ and $z(t)$ are real, it follows that

$$\tilde{v}^*(n)=\tilde{v}(-n), \qquad \forall n, \tag{A5}$$

and similarly for the $\tilde{z}(n)$.

The restatement of Lemma 1 then takes the following form.

Lemma 2: Under the conditions of Lemma 1,

$$\sum_{n=1}^{\infty} \operatorname{Re}\left(\tilde{z}^*(n)\tilde{v}(n)[1-\exp(2\pi i n\tau/T)]\right) \geq 0, \qquad \forall \tau.$$

Proof of Lemma 2: Substitute (A4), and the corresponding expression for $z(t)$, in Lemma 1, invoking Parseval's theorem [7]. Then use (A5), and the corresponding relation for $\tilde{z}(n)$, to express the result in terms of a summation over positive values of n. Q.E.D.

With a slight strengthening of assumptions, the next lemma follows.

Lemma 3: Under the conditions of Lemma 1, together with the assumption that either $v(t)$ or $z(t)$ is an absolutely continuous function with derivative in $L^2(0,T)$,

$$\sum_{n=1}^{\infty} n \operatorname{Re}[\tilde{z}^*(n)\tilde{v}(n)] \geq 0$$

and

$$\sum_{n=1}^{\infty} n \operatorname{Im}[\tilde{z}^*(n)\tilde{v}(n)] = 0.$$

Proof of Lemma 3: Let $\mu(\tau)$ denote the expression on the left-hand side of the inequality in Lemma 2. By virtue of the assumptions, $\mu(\tau)$ is a continuously differentiable function of τ in $(-\infty,\infty)$ and its derivative can be evaluated term-by-term.

In other words, since

$$\mu(\tau)\geq 0, \qquad \forall \tau$$

and

$$\mu(0)=0,$$

it follows that

$$\frac{d\mu}{d\tau}(0)=0,$$

proving the second result, since

$$\frac{d\mu}{d\tau}(0)=\left(\frac{2\pi}{T}\right)\sum_{n=1}^{\infty} n \operatorname{Im}[\tilde{z}^*(n)\tilde{v}(n)].$$

Further, the integral

$$\int_0^{\infty} [\mu(\tau)+\mu(-\tau)]\frac{d\tau}{\tau^2}=\left(\frac{2\pi^2}{T}\right)\sum_{n=1}^{\infty} n \operatorname{Re}[\tilde{z}^*(n)\tilde{v}(n)]$$

exists and can be evaluated term-by-term. Since the integrand is nonnegative, this proves the first result. Q.E.D.

Proof of Theorem 1: Let ϵ denote the infimum, over all positive integers n, of the minimum eigenvalues of $M(n)$. Then, on account of (2),

$$0<\epsilon \leq \min_j \left(\frac{2\operatorname{Re} d_j}{\kappa_j}\right).$$

Now, define a new m-vector $v(t)$ by

$$v_j=\left(\frac{\epsilon}{4\operatorname{Re} d_j}-\frac{1}{\kappa_j}\right)z_j-y_j, \qquad (j=1,\cdots,m).$$

By the contraction mapping theorem [4], this with (3) defines z_j as a Lipschitz-continuous nondecreasing function of v_j, for $j=1,\cdots,m$. The function is nondecreasing because

$$\frac{dz_j}{dv_j}=\frac{dz_j}{dy_j}\Big/\frac{dv_j}{dy_j}$$

where

$$-\frac{dz_j}{dy_j} \geqslant 0$$

and

$$-\frac{dv_j}{dy_j} = 1 - \left(\frac{1}{\kappa_j} - \frac{\epsilon}{4\operatorname{Re} d_j}\right)\left(-\frac{dz_j}{dy_j}\right) \geqslant \frac{\epsilon\kappa_j}{4\operatorname{Re} d_j} > 0.$$

Hence, if the system possesses a limit cycle of period T, then, for each j, $v_j(t)$ and $z_j(t)$ will be a pair of functions satisfying the conditions of Lemma 3, while their Fourier coefficients are related by

$$\tilde{v}(n) = \left(\frac{\epsilon}{2}(D+D^*)^{-1} - K^{-1} - H\left(\frac{2\pi in}{T}\right)\right)\tilde{z}(n).$$

But, by Lemma 3,

$$\sum_{n=1}^{\infty} n \operatorname{Re}\left[\tilde{z}^*(n) D \tilde{v}(n)\right] \geqslant 0$$

whence

$$\sum_{n=1}^{\infty} n\tilde{z}^*(n)\left[\frac{\epsilon I}{2} - M(n)\right]\tilde{z}(n) \geqslant 0,$$

so that, for every positive integer n,

$$\tilde{v}(n) = \tilde{z}(n) = \mathbf{0}. \qquad \text{Q.E.D.}$$

Proof of Theorem 2: With the notation of Theorem 1, setting

$$D = P^2\Phi$$

and defining

$$\Gamma(n) = \Lambda^{-1} Q\left(\frac{2\pi in}{T}\right)\Lambda^{-1},$$

it follows, after some algebra using (9) and (10), that

$$M(n) = H^*\left(\frac{2\pi in}{T}\right) P\Lambda\left[\Gamma^*(n)\Gamma(n) - I\right]\Lambda P H\left(\frac{2\pi in}{T}\right),$$

and so, since $H(2\pi in/T)$ is nonsingular by (9) and

$$\|\Gamma^{-1}(n)\| < 1,$$

$M(n)$ is positive-definite and the result follows as a consequence of Theorem 1. Q.E.D.

Proof of Theorem 3: With the notation of Theorems 1 and 2, and the definition

$$\Omega(n) = \Delta^{-1} R\left(\frac{2\pi in}{T}\right)\Delta^{-1},$$

there follows the relation

$$\left(I + G^*\left(\frac{2\pi in}{T}\right)A\right)M(n)\left(I + AG\left(\frac{2\pi in}{T}\right)\right) = P\Delta\left[\Omega^*(n)\Omega(n) - I\right]\Delta P,$$

and hence, since

$$\|\Omega^{-1}(n)\| < 1,$$

$M(n)$ is positive-definite and the result follows from Theorem 1. Q.E.D.

Lemma 4: Let C be an $m \times m$ matrix with real or complex elements c_{jk}, $(j,k = 1,\cdots,m)$, and let ν_j, $(j = 1,\cdots,m)$, be real positive numbers. Then, the following results hold.

1) If

$$\operatorname{Re} c_{jj} > \sum_{\substack{k=1\\(k\neq j)}}^{m} \frac{\nu_k}{\nu_j}\left(\frac{|c_{jk}| + |c_{kj}|}{2}\right), \qquad (j = 1,\cdots,m),$$

then the matrix $C + C^*$, is positive-definite.

2) If

$$|c_{jj}| > 1 + \sum_{\substack{k=1\\(k\neq j)}}^{m} \frac{\nu_k}{\nu_j}\left(\frac{|c_{jk}| + |c_{kj}|}{2}\right), \qquad (j = 1,\cdots,m),$$

then C is nonsingular and

$$\|C^{-1}\| < 1.$$

Proof of Lemma 4: Part 2) is proved in [3], and the method used there serves also to prove part (1). Q.E.D.

Proof of Theorem 4: The result follows from Theorem 1 and Lemma 4-1), on identifying the following:

$$D = \operatorname{diag}\left[p_j^2 \exp(i\theta_j)\right]$$
$$P = \operatorname{diag}(p_j)$$
$$C = P^{-1} D\left[H\left(\frac{2\pi in}{T}\right) + K^{-1}\right]P^{-1}$$
$$\nu_j = \chi_j(n). \qquad \text{Q.E.D.}$$

Proof of Theorem 5: The result follows from Theorem 2 and Lemma 4-2), on identifying the following:

$$C = \Gamma(n)$$
$$\nu_j = \chi_j(n)\lambda_j. \qquad \text{Q.E.D.}$$

Proof of Theorem 6: The result follows from Theorem 3 and Lemma 4-2), on identifying the following:

$$C = \Omega(n)$$
$$\nu_j = \chi_j(n)\delta_j. \qquad \text{Q.E.D.}$$

REFERENCES

[1] E. A. Coddington and N. Levinson, *Theory of Ordinary Differential Equations*. New York: McGraw-Hill, 1955.

[2] Y.-S. Cho and K. S. Narendra, "An off-axis circle criterion for the stability of feedback systems with a monotonic nonlinearity," *IEEE Trans. Automat. Contr.*, vol. AC-13, pp. 413–416, Aug. 1968.

[3] P. A. Cook, "Modified multivariable circle theorems," in *Recent Mathematical Developments in Control*, D. J. Bell, Ed. London: Academic, 1973, pp. 367–372.

[4] R. W. Brockett, *Finite Dimensional Linear Systems*. New York: Wiley, 1970.

[5] M. Araki and B. Kondo, "Stability and transient behavior of composite nonlinear systems," *IEEE. Trans. Automat. Contr.*, vol. AC-17, pp. 537–541, Aug. 1972.

[6] G. Zames and P. L. Falb, "Stability conditions for systems with monotone and slope-restricted nonlinearities," *SIAM J. Contr.*, vol. 4, pp. 89–108, Jan. 1968.

[7] R. E. A. C. Paley and N. Wiener, *Fourier Transforms in the Complex Domain*. Providence, RI: Amer. Math. Soc. Colloquium Publ., 1934.

Modern Wiener–Hopf Design of Optimal Controllers — Part II: The Multivariable Case

DANTE C. YOULA, FELLOW, IEEE, HAMID A. JABR, MEMBER, IEEE, AND JOSEPH J. BONGIORNO, JR., MEMBER, IEEE

Abstract—**In many modern-day control problems encountered in the fluid, petroleum, power, gas and paper industries, cross coupling (interaction) between controlled and manipulated variables can be so severe that any attempt to employ single-loop controllers results in unacceptable performance. In all these situations, any workable control strategy must take into account the true multivariable nature of the plant and address itself directly to the design of a compatible multivariable controller. Any practical design technique must be able to cope with load disturbance, plant saturation, measurement noise, process lag, sensitivity and also incorporate suitable criteria delimiting transient behavior and steady-state performance. These difficulties, when compounded by the fact that many plants (such as chemical reactors) are inherently open-loop unstable have hindered the development of an inclusive frequency-domain analytic design methodology. However, a solution based on a least-square Wiener–Hopf minimization of an appropriately chosen cost functional is now available. The optimal controller obtained by this method guarantees an asymptotically stable and dynamical closed-loop configuration irrespective of whether or not the plant is proper, stable, or minimum-phase and also permits the stability margin of the optimal design to be ascertained in advance. The main purpose of this paper is to lay bare the physical assumptions underlying the choice of model and to present an explicit formula for the optimal controller.**

I. Introduction

In many modern-day control problems encountered in the fluid, petroleum, power, gas, and paper industries, cross coupling (interaction) between controlled and manipulated variables can be so severe that any attempt to employ single-loop controllers results in unacceptable performance. In all these situations, any workable control strategy must take into account the true multivariable nature of the plant and address itself directly to the design of a compatible multivariable controller. Any practical design technique must be able to cope with load disturbance, plant saturation, measurement noise, process lag, sensitivity and also incorporate suitable criteria delimiting transient behavior and steady-state performance. These difficulties, when compounded by the fact that many plants (such as chemical reactors) are inherently open-loop unstable have hindered the development of an inclusive frequency-domain analytic design methodology. However, these obstacles have been overcome and a solution based on a least-squares Wiener–Hopf minimization of an appropriately chosen cost functional E is now available. This solution, which is the natural culmination of earlier work [1]–[4], offers the following concrete accomplishments:

1) There are no restrictions on the plant transfer matrix. It can be rectangular, unstable, improper,[1] and nonminimum phase.

2) The design incorporates input noise, load disturbance, measurement noise, and feedforward compensation. The noise can be colored.

3) The optimal controller minimizing E is proper and guarantees a dynamical asymptotically stable closed-loop design possessing proper sensitivity matrices equal to the identity matrix at $s=\infty$.

Manuscript received June 5, 1975; revised February 11, 1976. Paper recommended by J. B. Pearson, Chairman of the IEEE S-CS Linear Systems Committee. This work was supported by the National Science Foundation under Grant ENG 74-13054 and is taken in part from a Ph.D. dissertation submitted by H. A. Jabr to the Faculty of the Polytechnic Institute of New York.

D. C. Youla and J. J. Bongiorno, Jr., are with the Department of Electrical Engineering and Electrophysics, Polytechnic Institute of New York, Long Island Center, Farmingdale, NY 11735.

H. A. Jabr was with the Department of Electrical Engineering and Electrophysics, Polytechnic Institute of New York, Long Island Center, Farmingdale, NY 11735. He is now with the University of Jordan, Amman, Jordan.

[1] A transfer matrix $A(s)$ is proper if $A(\infty)$ is finite and strictly proper if $A(\infty)=O$, the zero matrix. Otherwise it is improper.

Reprinted from *IEEE Trans. Automat. Contr.*, vol. AC-21, pp. 319–338, June 1976.

4) The loop can track ramp-type inputs and recover from step-type disturbances of the correct order with zero steady-state error.

5) Transient response (system accuracy) can be traded off against linear operation.

6) The stability margin of the optimal design is ascertainable in advance.

7) The sensor transfer matrices are absorbed directly into the cost and various delays can be simulated by suitable preequalization.

The primary purpose of this paper is to lay bare the physical assumptions underlying the choice of model and to derive an explicit expression for the optimal controller. To achieve this objective it is first necessary to solve several difficult intermediate problems of the "model matching" variety and, for the sake of continuity and clarity, some of the more involved details have been relegated to two Appendixes. Finally, to help place the contributions of the present work in perspective we offer a comparison with the linear quadratic Gaussian (LQG) approach [17]. It is pointed out that the problem addressed and solved by LQG is quite different from the one considered in this paper. Nevertheless, there is a common class of problems that can be treated by both methods and for any such problem the optimal controller is the same. However, we show by actual example that forcing the optimal controller to be realized via the Kalman structure is not always possible. This limitation is inherent in LQG, but not in ours.

II. The Model

We focus our attention exclusively on the design of optimal controllers for multi-input–output finite-dimensional linear time-invariant plants imbedded in a multivariable single-loop configuration of generic type shown in Fig. 1.[2] Suppose $y_d(s)$, the *desired* closed-loop output is related to $u_i(s)$, the *actual* input set-point signal in the linear fashion

$$y_d(s)=T_d(s)u_i(s) \tag{1}$$

via the *ideal* transfer matrix $T_d(s)$. The *prefilter* $W(s)$ is selected in advance, but once chosen,[3]

$$u=W(u_i+n) \tag{2}$$

must be considered the best available linear version of $y_d(s)$. Any reasonable performance measure should be based on the vector error difference

$$e(s)=u(s)-y(s) \tag{3}$$

between the actual smoothed input $u(s)$ driving the loop and the plant output $y(s)$. If plant delays are excessive the suppression of load disturbance by means of feedback alone may not suffice and it is usually advisable to incorporate feedforward compensation $L(s)$ as an integral part of the design. For given choices of overall sensors $F(s)$ and $L(s)$, the design of the controller $C(s)$ evolves from an appropriate minimization procedure subject to a power-like constraint on $r(s)$ to avoid plant saturation and to extend the linear range. (In nonlinear applications the constraint on $r(s)$ is imposed to avoid permanent departures from the neighborhood of a desired equilibrium state.) Plant disturbance $d(s)$ and instrument noise $m(s)$, $l(s)$ are modeled in a perfectly general way by assuming that

$$y(s)=P(s)r(s)+P_o(s)d(s), \tag{4}$$

$$v(s)=F(s)y(s)+F_o(s)m(s) \tag{5}$$

and

$$z(s)=L(s)d(s)+L_o(s)l(s) \tag{6}$$

where $P(s)$, $P_o(s)$, $F(s)$, $F_o(s)$, $L(s)$, and $L_o(s)$ are real rational matrices.

In Fig. 1, $P(s)$ is $n\times m$, $F(s)$ is $n\times n$, and $C(s)$ is $m\times n$. Hence FPC is $n\times n$ and it is assumed of course that all other matrices are dimensioned compatible.[4] Straightforward analysis yields

$$y=PR(u-F_om-L_ol)+(P_o-PRP_d)d, \tag{7}$$

$$r=R(u-F_om-L_ol-P_dd), \tag{8}$$

$$e=(1_n-PR)u+PR(F_om+L_ol)-(P_o-PRP_d)d \tag{9}$$

where

$$R=CS, \tag{10}$$

$$S=(1_n+FPC)^{-1}, \tag{11}$$

$$P_d=FP_o+L. \tag{12}$$

In the absence of measurement noise and load disturbance, $y=(PR)u$. Thus,

$$T(s)=P(s)R(s) \tag{13}$$

is the closed-loop transfer matrix and $S(s)$ is the sensitivity matrix. In most industrial applications the available choices of physical sensing devices $L_t(s)$ and $F_t(s)$ are severely restricted and more or less dictated by the problem at hand. However, as explained later, low-power preequalizers $L_e(s)$ and $F_e(s)$ can and in many cases should be employed to improve stability margin, to assure

[2]To avoid proliferating symbols, all quantities are Laplace transforms, deterministic or otherwise. All stochastic processes are either zero-mean second-order stationary or shape-deterministic or a sum of both with rational spectral densities. For example, η/s, η a random variable, is the transform of a random step with spectral density

$$\langle(\eta/s)(\eta/s)_*\rangle=-\frac{\sigma^2}{s^2}$$

where $\sigma^2=\langle|\eta|^2\rangle$ and $\langle,\rangle$ denotes ensemble average.

[3]Function arguments are omitted wherever convenient and for any matrix A, A', $\bar{A}$, $A^*(\equiv\bar{A}')$ and det A denote the transpose, complex-conjugate, ajoint and determinant of A, respectively. Column vectors are written a, x, etc., or as $x=(x_1,x_2,\cdots,x_n)'$ to exhibit the components explicitly. Last, for any real rational matrix $A(s)$ of the complex frequency variable $s=\sigma+j\omega$, $A_*(s)\equiv A'(-s)$. Note that for $s=j\omega$, ω real, $A_*(j\omega)=A^*(j\omega)$.

[4]1_n is the $n\times n$ identity matrix and O_n, $O_{n,m}$, O_n denote the n-dimensional zero vector, the $n\times m$ and $n\times n$ zero matrices, respectively.

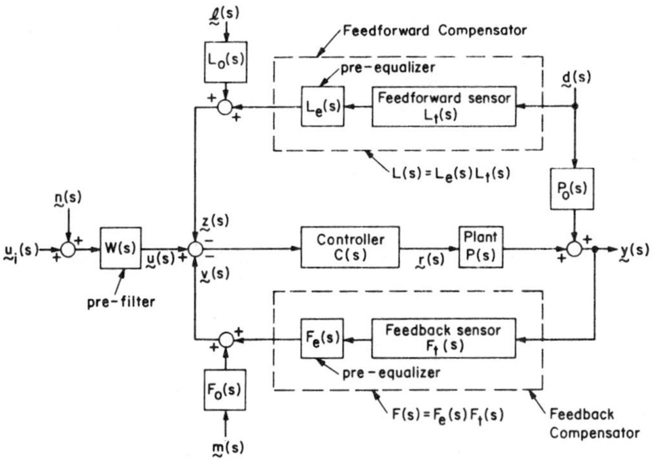

Fig. 1. Multivariable single-loop configuration.

zero steady-state error and to simulate delay in the feedback link. From this point on it is assumed that the data $P_o(s)$, $P(s)$, $L_o(s)$, $F_t(s)$, $L_t(s)$,

$$F(s)=F_e(s)F_t(s) \tag{14}$$

and

$$L(s)=L_e(s)L_t(s) \tag{15}$$

are prescribed in advance.

An interpretation of (9) with $F=1_n$ (unity feedback) and $z=O_n$ (no feedforward compensation) reveals most clearly the potential for tradeoff in the various frequency bands. In fact, for this case $1_n-PR=S$ and

$$\boldsymbol{e}=S(\boldsymbol{u}-P_o\boldsymbol{d})+(1_n-S)F_o\boldsymbol{m} \tag{16}$$

is composed of two contributions $\boldsymbol{e}_1(s)$ and $\boldsymbol{e}_2(s)$. The first,

$$\boldsymbol{e}_1=S(\boldsymbol{u}-P_o\boldsymbol{d}), \tag{17}$$

subsumes steady-state error, accuracy, and load disturbance while the second,

$$\boldsymbol{e}_2=(1_n-S)F_o\boldsymbol{m}, \tag{18}$$

is the error produced by measurement noise. The impossibility of making both $S(j\omega)$ and $1_n-S(j\omega)$ arbitrarily "small" over any frequency band is partly intrinsic and partly conditioned by the plant restrictions [5], [6]. This fundamental conflict is inevitable and responsible for a great deal of the difficulty surrounding practical analytic feedback design. According to (8), the spectral amplification from $\boldsymbol{m}(j\omega)$ to $\boldsymbol{r}(j\omega)$ must depend on the "size" of the matrix $R(j\omega)$. Since (with $F=1_n$)

$$P(j\omega)R(j\omega)=1_n-S(j\omega) \tag{19}$$

and plant bandwidth is usually confined to some low-frequency interval $0\leqslant\omega\leqslant\omega_o$, good transient response and sensitivity require

$$S(j\omega)\approx O_n, \qquad 0\leqslant\omega\leqslant\omega_o; \tag{20}$$

or, qualitatively,

$$C(j\omega)\approx\infty, \qquad 0\leqslant\omega\leqslant\omega_o. \tag{21}$$

Hence, even if $1_n-S(j\omega)$ approaches O_n as $\omega\to\infty$, there usually exists an intermediate high-frequency band $\omega_1\leqslant\omega\leqslant\omega_2$, $\omega_2-\omega_1\gg\omega_o$, over which $1_n-S(j\omega)\approx 1_n$ and $P(j\omega)\approx O_{n,m}$. In view of (19), this implies[5]

$$R(j\omega)\approx\infty, \qquad \omega_1\leqslant\omega\leqslant\omega_2, \tag{22}$$

and the rms value of $\boldsymbol{r}(j\omega)$ can easily exceed the saturation level of the plant because of the extremely wide-band nature of $\boldsymbol{m}(j\omega)$. If we assume the feedback sensors to be as noise free as possible the only remaining remedy is to concentrate on a "best" choice for $C(s)$ subject to the constraint that the closed loop be asymptotically stable. A successful quantitative reformulation of this latter requirement has enabled us to achieve a least-squares solution for $C(s)$ which takes into account all the pertinent performance criteria and is applicable to arbitrary open-loop unstable nonminimum-phase plants.

The McMillan degree, $\delta(A;s_o)$, of $s=s_o$ (finite or infinite) as a pole of the rational matrix $A(s)$ is the largest multiplicity it possesses as a pole of any minor of $A(s)$. The McMillan degree, $\delta(A)$, of $A(s)$ is the sum of the McMillan degrees of its distinct poles. Let the distinct *finite* poles of $A(s)$ be denoted by s_i and their associated McMillan degrees by δ_i, $i=1\to\mu$. The monic polynomial

$$\psi_A(s)=\prod_{i=1}^{\mu}(s-s_i)^{\delta_i} \tag{23}$$

is the *characteristic* denominator of $A(s)$. It is easily shown that $\psi_A(s)$ is also the monic least common multiple of all denominators of all minors of $A(s)$, each minor assumed expressed as the ratio of two relatively prime polynomials.

Lemma 1 (Appendix A): If the plant, feedback compensator, and controller (dynamical or otherwise) are free of unstable hidden modes, the closed loop of Fig. 1 is asymptotically stable iff

$$\varphi(s)\equiv\frac{\psi_P(s)\psi_C(s)\psi_F(s)}{\det S(s)} \tag{24}$$

is a strict Hurwitz polynomial.[6]

By assumption, $P(s)$ and $F(s)$ are given, but even granting that the plant and feedback compensator are free of unstable hidden modes, it may still be impossible to find a controller $C(s)$ which stabilizes the closed loop. Such is the case iff for some finite $s=s_o$, $\mathrm{Re}\, s_o\geqslant 0$,

$$\delta(FP;s_o)<\delta(P;s_o)+\delta(F;s_o). \tag{25}$$

This means that there exists at the output of the plant or feedback compensator an exponential ramp-modulated

[5] At this stage these arguments are intentionally informal. Incidentally, for nonminimum-phase unstable plants it is also possible to have $1_n-S(j\omega)\approx\infty$ over $\omega_1\leqslant\omega\leqslant\omega_2$. See the example in [6, p. 12] and the accompanying table in Fig. 5.

[6] A polynomial free of zeros in $\mathrm{Re}\, s\geqslant 0$ is said to be strict Hurwitz and "iff" abbreviates "if and only if." A system with transfer matrix $A(s)$ is dynamical if $A(s)$ is proper, i.e., if $A(\infty)$ is finite.

sinusoid whose growth in time exceeds that of the signal at the corresponding input and the necessary corrective action to effect stabilization is lacking.

Definition 1: The plant and feedback compensator form an admissible pair if each is individually free of unstable hidden modes and

$$\psi_{FP}^{+}(s)=\phi_F^{+}(s)\psi_P^{+}(s). \tag{26}$$

(The monic polynomials $\psi^{+}(s)$ and $\psi^{-}(s)$ absorb all the zeros of $\psi(s)$ in $\mathrm{Re}\,s \geqslant 0$ and $\mathrm{Re}\,s<0$, respectively. Thus, up to a multiplicative constant, $\psi=\psi^{+}\psi^{-}$.)

Lemma 2 (Appendix A): There exists a controller stabilizing the given plant and feedback compensator in the closed-loop configuration of Fig. 1 iff the pair is admissible.

Let the spectral densities of $\boldsymbol{u}(s)$, $\boldsymbol{d}(s)$, $\boldsymbol{l}(s)$, and $\boldsymbol{m}(s)$ be denoted by $G_u(s)$, $G_d(s)$, $G_l(s)$, and $G_m(s)$, respectively. Setting aside for the moment all questions of convergence,[7]

$$2\pi j E_t=\mathrm{Tr}\int_{-j\infty}^{j\infty}\langle \boldsymbol{e}(s)\boldsymbol{e}_*(s)\rangle ds \tag{27}$$

is the usual quadratic measure of steady-state response. Similarly, if $P_s(s)$ represents the transfer matrix coupling the plant input $\boldsymbol{r}(s)$ to those "sensitive" plant modes which must be especially guarded against excessive dynamic excursions,

$$2\pi j E_s=\mathrm{Tr}\int_{-j\infty}^{j\infty}\langle P_s(s)\boldsymbol{r}(s)\boldsymbol{r}_*(s)P_{s*}(s)\rangle ds \tag{28}$$

is a proven useful penalty function for saturation [7]. Hence,

$$E=E_t+kE_s, \tag{29}$$

k an adjustable positive constant, serves as a weighted cost combining both factors and the optimal controller is chosen to minimize E. Now referring to (8) and (9) it is seen that $R(s)$ determines $\boldsymbol{r}(s)$, $\boldsymbol{e}(s)$, and E. Consequently $R(s)$ embodies all the design freedom and the next lemma plays an obvious and indispensable role.

Lemma 3 (Appendix A): Let the given plant and feedback compensator form an admissible pair with transfer matrix descriptions $P(s)$, $F(s)$. Let

$$F(s)P(s)=A^{-1}(s)B(s)=B_1(s)A_1^{-1}(s) \tag{30}$$

where the pairs $A(s)$, $B(s)$ and $B_1(s)$, $A_1(s)$ constitute any left–right coprime polynomial decompositions of $F(s)P(s)$, respectively. Select polynomial matrices $X(s)$ and $Y(s)$ such that[8]

$$A(s)X(s)+B(s)Y(s)=1_n. \tag{31}$$

Then, 1) the closed-loop of Fig. 1 is asymptotically stable iff

$$R(s)=H(s)A(s) \tag{32}$$

where

$$H(s)=Y(s)+A_1(s)K(s)$$

and $K(s)$ is any $m\times n$ real rational matrix analytic in $\mathrm{Re}\,s\geqslant 0$ which satisfies the constraint

$$\det(X(s)-B_1(s)K(s))\not\equiv 0. \tag{33}$$

2) The stabilizing controller associated with a particular choice of admissible $K(s)$ possesses the transfer matrix

$$C=(Y+A_1K)(X-B_1K)^{-1}. \tag{34}$$

(From $AB_1=BA_1$ and (31) we deduce that

$$A(X-B_1K)+B(Y+A_1K)=1_n, \tag{35}$$

a useful relationship.)

In view of this lemma, the natural way to attack the problem of minimizing E is to vary over all $m\times n$ real rational matrices $K(s)$ analytic in $\mathrm{Re}\,s\geqslant 0$ which satisfy restriction (33). We are now ready to discuss in detail the assumptions which justify the entire optimization scheme.

1) Rate gyros and tachometers are examples of practical sensing devices which are not modeled as dynamical systems. Yet almost invariably sensors are stable and their transfer matrices are analytic in $\mathrm{Re}\,s\geqslant 0$. However, for our purposes it suffices to assume that the feedforward cascade is stable and that $F(s)$ is analytic on the finite $s=j\omega$-axis. In particular, $L(s)$ is analytic in $\mathrm{Re}\,s\geqslant 0$. If $P_o(s)$ and $F_o(s)$ represent distinct physical blocks, these blocks must be stable and both $P_o(s)$ and $F_o(s)$ are analytic in $\mathrm{Re}\,s\geqslant 0$. On the other hand, if $P_o(s)$ and $F_o(s)$ are merely part of the paper modeling, it is possible to relax the analyticity requirements.

2) A pole of $F(s)P(s)$ in $\mathrm{Re}\,s>0$ reveals true open-loop instability whereas a finite pole on the $s=j\omega$-axis is usually present because of intentional high-gain preconditioning. Recall that in the absence of load disturbance and measurement noise, a unity-feedback single-input–output loop enclosing a plant whose transfer function possesses a pole of order ν at $s=j\omega_o$ will track any causal linear combination of $e^{j\omega_o t}\cdot t^{k-1}$, $k=1\rightarrow\nu$, with zero steady-state error. The correct generalization to the multivariable case is easy to find. Setting $\boldsymbol{d}=\boldsymbol{O}$, $\boldsymbol{l}=\boldsymbol{O}$, and $\boldsymbol{m}=\boldsymbol{O}$ in (7) and (9) we obtain

$$\boldsymbol{y}=T\boldsymbol{u} \tag{36}$$

and

$$\boldsymbol{e}=(1_n-T)\boldsymbol{u}. \tag{37}$$

For a stable configuration $T(s)$ is analytic in $\mathrm{Re}\,s\geqslant 0$, but not necessarily proper (Appendix A). Nevertheless, there are cogent reasons for insisting on a dynamical closed-loop design. Consider the conditions that must prevail if

[7] $\mathrm{Tr}A=\mathrm{trace}A$. In (27) and (28), $s=j\omega$, ω real.

[8] The existence of real polynomial matrices $X(s)$, $Y(s)$ satisfying (31) is guaranteed by the left-coprimeness of $A(s)$ and $B(s)$ (Appendix A). These polynomials need not be unique.

the loop is to track any one-sided input of the form

$$e^{j\omega_o t}\cdot \sum_{k=1}^{\nu} t^{k-1} d_{\nu-k}, \tag{38}$$

d_k a constant vector, $k=1\to\nu$, with zero steady-state error. Clearly,[9]

$$e(s)=\sum_{k=1}^{\nu}\Gamma(k)\cdot\frac{1_n-T(s)}{(s-j\omega_o)^k}\cdot d_{\nu-k} \tag{39}$$

is the transform of a bounded time function which vanishes as $t\to\infty$ iff it is analytic in $\mathrm{Re}\, s\geqslant 0$ and $e(\infty)=O$. As necessary consequences, $T(s)$ must be proper and

$$(1_n-T(j\omega_o))d_o=O_n. \tag{40}$$

As is well known, (40) possesses a nontrivial solution d_o iff

$$\det(1_n-T(j\omega_o))=0. \tag{41}$$

Conversely, any ω_o satisfying (41) generates a generalized ramp-modulated sinusoid (38) capable of being tracked with zero steady-state error. These inputs and their finite linear combinations constitute a most important class of shape-deterministic information-bearing signals and play a key role in industrial applications. The set of all such possible "infinite gain" frequencies ω_o coincides with the totality of real solutions of (41).

In view of the arguments presented in the initial paragraph of 2), poles of $P(s)$ on the $s=j\omega$-axis enable the loop to track certain inputs with zero steady-state error. With unity feedback, $1_n-T=S$ and all plant poles in $\mathrm{Re}\, s\geqslant 0$, counted according to their McMillan degrees, are indeed zeros of $\det S$ (Appendix A). However, if $F\neq 1_n$, this perfect tracking capability is lost unless $F(s)$ is also conditioned suitably. Employing the easily derived formulas

$$S=(X-B_1K)A \tag{42}$$

and

$$FPR=1_n-S, \tag{43}$$

it is seen that

$$\begin{aligned}1_n-T&=S+(F-1_n)PR\\&=(X-B_1K+(F-1_n)P(Y+A_1K))A.\end{aligned} \tag{44}$$

Since $P(s)$ and $F(s)$ form an admissible pair,

$$\det{}^+A=\psi_{FP}^+=\psi_F^+\psi_P^+ \tag{45}$$

and (44) shows that the purely imaginary zeros of $\psi_P^+(s)$ will surely be zeros of $\det(1_n-T)$ provided

$$Z=X-B_1K+(F-1_n)P(Y+A_1K) \tag{46}$$

is designed to be analytic on the finite $s=j\omega$-axis.[10] This analyticity precludes any possibility of cancellation and is achieved iff $(F-1_n)P$ is analytic on the finite $s=j\omega$-axis. The proof of this assertion is somewhat tedious but because of its great importance we supply it in detail.

In 4) it is shown that $P(s)A_1(s)$ is automatically analytic for all finite $s=j\omega$ and it follows from (46) that the same is true of $Z(s)$ iff $(F-1_n)PY$ is analytic for all finite $s=j\omega$. Multiplication of both sides of (31) on the left by $A^{-1}(s)$ yields

$$X+FPY=A^{-1} \tag{47}$$

since $FP=A^{-1}B$. By assumption, $F(s)$ is analytic for $s=j\omega$ whence, by admissibility and (47), any finite purely imaginary pole $s_o=j\omega_o$ of $P(s)$ of McMillan degree ν_o must also be a pole of $P(s)Y(s)$ of the same degree. Write

$$PY=A_2^{-1}B_2 \tag{48}$$

and

$$P=A_p^{-1}B_p \tag{49}$$

where the polynomial pairs (B_2,A_2) and (B_p,A_p) are both left-coprime. By hypothesis,

$$(F-1_n)PY=(F-1_n)A_2^{-1}B_2 \tag{50}$$

is analytic for finite $s=j\omega$. But (X_2 and Y_2 are polynomial)

$$A_2X_2+B_2Y_2=1_n$$

implies

$$(F-1_n)X_2+(F-1_n)A_2^{-1}B_2Y_2=(F-1_n)A_2^{-1} \tag{51}$$

and $(F-1_n)A_2^{-1}$ is also analytic on the finite $s=j\omega$-axis. Substituting (49) into (48) we get

$$B_pY=A_pA_2^{-1}B_2 \tag{52}$$

and by an argument similar to the above, the analyticity of B_pY for finite $s=j\omega$ forces that of $A_pA_2^{-1}$. In other words,

$$A_2^{-1}=A_p^{-1}\mathcal{P} \tag{53}$$

where $\mathcal{P}(s)$ is analytic on the finite $s=j\omega$-axis. However, because the finite $j\omega$-axis poles of PY agree with those of P, McMillan degrees included, $\det A_2(s)$ and $\det A_p(s)$ possess the same $j\omega$-axis zeros, multiplicities included. Thus,

$$\det\mathcal{P}(s)\neq 0, \qquad s=j\omega \tag{54}$$

and $\mathcal{P}^{-1}(s)$ and $(F-1_n)A_2^{-1}$ are, therefore, both analytic on the finite $s=j\omega$-axis. It is now clear that

$$(F-1_n)P=(F-1_n)A_p^{-1}B_p=(F-1_n)A_2^{-1}\mathcal{P}^{-1}B_p \tag{55}$$

is analytic for all finite $s=j\omega$. Q.E.D.

This constraint is of decisive importance and replaces the usual unity-feedback desideratum $F=1_n$ which due to

[9] $\Gamma(k)$ is the Gamma function of argument k.

[10] The multiplicity of any zero of $\psi_P(s)$ equals its McMillan degree as a pole of $P(s)$. Hence, the purely imaginary zeros of $\psi_P^+(s)$ constitute the totality of finite $j\omega$-axis poles of $P(s)$.

ever-present delays and transducer inertia is never realizable. In the actual design the constraint is met by a correct choice of preequalizer $F_e(s)$ and the two degrees of freedom inherent in the problem are exploited to maximum advantage.

3) In process control the recovery of steady state under load disturbance $\boldsymbol{d}(s)$ is a requirement of paramount importance. From (9), with $\boldsymbol{u}$, $\boldsymbol{m}$, and $\boldsymbol{l}$ set equal to $\boldsymbol{O}$,

$$\boldsymbol{e}=(P_0-PRP_d)\boldsymbol{d} \tag{56}$$

$$=(1_n-PRF)P_o\boldsymbol{d}-(PRL)\boldsymbol{d}$$

$$=S_1P_o\boldsymbol{d}-TL\boldsymbol{d}=(S_1P_o-TL)\boldsymbol{d} \tag{57}$$

where

$$S_1=(1_n+PCF)^{-1}. \tag{58}$$

Again as in 2), the shape-deterministic component of $\boldsymbol{d}(s)$ is envisaged to be the transform of a sum of generalized ramp-modulated sinusoids and for bounded zero steady-state error, $\boldsymbol{e}(s)$ must vanish at infinity and be analytic in $\mathrm{Re}\, s \geqslant 0$. Assuming S_1P_o—TL proper and $S_1P_o\boldsymbol{d}$ and $L\boldsymbol{d}$ analytic in $\mathrm{Re}\, s\geqslant 0$ is evidently sufficient. Invoking closed-loop stability it can be shown (Appendix A) that

$$S_1(s)=\mathcal{P}_1(s)A_p(s), \tag{59}$$

$\mathcal{P}_1(s)$ analytic in $\mathrm{Re}\, s\geqslant 0$. Hence, $S_1P_o\boldsymbol{d}$ analytic in $\mathrm{Re}\, s \geqslant 0$ can be replaced by $A_pP_o\boldsymbol{d}$ analytic in $\mathrm{Re}\, s\geqslant 0$ and once again the $j\omega$-axis poles of the plant are brought into evidence through $A_p(s)$. Observe that the $j\omega$-axis analyticity of $A_p(P_oG_dP_{o*})A_{p*}$, LG_dL_*, and $LG_dP_{o*}A_{p*}$ is a corollary.

4) Let

$$P=B_{p1}A_{p1}^{-1} \tag{60}$$

be any right-coprime decomposition of $P(s)$. Then,

$$B_1A_1^{-1}=FP=FB_{p1}A_{p1}^{-1} \tag{61}$$

and it follows from the assumed analyticity of $F(s)$ on the finite $j\omega$-axis that

$$B_1A_1^{-1}A_{p1}=FB_{p1} \tag{62}$$

is also analytic for all finite $s=j\omega$. Hence, reasoning as in 2),

$$A_{p1}(s)=A_1(s)\mathcal{P}_2(s), \tag{63}$$

$\mathcal{P}_2(s)$ analytic and nonsingular for all finite $s=j\omega$. Consequently,

$$PA_1=B_{p1}A_{p1}^{-1}A_1=B_{p1}\mathcal{P}_2^{-1} \tag{64}$$

is analytic for all finite $s=j\omega$. Q.E.D.

5) From (8), (9) and the definitions (28), (27),[11]

$$2\pi jE_s=\mathrm{Tr}\int_{-j\infty}^{j\infty}QR\left(G_u+G_{ml}+P_dG_dP_{d*}\right)R_*\,ds \tag{65}$$

and

$$2\pi jE_t=\mathrm{Tr}\int_{-j\infty}^{j\infty}\big((1_n-PR)G_u(1_n-PR)_*+(PR)G_{ml}(PR)_*$$

$$+(P_o-PRP_d)G_d(P_o-PRP_d)_*\big)ds \tag{66}$$

where

$$Q(s)=P_{s*}(s)P_s(s) \tag{67}$$

and

$$G_{ml}=F_oG_mF_{o*}+L_oG_lL_{o*}. \tag{68}$$

In terms of

$$G=G_u+G_{ml}+P_dG_dP_{d*} \tag{69}$$

and H,

$$2\pi jE_s=\mathrm{Tr}\int_{-j\infty}^{j\infty}QH(AGA_*)H_*\,ds. \tag{70}$$

The nonnegative parahermetian matrices $G_{ml}(s)$ and $Q(s)$ are assumed to be free of finite $j\omega$-axis poles. (There is no physical reason for doing otherwise.) Since a stable closed-loop design forces $H(s)$ to be analytic in $\mathrm{Re}\, s\geqslant 0$ (Lemma 3), the integrand of (70) will be devoid of finite $j\omega$-axis poles if AGA_* is analytic on the $j\omega$-axis. Consider first AG_uA_* and the equality

$$P+(F-1_n)P=FP=A^{-1}B. \tag{71}$$

Write, as before, $P=A_p^{-1}B_p$ where A_p, B_p is a left-coprime pair and substitute into (71). Bearing in mind that $(F-1_n)P$ is assumed to be analytic on the finite $j\omega$-axis, familiar reasoning[12] permits us to conclude that $A(s)=\mathcal{P}_3(s)A_p(s)$, $\mathcal{P}_3(s)$ analytic and nonsingular for all finite $s=j\omega$. Hence, the analyticity of $A_pG_uA_{p*}$ on the finite $s=j\omega$-axis guarantees that of AG_uA_*. This $j\omega$-axis analyticity is in accord with our previous reasoning. Namely, the deterministic part of $\boldsymbol{u}(s)$ is the transform of a sum of generalized ramp-modulated sinusoids whose resonant frequencies coincide with the $j\omega$-axis poles of $P(s)$. These poles *and only these poles* should appear as $j\omega$-axis poles of $G_u(s)$. But these poles are also imbedded in the Smith canonic structure of $A_p(s)$ and the $j\omega$-axis analyticity of $A_pG_uA_{p*}$ is merely a succinct formulation of one design objective. Regarding $A(P_dG_dP_{d*})A_*$, its $j\omega$-axis analyticity follows from the assumptions in 3) and the readily deduced relation

$$AF=\mathcal{P}_4A_p, \tag{72}$$

$\mathcal{P}_4(s)$ analytic for $s=j\omega$.

Let us now examine the $j\omega$-axis analyticity of the individual terms making up the integrand of (66). First,

[11]All random processes are assumed to be independent. Note $\mathrm{Tr}(L_1L_2)=\mathrm{Tr}(L_2L_1)$.

[12]Both the admissibility of the pair $F(s)$, $P(s)$ and the $j\omega$-axis analyticity of $F(s)$ must be invoked.

$$(1_n - PR)G_u(1_n - PR)_*$$
$$= (1_n - PR)A^{-1}(AG_uA_*)A_*^{-1}(1_n - PR)_* \quad (73)$$
$$= (A^{-1} - PH)(AG_uA_*)(A^{-1} - PH)_* \quad (74)$$

and it suffices to prove that $A^{-1} - PH$ is analytic on the $j\omega$-axis. This is clear because K, PA_1, and $(F - 1_n)P$ are analytic on $j\omega$, $A^{-1} = X + FPY$ and

$$A^{-1} - PH = A^{-1} - P(Y + A_1K) = A^{-1} - PY - PA_1K$$
$$= X + (F - 1_n)PY - (PA_1)K. \quad (75)$$

The $j\omega$-axis analyticity of the second and third terms in (66) follows from that of $G_{ml}(s)$ and 3). In order to exclude meaningless, but mathematically allowed physical degeneracies, we must also impose the restriction

$$\det(AGA_*)\cdot\det(A_{1*}(P_*P + kQ)A_1) \neq 0, \qquad s = j\omega. \quad (76)$$

This inequality is essential (Appendix B). It is also shown in Appendix B[13] that

$$G_u(j\omega) \leqslant O(1/\omega^2) \quad (77)$$

and

$$P_oG_dP_{o*} \leqslant O(1/\omega^2) \quad (78)$$

are suggested naturally by the requirement of finite cost. Furthermore, if

$$(P_*P + kQ)G \approx \omega^{2\mu}1_m, \quad (79)$$
$$G_d(j\omega) \approx \omega^{-2i}1 \quad (80)$$

and

$$P(s) = O(s^\nu), \quad (81)$$

the inequalities

$$\mu \geqslant \nu - 1 \quad (82)$$

and

$$i \leqslant 1 \quad (83)$$

assure the properness of T and $S_1P_o - TL$, respectively. In most applications load disturbance contains a step-component and (80) is satisfied with $i = 1$. (The integers μ and ν can be negative.)

6) In general, the effects of parameter uncertainty on P and F are more pronounced as ω increases and closed-loop sensitivity is an important consideration. Let F, PC, S, S_1, and T undergo changes from $(F)_a$, $(PC)_a$, $(S)_a$, $(S_1)_a$, and $(T)_a$ to $(F)_b$, $(PC)_b$, $(S)_b$, $(S_1)_b$, and $(T)_b$ at a fixed ω. Noting that $T = PCS = S_1PC$,

$$(T)_b - (T)_a = (S_1)_b(PC)_b - (PC)_a(S)_a$$
$$= (S_1)_b[(PC)_b(1_n + (F)_a(PC)_a) - (1_n + (PC)_b(F)_b)(PC)_a](S_a)$$
$$= (S_1)_b[(PC)_b - (PC)_a - (PC)_b \cdot ((F)_b - (F)_a)(PC)_a](S)_a.$$

Thus

$$\Delta T = (S_1)_b\cdot\Delta(PC)\cdot(S)_a - (T)_b\cdot(\Delta F)\cdot(T)_a, \quad (84)$$

an exact formula valid for arbitrary increments ΔF, $\Delta(PC)$. To first order,

$$\delta T = S_1\cdot\delta(PC)\cdot S - T(\delta F)T \quad (85)$$

and we recover the classical differential version of (84). If $\det(FPC) \not\equiv 0$, (85) may also be rewritten as

$$T^{-1}\cdot\delta T = (PC)^{-1}\cdot\delta(PC)\cdot S - (\delta F)\cdot F^{-1}\cdot(1_n - S). \quad (86)$$

In words, at frequency ω,

left percent change in T = (left percent change in PC) $\cdot S(j\omega)$ − (right percent change in F)$\cdot(1_n - S(j\omega))$ (87)

and again $S(j\omega)$ and $1_n - S(j\omega)$ emerge as the pertinent matrix gain functions for the forward and return links, respectively. Clearly then, to combat the adverse effects of high-frequency uncertainty in the modeling of $F(j\omega)$ and the plant matrix $P(j\omega)$, it is sound engineering practice to insist on a design with $S(j\omega)$ proper and equal to 1_n at $\omega = \infty$. This feature is easily introduced into the analytic framework by means of the constraint

$$O(P) + O(F) \leqslant \mu \quad (88)$$

which simultaneously ensures that the Wiener–Hopf controller defined by (34) makes sense and is proper if $\mu \geqslant -1$ (Appendix B). Furthermore, (88) also forces $S_1 = (1_n + PCF)^{-1} \to 1_n$ as $\omega \to \infty$ which is consistent with the engineering interpretation of the right-percentage formula for T,

$$(\delta T)\cdot T^{-1} = S_1\cdot\delta(PC)\cdot(PC)^{-1} - (1_n - S_1)\cdot F^{-1}\cdot\delta F. \quad (89)$$

We should like to emphasize that the cost E already imposes a weighted penalty on the choice of forward and return-link sensitivities through the (somewhat disguised) presence of S and $1_n - S$ in the error $\boldsymbol{e}$. (Equation (16) for $F = 1_n$ illustrates the point.) All this is in accord with a basic tenet of the classical theory which states that good immunity to load disturbance and good forward-link sensitivity usually go hand in hand.

III. The Optimal Controller

By way of recapitulation we shall collate the major working assumptions.

[13] $A(s) \leqslant O(s^r)$ means that no entry in $A(s)$ grows faster than s^r as $s \to \infty$. The order of $A(s)$ equals r, i.e., $A(s) = O(s^r)$ if 1) $A(s) \leqslant O(s^r)$ and 2) *at least one* entry grows exactly like s^r. For $A(s)$ square, $A(s) \approx s^r 1$ abbreviates

$$\lim_{s\to\infty} s^{-r}A(s) = A_\infty,$$

A_∞ *a constant nonsingular matrix*. Note $A(s) \approx s^r1$ implies $A(s) = O(s^r)$, but not conversely.

Assumption 1: The plant and feedback compensator form an admissible pair (Definition 1), the feedforward compensator is asymptotically stable and the respective transfer matrices, $P(s)$, $F(s)$, $L(s)$ are prescribed in advance. (Note, in particular, that $L(s)$ is analytic in Re $s \geqslant 0$.)

Assumption 2: $P_o(s)$, $F_o(s)$, $L_o(s)$, $Q(s)=P_{s*}(s)P_s(s)$ and the spectral densities $G_u(s)$, $G_d(s)$, $G_m(s)$, $G_l(s)$ are given. Any block outside the loop which represents an actual physical component must be asymptotically stable and its transfer matrix is therefore analytic in Re $s \geqslant 0$. (On the other hand, if any such block is merely part of the paper modeling the analyticity requirement can be relaxed.) The input signal, load disturbance and measurement noises are stochastically independent.

Assumption 3: Let $P=A_p^{-1}B_p$ be any left-coprime factorization of $P(s)$ and let

$$G_{ml}=F_oG_mF_{o*}+L_oG_lL_{o*}. \tag{90}$$

The matrices Q, F, $(F-1_n)P$, $A_pG_uA_{p*}$, $A_p(P_oG_dP_{o*})A_{p*}$, LG_dL_*, and G_{ml} are analytic on the finite $s=j\omega$-axis.

Assumption 4: Let k be any positive constant,

$$G=G_u+P_dG_dP_{d*}+G_{ml} \tag{91}$$

and

$$P_d=FP_o+L. \tag{92}$$

The matrices AGA_* and $A_{1*}(P_*P+kQ)A_1$ are nonsingular on the finite $s=j\omega$-axis. (Their $j\omega$-analyticity is ensured by the above assumptions.)

Assumption 5: The data satisfy the order relations[14]

$$G_u \leqslant O(1/s^2); \qquad P_oG_dP_{o*} \leqslant O(1/s^2)$$

$$G_d \approx s^{-2i}1; \qquad P=O(s^{\nu}) \tag{93}$$

$$O(P)+O(F) \leqslant \mu \tag{94}$$

and

$$(P_*P+kQ)G \approx s^{2\mu}1_m \tag{95}$$

where

$$i \leqslant 1; \qquad \mu \geqslant \max(\nu-1,-1). \tag{96}$$

We are now in a position to state the master result.

Theorem 1 (Appendix B): Under Assumptions 1–5 the optimal design is carried out in the following manner.

1) Construct two square real rational matrices $\Lambda(s)$, $\Omega(s)$ *analytic together with their inverses in* Re $s \geqslant 0$ such that

$$A_{1*}(P_*P+kQ)A_1=\Lambda_*\Lambda \tag{97}$$

and

$$AGA_*=\Omega\Omega_*. \tag{98}$$

[14]Refer to footnote 13 for an explanation of the notation.

2) Let

$$I=A_{1*}P_*(G_u+P_oG_dP_{d*})A_* \tag{99}$$

and choose any two real polynomial matrices $X(s)$, $Y(s)$ such that

$$A(s)X(s)+B(s)Y(s)=1_n. \tag{100}$$

3) The transfer matrix of the optimal controller is given by

$$C=(Y+A_1K)(X-B_1K)^{-1} \tag{101}$$

where[15]

$$K=\Lambda^{-1}\left(\left\{\Lambda_*^{-1}I\Omega_*^{-1}\right\}_+ +\left\{\Lambda A_1^{-1}Y\Omega\right\}_-\right)\Omega^{-1}-A_1^{-1}Y; \tag{102}$$

or, in a form more suitable for numerical implementation,

$$C=H_o\left(A^{-1}\Omega-FPH_o\right)^{-1}, \tag{103}$$

$$H_o=A_1\Lambda^{-1}\left(\left\{\Lambda_*^{-1}I\Omega_*^{-1}\right\}_+ +\left\{\Lambda A_1^{-1}Y\Omega\right\}_-\right). \tag{104}$$

The (nonhidden) poles of the optimally compensated loop are *precisely* the *zeros* of the strict Hurwitz polynomial

$$\theta(s)=\frac{\psi_F^-(s)\psi_P^-(s)}{\psi_{FP}^-(s)} \tag{105}$$

plus the finite *poles* of $K(s)$, each of these poles counted according to its McMillan degree. Both $H_o(s)$ and $K(s)$ are analytic in Re $s \geqslant 0$ and the *distinct* finite poles of $K(s)$ are included in those of the primary data

$$FP,\ \left(A_{1*}(P_*P+kQ)A_1\right)^{-1},\ \left(AGA_*\right)^{-1},\ A_{1*}P_*\left(G_u+P_oG_dP_{d*}\right)A_* \tag{106}$$

located in Re $s<0$. Thus stability margin is ascertainable in advance.

Several comments are in order. First, there exist effective computer algorithms for the realization of the canonic factors $\Lambda(s)$, $\Omega(s)$ [8], [9]. Second, the combination of plant and feedback compensator is said to be nonminimum-phase if the polynomial matrix $B(s)$ appearing in the left-coprime decomposition $F(s)P(s)=A^{-1}(s)B(s)$ has rank *less* than row-rank for some finite $s=s_o$ in Re $s>0$.[16] As is shown in Appendix A, any such s_o is also a zero of $\det(1_n-S)$. Now for any choice of nonzero constant $\eta\neq 1$ the zeros of the stability polynomial

$$\varphi(s,\eta)=\psi_F\psi_P\psi_C\cdot\det(1_n+\eta FPC)$$
$$=\psi_F\psi_P\psi_C\cdot\det(1_n+FPC+(\eta-1)FPC) \tag{107}$$

[15]In the partial fraction expansion $\{\ \}_\infty+\{\ \}_++\{\ \}_-$ of any rational matrix, $\{\ \}_\infty$ is the part associated with the pole at infinity and $\{\ \}_+$, $\{\ \}_-$ the parts associated with all the finite poles in Re $s<0$ and Re $s\geqslant 0$, respectively. Clearly, $\{\ \}_+$ is analytic in Re $s\geqslant 0$, $\{\ \}_-$ in Re $s<0$ and both vanish at infinity.

[16]Although this definition is the most natural generalization of the one accepted in the scalar case, other definitions also make physical sense when examined in the context of the standard control problem [3].

coincide with those of[17]

$$\varphi(s,1)\cdot\det\left(\frac{1}{\eta-1}1_n+1_n-S\right). \tag{108}$$

Thus, by continuity, at least one of these zeros tends to $s=s_o$ as $|\eta|\to\infty$ and all attempts to decrease transient error to zero by a simple constant-gain modification of some already predetermined controller $C(s)$ must, therefore, fail.

Corollary 1: Suppose $F(s)P(s)$ is analytic in $\mathrm{Re}\,s\geqslant 0$. Then

$$C=H_o(\Omega_r-FPH_o)^{-1} \tag{109}$$

where

$$H_o=\Lambda_r^{-1}\{\Lambda_{r*}^{-1}I_r\Omega_{r*}^{-1}\}_+, \tag{110}$$

$$(P_*P+kQ)=\Lambda_{r*}\Lambda_r, \tag{111}$$

$$G=\Omega_r\Omega_{r*}, \tag{112}$$

$$I_r=P_*(G_u+P_oG_dP_{d*}) \tag{113}$$

and $\Lambda_r(s)$, $\Omega_r(s)$ are square, real rational matrices analytic together with their inverses in $\mathrm{Re}\,s\geqslant 0$. ($\Lambda_r,\Omega_r,I_r$ are "reduced" quantities.)

Proof: The analyticity of $F(s)P(s)$ in $\mathrm{Re}\,s\geqslant 0$ implies $\det^+A(s)=\det^+A_1(s)=\psi_{FP}^+(s)=1$. Thus $A\Omega_r=\Omega$, $\Lambda_rA_1=\Lambda$, $\{\Lambda A_1^{-1}Y\Omega\}_-=O$ and the rest follows by direct substitution. Q.E.D.

Under the conditions of the corollary, the feedback sensor and plant are asymptotically stable and the resulting simplification, as evidenced in (109)–(113), is striking. Note in particular that the polynomial factors $A(s)$, $A_1(s)$, and $Y(s)$ are no longer needed!

The general formula (103) for the optimal controller transfer matrix is excellently conditioned. In fact, it is easily shown (Appendix B) that in exact arithmetic

$$H_o=(Y+A_1K)\Omega \tag{114}$$

and

$$A^{-1}\Omega-FPH_o=(X-B_1K)\Omega. \tag{115}$$

Thus, in exact arithmetic both H_o and $A^{-1}\Omega-FPH$ are analytic in $\mathrm{Re}\,s\geqslant 0$. Consequently, if the numerical scheme employed to compute (103) automatically ensures the closed right half-plane analyticity of H_o and $A^{-1}\Omega-FPH_o$, the corresponding exact arithmetic K is such that A_1K and B_1K are also analytic in $\mathrm{Re}\,s\geqslant 0$.[18] But then,

$$X_1A_1K+Y_1B_1K=K \tag{116}$$

reveals that $K(s)$ is analytic in $\mathrm{Re}\,s\geqslant 0$ *and the closed-loop structure realized with the computed C(s) is asymptotically stable.*

[17] $1_n-S=(1_n+FPC)^{-1}FPC$.

[18] $\Omega^{-1}(s)$ is analytic in $\mathrm{Re}\,s\geqslant 0$.

Corollary 2: Let[19]

$$a=\Lambda_*^{-1}I\Omega_*^{-1}, \tag{117}$$

$$b=\Lambda A_1^{-1}Y\Omega, \tag{118}$$

$$c=\{a-b\}_- \tag{119}$$

and

$$\rho=G_u+P_oG_dP_{o*}-a_*a+c_*c. \tag{120}$$

Then, under the assumption[20]

$$a_\infty(s)=O, \tag{121}$$

the *minimum* cost $E_{\min}$ is given by

$$2\pi jE_{\min}=\mathrm{Tr}\int_{-j\infty}^{j\infty}\rho(s)\,ds. \tag{122}$$

In particular, if $F(s)P(s)$ is analytic in $\mathrm{Re}\,s\geqslant 0$ (the stable case) we can choose

$$\rho=G_u+P_oG_dP_{o*}-a_{+*}a_+. \tag{123}$$

Proof: From (B2), Appendix B,

$$a-b-\Lambda K\Omega=\Lambda_*^{-1}\Delta_*\Omega_*^{-1} \tag{124}$$

and it follows immediately that $c=\{a-b\}_-$ is analytic in $\mathrm{Re}\,s\leqslant 0$ (which includes the $j\omega$-axis). Now by combining (B19), (B22), and (B24) and exploiting the closed left half-plane analyticity of $c(s)$ with the aid of Cauchy's theorem, we easily reach (120)+(122). If $F(s)P(s)$ is analytic in $\mathrm{Re}\,s\geqslant 0$, $b_-(s)\equiv O$ and

$$\rho=G_u+P_oG_dP_{o*}-a_{+*}a_+-a_{+*}a_--a_{-*}a_+.$$

However, since $a_{+*}a_-$ is $O(1/\omega^2)$ and analytic in $\mathrm{Re}\,s\leqslant 0$, contour integration yields

$$\mathrm{Tr}\int_{-j\infty}^{j\infty}a_{+*}a_-\,ds=\mathrm{Tr}\int_{-j\infty}^{j\infty}a_{-*}a_+\,ds=0.$$

Thus

$$2\pi jE_{\min}=\mathrm{Tr}\int_{-j\infty}^{j\infty}(G_u+P_oG_dP_{o*}-a_{+*}a_+)\,ds.$$

Q.E.D.

In the stable case $G_u+P_oG_dP_{o*}$ and a_*a are both individually $j\omega$-analytic, but, in general, it is only the combination $G_u+P_oG_dP_{o*}-a_*a$ which is devoid of purely imaginary poles.

Corollary 3:[21] Let $P(s)$ be square and analytic *together with its inverse* in $\mathrm{Re}\,s\geqslant 0$, let $F=1$ (unity feedback), let $k=0$ (no saturation constraint) and assume feedforward compensation is not employed (L and G_l are zero). Then, if G and $G_u+P_oG_dP_{o*}$ are diagonal matrices, the optimal controller $C(s)$ satisfies the noninteraction condition

[19] Here $a_+\equiv\{a\}_+, b_-\equiv\{b\}_-, a_\infty\equiv\{a\}_\infty$, etc.

[20] Quite usual.

[21] Suggested some years ago by I. M. Horowitz [19].

$$P(s)C(s) = \text{diagonal matrix}. \tag{125}$$

Proof: Clearly, from (109)–(113) and the stipulated assumptions, it follows that $\Lambda_r = P$, Ω_r is diagonal and

$$I_r = \Lambda_{r*}(G_u + P_o G_d P_{o*}). \tag{126}$$

Thus

$$\Lambda_{r*}^{-1} I_r \Omega_{r*}^{-1} = (G_u + P_o G_d P_{o*})\Omega_{r*}^{-1}, \tag{127}$$

$$PH_o = \Lambda_r H_o = \left\{ (G_u + P_o G_d P_{o*})\Omega_{r*}^{-1} \right\}_+ \tag{128}$$

and

$$PC = PH_o(\Omega_r - PH_o)^{-1} \tag{129}$$

are also diagonal. Q.E.D.

Let us mention some obvious generalizations. First, suppose the integrand in (27) is also weighted so that

$$2\pi j E_t = \int_{-j\infty}^{j\infty} \langle e_*(s) Q_t e(s) \rangle ds$$

$$= \text{Tr} \int_{-j\infty}^{j\infty} Q_t \langle e(s) e_*(s) \rangle ds, \tag{130}$$

Q_t an arbitrary real, constant, symmetric nonnegative-definite matrix. Then we simply make the substitutions

$$(P_* P + kQ) \rightarrow P_* Q_t P + kQ, \tag{130a}$$

$$I \rightarrow A_{1*} P_* Q_t (G_u + P_o G_d P_{d*}) A_* \tag{130b}$$

and

$$\rho \rightarrow Q_t (G_u + P_o G_d P_{o*}) - a_* a + c_* c \tag{130c}$$

and continue to use the same formulas as before. In particular, the canonic factor $\Lambda(s)$ is found from the decomposition

$$\Lambda_* \Lambda = A_{1*}(P_* Q_t P + kQ) A_1 \tag{130d}$$

and (76) is altered to read

$$\det(A_{1*}(P_* Q_t P + kQ) A_1) \cdot \det(AGA_*) \neq 0, \qquad s = j\omega. \tag{130e}$$

Second, we have assumed all processes to be zero-mean. This is always true for the measurement noises $\boldsymbol{m}$ and $\boldsymbol{l}$ and almost invariably true for $\boldsymbol{u}$. In any case, if at least one of the means $\langle \boldsymbol{u} \rangle$ or $\langle \boldsymbol{d} \rangle$ vanishes, all formulas remain intact. Otherwise, $\boldsymbol{e}$ in the integrand of E_t and $\boldsymbol{r}$ in the integrand of E_s must be replaced by $\boldsymbol{e} - \langle \boldsymbol{e} \rangle$ and $\boldsymbol{r} - \langle \boldsymbol{r} \rangle$, respectively. This then entails identifying G_u with the spectral density of $\boldsymbol{u} - \langle \boldsymbol{u} \rangle$ and G_d with that of $\boldsymbol{d} - \langle \boldsymbol{d} \rangle$. The optimal controller now minimizes the steady-state rms error fluctuation subject to a steady-state rms constraint on the fluctuation of the plant input.

IV. Discussion and Conclusions

It would be superfluous to list the numerical problems which beset algorithms involving the factorization and manipulation of rational matrices. Nevertheless, work now in progress leads us to believe that a feasible computer implementation of the optimal controller is within reach. The availability of such an algorithm will undoubtedly suggest related simpler suboptimal strategies.

Although many of the physical ideas propounded in this paper have already been touched upon in the literature by several authors [14], [15], the various attempts to evolve an inclusive frequency-domain least-squares approach to multivariable controller design have by and large been unsuccessful because of an imprecise grasp of the full implications of closed-loop stability and a failure to recognize at the outset the need to condition the cost functional in a manner compatible with the physical constraints introduced by the given data $F(s)$, $P(s)$. As this paper clearly shows, within a linear framework a correct treatment depends essentially on an in-depth analytic characterization of all those engineering factors which figure meaningfully in any practical design scheme and a successful parametric solution of the concomitant "model-matching" problems associated with the matrix Wiener–Hopf equation.[22]

In LQG [17], [18] the objective is to optimally reset the state of the plant to a fixed known equalibrium state in the face of both Gaussian white background noise and Gaussian white measurement noise given the measured output. However, in the problem solved in this paper the "set point" excursion $\boldsymbol{u}(t)$ is both variable and stochastic and the functions of time to be reset are subsumed as components of an output vector $\boldsymbol{y}(t)$. The task of the optimal controller is to optimally reset $y(t)$ to a new level dictated by a shape-deterministic or second-order stationary $\boldsymbol{u}(t)$. This must be accomplished despite the presence of shape deterministic or second-order stationary load disturbance, measurement noise, nonideal sensor dynamics, a zero steady-state error requirement, etc. Accordingly, that part of the cost E_t reflecting loop accuracy has been imposed directly on $\boldsymbol{u}(t) - \boldsymbol{y}(t)$ and does not necessarily involve all the state variables. Nevertheless, these other variables are kept within bounds by an appropriate weighting of the saturation constraint E_s. It appears, therefore, that underlying our design philosophy is the assumption that any variable which is to be reset to a time-varying stochastic set-point must be available as a measured output. This attitude is of course consistent with the classical viewpoint and its true merit can only be judged after sufficient experience with applications of the optimal controller formula (103) to problems of industrial importance has been obtained.[23]

In LQG the optimal regulator structure is prescribed in advance in a manner which identifies the separate roles played by state estimation, Kalman-weighting (via the

[22]The Ph.D. dissertation of H. A. Jabr [16] contains some nontrivial fully worked numerical examples and also includes a transfer-matrix description of the stirred-tank chemical reactor linearized about its unstable equilibrium state.

[23]One possible way to enlarge LQG to encompass a special variable set-point problem is described in [18] but it appears to us that the proposed method can be very sensitive to parameter variations and we prefer the infinite-gain plant preconditioning scheme discussed in 2), Section II.

innovative input) and noise-free optimal deterministic state feedback [17]. However, it is easily shown that the entire configuration is simply a special case of Fig. 1 in which $\boldsymbol{u}=\boldsymbol{O}$, feedforward compensation is absent, $F(s)=1$, $F_o(s)=1$, $G_d(s)=\Sigma$ and $G_m(s)=\Theta$; Σ is real, constant, symmetric nonnegative-definite and Θ is real, constant, symmetric positive-definite. In the frequency-domain approach the objective is to find the optimal controller transfer matrix $C(s)$ and its mode of realization

$$C(s)=\frac{\left[(3+4c_1+4c_2+8c_1c_2)\sigma+4(1+2c_1+2c_2+4c_1c_2)\sigma_m\right]s-2\sigma}{\sigma_m c_1c_2s^2+\left[c_1c_2\sigma+(c_1+c_2+4c_1c_2)\sigma_m\right]s-\left[(3+3c_1+3c_2+4c_1c_2)\sigma+(3+4c_1+4c_2+8c_1c_2)\sigma_m\right]} \tag{141}$$

is based on other considerations. This shifting of the emphasis to $C(s)$ is really a restatement of the problem in invariantive fashion and has some distinct advantages.

For example, consider a time-invariant single-input, single-output plant with the constant-coefficient state-variable description

$$\dot{x}=\begin{bmatrix}0 & 1\\ 0 & 2\end{bmatrix}x+\begin{bmatrix}0\\ 1\end{bmatrix}u_o+\xi, \tag{131}$$

$$y=\begin{bmatrix}-1 & 1\end{bmatrix}x; \qquad z=y+\theta. \tag{132}$$

Here $u_o(t)$ is the plant input, $y(t)$ the output, and $z(t)$ the measured output. The noise processes $\xi(t)$ and $\theta(t)$ are both white Gaussian with respective covariance matrices

$$\langle\xi(t)\xi(\tau)\rangle=\begin{bmatrix}\sigma^2 & 0\\ 0 & 0\end{bmatrix}\cdot\delta(t-\tau)=\Sigma\cdot\delta(t-\tau) \tag{133}$$

and

$$\langle\theta(t)\theta(\tau)\rangle=\sigma_m^2\cdot\delta(t-\tau)=\Theta\cdot\delta(t-\tau). \tag{134}$$

Clearly,

$$P(s)=\frac{s-1}{s(s-2)}; \qquad P_o(s)=\left[-\frac{1}{s}\ \middle|\ \frac{s-1}{s(s-2)}\right] \tag{135}$$

$$G_d(s)=\Sigma; \qquad G_m(s)=\sigma_m^2. \tag{136}$$

Subject to the choices $k>0$ and

$$Q_o=\begin{bmatrix}1 & -1\\ -1 & 1\end{bmatrix}, \tag{137}$$

it is a consequence of the LQG solution that the cost functional

$$J=\operatorname*{limit}_{T\to\infty}\frac{1}{2T}\int_{-T}^{T}(x'Q_ox+ku_o^2)\,dt \tag{138}$$

is minimized by choosing the control law

$$u_o=-\frac{1}{k}\left[\sqrt{k}\ \middle|\ 2k+\sqrt{4k^2+2k\sqrt{k}+k}\right]\hat{x} \tag{139}$$

and placing the Kalman column-vector gain

$$W=\begin{bmatrix}\dfrac{3\sigma}{\sigma_m}+4\\[2ex] \hline \dfrac{4\sigma}{\sigma_m}+8\end{bmatrix} \tag{140}$$

at the innovative input.[24] The observer of course provides the state estimate $\hat{x}$. Since $x'Q_ox=y^2$, this problem also falls within the scope of our solution (with $\boldsymbol{u}=\boldsymbol{O}$) and we obtain[25] (141)

where

$$\sqrt{2}\,c_{1,2}=\sqrt{(4k+1)\pm\sqrt{(4k+1)^2-4k}}\,. \tag{142}$$

Now in view of (139) and (140), the LQG design fails if either $k=0$ or $\sigma_m=0$. Nevertheless, $C(s)$ is perfectly well-defined and, in fact, setting $k=0$ in (141) yields

$$C(s)=\frac{\left(\dfrac{7\sigma}{\sigma_m}+12\right)s-\dfrac{2\sigma}{\sigma_m}}{s-\left(\dfrac{6\sigma}{\sigma_m}+7\right)}; \qquad k=0. \tag{143}$$

If, in addition, σ_m also equals zero,

$$C(s)=\frac{1}{3}-\frac{7}{6}s; \qquad k=\sigma_m=0. \tag{144}$$

Thus, the LQG technique misses these extremely simple practical controllers. On the other hand, if $k\sigma_m\neq 0$, it is straightforward to show that (139) and (140) lead to an overall controller with transfer function given precisely by (141). It is interesting to note that in this limiting case ($k=\sigma_m=0$),

$$O(P)+O(F)=-1>-2=\mu$$

and since inequality (94) is violated it is not surprising to find that $C(s)$ is improper and $S(\infty)=-6\neq 1$.

The other Kalman gain alluded to in the previous footnote is given by

$$\hat{W}=\begin{bmatrix}-\dfrac{\sigma}{\sigma_m}\\[2ex] \hline 0\end{bmatrix} \tag{145}$$

and its associated cost

$$\hat{J}=\sigma^2+\sigma\sigma_m+\sigma^2\sqrt{4k+2\sqrt{k}+1} \tag{146}$$

is obviously *less* than the cost

[24]Actually, there is a second Kalman column-vector gain which yields a smaller cost than (139) but leads to an unstable closed-loop design. We address this point later on.

[25]All details are omitted.

$$J=\big(9+9\sqrt{4k+2\sqrt{k}+1}+24\sqrt{k}+32k+16\sqrt{4k^2+2k\sqrt{k}+k}\big)\sigma^2+$$
$$+\big(25+24\sqrt{4k+2\sqrt{k}+1}+80\sqrt{k}+128k+64\sqrt{4k^2+2k\sqrt{k}+k}\big)\sigma\sigma_m+$$
$$+\big(20+16\sqrt{4k+2\sqrt{k}+1}+64\sqrt{k}+128k+64\sqrt{4k^2+2k\sqrt{k}+k}\big)\sigma_m^2 \qquad (147)$$

induced by W, (140). The two gains W and $\hat{W}$ are generated by the two distinct solutions

$$Z_R=\left[\begin{array}{c|c}4\sigma^2+9\sigma\sigma_m+4\sigma_m^2 & 4\sigma^2+12\sigma\sigma_m+8\sigma_m^2\\ \hline 4\sigma^2+12\sigma\sigma_m+8\sigma_m^2 & 4\sigma^2+16\sigma\sigma_m+16\sigma_m^2\end{array}\right] \qquad (148)$$

and

$$\hat{Z}_R=\left[\begin{array}{c|c}\sigma\sigma_m & 0\\ \hline 0 & 0\end{array}\right], \qquad (149)$$

respectively, of the pertinent matrix Riccati equation. Although Z_R is positive-definite, $\hat{Z}_R$ is only semipositive-definite. Observe, that with our choice of Σ in (133), the plant described by (131) is not controllable from the equivalent scalar disturbance input and the various theorems relating to the uniqueness of the solution of the Riccati equation do not apply [18, p. 36].[26]

The controller[27]

$$\hat{C}(s)=\frac{\frac{\sigma}{\sigma_m}(2-s)}{ks^2+\left(\frac{k\sigma}{\sigma_m}+\sqrt{4k^2+2k\sqrt{k}+k}\right)s+\sqrt{k}\left(1+\frac{\sigma}{\sigma_m}\right)+\frac{\sigma}{\sigma_m}\sqrt{4k^2+2k\sqrt{k}+k}} \qquad (150)$$

paired with the choice $\hat{Z}_R$ possesses a zero at $s=2$ coincident with a pole of $P(s)$, and this fact makes the instability of the LQG design immediately apparent. It appears, therefore, that the optimal stabilizing controller (141) yields a relative and not an absolute minimum for the cost functional J. This observation suggests the following question. Since LQG prejudges the structure of the controller and does not invoke closed-loop stability as an *a priori* constraint, is it really clear that the optimal stabilizing Z_R is always included in its several solutions? In any reasonable topology the collection of stabilizing controllers for a given plant-feedback sensor combination should form an open set and the answer is probably yes, but in our opinion the conjecture is in need of strict proof. On the other hand, the frequency-domain solution advanced in this paper not only absorbs many important practical factors easily and naturally, but also succeeds in completely circumventing the above difficulty.

[26]The existence of this second solution $\hat{Z}_R$ was kindly brought to the authors' attention by Dr. J. Boyd Pearson of Rice University, Houston, TX, who also supplied some interesting insights regarding its implications for LQG. We gratefully acknowledge his comments and helpful editorial suggestions.

[27]All details are omitted.

Appendix A

For sound practical reasons the components in the loop of Fig. 1 must not be restricted to be dynamical and a stability criterion must be general enough to encompass this case. Let the zero-state Laplace transform descriptions of the feedback compensator, controller, and plant be given by

$$F_i(s)\boldsymbol{x}_i(s)=G_i(s)\boldsymbol{u}_i(s), \qquad (\text{A1})$$
$$\boldsymbol{y}_i(s)=J_i(s)\boldsymbol{u}_i(s)+H_i(s)\boldsymbol{x}_i(s), \qquad (\text{A2})$$

$i=2\rightarrow4$, respectively. All coefficient matrices are real and polynomial, all F_i's are square and as usual $\boldsymbol{x}_i$, $\boldsymbol{u}_i$, $\boldsymbol{y}_i$ denote, in the same order, the internal state, the input, and the output. Physical degeneracies are excluded by imposing the determinantal condition,

$$\prod_{i=2}^{4}\det F_i(s)\not\equiv 0. \qquad (\text{A3})$$

Clearly then

$$P_i(s)=J_i(s)+H_i(s)F_i^{-1}(s)G_i(s) \qquad (\text{A4})$$

is the transfer matrix of system no. i, $i=2\rightarrow4$. As is well known [10], [11], system number i is asymptotically stable iff the scalar polynomial

$$\Delta_i(s)\equiv\det F_i(s) \qquad (\text{A5})$$

has all its zeros in $\operatorname{Re}s<0$, $i=2\rightarrow4$. In the present notation,

$$\Delta_F(s)=\Delta_2(s); \qquad F(s)=P_2(s) \qquad (\text{A6})$$
$$\Delta_C(s)=\Delta_3(s); \qquad C(s)=P_3(s) \qquad (\text{A7})$$
$$\Delta_P(s)=\Delta_4(s); \qquad P(s)=P_4(s). \qquad (\text{A8})$$

In Fig. 2 the three systems are shown interconnected through a linear, time-invariant frequency-insensitive grid, and it is assumed that the inputs to this grid uniquely determine its outputs. Hence, there exist real constant matrices M_a and M_b such that

$$\boldsymbol{u}_t(s)=M_a\boldsymbol{y}_t(s)+M_b\boldsymbol{u}(s) \qquad (\text{A9})$$

where

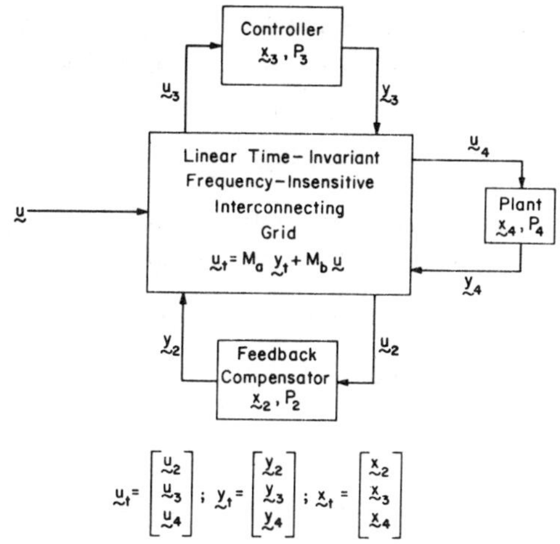

Fig. 2. Generalized interconnection scheme.

$$u_t(s)=\begin{bmatrix}u_2\\u_3\\u_4\end{bmatrix};\ y_t(s)=\begin{bmatrix}y_2\\y_3\\y_4\end{bmatrix};\quad x_t=\begin{bmatrix}x_2\\x_3\\x_4\end{bmatrix}. \tag{A10}$$

Eliminating u_t in (A1) and (A2) with the help of (A9) and (A10) we obtain

$$\left[\begin{array}{c|c}F & -GM_a\\ \hline -H & 1-JM_a\end{array}\right]\left[\begin{array}{c}x_t\\ \hline y_t\end{array}\right]=\left[\begin{array}{c}G\\ \hline J\end{array}\right]M_b u \tag{A11}$$

in which[28]

$$\begin{aligned}F&=F_2\dotplus F_3\dotplus F_4,\\ G&=G_2\dotplus G_3\dotplus G_4,\\ H&=H_2\dotplus H_3\dotplus H_4,\\ J&=J_2\dotplus J_3\dotplus J_4.\end{aligned} \tag{A12}$$

Consequently [10], [11], the interconnected system is asymptotically stable iff the determinant $\Delta(s)$ of the coefficient matrix on the left-hand side of (A11) has all its roots in $\mathrm{Re}\, s<0$. A straightforward row operation yields

$$\Delta(s)=\det(1-P_t(s)M_a)\cdot\prod_{i=2}^{4}\Delta_i(s), \tag{A13}$$

$$P_t(s)=P_2(s)\dotplus P_3(s)\dotplus P_4(s). \tag{A14}$$

The interconnection is nondegenerate iff

$$\det(1-P_t(s)M_a)\not\equiv 0 \tag{A15}$$

which is exactly the necessary and sufficient condition for the existence of an overall transfer matrix description $T_t(s)$. In fact if $y_t=T_t u$,

$$T_t(s)=(1-P_t(s)M_a)^{-1}P_t(s)M_b. \tag{A16}$$

(The easy derivation is left to the reader.)

For the topology depicted in Fig. 1,

$$\begin{bmatrix}u_2\\u_3\\u_4\end{bmatrix}=\begin{bmatrix}O & O & 1\\ -1 & O & O\\ O & 1 & O\end{bmatrix}\begin{bmatrix}y_2\\y_3\\y_4\end{bmatrix}+\begin{bmatrix}O\\1\\O\end{bmatrix}u. \tag{A17}$$

Thus,

$$1-P_tM_a=1-(F\dotplus C\dotplus P)\begin{bmatrix}O & O & 1\\ -1 & O & O\\ O & 1 & O\end{bmatrix} \tag{A18}$$

$$=\begin{bmatrix}1 & O & -F\\ C & 1 & O\\ O & -P & 1\end{bmatrix} \tag{A19}$$

and

$$\det(1-P_tM_a)=\det(1_n+FPC)=1/\det S. \tag{A20}$$

Expression (A13) for $\Delta(s)$ now assumes the form

$$\Delta(s)=\frac{\Delta_P(s)\Delta_C(s)\Delta_F(s)}{\det S(s)}. \tag{A21}$$

If all components have asymptotically stable hidden modes,

$$\begin{aligned}\Delta_P(s)&=h_P(s)\psi_P(s),\\ \Delta_C(s)&=h_C(s)\psi_C(s),\\ \Delta_F(s)&=h_F(s)\psi_F(s)\end{aligned} \tag{A22}$$

where the h's are strict Hurwitz and ψ_P, ψ_C, ψ_F are the characteristic denominators of plant, controller, and feedback compensator, respectively [10], [11].[29] Thus, the loop is asymptotically stable iff

$$\varphi(s)=\frac{\psi_P(s)\psi_C(s)\psi_F(s)}{\det S(s)} \tag{A23}$$

is strict Hurwitz which is precisely the assertion of Lemma 1. Q.E.D.

Let

$$F(s)P(s)=A^{-1}(s)B(s) \tag{A24}$$

be any left-coprime polynomial decomposition of $F(s)P(s)$ and

$$C(s)=B_C(s)A_C^{-1}(s) \tag{A25}$$

any right-coprime decomposition of $C(s)$.

Then [10], [12],

$$\psi_{FP}(s)=\det A(s) \tag{A26}$$

and

$$\psi_C(s)=\det A_C(s). \tag{A27}$$

[28] $A\dotplus B$ is the "direct sum" of matrices A and B.

[29] Equation (A22) is also obvious from (A4).

Evidently,

$$S=(1_n+FPC)^{-1}=A_C(AA_C+BB_C)^{-1}A \quad (A28)$$

and

$$\det S=\frac{\psi_C\psi_{FP}}{g(s)}\not\equiv 0 \quad (A29)$$

where

$$g(s)=\det(AA_C+BB_C) \quad (A30)$$

is a polynomial. Substituting into (A23),

$$\varphi=g\cdot\frac{\psi_F\psi_P}{\psi_{FP}}. \quad (A31)$$

Since the McMillan degree of any pole of $F(s)P(s)$ cannot exceed the sum of its degrees as a pole of $F(s)$ and $P(s)$, ψ_{FP} must divide $\psi_F\psi_P$ without remainder and the quotient $\psi_F\psi_P/\psi_{FP}$ is polynomial. Thus, if the loop is asymptotically stable $g(s)$ is necessarily strict Hurwitz. Furthermore, any zero of the product $\psi_F^+\psi_P^+$ must be cancelled by a zero of ψ_{FP}^+ whence

$$\psi_{FP}^+(s)=\psi_F^+(s)\psi_P^+(s) \quad (A32)$$

is also necessary for closed-loop stability.

Suppose now that (A32) is satisfied and let the real polynomial matrices $X(s)$ and $Y(s)$ be chosen so that[30]

$$A(s)X(s)+B(s)Y(s)=1_n \quad (A33)$$

and

$$\det X(s)\not\equiv 0. \quad (A34)$$

Select any controller with asymptotically stable hidden modes and with transfer matrix

$$C(s)=Y(s)X^{-1}(s). \quad (A35)$$

According to (A33), the pair (Y,X) is right-coprime and

$$AA_C+BB_C=AX+BY=1_n. \quad (A36)$$

Thus $g(s)=1$ and the associated stability polynomial $\varphi(s)$ is given by

$$\varphi=\frac{\psi_F\psi_P}{\psi_{FP}}=\frac{\psi_F^-\psi_P^-}{\psi_{FP}^-} \quad (A37)$$

which is devoid of zeros in $\mathrm{Re}\, s\geqslant 0$. Consequently, the closed-loop structure is asymptotically stable and Lemma 2 is established. Q.E.D.

Recall from (10) that $R=CS$ or, in terms of the polynomial factors A, B, B_C, and A_C,

$$R=B_C(AA_C+BB_C)^{-1}A=HA, \quad (A38)$$

$$H=B_C(AA_C+BB_C)^{-1}. \quad (A39)$$

[30]The left-coprimeness of the pair $A(s)$, $B(s)$ guarantees that such a choice is always possible [10], [12].

For a stable loop, $g=\det(AA_C+BB_C)$ is strict Hurwitz and it follows immediately that $H(s)$ is analytic in $\mathrm{Re}\, s\geqslant 0$. Let

$$F(s)P(s)=B_1(s)A_1^{-1}(s) \quad (A40)$$

be any right-coprime polynomial factorization of $F(s)\,P(s)$ and define $K(s)$ via the equation

$$Y+A_1K=B_C(AA_C+BB_C)^{-1}. \quad (A41)$$

With this choice of K,

$$\begin{aligned} X-B_1K&=X-B_1A_1^{-1}\big(B_C(AA_C+BB_C)^{-1}-Y\big)\\ &=X+FPY-FPB_C(AA_C+BB_C)^{-1}\\ &=A^{-1}\big(1_n-BB_C(AA_C+BB_C)^{-1}\big)\\ &=A_C(AA_C+BB_C)^{-1}=SA^{-1}. \end{aligned} \quad (A42)$$

Hence, if the polynomial matrices $X_1(s)$ and $Y_1(s)$ are constructed to satisfy

$$X_1A_1+Y_1B_1=1_m, \quad (A43)$$

(A41) and (A42) combine to give

$$K=(X_1B_C-Y_1A_C)(AA_C+BB_C)^{-1}+Y_1X-X_1Y \quad (A44)$$

which is obviously analytic in $\mathrm{Re}\, s\geqslant 0$. Conversely, let $K(s)$ be any real rational matrix analytic in $\mathrm{Re}\, s\geqslant 0$ such that $\det(X-B_1K)\not\equiv 0$ and select any controller with stable hidden modes and transfer matrix $C(s)$ given by

$$C=(Y+A_1K)(X-B_1K)^{-1}. \quad (A45)$$

Reasoning exactly as in Appendix B in the derivation of (B64) we find that

$$\varphi(s)=\frac{\psi_F^-(s)\psi_P(s)}{\psi_{FP}^-(s)}\cdot\psi_K(s). \quad (A46)$$

Since $K(s)$ is analytic in $\mathrm{Re}\, s\geqslant 0$, $\psi_K(s)$ and therefore $\varphi(s)$ are both strict Hurwitz and the closed-loop is asymptotically stable. This completes the proof of Lemma 3. Q.E.D.

The closed-loop transfer matrix

$$T=PR=PCS=(1_n+PCF)^{-1}PC. \quad (A47)$$

Let $PC=A_5^{-1}B_5$ and $F=B_FA_F^{-1}$ be left-and right-coprime polynomial factorizations. Evidently,

$$S_1=(1_n+PCF)^{-1}=A_F(A_5A_F+B_5B_F)^{-1}A_5 \quad (A48)$$

and

$$\det S_1=\det S=\frac{\psi_F\psi_{PC}}{g_1(s)}, \quad (A49)$$

$$g_1=\det(A_5A_F+B_5B_F). \quad (A50)$$

Hence

$$\varphi(s)=g_1(s)\cdot\frac{\psi_P(s)\psi_C(s)}{\psi_{PC}(s)} \quad (A51)$$

and it follows as before that the conditions $g_1(s)$ strict Hurwitz and $\psi_P^+\psi_C^+ = \psi_{PC}^+$ are both necessary for closed-loop stability. In particular,

$$T = PR = PCS = S_1PC = A_F(A_5A_F + B_5B_F)^{-1}B_5 \quad \text{(A52)}$$

is analytic in $\text{Re}\, s \geq 0$.

From (A42),

$$\det S = \det(X - B_1K)\cdot \det A = \det(X - B_1K)\psi_{FP} \quad \text{(A53)}$$

and because of the analyticity of $K(s)$ in $\text{Re}\, s \geq 0$, all zeros of $\psi_{FP}^+(s)$ are zeros of det $S(s)$, multiplicities included.

Introducing the left–right coprime polynomial decompositions $P = A_p^{-1}B_p$ and $CF = B_6A_6^{-1}$ into (A48) gives

$$S_1 = A_6(A_pA_6 + B_pB_6)^{-1}A_p = \mathcal{P}_1A_p \quad \text{(A54)}$$

and closed-loop stability forces $\mathcal{P}_1(s)$ to be analytic in $\text{Re}\, s \geq 0$. We have now justified the three comments preceeding (38), (42) and (59). Q.E.D.

Also, let us remark that for given polynomial matrices $A_7(s)$, $B_7(s)$, the existence of polynomial matrices $X_7(s)$, $Y_7(s)$ such that

$$X_7(s)A_7(s) + Y_7(s)B_7(s) = 1 \quad \text{(A55)}$$

is possible iff for every fixed finite s the homogeneous pair

$$A_7(s)\boldsymbol{a} = \boldsymbol{O}, \quad \text{(A56)}$$

$$B_7(s)\boldsymbol{a} = \boldsymbol{O} \quad \text{(A57)}$$

admits only the trivial solution $\boldsymbol{a} = \boldsymbol{O}$. Necessity is trivial and sufficiency is easily established by actually constructing a solution pair $X_7(s)$, $Y_7(s)$ with the help of the Smith–McMillan theorem. The idea underlying the construction is very simple to grasp. Let

$$\Omega_c(s) = \text{diag}\left[\frac{e_1(s)}{\psi_1(s)}, \frac{e_2(s)}{\psi_2(s)}, \cdots, \frac{e_k(s)}{\psi_k(s)}\right] \quad \text{(A58)}$$

be the canonic form of $F(s)P(s)$. Then [8], 1) k = normal rank $F(s)P(s)$; 2) the e's and ψ's are real monic polynomials uniquely determined by $F(s)P(s)$; 3) each $e_i(s)$ is relatively prime to its mate $\psi_i(s)$, $i = 1 \to k$; 4) $e_i(s)$ divides $e_{i+1}(s)$ and $\psi_{i+1}(s)$ divides $\psi_i(s)$, $i = 1 \to k-1$; 5) the distinct finite zeros and poles of $F(s)P(s)$ are identical, respectively, with the distinct zeros of $e_1(s)$ and $\psi_1(s)$; 6) the McMillan degree of any finite pole of $F(s)P(s)$ equals its multiplicity as a root of the characteristic denominator

$$\psi_{FP}(s) = \prod_{i=1}^{k} \psi_i(s). \quad \text{(A59)}$$

From the Smith–McMillan theorem [8],

$$FP = U(\Omega_c \dotplus O_{n-k,m-k})V \quad \text{(A60)}$$

where $U(s)$ and $V(s)$ are square, real elementary polynomial matrices.[31] Since $e_i(s)$ is relatively prime to $\psi_i(s)$ there exist [13] two real polynomials $\alpha_i(s)$, $\beta_i(s)$ such that $\beta_i(s) \not\equiv 0$ and

$$\alpha_i(s)e_i(s) + \beta_i(s)\psi_i(s) = 1, \qquad i = 1 \to k. \quad \text{(A61)}$$

Let[32]

$$\epsilon = \text{diag}[e_1, e_2, \cdots, e_k], \quad \text{(A62)}$$

$$\chi = \text{diag}[\psi_1, \psi_2, \cdots, \psi_k], \quad \text{(A63)}$$

$$\alpha = \text{diag}[\alpha_1, \alpha_2, \cdots, \alpha_k], \quad \text{(A64)}$$

$$\beta = \text{diag}[\beta_1, \beta_2, \cdots, \beta_k]. \quad \text{(A65)}$$

Then, putting

$$A = U(\chi \dotplus 1_{n-k})U^{-1}, \quad \text{(A66)}$$

$$B_1 = B = U(\epsilon \dotplus O_{n-k,m-k})V, \quad \text{(A67)}$$

$$A_1 = V^{-1}(\chi \dotplus 1_{m-k})V, \quad \text{(A68)}$$

$$X = U(\beta \dotplus 1_{n-k})U^{-1}, \quad \text{(A69)}$$

$$Y_1 = Y = V^{-1}(\alpha \dotplus O_{m-k,n-k})U^{-1} \quad \text{(A70)}$$

and

$$X_1 = V^{-1}(\beta \dotplus 1_{m-k})V, \quad \text{(A71)}$$

we verify by inspection that

$$\alpha\epsilon + \beta\chi = 1_k, \quad \text{(A72)}$$

$$AX + BY = 1_n, \quad \text{(A73)}$$

$$X_1A_1 + Y_1B_1 = 1_m, \quad \text{(A74)}$$

$$XA = AX = U(\chi\beta \dotplus 1_{n-k})U^{-1}, \quad \text{(A75)}$$

$$A^{-1}B = BA_1^{-1} = FP, \quad \text{(A76)}$$

$$XB = BX_1 = U(\beta\epsilon \dotplus O_{n-k,m-k})V, \quad \text{(A77)}$$

$$Y_1X = X_1Y = V^{-1}(\alpha\beta \dotplus O_{m-k,n-k})U^{-1}. \quad \text{(A78)}$$

Of course, other decompositions may not possess all the symmetry properties enumerated in (A66)–(A78).

According to (A29), any zero of the characteristic denominator $\psi_{FP}(s)$ in $\text{Re}\, s \geq 0$ of multiplicity μ is a zero of det S of at least the same multiplicity. Define

$$e_{FP}(s) = \prod_{i=1}^{k} e_i(s) \quad \text{(A79)}$$

to be the characteristic *numerator* of $F(s)P(s)$. Suppose $\det(1_n - S) \not\equiv 0$. Then, any zero of $e_{FP}(s)$ in $\text{Re}\, s \geq 0$ of multiplicity μ is a zero of $\det(1_n - S)$ of multiplicity at least μ. For the proof, note that

$$1_n - S = 1_n - (1_n + FPC)^{-1} = (1_n + FPC)^{-1}FPC;$$

or, using (A24), (A25), and (A30),

$$1_n - S = A_C(AA_C + BB_C)^{-1}\cdot(BB_C)A_C^{-1}. \quad \text{(A80)}$$

[31] Det $U(s)$ and det $V(s)$ equal nonzero constants.

[32] A square matrix A whose only nonzero elements are its main diagonal elements $a_1, a_2, \cdots, a_k$ is written $A = \text{diag}[a_1, a_2, \cdots, a_k]$.

$$\therefore\ \det(1_n - S) = \frac{\det(BB_C)}{g(s)} \tag{A81}$$

and it is clear from (A62) and (A67) with $n=k$ that $\det(BB_C)$ is divisible by $e_{FP}(s)$. Since $g(s)$ is a strict Hurwitz polynomial, the assertion follows. Q.E.D.

Appendix B

Adding (66) to $k\times(65)$ we obtain $2\pi j(E_t + kE_s) = 2\pi jE$. Since $R = (Y + A_1 K)A$,

$$\delta R = A_1(\delta K)A \tag{B1}$$

with $\delta K(s)$ analytic in $\mathrm{Re}\, s \geqslant 0$. Use of the standard variational argument [1] to examine the increment in E produced by the perturbation (B1) leads directly to the Wiener–Hopf equation

$$\Phi - A_{1*}(P_*P + kQ)A_1 K(AGA_*) = \Delta_* \tag{B2}$$

where

$$\Phi = A_{1*}P_*(G_u + P_o G_d P_{d*})A_* - A_{1*}(P_*P + kQ)Y(AGA_*) \tag{B3}$$

and $\Delta(s)$ is analytic in $\mathrm{Re}\, s \geqslant 0$. If (B2) possesses a real rational matrix solution $K(s)$ analytic in $\mathrm{Re}\, s \geqslant 0$ which satisfies (33) and has a finite associated cost E, then this $K(s)$ is optimal. According to 5) and (76), $A_{1*}(P_*P + kQ)A_1$ and AGA_* are analytic for all $s = j\omega$ and the existence of a $K(s)$ with the desired properties implies the $j\omega$-axis analyticity of $\Phi(s)$. Since the latter is a unique construct from the prescribed data it is important to verify at the outset that this is indeed the case.

Using (69),

$$\Phi = A_{1*}P_*(G + (P_o - P_d)G_d P_{d*} - G_{ml})A_* - A_{1*}(P_*P + kQ)Y(AGA_*) \tag{B4}$$

and its $j\omega$-analyticity follows from that of[33]

$$A_{1*}P_*(P_o - P_d)G_d P_{d*}A_* + \left(A_{1*}P_*A^{-1} - A_{1*}(P_*P + kQ)Y\right)AGA_*$$

which in turn follows from that of

$$A_{1*}P_*(P_o - P_d)G_d P_{d*}A_* \tag{B5}$$

and

$$A_{1*}P_*A^{-1} - A_{1*}(P_*P + kQ)Y \equiv \beta. \tag{B6}$$

Expanding (B5),

$$\begin{aligned}(P_o - P_d)G_d P_{d*}A_* &= ((1_n - F)P_o - L)G_d(FP_o + L)_*A_* \\ &= (1_n - F)P_o G_d P_{o*}(AF)_* - LG_d L_* A_* \\ &\quad + (1_n - F)P_o G_d L_* A_* - LG_d P_{o*}(AF)_*.\end{aligned} \tag{B7}$$

All four terms are $j\omega$-analytic. First, $AF = \mathcal{P}_4 A_p$, $\mathcal{P}_4(s)$ $j\omega$-analytic. Second, the analyticity of

$$(1_n - F)P_o G_d P_{o*}A_{p*} = (1_n - F)A_p^{-1}A_p P_o G_d P_{o*}A_{p*}, \tag{B8}$$

$$(1_n - F)P_o G_d L_* = (1_n - F)A_p^{-1}A_p P_o G_d L_*, \tag{B9}$$

$LG_d L_*$ and $LG_d P_{o*}A_{p*}$ is implied by that of $(F - 1_n)P$ and the assumptions introduced in 3).

With regard to (B6), replacing A^{-1} by $X + FPY$ transforms it into

$$A_{1*}P_*X + A_{1*}P_*(F - 1_n)PY - kA_{1*}QY \tag{B10}$$

which is eveidently analytic on the $j\omega$-axis since Q, PA_1 and $(F - 1_n)P$ are $j\omega$-analytic.

The solution of (B2) is now routine. Construct[34] two square real rational matrices $\Lambda(s)$, $\Omega(s)$ *analytic together with their inverses in* $\mathrm{Re}\, s \geqslant 0$ such that

$$A_{1*}(P_*P + kQ)A_1 = \Lambda_*\Lambda \tag{B11}$$

and

$$AGA_* = \Omega\Omega_*. \tag{B12}$$

From (B2),

$$\Lambda_*^{-1}\Phi\Omega_*^{-1} - \Lambda K\Omega = \Lambda_*^{-1}\Delta_*\Omega_*^{-1}. \tag{B13}$$

Effect the partial fraction decomposition

$$\Lambda_*^{-1}\Phi\Omega_*^{-1} = \{\Lambda_*^{-1}\Phi\Omega_*^{-1}\}_\infty + \{\Lambda_*^{-1}\Phi\Omega_*^{-1}\}_+ + \{\Lambda_*^{-1}\Phi\Omega_*^{-1}\}_- \tag{B14}$$

where $\{\ \}_\infty$ is the polynomial part of the Laurent expansion of $\Lambda_*^{-1}\Phi\Omega_*^{-1}$ associated with the pole at infinity and $\{\ \}_+$, $\{\ \}_-$ the parts associated with all the poles in $\mathrm{Re}\, s < 0$ and $\mathrm{Re}\, s \geqslant 0$, respectively. Clearly, since Φ is analytic on $j\omega$, $\{\ \}_+$ is analytic in $\mathrm{Re}\, s \geqslant 0$, $\{\ \}_-$ in $\mathrm{Re}\, s \leqslant 0$ and both vanish for $s = \infty$. The substitution of (B14) into (B13) yields

$$\{\Lambda_*^{-1}\Phi\Omega_*^{-1}\}_+ - \Lambda K\Omega = \Lambda_*^{-1}\Delta_*\Omega_*^{-1} - \{\Lambda_*^{-1}\Phi\Omega_*^{-1}\}_- - \{\Lambda_*^{-1}\Phi\Omega_*^{-1}\}_\infty. \tag{B15}$$

However, with $K(s)$ forced to be analytic in $\mathrm{Re}\, s \geqslant 0$, the left-hand side of (B15) is also analytic in $\mathrm{Re}\, s \geqslant 0$ and equals the right-hand side which is analytic in $\mathrm{Re}\, s \leqslant 0$. Thus (B15) is polynomial and we obtain

$$K = \Lambda^{-1}J\Omega^{-1} + \Lambda^{-1}\{\Lambda_*^{-1}\Phi\Omega_*^{-1}\}_+\Omega^{-1}, \tag{B16}$$

$J(s)$ a real polynomial matrix to be determined by the requirement of finite cost. Observe that $K(s)$, as defined by (B16) is actually analytic in $\mathrm{Re}\, s \geqslant 0$ while

[33] PA_1 and G_{ml} are $j\omega$-analytic.

[34] Inequality (76) guarantees the analyticity of the factors $\Lambda^{-1}(s)$, $\Omega^{-1}(s)$ in $\mathrm{Re}\, s \geqslant 0$. Without (76) analyticity is assured only in $\mathrm{Re}\, s > 0$. It can be shown that the factors are unique up to real constant orthogonal multipliers [8], [9].

$$\Delta_* = \Lambda_*\left(\{\Lambda_*^{-1}\Phi\Omega_*^{-1}\}_- + \{\Lambda_*^{-1}\Phi\Omega_*^{-1}\}_\infty - J\right)\Omega_* \quad \text{(B17)}$$

is analytic in $\mathrm{Re}\, s \leq 0$ (as it should be). In 5) we imposed conditions guaranteeing the $j\omega$-analyticity of all integrands in E_s and E_t and to study the convergence of the cost under the choice (B16) for K it suffices to examine the behavior of the integrand of E as $\omega \to \infty$. Denote this integrand by $\rho(s)$. Noting that $R = (Y + A_1K)A = HA$ and

$$\begin{aligned}\mathrm{Tr}\left(H_*(P_*P+kQ)H(AGA_*)\right) &= \mathrm{Tr}\left[kQRGR_* + (PR)G(PR)_*\right] \\ &= \mathrm{Tr}\left(\Omega_* H_*(P_*P+kQ)H\Omega\right), \quad \text{(B18)}\end{aligned}$$

simple algebra yields

$$\begin{aligned}\rho = \mathrm{Tr}\left(\Omega_* H_*(P_*P+kQ)H\Omega\right) + \mathrm{Tr}\, G_u + \mathrm{Tr}\left(P_oG_dP_{o*}\right) \\ -2\,\mathrm{Tr}\left(PRG_u\right) - 2\,\mathrm{Tr}\left(PRP_dG_dP_{o*}\right). \quad \text{(B19)}\end{aligned}$$

To evaluate the first term in ρ we need H. From (B16) and (B3),

$$\begin{aligned}K = \Lambda^{-1}J\Omega^{-1} + \Lambda^{-1}\{\Lambda_*^{-1}I\Omega_*^{-1}\}_+\Omega^{-1} \\ -\Lambda^{-1}\{\Lambda A_1^{-1}Y\Omega\}_+\Omega^{-1} \quad \text{(B20)}\end{aligned}$$

where

$$I = A_{1*}P_*(G_u + P_oG_dP_{d*})A_*. \quad \text{(B21)}$$

Multiplying (B20) on the left by A_1 and combining,

$$\Lambda A_1^{-1}H\Omega = J_1 + \{\Lambda_*^{-1}I\Omega_*^{-1}\}_+ + \{\Lambda A_1^{-1}Y\Omega\}_- \quad \text{(B22)}$$

where

$$J_1 = J + \{\Lambda A_1^{-1}Y\Omega\}_\infty \quad \text{(B23)}$$

is also polynomial. Since

$$\Omega_* H_*(P_*P+kQ)H\Omega = (\Lambda A_1^{-1}H\Omega)_*(\Lambda A_1^{-1}H\Omega), \quad \text{(B24)}$$

the integral of the first term in (B19) converges iff

$$\Lambda A_1^{-1}H\Omega \leq O(1/\omega), \qquad \omega \to \infty. \quad \text{(B25)}$$

Now both curly brackets in (B22) are already $\leq O(1/\omega)$ and, therefore, $J_1 \leq O(1/\omega)$. But being polynomial J_1 can only be $\leq O(1/\omega)$ for $\omega \to \infty$ if it is identically zero, whence

$$J = -\{\Lambda A_1^{-1}Y\Omega\}_\infty \quad \text{(B26)}$$

is identified. According to (B18) this convergence entails that of

$$\mathrm{Tr}\int_{-j\infty}^{j\infty}(PR)G(PR)_*\,ds \quad \text{(B27)}$$

which entails that of

$$\mathrm{Tr}\int_{-j\infty}^{j\infty}(PR)G_u(PR)_*\,ds, \quad \text{(B28)}$$

$$\mathrm{Tr}\int_{-j\infty}^{j\infty}(PR)G_{ml}(PR)_*\,ds \quad \text{(B29)}$$

and

$$\mathrm{Tr}\int_{-j\infty}^{j\infty}(PR)(P_dG_dP_{d*})(PR)_*\,ds. \quad \text{(B30)}$$

We can exploit the integrability of

$$\mathrm{Tr}\left[H_*(P_*P+kQ)H(AGA_*)\right] = \mathrm{Tr}\left((P_*P+kQ)RGR_*\right) \quad \text{(B31)}$$

to derive a sharp sufficient condition for $T(s) = PR$ to be proper. Let

$$G(j\omega) \approx \omega^{2l}1_n, \quad \text{(B32)}$$

$$(P_*P+kQ) \approx \omega^{2q}1_m \quad \text{(B33)}$$

and

$$R(j\omega) = O(\omega^r) \quad \text{(B34)}$$

for $\omega \to \infty$. Then[35]

$$(P_*P+kQ)RGR_* = O(\omega^{2l+2q+2r}) \quad \text{(B35)}$$

and invoking integrability, $l+q+r \leq -1$. Thus $r \leq -(1+l+q)$ and if $P(s) = O(s^\nu)$, order T = order $(PR) \leq \nu - (1+l+q)$. It follows that the constraint

$$\nu - 1 \leq l + q \quad \text{(B36)}$$

guarantees $T(s)$ proper. Stated differently, if

$$(P_*P+kQ)G \approx \omega^{2\mu}1_m, \quad \text{(B37)}$$

$$P(s) = O(s^\nu) \quad \text{(B38)}$$

and

$$\mu \geq \nu - 1, \quad \text{(B39)}$$

then $T(s)$ is proper. Irrespective of (B39), the assumptions

$$G_u(j\omega) \leq O(1/\omega^2) \quad \text{(B40)}$$

and

$$P_oG_dP_{o*} \leq O(1/\omega^2) \quad \text{(B41)}$$

plus the finiteness of (B28) and (B30) imply $E < \infty$. For, using Schwartz's inequality,[36]

$$|\mathrm{Tr}\int(PRG_u)\,d\omega|^2 \leq \mathrm{Tr}\int(PR)G_u(PR)\,d\omega \cdot \mathrm{Tr}\int G_u\,d\omega < \infty \quad \text{(B42)}$$

[35]This conclusion is reached by making use of some properties of positive-definite matrices.

[36]$|\mathrm{Tr}\int F_1F_2\,dx|^2 \leq \mathrm{Tr}\int F_1F_1^*\,dx \cdot \mathrm{Tr}\int F_2F_2^*\,dx$.

and

$$|\mathrm{Tr}\int PRP_dG_dP_{o*}\,d\omega|^2 \leqslant \mathrm{Tr}\int PR(P_dG_dP_{d*})(PR)_*\,d\omega \cdot \mathrm{Tr}\int P_oG_dP_{o*}\,d\omega < \infty. \quad (B43)$$

(The range of integration is over $|\omega| > \omega_o$, ω_o sufficiently large.) Writing $G_d = K_dK_{d*}$, it is seen that (B30) is finite iff

$$PRP_dK_d = ((1_n - S_1)P_o + TL)K_d \leqslant O(1/\omega). \quad (B44)$$

From (B41), $P_oK_d \leqslant O(1/\omega)$ and substituting into (B44) we obtain

$$(S_1P_o - TL)K_d \leqslant O(1/\omega). \quad (B45)$$

Obviously, if

$$G_d(j\omega) \approx \omega^{-2i}1, \qquad i \leqslant 1, \quad (B46)$$

then $K_d(j\omega) \approx \omega^{-i}1$ and (B45) forces $S_1P_o - TL$ to be proper.

From $FPR = 1_n - S$ and $PRF = 1_n - S_1$ it is clear that

$$O(P) + O(R) + O(F) \leqslant -1 \quad (B47)$$

is a sufficient condition for limit $S(j\omega) = $ limit $S_1(j\omega) = 1_n$ as $\omega \to \infty$. Since $O(R) \leqslant -(1+\mu)$, (B47) is certainly valid if

$$O(P) + O(F) \leqslant \mu. \quad (B48)$$

It now follows from $R = CS$ that $O(C) = O(R)$ and, therefore, $\mu \geqslant -1$ guarantees $C(s)$ proper. Note that $S(j\omega) \to 1_n$ as $\omega \to \infty$ implies det $S(j\omega) \not\equiv 0$ and in particular det $(X - B_1K) \not\equiv 0$ because $S = (X - B_1K)A$. This means that $C(s)$, as defined by (34), makes sense.

Employing the formulas $R = CS = HA$, $S = 1_n\text{-}FPR$ and (B22) with $J_1 = O$ we obtain

$$C = R(1_n - FPR)^{-1} = H(A^{-1} - FPH)^{-1} = H(1_n - BH)^{-1}A \quad (B49)$$

where

$$H = A_1\Lambda^{-1}(\{\Lambda_*^{-1}I\Omega_*^{-1}\}_+ + \{\Lambda A_1^{-1}Y\Omega\}_-)\Omega^{-1}. \quad (B50)$$

The product $A_1\Lambda^{-1}\{\Lambda A_1^{-1}Y\Omega\}_-\Omega^{-1}$ is obviously analytic in Re$s \geqslant 0$ and the closed right-half-plane analyticity of $H(s)$ is, therefore, apparent.[37]

According to Appendix A, to study the stability margin of the optimally compensated loop it is necessary to find the zeros of the associated polynomial[38]

$$\Delta(s) = \frac{\Delta_F(s)\Delta_P(s)\Delta_C(s)}{\det S(s)}. \quad (B51)$$

Granting that any hidden modes of the plant and feedback compensator are known or at least localizable and that $C(s)$ shall be realized minimally,[39] it suffices instead to locate the zeros of the polynomial

$$\varphi(s) = \frac{\psi_F(s)\psi_P(s)\psi_C(s)}{\det S(s)} \quad (B52)$$

where $\psi_F(s)$, $\psi_P(s)$ and $\psi_C(s)$ are the characteristic denominators of $F(s)$, $P(s)$, and $C(s)$, respectively. Since

$$\det S = \det(X - B_1K)\cdot\det A \quad (B53)$$

and $\psi_F^+\psi_P^+ = \psi_{FP}^+ = \det{}^+A$ (by admissibility),

$$\varphi = \frac{\psi_F^-\psi_P^-\psi_C}{\det(X - B_1K)\cdot\psi_{FP}^-}. \quad (B54)$$

Evidently, ψ_{FP}^- divides $\psi_F^-\psi_P^-$ and

$$\varphi = \frac{\psi_C}{\det(X - B_1K)}\cdot\theta \quad (B55)$$

where

$$\theta(s) = \frac{\psi_F^-(s)\psi_P^-(s)}{\psi_{FP}^-(s)} \quad (B56)$$

is a strict Hurwitz polynomial. To make further progress we must relate ψ_C to $\det(X - B_1K)$. Let $K = NM^{-1}$ be a right-coprime factorization of $K(s)$. Then

$$C = (Y + A_1K)(X - B_1K)^{-1} = (YM + A_1N)(XM - B_1N)^{-1} \quad (B57)$$

and the pair $(YM + A_1N,\ XM - B_1N)$ is right-coprime. For the proof it is necessary to show (Appendix A) that the equations

$$(YM + A_1N)\boldsymbol{a} = \boldsymbol{O}, \quad (B58)$$

$$(XM - B_1N)\boldsymbol{a} = \boldsymbol{O} \quad (B59)$$

possess only the trivial solution $\boldsymbol{a} = \boldsymbol{O}$ which we accomplish by using the identity

$$A(XM - B_1N) + B(YM + A_1N) = M. \quad (B60)$$

Clearly, in view of (B60) any $\boldsymbol{a}$ satisfying (B58) and (B59) must also satisfy

$$M\boldsymbol{a} = \boldsymbol{O}, \quad (B61)$$

$$A_1N\boldsymbol{a} = \boldsymbol{O}; \quad B_1N\boldsymbol{a} = \boldsymbol{O}. \quad (B62)$$

Since the pair (A_1, B_1) is right-coprime, (B62) implies $N\boldsymbol{a} = \boldsymbol{O}$ and invoking (B61) and the right-coprimeness of (N, M), $\boldsymbol{a} = \boldsymbol{O}$. Q.E.D.

Hence, up to a multiplicative constant,

$$\psi_C = \det(XM - B_1N) \quad (B63)$$

and substituting into (B55),

$$\varphi(s) = \theta(s)\cdot\det M(s). \quad (B64)$$

[37]Unfortunately, the best numerical scheme for carrying out the computation (B50) is not so apparent.

[38]$\Delta(s)$ in (B51) has no connection with the $\Delta(s)$ appearing in (B2).

[39]If $C(s)$ is not realized minimally its hidden modes must also be localizable.

It is seen therefore that the (nonhidden) poles of the optimally compensated loop are *precisely* the zeros of $\theta(s)$ plus the finite poles of $K(s)$, each of the latter counted according to its McMillan degree.

An examination of the formula

$$K=\Lambda^{-1}\left(\left\{\Lambda_*^{-1}I\Omega_*^{-1}\right\}_+ +\left\{\Lambda A_1^{-1}Y\Omega\right\}_-\right)\Omega^{-1}-A_1^{-1}Y \tag{B65}$$

reveals immediately that the distinct finite poles of $K(s)$ are *included* in those of $A_1^{-1}(s)$, $\Lambda^{-1}(s)$, $\Omega^{-1}(s)$, and $I(s)$ in $\mathrm{Re}\, s<0$; or, in terms of primary data, in those of

$$FP,\ \left(A_{1*}(P_*P+kQ)A_1\right)^{-1},\ (AGA_*)^{-1},\ A_{1*}P_*(G_u+P_oG_dP_{d*})A_*. \tag{B66}$$

Finally, instead of (B49), experience indicates that the formula

$$C=H_o\left(A^{-1}\Omega-FPH_o\right)^{-1} \tag{B67}$$

where

$$H_o=H\Omega=A_1\Lambda^{-1}\left(\left\{\Lambda_*^{-1}I\Omega_*^{-1}\right\}_+ +\left\{\Lambda A_1^{-1}Y\Omega\right\}_-\right) \tag{B68}$$

is more suitable for computer implementation. To complete the proof of Theorem 1, Section III, it is finally necessary to prove that the controller defined by (B67) and (B68) provides a global minimum for the cost E from among the class of all admissible controllers.

Combining (B16) and (B26), it is seen that

$$K_o(s)=\Lambda^{-1}\left(\left\{\Lambda_*^{-1}\Phi\Omega_*^{-1}\right\}_+ -\left\{\Lambda A_1^{-1}Y\Omega\right\}_\infty\right)\Omega^{-1} \tag{B69}$$

is the Wiener–Hopf solution for $K(s)$. Clearly, $K_o(s)$ is analytic in $\mathrm{Re}\, s\geqslant 0$ and as we have already shown in great detail, the associated cost

$$E(K_o)=E_s(K_o)+kE_t(K_o) \tag{B70}$$

obtained by substituting $R_o=(Y+A_1K_o)A$ into (65) and (66) is finite. According to Lemma 3, any $R(s)$ corresponding to a stable closed-loop design must be of the form $R=(Y+A_1K)A$ where $K(s)$ is analytic in $\mathrm{Re}\, s\geqslant 0$. Hence, for our present purposes we say that $K(s)$ is admissible if it is analytic in $\mathrm{Re}\, s\geqslant 0$ and the associated cost $E(K)<\infty$.[40] Our objective is to prove that $E(K)\geqslant E(K_o)$ for any choice of admissible $K(s)$.

Let

$$(R_1,R_2)_s\equiv \mathrm{Tr}\int_{-\infty}^{\infty} QR_1GR_{2*}\,d\omega, \tag{B71}$$

$$(R_1,R_2)_u\equiv \mathrm{Tr}\int_{-\infty}^{\infty} (1_n-PR_1)G_u(1_n-PR_2)_*\,d\omega, \tag{B72}$$

$$(R_1,R_2)_{ml}\equiv \mathrm{Tr}\int_{-\infty}^{\infty} (PR_1)G_{ml}(PR_2)_*\,d\omega \tag{B73}$$

and

$$(R_1,R_2)_d\equiv \mathrm{Tr}\int_{-\infty}^{\infty} (P_o-PR_1P_d)G_d(P_o-PR_2P_d)_*\,d\omega. \tag{B74}$$

In view of (66), (69), and (70),

$$2\pi E(K)=k(R,R)_s+(R,R)_u+(R,R)_{ml}+(R,R)_d. \tag{B75}$$

Moreover, since each of the four terms on the right-hand side of (B75) is nonnegative, $E(K)<\infty$ iff these terms are all finite.

Suppose R_1 and R_2 correspond to admissible choices K_1 and K_2, respectively. Then, $E(K_1)<\infty$, $E(K_2)<\infty$ and using the version of Schwartz's inequality given,[36] it is easily shown that

$$\begin{aligned}
|(R_1,R_2)_s|^2&\leqslant(R_1,R_1)_s\cdot(R_2,R_2)_s<\infty,\\
|(R_1,R_2)_u|^2&\leqslant(R_1,R_1)_u\cdot(R_2,R_2)_u<\infty,\\
|(R_1,R_2)_{ml}|^2&\leqslant(R_1,R_1)_{ml}\cdot(R_2,R_2)_{ml}<\infty,\\
|(R_1,R_2)_d|^2&\leqslant(R_1,R_1)_d\cdot(R_2,R_2)_d<\infty.
\end{aligned} \tag{B76}$$

For example, recalling that $Q=P_{s*}P_s$ and $G=\Omega\Omega_*$,

$$\begin{aligned}
|(R_1,R_2)_s|^2&=\left|\mathrm{Tr}\int_{-\infty}^{\infty}(P_sR_1\Omega)(P_sR_2\Omega)_*\,d\omega\right|^2\\
&\leqslant \mathrm{Tr}\int_{-\infty}^{\infty}(P_sR_1\Omega)(P_sR_1\Omega)_*\,d\omega\\
&\quad\cdot \mathrm{Tr}\int_{-\infty}^{\infty}(P_sR_2\Omega)(P_sR_2\Omega)_*\,d\omega=\\
&=\mathrm{Tr}\int_{-\infty}^{\infty}QR_1GR_{1*}\,d\omega\cdot \mathrm{Tr}\int_{-\infty}^{\infty}QR_2GR_{2*}\,d\omega\\
&=(R_1,R_1)_s\cdot(R_2,R_2)_s<\infty.
\end{aligned}$$

The other three inequalities are established in exactly the same way. (The result $\mathrm{Tr}\,AB=\mathrm{Tr}\,BA$ is used repeatedly.)

Identify R_1 with R_o and R_2 with any R defined by an admissible $K=K_o+\delta K$. Of course, $\delta K(s)$ is analytic in $\mathrm{Re}\, s\geqslant 0$ and $R=R_o+\delta R$ where $\delta R=A_1(\delta K)A$. Since

$$(R_o,R)_s=(R_o,R_o)_s+(R_o,\delta R)_s$$

is finite and $(R_o,R_o)_s<\infty$, it is also true that $\alpha_o=(R_o,\delta R)_s<\infty$. Similarly,

$$\begin{aligned}
\alpha_1&=(R_o,\delta R)_{ml}<\infty,\\
\alpha_2&=\mathrm{Tr}\int_{-\infty}^{\infty}(1_n-PR_o)G_u(P\delta R)_*\,d\omega<\infty
\end{aligned} \tag{B77}$$

and

$$\alpha_3=\mathrm{Tr}\int_{-\infty}^{\infty}(P_o-PR_oP_d)G_dP_{d*}(P\delta R)_*\,d\omega<\infty.$$

[40] The argument that follows is independent of the assumption $\det(X-B_1K)\not\equiv 0$ in (33).

From

$$(R,R)_s = (R_o,R_o)_s + 2(R_o,\delta R)_s + (\delta R,\delta R)_s$$

it now follows that $\beta_o = (\delta R,\delta R)_s < \infty$. In the same manner, exploiting the remaining inequalities in (B77), we get

$$\beta_1 = \mathrm{Tr}\int_{-\infty}^{\infty} (P\delta R)G_{ml}(P\delta R)_* d\omega < \infty,$$

$$\beta_2 = \mathrm{Tr}\int_{-\infty}^{\infty} (P\delta R)G_u(P\delta R)_* d\omega < \infty \qquad \text{(B78)}$$

and

$$\beta_3 = \mathrm{Tr}\int_{-\infty}^{\infty} (P\delta R)P_d G_d P_{d*}(P\delta R)_* d\omega < \infty.$$

Clearly, all four β's are nonnegative.

Let $E(K) = E(K_o) + \delta E$. By a straightforward expansion of (B75),

$$2\pi(\delta E) = 2(k\alpha_o + \alpha_1 - \alpha_2 - \alpha_3) + (k\beta_o + \beta_1 + \beta_2 + \beta_3). \qquad \text{(B79)}$$

However, it is readily verified by grouping terms that

$$-j(k\alpha_o + \alpha_1 - \alpha_2 - \alpha_3) = \mathrm{Tr}\int_{-j\infty}^{j\infty} \Delta_*(\delta K)_* ds \qquad \text{(B80)}$$

where $\Delta_*(s)$ is as defined in (B2) and (B3) and $K(s)$ replaced by $K_o(s)$. Now the Wiener–Hopf solution $K_o(s)$ guarantees the analyticity of $\Delta_*(s)$ in Re $s \leqslant 0$ and the finiteness of the α's implies that of the integral. The integrand

$$\mathrm{Tr}\left(\Delta_*(\delta K)_*\right)$$

is therefore analytic in Re $s \leqslant 0$ and $O(1/\omega^2)$ for large ω^2. By Cauchy's theorem the integral equals zero whence, $k\alpha_o + \alpha_1 - \alpha_2 - \alpha_3 = 0$ and

$$2\pi(\delta E) = k\beta_o + \beta_1 + \beta_2 + \beta_3 \geqslant 0.$$

Consequently, $E(K) \geqslant E(K_o)$ for every admissible $K(s)$.

Q.E.D.

References

[1] J. E. Weston and J. J. Bongiorno, Jr., "Extension of analytical design techniques to multivariable feedback control systems," *IEEE Trans. Automat. Contr.*, vol. AC-17, pp. 613–620, Oct. 1972.

[2] D. C. Youla, "Modern classical multivariable feedback control theory: Part I," Rome Air Development Center, Griffiss Air Force Base, NY, Tech Rep. RADC-TR-70-98, June 1970.

[3] D. C. Youla, J. J. Bongiorno, Jr., and C. N. Lu, "Single-loop feedback stabilization of linear multivariable dynamical plants," *Automatica*, vol. 10, pp. 159–173, 1974.

[4] D. C. Youla, J. J. Bongiorno, Jr., and H. A. Jabr, "Modern Wiener–Hopf design of optimal controllers—Part I: The single-input-output case," *IEEE Trans. Automat. Contr.*, vol. AC-21, pp. 3–13, Feb. 1976.

[5] H. W. Bode, *Network Analysis and Feedback Design*. New York: Van Nostrand, 1945.

[6] D. C. Youla, "Network ideas applied to the design of optimal multivariable feedback controllers," Polytechnic Inst. of New York, Farmingdale, Memo POLY-EE/EP-75-146, Dec. 1973.

[7] G. C. Newton, Jr., L.A. Gould, and J. F. Kaiser, *Analytical Design of Linear Feedback Controls*. New York: Wiley, 1957.

[8] D. C. Youla, "On the factorization of rational matrices," *IRE Trans. Inform. Theory*, vol. IT-7, pp. 172–189, July 1961.

[9] W. G. Tuel, Jr., "Computer algorithm for spectral factorization of rational matrices," *IBM J. Res. Develop.*, vol. 12, pp. 163–170, Mar. 1968.

[10] H. H. Rosenbrock, *State-Space and Multivariable Theory*. New York: Wiley-Interscience, 1970.

[11] R. E. Kalman, "Irreducible realizations and the degree of a rational matrix," *J. Soc. Industrial and Applied Mathematics*, vol. 13, pp. 520–544, June 1965.

[12] H. H. Rosenbrock, "Relatively prime polynomial matrices," *Electron. Lett.*, no. 4, pp. 227–228, 1968.

[13] K. Hoffman and R. Kunze, *Linear Algebra*. Englewood Cliffs, NJ: Prentice-Hall, 1961.

[14] R. T. Yanushevskii, "Synthesis of closed-loop multivariable control systems for a certain class of plants with delay," *Automation and Remote Control*, pp. 1394–1402, Feb. 1975; Russian original, vol. 35, no. 9, pt.1, Sept. 1974.

[15] I. M. Horowitz and U. Shaked, "Superiority of transfer function over state-variable methods in linear time-invariant feedback system design," *IEEE Trans. Automat. Contr.*, vol. AC-20, pp. 84–97, Feb. 1975.

[16] H. A. Jabr, "Modern analytical design of optimal multivariable control systems," Ph.D. dissertation, Polytechnic Institute of New York, Farmingdale, 1975.

[17] *IEEE Trans. Automat. Contr. (Special Issue on Linear-Quadratic-Gaussian Problem)*, vol. AC-16, Dec. 1971.

[18] H. Kwakernaak and R. Sivan, *Linear Optimal Control Systems*. New York: Wiley-Interscience, 1972.

[19] I. M. Horowitz, *Synthesis of Feedback Systems*. New York: Academic, 1963.

The generalized Nyquist stability criterion and multivariable root loci

A. G. J. MacFARLANE† and I. POSTLETHWAITE†

A comprehensive discussion is given of the background to the generalized Nyquist stability criterion for linear multivariable feedback systems. This leads to a proof based on the use of the Principle of the Argument applied to an algebraic function defined on an appropriate Riemann surface. It is shown how the matrix-valued functions of a complex variable which define the loop transmittance, return-ratio and return-difference matrices of feedback systems analysis may be associated with a set of characteristic algebraic functions, each associated with a Riemann surface. These characteristic functions enable the characteristic loci, which featured in previous heuristic treatments of the generalized Nyquist stability criterion, to be put on a sound basis. The relationship between the algebraic structure of the matrix-valued functions and the appropriate complex-variable theory is carefully discussed. These extensions of the complex-variable concepts underlying the Nyquist criterion are then related to an appropriate generalization of the root locus concept. It is shown that multivariable root loci are the 180° phase loci of the characteristic functions of a return-ratio matrix on an appropriate Riemann surface, plus some possibly degenerate loci each consisting of a single point.

1. Introduction

The Nyquist stability criterion (Nyquist 1932) is one of the most fundamental results in the theory of linear feedback systems and its generalization to the multivariable case is of great interest. Such a generalization was put forward (MacFarlane 1970 a) and used as part of a technique called the Characteristic Locus Method (MacFarlane and Belletrutti 1973) for feedback systems analysis and design, but no satisfactory proof was supplied. The proof of a generalized Nyquist stability theorem was undertaken by Barman and Katzenelson (1973, 1974) but their approach ignored certain key algebraic properties of the quantities involved ; it also leaned very heavily on the use of cuts in the complex plane ; this made their treatment technically complicated, and obscured the essential simplicity of the result. The purpose of this paper is to give a comprehensive discussion of the background to the generalized criterion and a rigorous proof based on a fundamental result in complex variable theory : the Principle of the Argument applied to an algebraic function (Bliss 1966) defined on an appropriate Riemann surface (Springer 1957).

The feedback configuration considered is shown in Fig. 1 (a). S_1 and S_2 are linear multivariable dynamical systems described by appropriate sets of state-space equations. Suppose all the feedback loops are broken at the point shown in Fig. 1 (b). Let $Z(s)$ be the loop-transmission transfer-function matrix relating signals injected at the point α to those returned at the point α'.

Received 22 June 1976.

† Control and Management Systems Group, Engineering Department, University of Cambridge.

Reprinted with permission from *Int. J. Control*, vol. 25, pp. 81-127, Jan. 1977.

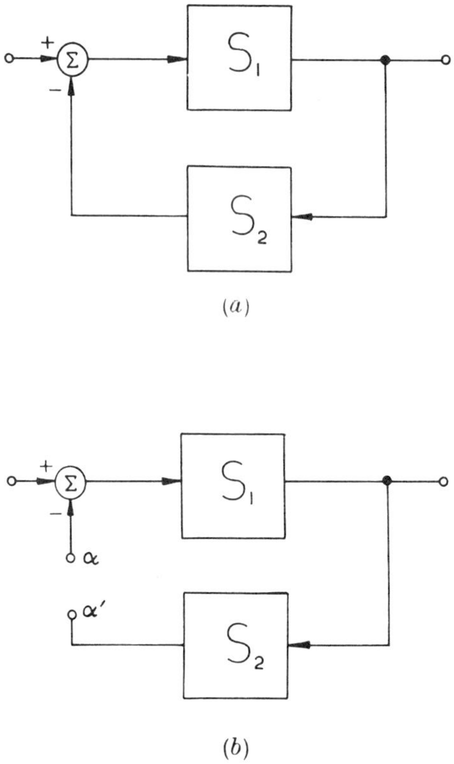

Figure 1. Multivariable feedback configuration. (a) Closed loop; (b) open loop.

Then the corresponding return-difference matrix (MacFarlane 1970 a) for this break point is

$$F(s) = I - Z(s) = I + L(s)$$

where $L(s)$ is defined as the system return-ratio matrix (MacFarlane 1970 a) and I is a unit matrix of appropriate order. A return-difference operator generates the difference between injected and returned signals from the injected signals. It plays a key role in feedback theory, since the essence of forging a feedback link is making two sets of signals identically equal and thus making the difference between them identically zero. Both $L(s)$ and $F(s)$ are matrix-valued functions of a complex variable s. The relevant basic properties of such entities are discussed in §§ 3, 4 and 5 from both the algebraic and the complex-variable point of view. The key concepts in the proof of the generalized criterion revolve around the properties of the eigenvalues of a matrix-valued function of a complex variable. It is shown in § 3 that a matrix-valued function of a complex variable is associated with a set of algebraic functions which may be called its characteristic functions. These characteristic functions accurately define the eigenvalues of the matrix-valued function as functions of a complex variable. It is also shown that the sets of characteristic functions have sets of poles and zeros. These sets of poles and zeros are related in § 4 to a set of poles and zeros for the matrix-valued function defined in algebraic terms.

There is a well-established theory of algebraic functions (Bliss 1966). This theory therefore provides the rigorous foundation on which the proof of the generalized stability criterion may be built. Each characteristic function is an algebraic function, which is a generalization of the elementary function of a complex variable. It is therefore associated with a Riemann surface (Springer 1957), on which domain of definition it becomes a single-valued function analytic everywhere except at a set of critical points. Many standard properties of analytic function theory hold in this extended domain. In particular the Principle of the Argument (Hille 1959) can be applied and this, together with the relationships between the poles and zeros of the set of characteristic functions of a return-difference matrix and the poles and zeros of the return-difference matrix itself, forms the basis of the proof.

Together with the Nyquist criterion (Nyquist 1932), and the related concept of Nyquist diagrams, the Root Locus method (Evans 1954) provides the basis for most single-loop linear feedback design techniques. It is therefore of interest and importance to relate these extensions of the Nyquist approach to root-locus concepts ; this is done in § 9, where it is shown that the multivariable root loci are the 180° phase loci of the characteristic functions of $L(s)$ on appropriate Riemann surfaces, plus some possibly degenerate loci each consisting of a single point.

2. Relationship between open-loop and closed-loop characteristic polynomials for basic feedback configuration

Consider the multivariable feedback arrangement shown in Fig. 1 (*a*). Let the state-space equation sets for the systems S_1 and S_2 be

$$\frac{dx_i}{dt} = A_i x_i + B_i u_i$$

$$y_i = C_i x_i + D_i u_i \quad i = 1, 2 \tag{2.1}$$

Let the transfer-function matrices for S_1 and S_2 be $G_1(s)$ and $G_2(s)$ respectively, and let their characteristic polynomials be $\Delta_1(s)$ and $\Delta_2(s)$ respectively. Then

$$G_i(s) = C_i(sI - A_i)^{-1}B_i + D_i \tag{2.2}$$

$$\Delta_i(s) = \det\,[sI - A_i] \qquad i = 1, 2 \tag{2.3}$$

$$G_i(\infty) = D_i \tag{2.4}$$

Further assume that

$$\det\,[I + G_2(\infty)G_1(\infty)] \neq 0 \tag{2.5}$$

Let the overall system, as shown in Fig. 2, have input vector u, state vector x and output vector y. Then breaking the feedback loops at y_2 puts the two

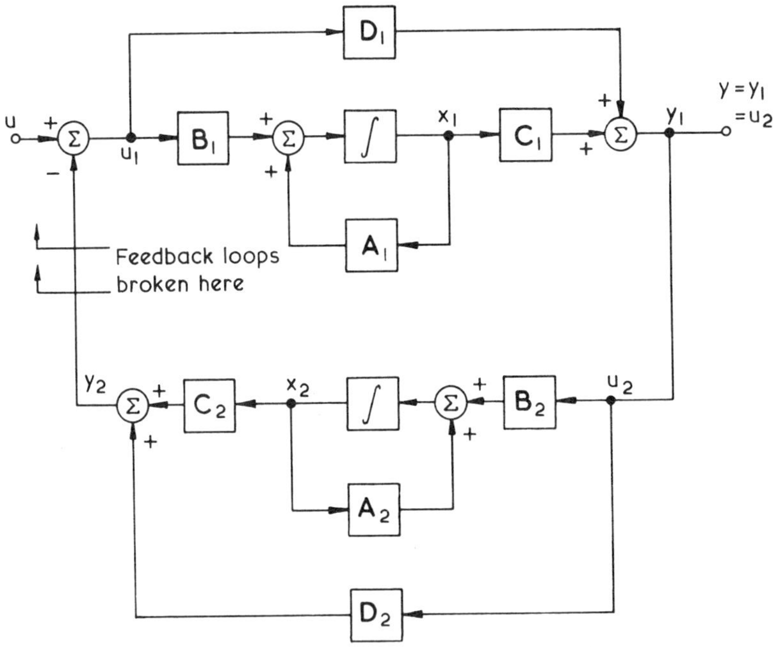

Figure 2. State-space representation of multivariable feedback system.

systems S_1 and S_2 in cascade, resulting in an open-loop system whose state-space description is given by :

$$\dot{x}_1 = A_1 x_1 + B_1 u_1 \tag{2.6}$$

$$\begin{aligned}\dot{x}_2 &= A_2 x_2 + B_2 u_2 \\ &= A_2 x_2 + B_2 C_1 x_1 + B_2 D_1 u_1\end{aligned} \tag{2.7}$$

$$\begin{aligned}y_2 &= C_2 x_2 + D_2 u_2 \\ &= C_2 x_2 + D_2 C_1 x_1 + D_2 D_1 u_1\end{aligned} \tag{2.8}$$

Combining these expressions we have that this open-loop system has a set of state-space equations

$$\dot{x} = Ax + Bu_1 \tag{2.9}$$

$$y_2 = Cx + Du_1 \tag{2.10}$$

where

$$x = \begin{bmatrix} x_1 \\ x_2 \end{bmatrix}$$

$$\left.\begin{aligned} A = \begin{bmatrix} A_1 & 0 \\ B_2 C_1 & A_2 \end{bmatrix}, \quad B = \begin{bmatrix} B_1 \\ B_2 D_1 \end{bmatrix} \\ C = [D_2 C_1 \quad C_2], \quad D = D_2 D_1 \end{aligned}\right\} \tag{2.11}$$

Now suppose the loops are all reconnected at y_2 so that

$$u_1 = u - y_2 \tag{2.12}$$

Substituting this into (2.9) and (2.10) we get

$$\dot{x} = Ax + B(u - y_2) \tag{2.13}$$

$$y_2 = Cx + D(u - y_2) \tag{2.14}$$

from which we obtain the set of closed-loop state-space equations

$$\begin{aligned}\dot{x} &= Ax + Bu - B(I+D)^{-1}Cx - B(I+D)^{-1}Du \\ &= [A - B(I+D)^{-1}C]x + [B - B(I+D)^{-1}D]u \end{aligned} \tag{2.15}$$

$$y_2 = (I+D)^{-1}Cx + (I+D)^{-1}Du \tag{2.16}$$

If we write the first of these closed-loop equations in the form

$$\dot{x} = A_c x + B_c u \tag{2.17}$$

then we have that

$$\begin{aligned} A_c &= A - B(I+D)^{-1}C \\ &= \begin{bmatrix} A_1 & 0 \\ B_2C_1 & A_2 \end{bmatrix} - \begin{bmatrix} B_1 \\ B_2D_1 \end{bmatrix} J\,[D_2C_1 \quad C_2] \\ &= \begin{bmatrix} A_1 - B_1JD_2C_1 & -B_1JC_2 \\ B_2C_1 - B_2D_1JD_2C_1 & A_2 - B_2D_1JC_2 \end{bmatrix} \end{aligned} \tag{2.18}$$

where

$$J = (I + D_2D_1)^{-1} \tag{2.19}$$

Let $F(s)$ be the return difference operator (MacFarlane 1970 a) for the set of opened loops. Then, applying Schur's formula (Gantmacher 1959) for the evaluation of partitioned determinants we have that

$$\begin{aligned} \det F(s) &= \det\,[C(sI - A)^{-1}B + D + I] \\ &= \det \begin{bmatrix} sI - A & B \\ -C & I + D \end{bmatrix} \div [\det\,(sI - A)] \\ &= \det \begin{bmatrix} sI - A_1 & 0 & B_1 \\ -B_2C_1 & sI - A_2 & B_2D_1 \\ -D_2C_1 & -C_2 & J^{-1} \end{bmatrix} \div \Delta_1(s)\Delta_2(s) \end{aligned} \tag{2.20}$$

Finally we may apply elementary column operations to the right-hand side of eqn. (2.20) in order to replace $-D_2C_1$ and $-C_2$ by zero blocks in the following way :

$$\begin{aligned}\det F(s)&\\ &=\det F(s)\det\begin{bmatrix} I & 0 & 0\\ 0 & I & 0\\ JD_2C_1 & JC_2 & I\end{bmatrix}\\ &=\det\begin{bmatrix} sI-A_1+B_1JD_2C_1 & B_1JC_2 & B_1\\ -B_2C_1+B_2D_1JD_2C_1 & sI-A_2+B_2D_1JC_2 & B_2D_1\\ 0 & 0 & J^{-1}\end{bmatrix}\div\Delta_1(s)\Delta_2(s)\end{aligned} \tag{2.21}$$

Then using eqns. (2.11), (2.18) and (2.19) we have

$$\begin{aligned}\det F(s)&=\det\begin{bmatrix} sI-A_c & B\\ 0 & J^{-1}\end{bmatrix}\div\Delta_1(s)\Delta_2(s)\\ &=\det\,[sI-A_c]\det\,[J^{-1}]\div\Delta_1(s)\Delta_2(s)\end{aligned} \tag{2.22}$$

so that

$$\frac{\det F(s)}{\det F(\infty)}=\frac{\det\,[sI-A_c]}{\det\,[sI-A]}=\frac{CLCP(s)}{OLCP(s)} \tag{2.23}$$

where $CLCP(s)$ and $OLCP(s)$ are the system closed-loop and open-loop characteristic polynomials respectively, and

$$OLCP(s)=\det\,[sI-A]=\det\,[sI-A_1]\det\,[sI-A_2] \tag{2.24}$$

The relationship has been derived for a restricted class of non-proper systems, that is one in which D is a finite constant matrix which ensures that $\det F(\infty)$ will be a finite constant. This type of system is considered throughout the paper.

3. Characteristic functions

Let $Q(s)$ be an $m\times m$ square matrix-valued function of a complex variable s whose elements are rational functions in s. For any specific value of complex frequency, $\bar{s}$ say, the corresponding matrix $Q(\bar{s})$ will be a matrix of complex numbers and will have a set of eigenvalues $\{q_i(\bar{s})\mid i=1,2,\ldots,m\}$ which are a set of complex numbers. In some sense therefore (which we hope to shortly make precise) the eigenvalues of $Q(s)$ are functions of a complex variable. However, if we form the relevant characteristic equation

$$\det\,[q(s)I_m-Q(s)]\triangleq\Delta(q,s)=0 \tag{3.1}$$

it is obvious that the polynomial in q, $\Delta(q,s)$, will not in general be expressible as a product of factors linear in q. Hence the matrix $Q(s)$ will not normally have eigenvalues which are rational functions of s. Or, to put it in another way, although the elements of $Q(s)$ are drawn from a field (the field of rational functions) the eigenvalues of $Q(s)$ do not all necessarily lie in that field. In general $\Delta(q, s)$ will be reducible to a form

$$\Delta(q, s) = \Delta_1(q, s)\Delta_2(q, s) \ldots \Delta_k(q, s) \tag{3.2}$$

where the factors $\{\Delta_i(q, s) : i = 1, 2, \ldots, k\}$ are polynomials which are irreducible over the field of rational functions in s. Let the irreducible factors $\Delta_i(q, s)$ have the form

$$\Delta_i(q, s) = q_i^{t_i}(s) + a_{i1}q_i^{t_i-1}(s) + \ldots + a_{it_i}(s) \quad i = 1, 2, \ldots, k \tag{3.3}$$

where t_i is the degree of the ith irreducible polynomial and the coefficients $\{a_{ij} : i = 1, 2, \ldots, k ; \; j = 1, 2, \ldots, t_i\}$ are rational functions in s.

If $b_{i0}(s)$ is the least common denominator of the coefficients $\{a_{ij}(s) : j = 1, 2, \ldots, t\}$, eqn. (3.3) can be put in the form

$$b_{i0}(s)q_i^{t_i} + b_{i1}(s)q_i^{t_i-1} + \ldots + b_{it_i}(s) = 0 \quad i = 1, 2, \ldots, k \tag{3.4}$$

where the coefficients $\{b_{ij}(s) : i = 1, 2, \ldots, k ; \; j = 1, 2, \ldots, t_i\}$ are now polynomials in s. The function of a complex variable $q_i(s)$ which is defined by eqn. (3.4) is called an algebraic function (Bliss 1966). Thus a square matrix-valued function of a complex variable $Q(s)$ is associated with a set of algebraic functions $\{q_i(s) : i = 1, 2, \ldots, k\}$ which play a role for $Q(s)$ related to its set of eigenvalues. The precise sense in which the set of eigenvalues of $Q(s)$ are functions of a complex variable is that they are the values of a set of algebraic functions ; and an algebraic function is a generalisation of the concept of a function of a complex variable. The *characteristic functions* of $Q(s)$ are defined to be the set of algebraic functions $\{q_i(s) : i = 1, 2, \ldots, k\}$.

The problems of finding the characteristic functions of the matrix $Q(s)$ is closely linked to the problem of finding an appropriate canonical form. If $\Delta(q, s)$ were reducible to factors linear in q then $Q(s)$ could be put into Jordan form (Cohn 1974). In general this will not be the case and a suitable canonical form is defined as follows.

Let

$$C(\Delta_i) \triangleq \begin{bmatrix} 0 & 0 \ldots 0 & -a_{i,t_i}(s) \\ 1 & 0 \ldots 0 & -a_{i,t_i-1}(s) \\ 0 & 1 \ldots 0 & -a_{i,t_i-2}(s) \\ \vdots & & \\ 0 & 1 & -a_{i1}(s) \end{bmatrix} \tag{3.5}$$

for $t_i > 1$ with

$$C(\Delta_i) \triangleq [-a_{i1}] \quad \text{if} \quad t_i = 1 \tag{3.6}$$

then a transformation matrix $T(s)$ exists such that

$$Q(s) = T(s)R(s)T^{-1}(s) \tag{3.7}$$

where $R(s)$ is a unique matrix, which we will define to be the *irreducible rational canonical form* of $Q(s)$ and given by

$$R(s) \triangleq \mathrm{diag}\,[C(\Delta_1), C(\Delta_2), \ldots, C(\Delta_k)] \tag{3.8}$$

It is clear that, given $R(s)$, the irreducible factors $\Delta_i(q, s)$ can easily be obtained. A proposed method for finding $R(s)$ for any given $Q(s)$ is given in Appendix 1.

3.1. *Riemann surface of a characteristic function*

Each characteristic function $q(s)$ is defined by an irreducible equation of the form

$$b_0(s)q^t + b_1(s)q^{t-1} + \ldots + b_t(s) = 0 \tag{3.9}$$

having in general t distinct roots. An exception occurs only if

(*a*) $b_0(s) = 0$, because the degree of the equation is then lowered, or if

(*b*) the equation has multiple roots.

This last situation can occur if, and only if, an expression, called the discriminant of the equation, vanishes. The discriminant (Barnett 1971) is an entire rational function of the equation coefficients ; it will be denoted by $D_q(s)$, and is discussed in Appendix 2†.

Ordinary points of the characteristic function

An ordinary point (Bliss 1966) of the characteristic function $q(s)$ is any point of the complex plane such that

$$b_0(s) \neq 0 \quad \text{and} \quad D_q(s) \neq 0$$

Critical points of the characteristic function

A critical point (Bliss 1966) of $q(s)$ is any point of the complex plane at which either

$$b_0(s) = 0 \quad \text{or} \quad D_q(s) = 0$$

or both.

Branch points of the characteristic function

Solutions of

$$D_q(s) = 0 \tag{3.10}$$

are called *branch points* of the characteristic function.

At every ordinary point the eqn. (3.9) defining the characteristic function has t distinct roots, since the discriminant does not vanish. The theory of algebraic functions (Bliss 1966) then shows that in a simply connected region of the complex plane punctured by the exclusion of the critical points the values of the characteristic function $q(s)$ form a set of analytic functions ; each of these analytic functions is called a *branch* of the characteristic function $q(s)$. Arguments based on standard techniques of analytic continuation, together with the properties of algebraic equations, show that the various branches can be organized into a single entity : the corresponding algebraic function.

† The point $s = \infty$ requires special discussion ; this is given in Appendix 7.

This is summarized in the following basic theorem of algebraic function theory : an irreducible algebraic equation of the form (3.9) defines precisely one t-valued regular function $q(s)$ in the punctured plane (Knopp 1947).

Functions defined in this way are called *algebraic functions*, and can be regarded as natural generalizations of the familiar elementary functions of a complex variable. An elementary function of a complex variable has the set of complex numbers **C** as both its domain and its range. An algebraic function has the complex number set **C** as its range but has a new and appropriately defined domain **R** which is called its *Riemann Surface* (Springer 1957). Since the Riemann surface of a characteristic function plays a crucial role in the proof of the generalized Nyquist stability criterion presented later, it is important to have an intuitive grasp of the ideas underlying its definition and formation, which is therefore now briefly considered.

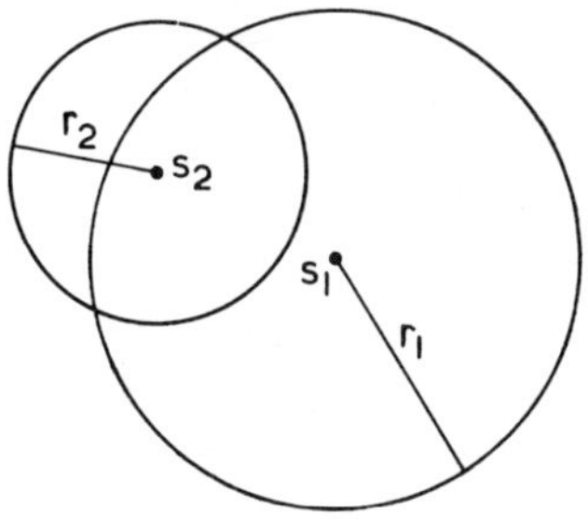

Figure 3. Analytic continuation.

Suppose we have a representation of part of one branch of an algebraic function in the form of a power series ; such a representation is usually called a functional element. Imagine its circle of convergence to be cut out of paper and that the individual points of the paper disc are made bearers of the unique functional values of the elements. If now this initial element is analytically continued by means of a second power series, another circle of convergence can be thought of as being cut out and pasted partly over the first, as illustrated by Fig. 3. The parts pasted together are made bearers of the same functional values and are accordingly treated as a single region covered once with values. If a further analytic continuation is carried out, a further disc is similarly pasted onto the preceding one. Now suppose that, after repeated analytic continuations, one of the discs lies over another disc, not associated with an immediately preceding analytic continuation, as shown in Fig. 4. Such an overlapping disc is pasted together with the one it overlaps if and only if both are bearers of the same functional values. If however they bear different functional values they are allowed to overlap but remain disconnected. Thus two sheets, which are bearers of different functional values, become superimposed on this part of the complex plane.

Continuing this process for as long as possible, a surface-like configuration is obtained covering t ' sheets ' of the complex plane, where t is the degree of the algebraic function. To form the Riemann surface these sheets can be joined together in the most varied of ways. This may involve connecting together two sheets which are separated by several other sheets lying between them. Although such a construction cannot be carried out in a three-dimensional space it is not difficult to give a perfectly satisfactory topological description of the process required. This surface-like configuration is called the *Riemann surface* of the multiple-valued algebraic function. On the Riemann surface the entire domain of values of the algebraic function is spread out in a completely single-valued manner so that, on every one of the t copies of the complex plane involved, every point is the bearer of one and only one value of the function.

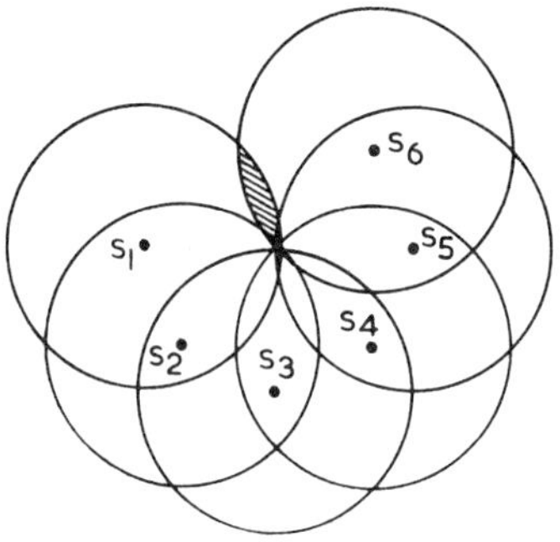

Figure 4. Repeated analytic continuation.

A method for building Riemann surfaces is given in Appendix 3. This involves the use of cuts in the complex plane and it may be helpful to say a word about them at this point. Let an algebraic function $q(s)$ have r critical points $\{a_1, a_2, \ldots, a_r\}$. Suppose them to be joined to one another and then to the point at infinity by a line L. Any line joining critical points will be called a *cut*. Let $\mathbf{L}$ denote the set of complex numbers defined by the line L. We then have that the solutions of eqn. (3.9) define a set of t ' distinct ' analytical functions $\{q_1(s), q_2(s), \ldots, q_t(s)\}$ in the cut plane $\mathbf{C}-\mathbf{L}$. Each of these functions can be analytically continued, by standard procedures, across the cut L. Now it follows from the fundamental principles of analytic continuation that if an analytic function satisfies an algebraic equation in one part of its domain of definition, it must satisfy that equation in every region into which it is analytically continued. We must therefore have that

(i) there are only t ' distinct ' analytic functions which satisfy the defining algebraic equation in the cut plane $\mathbf{C}-\mathbf{L}$;

(ii) each analytic continuation of any of these analytic functions $\{q_i(s) : i=1, 2, \ldots, t\}$ gives rise to an analytic function which also satisfies the defining algebraic equation. It follows from this that the set of analytic functions associated with one side of the cut L must be a simple permutation of the set of analytic functions associated with the other side of the cut. Therefore by identifying and suitably matching up corresponding analytic functions (via their sets of computed values) on opposite sides of the cut L, one can produce an appropriate domain on which a single analytic function may be specified which defines a continuous single-valued mapping from this domain into the complex plane. This function is of course the algebraic function, conceived of as a single entity, and the domain so constructed is its Riemann surface.

It is sufficient for the purposes of understanding this paper for the reader to know that a Riemann surface can be constructed for any given characteristic function, on which its values form a single-valued function of position. Many standard relationships and properties of analytic function theory generalize, using the Riemann surface concept, to the algebraic function case and, in particular the Principle of the Argument holds on the Riemann surface (Behnke *et al.* 1974).

3.2. *Poles and zeros of characteristic functions*

Consider the defining equation for a characteristic function $q(s)$:

$$b_0(s)q^t + b_1(s)q^{t-1} + \ldots + b_t(s) = 0$$

We will take both

$$b_0(s) \not\equiv 0 \quad \text{and} \quad b_t(s) \not\equiv 0$$

since, if either or both of these polynomial coefficients were to vanish identically, we could find a reduced-order equation such that both the coefficients of the highest and zeroth powers of $q(s)$ were non-zero ; this reduced-order equation would then be taken as defining an appropriate new algebraic function for whose defining equation the supposition would be true.

It may happen however that $b_0(s)$ and $b_t(s)$ share a common factor and thus both vanish together at some specific set of values of s. Before looking at the effect of this, consider the situation when $b_0(s)$ and $b_t(s)$ do not share a common factor. The algebraic function will obviously be zero when

$$b_t(s) = 0 \tag{3.11}$$

and will tend to infinity as

$$b_0(s) \to 0 \tag{3.12}$$

For this reason those values of s which satisfy eqn. (3.11) are defined to be the *zeros* of the algebraic function $q(s)$, and those values of s which satisfy the equation

$$b_0(s) = 0 \tag{3.13}$$

are defined to be the *poles* of the algebraic function $q(s)$†.

† The point $s = \infty$ requires special discussion ; this is given in Appendix 7.

In order to be able to take eqns. (3.11) and (3.13) as defining the zeros and poles of $q(s)$ in the general case, we must show that they remain appropriate when $b_0(s)$ and $b_t(s)$ share a common factor. Let us first dispose of the trivial case when all the coefficients $\{b_i(s) : i = 0, 2, \ldots, t\}$ share a common factor by saying that such a common factor would simply be divided out to get a new defining equation for an appropriate algebraic function. Suppose then that $b_0(s)$ and $b_t(s)$ have a common factor, but that some non-empty set of coefficients $\{b_k(s), \ldots, b_l(s)\}$ do not share this common factor. Then dividing through the left-hand side of eqn. (3.9) by $b_0(s)$ we get

$$q^t + \frac{b_1(s)}{b_0(s)} q^{t-1} + \ldots + \frac{b_k(s)}{b_0(s)} q^{t-k} + \ldots + \frac{b_l(s)}{b_0(s)} q^{t-l} + \ldots + \frac{b_t(s)}{b_0(s)} = 0 \qquad (3.14)$$

Then, as $s \to \bar{s}$, where $\bar{s}$ is a zero of the common factor of $b_0(s)$ and $b_t(s)$, the moduli of the coefficient set

$$\left\{ \frac{b_k(s)}{b_0(s)}, \ldots, \frac{b_l(s)}{b_0(s)} \right\}$$

all become arbitrarily large, and it is obvious that $q(s)$ will have a pole at $s = \bar{s}$.

Again, suppose that $b_0(s)$ and $b_t(s)$ have a common factor but that some non-empty set of coefficients $\{b_j(s), \ldots, b_m(s)\}$ do not. Then as $s \to \bar{s}$, where $\bar{s}$ is a zero of the common factor, the algebraic eqn. (3.9) may be replaced by

$$b_j(\bar{s}) q^{t-j}(\bar{s}) + \ldots + b_m(\bar{s}) q^{t-m}(\bar{s}) = 0 \qquad (3.15)$$

where

$$b_j(\bar{s}) \neq 0, \ \ldots, \ b_m(\bar{s}) \neq 0$$

so that we must have

$$q(\bar{s}) = 0$$

showing that $\bar{s}$ is indeed a zero of the algebraic function $q(s)$.

We thus conclude that eqns. (3.11) and (3.13) may be taken as defining the zeros and poles of the algebraic function $q(s)$, and that use of these definitions enables us to cope with the existence of coincident poles and zeros.

3.3. *The eigenvector functions for a matrix-valued function of a complex variable*

We have seen how a matrix-valued function of a complex variable $Q(s)$ is associated with a set of algebraic functions $q_i(s)$ whose values are the eigenvalues of $Q(s)$. It is shown in Appendix 4 that associated with each algebraic function $q_i(s)$ is a vector-valued function of a complex variable $w_i(s)$, whose elements are algebraic functions having the same Riemann surface as $q_i(s)$, and whose vector values are the eigenvectors of $Q(s)$.

4. Algebraic definition of poles and zeros of a transfer-function matrix

Let $G(s)$ be an $m \times l$ rational matrix-valued function of the complex variable s. Then there exists a canonical form for $G(s)$, the Smith-McMillan form (Rosenbrock 1970), such that

$$G(s) = H(s) M(s) J(s) \qquad (4.1)$$

where the $m \times m$ matrix $H(s)$ and the $l \times l$ matrix $J(s)$ are both unimodular (that is having a constant value for their determinants, independent of s). If r is the normal rank of $G(s)$ (that is $G(s)$ has rank r for almost all values of s) then $M(s)$ has the form

$$M(s) = \begin{bmatrix} M^*(s)_{rr} & 0_{r,\, l-r} \\ 0_{m-r,\, r} & 0_{m-r,\, m-r} \end{bmatrix} \tag{4.2}$$

with

$$M^*(s) = \text{diag}\left[\frac{\epsilon_1(s)}{\psi_1(s)}, \frac{\epsilon_2(s)}{\psi_2(s)}, \ldots, \frac{\epsilon_r(s)}{\psi_r(s)}\right] \tag{4.3}$$

where

(i) each $\epsilon_i(s)$ divides all $\epsilon_{i+j}(s)$ and

(ii) each $\psi_i(s)$ divides all $\psi_{i-j}(s)$.

With an appropriate partitioning of H, M and J we therefore have

$$\begin{aligned} G &= [H_1 \ H_2] \begin{bmatrix} M^* & 0 \\ 0 & 0 \end{bmatrix} \begin{bmatrix} J_1 \\ J_2 \end{bmatrix} \\ &= H_1 M^* J_1 \end{aligned} \tag{4.4}$$

where M^* is as defined in eqn. (4.3).

Thus $G(s)$ may be expressed in the form

$$\begin{aligned} G(s) &= H_1(s) \left[\text{diag}\, \frac{\epsilon_i(s)}{\psi_i(s)}\right] J_1(s) \\ &= \sum_{i=1}^{r} h_i(s) \frac{\epsilon_i(s)}{\psi_i(s)} j_i^t(s) \end{aligned} \tag{4.5}$$

where

(i) $\{h_i(s) : i = 1, 2, \ldots, r\}$ are the columns of the matrix $H_1(s)$;

(ii) $\{j_i^t(s) : i = 1, 2, \ldots, r\}$ are the rows of the matrix $J_1(s)$.

We know that

$$r \leqslant \min\,(l, m)$$

and that $H(s)$ and $J(s)$ are unimodular matrices of full rank m and l respectively for all s. Suppose $G(s)$ is the transfer-function matrix for a system with input transform vector $u(s)$ and output transform vector $y(s)$. Then any input vector $u(s)$ is turned into an output vector $y(s)$ by

$$y(s) = \sum_{i=1}^{r} h_i(s) \frac{\epsilon_i(s)}{\psi_i(s)} [j_i^t(s) u(s)] \tag{4.6}$$

For the single-input single-output case where

$$y(s) = \frac{k\epsilon(s)}{\psi(s)} u(s) \tag{4.7}$$

with k a constant, the transfer function

$$g(s)=\frac{k\epsilon(s)}{\psi(s)} \tag{4.8}$$

is defined as having zeros at those values of s where $\epsilon(s)$ vanishes and poles at those values of s where $\psi(s)$ vanishes. Thus for a non-zero $u(s)$ the modulus of $y(s)$ vanishes when s is a zero of $g(s)$, and becomes arbitrarily large when s is a pole of $g(s)$. A natural way therefore to characterize the zeros and poles of $G(s)$ is in terms of those values of s for which $\|y(s)\|$ becomes zero for non-zero $\|u(s)\|$, and arbitrarily large for finite $\|u(s)\|$ where $\|\cdot\|$ denotes the standard vector norm. This natural extension of scalar case ideas leads directly to definitions of zeros and poles of $G(s)$ in terms of the Smith–McMillan form quantities

$$\left\{\frac{\epsilon_i(s)}{\psi_i(s)}\right\}$$

because of the following pair of simple results.

Zero lemma. $\|y(s)\|$ vanishes for $\|u(s)\|\neq 0$ and s finite if and only if some $\epsilon_i(s)$ is zero.

Pole lemma. $\|y(s)\|\to\infty$ for $\|u(s)\|<\infty$ if and only if some $\psi_i(s)\to 0$.

These considerations lead naturally to the following definitions (Rosenbrock 1970).

Poles of $G(s)$. The poles of $G(s)$ are defined to be the set of all zeros of the set of polynomials $\{\psi_i(s): i=1, 2, \ldots, r\}$. In what follows we will usually denote the poles of $G(s)$ by $\{p_1, p_2, \ldots, p_n\}$ and put

$$p(s)=(s-p_1)(s-p_2)\ldots(s-p_n) \tag{4.9}$$

where $p(s)$ is conveniently referred to as the pole polynomial of $G(s)$ and is given by

$$p(s)=\sum_{i=1}^{r}\psi_i(s) \tag{4.10}$$

Zeros of $G(s)$. The zeros of $G(s)$ are defined to be the set of all zeros of the set of polynomials $\{\epsilon_i(s): i=1, 2, \ldots, r\}$. We will normally denote the zeros of $G(s)$ by $\{z_1, z_2, \ldots, z_q\}$ and put

$$z(s)=(s-z_1)(s-z_2)\ldots(s-z_q) \tag{4.11}$$

where $z(s)$ is conveniently referred to as the zero polynomial of $G(s)$ and is given by

$$z(s)=\prod_{i=1}^{r}\epsilon_i(s) \tag{4.12}$$

It is important to remember that $z(s)$ and $p(s)$ are not necessarily relatively prime; for this reason it is wrong to simply define $z(s)$ and $p(s)$ for a square matrix $G(s)$ as the numerator and denominator polynomials of det $G(s)$.

4.1. *Rules for calculating pole polynomials and zero polynomials*

The route via the Smith–McMillan form is not always convenient for the determination of the poles and zeros of $G(s)$, particularly if the calculation is being done by hand. The following rules (Kontakos 1973) can be shown to give the same results as the Smith–McMillan definitions.

Pole polynomial rule. $p(s)$ is the least common denominator of all non-zero minors of all orders of $G(s)$.

Zero polynomial rule. $z(s)$ is the greatest common divisor of the numerators of all minors of $G(s)$ of order r (r being the normal rank of $G(s)$) *which minors have all been adjusted to have $p(s)$ as their common denominator.*

4.2. *Example of pole and zero calculation* (*Kontakos* 1973)

In what follows, the expression

$$G^{i_1,\, i_2,\, \ldots,\, i_r}_{j_1,\, j_2,\, \ldots,\, j_r}$$

denotes the minor of $G(s)$ of order r formed by taking the determinant of the matrix obtained from $G(s)$ by deleting all rows except rows $i_1, i_2, \ldots, i_r$ and all columns except $j_1, j_2, \ldots, j_r$.

Let

$$G(s) = \frac{1}{(s+1)(s+2)(s-1)} \begin{bmatrix} (s-1)(s+2) & 0 & (s-1)^2 \\ -(s+1)(s+2) & (s-1)(s+1) & (s-1)(s+1) \end{bmatrix}$$

The minors of order 2 are

$$G^{1,\,2}_{1,\,2} = \frac{1}{(s+1)(s+2)} \qquad G^{1,\,2}_{1,\,3} = \frac{2}{(s+1)(s+2)} \qquad G^{1,\,2}_{2,\,3} = \frac{-(s-1)}{(s+1)(s+2)^2}$$

so that, considering the minors of all orders we get

$$p(s) = (s+1)(s+2)^2(s-1)$$

On adjusting the denominators of all minors of order 2 to be $p(s)$ we have

$$\bar{G}^{1,\,2}_{1,\,2} = \frac{(s-1)(s+2)}{p(s)} \qquad \bar{G}^{1,\,2}_{1,\,3} = \frac{2(s-1)(s+2)}{p(s)} \qquad \bar{G}^{1,\,2}_{2,\,3} = \frac{-s(s-1)^2}{p(s)}$$

and so

$$z(s) = s-1$$

The Smith–McMillan form of $G(s)$ can be calculated to be

$$M(s) = \begin{bmatrix} \dfrac{1}{(s+1)(s+2)(s-1)} & 0 & 0 \\ 0 & \dfrac{(s-1)}{(s+2)} & 0 \end{bmatrix}$$

which verifies the result.

5. Relationship between algebraically defined poles and zeros and the poles and zeros of the set of characteristic functions

As a key step in the establishment of a generalized Nyquist stability criterion, it is crucially important to relate the poles and zeros defined by algebraic means to complex variable theory, and thus to the poles and zeros of the set of characteristic functions.

The coefficients $a_i(s)$ in the expansion

$$\det [qI_m - Q(s)] = q^m + a_1(s)q^{m-1} + a_2(s)q^{m-2} + \dots + a_m(s) \tag{5.1}$$

are all appropriate sums of minors of $Q(s)$ since it can be shown that

$$\begin{aligned}\det [qI_m - Q(s)] &= q^m - [\text{trace } Q(s)]q^{m-1} \\ &+ [\textstyle\sum \text{principal minors of } Q(s) \text{ of order } 2]q^{m-2} - \dots + (-1)^m \det Q(s)\end{aligned} \tag{5.2}$$

and thus the term $b_0(s)$ in eqn. (3.9) is the least common denominator of all non-zero *principal* minors of all orders of $Q(s)$.

Now the pole polynomial $p(s)$ of a square matrix $Q(s)$ is the least common denominator of all non-zero minors of all orders of $Q(s)$. Therefore, if $e(s)$ is the least common denominator of all non-zero *non-principal* minors, with all factors common to $b_0(s)$ removed, we have that

$$p(s) = e(s)b_0(s) \tag{5.3}$$

Furthermore, since

$$a_m(s) = \det Q(s) \tag{5.4}$$

and

$$a_m(s) = \frac{b_m(s)}{b_0(s)} = \frac{b_m(s)e(s)}{p(s)} \tag{5.5}$$

and since the zero polynomial of a square matrix $Q(s)$ is the numerator of the rational function obtained from $\det Q(s)$ after adjusting $\det Q(s)$ in such a way as to obtain an equivalent rational function with $p(s)$ as its denominator, we must have that

$$z(s) = e(s)b_m(s) \tag{5.6}$$

In many cases the least common denominator of the non-zero non-principal minors of $Q(s)$ will divide $b_0(s)$, in which case $e(s)$ will be unity and the pole and zero polynomials for $Q(s)$ will be $b_0(s)$ and $b_m(s)$ respectively. In general a square-matrix-valued function of a complex variable $Q(s)$ will have a set of k irreducible characteristic functions in the form specified by eqn. (3.3) and the general form for the pole and zero polynomials can be written as

$$p(s) = e(s) \prod_{i=1}^{k} b_{i0}(s) \tag{5.7}$$

and

$$z(s) = e(s) \prod_{i=1}^{k} b_{i,\,t_i}(s) \tag{5.8}$$

where the pole and zero polynomials for the jth characteristic function $q_j(s)$ are $b_{j0}(s)$ and $b_{j,\,t_j}(s)$ respectively.

5.1. *Example demonstrating the pole-zero relationships*

Let

$$Q(s)=\frac{1}{(s+1)(s+2)(s-1)}\begin{bmatrix}(s-1)(s+2) & 0\\ -(s+1)(s+2) & (s-1)(s+1)\end{bmatrix}$$

$$=\begin{bmatrix}\dfrac{1}{s+1} & 0\\ \dfrac{-1}{s-1} & \dfrac{1}{s+2}\end{bmatrix}$$

The pole polynomial for $Q(s)$ is obviously

$$p(s)=(s+1)(s+2)(s-1)$$

and consequently the zero polynomial is

$$z(s)=(s-1)$$

The characteristic equation for $Q(s)$ is

$$\det\,[qI-Q(s)]=\left(q-\frac{1}{s+1}\right)\left(q-\frac{1}{s+2}\right)=0$$

so that the irreducible characteristic equations are

$$\Delta_1(s,\,q)=q-\frac{1}{s+1}=0$$

and

$$\Delta_2(s,\,q)=q-\frac{1}{s+2}=0$$

which may be written as

$$(s+1)q-1=0$$

and

$$(s+2)q-1=0$$

Therefore the pole and zero polynomials for the characteristic functions $q_1(s)$ and $q_2(s)$ are

$$p_{q_1}(s)=b_{10}(s)=(s+1) \quad z_{q_1}(s)=b_{11}(s)=1$$
$$p_{q_2}(s)=b_{20}(s)=(s+2) \quad z_{q_2}(s)=b_{21}(s)=1$$

Now for $Q(s)$ the least common denominator of all non-zero non-principal minors with all factors common to $b_0(s)$ $(=b_{10}(s)b_{20}(s))$ removed is given by

$$e(s)=(s-1)$$

which verifies the relationships

$$p(s)=e(s)\prod_{i=1}^{2}b_{i0}(s)$$

and

$$z(s)=e(s)\prod_{i=1}^{2}b_{i1}(s)$$

6. Extended principle of the argument

For each characteristic function $q(s)$ there is an appropriate Riemann surface $\mathbf{R}_q$ on which it becomes single-valued, and mappings from the Riemann surface to a q-plane of values are one-to-one and continuous. Suppose a characteristic function $q(s)$ has a defining algebraic equation of order t_j; then $\mathbf{R}_q$ is formed by piecing together t_j copies of the complex plane $\mathbf{C}$. Suppose now that a sub-set of $\mathbf{C}$ defining a closed Jordan contour $\mathbf{J}$ is drawn on every one of these copies of $\mathbf{C}$ before they are pieced together to form $\mathbf{R}_q$. Then, when the Riemann surface is formed, the set of copies of $\mathbf{J}$ will be joined into a set of closed contours on $\mathbf{R}_q$. The exact number of closed contours formed on $\mathbf{R}_q$ will lie between 1 and t_j and will depend on the location of the branch points of the characteristic function with respect to $\mathbf{J}$. Associated with each closed contour on $\mathbf{R}_q$ will be a set of values of the algebraic function $q(s)$ which will define a corresponding set of closed curves in the q-plane ($\mathbf{C}$).

Suppose that $q(s)$ has $^{\#}p$ poles and $^{\#}z$ zeros located within the set of closed contours on $\mathbf{R}_q$. Suppose that when $\mathbf{R}_q$ is formed the t_j copies of $\mathbf{J}$ join into a set of closed contours $\mathbf{A}_1, \mathbf{A}_2, \ldots, \mathbf{A}_l$ on $\mathbf{R}_q$ and that $\mathbf{A}_i$ encloses $^{\#}p_i$ poles and $^{\#}z_i$ zeros of $q(s)$. Let $\mathbf{\Gamma}_1, \mathbf{\Gamma}_2, \ldots, \mathbf{\Gamma}_l$ be the closed image curves in the q-plane corresponding to the closed curves $\mathbf{A}_1, \mathbf{A}_2, \ldots, \mathbf{A}_l$ on $\mathbf{R}_q$. For each closed curve on $\mathbf{R}_q$ the Principle of the Argument will apply and thus :

$$\sum \text{clockwise encirclements of origin by } \mathbf{\Gamma}_i = {}^{\#}z_i - {}^{\#}p_i$$

Thus

$$\text{Total} \sum \text{clockwise encirclements of origin by } \mathbf{\Gamma}_1, \ldots, \mathbf{\Gamma}_l$$
$$= \sum_{i=1}^{l} {}^{\#}z_i - \sum_{i=1}^{l} {}^{\#}p_i = {}^{\#}z - {}^{\#}p$$

7. Characteristic loci

Let $Q(s)$ be an $m \times m$ matrix-valued function of a complex variable. Associated with $Q(s)$ is a set of characteristic functions $\{q_1(s), \ldots, q_k(s)\}$ each having associated with it a corresponding Riemann surface $\mathbf{R}_1, \ldots, \mathbf{R}_k$. Let $\mathbf{D}$ denote the standard Nyquist contour in $\mathbf{C}$, as shown in Fig. 5, and suppose that there is a copy of $\mathbf{D}$ on each of the replicas of $\mathbf{C}$ out of which $\mathbf{R}_1, \ldots, \mathbf{R}_k$ are constructed. Then, associated with the standard Nyquist contour in $\mathbf{C}$ are sets of closed contours on each of the surfaces. Let $\mathbf{N}_1, \ldots, \mathbf{N}_k$ be the

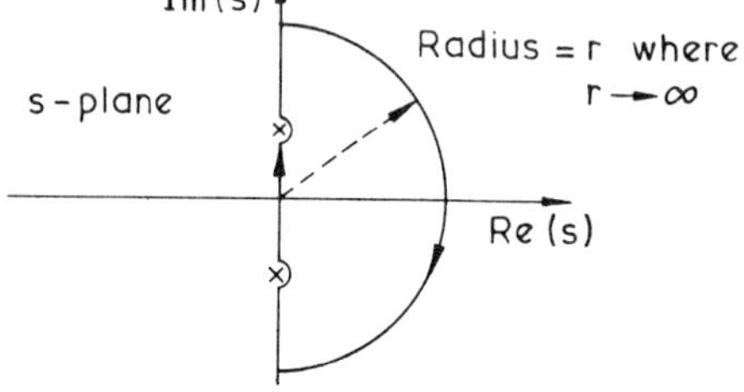

Figure 5. Standard Nyquist contour.

sets of closed image curves in the q-plane corresponding to the sets of closed contours on $\mathbf{R}_1, \ldots, \mathbf{R}_k$; then these subsets $\mathbf{N}_1, \ldots, \mathbf{N}_k$ of $\mathbf{C}$ are defined to be the *characteristic loci* of $Q(s)$ (MacFarlane and Belletrutti 1973).

In practice the characteristic loci are generated as the loci in the complex plane traced out by the eigenvalues of the matrix $Q(s)$ as s traverses the Nyquist contour in the standard (clockwise) direction. Suppose that we consider a portion of the imaginary axis. We can then compute a set of loci corresponding to the eigenvalues $q_1(j\omega), \ldots, q_m(j\omega)$ in the following way :

(i) Select a value of angular frequency, say ω_a.

(ii) Compute the complex matrix $Q(j\omega_a)$.

(iii) Use a standard computer algorithm to compute the eigenvalues of $Q(j\omega_a)$, which are a set of complex numbers denoted by $\{q_i(j\omega_a)\}$.

(iv) Plot the numbers $\{q_i(j\omega_a)\}$ in the complex plane.

(v) Repeat with further values of angular frequency $\omega_b, \omega_c, \ldots$, etc. and join the resulting plots up into continuous loci using a sorting routine based on the continuity of the various branches of the characteristic functions involved.

An example of the characteristic loci for a second order return-ratio matrix is given in Fig. 8 and discussed in § 10.

8. The generalized Nyquist stability criterion

We are now in a position to state and prove the generalized Nyquist stability criterion. The feedback system considered is shown in Fig. 1, and S_1 and S_2 are a pair of linear multivariable dynamical systems whose behaviour is governed by the state-space equation set (2.1) of § 2.

S_1 has m inputs and S_2 has m outputs and the set of feedback loops is broken at the point α. Let $L(s)$ be the system return-ratio matrix (MacFarlane 1970 a) for signals injected at point α and returned at point α'. Let $L(s)$ have a set of characteristic functions $\{l_1(s), l_2(s), \ldots, l_k(s)\}$ with characteristic loci $\mathbf{N}_1, \mathbf{N}_2, \ldots, \mathbf{N}_k$ in the complex plane as s traverses the standard Nyquist contour of Fig. 5 in a clockwise direction. Then we may state the generalized Nyquist criterion in the following form.

Generalized Nyquist stability criterion

Let the multivariable feedback system shown in Fig. 1 have no open-loop uncontrollable and/or unobservable modes whose corresponding characteristic frequencies lie in the right-half plane. Then this configuration will be closed-loop stable if and only if the net sum of anti-clockwise encirclements of the critical point $(-1+j0)$ by the set of characteristic loci of $L(s)$ is equal to the total number of right-half plane poles of $G_1(s)$ and $G_2(s)$.

Since uncontrollable and/or unobservable modes are not influenced by feedback, their possible presence adds a further necessary condition for stability : that all their corresponding characteristic frequencies must be in the left-half plane. In such a case the encirclement criterion above remains necessary but is no longer sufficient for closed-loop stability.

Since we are dealing with a return-ratio matrix, we must be careful, as pointed out by Desoer and Chan (1975), to consider the possibility of pole-zero cancellations between the cascade systems which make up the loop transmittance. The generalized Nyquist stability criterion statement given above, and the proof which follows below, both cope with this situation.

8.1. *Proof of generalized Nyquist criterion*

For the break point shown in Fig. 1 the corresponding return-difference matrix (MacFarlane 1970 a) is

$$F(s) = I_m + L(s) \tag{8.1}$$

Let

$OLCP(s)$ = open-loop characteristic polynomial of complete system with all loops broken at point α, as shown in Fig. 1 (*b*)

$CLCP(s)$ = closed-loop characteristic polynomial of complete system with all feedback loops closed, as shown in Fig. 1 (*a*)

Then, as shown in § 2 we have that

$$\frac{\det F(s)}{\det F(\infty)} = \frac{CLCP(s)}{OLCP(s)} \tag{8.2}$$

The eigenvalues of the return-difference matrix $F(s)$ are given by

$$\det [f(s)I_m - F(s)] = 0 \tag{8.3}$$

which in general, as explained in § 3, can be expressed as a product of irreducible characteristic equations of the form

$$b_{i0}(s)f_i^{t_i} + b_{i1}(s)f_i^{t_i-1} + \dots + b_{it_i}(s) = 0 \quad i = 1, 2, \dots, k \tag{8.4}$$

where the coefficients are polynomials in s. Therefore from § 5 we have that the pole and zero polynomials for $F(s)$ are

$$p(s) = e(s) \prod_{i=1}^{k} b_{i0}(s) \tag{8.5}$$

and

$$z(s) = e(s) \prod_{i=1}^{k} b_{it_i}(s) \tag{8.6}$$

respectively, where $e(s)$ is the least common denominator of all non-zero non-principal minors of $F(s)$, with all factors common to $\prod_{i=1}^{k} b_{i0}(s)$ removed.

By definition, the open-loop characteristic polynomial of the system of Fig. 1 is given by

$$OLCP(s) = \det [sI - A] = \det [sI - A_1] \det [sI - A_2] \tag{8.7}$$

where A, A_1 and A_2 are as defined in § 2. It is easily shown (MacFarlane and Karcanias 1976) that

$$\det [sI - A_i] = p_{G_i}(s) p_{d_i}(s) \quad i = 1, 2 \tag{8.8}$$

where $p_{G_i}(s)$ is the pole polynomial for the transfer function $G_i(s)$ and the polynomial $p_{d_i}(s)$ has as its zeros the decoupling zeros of the system associated with that set of characteristic frequencies (eigenvalues) of A_i which correspond to modes of the system which are uncontrollable and/or unobservable.

Let $p_l(s)$ be the pole polynomial for the return-ratio matrix $L(s)$, then

$$p_{G_1}(s)p_{G_2}(s)=p_l(s)p_x(s) \tag{8.9}$$

where $p_x(s)$ has as its zeros those poles of $G_1(s)$ and $G_2(s)$ which are lost when $L(s)$ is formed (Desoer and Chan 1975). Thus we have that

$$OLCP(s)=p_l(s)p_x(s)p_{d_1}(s)p_{d_2}(s)=p_l(s)p_x(s)p_d(s) \tag{8.10}$$

where

$$p_d(s)=p_{d_1}(s)p_{d_2}(s) \tag{8.11}$$

It is obvious, from an inspection of eqn. (8.1), that the return-ratio matrix $L(s)$ and the corresponding return-difference matrix $F(s)$ have the same poles, and therefore

$$OLCP(s)=p(s)p_x(s)p_d(s) \tag{8.12}$$

giving

$$OLCP(s)=p_x(s)p_d(s)e(s)\prod_{i=1}^{k} b_{i0}(s) \tag{8.13}$$

It then follows, using the fact that

$$\det F(s)=\frac{z(s)}{p(s)} \tag{8.14}$$

and using eqns. (8.2) and (8.6) that the closed-loop characteristic polynomial is given by

$$CLCP(s)=\frac{p_x(s)p_d(s)e(s)\prod_{i=1}^{k} b_{it_i}(s)}{\det F(\infty)} \tag{8.15}$$

An example of a situation in which the polynomial $p_x(s)\neq 1$ is given in Appendix 6.

For the set of irreducible characteristic equations associated with the return-difference operator $F(s)$, there is a corresponding set of Riemann surfaces on which the appropriate characteristic algebraic functions become single-valued, and mappings from these surfaces on to a corresponding f-plane are one-to-one and continuous. Consider the jth equation of the set defined in (8.4). The degree of the equation is t_j and therefore the corresponding Riemann surface $\mathbf{R}_j$ is formed by piecing together t_j copies of the complex s-plane $\mathbf{C}$. Suppose now that a standard Nyquist contour $\mathbf{D}$, as shown in Fig. 5, is drawn on every copy of $\mathbf{C}$ before they are pieced together to form $\mathbf{R}_j$. Then, when $\mathbf{R}_j$ is formed, the set of Nyquist contours will be joined into a set of closed contours on $\mathbf{R}_j$. Since the Principle of the Argument will apply to each closed contour on $\mathbf{R}_j$, the number of clockwise encirclements of the origin in $\mathbf{C}$, by the appropriate image curve, will be the difference between the number of zeros and poles of the characteristic function $f_j(s)$ which are enclosed by the domain curve on $\mathbf{R}_j$. Therefore, considering all the closed contours formed on $\mathbf{R}_j$ from the original Nyquist contour set, and applying the Argument Principle to each gives that

$$n_{f_j} = z_{f_j} - p_{f_j} \tag{8.16}$$

where :

(i) n_{f_j} is the net sum of clockwise encirclements of the origin in $\mathbf{C}$ by the set of image curves under f_j of the set of curves formed on $\mathbf{R}_j$ by piecing together the appropriate set of Nyquist contours when forming $\mathbf{R}_j$;

(ii) z_{f_j} is the number of right-half plane zeros of $f_j(s)$; and

(iii) p_{f_j} is the number of right-half plane poles of $f_j(s)$.

From eqn. (8.15) we have that necessary and sufficient conditions for the closed-loop stability of the feedback configuration shown in Fig. 1 are that

(*a*) $e(s)=0$ has no roots in the right-half plane ;

(*b*) $\prod_{i=1}^{k} b_{it_i}(s)=0$ has no roots in the right-half plane ;

(*c*) $p_x(s)=0$ has no roots in the right-half plane ; and

(*d*) $p_d(s)=0$ has no roots in the right-half plane.

Condition (*b*) is equivalent to saying that there are no zeros of

$$\{f_i(s) : i=1, 2, \ldots, k\}$$

in the right-half plane, and can therefore be replaced by

$$z_{f_i}=0 \qquad i=1, 2, \ldots, k \tag{8.17}$$

or

$$n_{f_i} = -p_{f_i} \quad i=1, 2, \ldots, k \tag{8.18}$$

which imply, and are implied by,

$$\sum_{i=1}^{k} n_{f_i} = -\sum_{i=1}^{k} p_{f_i} \tag{8.19}$$

We therefore conclude that an equivalent set of necessary and sufficient conditions for closed-loop stability are that

(*a*) $e(s)=0$ has no roots in the right-half plane ;

(*b*) $\sum_{i=1}^{k} n_{f_i} = -\sum_{i=1}^{k} p_{f_i}$;

(*c*) $p_x(s)=0$ has no roots in the right-half plane ; and

(*d*) $p_d(s)=0$ has no roots in the right-half plane.

Now, as shown by eqn. (8.5), $e(s)$ together with the set of pole polynomials for the set of characteristic functions $\{f_i(s) : i=1, 2, \ldots, k\}$ make up the pole polynomial for $F(s)$.

This leads us to consider combining the three conditions (*a*), (*b*) and (*c*) into the single equivalent condition

$$\sum_{i=1}^{k} n_{f_i} = -p \tag{8.20}$$

where p is the total number of right-half plane poles of $G_1(s)$ and $G_2(s)$.

Now the uncontrollable and/or unobservable parts of the system will not be affected by the feedback. We therefore confine our attention to the case where $p_d(s)=0$ has no roots in the right-half plane.

Necessity and sufficiency of condition (8.20) *for closed-loop stability when* $p_d(s)=0$ *has no roots in the right-half plane*

We have that

$$\sum_{i=1}^{k} n_{f_i} = \sum_{i=1}^{k} z_{f_i} - \sum_{i=1}^{k} p_{f_i} \tag{8.21}$$

and

$$p = \sum_{i=1}^{k} p_{f_i} + e + p_x \tag{8.22}$$

where e is the number of right-half plane roots of

$$e(s)=0 \tag{8.23}$$

and p_x is the number of right-half plane roots of

$$p_x(s)=0 \tag{8.24}$$

Combining the two relationships (8.21) and (8.22) we thus have

$$\sum_{i=1}^{k} n_{f_i} = \sum_{i=1}^{k} z_{f_i} + e + p_x - p \tag{8.25}$$

where $\sum_{i=1}^{k} z_{f_i}$, e, p_x and p are all positive integers or zero.

To establish the necessity of (8.20) suppose that

$$\sum_{i=1}^{k} n_{f_i} \neq -p$$

Then, from (8.25), this implies that

$$\sum_{i=1}^{k} z_{f_i} \neq 0, \quad \text{or} \quad e \neq 0, \quad \text{or} \quad p_x \neq 0$$

or any combination of these, and thus that the system will be closed-loop unstable. Hence we conclude that (8.20) is necessary for closed-loop stability.

For sufficiency suppose that

$$\sum_{i=1}^{k} n_{f_i} = -p$$

Then, from (8.25) we must have that

$$p_x = e = \sum_{i=1}^{k} z_{f_i} = 0$$

and hence that the system is closed-loop stable. Thus the sufficiency of condition (8.20) is established.

We have therefore shown that, when $p_d(s)=0$ has no roots in the right-half plane,

$$\sum_{i=1}^{k} n_{f_i} = -p$$

is a necessary and sufficiency condition for closed-loop stability. Now, using the eigenvalue shift theorem (MacFarlane 1970 b) we have that the characteristic functions $\{f_i(s) : i=1, 2, \ldots, k\}$ of $F(s)$ and $\{l_i(s) : i=1, 2, \ldots, k\}$ of $L(s)$ are related by

$$f_i(s) = 1 + l_i(s), \quad i=1, 2, \ldots, k \tag{8.26}$$

The image curve sets in $\mathbf{C}$ of the Nyquist contour sets mapped under $f_i(s)$ and $l_i(s)$ are therefore simply related by a unit horizontal shift in $\mathbf{C}$. Hence if n_{l_j} is defined as the net sum of clockwise encirclements of the critical point $(-1+j0)$ in $\mathbf{C}$ by the set of characteristic loci of $L(s)$ corresponding to the jth characteristic function, then the necessary and sufficient conditions for closed-loop stability in the case where $p_d(s)=0$ has no roots in the right-half plane simply become

$$\sum_{i=1}^{k} n_{l_i} = -p \tag{8.27}$$

Adding the obvious necessary qualifications regarding the role of uncontrollable and/or unobservable unstable open-loop modes then completes the proof of the generalized Nyquist stability criterion.

In the previous treatments of the generalized Nyquist stability criterion (MacFarlane and Belletrutti 1973) the necessary conditions on the uncontrollable and unobservable unstable modes are incorporated in the encirclement theorem : the closed-loop system is stable if and only if the net sum of anti-clockwise encirclements of the critical point $(-1+j0)$ by the set of characteristic loci of $L(s)$ is equal to the number of right-half plane zeros of $OLCP(s)$. The equivalence of this theorem with the stability criterion presented in this paper is established in Appendix 5 where a rigorous proof is given for the early statement of the generalized Nyquist stability criterion.

9. Multivariable root loci and their associated Riemann surfaces

Consider the feedback system shown in Fig. 6, where the linear dyanmical system S_1 has m inputs and S_2 has m outputs ; k is a scalar gain multiplier. Let $L(s)$ be the system return-ratio matrix for signals injected at point α and returned at point α' with $k=1$.

The return-difference for this configuration is given by

$$F(s, k) = I_m + kL(s) \tag{9.1}$$

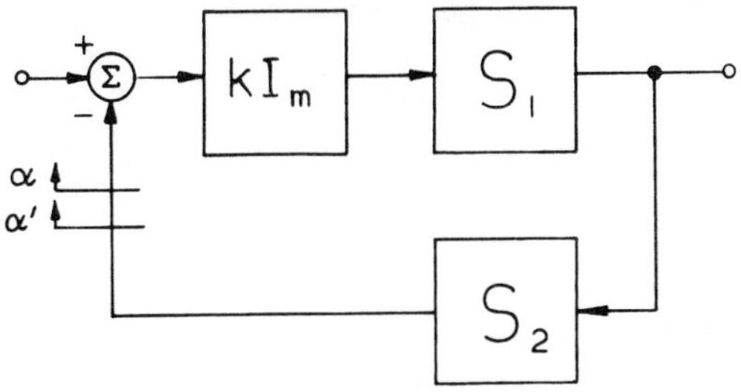

Figure 6. Multivariable feedback configuration with scalar gain k.

and the set of characteristic functions associated with this return-difference matrix are defined by

$$\det [f(s, k)I_m - F(s, k)] = 0 \tag{9.2}$$

Assume, for simplicity of exposition, that there is just one irreducible characteristic equation of the form

$$b_0(s)f^m(s, k) + b_1(s, k)f^{m-1}(s, k) + \ldots + b_m(s, k) = 0 \tag{9.3}$$

Denoting the system's open-loop and closed-loop characteristic polynomials by $OLCP(s)$ and $CLCP(s, k)$ respectively we will have that

$$\frac{\det F(s, k)}{\det F(\infty, k)} = \frac{CLCP(s, k)}{OLCP(s)} = \frac{b_m(s, k)}{b_0(s)} \tag{9.4}$$

and also that

$$OLCP(s) = p_x(s)p_d(s)e(s)b_0(s) \tag{9.5}$$

where $e(s)$ is here defined as the least common denominator of all non-zero non-principal minors of $L(s)$ with all factors common to $b_0(s)$ removed, $p_d(s)$ has as its zeros the decoupling zeros of the system, and $p_x(s)$ has as its zeros those poles of $G_1(s)$ and $G_2(s)$ which are lost when $L(s)$ is formed. In § 8, $e(s)$ was defined in terms of $F(s)$. It is shown in Appendix 6 that it is immaterial whether $e(s)$ is defined for $F(s)$ or $L(s)$ since the same polynomial results in either case.

It therefore follows that

$$CLCP(s, k) = \frac{p_x(s)p_d(s)e(s)b_m(s, k)}{\det F(\infty, k)} \tag{9.6}$$

so that the solution of the equation

$$p_x(s)p_d(s)e(s)b_m(s, k) = 0 \tag{9.7}$$

for s in terms of k will determine the dependence of the closed-loop poles on the scalar feedback gain parameter k. The graphical exhibition of this dependence in the complex plane is what constitutes the multivariable root loci of this system.

Note that for any value of k the solutions of

$$p_x(s)=0 \tag{9.8}$$

$$p_d(s)=0 \tag{9.9}$$

and

$$e(s)=0 \tag{9.10}$$

are solutions of eqn. (9.7). Thus for $e(s)\neq 1$ (an unusual condition) and/or $p_d(s)\neq 1$ (indicating unobservable and/or uncontrollable modes) and/or $p_x(s)\neq 1$ (indicating pole cancellations) some of the root loci degenerate to single points, these being the solutions of eqns. (9.8), (9.9) and (9.10). The other solutions of eqn. (9.7), which satisfy

$$b_m(s, k)=0 \tag{9.11}$$

are equivalent to finding the zeros of the characteristic function $f(s, k)$. If $l(s, k)$ is the characteristic function of $kL(s)$ (assumed irreducible), then the eigenvalue shift theorem gives us that

$$f(s, k)=1+l(s, k) \tag{9.12}$$

and thus finding the zeros of $f(s, k)$ is equivalent to finding those values of s for which

$$l(s, k)=-1 \tag{9.13}$$

The multivariable root loci for the feedback configuration of Fig. 6 are therefore defined by the solutions of

$$p_x(s)=0 \tag{9.14}$$

$$p_d(s)=0 \tag{9.15}$$

$$e(s)=0 \tag{9.16}$$

and

$$l(s, k)=-1 \tag{9.17}$$

for all values of k.

Now the characteristic equation for $L(s)$, the system return-ratio matrix with $k=1$, is

$$\det\,[l(s)I_m-L(s)]=0 \tag{9.18}$$

from which we can obtain the equation

$$c_0(s)l^m(s)+c_1(s)l^{m-1}(s)+\ldots+c_m(s)=0 \tag{9.19}$$

where the coefficients $\{c_i(s):\ i=1, 2, \ldots, m\}$ are polynomials in s. The characteristic equation for $kL(s)$ is given by

$$c_0(s)l^m(s)+c_1(s)kl^{m-1}(s)+\ldots+c_m(s)k^m=0 \tag{9.20}$$

Thus the introduction of the scalar gain multiplier k is equivalent to multiplying the characteristic function $l(s)$ by k. Thus the solutions of eqn. (9.17) are equivalent to those of

$$l(s)=-\frac{1}{k} \tag{9.21}$$

for all values of k, which is obviously a direct generalization of the defining equations for the single-loop root locus.

It is clear from this discussion that the complex loci defined by eqn. (9.21) are simply the 180° phase loci of the characteristic function $l(s)$ on its associated Riemann surface. The fact that multivariable root loci ' live ' on a Riemann surface explains their complicated behaviour (Kouvaritakis and Shaked 1976) as compared with the single-input single-output case, where the root loci lie in a simple complex plane. In the general case, there will be several irreducible characteristic equations for a given $L(s)$ and thus associated with a given $L(s)$ there will normally be several sets of root loci each on a different Riemann surface. It is also interesting to note that, when $e(s) \neq 1$, or $p_d(s) \neq 1$, or $p_x(s) \neq 1$ there will also be degenerate loci each consisting of a single point, a feature not present in the single-input single-output case. Note that the single point loci associated with $e(s)$ and $p_x(s)$ can be removed with feedback whereas those associated with $p_d(s)$ are invariant.

We have that

$$CLCP(s) = \frac{p_x(s)p_d(s)e(s) \prod_{i=1}^{k} b_{i0}(s)}{\det F(\infty)} \tag{9.22}$$

Now the solutions of

$$\prod_{i=1}^{k} b_{i0}(s) = 0 \tag{9.23}$$

are the zeros of $f_i(s)$ and are also values of s at which

$$l_i(s) = -1 \tag{9.24}$$

Consequently those points on the sheets of the Riemann surface at which the 0 dB contours cut the 180° phase contours are closed-loop poles of the system with direct unit-gain negative feedback. Note that, due to the presence of the factors $p_d(s)$, $p_x(s)$ and $e(s)$ in eqn. (9.22), not all the closed-loop poles appear on the Riemann surface.

10. An example of the generalized Nyquist stability criterion with Riemann surface construction and multivariable root loci illustration

As an illustrative example (Kontakos 1973) consider the standard multivariable feedback configuration of Fig. 7, where

$$G(s) = \frac{1}{1{\cdot}25(s+1)(s+2)} \begin{bmatrix} (s-1) & s \\ -6 & (s-2) \end{bmatrix}, \quad K(s) = kI_2 \quad \text{and} \quad H(s) = I_2$$

The pole polynomial for $G_1(s)$ $[=kG(s)]$ is

$$p_{G_1}(s) = (s+1)(s+2)$$

and for $G_2(s)[=H(s)]$ is

$$P_{G_2}(s) = 1$$

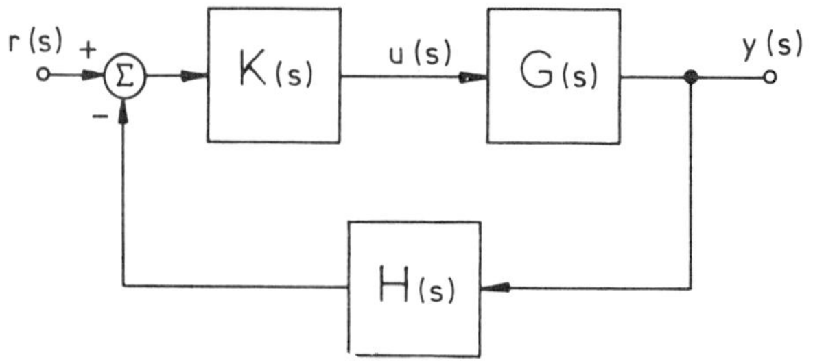

Figure 7. Standard multivariable feedback configuration.

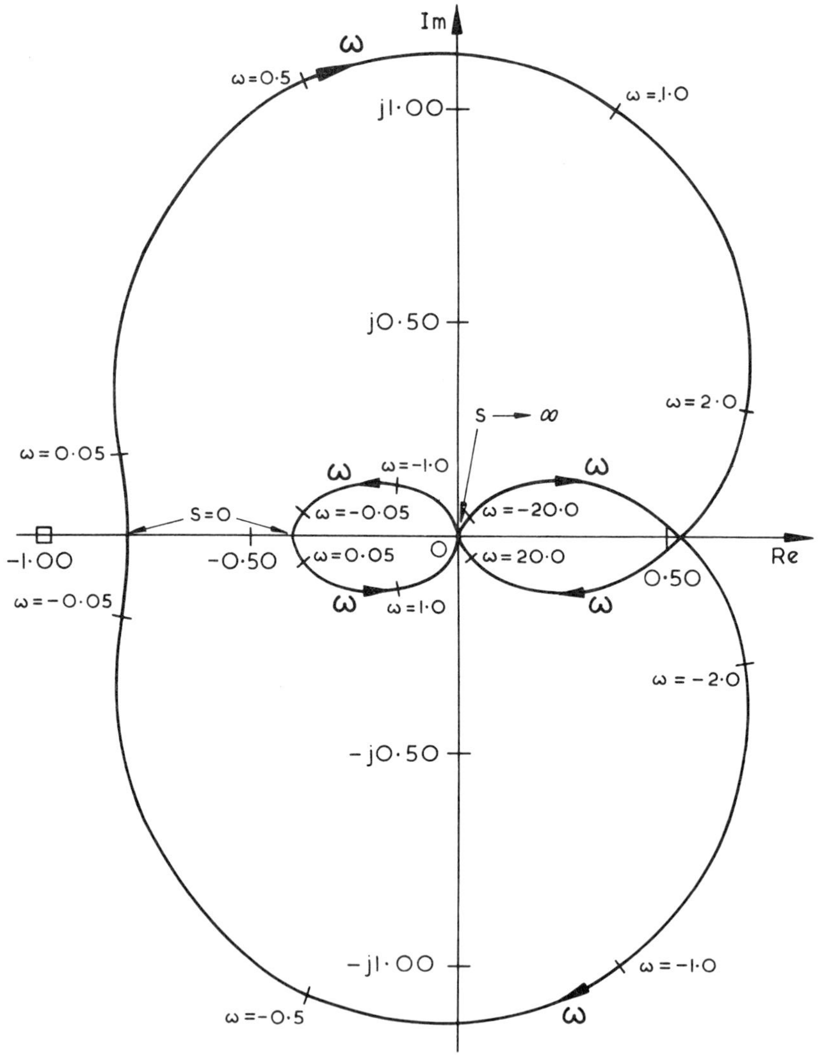

Figure 8. Example (§ 10) of characteristic loci.

and therefore the total number of poles in the right-half plane for $G_1(s)$ and $G_2(s)$ is $p=0$ and closed-loop stability will be ensured if

$$\sum_{i=1}^{k'} n_{l_i}=0$$

The characteristic loci of $L(s)$ [$=G(s)$ for $k=1$] are shown in Fig. 8.

Taking the critical point as $(-1/k, 0)$ the following stability conditions are obtained.

(i) For $-\infty < -1/k < -0{\cdot}8$ there are no encirclements of the critical point

$$\sum_{i=1}^{k'} n_{l_i}=0$$

and thus the closed loop system is stable for $0 \leqslant k < 1{\cdot}25$.

(ii) For $-0{\cdot}8 \leqslant -1/k \leqslant 0{\cdot}4$ there is one encirclement of the critical point, and therefore the system is closed-loop unstable for $1{\cdot}25 \leqslant k \leqslant 2{\cdot}5$.

(iii) For $-0{\cdot}4 < -1/k \leqslant 0$ the net sum of clockwise encirclements is zero,

$$\sum_{i=1}^{k'} n_{l_i}=0$$

and thus the closed-loop system is stable for $2{\cdot}5 < k < \infty$.

(iv) For $0 \leqslant -1/k \leqslant 0{\cdot}533$ there are two clockwise encirclements of the critical point and therefore the system is closed-loop unstable for $-\infty < k \leqslant -1{\cdot}875$.

(v) For $0{\cdot}533 < -1/k < \infty$ there are no encirclements of the critical point,

$$\sum_{i=1}^{k'} n_{l_i}=0$$

and thus the closed-loop system is stable for $-1{\cdot}875 < k \leqslant 0$. Note that conditions (iv) and (v) correspond to positive feedback.

The system exhibits the conditionally stable characteristic familiar in scalar feedback control systems. On increasing the gain (equally in both loops) the closed-loop system experiences stability, instability, and stability again. This phenomenon is linked with the presence of a branch point in the right-half plane (at $s=1/24$). The role of the branch point is best illustrated by looking at the Riemann surface corresponding to $L(s)$.

The two sheets of the surface are shown in Figs. 9 and 10, with constant phase and magnitude contours of $l(s)$ shown to emphasise the position of the cuts. The 180° phase contours are obviously the multivariable root loci and imply possible instability by being partly in the right-half plane on both sheets. The root locus branch starting at the -1 pole on sheet one moves with increasing gain into the right-half plane, implying instability; passes through the branch point to sheet two, still implying instability; and then moves into the stable left-half plane and off to infinity. The crossings of the imaginary axis into the right-half plane of sheet one, and out of the right-half plane of sheet two, are for $k=1{\cdot}25$ and $k=2{\cdot}5$ respectively. Therefore the system is closed-loop unstable for $1{\cdot}25 \leqslant k \leqslant 2{\cdot}5$ which is the condition obtained from the characteristic loci of $L(s)$.

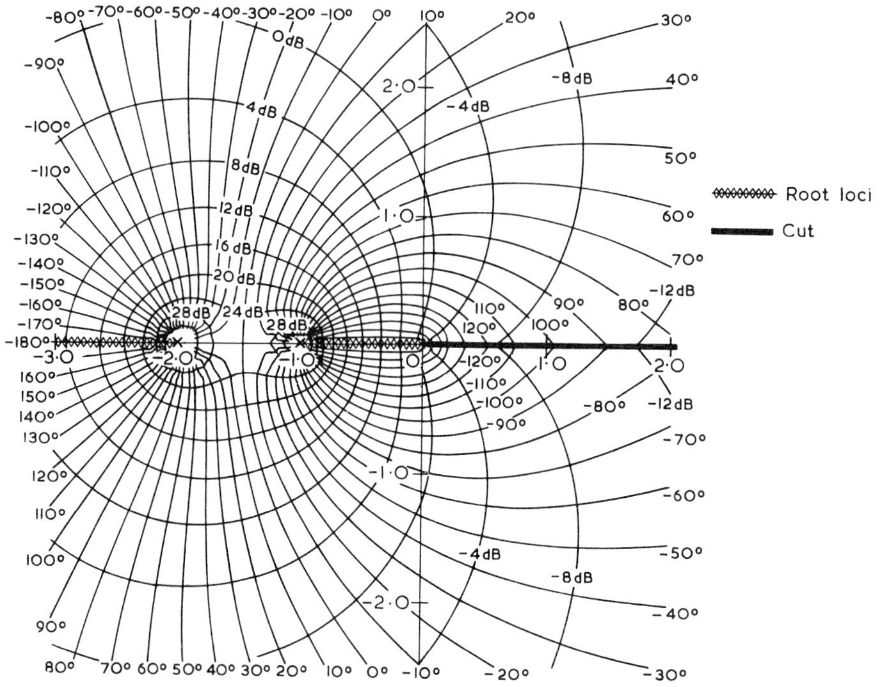

Figure 9. Sheet 1 of the Riemann surface for the example in § 10.

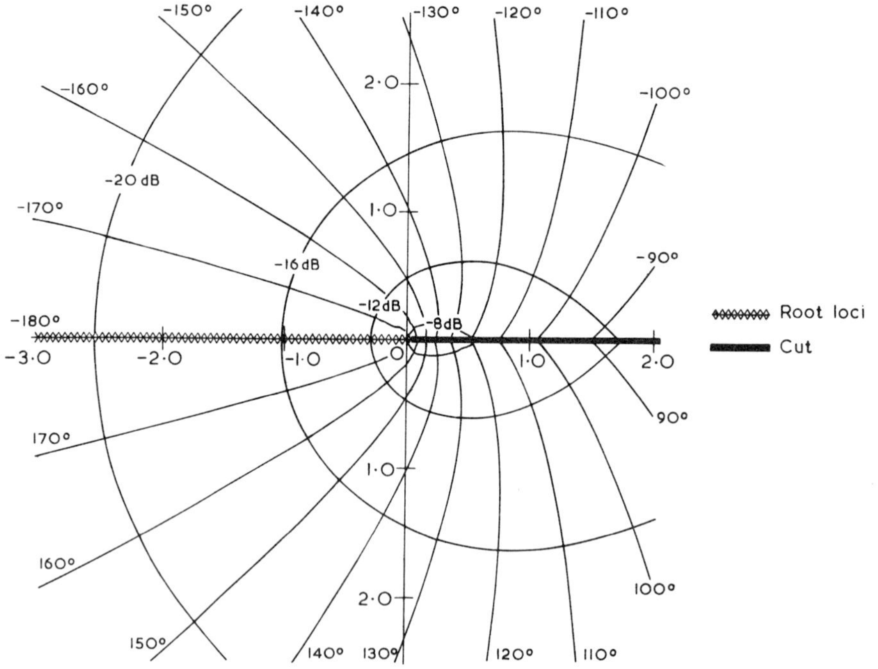

Figure 10. Sheet 2 of the Riemann surface for the example in § 10.

The movement of the root loci from poles to ' zeros at infinity ' is in agreement with work carried out by Kouvaritakis and Shaked (1976) on the asymptotic behaviour of the root loci of linear multivariable systems. Kouvaritakis and Shaked (1976) also pointed out that contrary to the scalar case the multivariable root loci can not only cross each other but two or more loci may even coincide in part. This is the case when the root loci are projected onto a single complex plane but when viewed on the Riemann surface the root loci can never cut each other, as demonstrated in Figs. 9 and 10.

A characteristic equation defining a single characteristic function $l(s)$ can equally well be viewed as an equation defining a single algebraic function $s(l)$ (assuming irreducibility). A Riemann surface, which is a domain for $s(l)$, can then be conceived and used to display constant phase and magnitude contours of $s(l)$. If $l(s)$ corresponds to a return-ratio matrix $L(s)$, then the 90° and -90° phase contours of $s(l)$ obviously represent the characteristic loci for $L(s)$. Therefore viewing the characteristic loci on appropriate surfaces they appear never to cut each other, as with the root loci on their corresponding surfaces.

For an open-loop stable system (i.e. $p=0$), it is necessary for closed-loop stability that the characteristic loci do not encircle the critical point $(-1+j0)$. If the characteristic loci are considered as subsets of points on an appropriate Riemann surface punctured by removal of the $-1+j0$ points, then it is sufficient for closed-loop stability that on this punctured surface the image of the Nyquist D-contour bounded by the characteristic loci can be continuously deformed into a point. This topological description of the criterion is intuitively more satisfying than considering an encirclement criterion for loci in $\mathbf{C}$. It arose out of a discussion between one of the authors (I.P.) and Professor R. Saeks of his generalized approach to Nyquist-type criteria (Saeks 1975) which uses such topological arguments.

Appendix 1

A reduction to the irreducible rational canonical form

In this Appendix a proposed method is given for reducing any m-square matrix to its *irreducible* rational canonical form. The method used is a variation on that given by Ayres (1965) for finding the rational canonical form of a square matrix. The rational canonical form of a square matrix Q is similar to the irreducible form except that its diagonal blocks correspond to the invariant factors of $qI-Q$, rather than the irreducible factors. The procedure given by Ayres (1965) for finding the rational canonical form is outlined below along with some necessary definitions.

Definitions

If the vectors

$$X, QX, Q^2X, \ldots, Q^{t-1}X \tag{A 1}$$

are linearly independent but

$$X, QX, Q^2X, \ldots, Q^{t-1}X, Q^tX \tag{A 2}$$

are not, then (A 1) is called a *chain* of length t having X as its *leader.*

Procedure

For a given m-square matrix Q over any field F :

(i) let X_m be the leader of a chain C_m of *maximum* length for all m-vectors over F ;

(ii) let X_{m-1} be the leader of a chain C_{m-1} of *maximum* length (any member of which is linearly independent of the preceding members and those of C_m) for all m-vectors over F which are linearly independent of the vectors of C_m ;

(iii) let X_{m-2} be the leader of a chain C_{m-2} of *maximum* length (any member of which is linearly independent of the preceding members and those of C_m and C_{m-1}) for all m-vectors over F which are linearly independent of the vectors C_m and C_{m-1} ; and so on. Then, for

$$T=[X_j, QX_j, \ldots, Q^{t_j-1}X_j ;\ X_{j+1}, QX_{j+1}, \ldots, Q^{t_{j+1}-1}X_{j+1} ;\ \ldots ;\ X_m, QX_m, \ldots, Q^{t_m-1}X_m]$$

we have that $T^{-1}QT$ is the rational canonical form of Q.

In this approach the chains of maximum length are used to pick out the invariant factors. Now the invariant factors are made up from products of the irreducible characteristic equations which are required in the irreducible rational canonical form. Therefore, if instead of using chains of maximum length those of *minimum* length are found, the transformation matrix T so formed is that required to give the irreducible rational canonical form R.

The problem with both of these methods is that no indication is given which enables one to know when a chain of maximum or minimum length has been obtained, except that in the contrary case there will appear a chain of longer or shorter length.

It is interesting to note that the chains of maximum and minimum length form bases for the Q-invariant subspaces of maximum and minimum dimensions respectively. Therefore the problem of finding the chains of minimum length is equivalent to that of finding the invariant subspaces of minimum dimension. It also happens that just as the 1-dimensional invariant subspace (eigenvector) picks out an eigenvalue, a t-dimensional invariant subspace (from the set of those of minimum dimensions) picks out an irreducible equation of degree t, defining t eigenvalues.

Example

To find the irreducible rational canonical form of

$$Q(s)=\begin{bmatrix} \dfrac{(s+3)}{(s+1)^2} & \dfrac{(s+2)}{(s+1)^2} & 0 \\ \dfrac{(s-3)}{(s+1)^2} & \dfrac{-2}{(s+1)^2} & 0 \\ \dfrac{-1}{(s+1)^2} & \dfrac{-(s+2)}{2(s+1)^2} & \dfrac{1}{s+1} \end{bmatrix}$$

Let $X=(0\ 0\ 1)^t$, where ' t ' denotes the transpose, then

$$QX=\frac{1}{(s+1)}X$$

and X is a chain of minimum length.

Let

$$Y=(0\ 1\ 0)^t$$

then

$$QY=\begin{bmatrix}\frac{s+2}{(s+1)^2} & \frac{-2}{(s+1)^2} & \frac{-(s+2)}{2(s+1)^2}\end{bmatrix}^t$$

and

$$Q^2Y=\begin{bmatrix}\frac{s+2}{(s+1)^3} & \frac{s-2}{(s+1)^3} & \frac{-(s+2)}{2(s+1)^3}\end{bmatrix}^t=\frac{1}{(s+1)}QY+\frac{s}{(s+1)^3}Y$$

No chain of smaller length can be found and therefore Y, QY completes the set of minimum length chains. The transformation matrix $T(s)$ is therefore given by

$$T(s)=[X\ Y\ QY]=\begin{bmatrix}0 & 0 & \frac{s+2}{(s+1)^2}\\ 0 & 1 & \frac{-2}{(s+1)^2}\\ 1 & 0 & \frac{-(s+2)}{2(s+1)^2}\end{bmatrix}$$

and

$$R(s)=T^{-1}(s)Q(s)T(s)$$

$$=\begin{bmatrix}\frac{1}{s+1} & 0 & 0\\ 0 & 0 & \frac{s}{(s+1)^3}\\ 0 & 1 & \frac{1}{(s+1)}\end{bmatrix}$$

which implies that the irreducible characteristic equations are

$$\Delta_1(s,g)=g-\frac{1}{s+1}$$

$$\Delta_2(s,g)=g^2-\frac{1}{(s+1)}g-\frac{s}{(s+1)^3}$$

Note that these are also obvious from the dependence relations obtained when finding the chains of minimum length.

Appendix 2

The discriminant

In this Appendix two methods are given for finding the discriminant of an equation of the form

$$b(s, q) = b_0(s)q^t + b_1(s)q^{t-1} + \dots + b_t(s)$$

Method 1 (Barnett 1971)

The resultant $R[a(q), c(q)]$ of two polynomials $a(q)$ and $c(q)$ given by

$$a(q) = a_0q^n + a_1q^{n-1} + \dots + a_n$$
$$c(q) = c_0q^m + c_1q^{m-1} + \dots + c_m$$

where $a_i, c_i \in \mathbf{C}$ is the determinant

$$R[a(q), c(q)] = \left| \begin{array}{cccccccccc} a_0 & a_1 & a_2 \cdots & & & & a_n & 0 & & \\ 0 & a_0 & a_1 \cdots & & & & a_{n-1} & a_n & & \\ \cdot & \cdot & \cdot\ \cdots & & & & & & & \\ \cdot & \cdot & \cdot\ \cdots & & & & & & a_{n-1} & a_n \\ \cdot & \cdot & \cdot\ \cdots & & & c_0 & c_1 & & c_{m-1} & c_m \\ \cdot & \cdot & \cdot\ \cdots & c_0 & c_1 & c_2 & & & c_m & 0 \\ \cdot & \cdot & \cdot\ \cdots & & & & & & & \\ c_0 & c_1 & c_2 \cdots & & & & & & & \end{array} \right| \begin{array}{l} \updownarrow\ m \text{ rows} \\ \\ \\ \\ \updownarrow\ n \text{ rows} \end{array}$$

The polynomials $a(q)$ and $c(q)$ have a common factor (of degree greater than zero) if and only if the $(n+m)$-order determinant $R[a(q), c(q)]$ is zero, provided that a_0 and c_0 are not both zero.

Let the derivative with respect to q of the polynomial $a(q)$ be denoted by $a'(q)$. Then the discriminant of the polynomial $a(q)$ is the determinant $D_q(a_0, a_1, \dots, a_n)$ defined by

$$D_q(a_0, \dots, a_n) = \frac{1}{a_0} R[a(q), a'(q)]$$

The polynomial $a(q)$ has a repeated factor if and only if the discriminant $D_q(a_0, \dots, a_n)$ is zero.

Now consider a polynomial of the type

$$b(s, q) = b_0(s)q^t + b_1(s)q^{t-1} + \dots + b_t(s), \quad t > 0$$

where the coefficients $\{b_i(s) : i = 1, 2, \dots, t\}$ are all polynomials in s. The discriminant of this polynomial in q is found from $D_q(b_0, b_1, \dots, b_t)$ as defined above by replacing $b_0, \dots, b_t$ by $b_0(s), \dots, b_t(s)$ respectively. Thus there is a function $D_q(s)$, again called the discriminant and defined by

$$D_q(s) = \frac{1}{b_0(s)} R[b(s, q), b'(s, q)]$$

where $b'(s, q)$ is the derivative with respect to q of $b(s, q)$.

Method 2 (Sansone and Gerretsen 1969)

Consider the polynomial

$$a(q) = a_0q^n + a_1q^{n-1} + \dots + a_n, \quad n > 0$$

where $a_i \in \mathbf{C}$; then the discriminant of $a(q)$ is given by the expression

$$D_q(a_0, \ldots, a_n) = a_0^{2n-2} P$$

where P is a determinant given by

$$P = \begin{vmatrix} \sigma_0 & \sigma_1 \cdots & \sigma_{n-1} \\ \sigma_1 & \sigma_2 \cdots & \sigma_n \\ \cdot & \cdot \quad \cdot & \cdot \\ \sigma_{n-1} & \sigma_n \cdots & \sigma_{2n-2} \end{vmatrix}$$

and the elements $\{\sigma_i : i = 1, 2, \ldots, 2n-2\}$ are functions of the coefficients $\{a_i : i = 0, 1, \ldots, n\}$, and

$$\sigma_0 = n$$

The elements $\sigma_1, \ldots, \sigma_{n-1}$ can be found from

$$\begin{aligned} a_1 + a_0\sigma_1 &= 0 \\ 2a_2 + a_1\sigma_1 + a_0\sigma_2 &= 0 \\ \cdots\cdots\cdots\cdots\cdots\cdots & \\ (n-1)a_{n-1} + a_{n-2}\sigma_1 \ldots + a_0\sigma_{n-1} &= 0 \end{aligned}$$

and $\sigma_n, \ldots, \sigma_{2n-2}$ from

$$\begin{aligned} a_n\sigma_0 + a_{n-1}\sigma_1 + \ldots + a_0\sigma_n &= 0 \\ a_n\sigma_1 + a_{n-1}\sigma_2 + \ldots + a_0\sigma_{n+1} &= 0 \\ \cdots\cdots\cdots\cdots\cdots\cdots & \\ a_n\sigma_m + a_{n-1}\sigma_{m+1} + \ldots + a_0\sigma_{n+m} &= 0 \\ \cdots\cdots\cdots\cdots\cdots\cdots & \end{aligned}$$

Consider now the polynomial $b(s, q)$ given by

$$b(s, q) = b_0(s)q^t + b_1(s)q^{t-1} + \ldots + b_t(s)$$

The discriminant of this polynomial in q is found from $D_q(b_0, \ldots, b_t)$ as defined above by replacing $b_0, \ldots, b_t$ by $b_0(s), \ldots, b_t(s)$ respectively. The polynomial $b(s, q)$ therefore has repeated factors if and only if

$$D_q(s) = b_0^{2t-2}(s)P$$

is zero, where P is the determinant of a matrix whose elements are functions of the coefficients $\{b_i(s) : i = 0, 1, 2, \ldots, t\}$.

Appendix 3

A method for constructing the Riemann surfaces of the characteristic functions corresponding to a transfer-function matrix

In § 3 it was shown that for a characteristic function of degree t the corresponding Riemann surface is made up from t sheets of the complex s-plane stitched together along cuts made between branch points and infinity. Although the cuts are in some sense arbitrary (i.e. there is no unique set of cuts), it is still a problem to choose a set that is consistent, and then to be able to identify in what order the sheets are connected together. In this Appendix a systematic method is given for solving this problem. The method is quite elegant in that the resulting cuts are symmetrical about the real axis and are always parallel to the imaginary axis except for possible cuts along the real axis. Also, the approach uses the transfer function matrix directly, so that there is no need to find the characteristic equations, and the resulting non-connected sets of connected sheets represent the Riemann surfaces for the irreducible characteristic equations.

The method is based on finding the eigenvalues of the matrix for a grid of values covering the s-plane and then sorting the eigenvalues in a continuous form along certain lines of the grid. If the transfer function is of order $m \times m$, m arrays which will effectively represent the m sheets of the Riemann surfaces are needed to store the eigenvalues. The process is analogous to the analytic continuation procedure described in § 3 where individual points of a circular disc are made bearers of unique functional values. Here individual points of the s-plane sheets (arrays) are being made the bearers of functional values.

The first line along which the eigenvalues are calculated and sorted is the real axis, and then the calculation and sorting are carried out along lines parallel to the imaginary axis and emanating from the real axis, as shown in Fig. 11. The calculation is only necessary in the upper-half plane since the eigenvalues in the lower-half plane are the complex conjugate of those in the upper half. Continuing this process the s-plane is covered, and m arrays of eigenvalues are obtained which are continuous along the real axis and along lines parallel to the imaginary axis but not necessarily crossing the real axis.

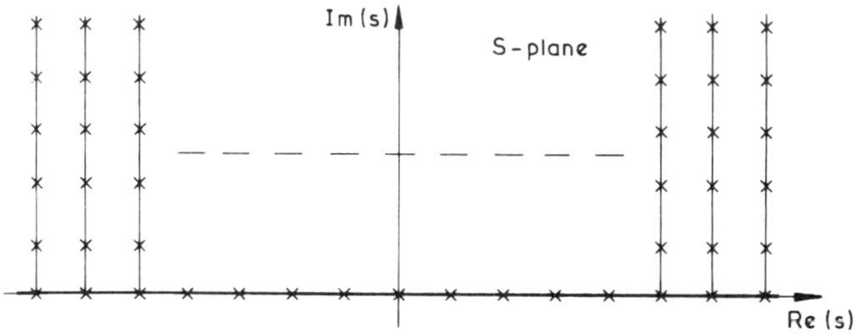

Figure 11. Lines along which eigenvalues are calculated and sorted. ×——× indicates continuity between eigenvalues.

By observation of each array or sheet the necessary cuts are obvious. If parallel to the imaginary axis a line of eigenvalues is not continuous with an adjacent line then these must be separated by a cut starting at a branch point and ending at a branch point or infinity as shown in Figs. 12 and 13. Eigenvalues corresponding to values of s in the upper-half plane are complex conjugate to those in the lower-half plane and therefore continuity of eigenvalues across the real axis is impossible if the eigenvalues situated on the real axis are complex. Therefore a cut along the real axis is necessary whenever the real axis eigenvalues are complex. Again all the cuts start at a branch point and end at a branch point or infinity, as shown in Fig. 14.

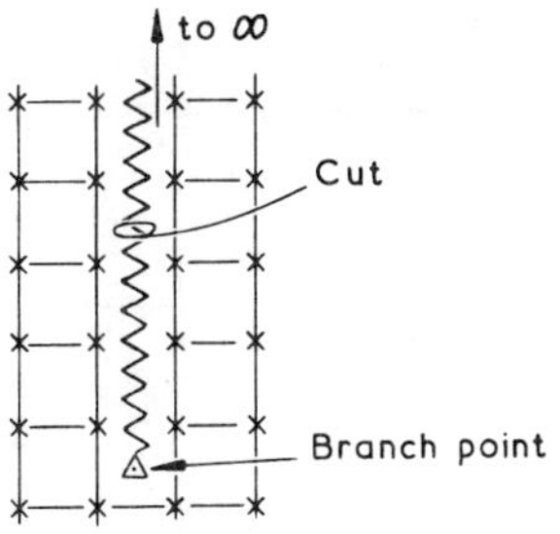

Figure 12. Infinite cut parallel to the imaginary axis. ×——× indicates continuity between eigenvalues.

The stitching together of the sheets also becomes obvious by matching eigenvalues on one side of a cut on one sheet to those on another. When the matching process is complete, in general, there will be sets of connected sheets each set defining a Riemann surface.

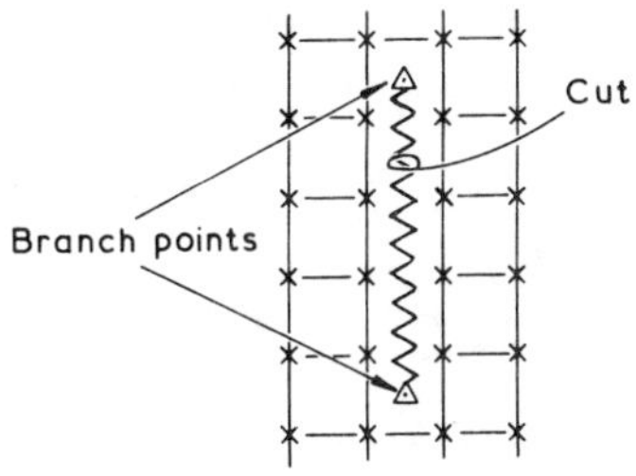

Figure 13. Finite cut parallel to the imaginary axis. ×——× indicates continuity between eigenvalues.

To facilitate the identification of cuts and the matching of sheets it is very useful to draw the constant phase and constant magnitude contours on each sheet ; this is demonstrated in the example given in § 10 of the paper.

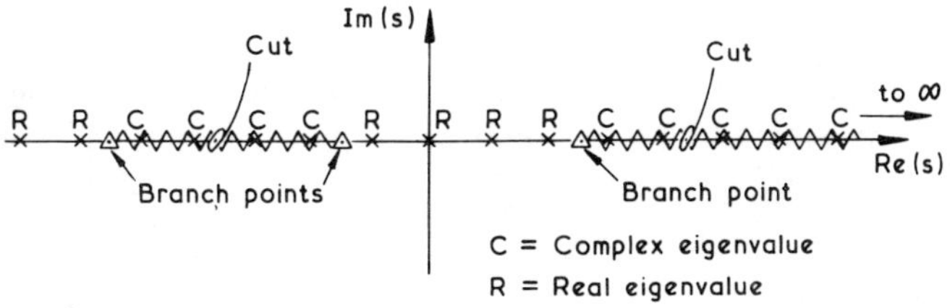

Figure 14. Cuts along the real axis.

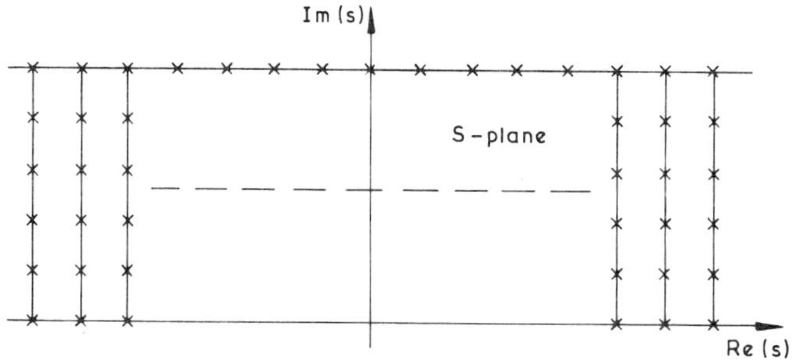

Figure 15. Lines along which eigenvalues are calculated and sorted (modified method). ×——× indicates continuity between eigenvalues.

Computationally sorting the eigenvalues along the real axis can be difficult because of the likelihood of real axis poles. This problem is overcome if the first line of calculation and sorting is changed to be a line parallel to, and a 'large' distance away from, the real axis. The rest of the calculations and sorting are then carried out along lines parallel to the imaginary axis starting at this new line and finishing at the real axis; as shown in Fig. 15. With this new approach the only possible cuts are either along the real axis, as before (see Fig. 14), or between complex conjugate branch points as shown in Fig. 16.

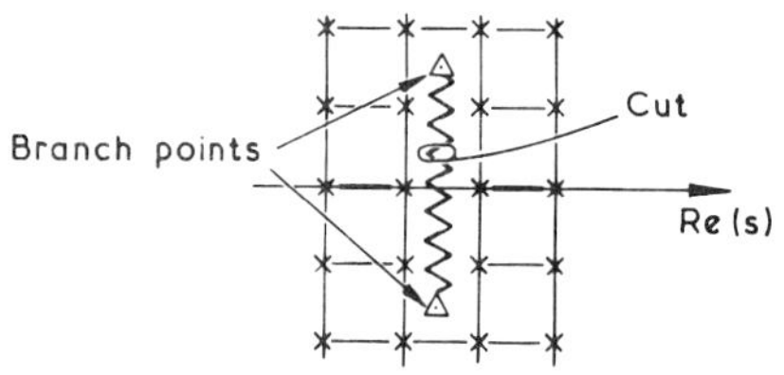

Figure 16. Cut parallel to the imaginary axis (modified method). ×——× indicates continuity between eigenvalues.

A Riemann surface construction for

$$L(s) = \frac{1}{1{\cdot}25(s+1)(s+2)} \begin{bmatrix} 5s-2 & 2s-1 \\ 3s-18 & s-8 \end{bmatrix}$$

is shown using the original method in Figs. 17 and 18, and using the modified method in Figs. 19 and 20, and illustrates the arbitrariness of the cuts.

Appendix 4

The eigenvector functions of a matrix-valued function of a complex variable

The eigenvalue functions of a matrix-valued function of a complex variable have been shown in § 3 to be associated with a set of algebraic functions called

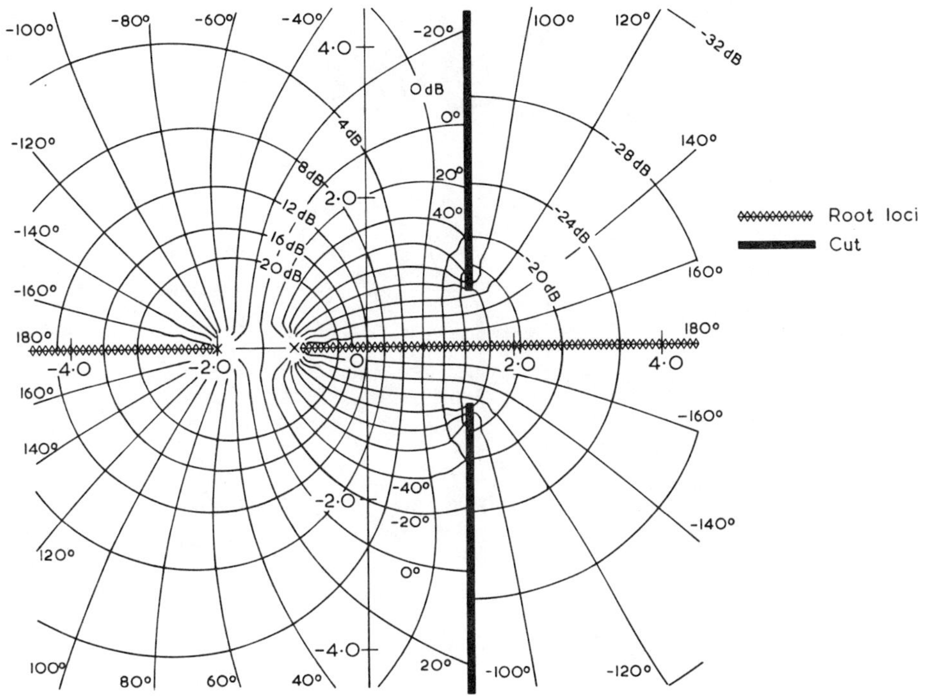

Figure 17. Sheet 1 of the Riemann surface for the example in Appendix 3.

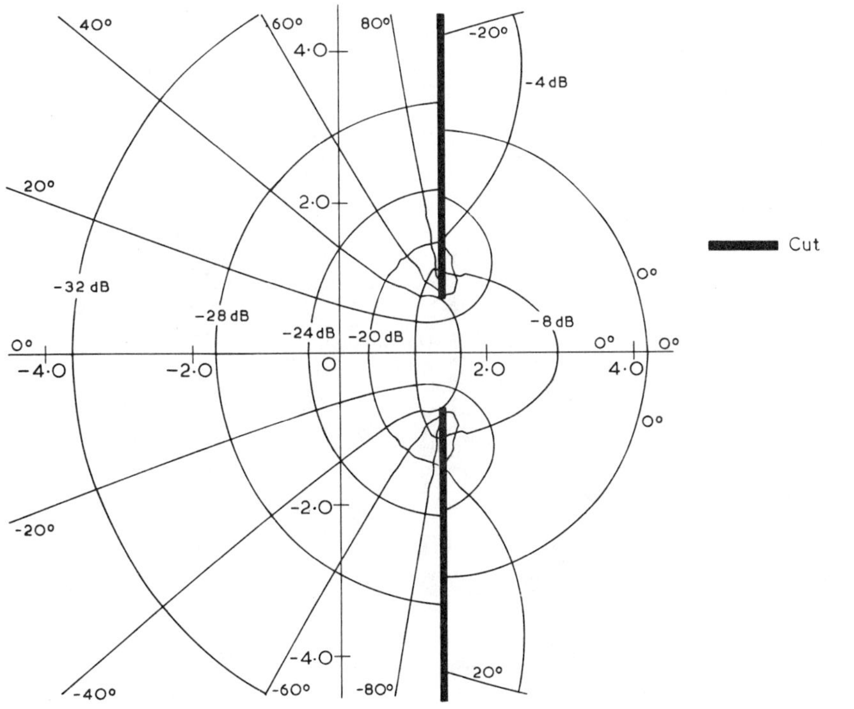

Figure 18. Sheet 2 of the Riemann surface for the example in Appendix 3.

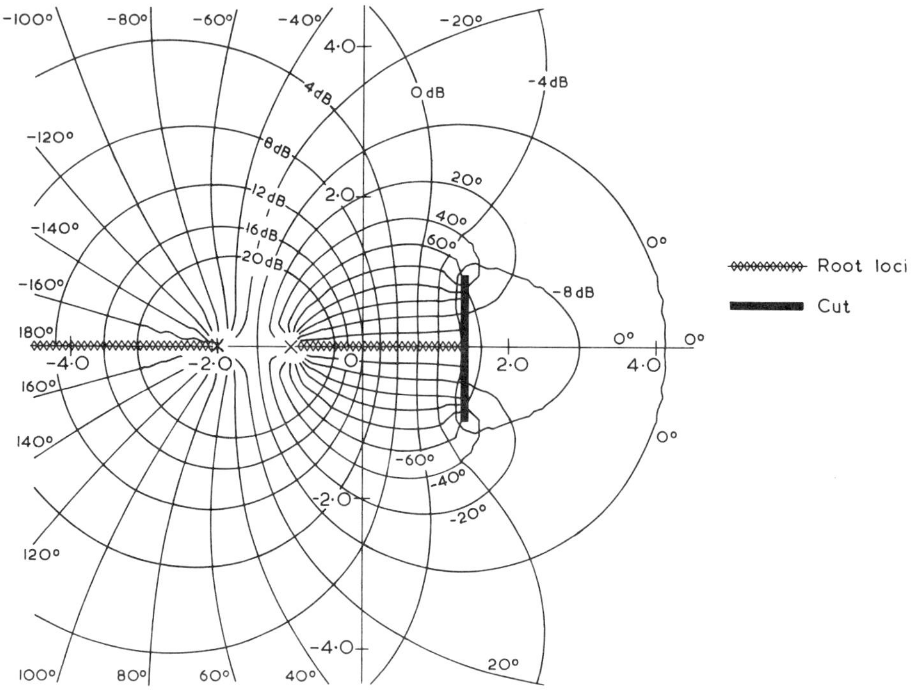

Figure 19. Sheet 1 of the Riemann surface for the example in Appendix 3 (modified method of construction).

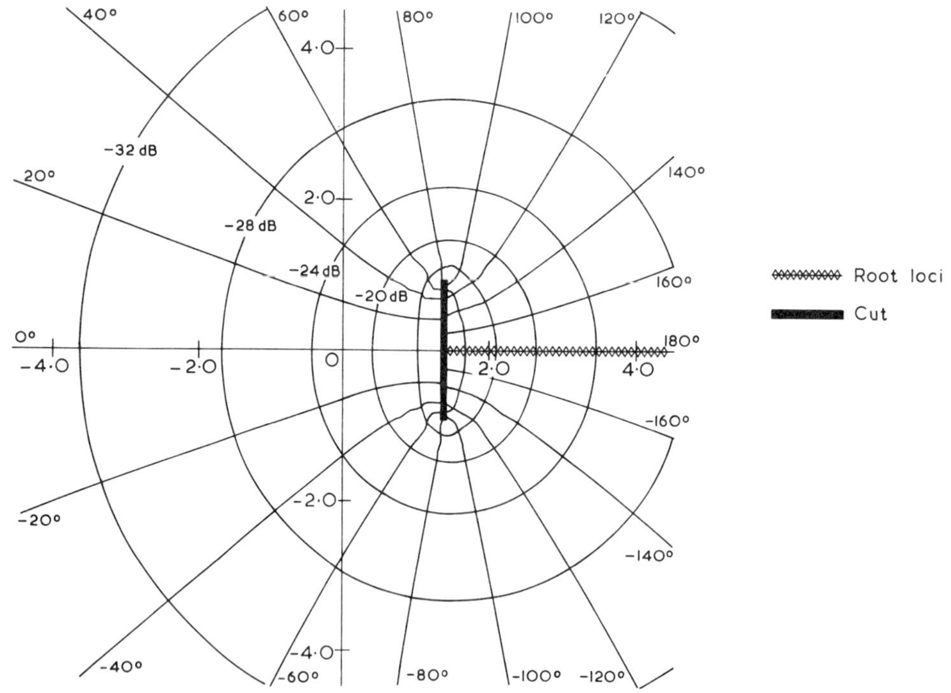

Figure 20. Sheet 2 of the Riemann surface for the example in Appendix 3 (modified method of construction).

the characteristic functions of the matrix. In order to complete the description of the relationships between the eigenstructure of a matrix-valued function of a complex variable and Riemann surfaces, we must consider the corresponding set of eigenvector functions.

For any given matrix-valued function of a complex variable $Q(s)$ there is a corresponding set of Riemann surfaces $\mathbf{R}_{qi}$ which are the domain sets for its characteristic functions $\{q_i : i=1, 2, \ldots, k\}$. It is shown in standard textbooks on complex function theory that the set of all algebraic functions having a given Riemann surface $\mathbf{R}$ as domain set form a field $K_{\mathbf{R}}$ (Behnke *et al.* 1974). For any such field $K_{\mathbf{R}}$ the set of all elementary rational functions are members, since such elementary functions are defined on the domain $\mathbf{C}$ and therefore on any domain formed out of multiple copies of $\mathbf{C}$. From an algebraic point of view each algebraic function defines a particular *extension* of the basic field of elementary rational functions. Now consider the equation defining the eigenvector function $w(s)$ corresponding to an eigenvalue function $q(s)$:

$$Q(s)w(s)=q(s)w(s)$$

The elements of $w(s)$ are found by solving linear sets of equations involving rational functions (the elements of $Q(s)$) and the algebraic function $q(s)$. They must therefore belong to the field of algebraic functions having $\mathbf{R}_q$, the Riemann surface for $q(s)$, as domain.

Thus, corresponding to every characteristic algebraic function $q(s)$ of a matrix-valued function of a complex variable $Q(s)$, we have a vector-valued function of a complex variable $w(s)$ whose elements are algebraic functions having the same Riemann surface domain as the characteristic function $q(s)$.

Appendix 5

Proof of an early statement of the generalized Nyquist stability criterion (MacFarlane and Belletrutti 1973)

Theorem

The closed-loop system is stable if and only if the net sum of anti-clockwise encirclements of the critical point $(-1+j0)$ by the set of characteristic loci of $L(s)$ is equal to the number of right-half plane zeros of $OLCP(s)$ where, as defined in § 2, $OLCP(s)=\det[sI-A_1]\det[sI-A_2]$.

Proof

From § 8 we have that the necessary and sufficient conditions for closed loop stability are that

(*a*) $e(s)=0$ has no roots in the right-half plane ;

(*b*) $\sum_{i=1}^{k} n_{f_i} = -\sum_{i=1}^{k} p_{f_i}$;

(*c*) $p_x(s)=0$ has no roots in the right-half plane ; and

(*d*) $p_d(s)=0$ has no roots in the right-half plane.

Also, from eqn. (8.13) the open loop characteristic polynomial is given by

$$OLCP(s)=p_x(s)p_d(s)e(s)\prod_{i=1}^{k} b_{i0}(s)$$

so that if p_0 is defined as the number of right-half plane zeros of $OLCP(s)$ we have that

$$p_0 = p_x + p_d + e + \sum_{i=1}^{k} p_{f_i}$$

where p_d is the number of right-half plane zeros of $p_d(s)$ and e and p_x are as defined in § 8.

This leads us to consider combining the four conditions (*a*), (*b*), (*c*) and (*d*) into the single equivalent condition

$$\sum_{i=1}^{k} n_{f_i} = -p_0 \tag{A 3}$$

Necessity and sufficiency of condition (A 3) for closed-loop stability

We have that

$$\sum_{i=1}^{k} n_{f_i} = \sum_{i=1}^{k} z_{f_i} - \sum_{i=1}^{k} p_{f_i}$$

and

$$p_0 = p_x + p_d + e + \sum_{i=1}^{k} p_{f_i}$$

and combining the two relationships we thus have

$$\sum_{i=1}^{k} n_{f_i} = \sum_{i=1}^{k} z_{f_i} + p_d + e + p_x - p_0 \tag{A 4}$$

where $\sum_{i=1}^{k} z_{f_i}$, p_d, e, p_x and p_0 are all positive integers or zero.

To establish the necessity of (A 3) suppose that

$$\sum_{i=1}^{k} n_{f_i} \neq -p_0$$

Then, from (A 4), this implies that

$$\sum_{i=1}^{k} z_{f_i} \neq 0, \quad \text{or} \quad p_d \neq 0, \quad \text{or} \quad e \neq 0, \quad \text{or} \quad p_x \neq 0$$

or any combination of these, and thus that the system will be closed-loop unstable.

Hence we conclude that (A 3) is necessary for closed-loop stability.

For sufficiency suppose that

$$\sum_{i=1}^{k} n_{f_i} = -p_0$$

Then, from (A 4) we must have that

$$p_x = p_d = e = \sum_{i=1}^{k} z_{f_i} = 0$$

and hence the system is closed-loop stable. Thus the sufficiency of condition (A 3) is established.

We have therefore shown that

$$\sum_{i=1}^{k} n_{f_i} = -p_0$$

is a necessary and sufficient condition for closed-loop stability. Using the eigenvalue shift theorem (MacFarlane 1970 b) and continuing as in § 8 it then follows that the necessary and sufficient condition for closed-loop stability becomes

$$\sum_{i=1}^{k} n_{l_i} = -p_0$$

where $\sum_{i=1}^{k} n_{l_i}$ is the net sum of clockwise encirclements of the critical point $(-1+j0)$ by the characteristic loci of $L(s)$. This then completes the proof of the early statement of the generalized Nyquist stability criterion.

Appendix 6

A note on the polynomials $e(s)$ and $p_x(s)$

In § 8 a polynomial $e(s)$ is defined in terms of the matrix $F(s)$ and in § 10 it is defined in terms of the matrix $L(s)$. The purpose of the first part of this brief Appendix is to show that the same polynomial $e(s)$ is obtained regardless of whether $F(s)$ or $L(s)$ is involved in the definition. The second part gives an example of the occurrence of a polynomial $p_x(s) \neq 1$.

We have that the pole polynomial for $F(s)$ is given by

$$p_f(s) = e_f(s) \prod_{i=1}^{k} b_{f_{io}}(s)$$

where $e_f(s)$ is the least common denominator of all non-zero non-principal minors of $F(s)$ with all factors common to $\prod_{i=1}^{k} b_{f_{io}}(a)$ removed. Also we have that the pole polynomial for $L(s)$ is given by

$$p_l(s) = e_l(s) \prod_{i=1}^{k} b_{l_{io}}(s)$$

with an obvious definition of $e_l(s)$.

Furthermore :

$$\text{pole polynomial for } f_i(s) = b_{f_{io}}(s)$$

and

$$\text{pole polynomial for } l_i(s) = b_{l_{io}}(s)$$

But

$$f_i(s) = 1 + l_i(s)$$

so that

$$b_{f_{io}}(s) = b_{l_{io}}(s)$$

and thus

$$\prod_{i=1}^{k} b_{fio}(s) = \prod_{i=1}^{k} b_{lio}(s)$$

Finally, since

$$F(s) = I_m + L(s)$$

we must have that

$$p_f(s) = p_l(s)$$

and so

$$e_f(s) = e_l(s) = e(s)$$

To see how a polynomial $p_x(s) \neq 1$ can arise suppose we have

$$G_1(s) = G_2(s) = \begin{bmatrix} \dfrac{2}{(s+1)} & \dfrac{1}{(s-1)} \\ 0 & \dfrac{2}{(s+1)} \end{bmatrix}$$

Then we have

$$L(s) = G_2(s)G_1(s) = \begin{bmatrix} \dfrac{4}{(s+1)^2} & \dfrac{4}{(s+1)(s-1)} \\ 0 & \dfrac{4}{(s+1)^2} \end{bmatrix}$$

so that

$$p_l(s) = (s+1)^4(s-1)$$

and

$$p_{G_1}(s) = p_{G_2}(s) = (s+1)^2(s-1)$$

Thus

$$p_x(s) = \frac{p_{G_1}(s)p_{G_2}(s)}{p_l(s)} = \frac{(s+1)^2(s-1)(s+1)^2(s-1)}{(s+1)^4(s-1)}$$

$$= (s-1).$$

Appendix 7.

Characterization of the point at infinity for the characteristic function $q(s)$

The characteristic function $q(s)$ is defined by an irreducible equation of the form

$$\Delta(q, s) = b_0(s)q^t + b_1(s)q^{t-1} + \ldots + b_t(s) = 0$$

For the purpose of considering $q(s)$ at the point $s = \infty$ one may put

$$s = \frac{1}{z}$$

Then

$$\Delta(q, s) = \Delta(q, z^{-1}) = z^{-n}\Psi(q, z) \qquad \text{(A 5)}$$

and in any neighbourhood of the value $z = 0$ (the point $z = 0$ itself being excluded from it) the equation $\Delta(q, s) = 0$ is equivalent to the equation $\Psi(q, z) = 0$. Considering the equation

$$\Psi(q, z) = \phi_0(z)q^t + \phi_1(z)q^{t-1} + \ldots + \phi_t(z) = 0 \qquad \text{(A 6)}$$

it therefore follows that :

(i) $s=\infty$ is a pole of the characteristic function $q(s)$ if and only if $\phi_0(0)=0$.
(ii) $s=\infty$ is a zero of the characteristic function $q(s)$ if and only if $\phi_t(0)=0$.
(iii) $s=\infty$ is a branch point of the characteristic function $q(s)$ if and only if $D(0)=0$, where $D(z)$ is the discriminant of $\Psi(q, z)$.

For a transfer function matrix describing a physically-realizable system it is not possible to have poles at infinity, and therefore they have not been considered when deriving the pole polynomial for $q(s)$ in § 3.2, or when determining the poles of a transfer function matrix $G(s)$ in § 4. Zeros at infinity are also neglected, but the reason for this is not so obvious since for any practical transfer function matrix they will always exist, and the relationship

$$z(s)=e(s)\prod_{i=1}^{k} b_{it_i}(s)$$

of § 5 only relates the finite zeros of a transfer-function matrix to the finite zeros of its set of characteristic functions. The infinite zeros need not be considered in this paper because the proof of the generalized Nyquist stability criterion is based on the return-difference matrix $F(s)$ which almost always has no infinite zeros. This can be shown very easily as follows.

The return-difference matrix $F(s)$ is defined as

$$F(s)=I+L(s)$$

where $L(s)$ is a transfer function matrix known as the system return-ratio matrix ; the corresponding characteristic functions of $F(s)$ and $L(s)$ are related by

$$f(s)=1+l(s)$$

Therefore providing $l(\infty)\neq -1$ the characteristic function $f(s)$ has no zeros at infinity, and it also follows that $F(s)$ will have no zeros at infinity.

For the restricted class of non-proper systems considered in this paper the condition $l(\infty)=-1$ is not possible because of the conditions imposed by eqn. (2.5), i.e. $\det[F(\infty)]\neq 0$. For a proper system, that is one in which $D_1=D_2=0$, we have $l(\infty)=0$ and hence $f(\infty)=1$. Consequently a return-difference matrix $F(s)$ almost always has no zeros at infinity, and thus this possibility has not been considered in formulating the proof of the generalized Nyquist criterion.

Example

$$G(s)=\frac{1}{1{\cdot}25(s+1)(s+2)}\begin{bmatrix} s-1 & s \\ -6 & s-2 \end{bmatrix}$$

$$\det[gI-Gs]=\left(g-\frac{(s-1)}{1{\cdot}25(s+1)(s+2)}\right)\left(g-\frac{(s-2)}{1{\cdot}25(s+1)(s+2)}\right)+\frac{6s}{1{\cdot}25^2(s+1)^2(s+2)^2}$$

$$=g^2-\frac{(2s-3)}{1{\cdot}25(s+1)(s+2)}g+\frac{1}{1{\cdot}25^2(s+1)(s+2)}$$

therefore

$$\Delta(g, s) = 1{\cdot}25^2(s+1)(s+2)g^2 - 1{\cdot}25(2s-3)g + 1 = 0$$

To consider $g(s)$ as $s \to \infty$ put $s = 1/z$

$$\Delta\left(g, \frac{1}{z}\right) = 1{\cdot}25^2\left(\frac{1}{z}+1\right)\left(\frac{1}{z}+2\right)g^2 - 1{\cdot}25\left(\frac{2}{z}-3\right)g + 1$$

$$= z^{-2}\Psi(g, z)$$

$$= 0$$

where

$$\Psi(g, z) = 1{\cdot}25^2(1+z)(1+2z)g^2 - 1{\cdot}25z(2-3z)g + z^2$$

Thus the coefficient $\phi_2(z)$ of eqn. (A 6) is given by

$$\phi_2(z) = z^2$$

$$\phi_2(0) = 0$$

which shows that there are two zeros located at infinity. Furthermore the discriminant of $\Psi(q, z)$ is given by

$$D(z) = 1{\cdot}25^2 z^2(2-3z)^2 - 4(1{\cdot}25)^2(1+z)(1+2z)z^2$$

so that

$$D(0) = 0$$

which shows that we have a branch point at infinity.

Acknowledgments

We are grateful to Dr. B. Kouvaritakis for the derivation of the relationship between open-loop and closed-loop characteristic polynomials used in § 2, and to Mr. J. Edmunds for the development of the computer algorithm, described in Appendix 3, used to construct the Riemann surfaces of Figs. 9, 10, 17, 18, 19 and 20. Both Dr. Kouvaritakis and Mr. Edmunds are with the Control and Management Systems Group, Engineering Department, University of Cambridge.

References

Ayres, F. M., 1965, *Theory and Problems of Modern Algebra* (New York : Schaum).

Barman, J. F., and Katzenelson, J., 1973, Memorandum ERL–383, Electronics Research Laboratory, College of Engineering, University of California, Berkeley ; 1974, *Int. J. Control*, **20**, 593.

Barnett, S., 1971, *Matrices in Control Theory* (London : Van Nostrand-Reinhold).

Behnke, H., Bachmann, F., Fladt, K., and Suss, W., 1974, *Fundamentals of Mathematics*, Vol. 3 *Analysis* (Cambridge, Mass. : MIT Press).

Bliss, G. A., 1966 (reprint of 1933 original), *Algebraic Functions* (New York : Dover).

Cohn, P. M., 1974, *Algebra*, Vol. 1 (London : Wiley).

Desoer, C. A., and Chan, W. S., 1975, *J. Franklin Inst.*, **300**, 335.

Evans, W. R., 1954, *Control System Dynamics* (New York : McGraw-Hill).

Gantmacher, F. R., 1959, *Theory of Matrices*, Vol. 1 (New York : Chelsea).

Hille, E., 1959, *Analytic Function Theory*, Vol. 1 (Waltham, Mass. : Blaisdell).

Knopp, K., 1947, *Theory of Functions*, Part 2 (New York : Dover).

Kontakos, T., 1973, Ph.D. Thesis, University of Manchester.

Kouvaritakis, B., and Shaked, U., 1976, *Int. J. Control*, **23**, 297.

MACFARLANE, A. G. J., 1970 a, *Proc. Inst. elect. Engrs*, **117,** 2037 ; 1970 b, *Dynamical System Models* (London : Harrap).
MACFARLANE, A. G. J., and BELLETRUTTI, J. J., 1973, *Automatica*, **9,** 575.
MACFARLANE, A. G. J., and KARCANIAS, N., 1976, *Int. J. Control*, **24,** 33.
NYQUIST, H., 1932, *Bell Syst. tech. J.*, **11,** 126.
ROSENBROCK, H. H., 1970, *State Space and Multivariable Theory* (London : Nelson).
SAEKS, R., 1975, *Trans. I.E.E.E. Circuits Systems*, **22,** 780.
SANSONE, G., and GERRETSEN, J., 1969, *Lectures on the Theory of Functions of a Complex Variable* Vol. 2 (Groningen : Wolters-Nordhoff).
SPRINGER, G., 1957, *Introduction to Riemann Surfaces* (Reading, Mass. : Addison-Wesley).

Characteristic frequency functions and characteristic gain functions

A. G. J. MacFARLANE† and I. POSTLETHWAITE†

In the transform analysis of linear systems the two classical approaches use complex functions to study gain as a function of frequency (the Nyquist–Bode approach), and to study frequency as a function of gain (the Evans root locus approach). The central feature of any transform approach to the analysis of linear multivariable systems is the use of transfer-function matrices, and it is the primary purpose of this paper to explain how the ideas of studying gain as a function of frequency, and frequency as a function of gain, can be extended to the multivariable case by associating with transfer-function matrices characteristic gain functions and characteristic frequency functions.

The characteristic gain function and characteristic frequency function are algebraic functions, each of which is defined on an appropriate Riemann surface. Considering the Riemann surface domain for the characteristic frequency function, a stability criterion for linear multivariable feedback systems is established which does not require a net sum of encirclements of the critical point.

1. Introduction

Complex numbers are used for two distinct purposes in the transform-domain analysis of linear systems : to represent frequencies and to represent gains. The two basic classical approaches to the analysis and design of linear single-loop feedback systems use complex functions to study gain as a function of frequency (the Nyquist–Bode approach), and frequency as a function of gain (the Evans root locus approach). The central feature of any transform approach to the analysis of linear multivariable systems is the use of transfer-function matrices, and it has been shown in a previous paper (MacFarlane and Postlethwaite 1977) how such a matrix-valued function of a complex variable can be associated with algebraic function theory (Bliss 1966). If $L(s)$ is a return-ratio matrix for a linear multivariable feedback system (MacFarlane 1970), then it can be associated with a set of characteristic algebraic functions by means of the characteristic equation

$$\Delta(l, s) = \det\,[lI_m - L(s)] = 0 \tag{1.1}$$

where I_m is a unit matrix of order m, the order of the square matrix $L(s)$. For simplicity of exposition in what follows, and because this is in any case the usual situation for transfer-function matrices arising from practical situations, it is assumed that $\Delta(l, s)$ is irreducible over the field of rational functions in the complex variable s.

If eqn. (1.1) is considered in terms of $\Delta(l, s)$ being regarded as a polynomial in l with coefficients which are rational functions of s, then it defines an algebraic function $l(s)$. This algebraic function will be called the *characteristic gain function* of the matrix $L(s)$. Alternatively, however, we may equally well consider eqn. (1.1) in terms of $\Delta(l, s)$ being regarded as a polynomial in s with

Received 22 October 1976.

† Control and Management Systems Group, Engineering Department, University of Cambridge, Mill Lane, Cambridge CB2 1RX, England.

Reprinted with permission from *Int. J. Control*, vol. 26, pp. 265–278, Aug. 1977.

coefficients which are rational functions of l. In this case it can be used to define another algebraic function $s(l)$ which will be called the *characteristic frequency function* of the matrix $L(s)$. Thus, associated with an irreducible characteristic equation like (1.1) are two characteristic algebraic functions : a characteristic gain function and a characteristic frequency function, each of which has as its domain an appropriate Riemann surface (Springer 1957). The Riemann surface associated with the characteristic gain function will be called the s-surface or frequency surface (since the domain of the gain function is comprised of frequencies). The Riemann surface associated with the characteristic frequency function of $L(s)$ will be called the l-surface or gain surface (since the domain of the frequency function is comprised of gains). A method of constructing the frequency surface for a given rational transfer-function has been given by MacFarlane and Postlethwaite (1977) and is briefly reviewed in § 3, and a method of constructing the corresponding gain surface is given in § 5.

The frequency surface (domain of $l(s)$), which should be intuitively thought of as built out of characteristic frequency values, contains the multivariable root loci for $L(s)$. As shown by MacFarlane and Postlethwaite (1977) these are, with the exception of some possible single-point loci, the 180°-phase contours of the characteristic gain function on the appropriate frequency surface. This is illustrated by an example in § 3 where a frequency surface is shown with a collection of constant-phase and constant-amplitude contours of the algebraic function $l(s)$. As a convenient and consistent terminology, we may call the multivariable root loci *characteristic frequency loci* and the characteristic loci used in previous treatments of the generalized Nyquist stability criterion may accordingly be called *characteristic gain loci*. It is shown in § 4 how these characteristic gain loci can be constructed from the calibrated frequency surface. If the gain surface is shown as a collection of constant-phase and constant-amplitude contours of $s(l)$, then the $\pm 90°$ phase contours will define the characteristic gain loci. This is illustrated by example in § 5, and in § 6 it is shown how to obtain the characteristic frequency loci from a calibrated gain surface.

A stability criterion for linear multivariable feedback systems is given in § 7 in a form which does not require a net sum of encirclements of the critical point. This is derived using arguments similar to those used by Saeks (1975) and DeCarlo and Saeks (1977). Finally, in § 8, a discussion is given of the relationship between the constant-real-part and constant-imaginary-part contours of $s(l)$ on a gain surface and the degree of relative stability of a closed-loop system.

2. Characteristic frequencies and characteristic gains

The archetypal feedback situation is when a set of outputs from one part of a system are connected back to a corresponding number of inputs to another part of the system. When such feedback connections are made the system characteristic frequencies are altered. A prime objective of all frequency-response approaches to the linear feedback problem is to find ways of relating closed-loop characteristic frequencies to open-loop gains.

Suppose, as shown in Fig. 1, we have a linear dynamical system S and select m outputs to be connected back to m selected inputs. Let the transfer-function matrix relating the selected set of inputs and outputs be $G(s)$, and suppose that this is a proper matrix of rational functions in s with a state space realization corresponding to the triple of matrices $\{A, B, C\}$. As shown in Fig. 1, let the outputs of S be connected back to the inputs through a gain matrix $g^{-1}I_m$, where g is a complex scalar gain and I_m is a unit matrix of order m. The basic idea behind what follows is that we can look at this situation from two points of view : we can examine the gain g as a function

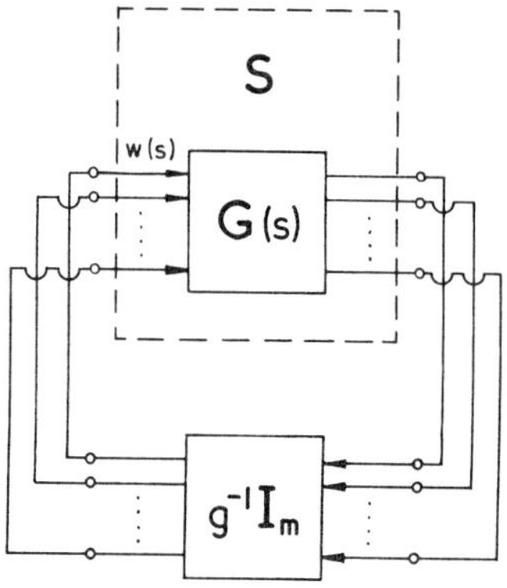

Figure 1. Arrangement for illustration of relationship between characteristic gains and characteristic frequencies.

of frequency s, or we can study the system closed-loop frequencies as a function of the gain g. As shown in Fig. 1, let $w(s)$ be the vector of transform inputs to $G(s)$. Then we must have that

$$G(s)w(s) = g(s)w(s) \tag{2.1}$$

and so, for a fixed value of frequency, $\bar{s}$ say, the corresponding values of gain $\{g_i(\bar{s}) : i=1, 2, \ldots, m\}$ must be eigenvalues of the complex matrix $G(\bar{s})$. As the frequency variable s takes all possible values, we can calculate the corresponding values of a characteristic gain function $g(s)$; this will obviously be an m-valued function of the complex variable s. This characteristic gain function will be defined via the equation

$$\det [gI_m - G(s)] = 0 \tag{2.2}$$

We can also take a fixed value of gain, $\bar{g}$ say, and determine the corresponding set of closed-loop characteristic frequencies $\{s_i(\bar{g}) : i=1, 2, \ldots, n\}$, where n is the order of the realization of $G(s)$. Thus we can investigate the properties of a characteristic frequency function $s(g)$. This may be defined, as discussed in § 5, by an equation of the form

$$\det [sI_n - S(g)] \tag{2.3}$$

where

$$S(g) = [A + g^{-1}BC] \tag{2.4}$$

The characteristic frequency function $s(g)$ is obviously an n-valued function of the complex variable g.

In the remainder of this paper we will mostly use a return-ratio matrix $L(s)$ for the purposes of discussion, rather than a plant transfer-function matrix $G(s)$, since return-ratio matrices are more directly related to a statement of stability results.

3. Characteristic frequency loci (root loci) on the *s*-surface

The feedback configuration considered is shown in Fig. 2 (a). S_1 has m inputs and S_2 has m outputs and they are both taken to be linear dynamical

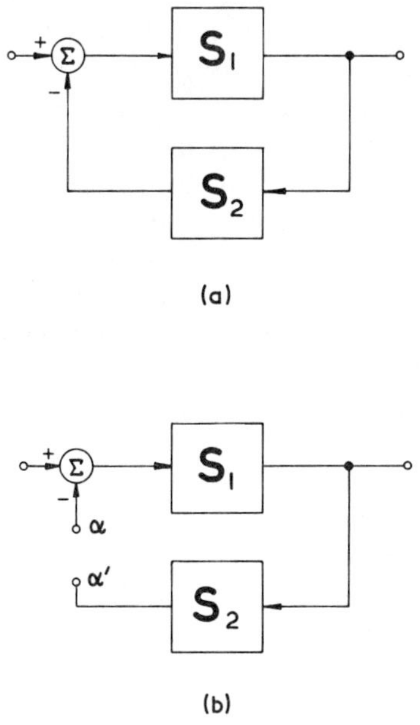

Figure 2. Multivariable feedback configuration. (a) Closed loop; (b) open loop.

systems having proper transfer-function matrices $G_1(s)$ and $G_2(s)$ with state-space realizations specified by the matrix triples $\{A_1\ B_1, C_1\}$ and $\{A_2, B_2, C_2\}$ respectively. The state-space description of the overall open-loop system is then given by the triple $\{A, B, C\}$, where

$$\left.\begin{aligned} A &= \begin{bmatrix} A_1 & 0 \\ B_2C_1 & A_2 \end{bmatrix} \\ B &= \begin{bmatrix} B_1 \\ 0 \end{bmatrix} \\ \text{and} \qquad C &= [0 \ \ C_2] \end{aligned}\right\} \tag{3.1}$$

Suppose all the feedback loops are broken at the point shown in Fig. 2 (*b*). Then the corresponding return-difference matrix (MacFarlane 1970) for this break point is

$$F(s) = I_m + L(s) \tag{3.2}$$

where

$$L(s) = G_2(s) G_1(s) \tag{3.3}$$

is the return-ratio matrix for this break point. The characteristic gain functions for $L(s)$ are obtained from the equation

$$\Delta(l, s) = \det\,[lI_m - L(s)] = 0 \tag{3.4}$$

The stability of the linear multivariable feedback system depends largely on the characteristic function $l(s)$, and a study of a plot of the constant-phase and constant-magnitude contours of this function on the s-surface is very instructive. A method for constructing the s-surface has been given by MacFarlane and Postlethwaite (1977), and is briefly restated here.

The method is based on finding the eigenvalues of the return-ratio matrix $L(s)$ for a grid of values covering the s-plane and then sorting these eigenvalues into a continuous form along certain lines of the grid. If the return-ratio matrix is of order $m \times m$, then m arrays are used to store the sorted eigenvalues. When the calculations and sorting are complete the m arrays represent the m sheets required to build the Riemann surface. The necessary cuts on a sheet are identified by a discontinuity between two lines of eigenvalues, and the ‘ stitching ’ together of the sheets becomes obvious by matching eigenvalues on one side of a cut on one sheet to those on another.

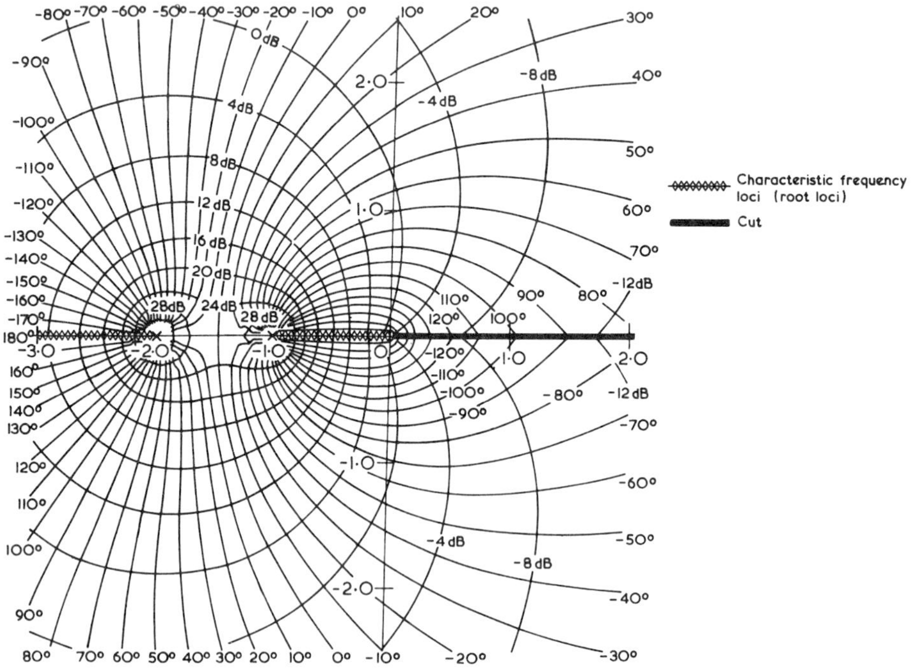

Figure 3. Sheet 1 of the s-surface for the return-ratio matrix of § 3.

As an illustrative example (MacFarlane and Postlethwaite 1977) the s-surface for

$$L(s)=\frac{1}{1\cdot 25(s+1)(s+2)}\begin{bmatrix} s-1 & s \\ -6 & s-2 \end{bmatrix} \tag{3.5}$$

characterized by constant-phase and constant-magnitude contours of $l(s)$ is shown in Figs. 3 and 4.

It has been shown (MacFarlane and Postlethwaite 1977) that for the multivariable feedback configuration of Fig. 5 the root loci are defined by solutions of the following equations :

$$p_x(s)=0 \tag{3.6}$$

$$p_d(s)=0 \tag{3.7}$$

$$e(s)=0 \tag{3.8}$$

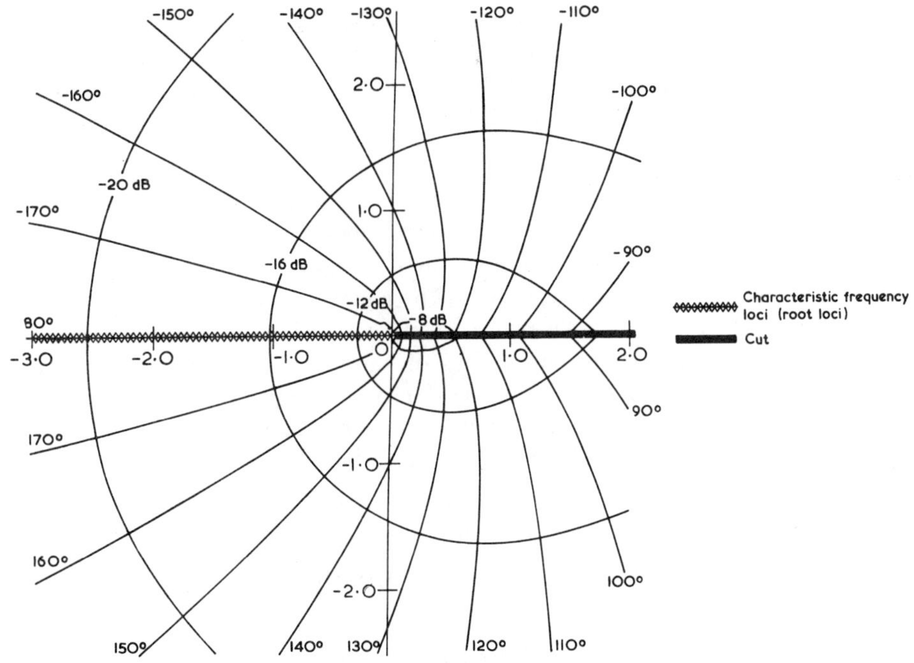

Figure 4. Sheet 2 of the s-surface for the return-ratio matrix of § 3.

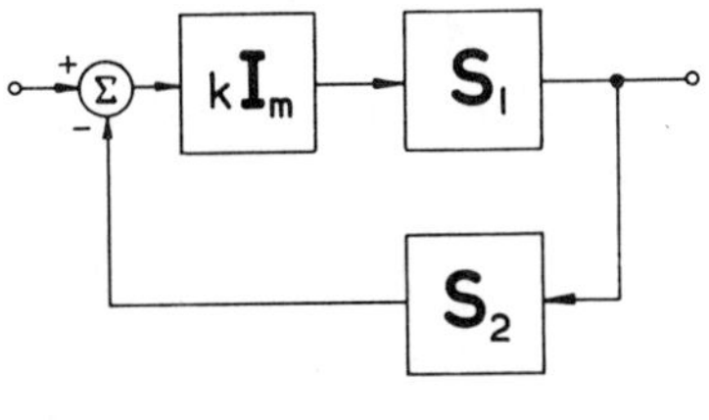

Figure 5. Multivariable feedback configuration with scalar gain k.

and

$$l(s) = -\frac{1}{k} \tag{3.9}$$

for all values of the scalar gain k. Here we have that

(i) $p_x(s)$ has as its zeros those poles of $G_1(s)$ and $G_2(s)$ which are lost when $L(s)$ is formed,
(ii) $p_d(s)$ has as its zeros the decoupling zeros of the overall system associated with the set of eigenvalues of A (A being the overall system matrix) which correspond to modes of the system which are uncontrollable and/or unobservable, and
(iii) $e(s)$ has as its zeros those poles of $L(s)$ which are not poles of the characteristic function $l(s)$.

Equation (3.9) is a direct generalization of the defining equation for a single-loop root locus, while for $e(s) \neq 1$, and/or $p_d(s) \neq 1$, and/or $p_x(s) \neq 1$ there will also be degenerate loci each consisting of a single point. It is clear therefore that with the exception of possible solutions from eqns. (3.6), (3.7) and (3.8) the multivariable root loci are simply the 180°-phase loci of the characteristic gain function $l(s)$ on its associated Riemann surface. This is illustrated in Figs. 3 and 4.

4. Determination of the characteristic gain loci from the *s*-surface

In practice the characteristic gain loci are generated as the loci in the complex plane traced out by the eigenvalues of the matrix $L(s)$ as s traverses the imaginary axis, $s = j\omega$. Therefore from an s-surface plot the characteristic gain loci are determined by the values of the constant-phase and constant-magnitude contours as they cross the $s = j\omega$ axes. Consequently if the contour patterns in the vicinity of the imaginary axes are relatively dense an accurate plot of the characteristic gain loci can be obtained.

5. Characteristic gain loci on the *l*-surface

In constructing the s-surface it is straightforward to substitute for s in the characteristic equation

$$\Delta(l, s) \triangleq \det\,[lI_m - L(s)] = 0 \tag{5.1}$$

and find l since this is a standard eigenvalue problem. To construct the Riemann surface for $s(l)$ using the same procedure as for the s-surface it is desirable to be able to find s easily for a given l; eqn. (5.1) does not allow this. A new relationship between s and l is therefore required. This is obtained using the state-space description of the overall system as follows.

From eqn. (3.9), that is

$$l(s) = -\frac{1}{k} \tag{5.2}$$

we have a relationship which gives the dependence of the closed-loop poles on the scalar feedback gain k. The reason for k being chosen to be scalar is so that the solutions of s trace out the standard root locus plot. In general, k can be considered as complex, and in considering eqn. (5.2) we will take this to be the case.

From the state-space point of view the closed-loop poles are given by

$$\det [sI_n - A + kBC] = 0 \tag{5.3}$$

where A, B and C are state-space matrices for the overall system. At a closed-loop pole eqn. (5.2) holds and therefore we can substitute for k in eqn. (5.3) to give

$$\det \left[sI_n - A - \frac{1}{l} BC \right] = 0 \tag{5.4}$$

This is the required relationship, since for a given l the required values of s can now be calculated as the eigenvalues of the matrix $[A + (1/l)BC]$.

Note that eqn. (5.4) also gives solutions, when they exist, for eqns. (3.6), (3.7) and (3.8).

The procedure for calculating the l-surface can now follow the same lines as for the s-surface. For a grid of values covering the l-plane the eigenvalues of the matrix $[A + (1/l)BC]$ are found, sorted along specified lines of the grid, and stored in n arrays, where n is the number of states for the overall system, If $p_x(s) \neq 1$, and/or $e(s) \neq 1$, and/or $p_d(s) \neq 1$, then some arrays will exist having the same value of s stored in every position. The surface made up from the arrays (sheets) with varying values of s is the required l-surface.

The l-surface for the example used in § 3 is shown characterized by constant phase and magnitude contours of $s(l)$ in Figs. 6 and 7. Now the characteristic

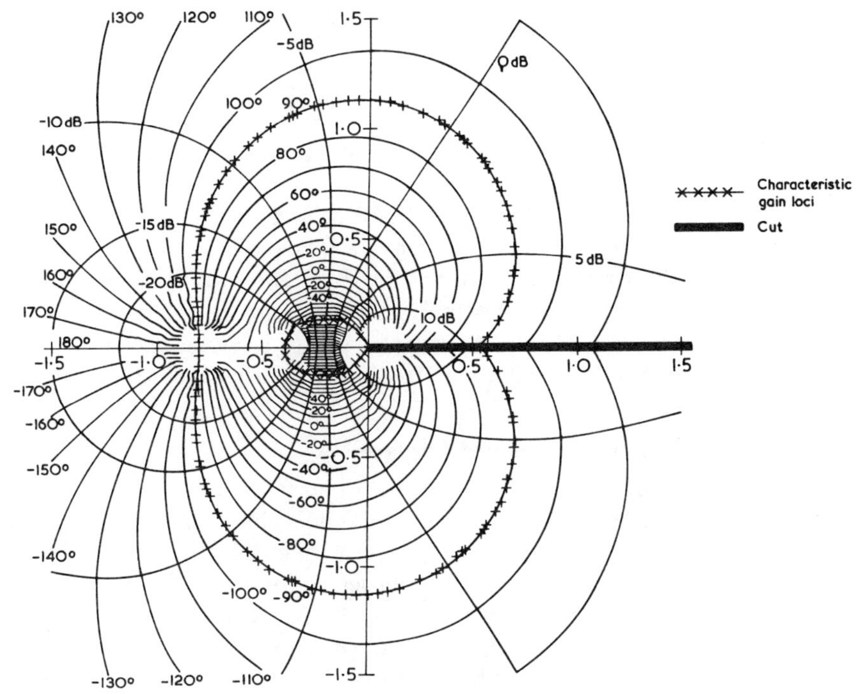

Figure 6. Sheet 1 of the l-surface for the return-ratio matrix of §3.

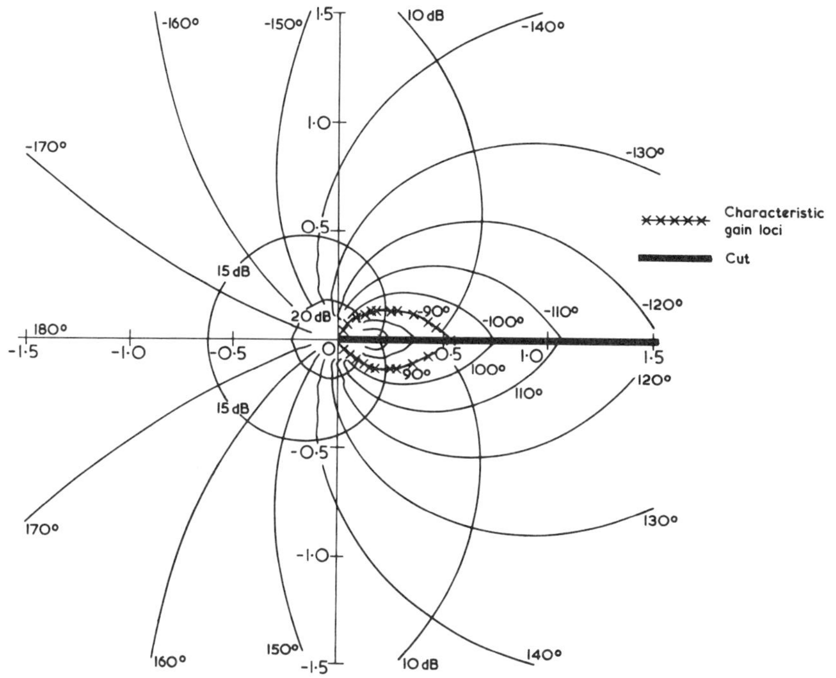

Figure 7. Sheet 2 of the l-surface for the return-ratio matrix of §3.

gain loci of $L(s)$ are the images of the imaginary axis ($s = j\omega$) and therefore on the l-surface the $\pm 90°$ phase contours trace out the characteristic gain loci ; this is illustrated in Figs. 6 and 7.

6. Determination of the characteristic frequency loci (root loci) from the l-surface plot

Apart from possible single-point loci, the root loci are simply the values of s at which the characteristic gain function has a phase of 180°. Therefore from the l-surface plot the root loci are determined by the values of the constant-phase and constant-magnitude contours as they cross the negative real axis on each sheet. Consequently if the contour patterns along the negative real axes are relatively dense, then an accurate plot of the root loci can be obtained.

7. Stability inference using a calibrated l-surface

Let the system of Fig. 2 (a) have no open-loop uncontrollable and/or unobservable modes whose characteristic frequencies lie in the right half-plane. Then by the generalized Nyquist stability criterion (MacFarlane and Postlethwaite 1977) this configuration will be closed-loop stable if and only if the net sum of anti-clockwise encirclements of the critical point $(-1+j0)$ by the set of characteristic gain loci of the return-ratio matrix $L(s)(=G_2(s)G_1(s))$ is equal to the total number of right half-plane poles of $G_1(s)$ and $G_2(s)$.

Work has been done by Saeks (1975), and DeCarlo and Saeks (1977), that suggests that having to count the number of encirclements of the critical point

$(-1+j0)$ is unnecessary. They argue that on a Riemann surface the image of the inside of the standard Nyquist D-contour will be one or more simply connected regions. If on removing the critical points $(-1+j0)$ from the surface these simply-connected regions can each be continuously deformed to a point, then this implies that the characteristic function $l(s)$ is never equal to -1 in the right half-plane. (Note that from eqn. (3.9) $l(s) = -1$ in the right half-plane corresponds to an unstable closed-loop pole.) Using the l-surface construction these arguments are now combined with knowledge of the polynomials $p_x(s)$ and $e(s)$ to give a multivariable feedback stability criterion which does not involve the number of encirclements of the critical point by the characteristic gain loci.

MacFarlane and Postlethwaite (1977) have shown that the following four conditions are necessary and sufficient for closed-loop stability :

(*a*) $e(s) = 0$ has no roots in the right half-plane ;
(*b*) $f(s)$ has no zeros in the right half-plane (where $f(s)$ is the algebraic function corresponding to the return-difference matrix $F(s)$), i.e. $l(s) \neq -1$ in the right half-plane ;
(*c*) $p_x(s) = 0$ has no roots in the right half-plane ;
(*d*) $p_d(s) = 0$ has no roots in the right half-plane.

Each sheet of an l-surface plot characterized by constant-phase and constant-magnitude contours is divided by branches of the characteristic gain loci into regions corresponding to the image of the left-half s-plane and that of the right-half s-plane. Therefore, given such a calibrated surface, one can see at a glance whether $l(s)$ is equal to -1 in the right half-plane without the need for counting encirclements. An equivalent statement of the generalized Nyquist stability criterion is therefore as follows.

Let the system have no open-loop uncontrollable and/or unobservable modes whose characteristic frequencies lie in the right half-plane. Then the system is closed-loop stable if and only if on the l-surface there are no '-1' points in regions corresponding to the right half-plane, and $p_x(s)$ and $e(s)$ have no zeros in the right half-plane.

Note that if the method proposed in § 5 for constructing the l-surface is used, then the zeros of $p_x(s)$, $e(s)$ and $p_d(s)$ are given explicitly as the values of s invariant with l, and therefore covering a whole array.

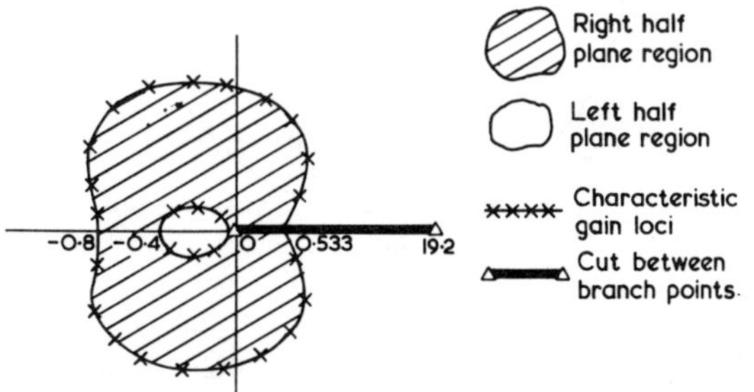

Figure 8. Sketch of Fig. 6 emphasizing right half and left half-plane regions.

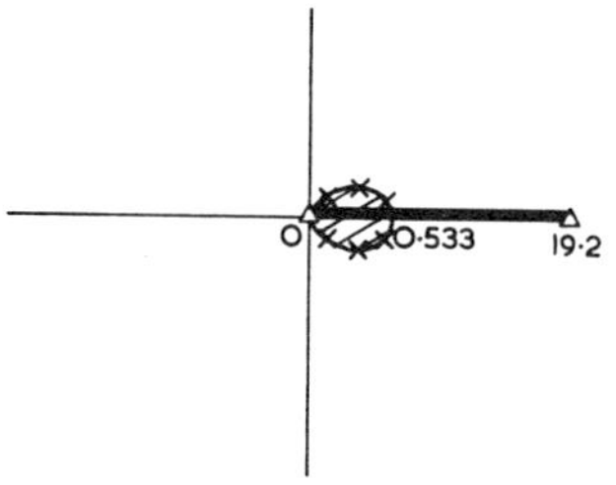

Figure 9. Sketch of Fig. 7 emphasizing right half and left half-plane regions (symbols as in Fig. 8).

To illustrate the stability criterion the example from § 3 is again considered. The l-surface is shown in Figs. 6 and 7, and in Figs. 8 and 9 sketches are made of the sheets to emphasize the right half-plane and left half-plane regions. Introducing a scalar gain k into the forward path, as shown in Fig. 5, gives critical points at $-1/k+j0$. As we increase k positively from zero, the critical points move from $-\infty$ towards the origin on each sheet. On sheet 1 the critical point is in a right half-plane region for $1{\cdot}25<k<2{\cdot}5$ while on sheet 2 for positive k the critical point never moves into a right half-plane region. Therefore, because we also have $p_x(s)=1$ and $e(s)=1$, the closed-loop system is stable for $0\leqslant k<1{\cdot}25$ and $2{\cdot}5<k<\infty$.

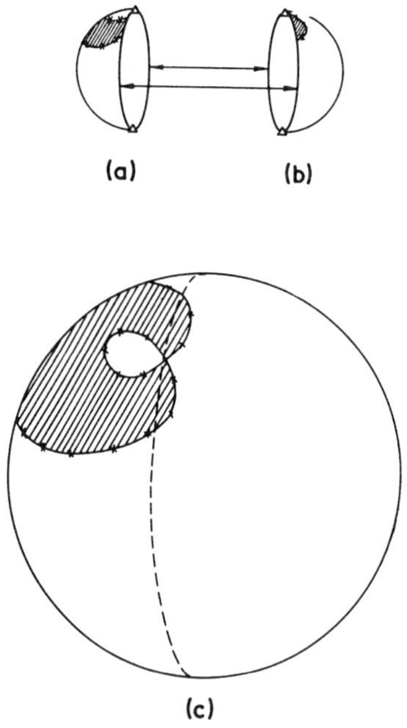

Figure 10. (*a*) Sheet 1 cut along line joining branch points and deformed into a hemisphere ; (*b*) sheet 2 cut along line joining branch points and deformed into a hemisphere ; (*c*) the complete l-surface topologically represented as a sphere by suitably joining up the hemispheres constructed from sheet 1 and sheet 2.

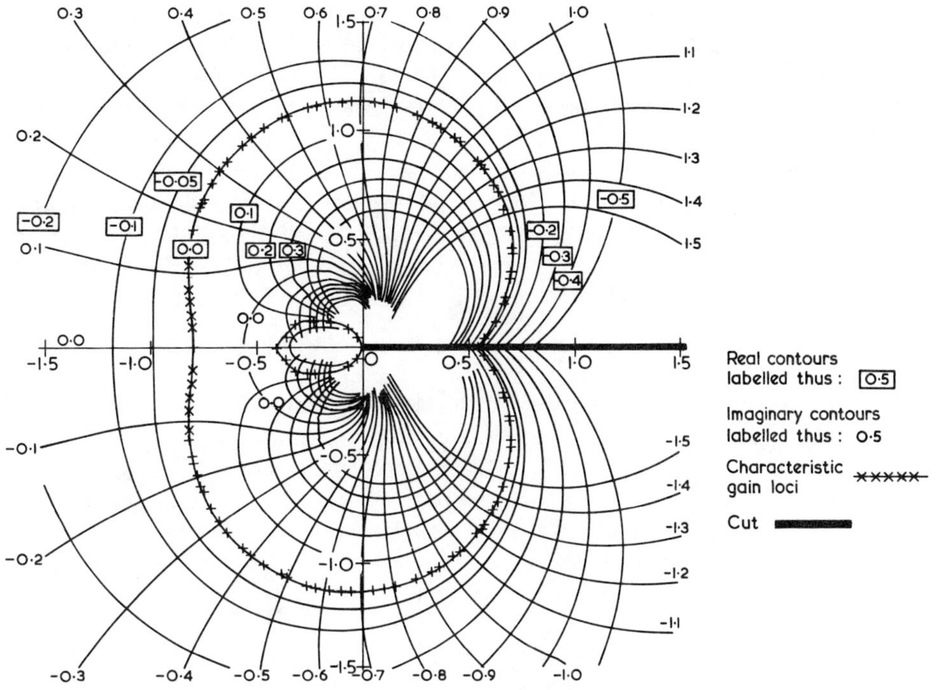

Figure 11 (*a*). Sheet 1 of the *l*-surface characterized by constant real and imaginary contours.

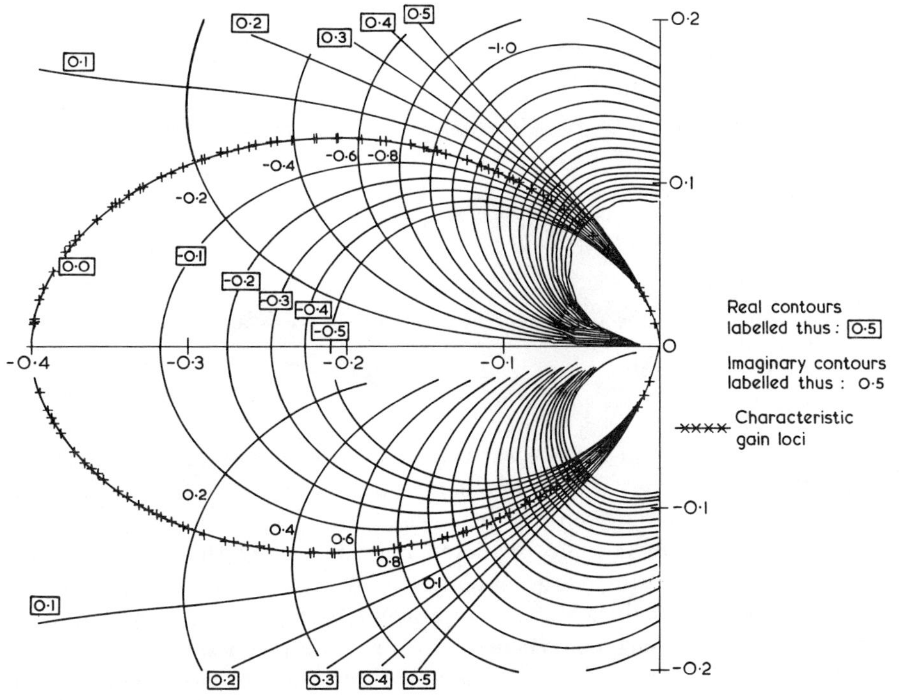

Figure 11 (*b*). Blown-up region close to the origin of Fig. 11 (*a*).

If k is increased negatively from zero the critical points move from ∞ towards the origin on each sheet. On both sheets the critical points are in right half-plane regions for $-\infty < k \leqslant -1{\cdot}875$. Therefore for negative k, which corresponds to positive feedback, the closed-loop system is stable for $-1{\cdot}875 < k \leqslant 0$.

Topologically, Riemann surfaces can be considered as spheres with handles (Springer 1957). The l-surface for this example is topologically equivalent to a simple sphere as shown in Fig. 10. It can be seen that the image of the inside of the Nyquist D-contour, i.e. the right half-plane region, is a simply-connected region on the surfaces as conjectured by DeCarlo and Saeks (1977).

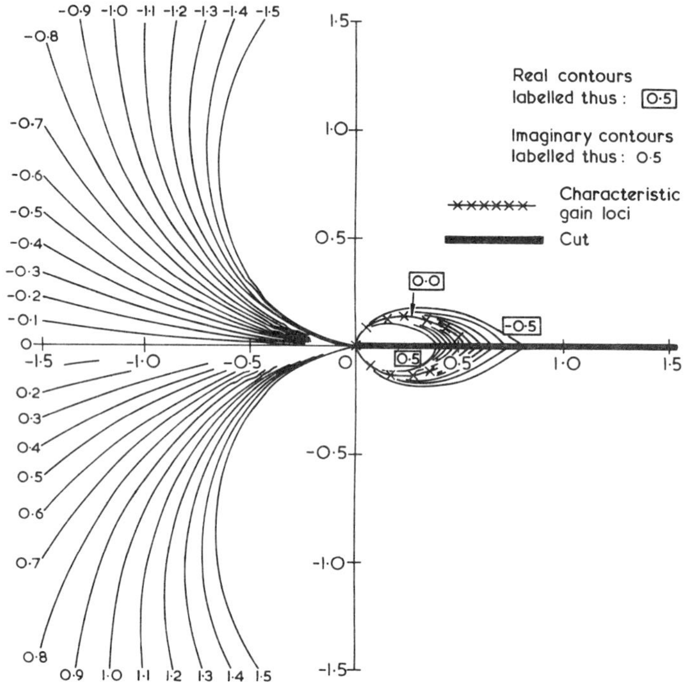

Figure 12. Sheet 2 of the l-surface characterized by constant real and imaginary contours.

If the calibrated gain surface is projected onto the complex gain plane **C**, we have the normal presentation of the characteristic gain loci, plus the superposition of contours representing both right half-plane and left half-plane regions. Stability can now be predicted by considering the right half-plane regions in relation to a single critical point $(-1+j0)$. However, this presentation will in general be difficult to comprehend because of the overlapping of contours. Therefore, although the counting of encirclements, in the generalized Nyquist stability criterion (MacFarlane and Postlethwaite 1977), is not fundamental to system stability, it does afford the simplest method for predicting closed-loop stability in the complex gain plane **C**.

8. Relative stability from an l-surface plot characterized by constant real and constant imaginary contours

From an l-surface plot of constant real and constant imaginary contours of $s(l)$ it is possible to accurately determine the closed-loop poles. This is illustrated by an example using the return-ratio matrix of § 3 to find the dominant closed-loop poles.

Let these dominant closed-loop poles be given by

$$s_c = \alpha \pm j\beta$$

Then α is the smallest (in magnitude) negative real contour that passes through any one of the critical -1 points, and β is the corresponding imaginary contour. The l-surface plot characterized by constant real and imaginary contours is shown in Figs. 11 (*a*), 11 (*b*) and 12 from which

$$\alpha \simeq -0{\cdot}05$$

and

$$\beta = 0$$

so that

$$s_c \simeq -0{\cdot}05$$

By hand calculation the dominant closed-loop pole is

$$s_c = -0{\cdot}0528$$

The l-surface representation therefore seems a useful tool for the engineer in practice, in that it enables him to assess stability at a glance and also to give a measure of the relative stability of the system by picking out the dominant closed-loop pole.

References

Bliss, G. A., 1966 (reprint of 1933 original), *Algebraic Functions* (New York : Dover Publications).

DeCarlo, R., and Saeks, R., 1977, *Int. J. Control*, **26,** 279.

MacFarlane, A. G. J., 1970, *Proc. Inst. elect. Engrs*, **117,** 2037.

MacFarlane, A. G. J., and Postlethwaite, I., 1977, *Int. J. Control*, **25,** 81.

Saeks, R., 1975, *Trans. I.E.E.E. Circuits Syst.*, **22,** 780.

Springer, G., 1957, *Introduction to Riemann Surfaces* (Reading, Massachusetts : Addison-Wesley).

Gain and Phase Margin for Multiloop LQG Regulators

MICHAEL G. SAFONOV, STUDENT MEMBER, IEEE, AND MICHAEL ATHANS, FELLOW, IEEE

***Abstract*—Multiloop linear-quadratic state-feedback (LQSF) regulators are shown to be robust against a variety of large dynamical linear time-invariant and memoryless nonlinear time-varying variations in open-loop dynamics. The results are interpreted in terms of the classical concepts of gain and phase margin, thus strengthening the link between classical and modern feedback theory.**

I. Introduction

HISTORICALLY, feedback has been used in control system engineering as a means for satisfying design constraints requiring

1) stabilization of insufficiently stable systems;
2) reduction of system response to noise;
3) realization of a specific input/output relation (e.g., specified poles and zeros);
4) improvement of a system's robustness against variations in its open-loop dynamics.

Classical feedback synthesis techniques include procedures which ensure directly that each of these design constraints is satisfied [1], [2]. Unfortunately, the direct methods of classical feedback theory become overwhelmingly complicated for all but the simplest feedback configurations. In particular, the classical theory cannot cope simply and effectively with multiloop feedback.

Linear-quadratic-Gaussian (LQG) control theory has made the solution of many multiloop control synthesis problems relatively simple. The LQG technique [3] provides a straightforward means for synthesizing stable linear feedback systems which are insensitive to Gaussian white noise. Variations of the LQG technique have also been devised for the synthesis of feedback systems with specified poles [4, pp. 77–87], [5], [6]. Thus, the LQG technique is a valuable design aid for satisfying the first three of the aforementioned design constraints.

The results which follow show how the multivariable LQG design can satisfy constraints of the fourth type, i.e., constraints requiring a system to be robust against variations in open-loop dynamics. The linear-quadratic state-feedback regulator, which we refer to as the LQSF regulator, is considered. The robustness of LQSF regulator designs against variations in open-loop dynamics is measured in terms of multiloop generalizations of the classical notions of *gain and phase margin*. Like classical gain and phase margin, the present results consider robustness as an input-output property characterizing variations in open-loop transfer functions which will not lead to closed-loop instability. Variations in system parameters (e.g., pole/zero locations) are considered by first determining how these variations map into variations in the open-loop frequency response matrix. It is shown that LQSF multivariable designs have the property of an infinite gain margin and at least $\pm 60°$ phase margin for each control channel. Similar results are derived for nonlinear perturbations in the feedback loop.

Such robustness results may appear incorrect at first glance, especially to control engineers familiar with classical servomechanism design. It should be noted that in classical servomechanism design the nature of the compensators used (e.g., lead-lag networks) generally leads to excessive phase lag at high frequencies, so that one may never have the infinite gain margin property. However, it should be stressed that when one uses *full state-variable feedback* one, in effect, introduces a multitude of phase-lag-correcting zeros in the compensator without introducing corresponding lag-producing poles. It is this abundance of zeros together with the linear-quadratic optimal design procedure that results in the surprising robustness properties of LQSF designs.

Exploiting the mathematical duality between Kalman filters and linear-quadratic optimal feedback controllers, the authors have shown that the robustness results of this paper lead to conditions for the nondivergence of the estimates generated by nonlinear filters of the type considered by Gilman and Rhodes [33]; these dual results will be the topic of a future publication. In contrast to the results presented here, the dual nonlinear filtering results require the availability of an exact description of the system under consideration and hence have no comparable robustness interpretation. It can be shown that substituting the nondivergent state estimate from this type of filter for the true state in a nonlinear state feedback regulator will not destabilize the closed-loop system.

In order to provide a more detailed and realistic bridge between the classical and modern approaches, especially with respect to robustness issues, one has to examine the case in which not all state variables are available for feedback. In the modern control approach, one would then have to use a state reconstructor (Luenberger observer or constant gain Kalman filter). The overall robust-

Manuscript received April 5, 1976; revised October 21, 1976. Paper recommended by P. R. Bélanger, Chairman of the IEEE S-CS Optimal Systems Committee. This work was conducted at the M.I.T. Electronic Systems Laboratory and supported in part by the NASA/AMES Research Center under Grant NGL-22-009-124 and by the AFOSR under Grant 72-2273.

The authors are with the Department of Electrical Engineering, Massachusetts Institute of Technology, Cambridge, MA 02139.

Reprinted with *IEEE Trans. on Automat. Contr.*, vol. AC-22, pp. 173–179, Apr. 1977.

ness properties of such designs are not entirely settled as yet; they will be addressed in a future publication. Also there are interesting and as yet unresolved issues of the robustness properties of output (or limited-state) variable feedback designs using quadratic performance criteria [31].

II. Previous Work

The fundamental work on the robustness of feedback systems is due to Bode [1, pp. 451–488]. Employing the Nyquist stability criterion, Bode showed how the notions of gain and phase margin can be exploited to arrive at a simple and useful means for characterizing the classes of variations in open-loop dynamics which will not destabilize single-input feedback systems. While Bode's concern was primarily with feedback amplifiers rather than control systems, his ideas have come to play a key role in the design of control systems. The control engineering implications of Bode's ideas are further developed by, for example, Horowitz [2]. Although the Nyquist criterion has been extended to multiloop feedback systems [7] and [8], there has as yet been only limited success in exploiting the multiloop version in the analysis of multiloop feedback system robustness [9]–[14].

Regarding the robustness properties specific to LQSF regulators, perhaps the most significant result is due to Anderson and Moore [4, pp. 70–76]. Exploiting the fact that single-input LQSF regulators have a return-difference greater than unity at all frequencies [15], these authors show that single-input LQSF regulator designs have $\pm 60°$ phase margin, infinite gain margin, and 50 percent gain reduction tolerance. It has also been shown that the gain properties extend to memoryless nonlinear gains of the type shown in Fig. 1 ([16] and [4, pp. 96–98]).[1] Related results by Barnett and Storey [18] and Wong [19], [35] parameterize a class of linear, constant perturbations in feedback gain which will not destabilize a multiloop LQSF regulator. A generalization of the latter result to multiloop nonlinearities in optimal nonlinear state-feedback regulators with quadratic performance index is incorrectly attributed to [16] by [20]. Insofar as the generalization stated in [20] applies to LQSF regulators, it is essentially equivalent to Theorem 1 of this paper.

Various other results have been produced which are more or less indirectly related to the question considered here. Issues related to the inverse problem of optimal control, i.e., the characterization of the properties of optimal systems, are considered by [15] and [20]–[24]. The question of sensitivity in LQSF regulators is considered by [10], [15], and [25]–[28]. The stability conditions of Zames [29], [30] involving loop gain, conicity, and positivity have many features in common with the results which are presented here.

[1]This result is attributed by Anderson [16] to Sage [17].

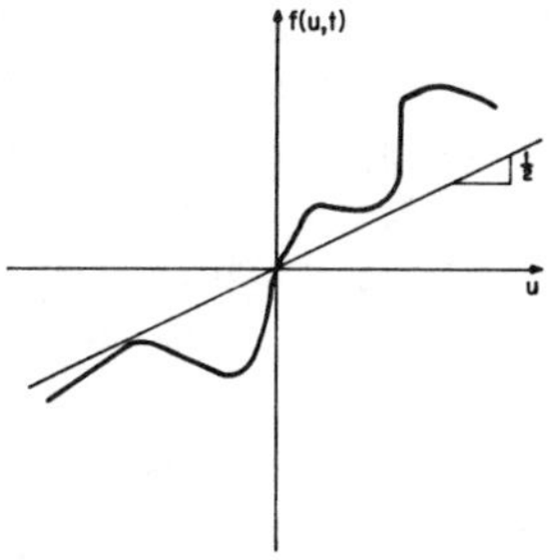

Fig. 1. Nondestabilizing nonlinear feedback gain.

III. Definitions and Notation

The following conventions of notation and terminology are used:

1) $A^T(x^T)$ denotes the transpose of the matrix A (the vector x).

2) A^* denotes the adjoint of the matrix A (i.e., the complex-conjugate of A^T).

3) We say that the function $x:[0,\infty)\rightarrow R^n$ is *square-integrable* if

$$\|x\|^2 \equiv \int_0^\infty x^T(t)x(t)\,dt < \infty.$$

For all square-integrable x, the quantity $\|x\|$ is called the *norm* of x.

4) The term *operator* is reserved for functions which map functions into functions. For example, a dynamical system may be viewed as an operator mapping input time-functions into output time-functions.

5) We say that an operator $\mathfrak{N}$ with $\mathfrak{N}\mathbf{0}=\mathbf{0}$ has *finite gain* if there exists a constant $k<\infty$ such that

$$\|\mathfrak{N}u\| < k\|u\|$$

for all square-integrable u.

6) We say that an operator mapping input time-functions into output time-functions is *nonanticipative* if the value assumed by the output function at any time t_0 depends only on the values of the input-function at times $t \leqslant t_0$.

7) If a function $x:[0,\infty)\rightarrow R^n$ has the property that

$$\lim_{t\rightarrow\infty} x(t) = \mathbf{0},$$

then we say that x is *asymptotically stable*. A system of ordinary differential equations is *asymptotically stable in the large* if every solution is asymptotically stable.

8) If (S) denotes the system $\dot{x}(t)=(\mathcal{F}x)(t)$ where $\mathcal{F}\mathbf{0}=\mathbf{0}$, we say that the pair $[H,S]$ is *detectable* if for each $x:[0,\infty)\rightarrow R^n$ satisfying (S) with x not square-integrable, Hx is also not square-integrable. The significance of detectability is most apparent if we consider $x(t)$ as a description of the internal dynamics of some physical system and $(Hx)(t)$ as the observed output. Viewed in this manner, detectability means essentially that unstable behavior in the system's internal dynamics always results in

an output which is unstable. For example, if H is a nonsingular square matrix, then $[H,S]$ will be detectable.

9) We say that an operator mapping time-functions into time-functions is *memoryless* if the value assumed by its output function at any instant t_0 depends only upon t_0 and the instantaneous value of the input function at time t_0.

10) $A>0$ ($A\geqslant 0$) is used to indicate that the matrix A is positive definite (semidefinite).

11) We say that a rational transfer function $P(s)$ is *proper* if $P(s)$ has at least as many poles as zeros.

IV. Problem Formulation

The linear-quadratic-state-feedback (LQSF) regulator problem can be formulated as follows:

$$\left.\begin{aligned}&\min_u J(x,u)\\ &\text{subject to}\\ &\dot{x}(t)=Ax(t)+Bu(t), \qquad x(0)=x_0\\ &x(t)\in R^n, u(t)\in R^m, A\in R^{n\times n}, B\in R^{n\times m}\end{aligned}\right\} \quad (1)$$

where the performance index $J(x,u)$ is given by

$$\left.\begin{aligned}&J(x,u)=\int_0^\infty \left[x^T(t)Qx(t)+u^T(t)Ru(t)\right]dt\\ &Q=Q^T\geqslant 0, \quad R=R^T>0.\end{aligned}\right\} \quad (2)$$

The optimal control $u^*(t)$ and the associated optimal state-trajectory $x^*(t)$ are given by

$$\left.\begin{aligned}&\dot{x}^*(t)=Ax^*(t)+Bu^*(t), \qquad x^*(0)=x_0\\ &u^*(t)=-Hx^*(t)\equiv -R^{-1}B^TKx^*(t)\end{aligned}\right\} \quad (\Sigma^*)$$

where $K=K^T\geqslant 0$ satisfies the Riccati equation

$$0=KA+A^TK-KBR^{-1}B^TK+Q. \quad (3)$$

The minimal value of the performance index is

$$J(x^*,u^*)=x_0^TKx_0. \quad (4)$$

The class of systems considered here are perturbed versions of (Σ^*) satisfying

$$\left.\begin{aligned}&\frac{d}{dt}\tilde{x}(t)=A\tilde{x}(t)+(B\mathfrak{N}\tilde{u})(t), \qquad \tilde{x}(0)=x_0\\ &\tilde{u}(t)=-H\tilde{x}(t)\end{aligned}\right\} \quad (\tilde{\Sigma})$$

where A, B, x_0, and H are the same as in (Σ^*). We assume that $\mathfrak{N}$ is a finite-gain, nonanticipative operator with $\mathfrak{N}0=0$ (see Fig. 2).[2]

[2]The condition $\mathfrak{N}0=0$ is not restrictive since we can always consider the dc or steady-state effects separately as is common engineering practice.

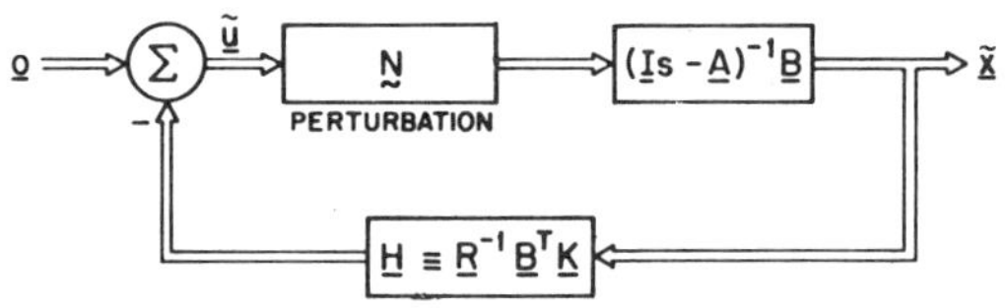

Fig. 2. Perturbed LQSF regulator $(\tilde{\Sigma})$.

V. Results

The two theorems which follow quantitatively characterize the tolerance of $(\tilde{\Sigma})$ to perturbations $\mathfrak{N}$. It is noted that the significance of these results is not restricted to systems with perturbations originating only at the point shown in Fig. 2. Rather, it is only necessary that the system under consideration have open-loop input/output behavior which is the same as the open-loop behavior of $(\tilde{\Sigma})$. Both of the theorems which follow have interpretations in terms of generalizations of the classical notions of gain and phase margin. The proofs are given in the Appendix.

Theorem 1 (LQSF Multiloop Nonlinear Gain Tolerance): Let the perturbation $\mathfrak{N}$ of $(\tilde{\Sigma})$ be a memoryless, time-varying nonlinearity

$$(\mathfrak{N}u)(t)=f(u(t),t). \quad (5)$$

If there exists a constant $\beta\geqslant 0$ and a constant $k<\infty$ such that

$$ku^Tu\geqslant u^Tf(R^{-1}u,t)\geqslant\frac{1+\beta}{2}u^TR^{-1}u \quad (6)$$

for all $u\in R^m$ and all $t\in[0,\infty)$, then

$$J(x^*,u^*)\geqslant\int_0^\infty\left[\tilde{x}^T(t)Q\tilde{x}(t)+\beta\tilde{u}^T(t)R\tilde{u}(t)\right]dt \quad (7)$$

and if, additionally, $[Q^{1/2},\tilde{\Sigma}]$ is detectable then $(\tilde{\Sigma})$ is asymptotically stable. □

In Theorem 1, the least conservative stability result is obtained with $\beta=0$. However, in this case, the bound (7) may be more conservative than necessary.

Theorem 2 (LQSF Multiloop Gain and Phase Margin): Let the perturbation $\mathfrak{N}$ of $(\tilde{\Sigma})$ be a finite-gain, linear-time-invariant operator $\mathfrak{L}$ with rational transfer function matrix $L(s)$. If for all ω

$$L(j\omega)R^{-1}+R^{-1}L^*(j\omega)-R^{-1}\geqslant 0 \quad (8)$$

and if $[Q^{1/2},\tilde{\Sigma}]$ is detectable, then $(\tilde{\Sigma})$ is asymptotically stable. □

The results of Theorems 1 and 2 apply only in situations where the perturbation $\mathfrak{N}$ is either memoryless or linear time-invariant. While this covers many interesting situations, these are not the most general results possible. In [34, Appendix B] it is shown that the stability conditions of Theorems 1 and 2 are actually special cases of a more abstract result concerning the input/output stability of a class of systems including $(\tilde{\Sigma})$ as a special case. The possibility of nonlinear time-varying dynamical perturbations in the A-matrix is also considered.

It is noted that conditions (7) and (8) may be difficult to verify in general, requiring ingenuity and perhaps the aid of a digital computer. Likewise, the condition of detectability may not be easy to verify rigorously, though physical considerations may often make detectability a virtual certainty. In the next section, a special case is considered in which detectability is assured and (7) and (8) are relatively easy to verify.

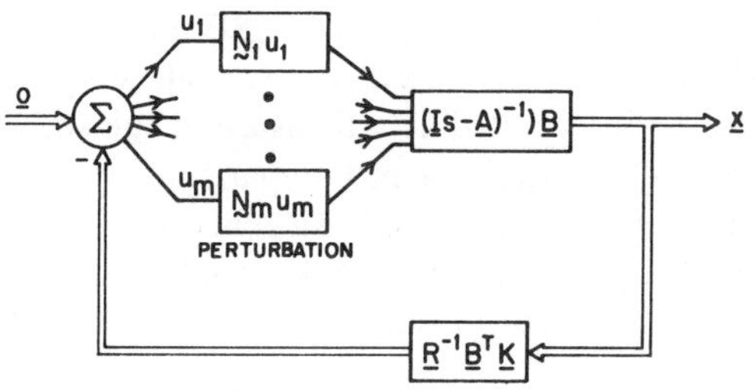

Fig. 3. LQSF regulator with noninteracting perturbations in each control loop.

VI. Discussion

Theorems 1 and 2 characterize a wide class of variations in open-loop dynamics which can be tolerated by LQSF regulator designs. To appreciate the significance of these results and, in particular, their relation to classical gain and phase margin, it is instructive to consider the special case depicted in Fig. 3 in which

$$\boldsymbol{Q}>\boldsymbol{0} \tag{9}$$

$$\boldsymbol{R}=\operatorname{diag}(r_1,\cdots,r_m)\equiv\begin{bmatrix} r_1 & 0 & \cdots & 0 \\ 0 & r_2 & \cdots & 0 \\ \cdots & \cdots & \cdots & \cdots \\ 0 & 0 & \cdots & r_m \end{bmatrix} \tag{10}$$

and the perturbation $\mathfrak{N}$ satisfies

$$\mathfrak{N}\boldsymbol{u}=\begin{bmatrix} \mathfrak{N}_1 u_1 \\ \cdot \\ \cdot \\ \cdot \\ \mathfrak{N}_m u_m \end{bmatrix} \tag{11}$$

so that the perturbations in the various feedback loops are noninteracting. Condition (9) ensures that $[Q^{1/2},\tilde{\Sigma}]$ is detectable and (10) and (11) simplify the verification of conditions (7) and (8).

In this case Theorem 1 specializes to the following.

Corollary 3: If the perturbed system $(\tilde{\Sigma})$ satisfies (9)–(11), if each of the perturbations $\mathfrak{N}_i$ is memoryless with $(\mathfrak{N}_i u_i)(t)\equiv f_i(u_i(t),t)$, and if for some $k<\infty$, some $\beta\geqslant 0$, and all $t\in[0,\infty)$,

$$f_i(0,t)=0 \tag{12a}$$

$$k\geqslant\frac{1}{u}f_i(u,t)\geqslant\frac{\beta+1}{2},\qquad \text{for all } u\neq 0 \tag{12b}$$

(see Fig. 1), then $(\tilde{\Sigma})$ is asymptotically stable in the large and (7) holds. □

Proof: This follows immediately from Theorem 1. □

If we consider the case in which the $\mathfrak{N}_i$'s of the system in Fig. 3 are linear time-invariant operators, then Theorem 2 becomes Corollary 4.

Corollary 4: If the perturbed system $(\tilde{\Sigma})$ satisfies (9)–(11) and if each of the perturbations $\mathfrak{N}_i$ is linear-time-invariant with proper rational transfer function $P_i(s)$, $\operatorname{Re}[s_j]<0$ for each pole s_j of $P_i(s)$, and $\operatorname{Re}[P_i(j\omega)]\geqslant 1/2$ for all ω, then $(\tilde{\Sigma})$ is asymptotically stable in the large. □

Proof: The condition $\operatorname{Re}[s_j]<0$ assures that $\mathfrak{N}$ has finite gain. Taking $\boldsymbol{L}(s)=\operatorname{diag}(P_i(s))$, the result follows immediately from Theorem 2. □

From Corollary 3, it is clear that the sufficient condition for stability

$$\frac{1}{u}f(u)>\frac{1}{2}, \tag{13}$$

proved in [4, pp. 96–98] and [16] for single-input LQSF regulators, generalizes to multiloop systems when $R=\operatorname{diag}(r_1,\cdots,r_m)$.

From Corollary 4, the following two results follow directly.

Corollary 5 (LQSF ± 60° Multiloop Phase Margin): If $\boldsymbol{Q}$ and $\boldsymbol{R}$ satisfy (9) and (10), then a phase shift ϕ_i with $|\phi_i|\leqslant 60°$ in the respective feedback loops of each of the controls u_i will leave an LQSF regulator asymptotically stable in the large. □

Proof: Take $P_i(j\omega)=e^{j\phi_i(\omega)}$. From Corollary 4, we require $\cos\phi_i(\omega)\geqslant\frac{1}{2}$ or $|\phi_i(\omega)|\leqslant\cos^{-1}(1/2)=60°$. □

Corollary 6 (Multiloop LQSF Infinite Gain Margin and 50 Percent Gain Reduction Tolerance): If $\boldsymbol{Q}$ and $\boldsymbol{R}$ satisfy (9) and (10), then the insertion of linear constant gains $a_i\geqslant\frac{1}{2}$ into the feedback loops of the respective controls u_i will leave an LQSF regulator asymptotically stable in the large. □[3]

Proof: Follows trivially from Corollary 4. □

Corollaries 5 and 6 are obvious *multiloop* generalizations of the previously established result [4, pp. 70–76] that single-input LQSF regulators have infinite gain margin, at least ±60° phase margin, and at least 50 percent gain reduction tolerance.

VII. Conclusions

Results have been generated which quantitatively characterize a wide class of variations in open-loop dynamics which will not destabilize LQSF regulators. A ±60° phase margin property of LQSF regulators has been established for multiloop systems (Corollary 5). The class of nondestabilizing linear feedback perturbations for multiloop LQSF regulators has been extended to include dynamical, transfer-function perturbations (Theorem 2). A nonlinearity tolerance property for LQSF regulators has been proved (Theorem 1). An upper bound on the performance

[3]Corollary 6 is a special case of a result proved by Wong [19], [35].

index change in a perturbed LQSF system has been established [(7) of Theorem 1 and Corollary 3]. The latter result can be interpreted as a measure of the stability of a perturbed LQSF regulator in comparison with the unperturbed regulator. The process of generating these results has brought pertinent previous results [4, pp. 70–76, 96–98], [16], [18]–[20] together under a unified theoretical framework.

The results presented show that modern multiloop LQSF regulators have excellent robustness properties as measured by the classical criteria of gain and phase margin, thus strengthening the link between modern and classical feedback theory. Additionally, these results show that multiloop LQSF regulator designs can tolerate a good deal of nonlinearity. The quantitative nature of the results suggests that they may be useful in the synthesis of robust controllers.

Although the results presented all specify that the tolerable perturbations be measured with respect to a perfect state-measurement LQSF system, it is apparent that statements may also be made about the general LQG regulator if the effect of the Kalman filter on the system's open-loop dynamics is viewed as a component of the perturbation $\mathfrak{N}$.

Appendix

Proofs of Theorems 1 and 2

We begin by introducing the following notation to facilitate the proofs.

1) The inner-product space $L_2^n[0,\infty)$ is defined by

$$L_2^n[0,\infty)=\left\{x|x:[0,\infty)\to R^n, \int_0^\infty x^T(t)x(t)\,dt<\infty\right\} \tag{A1a}$$

$$\langle x,y\rangle=\int_0^\infty x^T(t)y(t)\,dt. \tag{A1b}$$

2) The extension $L_{2e}^n[0,\infty)$ of $L_2^n[0,\infty)$ is defined by

$$L_{2e}^n[0,\infty)=\left\{x|x:[0,\infty)\to R^n, \int_0^\tau x^T(t)x(t)\,dt<\infty \text{ for all } \tau\right\} \tag{A2a}$$

$$\langle x,y\rangle_e=\begin{cases}\langle x,y\rangle, & \text{if the integral (A1b) converges}\\ \infty, & \text{otherwise.}\end{cases} \tag{A2b}$$

3) The linear truncation operator $\mathcal{P}_\tau: L_{2e}^n[0,\infty)\to L_2^n[0,\infty)$ is defined by

$$(\mathcal{P}_\tau x)(t)=\begin{cases}x(t), & \text{if } t\in[0,\tau]\\ 0, & \text{otherwise.}\end{cases} \tag{A3}$$

For brevity of notation we denote $\mathcal{P}_\tau x$ by x_τ.

The key result in the proofs of Theorems 1 and 2 is the following.

Theorem A.1: If the perturbation $\mathfrak{N}$ of $(\tilde{\Sigma})$ is such that for some $\beta\geq 0$

$$\langle u,(2\mathfrak{N}-(1+\beta)I)R^{-1}u\rangle\geq 0 \tag{A4}$$

for all $u\in L_2^m[0,\infty)$, then 1)

$$x_0^TKx_0\geq\langle\tilde{x},Q\tilde{x}\rangle+\beta\langle\tilde{u},R\tilde{u}\rangle \tag{A5}$$

where $\tilde{x},\tilde{u}$ is the solution of $(\tilde{\Sigma})$, and 2) if, additionally, $[Q^{1/2},\tilde{\Sigma}]$ is detectable, then $\tilde{x}$ is asymptotically stable and square-integrable.

Proof: For K the solution of (3) and $\tilde{x}$ the solution of $(\tilde{\Sigma})$ with $\tilde{x}(0)=x_0$, we have that for every $\tau\in[0,\infty)$

$$\begin{aligned}x_0^TKx_0&=\tilde{x}^T(\tau)K\tilde{x}(\tau)-\int_0^\tau\frac{d}{dt}\left(\tilde{x}^T(t)K\tilde{x}(t)\right)dt\\&=\tilde{x}^T(\tau)K\tilde{x}(\tau)-2\langle K\tilde{x}_\tau,(A-B\mathfrak{N}R^{-1}B^TK)\tilde{x}_\tau\rangle\\&\geq-2\langle\tilde{x}_\tau,K(A-B\mathfrak{N}R^{-1}B^TK)\tilde{x}_\tau\rangle\\&=\langle\tilde{x}_\tau,\left(KB(2\mathfrak{N}-I)R^{-1}B^TK+Q\right)\tilde{x}_\tau\rangle.\end{aligned} \tag{A6}$$

Using (A4) and the fact that $\tilde{u}=-R^{-1}B^TK\tilde{x}$, we have

$$\begin{aligned}&x_0Kx_0-\langle\tilde{x}_\tau,Q\tilde{x}_\tau\rangle-\beta\langle\tilde{u}_\tau,R\tilde{u}_\tau\rangle\\&\quad\geq\langle x_\tau,KB(2\mathfrak{N}-(1+\beta)I)R^{-1}B^TK\tilde{x}_\tau\rangle\\&\quad=\langle B^TK\tilde{x}_\tau,(2\mathfrak{N}-(1+\beta)I)R^{-1}B^TK\tilde{x}_\tau\rangle\\&\quad\geq 0.\end{aligned} \tag{A7}$$

Rearranging and taking the limit $\tau\to\infty$, (A5) follows. Now, suppose for the purpose of argument that $\tilde{x}$ is not square-integrable. Since $[Q^{1/2},\tilde{\Sigma}]$ is detectable, this means $\langle Q^{1/2}\tilde{x}_\tau, Q^{1/2}\tilde{x}_\tau\rangle$ increases without bound as τ increases, contradicting (A5). Therefore, $\tilde{x}$ is square-integrable. By hypothesis $\mathfrak{N}$ and hence $A-B\mathfrak{N}R^{-1}B^TK$ have finite gain. Thus, $\dot{\tilde{x}}=(A-B\mathfrak{N}R^{-1}B^TK)\tilde{x}$ is also square-integrable. Since both $\tilde{x}$ and $\dot{\tilde{x}}$ are square-integrable, it follows (cf. [32, pp. 235–37]) that $\tilde{x}$ is asymptotically stable. □

Proof of Theorem 1: Equation (6) ensures that (A4) is satisfied. Since, for memoryless $\mathfrak{N}$, $\tilde{x}$ is the state of $(\tilde{\Sigma})$ and since the initial time $t=0$ is not distinguished, the asymptotic stability in the large of $(\tilde{\Sigma})$ is assured if $\tilde{x}$ is asymptotically stable for every initial state $\tilde{x}(0)=x_0$. Theorem 1 follows from (4) and Theorem A1. □

Proof of Theorem 2: From (8) and Parseval's theorem it follows that, for every $u\in L_2[0,\infty)$

$$\begin{aligned}&\langle u,(2\mathfrak{N}-I)R^{-1}u\rangle\\&\quad=\langle u,(2\mathcal{L}-I)R^{-1}u\rangle\\&\quad=\frac{1}{2\pi}\int_{-\infty}^{\infty}\mathfrak{U}^*(j\omega)\left(L(j\omega)R^{-1}+R^{-1}L^*(j\omega)-R^{-1}\right)\mathfrak{U}(j\omega)\,d\omega\\&\quad\geq 0\end{aligned} \tag{A8}$$

where $\mathfrak{U}(j\omega)$ is the Fourier transform of u. Thus, (A4) is satisfied with $\beta=0$. Since $[Q^{1/2},\tilde{\Sigma})$ is detectable, Theorem A1 implies that $\tilde{x}$ is asymptotically stable, regardless of the value of x_0. It follows that the weighting pattern $W(t)$

(i.e., the response of $(\tilde{\Sigma})$ to an impulse $I_n\delta(t)$ where $\delta(t)$ is the Dirac delta function) is asymptotically stable. Thus, provided there are no unstable modes which are uncontrollable or unobservable, the closed-loop system is asymptotically stable in the large. Such modes correspond to "pole-zero cancellations" in the Laplace transform of $W(t)$,

$$\mathcal{W}(s)=\left[Is+A-BL(s)R^{-1}B^TK\right]^{-1}. \tag{A9}$$

The dynamics of $(\tilde{\Sigma})$ are described (not necessarily minimally) by the differential equations

$$\begin{bmatrix} Is-A & -B \\ L_N(s)R^{-1}B^TK & L_D(s) \end{bmatrix}\begin{bmatrix} \tilde{x} \\ \tilde{u} \end{bmatrix}=0 \tag{A10}$$

where $s=d/dt$, $L_N(s)$ and $L_D(s)$ are polynomial matrices satisfying $L(s)=L_D^{-1}(s)L_N(s)$, and the roots of $\det[L_D(s)]$ are the poles of $L(s)$. For $(\tilde{\Sigma})$ to be asymptotically stable in the large, we require that the roots of the characteristic polynomial $p(s)$ associated with (A10) all have negative real parts. Using a well-known matrix identity, we have from (A9) and (A10)

$$\begin{aligned} p(s) &\equiv \det\begin{bmatrix} Is-A & -B \\ L_N(s)R^{-1}B^TK & L_D(s) \end{bmatrix} \\ &= \det\left[L_D(s)\right]\cdot\det\left[Is-A+BL(s)R^{-1}B^TK\right] \\ &= \frac{\det\left[L_D(s)\right]}{\det\left[\mathcal{W}(s)\right]} \end{aligned} \tag{A11}$$

and therefore

$$\det\left[\mathcal{W}(s)\right]=\frac{\det\left[L_D(s)\right]}{p(s)}. \tag{A12}$$

Now, from standard results on linear systems we have that $W(t)$ is of the form

$$W(t)=\sum_{s_i\in\mathcal{C}(W)} C_i(t)e^{s_it} \tag{A13}$$

where $C_i(t)$ are nonzero matrices of polynomials in t and the set $\mathcal{C}(W)$ satisfies

$$\left.\begin{aligned} &P(W)-Z(W)\subseteq\mathcal{C}(W)\subseteq P(W) \\ &\text{where, in view of (A12),} \\ &Z(W)\equiv\{s_i \mid \det\left[L_D(s_i)\right]=0\} \\ &P(W)\equiv\{s_i \mid p(s_i)=0\}. \end{aligned}\right\} \tag{A14}$$

[We call the members of $Z(W)$ and $P(W)$, respectively, the zeros and the poles of $\mathcal{W}(s)$.] Since $W(t)$ is square-integrable,

$$\operatorname{Re}\left[s_i\right]<0, \qquad \text{for all } s_i\in\mathcal{C}(W). \tag{A15}$$

From (A12) and (A14) it follows that, except for roots of $p(s)$ which cancel with the roots of the polynomial $\det[L_D(s)]$, all roots of the characteristic polynomial $p(s)$ are contained in $\mathcal{C}(W)$. Since L has finite gain, it follows that all the roots of $\det[L_D(s)]$ have negative real parts. Thus any cancellations in (A12) can involve only roots with negative real parts. We conclude that all the roots of the characteristic polynomial $p(s)$ have negative real parts, and, hence, $(\tilde{\Sigma})$ is asymptotically stable in the large. □

References

[1] H. W. Bode, *Network Analysis and Feedback Amplifier Design.* New York: Van Nostrand, 1945.

[2] I. M. Horowitz, *Synthesis of Feedback Systems.* New York: Academic, 1963.

[3] M. Athans, "The role and use of the stochastic linear-quadratic-Gaussian problem in control system design," *IEEE Trans. Automat. Contr.*, vol. AC-16, pp. 529–552, Dec. 1971.

[4] B. D. O. Anderson and J. B. Moore, *Linear Optimal Control.* Englewood Cliffs, NJ: Prentice-Hall, 1971.

[5] C. H. Houpis and C. T. Constantinides, "Relationship between conventional-control-theory figures of merit and quadratic performance index in optimal control theory for a single-input/single-output system," *Proc. Inst. Elec. Eng.*, vol. 120, pp. 138–142. July 1973.

[6] M. A. Woodhead and B. Porter, "Optimal modal control," *Trans. Inst. Meas. Contr.*, vol. 6, pp. 301–303, 1973.

[7] H. H. Rosenbrock, "Design of multivariable control systems using inverse Nyquist array," *Proc. Inst. Elec. Eng.*, vol. 116, pp. 1929–1936, 1969.

[8] P. D. McMorran, "Extension of the inverse Nyquist method," *Electron. Lett.*, vol. 6, pp. 800–801, 1970.

[9] J. J. Belletrutti and A. G. J. MacFarlane, "Characteristic loci techniques in multivariable-control-system design," *Proc. Inst. Elec. Eng.*, vol. 118, pp. 1291–1296, 1971.

[10] A. G. J. MacFarlane, "Return-difference and return-ratio matrices and their use in the analysis and design of multivariable feedback control systems," *Proc. Inst. Elec. Eng.*, vol. 117, pp. 2037–2049, Oct. 1970.

[11] H. H. Rosenbrock, "Progress in the design of multivariable control systems," *Trans. Inst. Meas. Contr.*, vol. 4, pp. 9–11, 1971.

[12] A. G. J. MacFarlane, "A survey of some recent results in linear multivariable feedback theory," *Automatica*, vol. 8, pp. 455–492, 1972.

[13] A. G. J. MacFarlane and J. J. Belletrutti, "The characteristic locus design method," *Automatica*, vol. 9, pp. 575–588, 1973.

[14] I. Horowtiz and M. Sidi, "Synthesis of cascaded multiple-loop feedback systems with large plant parameter ignorance," *Automatica*, vol. 9, pp. 589–600, Sept. 1973.

[15] R. E. Kalman, "When is a linear control system optimal," *Trans. ASME* (J. Basic Eng.), vol. 86, pp. 51–60, Mar. 1964.

[16] B. D. O. Anderson, "Stability results for optimal systems," *Electron. Lett.*, vol. 5, p. 545, Oct. 1969.

[17] A. P. Sage, *Optimum Systems Control.* Englewood Cliffs, NJ: Prentice-Hall, 1968.

[18] S. Barnett and C. Storey, "Insensitivity of optimal linear control systems to persistent changes in parameters," *Int. J.Contr.*, vol. 4, pp. 179–184, 1966.

[19] P. K. Wong, "On the interaction structure of multi-input feedback control systems," M. S. thesis, Massachusetts Inst. Technol., Cambridge, MA, Sept. 1975.

[20] P. J. Moylan and B. D. O. Anderson, "Nonlinear regulator theory and an inverse optimal control problem," *IEEE Trans. Automat. Contr.*, AC-18, pp. 460–465, Oct. 1973.

[21] B.D.O. Anderson, "The inverse problem of optimal control," Stanford Electron. Lab., Stanford, CA, Rep. SEL-66-038 (TR 6560-3), Apr. 1966.

[22] B. P. Molinari, "The stable regulator and its inverse," *IEEE Trans. Automat. Contr.*, vol. AC-18, pp. 454–459, Oct. 1973.

[23] J. C. Willems, "Least squares optimal control and the algebraic Riccati equation," *IEEE Trans. Automat. Contr.*, vol. AC-16, pp. 621–634, Dec. 1971.

[24] R. Yokoyama and E. Kinnen, "The inverse problem of the optimal regulator," *IEEE Trans. Automat. Contr.*, vol. AC-17, pp. 497–504, Aug. 1972.

[25] W. R. Perkins and J. B. Cruz, "The parameter variation problem in state feedback control systems," *Trans. ASME* (J. Basic Eng.), vol. 87, pp. 120–124, Mar. 1965.

[26] ——, "Feedback properties of linear regulators," *IEEE Trans. Automat. Contr.*, vol. AC-16, pp. 659–664, Dec. 1971.

[27] J. B. Cruz, Ed., *Feedback Systems.* New York: McGraw-Hill, 1972.

[28] ——, *System Sensitivity Analysis.* Stroudsburg, PA: Dowden, Hutchinson and Ross, 1973.

[29] G. Zames, "On the input-output stability of time-varying nonlinear feedback systems—Part I: Conditions using concepts of loop gain, conicity, and positivity," *IEEE Trans. Automat. Contr.*, vol. AC-11, pp. 228–238, Apr. 1966.

——, "On the input-output stability of time-varying nonlinear feedback systems—Part II: Conditions involving circles in the frequency plane and sector nonlinearities," *IEEE Trans. Automat. Contr.*, vol. AC-11, pp. 465–476, July 1966.

[31] W. S. Levine and M. Athans, "On the determination of the optimal constant output-feedback gains for linear multivariable systems," *IEEE Trans. Automat. Contr.*, vol. AC-15, pp. 44–48, Feb. 1970.

[32] C. A. Desoer and M. Vidyasagar, *Feedback Systems: Input-Output Properties.* New York: Academic, 1975.

[33] A. S. Gilman and I. S. Rhodes, "Cone-bounded nonlinearities and mean-square bounds—estimation upper bounds," *IEEE Trans. Automat. Contr.*, vol. AC-18, pp. 260–265, June 1973.

[34] M. G. Safonov and M. Athans, "Gain and phase margin for multiloop LQG regulators," in *Proc. 1976 IEEE Conf. Decision and Control*, Dec. 1976.

[35] P. K. Wong and M. Athans, "Closed-loop structural stability for linear-quadratic optimal systems," in *Proc. 1976 IEEE Conf. Decision and Control*, Dec. 1976; also *IEEE Trans. Automat. Contr.*, vol. AC-22, pp. 94–99, Feb. 1977.

Output Regulation and Internal Models—a Frequency Domain Approach*

GUNNAR BENGTSSON†‡

To regulate a plant against exogenous signals, a minimal order feedback compensator creates an internal model of the environment in the open loop cascaded compensator and plant; the loop being closed with any stabilizing feedback.

Key Word Index—Algebraic system theory; closed loop systems; control system synthesis; control theory; multivariable control systems; regulator theory; servomechanisms; Internal models.

Summary—The algebraic regulator problem is formulated and solved in a transfer matrix setting. It is shown that, provided the closed loop system disregarding disturbances is stable, a necessary and sufficient condition for output regulation to take place is that the open loop path consisting of the plant and compensator in cascade, contains a suitably defined internal model of the environment. The disturbance model is more general than the ones used before. The results also generalize earlier results on internal models since they are necessary and sufficient under weaker assumptions. The internal model property is used to construct a compensator which achieves output regulation and internal stability. It is shown that any such compensator can be obtained in two steps: (a) create an internal model of the environment in the forward path and (b) stabilize the system. Our concept of internal model generalize earlier definitions and, unlike most earlier results, is valid even if structural stability (robustness) is not imposed.

1. INTRODUCTION

A BASIC requirement on a closed loop system must be its ability to regulate against disturbances and/or track reference signals, described by suitable dynamic model classes. One aspect of this problem is the so-called algebraic regulator problem, which has attained much interest during the last few years, see e.g. [1–8]. With a few exceptions, see e.g. [6], the problem has been treated in a state space setting. In this paper we give a frequency analog and generalize some earlier results.

The concept of internal models plays a crucial role in regulator problems. The internal model principle can intuitively be expressed as: '*Any good regulator must create a model of the dynamic structure of the environment in the closed loop system*'.

The necessity of internal models is discussed in [9] and more abstractly in [10]. In [3], [8], and implicitly in [1], it is shown that a regulator which is to achieve steady state regulation despite certain small perturbations in system data (structural stability) must contain a certain duplicated model of the environment in the feedback part. This feature is thus necessary under the perturbations considered.

To establish the internal model principle mathematically it is desirable to formalize the problem under as weak assumptions as possible both on the concept of regulation and the model classes considered. In this paper, the existence of internal models is established in a frequency domain setting. This is done under fairly weak assumptions (structural stability is not imposed) and using a more general disturbance model than before. The necessity of internal models when structural stability is not imposed has also been shown in [11] in a state space setting.

We assume that the regulated variables coincide with the variables accessible for feedback. It is then both *necessary and sufficient* for output regulation to take place that the open loop path, consisting of the plant and the compensator in cascade, contains a suitably defined internal model of the environment. Our definition of the concept of internal model is different from that of [3], [8], especially in that it is property of the cascade of regulator and plant rather than the regulator alone. The difference is, of course, due to the requirement of structural stability used in [3], [8]. If this requirement is not imposed, there seems to be no reason to differ between the 'plant' and the 'regulator' in the feedback loop. Note also, that our definition of internal model is directly related to output regulation. The internal model criterion is stated in some different ways to show the relationships between different representations of a linear system and to illustrate the presence of an internal model in a signal flow graph.

An important feature of the internal model property is that it provides insight into the regulation problem without too much algebraic detail. Such considerations are of great importance in synthesis. Based on the internal model criterion, a compensator which achieves output regulation and internal stability is constructed. It is shown that any such compensator can be obtained as a cascade of two compensators, one which creates an internal model of the environment in the forward path and

*Received 27 April 1976; revised 14 February 1977. The original version of this paper was not presented at any IFAC Meeting. It was recommended for publication in revised form by associate editor T. Davidson.

†ASEA, Central Research and Development Dept. System Analysis KYYS, S-72183 Västerås, Sweden.

‡Part of this work was done while the author was visiting Dept. of Electrical Engineering, University of Toronto, Toronto, Canada.

one which stabilizes the system. The first one will be of minimal order. This direct use of internal models for compensation is believed to be new. Also the results generalize earlier results since they are valid for a more general disturbance model.

The paper is organized as follows. Some notations and algebraic preliminaries are given in Section 2. The class of models and output regulation in a transfer matrix setting are discussed in Section 3. Necessary and sufficient conditions for output regulation to take place are given in Section 4. In the same section we also discuss the role of internal models in the regulator problem. A compensator design based on internal models is outlined in Section 5. In the appendix, we discuss the solvability of a certain algebraic equation which is crucial for the compensator synthesis.

2. PRELIMINARIES

Notations

$\mathfrak{R}$, $\mathfrak{C}$ and $\mathfrak{R}(s)$ denote the fields of real numbers, complex numbers and rational functions in s with coefficients in $\mathfrak{R}$ respectively. $\mathfrak{R}[s]$ is the ring of polynomials in s with coefficients in $\mathfrak{R}$. Capital letters A, B, C,... denote real matrices. A rational function $r(s)$ is said to be proper if $r(\infty)<\infty$ and strictly proper if $r(\infty)=0$. A rational matrix is (strictly) proper if all its elements are (strictly) proper. A polynomial matrix $P(s)$ is said to be unimodular if $P(s)^{-1}$ exists and is also a polynomial matrix. A right divisor of a polynomial matrix $P(s)$ is a polynomial matrix $R(s)$ such that $P(s)=P_1(s)R(s)$ for some polynomial matrix $P_1(s)$. Two polynomial matrices are relatively right prime if they have no common right divisors except unimodular matrices. The analogous definitions are made for left divisors. The order of a rational matrix $T(s)$, written $\partial T(s)$, is defined as the sum of the degrees of the denominator polynomials in the Smith–McMillan form of $T(s)$. For proper rational matrices, the order of a rational matrix equals the order of a minimal state realization (and also the McMillan degree).

An arbitrary rational matrix $T(s)$ can uniquely be written as

$$T(s)=T(s)_c+T(s)_p \tag{2.1}$$

where $T(s)_c$ is strictly proper and $T(s)_p$ a polynomial matrix.

Many arguments from realization theory[12, 16] are used in the sequel.

Polynomial fraction representations

The following results can be found in [12, 13, 14]. The exposition given here follows basically that of [12]. A (left) fraction representation of a rational matrix $T(s)$ is a pair of polynomial matrices $P(s)$ and $Q(s)$ such that

$$T(s)=Q(s)^{-1}P(s)$$

Such a representation is said to be *minimal* if $\deg(\det Q(s))$ is the least possible. The *characteristic polynomial* for $T(s)$ is defined as $\det(Q(s))$ where $Q(s)$, $P(s)$ is minimal.

The following result is taken from [12].

Lemma 1. The following statements are equivalent:

(i) $Q(s)^{-1}P(s)$ *is a minimal fraction representation of* $T(s)$.

(ii) $Q(s)$ *and* $P(s)$ *are relatively left prime.*

(iii) $\partial T(s)=\deg(\det Q(s))$

(iv) *There are polynomial matrices* $X(s)$ *and* $Y(s)$ *such that* $Q(s)X(s)+P(s)Y(s)=I$.

Furthermore, if $Q_1(s)^{-1}P_1(s)$ and $Q_2(s)^{-1}P_2(s)$ are two minimal fraction representations of $T(s)$ then there exists a unimodular matrix $M(s)$ such that $Q_1(s)=M(s)Q_2(s)$ and $P_1(s)=M(s)P_2(s)$. The analogous results can directly be given for (right) fraction representations

$$T(s)=N(s)D(s)^{-1}$$

where $N(s)$ and $D(s)$ are polynomial matrices (consider the transpose).

3. FORMALIZATION

The model

The plant and its environment is described by one common linear, time invariant system Unlike [3], where an internal (state space) model is used, the total system is in this case described by an external (transfer matrix) model

$$y(s)=T(s)u(s)+D(s)w(s) \tag{3.1}$$

where $y(s)$ is the q-dimensional regulated output, $u(s)$ the m-dimensional control input and $w(s)$ an r-vector comprising all exogenous signals acting on the system. In (3.1), $D(s)$ is a proper rational matrix and $T(s)$ a strictly proper rational matrix. We assume that the regulated variables coincide with the variables accessible for feedback. The rational matrices $T(s)$ and $D(s)$ represent dynamic models of how the regulated variables are influenced by the control inputs and the exogenous inputs respectively. Therefore, we regard $T(s)$ as the *plant model* and $D(s)$ as the *disturbance model.*

To give physical interpretation to the concept of regulation below, the exogenous signal w can be either an impulse, the initial condition of a linear, time invariant system or the laplace transform of a bounded signal. It also makes sense to regard w as a white noise process.

A distinction should be made between the exogenous signal w and the actual disturbance or reference signal. The difference may be best illustrated by comparing with the state space formulation in [3]. In [3] the overall system is described by a state equation

$$\begin{aligned} \dot{x}_1 &= A_1x_1 + A_3x_2 + B_1u \\ \dot{x}_2 &= A_2x_2 \qquad x_2(0) = x_{20} \\ y &= C_1x_1 + C_2x_2. \end{aligned} \tag{3.2}$$

In (3.2) x_1 is the state of the plant and x_2 the disturbance. A laplace transform of (3.2) yields the description (3.1) with

$$\begin{aligned} T(s) &= C_1(s - A_1)^{-1}B_1 \\ D(s) &= (C_1(s - A_1)^{-1}A_3 + C_2)(s - A_2)^{-1} \\ w(s) &= x_{20}. \end{aligned} \tag{3.3}$$

In this case the exogenous signal is the initial state x_{20} while the actual disturbance is x_2. Working with external descriptions, there is no need to identify the internal variable x_2 unless more specific properties such as e.g. internal stability is desired. Internal stability will be an issue first when the compensator design is discussed in Section 5. Here we follow basically the same approach as is done for state space descriptions in [7], i.e. identify the plant by a minimal realization of $T(s)$ and regard the disturbance as described by the 'remaining' dynamics.

We also see that our disturbance model is more general than the one used in (3.2) since $D(s)$ is allowed to be an arbitrary proper rational matrix, cf. also (3.3).

Output regulation

The class of admissible controls in (3.1) is

$$u(s) = -F(s)y(s) \tag{3.4}$$

where $F(s)$ is a proper rational matrix. The purpose of control is to regulate $y(s)$ against the exogenous signal $w(s)$. Before giving a rigorous definition of output regulation, consider the following simple example. Assume the disturbance model in (3.1) is a ramp, i.e.

$$D(s) = \frac{I_r}{s^2}; \qquad w(s) = w_0 \in \Re^r.$$

There is no steady state error in y for any w_0 if and only if the transfer matrix from w to y in the closed loop system is stable, i.e. if and only if the poles of

$$(I + T(s)F(s))^{-1}\frac{I_r}{s^2}$$

are all within the open left halfplane of the complex plane.

With this simple example in mind, let

$$\mathfrak{C} = \mathfrak{C}^+ \cup \mathfrak{C}^- \tag{3.5}$$

be a disjoint portion of the complex plane, where $\mathfrak{C}^-$ is symmetric with respect to the real axis and contains at least one real point. Here, $\mathfrak{C}^-$ represents the 'good' part and $\mathfrak{C}^+$ the 'bad' part of the complex plane as judged by the position of the poles of the transfer functions. Note that $\mathfrak{C}^-$ is quite arbitrary and not just the open left halfplane, say.

A rational matrix $T(s)$ can be written uniquely as the sum of two strictly proper rational matrices $T(s)_+$ and $T(s)_-$ and a polynomial matrix $T(s)_p$ as

$$T(s) = T(s)_+ + T(s)_- + T(s)_p \tag{3.6}$$

where the poles of $T(s)_+$ and $T(s)_-$ are all within the regions $\mathfrak{C}^+$ and $\mathfrak{C}^-$ respectively. Such factorizations can easily be done e.g. using partial fraction expansions. A rational matrix $T(s)$ having all its poles within $\mathfrak{C}^-$ can then be expressed as $T(s)_+ = 0$. A rational matrix with this property is said to be *stable* with respect to $\mathfrak{C}^-$.

In analogy with the simple example above, it is required for *output regulation* that the closed loop transfer matrix from w to y obtained with feedback (3.4) is stable w.r.t. $\mathfrak{C}^-$, i.e.

$$((I + T_0(s))^{-1}D(s))_+ = 0 \tag{3.7}$$

where

$$T_0(s) = T(s)F(s). \tag{3.8}$$

This formulation simply reflects the fact that the environment has an unsatisfactory dynamic behaviour, e.g. too slow, oscillative, unstable etc., in comparison with what is required from the closed loop system. Physically, (3.7) can be interpreted in different ways depending on the signal w and the choice of stable region $\mathfrak{C}^-$. If w is an impulse and $\mathfrak{C}^-$ the open left half plane, (3.7) is equivalent to that y tends to zero when time tends to infinity. The same is true if w represents an initial condition as in (3.3). Classical control problems such as steady state regulation against steps, ramps, sinusoids etc. are therefore included. Also (3.7) is equivalent to y being bounded for all bounded signals w. If w represents white noise, (3.7) implies that we 'shape' the frequency spectrum for y by insisting that the poles of the closed loop transfer matrix are all within $\mathfrak{C}^-$.

4. OUTPUT REGULATION AND INTERNAL MODELS

The purpose of this section is to establish some principles for output regulation against modelled disturbances. It is shown that a model of the environment must be included in the feedback loop in a specified way. This is both necessary and sufficient for output regulation to take place, provided the closed loop system disregarding disturbances is stable.

Output regulation

Consider the total system (3.1) with feedback control (3.4). The signal flow for the closed loop system with exogenous signals is shown in Fig. 1. In Fig. 1 let $T_0(s) = T(s)F(s)$ be the open loop cascade of plant and compensator. Assume that $F(s)$ must be chosen so that the loop in Fig. 1 disregarding disturbances, is stable for a signal injection at node y, i.e.

$$(I+T_0(s))_+^{-1}=0 \tag{4.1}$$

where $(\cdot)_+$ is defined with respect to (3.5), i.e. all the poles of (4.1) must be within $\mathfrak{C}^-$. The property (4.1)

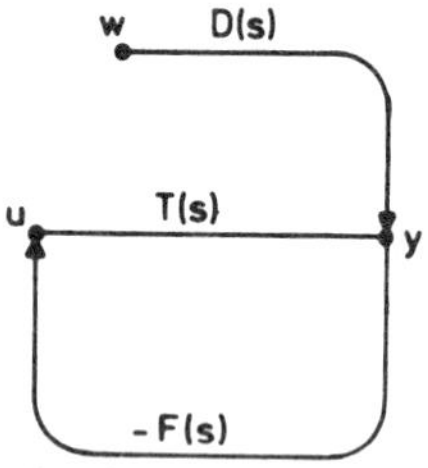

FIG. 1. Signal flow for the closed loop system with exogenous signals.

is denoted *loop stability*. Note that loop stability is a weaker assumption than internal stability* since unstable cancellations may occur in the cascade $T(s)F(s)$. Loop stability is, however, sufficient to establish the existence of an internal model as will be seen below. It is also required that *output regulation* takes place, i.e.

$$((I+T_0(s))^{-1}D(s))_+=0. \tag{4.2}$$

It is now possible to establish the following result.

Theorem 1. Assume that $F(s)$ is chosen so that loop stability holds. Output regulation takes place if and only if

$$\partial T_0(s)=\partial[T_0(s)\ D(s)_+] \tag{4.3}$$

where $\partial(\cdot)$ is the order of a rational matrix and $(\cdot)_+$ is defined with respect to (3.5).

To prove this theorem, the following lemma is used.

Lemma 2. Let $R_1(s)$ and $R_2(s)$ be two arbitrary rational matrices with minimal fraction representations $Q_1(s)^{-1}P_1(s)$ and $Q_2(s)^{-1}P_2(s)$ respectively. Then $\partial R_1(s)=\partial[R_1(s)\ R_2(s)]$ if and only if $Q_2(s)$ is a right divisor of $Q_1(s)$.

Proof. For brevity in exposition, we omit the argument s.

(if) There is a polynomial matrix D such that $Q_1 = DQ_2$. Hence,

$$[R_1\quad R_2]=Q_1^{-1}[P_1\quad DP_2]$$

is a fraction representation. Therefore, by Lemma 1 (iii),

$$\partial[R_1\quad R_2]\leqq \deg\det Q_1=\partial R_1.$$

Since the inequality trivially holds in the other direction, equality must be the case.

(only if) Let $Q^{-1}P=Q_1Q_2^{-1}P_2$ for a minimal fraction representation $Q^{-1}P$. Then

$$[R_1\quad R_2]=(QQ_1)^{-1}[QP_1\quad P] \tag{4.4}$$

is also a fraction representation. By Lemma 1, there are polynomial matrices X_i, $i=1, 2, 3, 4$, such that $QX_1+PX_2=I$ and $Q_1X_3+P_1X_4=I$. Multiply the second expression from right by X_1 and from left by Q and substitute QX_1 from the first expression. This yields

$$QQ_1(X_3X_1)+[QP_1\quad P]\begin{pmatrix}X_4X_1\\ X_2\end{pmatrix}=I$$

i.e. (4.4) is a minimal fraction representation according to Lemma 1. Therefore, by Lemma 1 (iii)

$$\partial[R_1\quad R_2]=\deg\det(QQ_1)=\deg\det Q_1+\deg\det Q$$

$$\partial R_1=\deg\det Q_1.$$

Since equality holds, $\deg(\det Q)=0$, i.e. $\det Q$ must be a nonzero real number since Q^{-1} exists. Hence, Q is unimodular and therefore $Q_1Q_2^{-1}P_2$ is a polynomial matrix, and since Q_2 and P_2 are relatively left prime, $Q_1Q_2^{-1}$ is a polynomial matrix.

Proof of Theorem 1. Write $D=D_++D_-+D_P$ analogous to (3.6). Then

$$(I+T_0)^{-1}D=(I+T_0)^{-1}D_++(I+T_0)^{-1}(D_-+D_P).$$

Since $(I+T_0)^{-1}$ is stable w.r.t. $\mathfrak{C}^-$ by assumption, the second term must always be stable. Therefore, (4.2) is equivalent to

$$((I+T_0)^{-1}D_+)_+=0.$$

Now, let $T_0=Q_0^{-1}P_0$ and $D_+=Q_1^{-1}P_1$ be minimal fraction representations. Then

$$(I+T_0)^{-1}=(Q_0+P_0)^{-1}Q_0$$

*The concept of internal stability is discussed in Section 5.

which shows that $\det(Q_0+P_0)$ has all its zeros within $\mathbb{C}^-$. Furthermore,

$$T^*=(I+T_0)^{-1}D_+=(Q_0+P_0)^{-1}Q_0Q_1^{-1}P_1.$$

Since $(Q_0+P_0)^{-1}$ is stable and Q_1^{-1} completely unstable, T^* is stable iff $Q_0Q_1^{-1}P_1$ is a polynomial matrix. Since Q_1, P_1 is relatively left prime, T^* is stable iff $Q_0Q_1^{-1}$ is a polynomial matrix, which by Lemma 2 is equivalent to the condition in the theorem. □

The relationship between the result of Theorem 1 and internal models is discussed in more detail below.

Internal models

Condition (4.3), which thus is necessary and sufficient for output regulation to take place under loop stability, can be viewed as a property of the open loop paths of the signal flow shown in Fig. 2, i.e.

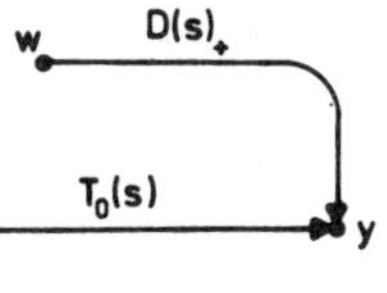

FIG. 2. Open loop paths from the signal flow in Fig. 1 where $T_0(s) = T(s)F(s)$.

The rational matrix $T_0(s)$ is here the open loop cascade of the plant and the compensator and $D(s)_+$ represents the 'unstable' part of the disturbance model as determined by the expression (3.6). Condition (4.3) says that a minimal state realization of the total signal flow in Fig. 2 yields the same dynamic order as a minimal realization of $T_0(s)$ alone. In other words, $T_0(s)$ contains a model of $D(s)_+$ in the sense that, *given a minimal state realization of* $T_0(s)$ *in Fig. 2, no extra state variables have to be introduced to realize the total signal flow including* $D(s)_+$.

Let us therefore take the following definition.

Definition 1. Let $T(s)$ and $D(s)$ be arbitrary rational matrices. Then $T(s)$ is said to contain an internal model of $D(s)$ if

$$\partial T(s)=\partial[T(s) \quad D(s)]. \qquad \square$$

To illustrate the internal model criterion for different representations of a linear system and to illustrate the presence of an internal model in a signal flow graph, the following theorem is given.

Theorem 2. Let $R(s)$ and $H(s)$ be arbitrary proper rational matrices with the same number of rows. The following statements are equivalent.

(i) $R(s)$ *contains an internal model of* $H(s)$.

(ii) *A minimal (state) realization of*

$$y=[R(s) \quad H(s)]\begin{pmatrix}u_1\\u_2\end{pmatrix}$$

is controllable from u_1 *alone.*

(iii) *Let* $R(s)=Q_1(s)^{-1}P_1(s)$ *and* $H(s)=Q_2(s)^{-1}P_2(s)$ *be minimal fraction representations. Then* $Q_2(s)$ *is a right divisor of* $Q_1(s)$.

(iv) *Let* (A_R, B_R, C_R, D_R) *and* (A_H, B_H, C_H, D_H) *be minimal state realizations of* $R(s)$ *and* $H(s)$ *respectively. Let their state dimensions be* n_R *and* n_H. *There is a monomorphism* P *such that the following diagram commutes*

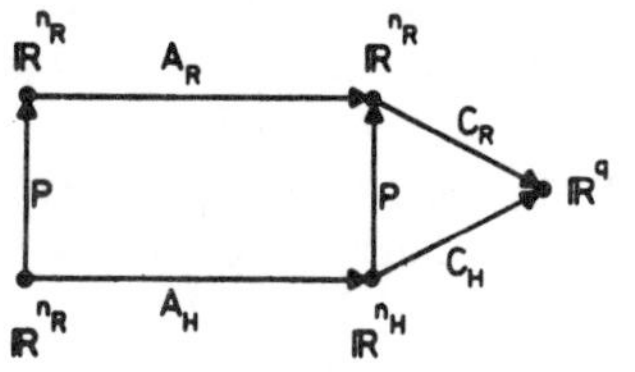

Theorem 2.

(v) *There are rational matrices* $R_i(s)$, $i=1, 2, 3$, *such that*

$$R(s)=(R_1(s)+H(s)R_2(s))R_3(s)$$

$$\partial R(s)=\sum_{i=1}^{3} \partial R_i(s)+\partial H(s)$$

(vi) *There is a real matrix* E *and proper rational matrices* $R_1(s)$ *and* $R_2(s)$ *such that*

$$R(s)=R_1(s)R_2(s); \partial R(s)=\partial R_1(s)+\partial R_2(s)$$

$$H(s)=R_1(s)E.$$

Proof. The equivalence between (i) and (iii) is proven in Lemma 2.

((i)⇔(ii)) Let

$$(A,[B_1 \quad B_2],C,[D_1 \quad D_2]) \qquad (4.6)$$

be a minimal state realization of $[R(s) \quad H(s)]$, i.e.

$$R(s)=C(s-A)^{-1}B_1+D_1$$

$$H(s)=C(s-A)^{-1}B_2+D_2.$$

Then (i) implies that (A, B_1, C, D_1) is a minimal realization of $R(s)$, i.e. (A, B_1) is a controllable pair. Conversely, if (4.6) is a minimal realization with (A, B_1) controllable, then (A, B_1, C, D_1) is a minimal realization of $R(s)$ since (A, C) is an observable pair. This yields the same order of the minimal realization and therefore (i) holds.

((ii)⇔(iv)) First, (iv) implies that (A_R, E, C_R, D_H) is a realization of $H(s)$ with $E=PB_H$. Therefore, $(A_R,$

$[B_R \ E]$, C_R, $[D_R \ D_H]$) is a minimal realization of $[R(s) \ H(s)]$ with (A_R, B_R) being controllable. Conversely, let $(A, [B_R \ E], C, [D_R \ D])$ be a realization of $[R(s) \ H(s)]$ with (A, B_R) being controllable. Then (A, B_R, C, D_R) is a minimal realization of $R(s)$. Moreover, let $\mathscr{R}$ be the controllable subspace for the pair (A, E) and let P be the inclusion of $\mathscr{R}$ into $\mathfrak{R}^{n_R}$. Define (A_H, B_H, C_H, D_H) by

$$AP = PA_H; \quad E = PB_H; \quad C_H = CP \qquad (4.7)$$
$$D_H = D.$$

It is easily verified that (A_H, B_H, C_H, D_H) is a realization of $H(s)$. Also, (A_H, B_H) is controllable by construction. Since (A, C) is observable, so is (A_H, C_H). Therefore, the realization is minimal. The diagram commutes by (4.7). Since all minimal realization are isomorphic, there obviously exists a P such that the diagram commutes for arbitrary minimal realizations.

((iii)⇔(v)) Let D be a polynomial matrix such that $Q_1 = DQ_2$. There are polynomial matrices X and Y such that $Q_2X + P_2Y = I$. Multiply from left by Q_2^{-1} and from right by $D^{-1}P_1$. Then

$$R = Q_1^{-1}P_1 = (X + HY)D^{-1}P_1$$

and

$$\begin{aligned} &\partial X + \partial Y + \partial D^{-1}P_1 + \partial H \\ &\quad = 0 + 0 + \deg\det D + \deg\det Q_2 \\ &\quad = \deg\det(DQ_2) = \partial R \end{aligned}$$

To prove the converse statement, first write

$$R = (R_1 + HR_2)R_3 = Q_2^{-1}(Q_2R_1 + P_2R_2)R_3$$

where $H = Q_2^{-1}P_2$ is a minimal fraction representation. Also let $S_2^{-1}D_2$ be a minimal fraction representation of $(Q_2R_1 + P_2R_2)R_3$. Then $Q_2^{-1}S_2^{-1}D_2$ is a minimal fraction representation of R by the dimensional equality and (iii) follows.

((vi) ⇒ (i)) The conditions in (vi) imply that

$$[R \quad H] = R_1[R_2 \quad E].$$

Let (A_i, B_i, C_i, D_i) be minimal realizations of $R_i(s)$, $i = 1, 2$, with state dimensions n_i. A realization (A, B, C, D) of $[R \ \ H]$ is then given by

$$A = \begin{pmatrix} A_1 & B_1C_2 \\ 0 & A_2 \end{pmatrix} \qquad B = \begin{pmatrix} B_1D_2 & B_1E \\ B_2 & 0 \end{pmatrix}$$
$$C = (C_1 \quad D_1C_2) \qquad D = (D_1D_2 \quad D_1E)$$

with dimension $n = n_1 + n_2$. Hence

$$\partial R = \partial R_1 + \partial R_2 = n_1 + n_2 \geq \partial[R \quad H]$$

and equality must hold since the inequality always holds in the other direction.

((ii)⇔(vi)) Let $(A, [B_1 \ B_2], C, [D_1 \ D_2])$ be a minimal realization with (A, B_1) controllable. Let

$$R_1(s) = [C(s-A)^{-1} \quad I]$$
$$R_2(s) = \begin{pmatrix} B_1 \\ D_1 \end{pmatrix} \qquad E = \begin{pmatrix} B_2 \\ D_2 \end{pmatrix}.$$

By this choice, all the conditions in (vi) are satisfied. □

Let us briefly discuss the implications of this theorem by illustrating the condition (4.3), i.e. put $R(s) = T_0(s)$ and $H(s) = D(s)_+$ in Theorem 2. Condition (v) implies that $T_0(s)$ can be represented by the following signal flow graph.

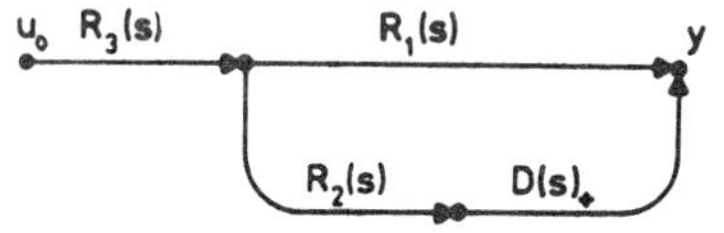

FIG. 3. Signal flow for $T_0(s)$ with internal model $D(s)_+$.

In Fig. 3 the order of $T_0(s)$ equals the sum of the orders of the component transfer matrices. The latter condition guarantees that no cancellation occurs. The presence of a model of $D(s)_+$ in $T_0(s)$ is apparent. Note, however, that $R_i(s)$, $i = 1, 2, 3$, are not necessarily proper.

To have a description with proper rational matrices, condition (vi) can be used. This condition implies that the signal flow in Fig. 2 can be given the following alternative form.

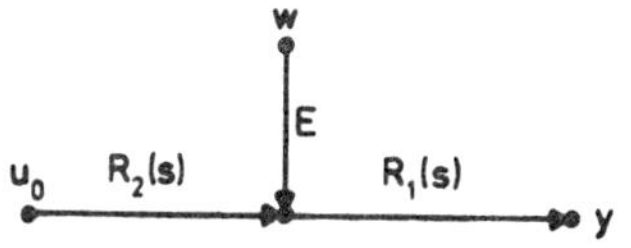

FIG. 4. Alternative signal flow for the system in Fig. 2 if $T_0(s)$ contains internal model of $D(s)_+$.

In Fig. 4, $T_0(s) = R_1(s)R_2(s)$ and $D(s)_+ = R_1(s)E$ and no cancellation occurs in the cascade $R_1(s)$ $R_2(s)$. In this case $R_1(s)$ contains the dynamics of $D(s)_+$.

Finally, (iv) represents the state space analog and implies that there exists a nonsingular matrix T such that

$$TA_0T^{-1} = \begin{pmatrix} A_{11} & A_{12} \\ 0 & A_+ \end{pmatrix}$$
$$C_0T^{-1} = (C_1 \quad C_+)$$

for some real matrices A_{11}, A_{12} and C_1.*

Some immediate *necessary* conditions for output regulation to take place can be derived using Theorem 2. If $d_0(s)$ and $d_+(s)$ are the characteristic polynomials for $T_0(s)$ and $D(s)_+$ respectively, a

*(A_0, B_0, C_0, D_0) and (A_+, B_+, C_+, D_+) are minimal realizations of $T_0(s)$ and $D(s)_+$ respectively.

necessary condition for output regulation is obtained directly from Theorem 2 (iii) as

$$d_+(s)\,|\,d_0(s). \tag{4.8}$$

This is also sufficient if $m=q=1$. If in the state space model (3.2) the eigenvalues of A_2 are all within $\mathbb{C}^+$, a necessary condition for output regulation is also

$$d_2(s)\,|\,d_0(s)$$
$$d_2(s)=\det(s-A_2). \tag{4.9}$$

These results can be strengthened using the following observation, which follows from Theorem 2 (iii).

Proposition 1. If $R(s)$ contains an internal model of $H(s)$ then also $M(s)R(s)$ contains an internal model of $M(s)H(s)$ for any polynomial matrix $M(s)$ such that the matrix products are defined.

Proof. Let $R=Q^{-1}P$ and $H=D^{-1}N$ be minimal fraction representations. Then by Theorem 2 (iii), $QD^{-1}=S$ is a polynomial matrix.

Consider

$$R_1=MQ^{-1}P$$
$$H_1=MD^{-1}N.$$

Let $MQ^{-1}=Q_1^{-1}M_1$ and $MD^{-1}=Q_2^{-1}M_2$ where the right hand sides are minimal fraction representations. Then

$$R_1=Q_1^{-1}M_1P$$
$$H_1=Q_2^{-1}M_2N$$

are also minimal fraction representations. Since, Q_2 and M_2 are relatively left prime, there are polynomial matrices X and Y such that $Q_2X+M_2Y=I$. By some straightforward calculations

$$X+Q_2^{-1}M_2Y=Q_2^{-1}$$
$$Q_1X+Q_1Q_2^{-1}M_2Y=Q_1Q_2^{-1}$$
$$Q_1X+Q_1MD^{-1}Y=Q_1Q_2^{-1}$$
$$Q_1X+M_1QD^{-1}Y=Q_1Q_2^{-1}$$

which shows that $Q_1Q_2^{-1}$ is a polynomial matrix since QD^{-1} is a polynomial matrix. The result then follows by Theorem 2 (iii). □

This proposition shows that if in the composite system shown in Fig. 2, $T_0(s)$ contains an internal model of $D(s)_+$, all subsystems of the form

$$\hat{y}(s)=M(s)y(s)=M(s)T_0(s)u_0+M(s)D(s)_+w$$

where $M(s)$ is a polynomial matrix, are such that $M(s)T_0(s)$ contains an internal model of $M(s)D(s)_+$. Especially, we can take $M(s)=e_i^T$, where e_i is the unit vector with a nonzero element in the ith position only. Combining this with (4.8) shows that

$$d_{i+}(s)\,|\,d_{i0}(s)$$

where $d_{i+}(s)$ and $d_{i0}(s)$ are least common denominators of the ith rows of $D(s)_+$ and $T_0(s)$ respectively.

For synthesis, it is necessary to find a compensator $F(s)$ which *creates* an internal model of $D(s)_+$ in the forward path. This is the topic of the next section.

Remark. Theorem 1 holds even if $D(s)$ and $T(s)$ are not proper rational matrices. The properness assumptions were introduced merely to restrict the attention to causal systems. Also Theorem 2 holds (except condition (vi)) if $R(s)$ and $H(s)$ are nonproper if we by a minimal realization of a nonproper rational matrix $R(s)$ mean $(A, B, C, R(s)_p)$ where (A, B, C) is a minimal realization of $R(s)_c$, cf. (2.1).

5. COMPENSATOR DESIGN

In this section it is shown how a compensator $F(s)$ can be designed using the internal model property. First, the following concept of *internal stability* is introduced. In the composite system shown in Fig. 1, let

$$\dot{x}=Ax+Bu$$
$$y=Cx \tag{5.1}$$

be a minimal realization of the plant $T(s)$. Also let

$$\dot{x}_c=A_cx_c+B_cy$$
$$u=C_cx_c+D_cy \tag{5.2}$$

be a minimal realization of the compensator $-F(s)$. The closed loop system is said to be *internally stable* with respect to $\mathbb{C}^-$ if the composite system (5.1) and (5.2) is stable w.r.t. $\mathbb{C}^-$, i.e. if the following matrix

$$\begin{pmatrix} A+BD_cC & -BC_c \\ B_cC & A_c \end{pmatrix} \tag{5.3}$$

has all its eigenvalues within $\mathbb{C}^-$. A compensator $F(s)$ with this property is said to be a *stabilizer* for $T(s)$. It is well known from observer and pole assignment theory, see e.g. [15, 17], that stabilizers always exist and can be fairly easily constructed.

The effect of closing a system with a stabilizer is explained in the following proposition.

Proposition 2. Assume that $T_0(s)$ is strictly proper and contains an internal model of $D(s)_+$ and let $F_s(s)$ be a stabilizer for $T_0(s)$. Then $T_0(s)F_s(s)$ contains an internal model of $D(s)_+$.

Proof. Using Theorem 2 (vi), the composite

system shown in Fig. 2, closed by F_s, can be represented by the following signal flow graph.

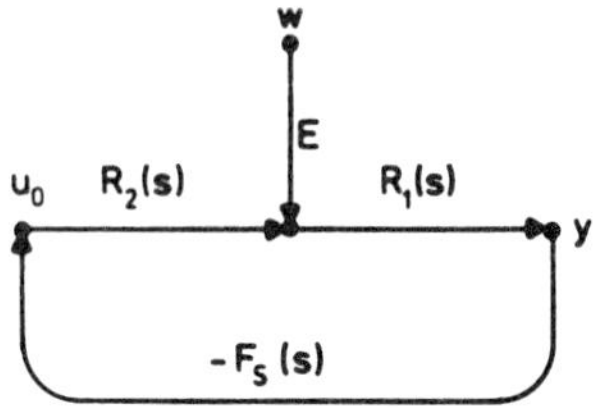

FIG. 5. Signal flow for composite system shown in Fig. 2 with a stabilizer.

Here, R_1 and R_2 are proper and $\partial(R_1R_2)=\partial R_1+\partial R_2$. Since F_s is a stabilizer for $T_0=R_1R_2$, the transfer matrix from w to y must be stable. Moreover, loop stability holds. By Theorem 1, T_0F_s contains an internal model of $R_1E=D$. □

The purpose of design is to find a proper compensator $F(s)$, connected as in Fig. 1, such that (a) output regulation and (b) internal stability hold. Since internal stability implies loop stability, there follows by Theorem 1 that $F(s)$ has the desired properties if and only if

(a) $F(s)$ creates an internal model of $D(s)_+$ in the cascade $T(s)F(s)$
(b) $F(s)$ is stabilizer for $T(s)$. (5.4)

To proceed, note that any $F(s)$ which is a candidate for (b) must avoid unstable cancellation in the cascade $T(s)F(s)$, or more precisely

$$\partial(T(s)F(s))_+=\partial T(s)_+ +\partial F(s)_+. \qquad (5.5)$$

Otherwise, there appear eigenvalues in (5.3) which are within $\mathfrak{C}^+$. Conversely, if there is no unstable cancellation in $T(s)F_1(s)$ and $T(s)F_1(s)$ contains an internal model of $D(s)_+$, there follows from Proposition 2 that we can take an arbitrary stabilizer $F_s(s)$ for $T(s)F_1(s)$ and

$$F(s)=F_1(s)F_s(s)$$

satisfies (5.4). Hence, the problem of finding a proper $F(s)$ satisfying (5.4a) and (5.4b) can be solved if and only if there is a proper $F(s)$ satisfying (5.4a) and (5.5).

Finally, the following proposition shows that if we can find *any* (including nonproper) compensator $F(s)$ satisfying (5.4a) and (5.5) we can also find a *proper* compensator of the same order satisfying (5.4a) and (5.5).

Proposition 3. Assume there exists a rational matrix $F(s)$, not necessarily proper, such that (5.4a) and (5.5) are satisfied. Also let

$$F(s)_c=C_c(s-A_c)^{-1}B_c \qquad (5.6)$$

where $F(s)_c$ is defined as in (2.1) and (A_c, B_c, C_c) is a minimal state realization of $F(s)_c$. Then the following proper compensators also satisfy (5.4a) and (5.5)

$$F_1(s)=[I \quad F_c(s)]$$
$$F_2(s)=[I \quad C_c(s-A_c)^{-1}] \qquad (5.7)$$

Lemma 3. Assume that

$$\partial R(s)=\partial[R(s) \quad H(s)].$$

Then also

$$\partial[R(s) \quad S(s)]=\partial[R(s) \quad S(s) \quad H(s)]$$

for an arbitrary rational matrix $S(s)$.

Proof. Let $R=Q_1^{-1}P_1$, $H=Q_2^{-1}P_2$ be minimal fraction representations. By Lemma 2, $Q_1Q_2^{-1}=M$ is a polynomial matrix. Also, let $Q_1S=Q_3^{-1}P_3$ be a minimal fraction representation. Then

$$[R \quad S]=(Q_3Q_1)^{-1}[Q_3P_1 \quad P_3]$$

is a minimal fraction representation. Moreover, $Q_3Q_1Q_2^{-1}=Q_3M$ and the lemma follows by Lemma 2. □

Proof of Proposition 3. By Lemma 3, it follows directly that

$$\partial[T[I \quad F]]=\partial[T[I \quad F] \quad D_+]$$

so $T[I \quad F]$ contains an internal model of D_+. Write $F=F_c+F_p$. Generally, if R_1 contains an internal model of R_2, then also R_1M contains an internal model of R_2 if M is a unimodular matrix. This follows e.g. from Lemma 2. Now

$$T[I \quad F]\begin{pmatrix} I & -F_p \\ 0 & I \end{pmatrix}=T[I \quad F_c]. \qquad (5.8)$$

Since we have multiplied with a unimodular matrix, $T[I \quad F_c]$ contains an internal model of D_+. Again using Lemma 3, $T[I \quad C_c(s-A_c)^{-1}]$ contains an internal model of D_+, and therefore F_1 and F_2 both satisfy (5.4a). Next, it is obvious that if TF does not contain any unstable cancellation, neither does $T[I \quad F]$. Furthermore, by (5.8) there follows that $T[I \quad F_c]$ does not contain any unstable cancellation and the same is true for $T[I \quad C_c(s-A_c)^{-1}]$. □

The original design problem has now been converted to a pure mathematical problem: *find a rational matrix $F(s)$ such that*

(a) *$T(s)F(s)$ contains an internal model of $D(s)_+$*
(b) $\partial(T(s)F(s))_+=\partial T(s)_+ +\partial F(s)_+$. (5.9)

Once such a compensator has been found, a proper compensator of the same order is directly constructed using Proposition 3 and a stabilizer using Proposition 2.

Represent $T(s)$ and $D(s)_+$ by minimal fraction representations:

$$T(s)=Q(s)^{-1}P(s)$$

$$D(s)_+=Q_1(s)^{-1}P_1(s). \tag{5.10}$$

Also, let

$$Q(s)Q_1(s)^{-1}=Q_A(s)^{-1}P_A(s). \tag{5.11}$$

where the right hand side is a minimal fraction representation.

Theorem 3. There is a compensator $F(s)$ such that (a) $T(s)F(s)$ contains an internal model of $D(s)_+$ and (b) $T(s)F(s)$ contains no unstable cancellation, if and only if there is a polynomial solution $X(s)$, $Y(s)$ to the linear equation

$$P(s)X(s)+Y(s)Q_A(s)=I. \tag{5.12}$$

Further, if a solution $X(s)$, $Y(s)$ to (5.12) exists, a compensator of least possible order satisfying (a) and (b) is given by

$$F(s)=[I_m \quad X(s)Q_A(s)^{-1}]. \tag{5.13}$$

A corresponding proper compensator is directly obtained using Proposition 3.

To prove this theorem, the following lemma is used.

Lemma 3. If $T(s)H(s)^{-1}$ contains an internal model of $D(s)_+$ and $H(s)$ is a polynomial matrix such that $\det H(s)$ is nonzero and has all its zeros within $\mathbb{C}^-$, then also $T(s)$ contains an internal model of $D(s)_+$.

Proof. Let $T=Q^{-1}P$ and $D_+=Q_1^{-1}P_1$ be minimal fraction representations. Now

$$TH^{-1}=Q^{-1}PH^{-1}=Q^{-1}\tilde{D}^{-1}\tilde{P} \tag{5.14}$$

where $\tilde{D}^{-1}\tilde{P}=PH^{-1}$ and the left hand side is a minimal fraction representation. Then, (5.14) is also minimal. By Theorem 2 (iii), $\tilde{D}QQ_1^{-1}=M$, where M is a polynomial matrix. Hence, $\tilde{D}^{-1}M=QQ_1^{-1}$. Now $\det\tilde{D}$ divides $\det H$ which implies that the left hand side is stable. Also, the righthand side is completely unstable. Therefore, both $\tilde{D}^{-1}M$ and QQ_1^{-1} must be polynomial matrices, i.e. Q_1 is a right divisor of Q which proves the result by Theorem 2.

Proof of Theorem 3. (If) First consider

$$TF=Q^{-1}P[I \quad XQ_A^{-1}]$$
$$=Q^{-1}[P \quad PX]\begin{pmatrix} I & 0 \\ 0 & Q_A \end{pmatrix}^{-1}=Q^{-1}\hat{P}\hat{Q}^{-1}$$

Using (5.12) we have

$$\begin{pmatrix} 0 \\ I \end{pmatrix}[P \quad PX]+\begin{pmatrix} I & 0 \\ -P & Y \end{pmatrix}\begin{pmatrix} I & 0 \\ 0 & Q_A \end{pmatrix}=\begin{pmatrix} I & 0 \\ 0 & I \end{pmatrix}$$

and therefore $\hat{P}\hat{Q}^{-1}$ is minimal by Lemma 1. Since $Q^{-1}P$ is minimal, so is $Q^{-1}\hat{P}$. Hence

$$\partial(TF)=\deg(\det Q)+\deg(\det \hat{Q})$$
$$=\deg(\det Q)+\deg(\det Q_A)=\partial T+\partial F \tag{5.15}$$

which shows that no cancellation occurs (and therefore no unstable one). Rewrite (5.12) as

$$PXQ_A^{-1}=Q_A^{-1}(I-Q_AY).$$

Then

$$TF=Q^{-1}Q_A^{-1}[Q_AP \quad (I-Q_AY)].$$

This fraction representation is minimal by (5.15) and Lemma 1. Using (5.11), we have $Q_AQQ_1^{-1}=P_A$ and therefore TF contains an internal model of $D(s)_+$, cf. Theorem 2 (ii).

(Only if) Let F be a compensator such that (a) and (b) in (5.9) are satisfied and let $F=NR^{-1}$ be a minimal fraction representation. Also represent T by (5.10). Factorize R and Q as $R=R_2R_1$ and $Q=Q_3Q_2$, where the zeros of $\det Q_1$ and $\det R_1$ are within $\mathbb{C}^+$ and the zeros of $\det Q_2$ and $\det R_2$ within $\mathbb{C}^-$. Now

$$TF=Q_2^{-1}Q_3^{-1}PNR_1^{-1}R_2^{-1} \tag{5.16}$$

Since TF contains an internal model of D_+, there follows by Proposition 1 and Lemma 3 that

$$T_1=Q_3^{-1}PNR_1^{-1} \tag{5.17}$$

contains an internal model of Q_2D_+, i.e. of $Q_2Q_1^{-1}P_1$. By (5.16), Q_3, PN are relatively left prime and PN, R_1 are relatively right prime, since otherwise an unstable cancellation occurs. Now, write $\tilde{R}^{-1}\tilde{P}=PNR_1^{-1}$ where $\tilde{R}^{-1}\tilde{P}$ is a minimal fraction representation. A substitution into (5.17) yields $T_1=Q_3^{-1}\tilde{R}^{-1}\tilde{P}$ which is also a minimal fraction representation. Since T_1 contains an internal model of $Q_2Q_1^{-1}P_1$. Theorem 2 (iii) implies that

$$\tilde{R}Q_3Q_2Q_1^{-1} = \tilde{R}QQ_1^{-1} = \tilde{R}Q_d^{-1}P_d$$

is a polynomial matrix. This can only be true if Q_d is a right divisor of $\tilde{R}$ i.e.

$$\tilde{R} = \hat{R}Q_d \tag{5.18}$$

for some polynomial matrix $\hat{R}$. Since $\tilde{R}$ and $\tilde{P}$ are relatively left prime, there are polynomial matrices Z and W such that $\tilde{P}Z + \tilde{R}W = I$. Some straightforward manipulations give

$$\tilde{R}^{-1}\tilde{P}Z + W = \tilde{R}^{-1}$$
$$PNR_1^{-1}Z + W = \tilde{R}^{-1}$$
$$PNR_1^{-1}Z\tilde{R} + W\tilde{R} = I.$$

This shows that $PNR_1^{-1}Z\tilde{R}$ is a polynomial matrix. Since PN and R_1 are relatively right prime, $R_1^{-1}Z\tilde{R} = M$ is a polynomial matrix. This together with (5.18) yields

$$PNM + W\hat{R}Q_d = I$$

i.e. $X = NM$ and $Y = W\hat{R}$ is a solution to (5.12).

Finally, to see that the compensator (5.13) is minimal, we note that for any compensator (5.18) holds, i.e.

$$\partial F = \deg(\det R) \geqq \deg(\det R_1) = \deg\det\tilde{R}$$
$$\geqq \deg\det Q_d.$$

However, $\deg(\det Q_d)$ is the order of the compensator in (5.13). □

The compensator design is now complete. The synthesis is summarized in Fig. 6 which shows the final compensator.

In this compensator structure, the components are obtained as follows.

(1) By solving the linear matrix equation (5.12) we directly obtain a compensator

$$F(s) = [I_m \quad X(s)Q_d(s)^{-1}]$$

of least possible order which creates an internal model of $D(s)_+$ in $T(s)F(s)$ without unstable cancellations. Minimal proper compensators with the same properties are obtained via Proposition 3 as

$$F_1(s) = [I_m \quad R(s)_c]; \quad R(s) = X(s)Q_d(s)^{-1} \tag{5.19}$$

or

$$F_2(s) = [I_m \quad C_c(s - A_c)^{-1}] \tag{5.20}$$

where $R(s)_c$ is the strictly proper part as in (2.1) and (A_c, B_c, C_c) is a minimal state realization of $R(s)_c$. Hence

$$F_{IM}(s) = R(s)_c \tag{5.21}$$

or

$$F_{IM}(s) = C_c(s - A_c)^{-1} \tag{5.22}$$

The sole purpose of F_{IM} is thus to create an internal model without unstable cancellation with the least possible dynamics.

(2) With F_{IM} defined as in (1), find a stabilizer

$$F_S(s) = \begin{pmatrix} F_{S1}(s) \\ F_{S2}(s) \end{pmatrix} \tag{5.23}$$

for $T(s)[I\ F_{IM}]$. This stabilization can be done using any standard technique, e.g. pole assignment and observers or generalized Nyquist criteria. To have as much freedom as possible available in the stabilization step, it is advantageous to select the second form (5.22) for F_{IM}. If we use a minimal dual observer[10], the order of the final compensator becomes $n + n_c - m$ where $n = \partial T$, $n_c = \partial F_{IM}$ and m is the number of control inputs to the plant.

The main computational step is to solve the algebraic equation (5.12). Since it is linear this is in principle simple. For instance, by identifying the coefficient matrices for different powers in s on both sides of (5.12), we get a number of linear equations for the coefficients in $X(s)$ and $Y(s)$ which can be solved by standard techniques, see also Appendix. Also, (5.12) can be solved by hand in many cases. Note that once (5.12) is solved, we obtain the minimal compensator almost directly from the solution, cf. (5.13).

The section is concluded by a simple example.

Example. Consider the system

$$y(s) = \begin{pmatrix} \frac{s-1}{s^2} & \frac{2}{s} \\ \frac{2s-1}{s^2} & \frac{2}{s} \end{pmatrix} u(s) + \begin{pmatrix} \frac{1}{s+1} \\ \frac{2}{s+1} \end{pmatrix} w_1(s)$$

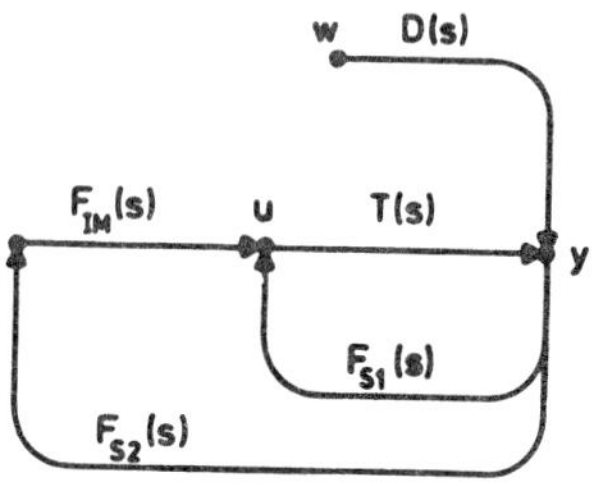

FIG. 6. Signal flow for the final compensator.

Find a compensator such that there is no steady state error in y for ramp disturbances $w_1(s)=w/s^2$. This is a problem of type (4.1) and (4.2) with $\mathbb{C}^-$ being the open left halfplane. In this case

$$T(s)=\begin{pmatrix} \frac{s-1}{s^2} & \frac{2}{s} \\ \frac{2s-1}{s^2} & \frac{2}{s} \end{pmatrix} \quad D(s)=\begin{pmatrix} \frac{1}{s^2(s+1)} \\ \frac{2}{s^2(s+1)} \end{pmatrix}$$

A partial fraction expansion of $D(s)$ yields

$$D(s)_+=\begin{pmatrix} \frac{1-s}{s^2} \\ \frac{2(1-s)}{s^2} \end{pmatrix}$$

The polynomial fraction representations become

$$T(s)=\begin{pmatrix} s-1 & 1 \\ -s & s \end{pmatrix}^{-1}\begin{pmatrix} 1 & 2 \\ 1 & 0 \end{pmatrix}$$

$$D(s)_+=\begin{pmatrix} s^2 & 0 \\ -2 & 1 \end{pmatrix}^{-1}\begin{pmatrix} 1-s \\ 0 \end{pmatrix}$$

Moreover, (5.11) becomes

$$Q(s)Q_1(s)^{-1}=\begin{pmatrix} \frac{s+1}{s^2} & 1 \\ \frac{1}{s} & s \end{pmatrix}=\begin{pmatrix} s & -1 \\ 0 & s \end{pmatrix}^{-1}\begin{pmatrix} 1 & 0 \\ 1 & s^2 \end{pmatrix}$$

To obtain a compensator $F(s)$ which creates an internal model in $T(s)F(s)$ with no unstable cancellation, solve (5.12) i.e.

$$\begin{pmatrix} 1 & 2 \\ 1 & 0 \end{pmatrix}X(s)+Y(s)\begin{pmatrix} s & -1 \\ 0 & s \end{pmatrix}=\begin{pmatrix} 1 & 0 \\ 0 & 1 \end{pmatrix}.$$

One solution is

$$X(s)=\tfrac{1}{2}\begin{pmatrix} 0 & 2(1-s) \\ (1-s) & s \end{pmatrix} \qquad Y(s)=\begin{pmatrix} 1 & 0 \\ 0 & 1 \end{pmatrix}.$$

Then from (5.13)

$$X(s)Q_d(s)^{-1}=\tfrac{1}{2}\begin{pmatrix} 0 & \frac{2(1-s)}{s} \\ \frac{1-s}{s} & \frac{1-s}{s^2}+1 \end{pmatrix}$$

Taking the strictly causal part yields

$$F_{IM}=(X(s)Q_s(s))_c^{-1}=\tfrac{1}{2}\begin{pmatrix} 0 & \frac{2}{s} \\ \frac{1}{s} & \frac{1-s}{s^2} \end{pmatrix}$$

Here F_{IM} is a minimal compensator such that $T[I\ F_{IM}]$ contains an internal model of $D(s)_+$, cf. Fig. 6. The problem is then solved by taking any stabilizer

$$\begin{pmatrix} F_{S1}(s) \\ F_{S2}(s) \end{pmatrix}$$

in Fig. 6. Since this is a standard problem, it is omitted here.

6 CONCLUSIONS

The concept of internal model as defined here has shown to be useful to characterize steady state regulation in terms of necessity and sufficiency, the existence of a controller which achieves output regulation and the structure of that controller. This is done without imposing assumptions on structural stability.

Contrary to most other papers in the genre, we operate mainly on transfer matrices. The internal model is given a simple and precise definition in this setting. The internal model criterion is made plausible by illustrating the presence of the model in signal flow graphs.

The internal model is used directly for synthesis by selecting the feedback compensator so that an internal model is created in the open loop cascade of compensator and plant. The existence of such a compensator is by Theorem 3 equivalent to the solvability of a linear polynomial equation. Moreover, the solution of this equation directly gives the compensator of minimal order. This direct relationship between solvability and synthesis is believed to be new.

One motivation for introducing a concept of internal models is its intuitive appeal[3]. It provides insight to the regulator problem without too much algebraic detail. Therefore it would be nice to generalize the concept of internal model to other systems than linear and finite dimensional. One such generalization would be to systems with time delays. Since we mainly operate on transfer matrices in this paper, this generalization should not be too difficult.

Acknowledgements—This work has been supported by The Research Council of Canada under Grant Nos. A-7399 and A-4165 and the Swedish Board for Technical Development under Grant No. 755776. The author thans Prof. W. M. Wonham for many stimulating discussions on the concept of internal models and other aspects of linear control theory.

REFERENCES

[1] E. J. DAVISON: A generalization of the output control of linear multivariable systems with unmeasurable arbitrary disturbances. *IEEE Trans. Aut. Control* **AC-20**(6) 788–795 (1975).

[2] E. J. DAVISON: The feedforward and feedback control of a general servomechanism problem, Parts I and II. *Proc. 11th Allerton Conference on Circuit and System Theory*, Univ. of Illinois (1973).

[3] B. A. FRANCIS and W, M. WONHAM: The internal model principle for linear multivariable regulators. *App. Maths. Optimization* **2**(2) 170–194 (1975).

[4] C. D. JOHNSON: Further study of the linear regulator with disturbances—The case of vector disturbances satisfying a linear differential equation. *IEEE Trans. Aut. Control* **AC-15**(2) 222–228 (1970).

[5] J. B. PEARSON and P. W. STAATS: Robust controllers for linear regulators. *IEEE Trans. Aut. Control* **AC-19**(3) 231–234 (1974).

[6] W. A. WOLOWICH: Multivariable system synthesis with step disturbance rejection. *IEEE Trans. Aut. Control* **AC-19**(2) (1974).

[7] W. M. WONHAM and J. B. PEARSON: Regulation and internal stabilization in linear multivariable systems. *SIAM J. Control* **12**(1) 5–18 (1974).

[8] E. J. DAVISON and A. GOLDENBERG: Robust control of a general servomechanism problem: the servo compensator. *Automatica* **11**, 461–471 (1975).

[9] C. R. KELLEY: *Manual and Automatic Control*. Wiley, New York (1968).

[10] W. R. ASHBY and R. C. CONSTANT: Every good regulator of a system must be a model of that system. *Int. J. Systems Sci.* **1**(2) 89–97 (1970).

[11] B. A. FRANCIS and W. M. WONHAM: *Int. J. Control* **22**(5) 657–681 (1975).

[12] M. HEYMANN: *Structure theory and realization problems in the theory of dynamical systems*. Lectures delivered at Int. Center for Mech. Sci., Udine, Italy (1972).

[13] H. H. ROSENBROCK: *Multivariable and State Space Theory*. Wiley, New York (1970).

[14] W. A. WOLOWICH: *Linear Multivariable Systems*. Springer-Verlag, New York (1974).

[15] D. G. LUENBERGER: An introduction to observers. *IEEE Trans. Aut. Control* **AC-16**(6) 596–602 (1971).

[16] R. E. KALMAN, P. L. FALB and M. A. ARBIB: *Topics in Mathematical Systems Theory*. McGraw-Hill, New York (1969).

[17] W. M. WONHAM: Pole assignment in multi-input controllable linear systems. *IEEE Trans. Aut. Control* **AC-12**(6) 660–665 (1967).

APPENDIX A—ON THE LINEAR EQUATION (5.12)

Consider the linear equation (5.12), i.e.

$$P(s)X(s)+Y(s)Q_d(s)=I \qquad \text{(A.1)}$$

which shall be solved for some polynomial matrices $X(s)$ and $Y(s)$. Here, $Q_d(s)$ is obtained via the minimal fraction representation (5.11). Given one $Q_d(s)$, the set of all is generated by $N(s)Q_d(s)$, $N(s)$ unimodular, i.e. all polynomial matrices that are row equivalent with $Q_d(s)$. Since Theorem 3 is independent of the choice of $Q_d(s)$ within the equivalent class, we may assume that $Q_d(s)$ is such that the rational matrix

$$T(s)=Q_d(s)^{-1} \qquad \text{(A.2)}$$

is strictly proper. If we are given one $Q_d(s)$ which does not satisfy this condition, we may transform $Q_d(s)$ to row proper forms ([13], Th. 2.5.11) in which case (A.2) is strictly proper.

To proceed we need a different version of the division algorithm.

Lemma A.1. Let $P(s)$, $m\times r$, and $Q(s)$, $m\times m$, be polynomial matrices such that $\det Q(s)\neq 0$. There are polynomial matrices $H(s)$ and $R(s)$ such that

$$P(s)=H(s)Q(s)+R(s) \text{ where}$$

$$\deg R(s)<\deg Q(s)$$

and $R(s)Q(s)^{-1}$ is strictly proper.

Proof. Consider the rational matrix $T=PQ^{-1}$. Using conventional realization theory, there are real matrices A, B and C and a polynomial matrix $D(s)$ such that

$$T(s)=C(s-A)^{-1}B+D(s).$$

Let $P_1Q_1^{-1}=(s-A)^{-1}B$ be a minimal fraction representation; then also

$$T=(CP_1+DQ_1)Q_1^{-1}$$

is a minimal fraction representation. Therefore, there is a nonsingular pol. matrix N such that $Q=Q_1N$ and

$$P=CP_1N+DQ_1N=CP_1N+DQ.$$

Let $R=CP_1N$ and $H=D$. Then $P=HQ+R$. By the equality $(s-A)P_1N=BQ$, there follows that

$$\deg(P_1N)<\deg Q,$$

and since C is real, $\deg R<\deg Q$. Also

$$RQ^{-1}=CP_1N(Q_1N)^{-1}=C(s-A)^{-1}B$$

which is strictly proper. □

The following bounds on the degree of $X(s)$ and $Y(s)$ in (A.1) can now be given.

Proposition A.1. Assume that $Q_d(s)$ has been chosen so that $Q_d(s)^{-1}$ is strictly proper. If there exists any solution to (A.1), there exists one with

$$\deg X(s)<\deg Q_d^{(s)} \quad\text{and}\quad \deg Y(s)<\deg P(s).$$

Proof. Let $X_0(s)$ and $Y_0(s)$ be any solution to (A.1). Applying Lemma A.1, there exists polynomial matrices X and D such that $X=X_0-DQ_d$, where $\deg X<\deg Q_d$ and XQ_d^{-1} is strictly proper. Then $X=X_0-DQ_d$ and $Y=Y_0+PD$ also satisfies (A.1) and we have satisfied the bound on $\deg X$. Next, by (A.1)

$$Y=Q_d^{-1}-PXQ_d^{-1}=\frac{Adj\,Q_d-PX\,Adj\,Q_d}{\det Q_d}$$

Now, Q_d^{-1} and XQ_d^{-1} are both strictly proper and therefore

$$\deg(Adj\,Q_d)<\deg\det Q_d$$

$$\deg(X\,Adj\,Q_d)<\deg\det Q_d.$$

Since Y is a polynomial matrix, $\det Q_d$ must divide each element in $Adj\,Q_d-PX\,Adj\,Q_d$. Hence

$$\begin{aligned}\deg Y&=\deg(Adj\,Q_d-PX\,Adj\,Q_d)-\deg\det Q_d\\&\leq\deg P+\deg(X\,Adj\,Q_d)-\deg\det Q_d\\&<\deg P.\end{aligned}$$

Since we can set *a priori* bounds on the degrees of $X(s)$ and $Y(s)$ in (A.1) we can now transform (A.1) to a linear equation with real numbers by identifying the coefficients in (A.1). On substituting

$$P(s)=\sum_{i=0}^{p} P_i s^i$$

$$Q_d(s)=\sum_{i=0}^{q} Q_i s^i$$

and (using Prop. A.1)

$$X(s)=\sum_{i=0}^{q-1} X_i s^i$$

$$Y(s)=\sum_{i=0}^{p-1} Y_i s^i$$

into (A.1), i.e.

$$\left(\sum_{i=0}^{p} P_i s^i\right)\left(\sum_{i=0}^{q-1} X_i s^i\right)+\left(\sum_{i=0}^{p-1} Y_i s^i\right)\left(\sum_{i=0}^{q} Q_i s^i\right)=I \qquad \text{(A.3)}$$

we get a set of linear equations in the coefficients X_i and Y_i by identifying the coefficients for different powers in s. Hence, by arranging the data X_i, Y_i into a vector x, we can rewrite as

$$Ax=b \qquad \text{(A.4)}$$

with suitable A and b. Equation (A.4) can be solved by standard techniques. Rewriting the equations in the form (A.4) is straightforward but somewhat tedious and is therefore omitted here.

Note that the procedure above is just one way to solve (A.1). Other procedures may be computationally more efficient.

Part V
Multidimensional Systems

The theory of multidimensional systems is principally associated with image processing in several spatial dimensions, and in particular with the use of multidimensional recursive digital filters. Its special interest, in the context of this survey volume, arises from the emergence of an appropriate multidimensional generalization of Nyquist-type stability theory. Such a generalization, following upon that to the multivariable case, is of great intrinsic interest, and a wider knowledge of these developments among the control engineering community may well lead to a suitable adaption for use in the control field, possibly in the study of stability under parameter variation. For simplicity of exposition most of the discussion given here will be confined to the two-dimensional case. An excellent summary of stability theory for multidimensional systems is given in the survey paper by Jury [13]; the availability of an early draft of this paper, kindly supplied by Prof. Jury, proved invaluable in preparing the brief summary presented here. Since the great bulk of the existing literature in this area is concerned with digital signal processing, the results discussed here are presented in terms of the z-domain; details of the analogous s-domain results are given by Jury [13]. An IEEE Press Reprint Volume on the theory and applications of multidimensional systems is available and should be consulted for a wider survey of this field [3].

A two-dimensional causal recursive digital filter has an associated two-dimensional z-transfer-function

$$G(z_1, z_2) = \frac{P(z_1, z_2)}{Q(z_1, z_2)} \tag{5.1}$$

where $P(z_1, z_2)$ and $Q(z_1, z_2)$ are polynomials in z_1 and z_2:

$$P(z_1, z_2) = \sum_{k=0}^{K} \sum_{l=0}^{L} p(k, l) z_1^k z_2^l \tag{5.2}$$

$$Q(z_1, z_2) = \sum_{i=0}^{I} \sum_{j=0}^{J} q(i, j) z_1^i z_2^j, \tag{5.3}$$

and it is assumed that all irreducible factors common to $P(z_1, z_2)$ and $Q(z_1, z_2)$ have been cancelled. Shanks attempted to show [15] that the two-dimensional recursive digital filter characterized by the two-dimensional transfer function (5.1) would be stable in the bounded-input bounded-output sense if and only if:

$$Q(z_1, z_2) \neq 0, \quad \text{for all } \{(z_1, z_2): |z_1| \leq 1, |z_2| \leq 1\}. \tag{5.4}$$

Unfortunately, as shown by Goodman [9], such a straightforward generalization of the one-dimensional criterion is only a sufficient condition for bounded-input bounded-output stability. Goodman showed that, unlike the single-dimensional situation, the stability of the two-dimensional digital filter is influenced by the numerator of the transfer function as well as by denominator. This vital difference from the familiar one-dimensional case arises from the fact that the zero sets of $P(z_1, z_2)$ and $Q(z_1, z_2)$ in the two-dimensional complex space $\mathbb{C}^2$ lie on infinite continua defined in terms of appropriate algebraic curves. The possibility therefore arises that the zero sets of $P(z_1, z_2)$ and $Q(z_1, z_2)$ may intersect. When this happens one gets a new kind of singularity which has no counterpart in the one-dimensional case. Such a singularity of $G(z_1, z_2)$ is called a nonessential singularity of the second kind. (The term nonessential is used because only rational functions are being considered and thus essential singularities are excluded.) A zero of $Q(z_1, z_2)$ which is not simultaneously a zero of $P(z_1, z_2)$ is called a (nonessential) singularity of the first kind; such singularities of $G(z_1, z_2)$ are the natural analogs of the familiar poles in the one-dimensional case. The snag with Shanks' original straightforward extension of the single-dimensional criterion for the nonexistence of denominator zeros in a unit disk

$$D^1 = \{z_1 : |z_1| \leq 1\} \tag{5.5}$$

to a polydisk

$$D^2 = \{(z_1, z_2): |z_1| \leq 1, |z_2| \leq 1\} \tag{5.6}$$

arises from the possibility of (nonessential) singularities of the second kind existing on the boundary of the polydisk D^2. When restated as a sufficient criterion for bounded-input bounded-output stability, or when suitably reformulated so as to exclude (nonessential) singularities of the second kind on the boundary of the unit bidisk, Shanks' result is the basis for the determination of bounded-input bounded-output stability of a two-dimensional causal recursive digital filter given in the form of a transfer-function description. An existence criterion for nonessential singularities of the second kind has been given by Bickart [2].

The determination of the stability of the filter having the transfer function $G(z_1, z_2)$ thus involves finding whether the polynomial $Q(z_1, z_2)$ has any zeros in the appropriate unit bidisk in $\mathbb{C}^2$. Such an investigation, as might be expected, is computationally involved and difficult. However, a simpler test may be sought by making use of the fact that the pole set of $G(z_1, z_2)$ is a continuum in $\mathbb{C}^2$. Roughly speaking, one seeks to exploit the fact that, as explained by DeCarlo, Murray, and Saeks [7], the pole set of $G(z_1, z_2)$ is extended in $\mathbb{C}^2$ in such a way that it cannot pass through the unit bidisk which is to be examined without also passing through some suitably selected subset of it. The first step in exploiting this fact, in order to devise tests for stability which are simpler from a computational point of view, was taken by Huang [10] who showed that Shanks' test, for the purpose of determining stability, is equivalent to the requirements that

(i) $Q(z_1, 0) \neq 0, \quad |z_1| \leqslant 1$

and

(ii) $Q(z_1, z_2) \neq 0, \quad |z_1| = 1 \; |z_2| \leqslant 1$

both hold. Huang's original proof of this equivalence has been corrected and extended by Davis [4], Goodman [8], and Murray [14].

Huang's idea of devising tests for the nonexistence of zeros in equivalent regions of $\mathbf{C}^2$ is of fundamental importance in multidimensional stability theory. Strintzis [16] and DeCarlo, Murray, and Saeks [7] have shown independently that another criterion for $G(z_1, z_2)$ to be stable is given by:

(i) $Q(a, z_2) \neq 0$, for some a such that $|a| \leqslant 1$, when $|z_2| \leqslant 1$
(ii) $Q(z_1, b) \neq 0$, for some b such that $|b| = 1$, when $|z_1| \leqslant 1$

and

(iii) $Q(z_1, z_2) \neq 0$, for $|z_1| = 1$ and $|z_2| = 1$.

In particular, on putting $a = b = 1$, one obtains the criterion specified by

(i) $Q(1, z_2) \neq 0, \quad |z_2| \leqslant 1$
(ii) $Q(z_1, 1) \neq 0, \quad |z_1| \leqslant 1$
(iii) $Q(z_1, z_2) \neq 0, \quad |z_1| = |z_2| = 1.$

DeCarlo, Murray, and Saeks [7] have shown that yet another equivalent criterion is specified by

(i) $Q(z_1, z_2) \neq 0$, for $z_1 = z_2 = z$ when $|z| \leqslant 1$
(ii) $Q(z_1, z_2) \neq 0$, for $|z_1| = |z_2| = 1$.

I. Two-Dimensional Nyquist-Like Criteria

Since the Nyquist stability criterion for feedback systems associated with a one-dimensional rational transfer-function can be considered in terms of determining whether or not some function has zeros in a particular region of the complex plane by examining the image of the function on the boundary of the region, it is natural, given Shanks' criterion, to seek a suitable extension of the Nyquist stability criterion to two-dimensional systems. In doing so one must remember Goodman's result on the effect of nonessential singularities of the second kind, and one can seek to use Huang's idea to replace the original region of $\mathbf{C}^2$ in which zeros are forbidden by some other, computationally simpler, region. Such an extension has been provided by DeCarlo, Murray, and Saeks in a series of papers [5]-[7].

Let a polydisk D_α in $\mathbf{C}^2$ be defined by

$$D_\alpha = \{(e^{j\alpha}, z_2) : |z_2| \leqslant 1\} \tag{5.7}$$

where α is real and such that $0 \leqslant \alpha \leqslant 2\pi$, and let a disk D be defined by

$$D = \{(z_1, 0) : |z_1| \leqslant 1\}. \tag{5.8}$$

Then DeCarlo, Murray, and Saeks have established the following results.

a) A causal recursive digital filter characterized by the rational two-dimensional transfer-function

$$G(z_1, z_2) = \frac{P(z_1, z_2)}{Q(z_1, z_2)},$$

where any irreducible common factors of $P(z_1, z_2)$ and $Q(z_1, z_2)$ have been cancelled and where $G(z_1, z_2)$ has no nonessential singularity of the second kind on the boundary of the unit bidisk, is stable in the bounded-input bounded-output (BIBO) sense if and only if the Nyquist plots for the family of one-dimensional functions

$$Q(e^{j\alpha}, z_2), \quad 0 \leqslant \alpha \leqslant 2\pi$$

and

$$Q(z_1, 0)$$

do not equal or encircle zero in the complex plane.

b) The two-dimensional digital filter described in a) is BIBO stable if and only if

1) $Q(z_1, z_2)$ has no zeros on $|z_1| = |z_2| = 1$,
2) the Nyquist plots for the one-dimensional functions $Q(1, z_2)$ and $Q(z_1, 1)$ do not encircle zero.

c) The two-dimensional filter described in a) is BIBO stable if and only if

1) $Q(z_1, z_2)$ has no zeros for $|z_1| = |z_2| = 1$,
2) the Nyquist plot for the single-variable function $Q(z, z)$ does not encircle zero.

II. Further Results for Multidimensional Systems

Jury's excellent survey [13] deals comprehensively with the extension of investigations and results of this sort to higher-dimensional systems in both the discrete and continuous domains; Jury [12] should also be consulted. In particular, Anderson and Jury [1] have extended Shanks' stability criterion to higher-dimensional systems, Murray [14] has discussed the extension of Huang's idea, and DeCarlo, Murray, and Saeks [7] have developed higher-dimensional forms of Nyquist-type stability criteria. A tentative start has been made on an exploration of the "matrix" or "multivariable" version of the multidimensional system problem [11], [13].

References

[1] B. D. O. Anderson and E. I. Jury, "Stability of multidimensional digital filters," *IEEE Trans. Circuits and Syst.*, CAS-21, 300–304, 1974.
[2] T. Bickart, "Existence criterion for nonessential singularities of the second kind," *Proc. IEEE*, 66 (8), 1978.
[3] N. K. Bose, Ed., *Multidimensional Systems: Theory & Applications*, IEEE Press Reprint Volume. New York: IEEE, 1979.
[4] D. L. Davis, "A correct proof of Huang's theorem on stability," *IEEE Trans. ASSP*, ASSP-24, 423–426, 1976.
[5] R. DeCarlo, R. Saeks, and J. Murray, "A Nyquist-like test for the stability of two-dimensional digital filters," *Proc. IEEE*, 65, 978–979, 1977.

[6] —, "Three graphical tests for the stability of multidimensional digital filters," *1977 IEEE Int. Symp. Circuits and Systems*, 665–669.
[7] R. A. DeCarlo, J. Murray, and R. Saeks, "Multivariable Nyquist theory," *Int. J. Control*, 25, 657–675, 1977.
[8] D. Goodman, "An alternate proof of Huang's stability theorem," *IEEE Trans. ASSP*, ASSP-24, 426–427, 1976.
[9] —, "Some stability properties of two-dimensional shift invariant digital filters," *IEEE Trans. Circuits and Syst.*, CAS-24, 201–208, 1977.
[10] T. S. Huang, "Stability of two-dimensional and recursive filters," *IEEE Trans. Audio Electroacoustics*, AU-20, 158, 1972.
[11] A. F. Humes, and E. I. Jury, "A graphical stability test of two-dimensional multi-input multi-output digital filters," *Proc. 11th Asilomar Conf. Circuits and Systems*, Monterey, CA, 75–77, 1977.
[12] E. I. Jury, "Stability tests for one-, two- and multidimensional linear systems," *Proc. IEE*, 124, 1237–1240, 1977.
[13] —, "Stability of multidimensional scalar and matrix polynomials," *Proc. IEEE*, 66 (9), 1018–1047, 1978.
[14] J. Murray, "Another proof and a sharpening of Huang's theorem," *IEEE Trans. ASSP*, ASSP-25, 581–582, 1977.
[15] J. L. Shanks, S. Treitel, and J. H. Justice, "Stability and synthesis of two dimensional recursive filters," *IEEE Trans. Audio Electroacoustics*, AU-20, 115–128, 1972.
[16] M. G. Strintzis, "Tests of stability of multidimensional filters," *IEEE Trans. Circuits Syst.*, CAS-24, 432–437, 1977.

A Nyquist-Like Test for the Stability of Two-Dimensional Digital Filters

R. DECARLO, R. SAEKS, AND J. MURRAY

***Abstract*—This paper constructs a Nyquist-like test for the stability of two-dimensional digital filters. The test takes the form of a continuum of classical one-variable Nyquist plots parameterized by the elements of the unit circle of the complex plane. Since the parameter space is compact, the test can be accurately approximated by a finite number of classical one-variable Nyquist plots and is therefore readily implemented on a computer.**

INTRODUCTION

A two-dimensional digital filter is characterized by a rational transfer function in two complex variables

$$\frac{B(z_1, z_2)}{A(z_1, z_2)} \tag{1}$$

where $A(z_1, z_2)$ and $B(z_1, z_2)$ are relatively prime polynomials in z_1 and z_2. For the purpose of this paper we say that the digital filter is stable if $A(z_1, z_2) \neq 0$ for $|z_1| \leq 1$ and $|z_2| \leq 1$. This *structural stability* condition implies that the filter is bounded-input bounded-output stable, though as recently shown by Goodman [1] the condition is actually slightly stronger. Huang showed that this four-dimensional stability condition was actually equivalent to the three-dimensional condition that $A(z_1, z_2) \neq 0$ for $|z_1| = 1$ and $|z_2| \leq 1$ or $|z_1| \leq 1$ and $z_2 = 0$ which we use as the basis of our theory.

The key to the formulation of our Nyquist-like theory is the observation that from an abstract analytic function point of view the classical one-variable Nyquist plot is simply a method of determining whether or not an analytic function in one variable has zeros in an appropriate region by plotting the image of the function on the boundary of the region. To obtain a Nyquist theory in two variables we therefore decompose the region of C^2, in which $A(z_1, z_2)$ is forbidden to have zeros by Huang's theorem into the union of a family of one-variable regions to which the classical Nyquist theorem applies. More precisely, for real α, $0 \leq \alpha < 2\pi$, we define the disk D_α in C^2 by

$$D_\alpha = \{(e^{i\alpha}, z_2) \quad |z_2| \leq 1\} \tag{2}$$

and we define the disk D by

$$D = \{(z_1, 0) \quad |z_1| \leq 1\}. \tag{3}$$

Now, Huang's theorem may be restated as "the digital filter is stable if and only if $A(z_1, z_2)$ has no zeros in the disks D and D_α, $0 \leq \alpha < 2\pi$." Observing that each disk is fixed in one of its variables, the polynomial $A(z_1, z_2)$ (restricted to any of the above defined disks) is an analytic function of one variable and hence the classical Nyquist test can be used to check for zeros within the disk. In particular, $A(z_1, z_2)$ has zeros in the disk D_α if and only if the Nyquist plot for the one-variable function $A(e^{i\alpha}, z_2)$ does not equal or encircle zero. Similarly, $A(z_1, z_2)$ has no zeros in the disk D if and only if the Nyquist plot for the one-variable function $A(z_1, 0)$ does not equal or encircle zero. Combining these observations we obtain the following stability theorem.

Theorem

A digital filter characterized by the two-variable transfer function

$$\frac{B(z_1, z_2)}{A(z_1, z_2)}$$

where $A(z_1, z_2)$ and $B(z_1, z_2)$ are relatively prime polynomials in two variables, is stable (structurally stable) if and only if the Nyquist plots for the family of one-variable functions

$$A(e^{i\alpha}, z_2) \quad 0 \leq \alpha < 2\pi$$

and

$$A(z_1, 0)$$

do not equal or encircle zero.

Manuscript received January 6, 1977. This research was supported in part by AFOSR Grant 74-2631 and ONR Contract 76-C-1136.

The authors are with the Department of Electrical Engineering, Texas Tech. University, Lubbock, TX 79409.

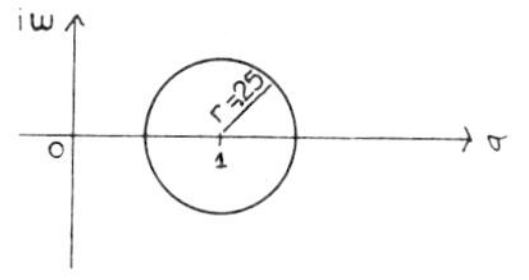

Fig. 1. Nyquist plot of $A(z_1, 0)$ for Example 1.

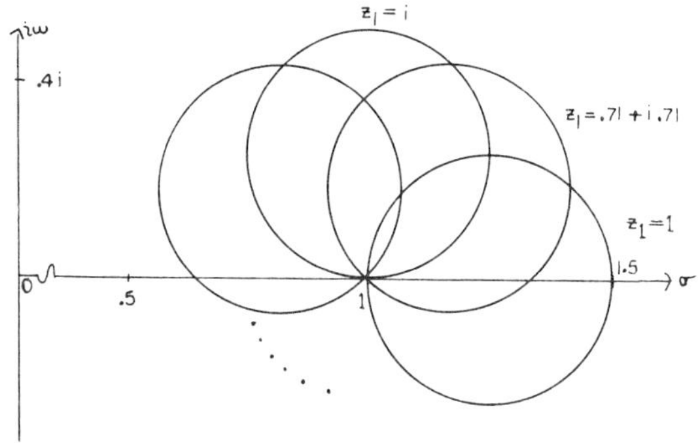

Fig. 2. Nyquist plots for $A(e^{i\alpha}, z_2)$ for Example 1.

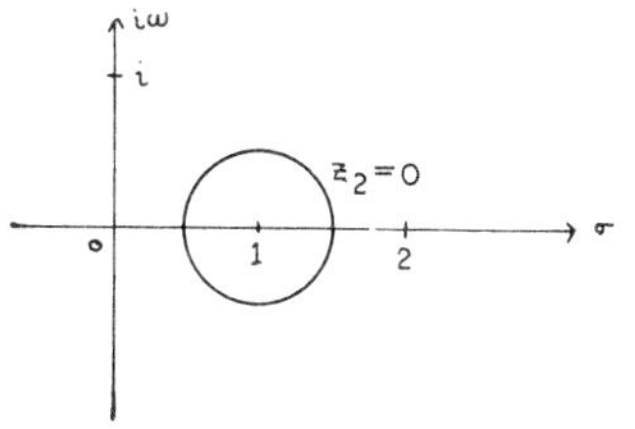

Fig. 3. Nyquist plot for $A(z_1, 0)$ for Example 2.

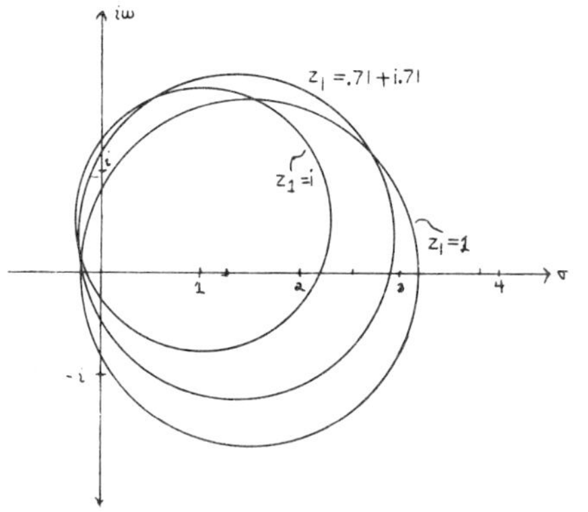

Fig. 4. Nyquist plots for $A(e^{i\alpha}, z_2)$ for Example 2.

Although the theorem formally implies that one check a continuum of Nyquist plots parameterized by the complex numbers of magnitude one, in fact, since this set of numbers is compact, one can obtain a test with arbitrarily good resolution using only a finite number of plots. Indeed, in a somewhat different context, the authors have shown that a similar continuum of Nyquist plots can actually be reduced to a single plot without inducing any error into the stability test [2]. The following examples are based on a finite approximation to the continuum of plots required by the theorem.

Example 1: Let the transfer function of a digital filter be

$$H(z_1, z_2) = \frac{1}{1 + 0.25z_1 + 0.25z_2} = \frac{B(z_1, z_2)}{A(z_1, z_2)}. \tag{4}$$

Step 1: Draw the Nyquist plot for $A(z_1, 0)$. This curve, shown in Fig. 1, does not encircle zero. So we proceed to the next step as outlined in the theorem.

Reprinted from *Proc. IEEE*, vol. 65, pp. 978-979, June 1977.

Step 2: Now consider the family of Nyquist plots for the functions $A(e^{i\alpha}, z_2)$; $0 \leqslant \alpha < 2\pi$. This family of curves does not encircle "0" as indicated in Fig. 2. Thus the filter is stable.

Example 2: Now consider the filter whose transfer function is

$$H(z_1, z_2) = \frac{1}{1 + 0.5z_1 + 0.5z_2 + 1.2z_1z_2} = \frac{B(z_1, z_2)}{A(z_1, z_2)}. \tag{5}$$

Step 1: Consider $A(z_1, 0)$. This Nyquist plot is illustrated in Fig. 3 and does not encircle zero.

At this point no decision can be made so proceed to Step 2.

Step 2: Consider the family of functions $A(e^{i\alpha}, z_2)$; $0 \leqslant \alpha < 2\pi$. Nyquist plots for some of these functions are shown in Fig. 4. They indicate that the filter is indeed unstable.

References

[1] D. Goodman, "Some stability properties of two-dimensional linear shift-invariant digital filters," *IEEE Trans. Circuits Syst.*, to appear.
[2] R. A. DeCarlo, J. Murray, and R. Saeks, "Multivariable Nyquist theory," *Int. J. Contr.*, to be published.

Multivariable Nyquist theory

R. A. DECARLO†, J. MURRAY† and R. SAEKS†

It is shown that a multivariable digital filter is stable if and only if $A(z_1, z_2, \ldots, z_n) \neq 0$ when $|z_1| = |z_2| = \ldots = |z_n| = 1$ and the Nyquist plot for the single-variable function $A(z, z, \ldots, z)$ does not encircle zero. Here $A(z_1, z_2, \ldots, z_n)$ is the denominator polynomial of the relatively prime rational transfer function of the digital filter.

1. Introduction

Although the Nyquist criterion (Nyquist 1932) has been known for over half a century, it has resisted generalization until recently. Interestingly, those generalizations which have been formulated retain the simple graphical character of the classical test, even when one is studying systems defined on abstract spaces. The earliest generalizations of the Nyquist criterion were the Circle and Popov criteria formulated in the early sixties as non-linear and/or time-variable perturbations of the classical test (Sandberg 1964, Popov 1961). More recently MacFarlane (1972), and Barman and Katznelson (1974) have extended the test to the case of frequency response matrices, while one of the authors has formulated a Nyquist-like sufficiency condition for Lipschitz continuous operators on abstract spaces (Saeks 1975). Finally, in a recent paper the authors gave a stability test for multivariable digital filters which was formulated in terms of a continuum of Nyquist plots (DeCarlo 1976, DeCarlo *et al.* 1977). In all cases the tests remain simple graphical conditions on the complex plane. The resultant criteria yield necessary and sufficient conditions in the case of linear time-invariant systems (including the multivariable and matrix generalizations) and sufficient conditions in the cases of non-linear and time-variable systems.

The thrust of this paper is to show that with a slight modification the continuum of Nyquist plots used in the multivariable Nyquist test of DeCarlo *et al.* (1977) can be reduced to a classical single-variable Nyquist plot plus a test to verify that the filter has no poles in the region $|z_1| = |z_2| = \ldots = |z_n| = 1$, the multivariable analogue of the $i\omega$-axis.

Although every attempt is made to minimize details the theorem illustrates the essential algebraic topological nature of the Nyquist criterion, with homotopic arguments playing a significant role in derivation. For a more detailed discussion of the algebraic topological nature of the Nyquist theory the reader is referred to DeCarlo (1976), DeCarlo *et al.* (1976) and DeCarlo and Saeks (1977). In particular, DeCarlo and Saeks (1977) give an algebraic topological derivation of the classical Nyquist criterion.

In the following section several Hurwitz-like stability tests are reviewed and a new test of the Hurwitz-type test is formulated. In the third section a homotopic interpretation of the classical Nyquist criterion is formulated, this

Received 10 September 1976.

† Department of Electrical Engineering, Texas Technical University, Lubbock, Texas 79409.

Reprinted with permission from *Int. J. Control*, vol. 25, pp. 657–675, May 1977.

being used to derive the desired multivariable Nyquist criterion from the Hurwitz conditions in the third and fourth sections. Finally some examples of the theory are given in § 5.

2. Hurwitz-like tests

Denote the vector space of complex n-tuples by $\mathbb{C}^n$. For the purposes of our multivariable stability theory, there are five interesting subsets of $\mathbb{C}^n$. First there is the *polydisk*, defined as

$$P^n = \{(z_1, \ldots, z_n) \text{ in } \mathbb{C}^n \mid |z_i| \leqslant 1, \quad i = 1, \ldots, n\} \tag{1}$$

It plays the same role in the multivariable theory as the unit disk (or right half-plane) in single-variable theory.

Next, there are three separate notions of the boundary of P^n. All are necessary for the theory of this paper. First is the *distinguished boundary* denoted by T^n, where

$$T^n = \{(z_1, \ldots, z_n) \text{ in } \mathbb{C}^n \mid |z_i| = 1, \quad i = 1, \ldots, n\} \tag{2}$$

T^n serves as the multidimensional analogue of the $i\omega$-axis. In particular, the frequency response (Jury 1975) of a digital filter is the evaluation of its transfer function over T^n. Geometrically T^n is an n-dimensional torus which reduces to the unit circle of the complex plane in the single-variable case. T^n is a ' boundary ' for P^n in the sense that it is a subset of P^n for which all coordinates of P^n simultaneously take on extremal values.

A second notion of boundary for P^n is defined by requiring only that $n-1$ coordinates take on extremal values. This boundary set is denoted by M^n, where

$$M^n = \{(z_1, \ldots, z_n) \text{ in } \mathbb{C}^n \mid |z_i| = 1, \quad i = 1, \ldots, k-1, k+1, \ldots, n\,; \quad |z_k| \leqslant 1\} \tag{3}$$

and where k ranges from 1 to n.

The final notion of the boundary requires that at least one of the coordinates take on extremal values. This notion is the usual *topological boundary* since it coincides with the usual concept of the boundary of the set P^n in the sense of point-set topology (Massey 1967). The topological boundary is denoted by B^n, where

$$B^n = \{(z_1, \ldots, z_n) \text{ in } \mathbb{C}^n \mid |z_i| \leqslant 1, \quad i = 1, \ldots, n \text{ and } |z_k| = 1 \text{ for some } k\} \tag{4}$$

Finally we define a subset, H^n, of P^n whose relevance to the stability problem was originally indicated by Huang (1972) :

$$H^n = \{(z_1, \ldots, z_n) \text{ in } \mathbb{C}^n \mid |z_i| = 1, \quad i = 1, \ldots, k-1\,; \quad |z_k| \leqslant 1\,; \quad z_i = 0, \quad i = k+1, \ldots, n\} \tag{5}$$

Here k varies from 1 to n. Note that $M^1 = H^1 = P^1$ and $T^1 = B^1$, hence these sets become redundant and all reduce to either the unit disk or unit circle in the single variable case.

Shanks *et al.* were the first to give a Hurwitz-like test for the stability of multidimensional digital filters. Their condition states essentially that the filter transfer function must have no poles in P^n. In the single-variable case the pole set of a transfer function is discrete. However, in the case of higher dimensional filters, the pole set is an infinite continuum. Using this fact, Huang (1972) showed that a transfer function has a pole in P^2 if and only if it also has a pole in H^2. This is not to imply that the only poles of the transfer function lie in H^2 but rather that the pole set is so large that it cannot pass through P^2 without intersecting the subset H^2. Anderson and Jury (1974) extended Huang's theorem to the n-dimensional case by showing that a transfer function has a pole in P^n if and only if it has a pole in H^n. The proof of Huang's theorem and its generalization are tediously straightforward but require a clever application of the maximum modulus theorem.

A result somewhat similar to Huang's can be formulated in terms of the topological boundary. To derive such a condition, one exploits the fact that the pole set of a multivariable ($n \geqslant 2$) rational function is an infinite continuum (more precisely no connected component of the pole set is compact (Bers 1964)). As such, the only way the pole set can intersect P^n is if it crosses the topological boundary, B^n. This implies that a transfer function has a pole set intersecting P^n if and only if the pole set has a non-void intersection with B^n.

Now observe that B^n can be viewed as the union of a family of $(n-1)$ variable polydisks (parameterized by k and the value of z_k, $|z_k|=1$). Hence the above argument can be repeated to show that the transfer function has a pole set intersecting the topological boundary of such a $(n-1)$-variable polydisk if it has a pole set intersecting P^n. Upon iterating the argument $(n-1)$ times and eliminating redundant sets, one eventually arrives at the following condition : the transfer function has a pole in P^n if and only if it has a pole in M^n.

The above various Hurwitz-like stability tests for multivariable digital filters are summarized as follows.

Theorem 1

Let a causal multidimensional digital filter be characterized by a rational transfer function in several complex variables. Assume the numerator and denominator polynomials are relatively prime. Then the following are equivalent stability conditions :

(i) the pole set of the transfer function has a null intersection with P^n ;

(ii) the pole set of the transfer function has a null intersection with B^n ;

(iii) the pole set of the transfer function has a null intersection with H^n ;

(iv) the pole set of the transfer function has a null intersection with M^n.

The easiest way to evaluate the stability tests based on the above conditions is by a comparison of the (topological) dimension of the sets where one checks for the existence of poles. In particular, P^n is $2n$ dimensional, B^n is $(2n-1)$ dimensional, while H^n and M^n are both $(n+1)$ dimensional. Again realize that the equivalences of Theorem 1 follow from the fact that the pole set is an infinite continuum whose complex dimension is $(m-1)$, where m is the number of complex variables of the specific function. Finally observe that a pole is implicitly used to mean a specific point in the ' pole set '.

3. Nyquist theory

The task of this section is to construct the concepts of a Nyquist contour, a Nyquist plot, encirclement, and degree, all in topological terms which are thus extendable to the multivariable case. All of our conditions will be stated in terms of the zero set of a relatively prime denominator polynomial of a transfer function. Hence we will deal exclusively with polynomials in several complex variables rather than rational transfer functions.

Traditionally engineers view the Nyquist contour as a subset of the complex plane. This point of view is somewhat erroneous. Mathematically speaking the *Nyquist contour* (the usual closed semicircle, the imaginary axis, or the unit circle) is a continuous map (of bounded variation) from T^1 to $\mathbb{C}^n$. The image of this map, called the trace of the map, is the traditional engineering notion of the Nyquist contour. In this paper T^1 is the unit circle of the complex plane. In the single-variable case (classical digital filter stability) one works with a 'Nyquist contour' defined by $\Gamma(\alpha)=\alpha=\exp(i\theta)$ for $0\leqslant\theta<2\pi$, $\theta=\arg(\alpha)$. In the multivariable case the map will take on values in $\mathbb{C}^n$ forcing the 'Nyquist contour' to be a more involved entity. Observe that we are taking liberties with the classical definition of the Nyquist contour and plot. In an abstract sense, there is no essential difference, although the specific applications (classical feedback stability or presently digital filter stability) are somewhat alien.

In this paper a *Nyquist plot* is defined as the composition of the Nyquist contour, Γ, with a polynomial in several complex variables, A, as Fig. 1. Note that the polynomial map from $\mathbb{C}^n$ to $\mathbb{C}$ is analytic and it is this property which makes the theory go. Thus the Nyquist plot is a continuous map of bounded variation from T^1 to $\mathbb{C}$.

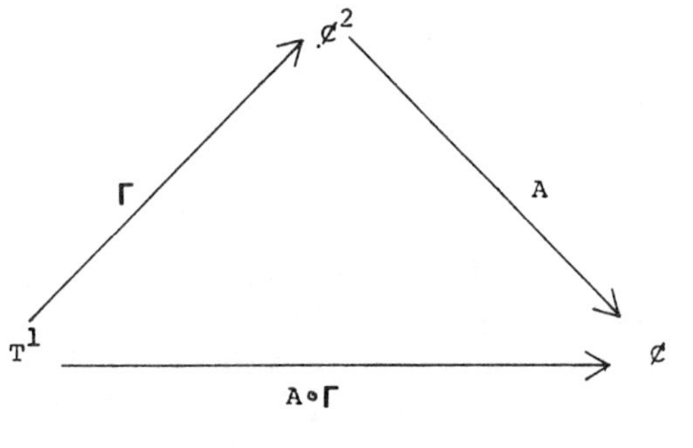

Figure 1. The Nyquist plot as a composition of maps.

The concept of encirclement is intimately related to the topological concept of homotopy. Keeping this association in mind, let X be an arbitrary topological space and let μ and γ be continuous functions of bounded variation defined on T^1 with values in X : μ : $T^1\rightarrow X$ and λ : $T^1\rightarrow X$. The maps μ and λ are said to be *homotopic* if there exists a continuous map, ϕ, defined on the product space $T^1\times I$, $I=[0, 1]$, with values in X such that $\phi(\alpha, 0)=\mu(\alpha)$ and $\phi(\alpha, 1)=\lambda(\alpha)$. In essence, a homotopy is a continuous deformation of the curve μ into the curve λ. This concept defines an equivalence relation on the set of continuous maps from T^1 to X—i.e. two curves are equivalent if one can be continuously deformed into the other. A curve is said to be homotopically trivial if it is homotopic to a constant map. Note that the use of an abstract topological space, X, in the definition of homotopy, is fundamental to the concept, since all curves with values in $\mathbb{C}^n$ or R^n are homotopically trivial. Although we are interested in the properties of functions defined on $\mathbb{C}^n$, a number of non-trivial topological spaces arise in our analysis; in particular the torus, T^n, and the punctured plane. Here the concept of *encirclement* may be defined for maps taking their values in $\mathbb{C}-\{0\}$. This is a highly non-trivial space in which the distinct equivalence classes of homotopic maps can be indexed by the integers corresponding to the number of times a curve encircles the point zero. This number is termed the degree, $n(\gamma, 0)$, of the map, γ, and can be computed by the formula (Massey 1967)

$$n(\gamma, 0)=\frac{1}{2\pi i}\int_{\gamma}(z-0)^{-1}\,dz \tag{6}$$

where γ is the curve in question and γ does not take on the value zero. The desire is to make a binary decision on whether or not the map encircles zero. This may be defined in purely homotopic terms by saying that a map $\mu: T^1\rightarrow\mathbb{C}-\{0\}$ does not encircle zero if it is homotopically trivial (homotopic to a constant map). The concept may then be extended to maps taking values in $\mathbb{C}$ which do not pass through the point zero by viewing them as maps with values in $\mathbb{C}-\{0\}$.

The significance of these homotopic concepts in algebraic topology (Massey 1967) is due to the fact that the equivalence classes of homotopic maps form a group, $\pi(X)$, where X is the space in question. $\pi(X)$ is called the fundamental group of X. More precisely, if we have two maps $\mu: T^1\rightarrow X$ and $\lambda: T^1\rightarrow X$, such that $\mu(1)=\lambda(1)$, their concatenation $\mu*\lambda: T^1\rightarrow X$ is defined by

$$[\mu*\lambda](\alpha)=\begin{cases}\lambda(\alpha^2) & 0\leqslant \arg(\alpha)\leqslant\pi\\ \mu(\alpha^2) & \pi\leqslant\arg(\alpha)<2\pi\end{cases}$$

Intuitively, $\mu*\lambda$, is a curve which first follows λ as arg (α) goes from 0 to π and then follows μ as arg (α) goes from π to 2π. Moreover, since $\mu(1)=\lambda(1)$, then $\mu*\lambda$ is continuous if μ and λ are continuous. Clearly concatenation is invariant under homotopic equivalence (Massey 1967) (i.e. if μ_1 is homotopic to μ_2 and λ_1 is homotopic to λ_2, then $\mu_1*\lambda_1$ is homotopic to $\mu_2*\lambda_2$). As such it defines a binary operation on the equivalence classes of homotopic curves $\mu: T^1\rightarrow X$ with a fixed value for $\mu(1)$. Thus the group operation of $\pi(X)$ is concatenation (Massey 1967). In classical algebraic topology, the properties of $\pi(\mathbb{C}^n)=0$, since all maps taking values in $\mathbb{C}^n$ are homotopically trivial. On the other hand, $\pi(\mathbb{C}-\{0\})$ is isomorphic to the additive group of integers where the 'degree function' is the isomorphism.

Using this machinery we now formalize a statement of the 'classical' Nyquist criterion. Consider the 'obvious' Nyquist contour, $\Gamma: T^1\rightarrow\mathbb{C}$ defined as $\Gamma(\alpha)=\alpha=\exp[i\arg(\alpha)]$ with the corresponding Nyquist plot $A\circ\Gamma: T^1\rightarrow\mathbb{C}$, where A is a polynomial in one variable.

Theorem 2 (Nyquist)

Let A be a polynomial on $\mathbb{C}$. Then A has no zeros in P^1 (the unit closed disk) if and only if $A \circ \Gamma$ does not pass through nor encircle zero.

4. Main theorems

Here the multivariable Nyquist theory is derived from condition (iv) of Theorem 1. Let a causal digital filter transfer function be

$$H(z_1, \ldots, z_n) = B(z_1, \ldots, z_n)/A(z_1, \ldots, z_n)$$

where A and B are relatively prime. The system so characterized is stable if and only if A has no zeros in M^n—i.e. the zero set of A does not intersect M^n. Now M^n can be expressed as a union of single-variable polydisks as follows. First, for any given set of $(n-1)$ elements, α_i, of T^1, indexed by the integers $1, 2, \ldots, k-1, k+1, \ldots, n$, embed a single-variable polydisk into $\mathbb{C}^n$ as

$$\begin{aligned} &P^1(\alpha_1, \ldots, \alpha_{k-1}, \cdot, \alpha_{k+1}, \ldots, \alpha_n) \\ &= \{(z_1, \ldots, z_n) \text{ in } \mathbb{C}^n \mid z_i = \alpha_i, \quad i = 1, \ldots, k-1, k+1, \ldots, n\,; \ |z_k| \leqslant 1\} \end{aligned} \tag{8}$$

By comparison with eqn. (3), one can verify that

$$M^n = \bigcup_{k=1}^{n} \alpha_k \bigcup_{\alpha_i \in T^1} P^1(\alpha_1, \ldots, \alpha_{k-1}, \cdot, \alpha_{k+1}, \ldots, \alpha_n)$$

Hence the digital filter is stable if and only if A has no zeros in each of the polydisks $P^1(\alpha_1, \ldots, \alpha_{k-1}, \cdot, \alpha_{k+1}, \ldots, \alpha_n)$. Moreover, since these are dependent on only one coordinate, one may test for zeros of A in

$$P^1(\alpha_1, \ldots, \alpha_{k-1}, \cdot, \alpha_{k+1}, \ldots, \alpha_n)$$

by sequentially testing for zeros of the single variable polynomial

$$A(\alpha_1, \ldots, \alpha_{k-1}, z_k, \alpha_{k+1}, \ldots, \alpha_n)$$

in the single-variable polydisk P^1 as defined in the introduction. Each such test can be executed using the 'Nyquist theorem'. This yields a stability test for a function of several variables which takes the form of a continuum of classical Nyquist plots.

Lemma 3

Let A be a polynomial mapping $\mathbb{C}^n$ to $\mathbb{C}^n$. Then A has no zeros in P^n if and only if each of the Nyquist plots for the family of single variable polynomials $A(\alpha_1, \ldots, \alpha_{k-1}, z_k, \alpha_{k+1}, \ldots, \alpha_n)$ for $k+1, \ldots, n$ and α_i in T^1, do not pass through nor encircle zero.

Lemma 3 is essentially equivalent to the condition formulated by DeCarlo (1976) and DeCarlo *et al.* (1977). However, the present condition arose from the fact that A has no zeros in M^n whereas the previous test grew from the fact that A has no zeros in H^n. As was shown by DeCarlo *et al.* (1977) the lemma can be implemented as a practical test in the two-dimensional case. Here one simply chooses a finite set of α's in T^1 and plots the corresponding Nyquist loci. Since T^1 is compact, this discretization can be made to yield as much accuracy as desired. Unfortunately, in the multivariable case our family of Nyquist plots is parameterized by n, $(n-1)$-dimensional tori.

The purpose of the first main theorem is to show that the family of Nyquist plots of Lemma 3 is reducible to n classical single variable Nyquist plots and one further test. To this end we reformulate the classical Nyquist contour used to test the single-variable function $A(\alpha_1, \ldots, \alpha_{k-1}, z_k, \alpha_{k+1}, \ldots, \alpha_n)$ as a Nyquist contour taking its values in $\mathbb{C}^n$; define the Nyquist contour, $\Gamma(\alpha_1, \ldots, \alpha_{k-1}, \cdot, \alpha_{k+1}, \ldots, \alpha_n) : T^1 \to \mathbb{C}^n$ by the equality

$$\Gamma(\alpha_1, \ldots, \alpha_{k-1}, \alpha, \alpha_{k+1}, \ldots, \alpha_n) = (\alpha_1, \ldots, \alpha_{k-1}, \alpha, \alpha_{k+1}, \ldots, \alpha_n) \tag{9}$$

Clearly, the Nyquist plot $A \circ \Gamma(\alpha_1, \ldots, \alpha_{k-1}, \alpha, \alpha_{k+1}, \ldots, \alpha_n)$ coincides with the Nyquists plots of Lemma 3. Thus Lemma 3 can be reformulated in terms of these plots. The key attribute of these multivariable Nyquist contours is that the entire family of Nyquist contours for a fixed k are homotopically equivalent.

Lemma 4

For any given set of α_i's in T^1, $i = 1, \ldots, k-1, k+1, \ldots, n$, the Nyquist contour $\Gamma(\alpha_1, \ldots, \alpha_{k-1}, \cdot, \alpha_{k+1}, \ldots, \alpha_n)$ is homotopic in T^n to the Nyquist contour $\Gamma(1, \ldots, 1, \cdot, 1, \ldots, 1)$.

Proof

Consider the homotopy $\phi : T^1 \times I \to T^n$ defined by

$$\phi(\alpha, t) = (\exp[i\theta_1(1-t)], \ldots, \exp[i\theta_{k-1}(1-t)], \alpha, \exp[i\theta_{k+1}(1-t)], \ldots, \exp[i\theta_n(1-t)]) \tag{10}$$

where $\theta_i = \arg(\alpha_i)$ for any set $\lambda_i \in T^1$, $i = 1, \ldots, k-1, k+1, \ldots, n$. Here $\phi(\alpha, t)$ is in T^n for all α and t. Moreover

$$\phi(\alpha, 0) = [\exp(i\theta_1), \ldots, \exp(i\theta_{k-1}), \alpha, \exp(i\theta_{k+1}), \ldots, \exp(i\theta_n)]$$
$$= \Gamma(\alpha_1, \ldots, \alpha_{k-1}, \alpha, \alpha_{k+1}, \ldots, \alpha_n) \tag{11}$$

and

$$\phi(\alpha, 1) = (1, \ldots, 1, \alpha, 1, \ldots, 1) = \Gamma(1, \ldots, 1, \alpha, 1, \ldots, 1) \tag{12}$$

Hence ϕ is the desired homotopy.

Theorem 3

Let A be a polynomial on $\mathbb{C}^n$. Then A has no zeros in P^n if and only if

(i) A has no zeros on T^n, and

(ii) the Nyquist plots for the single-variable functions $A(1, \ldots, 1, z_k, 1, \ldots, 1)$ $k = 1, \ldots, n$ do not encircle zero.

Proof

Since the images of the family of Nyquist contours defined by eqn. (9) cover T^n, the fact that none of the Nyquist plots of Lemma 3 go through zero implies that A has no zeros on T^n. This verifies the necessity of condition (i). To verify the necessity of condition (ii) observe that the n Nyquist plots of condition (ii) are a subset of the family of Nyquist plots of Lemma 3.

To verify the sufficiency of the theorem, observe that, if A has no zeros on T^n, then A restricted to T^n is a continuous map from T^n to $\mathbb{C}-\{0\}$. Now, since the continuous images of homotopic maps are homotopic, the fact that the Nyquist contours $\Gamma(\alpha_1, \ldots, \alpha_{k-1}, \cdot, \alpha_{k+1}, \ldots, \alpha_n)$ and $\Gamma(1, \ldots, 1, \cdot, 1, \ldots, 1)$ are homotopic for any fixed k with α_i in T^1, $i=1, \ldots, k-1, k+1, \ldots, n$, implies that the Nyquist plots $A \circ \Gamma(\alpha_{k-1}, \cdot, \alpha_{k+1}, \ldots, \alpha_n)$ and $A \circ \Gamma(1, \ldots, 1, \cdot, 1, \ldots, 1)$ are homotopic in $\mathbb{C}-\{0\}$; hence all such Nyquist plots encircle zero if and only if the Nyquist plot for $A \circ \Gamma(1, \ldots, 1, \cdot, 1, \ldots, 1)$ encircles. As such, if A has no zeros on T^n we are assured that none of the Nyquist plots of Lemma 3 go through zero, whereas if the n Nyquist plots $A \circ \Gamma(1, \ldots, 1, \cdot, 1, \ldots, 1)$ do not encircle zero, then none of the Nyquist plots of Lemma 3 encircle zero. With the final observation that the Nyquist plot for the single-variable function $A(1, \ldots, 1, z_n, 1, \ldots, 1)$ coincides with $A \circ \Gamma(1, \ldots, 1, \cdot, 1, \ldots, 1)$, this verifies the sufficiency of the theorem.

Surely this theorem is a true generalization of the classical Nyquist theorem, in that it tests for stability, using only distinguished boundary ($i\omega$-axis) information. Moreover, the test is n-dimensional, hence superior to any of the Hurwitz-type tests.

Intuitively speaking, the result is both surprising and expected. It is surprising because one tests for zeros of an n-variable function using single variable Nyquist plots as opposed to some type of n-dimensional encirclement. It was expected, however, since a polynomial contains a finite amount of information (a finite number of coefficients), so that only a finite number of tests need be executed. In this light the condition of Lemma 3 seemed superfluous.

Again, Theorem 3 is aesthetically pleasing, since it uses only frequency response information. However, by cleverly considering the implications of this information as shown by Huang (1972) and Shanks *et al.* (1972), one may concoct an equivalent test. Essentially the test will be a consequence of condition (iii) of Theorem 1 and hopefully will be easier to implement.

Theorem 4

Let A be a polynomial mapping $\mathbb{C}^n$ to $\mathbb{C}^n$. Then A has no zeros in P^n if and only if

(i) A has no zeros on T^n, and
(ii) the Nyquist plots for the single variable functions $A(1, \ldots, 1, z_k, 0, \ldots, 0)$ $k=1, \ldots, n$, do not encircle zero.

Proof

Note first that it is known (DeCarlo 1976, DeCarlo *et al.* 1977) that A has no zeros in P^n if and only if the Nyquist plots of $A(\alpha_1, \ldots, \alpha_{k-1}, z_k, 0, \ldots, 0)$ for $k=1, \ldots, n$ and for each and every α_i in T^1 do not encircle nor pass through zero.

Since A has no zeros in P^n, it immediately follows that A has no zeros in T^n. Moreover, the Nyquist plots of condition (ii) are a subset of the Nyquist plots of the stability result noted above. Thus the forward direction is shown.

Conversely, suppose condition (i) and condition (ii) hold. Since A has no zeros in T^n, Lemma 4 guarantees that the Nyquist plots of $A(\alpha_1, \ldots, \alpha_{n-1}, z_n)$

for each and every α_i in T^1 are homotopic to one another. In particular, they are homotopic to $A(1, \ldots, 1, z_n)$. Thus any member of this family of Nyquist plots encircles zero if and only if $A(1, \ldots, 1, z_n)$ encircles zero.

Now if the Nyquist plot of $A(1, \ldots, 1, z_n)$ does not encircle zero, then $A(\alpha_1, \ldots, \alpha_{n-1}, 0) \neq 0$ for each and every α_i in T^1. In other words $A(z_1, \ldots, z_{n-1}, 0)$ has no zeros on the $n-1$-dimensional torus ;

$$\{(z_1, \ldots, z_n) \in C^n \mid |z_i| = 1 \; ; \quad i = 1, \ldots, n-1 \; ; \quad z_n = 0\}$$

Repeating the above arguments we conclude that the Nyquist plot of $A(1, \ldots, 1, z_{n-1}, 0)$ encircles zero if and only if each of the Nyquist plots of $A(\alpha_1, \ldots, \alpha_{n-2}, \alpha_{n-1}, 0)$ encircles zero. Continuing in this fashion, one verifies that the conditions of the theorem are equivalent to the conditions shown by DeCarlo (1976) and DeCarlo *et al.* (1977) as stated at the beginning of the proof. The statement of the theorem now follows.

Observe that this theorem does not explicitly use distinguished boundary (frequency response) information. However, the sequential manner of the test does use such information in an implicit way. Also the test of Theorem 4 may be easier to implement since the zero dependence of $A(1, \ldots, z_k, 0, \ldots, 0)$ tends to cancel terms in the original polynomial which effectively diminishes the complexity of the test.

At this point we state and prove the final theorem of the section. This theorem combines the n Nyquist plots of Theorem 3 into a single Nyquist plot.

Theorem 5

Let A be a polynomial mapping $\mathbb{C}^n$ into $\mathbb{C}$. Then A has no zeros in P^n if and only if

(i) A has no zeros on T^n, and
(ii) the Nyquist plot for the single-variable function $A(z, z, \ldots, z)$ does not encircle zero.

Before giving the formal proof of this theorem, we will sketch its derivation as a corollary to Theorem 3. First observe that since an analytic function is orientation preserving (Conway 1973), the degree of each of the single variable Nyquist plots, $A \circ \Gamma(1, 1, \ldots, 1, \cdot, 1, \ldots, 1)$ of Theorem 3 is non-negative Moreover, the degree function associated with the set of closed curves is an isomorphism from $\pi(C - \{0\})$ onto the additive group of integers. Thus the degree of the concatenation (the group operation in $\pi(C - \{0\})$) of closed curves, will be the sum of the degrees of the individual curves. Furthermore, the sum of non-negative integers is zero if and only if each integer is zero. This implies that the second hypothesis of Theorem 3 holds if and only if the single Nyquist plot, obtained by concatenating the n Nyquist plots of Theorem 3, does not encircle zero. Consequently Theorem 3 reduces to verifying that A has no zeros on T^n and checking the encirclement of zero by the single Nyquist plot :

$$\begin{aligned}[A \circ \Gamma(\cdot, 1, \ldots, 1)] * [A \circ \Gamma(1, \cdot, 1, \ldots, 1)] * \ldots * [A \circ \Gamma(1, \ldots, 1, \cdot)] \\ = A \circ [\Gamma(\cdot, 1, \ldots, 1) * \Gamma(1, \cdot, 1, \ldots, 1) * \ldots * \Gamma(1, \ldots, 1, \cdot)] \qquad (13)\end{aligned}$$

where the equality of eqn. (13) is due to the fact (Massey 1967) that composition distributes over concatenation.

Although eqn. (13) reduces the multivariable stability test to a single Nyquist plot, this plot is just the concatenation of the n plots of Theorem 3. The resultant test, then, is no easier to implement than the original test. Fortunately, this Nyquist plot is homotopic in $\mathbb{C}-\{0\}$ to the Nyquist plot for the single-variable function $A(z, z, \ldots, z)$, obtained by setting each of the dependent variables of A equal to one another. To verify this contention, first observe that this single-variable Nyquist plot is equal to the Nyquist plot $A \circ \Gamma(\cdot, \cdot, \ldots, \cdot)$, where $\Gamma(\cdot, \cdot, \ldots, \cdot): T^1 \to C^n$ by taking the point α in T^1 to $(\alpha, \alpha, \ldots, \alpha)$ in $\mathbb{C}^m$. Now, A has no zeros on T^n. Hence A maps T^n continuously to $\mathbb{C}-\{0\}$. The Nyquist plot $A \circ \Gamma(\cdot, \cdot, \ldots, \cdot)$ will thus be homotopic in $\mathbb{C}-\{0\}$ to the Nyquist plot of eqn. (13) provided their corresponding Nyquist contours are homotopic in T^n. This is, indeed, the case. However, the required homotopy is extremely complex. As such, rather than wading through the details, we will simply sketch the required homotopy in the two-variable case. Then we proceed to an alternative proof of the theorem based on a known, but non-intuitive, theorem of functions of several complex variables.

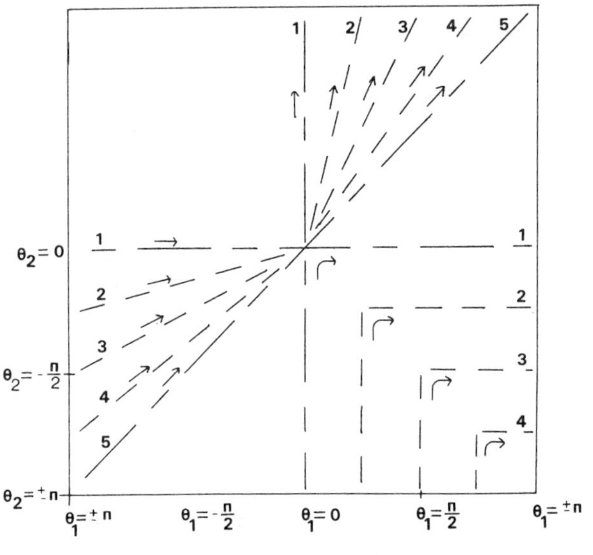

Figure 2. Diagram of homotopy.

To sketch the required homotopy in the two-variable case, represent the torus, T^2, as a square on the plane. Topologically identify opposite sides of the square. Figure 2 illustrates such a square. The point (z_1, z_2), $|z_1| = |z_2| = 1$, in T^2, corresponds to the point (θ_1, θ_2) on the plane, where $\theta_1 = \arg(z_1)$ and $\theta_2 = \arg(z_2)$, i.e. $(z_1, z_2) = [\exp(i\theta_1), \exp(i\theta_2)]$. In other words, the upper and lower boundaries of the square represent the same line on the torus since $\exp(i\pi) = \exp(-i\pi)$ and similarly for the right and left boundaries of the square. Moreover, all four corners of the square represent the same point, $(-1, -1)$. In the sketch of Fig. 2, the Nyquist contour $\Gamma(\cdot, 1) * \Gamma(1, \cdot)$ of eqn. (13) corresponds to the curve, number 1, which starts at $(\theta_1, \theta_2) = (0, 0)$ in the centre of the square travelling vertically to the top of the square. It then goes from the bottom of the square vertically back to the centre, from the centre of the square curve 1, then passes horizontally to the right-hand boundary, and finally it returns from the left-hand boundary of the square back to the centre. Since the upper and lower boundaries of the square are identified, when the curve ' jumps ' from the upper to lower boundary, it remains continuous (think of the square being rolled up into a cylinder with the upper and lower boundaries glued together) ; and similarly for the ' jump ' from the right to left boundary. Of course, curve 1 is closed, since it starts and ends at the same point.

The Nyquist contour $\Gamma(\cdot, \cdot)$ is represented in Fig. 2 by curve 5, which starts at the centre of the square, goes diagonally to the upper right-hand corner of the square and then ' jumps ' to the lower left-hand corner of the square, from which point it returns diagonally back to the centre. As before, the curve is continuous and closed.

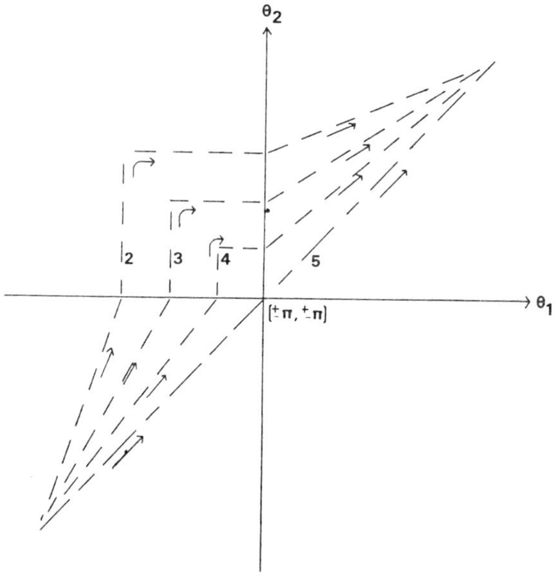

Figure 3. Diagram of homotopy.

The required homotopy between curves 1 and 5 is indicated on Fig. 2 by the three intermediary curves numbered 2, 3 and 4. As before, these curves are continuous, since the upper and lower boundaries and the left and right boundaries of the square are identified. Also all the intermediary curves begin and end at the base point $(\theta_1, \theta_2) = (0, 0)$. The continuity of the intermediary curves is illustrated graphically in Fig. 3 wherein we have redrawn Fig. 2 with the point $(\theta_1, \theta_2) = (\pm\pi, \pm\pi)$ taken as the centre point. In this representation it is clear that curves 2, 3 and 4 are continuous and converge to curve 5.

Although the homotopy required to complete our proof is neatly illustrated in Fig. 2, its explicit mathematical description is by no means simple, even for the two-variable case. Consequently, rather than formalizing the tedious details of the required n-variable homotopy, we construct an alternative proof of Theorem 5 based on a theorem of several complex variables. Since the theorem is applicable to analytic functions as well as polynomials this proof will also allow us to extend Theorem 5 to the case of meramorphic transfer functions in several complex variables.

Lemma 5

Let $f=(f_1, f_2, \ldots, f_n)$ be a continuous function mapping P^1 to $\mathbb{C}^n$, $n \geqslant 2$, such that $f(T^1) \subset T^n$ and each of its coordinate functions, f_i, have positive degree when viewed as functions from T^1 to C, $f_i|_{T^1} : T^1 \to \mathbb{C}$. Then for any analytic function $g : \mathbb{C}^n \to C$, g has a zero in P^n if and only if g has a zero in $T^n \cup f(P^1)$. The theorem appears on page 87 of Rudin (1969) and its proof will not be repeated here. In essence the theorem yields an entire family of n-dimensional Hurwitz-like tests (since T^n is n-dimensional and $f(P^1)$ is 2-dimensional) one for each f satisfying the hypotheses of the theorem.

Proof of Theorem 5

To prove Theorem 5, we apply Lemma 5 with f defined by $f(z)=(z, z, \ldots, z)$. Since each coordinate function $f_i(z)=z$ is the identity map the coordinates all have degree one and the hypotheses of Theorem 5 are satisfied. As such, the polynomial $A : \mathbb{C}^n \to \mathbb{C}$ (an arbitrary analytic function, $g : \mathbb{C}^n \to \mathbb{C}$, could be used with equal validity) has a zero in P^n if and only if it has a zero in $T^n \cup f(P^1)$. Now

$$f(P^1)=\{(z, z, \ldots, z) \text{ in } \mathbb{C}^n \mid |z| \leqslant 1\} \tag{14}$$

is just a polydisk in one variable embedded in $\mathbb{C}^n$. As such, via the classical single-variable Nyquist criterion the existence of zeros of A in $f(P^1)$ may be determined using the Nyquist plot $A \circ \Gamma(\cdot, \cdot, \ldots, \cdot)$ whose Nyquist contour $\Gamma(\cdot, \cdot, \ldots, \cdot)$ follows the boundary of $f(P^1)$. This Nyquist plot is, however, just the classical Nyquist plot for the single variable function $A(z, z, \ldots, z)$. Thus, if we check to see if A has no zeros on T^n and that the Nyquist plot for

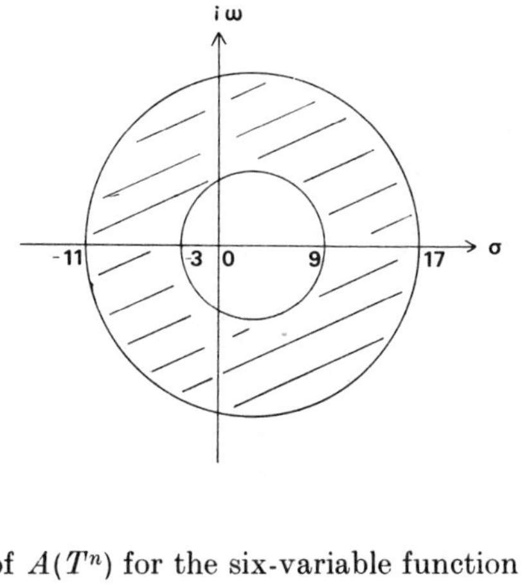

Figure 4. Plot of $A(T^n)$ for the six-variable function of eqn. (15).

Fig. 5

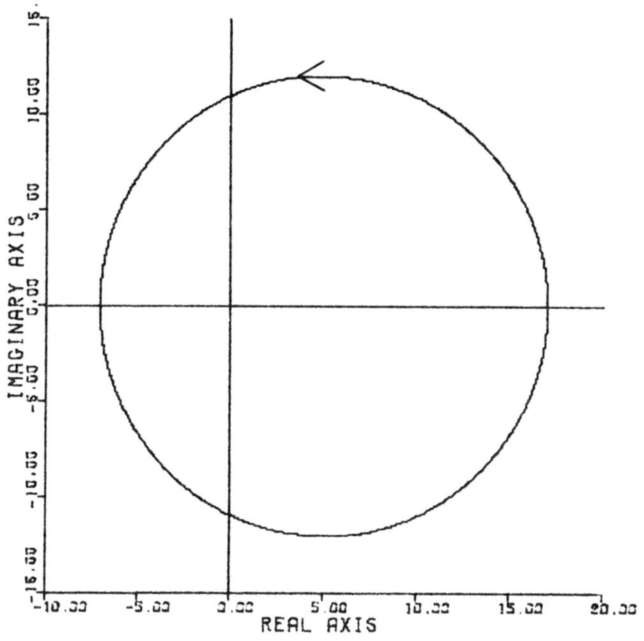
IMAGINARY AXIS
REAL AXIS
15.00
10.00
5.00
0.00
-5.00
-10.00
-15.00
-10.00
-5.00
0.00
5.00
10.00
15.00
20.00

(*a*)

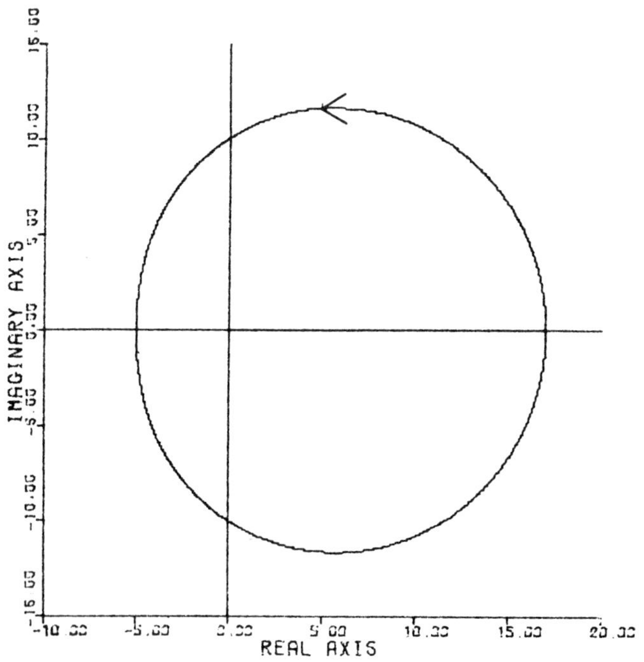
IMAGINARY AXIS
REAL AXIS
15.00
10.00
5.00
0.00
-5.00
-10.00
-15.00
-10.00
-5.00
0.00
5.00
10.00
15.00
20.00

(*b*)

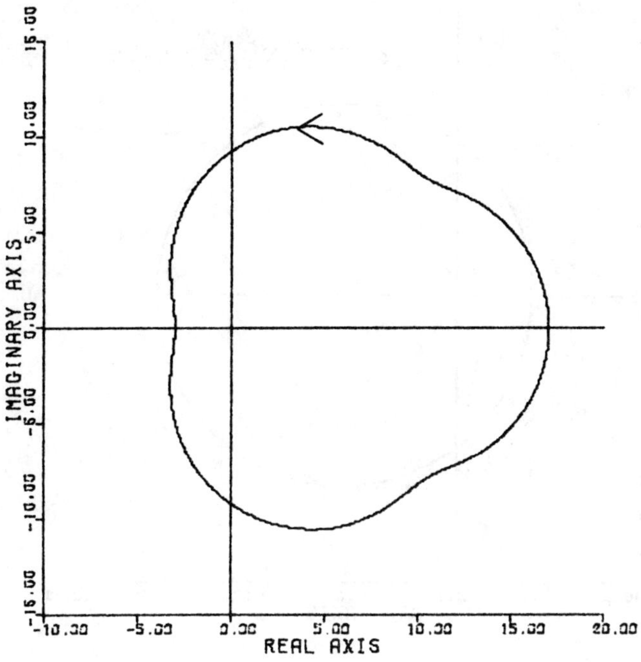
IMAGINARY AXIS
15.00
10.00
5.00
0.00
-5.00
-10.00
-15.00
-10.00
-5.00
0.00
5.00
10.00
15.00
20.00
REAL AXIS

(c)

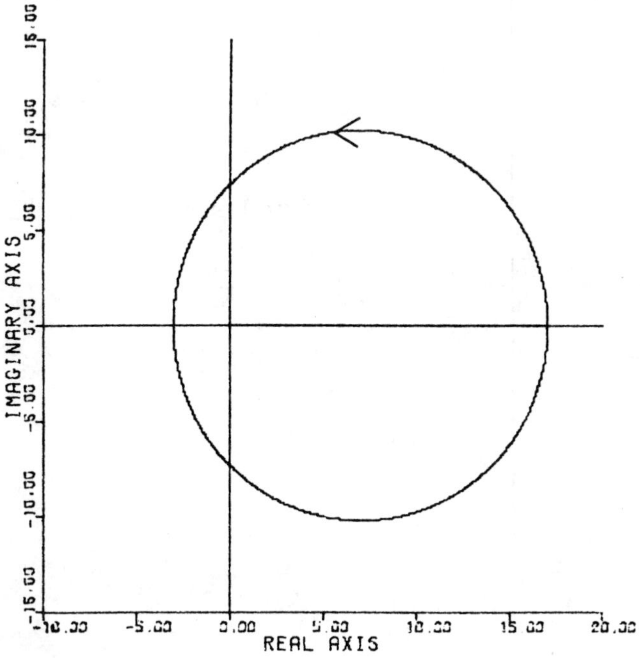
IMAGINARY AXIS
15.00
10.00
5.00
0.00
-5.00
-10.00
-15.00
-10.00
-5.00
0.00
5.00
10.00
15.00
20.00
REAL AXIS

(d)

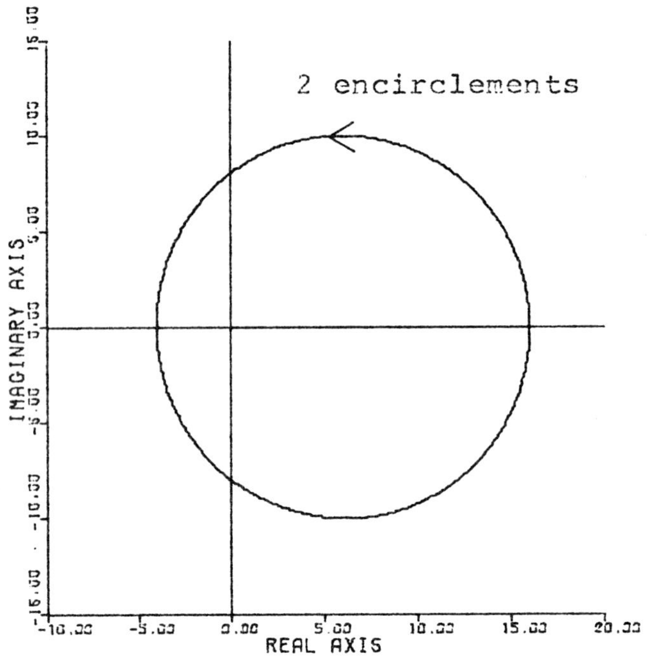

(*e*)

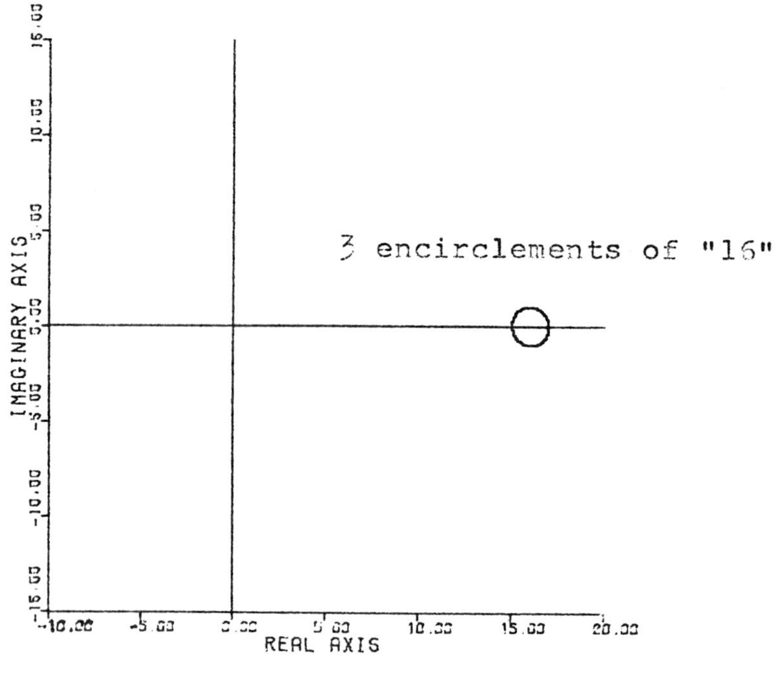

(*f*)

Figure 5. Nyquist plots for the six single-variable functions of eqns. (16) to (21).

$A(z, z, \ldots, z)$ does not encircle zero we are assured that A has no zeros in $T^n \cup f(P^1)$ and thus by Theorem 6 we are assured that A has no zeros in P^n as was to be shown.

5. Examples

Example 1

Consider the six-variable fourth-order polynomial

$$A(z_1, z_2, z_3, z_4, z_5, z_6) = 10z_1z_2z_3z_4z_5^2 + 2z_1^2 z_2 + z_1z_3^2 z_4^4 + z_6^3 + 3 \quad (15)$$

for which the image of A restricted to T^n is plotted in Fig. 4. Since zero is not in the image, condition A of the theorem is satisfied and we may proceed to check condition B. This requires that we test the Nyquist plots for the six one-variable functions

$$A(z_1, 1, 1, 1, 1, 1) = 11z_1 + 2z_1^2 + 4 \quad (16)$$

$$A(1, z_2, 1, 1, 1, 1) = 12z_2 + 5 \quad (17)$$

$$A(1, 1, z_3, 1, 1, 1) = 10z_3 + z_3^2 + 6 \quad (18)$$

$$A(1, 1, 1, z_5, 1, 1) = 10z_4 + z_4^4 + 6 \quad (19)$$

$$A(1, 1, 1, 1, z_5, 1) = 10z_5^2 + 7 \quad (20)$$

and

$$A(1, 1, 1, 1, 1, z_6) = z_6^3 + 16 \quad (21)$$

for encirclements of zero. The resultant plots are sketched in Figs. 5 (*a*) to 5 (*f*), where we see that five of the six plots encircle zero. As such, the system is unstable.

Example 2

In this case we apply Theorem 4 to the same polynomial of Example 1. Again the image of T^n under A does not contain zero so we must perform the sequential tests outlined in Theorem 4.

Step 1. Consider the Nyquist plot of $A(1, \ldots, 1, z_6) = z_6^3 + 16$

Step 2. Since the first Nyquist plot fails to encircle zero, consider the Nyquist plot of $A(1, \ldots, 1, z_5, 0) = 10z_5^2 + 6$. Clearly this Nyquist plot encircles, so the filter is unstable.

Example 3

In this we apply Theorem 5 to the same polynomial of the previous examples. Notice that in this case the curve is of higher order and appears complicated. There also may be some numerical problems in obtaining an accurate Nyquist plot of this curve.

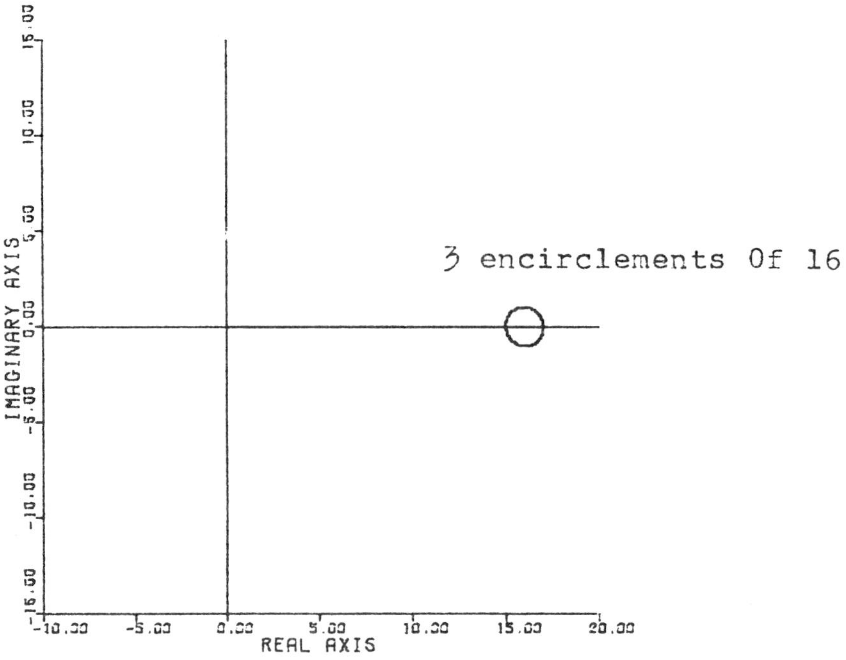

Figure 6. Nyquist plot of $A(1, \ldots, z_6)$ does not encircle zero.

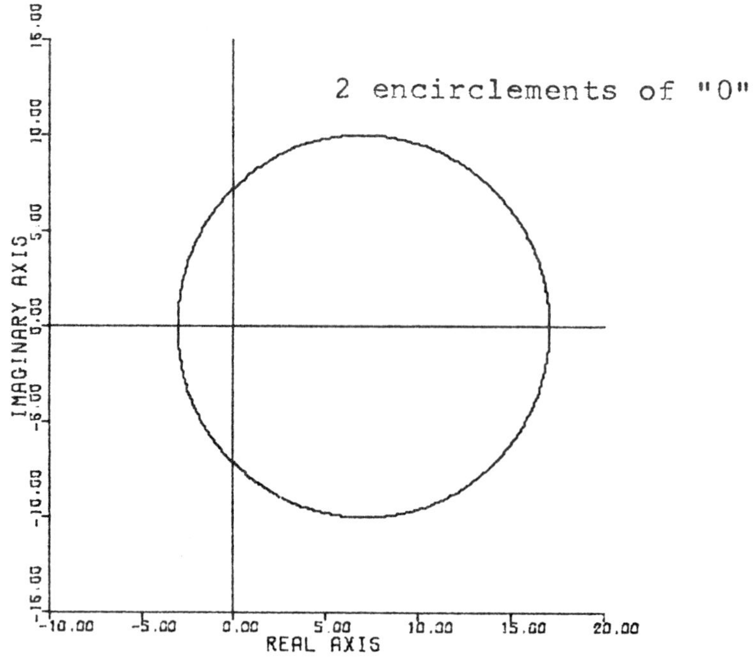

Figure 7. Nyquist plot of $A(1, \ldots, 1, z_5, 0)$.

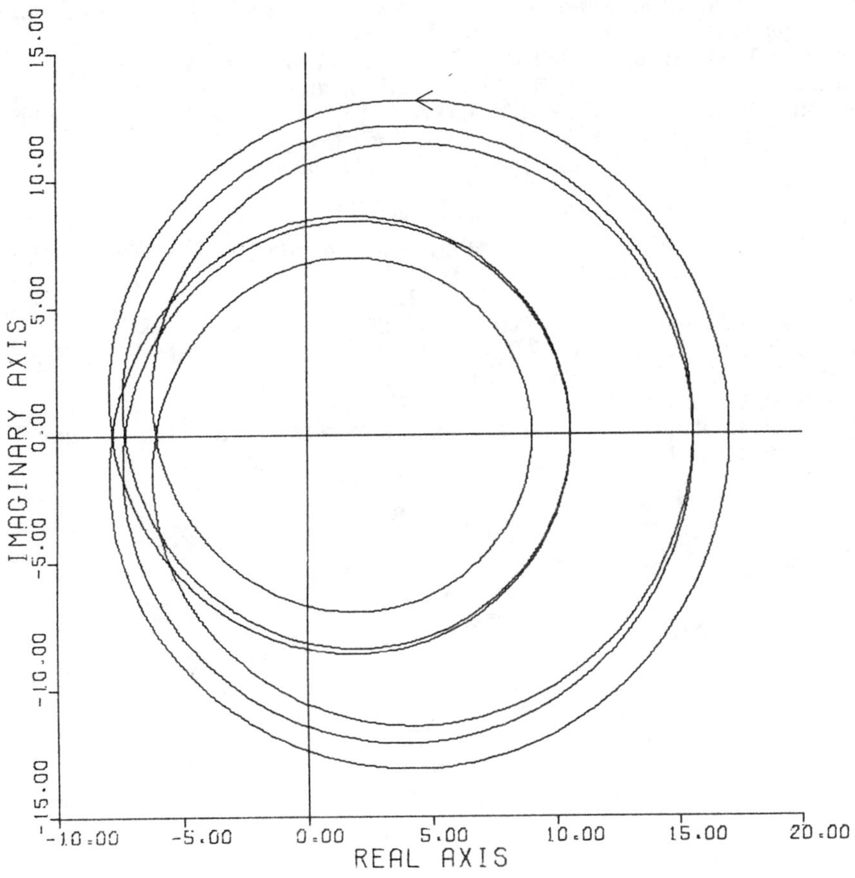

Figure 8. The single Nyquist plot of $A(z, z, z, z, z, z)$.

Clearly $A(T^n) \neq 0$ as in the previous examples. Thus consider the Nyquist plot of $A(z_1, \ldots, z_6) = z^7 + 10z^6 + 3z^3 + 3$ where we have set $z = z_1 = \ldots = z_6$.

Observe that the number of times the curve of Fig. 8 encircles zero equals the number of times all the curves of Fig. 5, taken together, encircle zero.

Lastly, it is interesting to wonder at the usefulness of these plots for the design engineer. The authors believe that in time these plots will be shown to supply a large amount of information on the behaviour of a system.

Acknowledgment

The authors wish to acknowledge Rodney Trotter who ran numerous computer programmes verifying the Nyquist tests herein.

References

Anderson, B. O. O., and Jury, E. I., 1974, *I.E.E.E. Trans. Circuits Systems.*, **21,** 300.

Barman, J., and Katzenelson, J., 1974, *Int. J. Control*, **20,** 593.

Bers, L., 1964, *Introduction to Several Complex Variables* (New York: Courant Institute of Mathematical Sciences).

Conway, John, 1973, *Functions of One Complex Variable* (New York : Springer-Verlag).
DeCarlo, R. A., 1976, Ph.D. Thesis, Texas Tech University, Lubbock, Texas.
DeCarlo, R. A., and Saeks, R., 1977, *Int. J. Control* (to be published).
DeCarlo, R. A., Saeks, R., and Murray, J., 1977, *Proc. I.E.E.E.* (to be published).
Huang, T. S., 1972, *I.E.E.E. Trans. Audio Electroacoust.*, **20,** 158.
Jury, E. I., 1975, *Inners and the Stability of Dynamical Systems* (New York : J. Wiley & Sons).
MacFarlane, A. G. J., 1972, *Automatica*, **8,** 455.
Massey, W. S., 1967, *Algebraic Topology : An Introduction* (New York : Hartcourt Brace & World Inc.).
Nyquist, H., 1932, *Bell Syst. tech. J.*, **11,** 126.
Popov, V. M., 1961, *Automn remote Control*, **22,** 857.
Rudin, Walter, 1969, *Function Theory in Polydisks* (Amsterdam : W. A. Benjamin).
Saeks, R., 1975, *I.E.E.E. Trans. Circuits Syst.*, **22,** 780.
Sandberg, I. W., 1964, *Bell Syst. tech. J.*, **43,** 1501.
Shanks, J. L., Treital, S., and Justice, J., 1972, *I.E.E.E. Trans. Audio Electroacoust.*, **20,** 115.

Bibliography

References are grouped into the following sections.

I. HISTORICAL

1.0 General historical material
1.1 Early development of control
1.2 Genesis of frequency-response methods
1.3 Second World War developments and postwar spread of frequency-response methods

II. CLASSICAL SINGLE-LOOP LINEAR THEORY AND APPLICATIONS

2.0 General background material
2.1 Nyquist's stability criterion, its proof, and further development
2.2 Mikhailov criterion and other locus methods
2.3 Bode's work and its development
2.4 Root-locus method
2.5 Other work related to feedback systems
2.6 Frequency-response treatment of random signals
2.7 Discrete-time systems
2.8 Design and applications

III. NONLINEAR, TIME-VARYING AND STOCHASTIC SYSTEMS

3.0 General background material
3.1 Aizerman and Kalman conjectures
3.2 Describing function
3.3 Popov criterion
3.4 Circle criterion and related topics
3.5 Other work on nonlinear feedback system stability
3.6 Time-varying systems
3.7 Stochastic systems

IV. MULTIVARIABLE SYSTEMS

4.0 General background material
4.1 Early work on multivariable problems
4.2 Noninteractive control and decoupling theory
4.3 Inverse Nyquist array method
4.4 Generalized Nyquist and generalized root-locus methods
4.5 Sequential return difference method
4.6 Dyadic decomposition methods
4.7 Optimal control and optimal filtering
4.8 Modal control and pole shifting
4.9 Algebraic theory
4.10 Geometric theory
4.11 Internal model principle
4.12 Multivariable regulator and multivariable servomechanism problems
4.13 Zeros
4.14 Analytical design techniques and Wiener-Hopf approach
4.15 Multivariable circle criteria
4.16 Nonlinear multivariable systems
4.17 Other work on multivariable systems

V. MULTIDIMENSIONAL SYSTEMS

5.0 General background material
5.1 Multidimensional Nyquist theory

I. HISTORICAL

1.0 General Historical Material

Bateman, H., 1945, "The control of an elastic fluid," *Bull. Amer. Math. Soc.*, 51, 601-646.

Bellman, R. and R. Kalaba (Eds.), 1964, *Selected Papers on Mathematical Trends in Control Theory.* New York: Dover.

Bode, H. W., 1978, "Harry Nyquist," *IEEE Trans. Automat. Control*, AC-22, 897-898.

Brittain, J. E., (Ed.), 1977, *Turning Points in American Electrical History,* New York: IEEE Press.

Coales, J. F., 1956, "Historical and scientific background of automation," *Engineering*, 182, 363-370.

Derby, T. K. and T. I. Williams, 1960, *A Short History of Technology,* Oxford: Oxford Univ. Press.

Fuller, A. T., 1963, "Directions of research in control," *Automatica*, 1, 289-296.

Fuller, A. T., (Ed.), 1975, *Stability of Motion*. London: Taylor and Francis.

Heathcoate, N., 1953, *Nobel Prize Winners in Physics 1901-1950*. New York: Schuman.

Lerner, A. Y., 1974, "A survey of Soviet contributions to control theory," in *Control and Dynamic Systems—Advances in Theory and Applications,* Vol. 11, Ed. by C. T. Leondes. New York: Academic Press, pp. 491-514.

Mayr, O., 1970, *The Origins of Feedback Control*. Cambridge, MA: M.I.T. Press.

Rörentrop, K., 1971, *Entwicklung der modernen Regelungstechnik*. Munich: Oldenbourg.

Thaler, G. J., (Ed.), 1974, *Automatic Control: Classical Linear Theory*. Stroudsberg, Pa: Dowden, Hutchinson and Ross.

1.1 Early Development of Control

Airy, G. B., 1840, " On the regulator of the clockwork for effecting uniform movement of equatoreals," *Mem. Roy. Astr. Soc.*, 11, 249-267.

Airy, G. B., 1851a, "Supplement to a paper on the regulation of the clockwork for effecting uniform movement of equatoreals," *Mem. Roy. Astr. Soc.*, 20, 115-119.

Airy, G. B., 1851b, " On a method of regulating the clockwork for equatoreals," *Monthly Notices of the Royal Astronomical Society*, 11, 17-18.

Andronov, A. A. and I. N. Vosnesenskii, 1956, "The work of J. C. Maxwell, I. A. Vyshnegradsky and A. Stodola in the theory of machine control" (in Russian), A. A. Andronov: Sobranie Trudov, Izdat, ANNSSSR, Moscow.

Barkhausen, H., 1907, *Das problem der Schwingungserzeugung*, Leipzig.

Barkhausen, H., 1921, *Lehrbuch der Elektronenrohren*, Leipzig: Hirzel.

Bethell, P., 1946, "The development of the torpedo," *Engineering*, 160, 4-5.

Bennett, S., 1975, "The search for uniform and equable motion: a study of the early methods of control of the steam engine," *Int. J. Control*, 21, 113-147.

Callendar, A., D. R. Hartree and A. Porter, 1936, "Time lag in a control system," *Phil. Trans. Roy. Soc. London*, 235A, 415-444.

Farcot, J., 1873, *Le Servo-Moteur ou Moteur Asservi*. Paris: Baudrey.

Fuller, A. T., 1976a, "The early development of control theory," *Trans. ASME J. Dynamic Systems, Measurement and Control*, 98, 109-118.

Fuller, A. T., 1976b, "The early development of control theory II," *Trans. ASME, J. Dynamic Systems, Measurement and Control*, 98, 224-235.

Gassiot, J. P., 1866, "On Appold's apparatus for regulating temperature and keeping the air in a building at any desired degree of moisture," *Proc. Roy. Soc. London*, 144.

Gray, J., 1867, "Description of the steam steering engine in the Great Eastern steamship," *Proc. Inst. Mech. Engrs*.

Gray, E., 1975, *The Devil's Device: The Story of Robert Whitehead, Inventor of The Torpedo*. London: Seeley Service.

Hartree, D. R., A. Porter, A. Callender and A. B. Stephenson, 1937, "Time lag in a control system—II," *Proc. Roy. Soc. London*, 161A, 460-476.

Henderson, J. B., 1884, "On the application of hydraulic machinery to the loading, discharging, steering and working of steamships," *Trans. Inst. Nav. Arch.*, pp. 153 ff.

Hermite, C., 1854, "Sur le nombre des racines d'une equation algebrique comprise entre des limites donees," *J. Reine Angew, Math*, 52, 39-51.

Hort, W., 1904, "Die Entwicklung des Problems der stetigen Kraftmaschinen-regelung nebst einem Versuch der Theorie unstetiger Regelungsvorgänge," *Zeitschrift Math. und Phys.*, 50, 233-279.

Hurwitz, A., 1895, "Uber die Bedingungen, unter welchen eine Gleichung nur Wurzeln mit negativen reelen Teilen besitzt," *Mathematische Annalen*, 273-284.

Ivanoff, A., 1934, Theoretical foundations of the automatic regulation of temperature, *J. Inst. Fuel*, 7, 117-138.

Lincke, M., 1879, *Das mechanische Relais*. VDI-Zeitschrift.

Luders, J., 1861 and 1865, *Uber die Regulatoren.* VDI-Zeitschrift.

Marié, G., 1878, "Etude comparee des regulateurs de vitesse, de pression, de temperature," *Annals. Mines*, 7th series, 14, 450-548.

Maxwell, J. C., 1868, "On governors," *Proc. Roy. Soc. London*, 16, 270-283.

Mayr, O., 1971a, "Victorian physicists and speed regulation: an encounter between science and technology," *Notes and Records of the Royal Society of London*, 26, 205-228.

Mayr, O., 1971b, "Maxwell and the origins of cybernetics," *Isis*, 62, 424-444.

Minorsky, N., 1922, "Directional stability of automatically steered bodies," *J. Am. Soc. Naval Eng.*, 42, 280-309.

Minorsky, N., 1930, "Automatic steering tests," *J. Amer. Soc. Naval Engrs*, 42, 285-310.

Möller, H. G., 1920, *Die Elektronenröhren und ihre technischen Anwendungen*, Vieweg, Braunschweig.

Preuss, J., 1823, "On a new steam-engine governor," *Philosophical Magazine*, 62, 297-299.

Siemens, C. W., 1853, "On an improved governor for steam engines," *Proc. Inst. Mech. Eng.*, 75-87.

Siemens, C. W., 1866, "On uniform rotation, Phil. Trans." *Roy. Soc. London*, 156, 657-670.

Stodola, A., 1893 and 1894, "Uber die Regulierung von Turbinen," *Schweiz, Bauzeitung*, 22, 27-30 and 23, 17-18.

Tolle, M., 1895 and 1896, *Beiträge zur Beurteilung der Zentrifugalregulatoren*, VDI-Zeitschrift.

Tolle, M., 1905, *Die Regelung der Kraftmaschinen*. Berlin: Springer.

Trinks, W., 1919, *Governors and the Governing of Prime Movers.* New York: Van Nostrand.

Von Mises, R., 1911, "Regulierung des Maschinenganges," *Encyklopadie der Mathematischen Wissenschaften*, 4, Part 2, Article 10, 254-296.

Vyschnegradskii, J. A., 1876, "Sur las theorie des regulateurs," *Comptes Rendus*, 83, 318-321.

Vyschnegradskii, J. A., 1877, "Uber direkt wirkende Regulatoren," *Civilingenieur*, 23, 95-131.

1.2 Genesis of Frequency-Response Methods

Black, H. S., 1934, "Stabilized feedback amplifiers," *Bell System Technical Journal*, 13, 1-18.

Black, H. S., 1977, "Inventing the negative feedback amplifier," IEEE *Spectrum*, 14, 54-60.

Blackman, R. B., 1943, "Effect of feedback on impedance," *Bell System Tech. Journal*, 22, 268-277.

Bloch, O., 1917, "Die Ortskurven der graphischen Elektrotechnik, nach einheitlicher Methode behandelt," Dissertation, ETH, Zürich.

Bode, H. W., 1960, "Feedback—The history of an idea," *Proc. Symp. Active Networks and Feedback Systems*, Polytechnic Institute of Brooklyn: Polytechnic Press, 1-17.

Bromwich, T. J. I'A., 1916, "Normal co-ordinates in dynamical systems," *Proc. Lond. Math. Soc.*, 15, 401-448.

Bush, V., 1929, *Operational Circuit Analysis.* New York: Wiley.

Campbell, G. A., 1911, *Trans. AIEE*, 38, 873.

Campbell, G. A. and R. M. Foster, 1931, "Fourier integrals for practical applications," *Bell Telephone System Monograph* B584, N.Y.

Carslaw, H. S., 1930, *Fourier's Series and Integrals* 3rd Edition, London.

Carson, J. R., 1922, "The Heaviside operational calculus," *Bell Sys. Tech. Journ.*, 1, 43.

Carson, J. R., 1926, *Electrical Circuit Theory and the Operational Calculus*, New York: McGraw-Hill.

Cauchy, A., 1842, *Comptes Rendus Acad. Science*, Paris, 14, 1020 and 15, 14.

Doetsch, G., 1937, *Theorie und Anwendung der Laplace-Transformation*, Springer, Berlin.

Feiss, R., 1939, "Untersuchung der Stabilität von Regulierungen anhand des Vektorbildes," Dissertation, ETH, Zurich.

Feiss, R., 1940, "Regenerations theorie und Stabilität von Regulierungen," *Schweiz Bauzietung*, 115, 97-99.

Feiss, R., 1941, "Eine neue Methode zur Bestimmung der Stabilitat von Regulierungen," *Schweiz Bauzietung*, 118, 61-65.

Gardner, M. F. and J. L. Barnes, 1942, *Transients in Linear Systems*, Vol. I, New York: Wiley.

Heaviside, O., 1899, *Electromagnetic Theory*, London.

Küpfmüller, K., 1928a, "Uber Beziehungen zwischen Frequenzcharakteristiken und Ausgleichsvorgangen in linearen Systemen," *Elektr. Nachr.-Technik*, 5, 18-32.

Küpfmüller, K., 1928b, "Die dynamik der selbsttätigen Verstarkungsregler," *Elektr Nachrichtentechnik*, 5, 459.

Küpfmüller, K., 1941, *Theoretische Elecktrotechnik*. Berlin.

Lauer, H., R. Lesnick and L. E. Matson, 1947, Servomechanism Fundamentals. New York: McGraw-Hill.

Lee, Y. W., 1932, "Synthesis of electrical networks by means of Fourier transforms of Laguerre's functions," *J. Math. Phys.*, 11, 83-113.

Leonhard, A., 1940, *Die selbsttätige Regelung in der Elektrotechnik.* Berlin: Springer.

Ludwig, E. H., 1940, "Die Stabilisierung von Regelanordnungen mit Röhrenverstärkern durch Dämpfung oder elastische Rückführung," *Arch. Elektrotechnik*, 34, 269 ff.

Mikhailov, A. W., 1938, "Methods for harmonic analysis in the automatic control system theory (in Russian)," *Avtomatika i Telemekhanika*, 3, 27.

Nyquist, H., 1956, in *Frequency Response* edited by R. Oldenburger. New York: MacMillan.

Oldenbourg, R. C. and H. Sartorius, 1944, *Dynamik Selbsttätiger Regelungen.* Munich: Oldenbourg.

Paley, R. E. A. C. and N. Wiener, 1934, "Fourier transforms in the complex domain," *American Mathematical Society Colloquium Publication No. 19*, Providence, R.I.

Peterson, E., J. G. Kreer and L. A. Ware, 1934, "Regeneration theory and experiment," *Bell System Technical Journal*, I3, 680-700.

Phillips, R. S., 1942, "Servomechanisms," *R L Report* No. 372.

Schenkel, 1901, *Geometrische Örter an Wechselstromdiagrammen, Elektrotechn*. Zeitschrift, p. 1043.

Steinmetz, C. P., 1897, "Theory and calculation of alternating current phenomena."

Strecker, F., 1947, *Die elektrische Selbsterregung, mit einer Theorie der aktiven Netzwerke*. Stuttgart: Hirzel.

Strecker, F., 1949, "Aktive Netzwerke und das allgemeine Ortskriterium für Stabilität," *Frequenz*, 3, 78-84.

Strecker, F., 1950a, *Praktische Stabilitätsprüfung mittels Ortskurven und numerischer Verfahren.* Berlin: Springer

Strecker, F., 1950b, "Stabilitatsprufung durch geschlossene und offene Ortskurven," *Arch. Elektr. Übertragg*, 4, 199.

Taylor, G. I., 1920, "Diffusion by continuous movements," *Proc. Lond. Math. Soc.*, 20, 196-212.

Tsypkin, Ya. Z., 1946, "Stability of system with time delay feedback," (in Russian), *Avtomatika i Telemekhanika*, 7, 107-129.

Wagner, K. W., 1916, "On a formula of Heaviside's for the solution of transients," (in German), *Archiv. fur Elecktrotech.*, 4, 159-193.

1.3 Second World War Developments and Postwar Spread of Frequency-Response Methods

Ahrendt, W. R. and J. F. Taplin, 1951, *Automatic Feedback Control.* New York: McGraw-Hill.

Ahrendt, W. R., 1954, *Servomechanism Practice*. New York: McGraw-Hill.

Bennett, S., 1976, "The emergence of a discipline: Automatic control 1940-1960," *Automatica*, 12, 113-121.

Brown, G. S., 1940, "Behaviour and design of servomechanisms," report privately printed under the auspices of the Fire Control Committee (Sec D-2) of the National Defence Research Committee.

Brown, G. S. and A. C. Hall, 1946, "Dynamic behaviour and design of servomechanisms," *Trans. ASME*, 68, 503-524.

Brown, G. and D. Campbell, 1948, *Principles of Servomechanisms*. New York: Wiley.

Campbell, D. P., 1958, *Process Dynamics.* New York: Wiley.

Chestnut, H. and R. Mayer, 1951 and 1955, *Servomechanisms and Regulating System Design*, Vols. I and II. New York: Wiley.

Cremer, L., 1947, "Ein neues Verfahren zur Beurteilung der Stabilität linearer Regelungs-systeme," *Z. für angew. Mathematik und Mechanik*, 25-27, 5/6.

Ferrell, E. B., 1945, "The servo problem as a transmission problem," *Proc. IRE*, 33, 763-767.

Gille, J-C, M. J. Pelegrin and P. Decaulne, 1959, *Feedback Control Systems: Analysis, Synthesis and Design*. New York: McGraw-Hill.

Graham, R. E., 1946, "Linear servo theory." *Bell System Tech. Journ.* 25, 616-651.
Greenwood, I. A. Jr., J. V. Holdam Jr. and D. Macrae Jr., 1948, *Electronic instrumentation*, New York: McGraw-Hill.
James, H. M., N. B. Nichols and R. S. Phillips, 1947, *Theory of Servomechanisms*, New York: McGraw-Hill.
Hall, A. C., 1943, "The analysis and synthesis of linear servomechanisms," *MIT Technology Press.*
Hall, A. C., 1946, "Application of circuit theory to the design of servomechanisms," *J. Franklin Inst.* 242, 279-307.
Harriott, P., 1964, *Process Control*. New York: McGraw-Hill.
Harris, H., 1942, "The analysis and design of servomechanisms," OSRD Report No. 454.
Harris, Jr., H., 1946, "The frequency response of automatic control systems," *Trans. AIEE*, 65, 539-546.
Hazen, H. L., 1934, "Theory of servomechanisms," *J. Franklin Inst.*, 218, 279-331.
Herwald, S. W., 1944, "Considerations in servomechanism design," *Trans. AIEE*, 63, 871-876.
Lauer, H., R. Lesnick and L. E. Matson, 1947, *Servomechanism Fundamentals.* New York: McGraw-Hill.
Leonhard, A., 1944, "Neues Verfahren zur Stabilitatsuntersuchung," *Arch. der Elektrotechnik*, 38, 17-28.
Leonhard, A., 1940, *Die selbsttätige Regelung in der Elektrotechnik.* Berlin: Springer.
Leonhard, A., 1949 and 1957, *Die Selbsttatige Regelung*, Berlin: Springer.
MacColl, L. A., 1943, *"The analysis and synthesis of linear servomechanisms,"* NRDC Report (Section D-2 Fire Control).
MacColl, L. A., 1945, *Fundamental Theory of Servomechanisms*, New York: Van Nostrand.
Marcy, H. T., 1946, "Parallel circuits in servomechanisms," *Trans. AIEE*, 65, 521.
Naslin, P., 1951, "Les systems asservis," *Revue d'Optique,* Paris.
Oldenburger, R., 1956, *Frequency Response*. New York: MacMillan.
Pelegrin, M. J., 1952, "Application of the statistical technique to the servomechanism field," in *Automatic and Manual Control*, A. Tustin (Ed.). London: Butterworths, 123-137.
Porter, A., 1965, "The servo panel—A unique contribution to control-systems engineering," *Electronics and Power*, 11, 330-333.
Profos, P., 1945, "A new method for the treatment of regulation problems," *Sulzer Technical Review*, 2, l.
Tustin, A., (Ed.), 1952, *Automatic and Manual Control*. London: Butterworths.
Westcott, J. H., 1965, "Twenty years after: A review of postwar developments," *Electronics and Power*, 11, 334-340.
Whiteley, A. L., 1946, "Theory of servo systems with particular reference to stabilization," J. IEE, 93, Pt. II, 353-372.
Whiteley, A. L., 1947, "Fundamental principles of automatic regulators and servomechanisms," J. IEE, 94, Part IIA, 5-22.
Ziegler, J. G., and N. B. Nichols, 1942, "Optimum settings for automatic controllers," *Trans. ASME*, 64, 759-768.

II. CLASSICAL SINGLE-LOOP LINEAR THEORY AND APPLICATIONS

2.0 General Background Material

Desoer, C. A., and M. Vidyasagar, 1975, *Feedback Systems: Input-Output Properties*. New York: Academic Press.
Guillemin, E. A., 1935, *Communication Networks*, Vols. 1 and 2. New York: Wiley.
Horowitz, I., 1959, "Fundamental theory of automatic linear feedback control systems," *IRE Trans.*, AC-4, 5-19.
Horowitz, I., 1963, *Synthesis of Feedback Systems*. New York: Academic Press.
Lehningk, S., 1966, *Stability Theorems for Linear Motions*. Englewood Cliffs, N.J.: Prentice-Hall.
Smith, O. J. M., 1958, *Feedback Control Systems*. New York: McGraw-Hill.
Truxal, J. G., 1955, *Automatic Feedback Control System Synthesis*. New York: McGraw-Hill.
Tsien, H. S., 1954, *Engineering Cybernetics*. New York: McGraw-Hill.
Willems, J. C., 1971, *The Analysis of Feedback Systems*. Cambridge, MA: MIT Press.

2.1 Nyquist's Stability Criterion, Its Proof and Further Development

Callier, F. M. and C. A. Desoer, 1972, "A graphical test for checking the stability of a linear time-invariant feedback system," *IEEE Trans. Automat. Control*, AC-17, 773-780.
Callier, F. M. and C. A. Desoer, 1976, "On simplifying a graphical stability criterion for linear distributed feedback systems," *IEEE Trans. Automat. Control*, AC-21, 128-129.
Choksy, N. H., C. F. Chen and P. N. Nikiforuk, 1966, "[Comments on] On dual locus diagrams," *IEEE Trans. on Automat. Control*, AC-11, 142-143.
Davis, J. H., 1972, "Encirclement conditions for stability and instability of feedback systems with delays," *Int. J. Control*, 15, 793-799.
Davis, J. H., 1972, "Fredholm operators, encirclements, and stability criteria," *SIAM J. Control*, 10, 608-622.
Decarlo, R. and R. Saeks, 1977, "The encirclement condition: An approach using algebraic topology, *Int. J. Control*," 26, 279-287.
Desoer, C. A., 1965, "A general formulation of the Nyquist criterion," *IEEE Trans. Circuit Theory*, CT-12, 230-234.
Desoer, C. A. and M. Y. Wu, 1968, "Stability of linear time-invariant systems," *IEEE Trans. Circuit Theory*, CT-15, 245-250.
Dzung, L. S., 1951, "The stability criterion," in *Automatic and Manual Control*, A. Tustin, Ed. London: Butterworths, 13-23.
Frey, W., 1946, "A generalization of the Nyquist and Leonhard stability criteria," *Brown Boveri Review*, 33, 59-65.
Goldberg, E. A., 1960, "An analog computer Nyquist plotter," *IRE Trans on Circuit Theory*, CT-7, 130-135.
Görk, E., 1950, "Stabilitätskriterium," *Arch. Elekt. Uebertrag*, 4, 89-96.
Jones, P., 1954, "Stability of feedback systems using dual Nyquist diagram," *IRE Trans. Circuit Theory*, CT-1, 35-44.
Kirschstein, F., 1949, "Zum Stabilitätskriterium von H. Nyquist," *Arch. Elekt. Uebertrag*, 3, 195-198.
Kusters, N. L. and W. J. M. Moore, 1951, "A generalization of the frequency response method for the study of feedback control systems," in *Automatic and Manual Control*, A. Tustin, Ed. London: Butterworths, 105-117.
Lefevre, P., 1952, "L'étude de la stabilité des systems lineaires par la methode de diagramme de phase generalise," *Mémor. Artill. fr.*, Pt 2.
Lefevre, P., 1958, "Development of the generalized phase diagram method," *Trans. Amer. Soc. Mech. Eng.*
Leonhard, A., 1951, "Relative damping as criterion for stability and as an aid in finding the roots of a Hurwitz polynomial," in *Automatic and Manual Control*, A. Tustin, Ed. London: Butterworths, 25-35.
Lepschy, A. and A. Ruberti, 1960, "A rule for direct verification of the Nyquist criterion in nonpolar diagrams," *Proc. First IFAC Congress*, Moscow, 1960. London: Butterworths, 1961, Vol. 1, 13-16.
Natesan, T. R., 1967, "A supplement to the note on the generalized Nyquist criterion," *IEEE Trans. Automat. Control*, AC-12, 215-216.
Nikiforuk, P. N. and D. R. Westlund, 1965, "Relative stability from the dual-locus diagram," *IEEE Trans. Automat. Control*, AC-10, 103-104.
Nikiforuk, P. N. and D. D. G. Nunweiler, 1965, "Dual-locus stability analysis," *Int. J. Control*, 1, 157-166.
Northouse, R. A., 1973, "Inverse Nyquist and INAP," *Int. J. Control*, 17, 721-739.
Nyquist, H., 1932, "Regeneration theory," *Bell System Technical Journal*, 11, 126-147.
Oppelt, W., 1961, "A stability criterion based on the method of two hodographs," *Avtomat. i. Telemekh*, 22, 1175-1178.
Peters, J., 1950, "Wann gilt das stabilitätskriterium nach Nyquist?," *Arch. Elekt. Uebertrag*, 4, 17-22.
Saeks, R., 1975, "On the encirclement condition and its generalization," *IEEE Trans. Circuits and Systems*, CAS-22, 780-785.
Siljak, D. D., 1966, "A note on the generalised Nyquist criterion," *IEEE Trans. Automat. Control*, AC-11, 317.
Stewart, R. M., 1951, "A simple graphical method for constructing families of Nyquist diagrams," *J. Aeronaut Sci.* 18, 767-768.
Stojic, M. R. and D. D. Siljak, 1965, "Generalization of Hurwitz, Nyquist and Mikhailov stability criteria," *IEEE Trans. Automat. Control*, AC-10, 250-254.
Tsypkin, Ya. Z., 1946, "Stability of system with time-delay feedback," (in Russian), *Avtomatika i Telemekhanika*, 7, 107-129.
Vazsonyi, A., 1949, "A generalization of Nyquist's stability criterion," *J. Appl. Phys.* 20, 863-867.

2.2 Mikhailov Criterion and Other Locus Methods

Choe, H. H. and G. J. Thaler, 1966, "An extension of Mitrovic's method: Frequency response techniques," *IEEE Trans. Automat. Control*, AC-11, 569-573.

Genin, J. and R. Genin, 1972, "Note on the Meadows method for automatic Mikhailov hodograph plotting," *Int. J. Control*, 16, 603–605.

Karmarkar, J. S., 1970, "Graphical stability criterion for linear systems," *Proc. IEE*, 117, 1430–1433.

Karmarkar, J. S., 1970, "Stability analysis of systems with distributed delay," *Proc. IEE*, 117, 1425–1429.

Karmarkar, J. S. and D. D. Siljak, 1970, "Stability analysis of systems with time delay," *Proc. IEE*, 117, 1421–1424.

Levine, D., 1959, "Stability criteria in ρ–ϕ rectangular coordinates," *IRE Trans. Automat. Control*, AC-4, 69–70.

Meadows, N. G., 1968, "An analogue computer technique for plotting Mikhailov stability curves," *Int. J. Control*, 8, 353–363.

Mikhailov, A. V., 1938, "Metod garmonicheskovo analiza v teorii regulirovanija (Methods for harmonic analysis in automatic control theory)," *Avtomatika i Telemekhanika*, 3, 27.

Mikhailov, A. V., 1939, "Stability theory of linear feedback circuit with lumped parameters," (in Russian), *J. Technical Physics*, 1, 20–31.

2.3 Bode's Work and Its Development

Bode, H. W., 1940, "Relations between attenuation and phase in feedback amplifier design," *Bell System Technical Journal*, 19, 421–454.

Bode, H. W., 1945, *Network Analysis and Feedback Amplifier Design*. Princeton, NJ: Van Nostrand.

Horowitz, I. M., 1963, *Synthesis of Feedback Systems*. New York: Academic Press.

Horowitz, I., 1973, "Optimum loop transfer function in single-loop minimum-phase feedback systems," *Int. J. Control*, 18, 97–113.

Leake, R. J., 1965, "Return difference Bode diagram for optimal system design," *IEEE Trans on Automatic Control*, AC-10, 342–344.

Mitchell, J. R., 1977, "Comments on 'Bode Compensator Design'," IEEE Trans. on Automatic Control AC-22, 869–870.

Thomas, D. E., 1947, "Tables of phase associated with a semi-infinite unit slope attenuation," *Bell System Tech. Journal*, 26, 870–899.

Wakeland, W. R., 1976, "Bode compensator design," *IEEE Trans. Automat. Control*, AC-21, 771–773.

2.4 Root-Locus Method

Bhattacharyya, B. P., 1965, "Root-locus equations of the fourth degree," *Int. J. Control*, 1, 533–556.

Chang, C. S., 1965, "An analytical method for obtaining the root locus with positive and negative gain," *IEEE Trans. Automat. Control*, AC-10, 92–94.

Chen, C. F., 1965, "A new rule for finding breakaway points of root loci involving complex roots," *IEEE Trans. Automatic Control*, AC-10, 373–374.

Chu, Y., 1952, "Feedback control systems with dead time lag or distributed lag by root-locus method," *AIEE Trans. (Applications and Industry)* 71, 291–292.

Chu, Y., 1962, "Synthesis of feedback control system by phase-angle loci," *AIEE Trans. Applications and Industry*, 71, 330–339.

Evans, W. R., 1948, "Graphical analysis of control systems," *Trans. AIEE*, 67, 547–551.

Evans, W. R., 1950, "Control system synthesis by root locus method," *Trans. AIEE*, 69, 1–4.

Evans, W., 1953, *Control System Dynamics*. New York: McGraw-Hill.

Feinstein, J. and A. Fregosi, 1969, "Some invariances of the root locus," *IEEE Trans. Automat. Control*, AC-14, 102–103.

Fitzgerald, R. J., 1966, "Finding root-locus breakaway points with a spirule," *IEEE Trans. Automat. Control*, AC-11, 317–318.

Huang, I. -B. and L. L. -C. LI, 1967, "Root locus determination of linear systems with transport lag," *IEEE Trans. Automat. Control*, AC-12, 632–634.

Johnston, W. G., 1958, "Relating the Nyquist plot to the root-locus plot," *J. Electronics and Control*, 5, 89–96.

Kingma, Y. J. and S. J. Deitch, 1970, "Root-locus method for the Tsypkin and Jury and Lee criteria," *Int. J. Control*, 12, 577–591.

Klagsbrunn, Z. and Y. Wallach, 1968, "On computer implementation of analytic root-locus plotting," *IEEE Trans. Automat. Control*, AC-13, 744–745.

Kocourek, C. J. and R. A. Northouse, 1974, "Unsupervised root locus gain selection," *Int. J. Control*, 19, 517–527.

Koziol, J. S., Jr., 1971, "An approximate root locus method in the s-plane for sampled-data systems," *IEEE Trans. Automat. Control*, AC-16, 101–102.

Krishnan, V., 1966, "Semi-analytic approach to root locus," *IEEE Trans. Automat. Control*, AC-11, 102–108.

Labounty, R. A. and C. H. Houpis, 1966, "Root locus analysis of a high-gain linear system with variable coefficients; application of Horowitz's method," *IEEE Trans. Automat. Control*, AC-11, 255–263.

Lorens, C. S. and R. C. Titsworth, 1960, "Properties of root locus asymptotes," *IRE Trans. Automat. Control*, AC-5, 71–72.

McDaniel, W. L. and J. W. Dalton, 1967, "A modified root locus technique for a class of sampled-data systems," *Proc. Asilomar Conf. Circuits and Systems*.

Mitchell, J. R. and W. L. McDaniel, Jr., 1970, "A generalized root locus following technique," *IEEE Trans. Automat. Control*, AC-15, 483–486.

Muhlenberg, J. D. S., 1967, "Quartic root locus types," *IEEE Trans. Automat. Control*, AC-12, 228–229.

Narendra, K. S., 1961, "Inverse root-locus, reversed root-locus or complementary root-locus," *IRE Trans. Automat. Control*, AC-6, 359–360.

Power, H. M., 1969, "Approximation theorem for establishing root-locus topology," *Electronics Letters*, 5, 97.

Power, H. M., 1969, "Contribution to the theory of phase-angle loci," *Electronics Letters*, 5, 703.

Power, H. M., 1970, "Application of bilinear transformation to root locus plotting," *IEEE Trans. Automat. Control*, AC-15, 693–694.

Power, H. M., 1971, "Root loci having a total of four poles and zeros," *IEEE Trans. Automat. Control*, AC-16, 484–486.

Power, H. M., 1972, "Correction to 'Application of bilinear transformation to root locus plotting'," *IEEE Trans. Automat. Control*, AC-17, 180.

Sambandam, M. K., 1968, "Comments on 'Semi-analytic approach to root locus'," *IEEE Trans. Automat. Control*, AC-13, 221.

Stapleton, C. A., 1962, "On root-locus breakaway points," *IRE Trans. Automat. Control*, AC-7, 88–89.

Steiglitz, K., 1961, "An analytical approach to root loci," *IRE Trans. Automat. Control*, AC-6, 326–332.

Wakeland, W. R., 1967, "Analytic technique for root locus compensation with quadratic factors," *IEEE Trans. Automat. Control*, AC-12, 631–632.

Williamson, S. E., 1969, "Accurate root locus plotting including the effects of pure time delay," *Proc. IEE*, 116, 1269–1271.

Williamson, S. E. and W. F. Lovering, 1969, "The root-loci of four pole systems," *Int. J. Control*, 10, 625–643.

2.5 Other Work Related to Feedback Systems

Acar, C., 1969, "New return difference," *Electronics Letters*, 5, 543.

Araki, M., 1976, "Input-output stability of composite feedback systems," *IEEE Trans. Automat. Control*, AC-21, 254–259.

Baker, R. A. and D. J. Vakharia, 1970, "Input-output stability of linear time-invariant systems," *IEEE Trans. Automat. Control*, AC-15, 316–319.

Barman, J. F., F. M. Callier and C. A. Desoer, 1973, "L^2-stability and L^2-instability of linear time-invariant distributed feedback systems perturbed by a small delay in the loop," *IEEE Trans. Automat. Control*, AC-18, 479–484.

Bickart, T. A. and G. Prada, 1971, "Bounded input power-bounded output power stability criterion," *Automatica*, 7, 261–264.

Bittanti, S., G. Fronza and G. Guardabassi, 1973, "Periodic control: A frequency domain approach," *IEEE Trans. Automat. Control*, AC-18, 33–38.

Bridgland, T. F. and R. E. Kalman, 1963, "Some remarks on the stability of linear systems," *IRE Trans. Circuit Theory*, CT-10, 539–542.

Desoer, C. A. and Tomasian, 1963, "A note on zero-state stability of linear systems," *Proc. First Allerton Conference on Circuit and System Theory*, University of Illinois, Urbana, IL.

Desoer, C. A., 1970, "Singular perturbation and bounded-input bounded-state stability," *Electronics Letters*, 6, 496.

George, J. H., 1967, "On parameter stability regions for several parameters using frequency response," *IEEE Trans. Automat. Control*, AC-12, 197–200.

Hale, F. J., 1973, "Linear systems and nonunity feedback," *IEEE Trans. Automat. Control*, AC-18, 319–321.

Hamaker, J. P., 1966, "On the approximation of algebraic irrational functions by means of rational fractions," *IEEE Trans. Circuit Theory*, CT-13, 293–297.

Harris, N. G., 1969, "Dynamic *D* partition," *Electronics Letters*, 5, 631.

Kalman, R. E., 1964, "When is a linear control system optimal?," *Trans. ASME, J. Basic Eng.*, Ser. D., 86, 51–60.

Karmarkar, J. S. and G. J. Thaler, 1970, "Generalisation of parameter methods and *D*-decomposition," *Proc. IEE*, 117, 2030–2032.

Krishnamurthi, V., 1972, "Gain margins of conditionally stable systems from Routh's stability criterion," *IEEE Trans. Automat. Control*, AC-17, 551–552.

Krishnamurthi, V., 1972, "Correlation between Routh's stability criterion and relative stability of linear systems," *IEEE Trans. Automat. Control*, AC-17, 144–145.

Nasburg, R. E. and R. A. Baker, 1972, "Stability of linear time-invariant distributed parameter single-loop feedback systems," *IEEE Trans. Automat. Control*, AC-17, 567–569.

O'Shea, R. P., 1966, "A combined frequency-time domain stability criterion for autonomous continuous systems," *IEEE Trans. Automat. Control*, AC-11, 477–484.

O'Shea, R. P., 1967, "An improved frequency time domain stability criterion for autonomous continuous systems," *IEEE Trans. Automat. Control*, AC-12, 725–731.

Polak, E., 1964, "A note on *D*-decomposition theory," *IEEE Trans. Automat. Control*, AC-9, 107–109.

Siljak, D. D., 1964, "Generalization of Mitrovic's method," *IEEE Trans.*, IGA-83, 314–320.

Siljak, D., 1968, "Analytic test for absolute stability," *Electronics Letters*," 4, 358.

Siljak, D., 1969, "Parameter analysis of absolute stability," *Automatica*, 5, 385–387.

Siljak, D. D., 1970, "Algebraic criterion for absolute stability, optimality and passivity of dynamic systems," *Proc. IEE*. 117, 2033–2036.

Vidyasagar, M., 1977, "Instability of feedback systems," *IEEE Trans. Automat. Control*, AC-22, 466–468.

Vidyasagar, M. and M. A. L. Thathachar, 1977, "A note on feedback stability and instability in the Marcinkiewicz space M_2," *IEEE Trans. Circuits and Systems*, CAS-24, 127–131.

Wang, K. P. C., 1968, "Theory of stability and control for distributed parameter systems (a bibliography)," *Int. J. Control*, 7, 101–116.

Wax, N., 1962, "A note on stable, physically realizable, linear, time invariant systems," *IRE Trans. Circuit Theory*, CT-9, 405–408.

Westcott, J. H., 1951, "The development of relationships concerning the frequency bandwidth and the mean square error of servo systems from properties of gain-frequency characteristics," in *Automatic and Manual Control*, A. Tustin, Ed. London: Butterworths, 45–60.

Willems, J. C., 1976, "Mechanisms for the stability and instability in feedback systems," *Proc. IEEE* 64, 24–35.

Wohlers, M. R., 1965, "On gain-bandwidth limitations for physically realizable systems," *IRE Trans. Circuit Theory*, CT-12, 329–333.

2.6 Frequency-Response Treatment of Random Signals

Åström, K. J., 1970, *Introduction to Stochastic Control Theory*. New York: Academic Press.

Bendat, J. S., 1958, *Principles and Applications of Random Noise Theory*. New York: Wiley.

Bode, H. W. and C. E. Shannon, 1950, "A simplified derivation of linear least square smoothing and prediction theory," *Proc. IRE*, 38, 417–425.

Davenport, W. B. and W. L. Root, 1958, *An Introduction to the Theory of Random Signals and Noise*. New York: McGraw-Hill.

Kolmogorov, A. N., 1941, "Interpolation and extrapolation of stationary time series," *Bull. Acad. Sci.* USSR Math, Ser. 5.

Kushner, H., 1971, *Introduction to Stochastic Control*. New York: Holt, Rinehart, and Winston.

Laning, J. H. and R. H. Battin, 1956, *Random processes in Automatic Control*. New York: McGraw-Hill.

Lee, Y. W., 1960, *Statistical Theory of Communication*. New York: Wiley.

Papoulis, A., 1965, *Probability, Random Variables and Stochastic Processes*. New York: McGraw-Hill.

Schwartz, M., 1970, *Information Transmission, Modulation, and Noise*. New York: McGraw-Hill.

Solodovnikov, V. V. 1960, *Introduction to the Statistical Dynamics of Automatic Control Systems*. New York: Dover, (Translation of 1952 Russian version).

Sveshnikov, A. A., 1966, *Applied Methods of the Theory of Random Functions*. London: Pergamon, (Translation of 1961 Russian version).

Wiener, N., 1930, "Generalized harmonic analysis," *Acta. Math.*, 55, 117–258.

Wiener, N., 1948, *Cybernetics or Control and Communication in the Animal and the Machine*. Cambridge, MA: M.I.T. Press.

Wiener, N., 1949, *Extrapolation, Interpolation and Smoothing of Stationary Time Series*. Cambridge MA: M.I.T. Press.

Wong E., 1971, *Stochastic Processes in Information and Dynamical Systems*. New York: McGraw-Hill.

2.7 Discrete-Time Systems

Barker, R. H., 1950, "The theory of pulse monitored servomechanisms and their use for prediction," Report No. 1046, Signals Research and Development Establishment, Christchurch, England.

Barker, R. H., 1952, "The pulse transfer function and its application to sampling servomechanisms," *Proc. IEE*, 99 (4), 302–317.

Barkin, A. I., 1970, "Sufficient conditions for the absence of autooscillations in pulse-systems, *Automat. Remote Control*, 31, 942–946.

Bergen, A. R. and J. R. Ragazzini, 1954, "Sampled-data processing techniques for feedback control systems," *Trans. AIEE*, 73 (2), 236–247.

Bubnicki, Z., 1968, "Frequency condition for the stochastic stability of a class of discrete-time control systems," *Electronics Letters*, 4, 200.

Davis, J. H., 1972, "Stability conditions derived from spectral theory: Discrete systems with periodic feedback, *SIAM J. Control*, 10, 1–13.

Freeman, H. and O. Lowenschuss, 1958, "Bibliography of sampled-data control systems and *Z*-transform applications," *IRE Trans. Automat. Control*, PGAC-4, 28–30.

Freeman, H., 1965, *Discrete-Time Systems*. New York: Wiley.

Helm, H. A., 1959, "The *z* transformation," *Bell Syst. Tech. J.*, 38 (1), 177–196.

Higgins, R. A., 1972, "An exact method for compensation of discrete data systems in the *z*-plane," *Int. J. Control*, 15, 21–27.

Jury, E. I., 1954, "Analysis and synthesis of sampled-data control systems," *Trans. AIEE*, 73 (1), 332–346.

Jury, E. I., 1958, *Sampled-Data Control Systems*. New York: Wiley.

Jury, E. I., 1964, *Theory and Application of the z-Transform Method*. New York: Wiley.

Jury, E. I. and Ya. Z. Tsypkin, 1971, "On the theory of discrete systems," *Automatica*, 7, 89–107.

King-Smith E. A., 1971 "Stability analysis of linear continuous timedelay feedback systems," *Int. J. Control*, 13, 633–655.

King-Smith, E. A., 1971, "Stability analysis of linear sampled-data time-delay feedback systems," *Int. J. Control*, 14, 1–26.

Kuo, B., 1963, *Analysis and Synthesis of Sampled-Data Control Systems*. Englewood Cliffs, NJ: Prentice-Hall.

Linvill, W. K., 1951, "Sampled-data control systems studied through comparison of sampling with amplitude modulation," *Trans. AIEE*, 70, Part II, 1779–1788.

O'Shea, R. P. and M. I. Younis, 1967, "A frequency-time domain stability criterion for sampled-data systems," *IEEE Trans. Automat. Control*, AC-12, 719–724.

Phillips, C. L., 1970, "A note on the frequency-response design technique for multirate digital controllers," *IEEE Trans. Automat. Control*, AC-15, 263–264.

Ragazzini, J. R. and L. A. Zadeh, 1952, "The analysis of sampled-data systems," *Trans. AIEE*, 71 (2), 225–232.

Ragazzini, J. R. and G. Franklin, 1958, *Sampled-Data Control Systems*. New York: McGraw-Hill.

Reddy, D. C. and L. A. Ware, 1966, "A graphical technique for compensation in the *z*-plane," *Int. J. Control*, 4, 87–95.

Roberts, P. D., 1969, "Stability regions of linear continuous or discrete data control systems," *Proc. IEE*, 116, 1937–1939.

Shortle, G. E., Jr. and F. J. Alexandro, Jr., 1970, "An extended frequency-domain stability criterion for a class of sampled-data systems," *IEEE Trans. Automat. Control*, AC-15, 232–234.

Steiglitz, K, 1965, "The equivalence of digital and analog signal processing," *Information and Control*, 8, 455–467.

Sun, C. K. and D. Siljak, 1969, "Absolute-stability test for discrete systems," *Electronics Letters*, 5, 236.

Tsai, S. C. and P. R. Ukrainetz, 1970, "Relative stability of sampled-data control systems by a hodograph method," *Electronics Letters*, 6, 714.

Tsypkin, Ya. Z., 1962, "On the global stability of nonlinear sampled-data systems," *Dokl. Akad. Nauk. SSSR*, 145, 1.

Tsypkin, Ya. Z., 1956, "Frequency method of analysing intermittent regulating systems," in *Frequency Response*, edited by R. Oldenburger, New York: Macmillan.

Tsypkin, Ya. Z., 1958, "Theorie der Relaissysteme der Automatischen Regelung," Munchen, Berlin: Verlag Technik.

2.8 Design and Applications

Bongiorno, J. J., Jr. and D. C. Youla, 1977, "On the design of single-loop single-input-output feedback control systems in the complex-frequency domain," *IEEE Trans. Automat. Control*, AC-22, 416–423.

D'Azzo, J. J. and Houpis C. H., 1966, *Feedback Control System Analysis and Synthesis*, New York: McGraw-Hill,

Gould, L. A., 1969, *Chemical Process Control: Theory and Applications*. Reading, MA: Addison-Wesley,

Grodins, F. S., 1963, *Control Theory and Biological Systems*. New York: Columbia University Press.

Horowitz, I. M., 1963, *Synthesis of Feedback Systems*. New York: Academic Press.

Horowitz, I., 1962, "Plant adaptive systems vs ordinary feedback systems," *IRE Trans.*, AC-7, 48–56.

Horowitz, I. and M. Sidi, 1972, "Synthesis of feedback systems with large plant ignorance for prescribed time-domain tolerances," *Int. J. Control*, 16, 287–309.

Horowitz, I., 1975, "A synthesis theory for linear time-varying feedback systems with plant uncertainty," *IEEE Trans. Automat. Control*, AC-20, 454–464.

Horowitz, I. and M. Sidi, 1978, "Synthesis of linear time-varying nonminimum-phase systems with plant uncertainty," *Int. J. Control*, 27, 351–359.

Horowitz, I. and M. Sidi, 1978, "Optimum synthesis of non-mimimum phase feedback systems with plant uncertainty," *Int. J. Control*, 27, 361–386.

Merriam C. W., 1974, *Automated Design of Control Systems*. New York: Gordon and Breach.

Milhorn, H. T., 1966, *The Application of Control Theory to Physiological Systems*. Philadelphia: W. B. Saunders Co.

Milsum, J. H., 1966, *Biological Control Systems Analysis*. New York: McGraw-Hill.

Mitrovic, D., 1959, "Graphical analysis and synthesis of feedback control systems, Part I—Theory and analysis," *AIEE Trans. on Applications and Industry* 77, 479–496.

Murphy, G. J., 1957, *Basic Automatic Control Theory*. Princeton, NJ: Van Nostrand.

Murphy, G. J., 1959, *Control Engineering*. Princeton, NJ: Van Nostrand.

Newton, G. C., Jr., L. A. Gould and J. Kaiser, 1957, *Analytical Design of Linear Feedback Controls*. New York: Wiley.

Oizumi, J. and M. Kimura, 1957, "Design of conditionally stable feedback systems," *Trans. IRE Circuit Theory*, CT-4, 157–166.

Rolnik, J. A. and I. Horowitz, 1969, "Feedback control system synthesis for plants with large parameter variations," *IEEE Trans. Automat. Control*, AC-14, 714–718.

Rosenbrock, H. H., 1974, *Computer-Aided Control System Design*. New York: Academic Press,

Saucedo, R. and E. E. Schiring, 1968, *Introduction to Continuous and Digital Control Systems*. New York: Collier-MacMillan.

Savant, C. J., 1958, *Control System Design*. New York: McGraw-Hill.

Shinners, S. M., 1964, *Control System Design*. New York: Wiley

Siefert, W. W. and C. W. Steeg, Jr., (Editors), 1960, *Control Systems Engineering*. New York: McGraw-Hill.

Stark, L., 1959, "Stability, oscillations and noise in human pupil servomechanism," *Proc. IRE*, 47, 1925–1938.

Stark, L., 1960, "Vision, servoanalysis of pupil reflex to light," in *Medical Physics*, O. Grasser (Ed.), Chicago: The Year Book Pub. Co., Vol. III, 702–719.

Stark, L., 1968, "Neurological control system," in *Studies in Bioengineering*, New York: Plenum Press.

Thaler, G. J., 1973, *Design of Feedback Systems*. Stroudsberg, PA. Dowden Hutchinson and Ross.

Truxal, J. G., 1955 *Automatic Feedback Control System Synthesis*. New York: McGraw-Hill.

Truxal, J. G., 1958, *Control Engineers' Handbook. New York: McGraw-Hill.*

Westheimer, G., 1954, "Mechanism of saccadic eye movements," *AMA Arch. Opth.*, 52, 710–724.

Youla, D. C., J. J. Bongiorno and H. A. Jabr, 1976, "Modern Wiener-Hopf design of optimal controllers Part I: The single-input-output case," *IEEE Trans. Automat. Control*, AC-21, 3–13.

III NONLINEAR, TIME-VARYING AND STOCHASTIC SYSTEMS

3.0 General Background Material

Aizerman, M. A. and F. R. Gantmacher, 1964, *Absolute Stability of Regulator Systems*. San Francisco: Holden-Day.

Blaquiere, A., 1966, *Nonlinear System Analysis*. New York: Academic Press.

Brockett, R. W., 1966, "The status of stability theory for deterministic systems," *IEEE Trans. Automat. Control*, AC-11, 596–606.

Graham, D. and D. McRuer, 1961, *Analysis of Nonlinear Control Systems*. New York: Wiley.

Higgins, T. J., 1957, "A resume of the development and literature of nonlinear control-system theory," *Trans. ASME*, 79, 445–453.

Holtzmann, J. M., 1970, *Nonlinear System Theory*. New York: Prentice-Hall.

Krylov, N. and N. Bogoliubov, 1943, *Introduction to Nonlinear Mechanics*, Princeton, NJ: Princeton Univ. Press.

Liapunov, A. M., 1907, "Probleme generale de la stabilite du mouvement," *Annales de la Faculte des Sciences de Toulouse*, reprinted as *Annals of Mathematics Study*, No. 17, 1947, Princeton Univ. Press, Princeton, NJ.

Lighthill, M. J. and A. I. Mees, 1973, "Stability of nonlinear feedback systems," in *Recent Mathematical Developments in Control*, D. J. Bell (Ed.). London: Academic Press, 1–20.

Minorsky, N., 1969, *Theory of Nonlinear Control Systems*, New York: McGraw-Hill.

Narendra, K. S. and J. H. Taylor, 1973, *Frequency Domain Criteria for Absolute Stability*. New York: Academic Press.

Popov, V. M., 1973, *Hyperstability of Control Systems*. Berlin: Springer-Verlag.

Siljak, D. D., 1969, *Nonlinear Systems*. New York: Wiley.

West, J. C., 1960, *Analytical Techniques for Nonlinear Control Systems*. London: English Universities Press.

Wienberg, L. and P. Slepian, 1960, "Positive real matrices," *Journal for Math. and Mechanics*, 9, 71–83.

Willems, J. L., 1970, *Stability Theory of Dynamical Systems*. London: Nelson.

Willems, J. C., 1971, *The Analysis of Feedback Systems*. Cambridge, MA: M.I.T. Press.

Zadeh, L. A., 1950, "Frequency analysis of variable networks," *Proc. IRE*, 38, 291–299.

3.1 Aizerman and Kalman Conjectures

Aizerman, M. A., 1949, "On a problem concerning the stability in the large of dynamic systems," *Usp. Mat. Nauk.*, 4, 187–188.

Bergen, A. and I. J. Williams, 1962, "Verification of Aizerman's conjecture for a class of third-order systems," *IRE Trans. Automat. Control*, 7, 42–47

Bergen, A. R. and R. A. Baker, 1972, "On third-order systems and Aizerman's conjecture," *IEEE Trans. Automat. Control*, AC-17, 220–222.

Dewey, A. G. and E. I. Jury, 1965, "A note on Aizerman's conjecture," *IEEE Trans. Automat. Control*, AC-10, 482–483.

Fannin, D. R., 1975, "Further comments on two counterexamples to Aizerman's conjecture," *IEEE Trans. Automat. Control*, AC-20, 697–700.

Fitts, R., 1966, "Two counter-examples to Aizerman's conjecture," *IEEE Trans. Automat. Control*, AC-11, 553–556.

Fujii, K. and K. Shoji, 1972, "Verification of the Aizerman and/or Kalman conjecture," *IEEE Trans. Automat. Control*, AC-17, 406–408.

Kalman, R. E., 1957, "Physical and mathematical mechanisms of instability in nonlinear automatic control systems," *Trans. ASME*, 79, 553–566.

Kaszkurewicz E. and L. Hsu, 1978, "Stability of nonlinear systems: A structural approach," Preprints Seventh IFAC World Congress, Helsinki, 2, 1141–1147.

Mukerjee, M. R., 1975, "A note on Aizerman's conjecture for third-order systems," *IEEE Trans. Automat. Control*, AC-20, 552–553.

Pliss, V. A., 1958, "On the Aizerman problem for a system of three differential equations," *Dokl. Akad. Nauk. SSSR*, 121, 3.

Pliss, V. A., 1958, "Necessary and sufficient conditions for the global stability of a certain system of three differential equations," *Dokl. Akad. Nauk SSSR*, 120, 4.

Singh, V., 1976, "A note on Kalman's conjecture for a class of third-order systems," *Proc. IEEE*, 1246–1247.

Vogt, W. G., 1967, "On Aizerman's conjecture and boundedness," *IEEE Trans. Automat. Control*, AC-12, 338–339. See correction: *Ibid.* p. 799.

3.2 Describing Function

Allwright, D. J., 1977, "Harmonic balance and the Hopf bifurcation," *Math. Proc. Camb. Phil. Soc.*, 82, 453–467.

Atherton, D. P., 1975, *Nonlinear Control Engineering*. London: Van Nostrand Reinhold.

Bass, R. W., 1956, "Equivalent linearization, nonlinear circuit synthesis and the stabilization and optimization of control systems," *Proc. Symp. Nonlinear Circuit Analysis*, M.R.I. Series, Polytechnic Institute of Brooklyn, New York, pp. 163–198.

Bass, R. W., 1960, "Mathematical legitimacy of equivalent linearization by describing functions," *Proc. First IFAC Congress*, Moscow, Butterworths London, 1961, Vol. 2, 895–905.

Bergen, A. R. and R. L. Franks, 1971, "Justification of the describing function method," *S.I.A.M. J. Control*, 9 (4), 568–589.

Bickart, T. A., 1966, "The exponential describing function in the analysis of nonlinear systems," *IEEE Trans. Automat. Control*, AC-11, 491–497.

Blaquière, A., 1951, "Extension de la theorie de Nyquist au cas de caractéristiques non lineaires," *Compt. Rend.*, 233, 345.

Blaquière, A., 1952, "Adaptation generale de la methode du diagramme de Nyquist dans le domaine non lineaire," *J. Phys. Radium*, 13, 527–540, 636–644.

Bulgakov, B. V., 1943, "Periodic processes in free pseudo-linear oscillatory systems," *J. Franklin Inst.*, 235, 591–616.

Chandran, S. R. and M. V. C. Rao, 1977, "Comments on limitations of the describing function method," *IEEE Trans. Automat. Control*, AC-22, 283–284.

Chen, C. F. and I. J. Haas, 1965, "An extension of Oppelt's stability criterion based on the method of two hodographs," *IEEE Trans. Automat. Control*, AC-10, 99–102.

Cook, P. A., 1973, "Describing function for a sector nonlinearity," *Proc. IEE*, 120, 143–144.

Dutilh, J., 1950, "Theorie des servomechanisms a relais," *Onde Elec.*, 438–445.

Gelb, A. and W. E. Vander Velde, 1968, *Multiple-Input Describing Functions and Nonlinear System Design*. New York: McGraw-Hill.

Goldfarb, L. C., 1947, "On some nonlinear phenomena in regulatory systems," *Avtomatika i Telemekhanika*, 8 (5), 349–383. Also translated in *Frequency Response*, U. Oldenburger (Ed.). New York: MacMillan, 1956.

Grensted, P. E. W., 1955, "The frequency-response analysis of non-linear systems," *Proc. IEE*, 102C, 244–253.

Grensted, P. E. W., 1962, "Frequency response methods applied to nonlinear systems," in *Progress in Control Engineering*, Vol. 1. New York: Academic Press, pp. 103–141.

Johnson, B. C., 1952, "Sinusoidal analysis of feedback control systems containing nonlinear elements," *Trans. AIEE*, Part II, 71, 169–181.

Kochenburger, R. J., 1950, "A frequency response method for analysing and synthesizing contractor servomechanisms," *Trans. AIEE*, 69, 270–283.

Kou, S. Y. and K. W. Han, 1975, "Limitations of the describing function method," *IEEE Trans. Automat. Control*, AC-20, 291–292.

Kudrewicz, J., 1969, "Theorems on the existence of periodic vibrations based upon the describing function method," *Proc. Fourth IFAC World Congress*, Warsaw, Session 4.1, pp. 46–60.

Mees, A. I., 1972, "The describing function matrix," *J. Inst. Maths. Applics.*, 10, 49–67.

Mees, A. I., 1973, "Describing functions, circle criteria and multiple-loop feedback systems," *Proc. IEE*, 120, 126–130.

Mees, A. I., 1973, "Limit cycle stability," *J. Inst. Maths. Applicns.*, 11, 281–295.

Mees, A. I. and A. R. Bergen, 1975, "Describing functions revisited," *IEEE Trans. Automat. Control*, AC-20, 473–478.

Oppelt, W., 1948, "Locus curve method for regulators with friction," *Z. Deut. Ingr.*, Berlin, 90, 179–183. Translated as Report 1691, National Bureau of Standards, Washington, 1952.

Ramani, N. and D. P. Atherton, 1973, "Describing functions, circle criteria and multiple-loop feedback systems," *Proc. IEE*, 120, 814.

Rao, M. V. C. and P. V. Rao, 1970, " A comment on the discrete describing function method," *IEEE Trans. Automat. Control*, AC-15, 270–271.

Rapp, P. E. and A. I. Mees, 1977, "Spurious predictions of limit cycles in a non-linear feedback system by the describing function method," *Int. J. Control*, 26, 821–829.

Sen, A. K. and C. F. Chen, 1966, "Comments on an extension of Oppelt's stability criterion based on the method of two hodographs and relative stability from the dual-locus diagram," *IEEE Trans. Automat. Control*, AC-11, 141–142.

Snelsire, R., 1967, "On the use of the describing function as a stability criterion," *IEEE Trans. Automat. Control*, AC-12, 788–789.

Teodorescu, D., 1970, "Describing-function series: A new means for non-linear-control-system analysis," *Proc. IEE*, 117, 2175–2180.

Tustin, A., 1947, "The effects of backlash and of speed dependent friction on the stability of closed-cycle control systems," *J. IEE*, 94, Part II, 143–151.

West, J. C., J. L. Douce and R. K. Livesley, 1956, "The dual input describing function and its use in the analysis of nonlinear feedback systems," *Proc. IEE*, 103-B, 463–474.

3.3 Popov Criterion

Cartianu, Gh. and F. Pilat, 1975, "Extension of applicability of Popov's steady-state absolute-stability frequency criterion of nonlinear systems," *Electronics Letters*, 11, 111–113.

Chang, T. L. and M. S. Davies, 1972, "Regions of transient stability for power systems involving saliency using the Popov criterion," *Proc. IEE*, 119, 625–628.

Desoer, C. A., 1965, "A generalization of the Popov criterion," *IEEE Trans. Automat. Control*, AC-10, 182–185.

Garg, D. P., 1971, "A Popov-criterion-based algorithm for control system synthesis using non-linear compensators," *Int. J. Control*, 13, 155–163.

Huseyin, O., 1973, "On the Popov criterion, *Int. J. Control*, 17, 1137–1142.

Huseyin, O., 1973, "The Popov criterion and the inverse Nyquist method," *Int. J. Control*, 18, 1303–1312.

Jackson, E. K. and J. K. Aggarwal, 1966, "Popov and Hurwitz stability criterions: A comparison," *IEEE Trans. Automat. Control*, AC-11, 623–624.

Janakiraman, P. A. and P. V. Rao, 1970, "Application of Popov's criterion to signal stabilization in discrete systems," *IEEE Trans. Automat. Control*, AC-15, 142–143.

Kan, E. P. F. and E. I. Jury, 1971, "On Popov criteria for ΣPFM systems," *Int. J. Control*, 13, 1121–1129.

Krikorian, J. S. Jr. and T. A. Bickart, 1969, "Popov-like stability criterion for a class of time-varying discrete systems," *IEEE Trans. Automat. Control*, AC-14, 208–210.

Krikorian, J. S. and T. Bickart, 1968, "Popov-like stability criterion for a class of time-varying continuous systems," *Electronics Letters*, 4, 344.

Ku, Y. H. and H. T. Chieh, 1965, "Extension of Popov's theorems for stability of nonlinear control systems," *J. Franklin Inst.*, 279, 401–416.

Lee, B. W., 1971, "Comments on application of Popov's criterion to signal stabilization in discrete systems," *IEEE Trans. Automat. Control*, AC-16, 103–104.

Moore, J. B. and B. D. O. Anderson, 1967, "Applications of the multivariable Popov criterion," *Int. J. Control*, 345–353.

Morozan, T., 1966, "The method of V. M. Popov for control systems with random parameters," *J. Math. Anal. Appl.*, 16, 201–215.

Moore, J. B. and B. D. O. Anderson, 1968, "A generalization of the Popov criterion," *J. Franklin Inst.*, 285, 488–492.

Noldus, E., 1971, "A counterpart of Popov's theorem for the existence of periodic solutions," *Int. J. Control*, 13, 705–719.

Narendra, K. S. and J. H. Taylor, 1973, *Frequency Domain Criteria for Absolute Stability*. New York: Academic Press.

Noldus, E. J., 1975, "Oscillation criteria of the Popov type," *IEEE Trans. Automat. Control*, AC-20, 577–579.

Popov, V. M., 1961, "New graphical criteria for the stability of the steady state of nonlinear control systems," *Revue d'Electrotech. et d'Energ.*, Acad. Rep. Pop. Romaine, 6, No. 1.

Popov, V. M., 1961, "Absolute stability of nonlinear systems of automatic control," (in Russian), *Avtomatika i Telemekhanika*, 21, 961–979.

Popov, V. M., 1962, "Absolute stability of nonlinear control systems of automatic control," *Automation and Remote Control*, 22, 857–875.

Popov, V. M. and A. Halanay, 1963, "On the stability of nonlinear automatic control systems with lagging argument," *Automat. Remote Control*, 23, 783–786.

Pincura, S. C., 1967, "On the inapplicability of the Popov stability criterion in certain classes of control systems," *IEEE Trans. Automat. Control*, AC-12, 465–466.

Ramapriyan, H. K., M. D. Srinath and M. A. L. Thatachar, 1966, "A root-locus interpretation of the Popov criterion," *Int. J. Control*, 3, 149–161.

Rekasius, Z. V. and J. R. Rowland, 1966, "A counter example for the generalization of the Popov criterion to systems containing a single time-varying element," *IEEE Trans. Automat. Control*, AC-11, 139–140.

Sandberg, I. W., 1965, "Some stability results related to those of V. M. Popov," *Bell Syst. Tech. Journal*, 44, 2133–2148.

Sandberg, I. W., 1966, "On generalizations and extensions of the Popov criterion," *IEEE Trans. Circuit Theory*, CT-13, 117–118.

Sandberg, I. W., 1966, "Correction to 'On generalizations and extensions of the Popov criterion'," *IEEE Trans. Circuit Theory*, CT-13, 240.

Wu, S. H. and Manke, 1967, "Popov criterion and Lagrange stability of nonlinear systems," *IEEE Trans. Automat. Control*, AC-12, 627.

Zimmerman, C. E. and G. J. Thaler, 1971, "Application of the Popov criterion to design of nonlinear systems," *IEEE Trans. Automat. Control*, AC-16, 76–79.

3.4 Circle Criterion and Related Topics

Bergen, A. R. and M. A. Sapiro, 1967, "The parabola test for absolute stability," *IEEE Trans. Automat. Control*, AC-12, 312–314.

Bonenn, Z., 1968, "The circle criterion and describing function analysis," *IEEE Trans. Automat. Control*, AC-13, 588–589.

Brockett, R. W., 1965, "Optimization theory and the converse of the circle criterion," *Proc. of the N.E.C. of the USA*, 21, 697–701.

Brockett, R. W. and Willems, J. L. 1965, "Frequency domain stability criteria," *IEEE Trans. Automat. Control*, AC-10, 255–261 and 407–413.

Brockett, R. W. and Lee, H. B., 1967, "Frequency domain instability criteria for time-varying and nonlinear systems," *Proc. IEEE*, 55, 604–619.

Cho, Y.-S, and K. S. Narendra, 1968, "An off-axis circle criterion for the stability of feedback systems with a monotonic nonlinearity," *IEEE Trans. Automat. Control*, AC-13, 413–416.

Cook, P. A., 1975, "Circle criteria for stability in Hilbert space," *SIAM J. Control*, 13, 593–610.

Cook, P. A., 1978, "Stability of systems containing slope-restricted non-linearities," in *Recent Theoretical Developments in Control*. New York: Academic Press, 161–174.

Desoer, C. A., 1968, "An extension to the circle criterion," *IEEE Trans. Automat. Control*, AC-13, 587–588.

Falb, P. L. and G. Zames, 1968, "Multipliers with real poles and zeros: An application of a theorem on stability conditions," *IEEE Trans. Automat. Control*, AC-13, 125–126.

Gruber, M. and J. L. Willems, 1966, "On a generalization of the circle criterion," *Proc. of the 4th Annual Allerton Conf. on Circuit and System Theory*, 827–835, University of Illinois, Urbana, IL.

Huseyin, O., 1973, "On the circle criterion," *Int. J. Control*, 18, 9–16.

Lambda, S. S., 1972, "Comments on a correlation between the Fukuma-Matsubara and circle criteria for the determination of jump resonance," *IEEE Trans. Automat. Control*, AC-17, 176–177.

Mees, A. I., 1978, "On using the circle criterion to predict existence of solutions," in *Recent Theoretical Developments in Control*. New York: Academic Press, 175–190.

Moore, J. B., 1968, "A circle criterion generalization for relative stability," *IEEE Trans. Automat. Control*, AC-13, 127–128.

Moore, J. B., 1968, "Circle criteria in the parameter plane," *Proc. IEE*, 115, 557–580.

Moore, J. B. and Bartlett, 1969, "Two-dimensional circle criterion on the parameter plane," *IEEE Trans. Automat. Control*, AC-14, 108–109.

Narendra, K. S. and R. M. Goldwyn, 1964, "A geometrical criterion for the stability of certain nonlinear nonautonomous systems," *IEEE Trans. Circuit Theory*, CT-11, 406–408.

Narendra, K. S. and C. P. Neuman, 1966, "Stability of a class of differential equations with a single monotonic nonlinearity," *SIAM J. Control*, 4 (2).

Narendra, K. S. and Y.-S. Cho, 1968, "An off-axis circle criterion for the stability of feedback systems with a monotonic nonlinearity," *IEEE Trans. Automat. Control*, AC-13, 413–416.

Parks, P. C., 1966, "The circle criterion and the undamped Mathieu equation," *Electronics Letters*, 2, 315.

Power, H. M. and A. C. Tsoi, 1973, "Improving the predictions of the circle criterion by combining quadratic forms," *IEEE Trans. Automat. Control*, AC-18, 65–67.

Riemenschneider, A. L. and E. J. Mastascusa, 1970, "A correlation between the Fukuma-Matsubara and circle criteria for the determination of jump resonance," *IEEE Trans. Automat. Control*, AC-15, 507–508.

Rozenwasser, E. N., 1963, "The absolute stability of nonlinear systems," *Avtomat. i. Telemekh.* 24 (3), 283–294.

Sandberg, I. W., 1964, "On the response of nonlinear control systems to periodic input signals," *Bell Syst. Tech. J.*, 43, 911–926.

Sandberg, I. W., 1964, "A frequency domain condition for the stability of systems containing a single time-varying nonlinear element," *Bell Syst. Tech. J.*, 43, 1901–1908.

Tsoi, A. C. and H. M. Power, 1972, "Equivalent predictions of the circle criterion and an optimum quadratic form for a second-order system," *IEEE Trans. Automat. Control*, AC-17, 565–566.

Willems, J. L., 1973, "The circle criterion and quadratic Lyapunov functions for stability analysis," *IEEE Trans. Automat. Control*, AC-18, 184–186.

Willems, J. C. and R. W. Brockett, 1973, "Average value stability criteria for symmetric systems," *Ricerche di Automatica*, 4, 87–108.

Zames, G., 1964, "On the stability of nonlinear, time-varying feedback systems," *Proc. NEC*, 20, 725–730.

Zames, G., 1966, "On the input-output stability of time-varying nonlinear feedback systems," *IEEE Trans. Automat. Control*, AC-11, 228–238 and 465–476.

Zames, G. and R. R. Kallman, 1970, "On spectral mappings, higher order circle criteria and periodically varying systems," *IEEE Trans. Automat. Control*, AC-15, 649–652.

3.5 Other Work on Nonlinear Feedback System Stability

Aizerman, M. A., 1946, "On the convergence of a control process after large initial deviations," *Avtom. i. Telemekh.*, 7, 2–3.

Aizerman, M. A., 1947, "On the effect of nonlinear functions of several variables on the stability of automatic control systems," *Avtom. i. Telemekh*, 8, 1.

Bergen, A. R., R. P. Iwens and A. J. Rault, 1966, "On input-output stability of nonlinear feedback systems," *IEEE Trans. Automat. Control*, AC-11, 742–744.

Blodgett, R. E. and R. E. King, 1968, "Quasiasymptotic stability of a class of non-linear systems," *Int. J. Control*, 8, 245–252.

Bogoliubov, N. N. and Y. A. Mitropolsky, 1958, *Asymptotic Methods in the Theory of Nonlinear Oscillations*, Moscow, English translation published by Gordon and Breach, New York, 1961.

Brockett, R. W., 1964, "On the stability of nonlinear feedback systems," *Proc. Joint Automatic Control Conference*.

Byrne, P. C., 1975, "Frequency-domain stability theorem for the Lurie system with multiple nonlinearities specified by sector and slope information," *Electronics Letters*, 11, 394–396.

Chang, J. L. and M. S. Davies, 1970, "Stability criteria for a class of non-linear systems," *Int. J. Control*, 11, 949–955.

Cho, Y. S. and K. S. Narendra, 1968, "Stability of nonlinear time-varying feedback systems," *Automatica*, 4, 6.

Desoer, C. A., 1962, "Nonlinear distortion in feedback amplifiers," *IRE Trans. Circuit Theory*, CT-9, 2–6.

Desoer, C. A., 1965, "A stability criterion obtained by a method of comparison," *IEEE Trans. Automat. Control*, AC-10, 185–186.

Desoer, C. A., R. Liu and L. V. Auth, Jr., 1965, "Linearity vs nonlinearity and asymptotic stability in the large," *IEEE Trans. Circuit Theory*, CT-12, 117–118.

Desoer, C. A. and M. Y. Wu, 1969, "Stability of a nonlinear time-invariant feedback system under almost constant inputs," *Automatica*, 5, 231–233.

Dewey, A. G., 1966, "On the stability of feedback systems with one differentiable nonlinear element," *IEEE Trans. Automat. Control*, AC-11, 485–491.

Fukuma, A. and M. Matsubara, 1966, "Jump resonance criteria of nonlinear control systems," *IEEE Trans. Automat. Control*, AC-11, 699–706.

Garber, E. D., 1967, "Frequency criteria for the absence of periodic responses," *Automat. Remote Control*, 28.

Hahn, W., 1963, *Theory and Application of Liapunov's Direct Method*, Englewood Cliffs, NJ: Prentice-Hall.

Hill, D. J. and P. J. Moylan, 1977, "Stability results for nonlinear feedback systems," *Automatica*, 13, 377–382.

Hirai, K., 1969, "A stability criterion of nonlinear control systems," *IEEE Trans. Automat. Control*, AC-14, 601–602.

Holtzmann, J. M., 1967, "Contraction maps and equivalent linearization," *Bell Syst. Tech. J.* 46, 2405–2435.

Ibrahim, E. S. and S. V. Rekasius, 1964, "A stability criterion for nonlinear feedback systems," *IEEE Trans. Automat. Control*, AC-9, 154–159.

Iwens, R. P. and A. R. Bergen, 1967, "Frequency criteria for bounded-input-bounded-output stability of nonlinear sampled-data systems," *IEEE Trans. Automat. Control*, AC-12, 46–53.

Jury, E. I. and B. W. Lee, 1964, "On the stability of a certain class of nonlinear sampled-data systems," *IEEE Trans. Automat. Control*, AC-9, 51-61.

Jury, E. I. and B. W. Lee, 1965, "The absolute stability of systems with many nonlinearities," *Automat. Remote Control*, 26, 943-961.

Jury, E. I. and B. W. Lee, 1966, "A stability theory for multinonlinear systems," *Proc. Third World Congress of IFAC*, London, Session 28, Paper 28a.

Johnson, C. D., 1966, "A note on control systems with one nonlinear element," *IEEE Trans. Automat. Control*, AC-11, 122-124.

Kalman, R. E., 1963, "Liapunov functions for the problem of Lur'e in automatic control," *Proc. Nat. Acad. of Science USA*, 49, 201-205.

Krassovskii, N. N., 1952, "Theorems on the stability of a motion defined by a system of two equations," *Prikl. Matem. i. Mekh.*, 16, 5.

Krassovskii, N. N. 1953, "On the stability of the solutions of a system of two differential equations," *Prikl. Matem. i Mekh*, 17, 6.

Krikorian, J. S., Jr., 1972, "An l_2 stability criterion with frequency domain interpretation for a class of nonlinear discrete systems," *IEEE Trans. Automat. Control*, AC-17, 365-368.

Lasalle, J. P. and S. Lefschetz, 1961, *Stability by Liapunov's Direct Method with Applications*. New York/London: Academic Press.

Lecoq, L. P. and A. M. Hopkin, 1972, "A functional analysis approach to L_∞ stability and its applications to systems with hysteresis," *IEEE Trans. Automat. Control*, AC-17, 328-338.

Letov, A. M., 1953, "Stability of control systems with two power elements," *Prikl. Matem. i Mekh.*, 17, 4.

Lur'e, A. I., and V. N. Postnikov, 1944, "On the theory of stability of control systems," *Prikl. Mat. i Mekh*, 8, 3.

Lur'e, A. I., 1951, *Some Nonlinear Problems in the Theory of Automatic Control*. Moscow: Gostekhizdat.

Lur'e, A. I., 1951, "On the problem of stability of control systems," *Prikl. Matem. i Mekh.*, 15, 1.

Maeda, H., and S. Kodama, 1970, "A new stability criterion of a relay servomechanism," *IEEE Trans. Automat. Control*, AC-15, 275-276.

Maeda, H., M. Ikeda and S. Kodama, 1970, "Stability criterion for a feedback system with backlash an extension of frequency-domain condition by the multiplier method," *IEEE Trans. Automat. Control*, AC-15, 703-705.

Mahalanabis, A. K. and S. Purkayasta, 1973, "Frequency-domain criteria for stability of a class of nonlinear stochastic systems," *IEEE Trans. Automat. Control*, AC-18, 266-270.

Malkin, I. G., 1951, "On the theory of stability of control systems," *Prikl. Matem. i Mekh*, 15, I.

Malkin, I. G., 1952, "On a particular problem of stability in automatic control systems," *Prikl. Matem. i Mekh*, 16, 3.

McGee, R. W., 1968, "Application of frequency-domain stability criteria to certain nonlinear position control systems," *Electronics Letters*, 4, 536.

Mess, A. I. and L. O. Chua, 1977, "The Hopf bifurcation theorem and its applications to nonlinear oscillations in circuits and systems," Memo No UCB/ERL M77/63, Electronics Res. Lab. College of Engineering, Univ. California, Berkely.

Moore, J. B., 1967, "Stability of linear dynamical systems with memoryless nonlinearities," *Int. J. Control*, 6, 373-379.

Murgan, A. T., 1976, "Stability criterion of oscillations in nonlinear autonomous systems," *IEEE Trans. Automat. Control*, AC-21, 778-779.

Murphy, G. J., 1967, "A frequency-domain stability chart for nonlinear feedback systems," *IEEE Trans. Automat. Control*, AC-12, 740-743.

Narendra, K. S. and R. M. Goldwyn, 1964, "A geometrical criterion for the stability of certain nonlinear nonautonomous systems," *IEEE Trans. Circuit Theory*, CT-11, (3), 406-408.

Narendra, K. S. and Y. S. Cho, 1967, "Stability of feedback systems containing a single odd monotonic nonlinearity," *IEEE Trans. Automat. Control*, AC-12, 448-450.

Naumov, B. N., and Ya. Z. Tsypkin, 1964, "Frequency criterion for process absolute stability in nonlinear automatic control system," (in Russian), *Avtomatika i Telemekhanika*, 25(6), 852-866.

Naumov, B. N. and Y. Z. Tsypkin, 1965, "Frequency criterion for absolute process stability in nonlinear automatic control systems," *Automation and Remote Control*, 25, 765-778.

Noldus, E. J., 1974, "Comments on periodic control: A frequency domain approach," *IEEE Trans. Automat. Control*, AC-19, 287-289.

Noldus, E. J., 1974, "Autonomous periodic motion in nonlinear feedback systems," *IEEE Trans. Automat. Control*, AC-19, 381-387.

Pliss, V. A., 1958, *Some Problems of the Theory of the Overall Stability of Motion*. Izd. L.G.U. (in Russian).

Pliss, V. A., 1958, *Certain Problems in the Theory of Stability in the Whole*. L.G.U.

Pliss, V. A., 1966, *Nonlocal Problems of the Theory of Oscillations*. New York: Academic Press.

Popov, V. M., 1959, "Criterii de stabilitate pentru sistemele neliniare de reglare automata, bazate pe utilizarea transformatei Laplace," *Studii si cercetari de energetica, Acad. R.P.R.*, 9, I.

Popov, V. M., 1959, "Criterii suficiente de stabilitate asimptotica in mare pentru sistemele automate neliniare cu mai multe organie de executie," *Studii si certari de energetica, Acad R.P.R.*, 9, 4.

Popov, V. M., 1960, "Criterii de stabilitate pentru sistemele automate contininf rlemente neunivoce," *Probleme de automatizare*, Oct. 13, 1960.

Popov, V. M., 1960, "Criterion of quality for nonlinear controlled systems," *Proc. First IFAC Congress*, Moscow, Butterworths, London, 1961, Vol. 1, 173-177.

Popov, V. M., 1960, "Noi criterii grafice pentru stabilitates starii stationare a sistemenlor automate neliniare," English translation in *Revue d'Electrotechnique et d'Energetique*, 5, 1.

Popov, V. M., 1960, "Noi criterii de stabilitate pentru sistemele automate neliniare, *Studii si cercetari de energetica Acad R.P.R.*, 10, I, French translation in *Revue d'Electrotechnique et d'Energetique*, 5, 1, 1960.

Popov, E. P., 1960, "Certain problems of the synthesis of non-linear systems of automatic control," *Proc. First IFAC Congress*, Moscow, Butterworths, London, 1961, Vol. 1, 165-172.

Popov, V. M., 1960, "Nouveaux criteriums de stabilite pour les systemes automatiques non-linearies," *Reveu d'Electrotechnique et d'Energetique*, Acad. de la Rep. Populaire Romaine, 5, No. 1.

Popov, V. M., 1961, "On the absolute stability of nonlinear control systems," *Avtom. i Telemekh*, 22, 8.

Popov, V. M., 1962, "On a certain critical case of absolute stability," *Avtomatika i Telemekhanika*, 23, No. 1.

Popov, V. M., 1963, "The solution of a new stability problem for controlled systems," *Automation and Remote Control*, 24(1), 1-23.

Popov, V. M., 1964, "Hyperstability and optimality of automatic systems with several control functions," *Revue d'Electrotech. et d'Energ.*, Acad. Rep. Pop. Romaine, 9.

Power, H. M. and A.-C. Tsoi, 1974, "A note on Brockett's variational technique and a conjecture in stability theory," *IEEE Trans. Automat. Control*, AC-19, 251-252.

Rae, W. G., 1968, "Stability criteria for control systems with one nonlinear element," *Int. J. Control*, 8, 659-663.

Ramarajan, S. and M. A. L. Thathachar, 1973, "Construction of stability multipliers with prescribed phase characteristics: An improved value for σ_*, *SIAM J. Control*, 11, 94-99.

Ramarajan, S. and K. L. P. Mishra, 1977, "L_2-stability of nonlinear time-varying systems—noncausal multipliers," *IEEE Trans. Automat. Control*, AC-22, 476-479.

Rekasius, Z. V. 1964, "A stability criterion for feedback systems with one nonlinear element," *IEEE Trans. Automat. Control*, AC-9, 46-50.

Rootenberg, J. and J. B. Oso, 1971, "On cross coupling and stability in nonlinear control systems," *IEEE Trans. Automat. Control*, AC-16, 73-74.

Rootenberg, J. and R. Walk, 1973, "Frequency criteria for the absence of the limit cycles in nonlinear systems," *IEEE Trans. Automatic Control*, AC-18, 64-65.

Rozenvasser, E. N. 1957, "On the stability of nonlinear control systems," *Dokl. Akad. Nauk. SSSR*, 117, 4.

Rozenvasser, E. N., 1960a, "On the constructions of a Liapunov function for a class of nonlinear systems," *Tzevestia Akad. Nauk. SSSR*, OTN, 2.

Rozenvasser, E. N., 1960b, "Remarks on a method for constructing a Liapunov function," *Prikl. Matem i Mekh.*, 24, 4.

Sandberg, I. W., 1964, "On the L_2-boundedness of nonlinear functional equations," *Bell System Tech. Journal*, 43, No. 4.

Sandberg, I. W., 1965, "On the boundedness of solutions of nonlinear integral equations," *Bell Syst. Tech. J.*, 44, 439-453.

Sandberg, I. W., 1965, "Some results on the theory of physical systems governed by nonlinear functional equations," *Bell System Tech. Journal*, 44, 871-894.

Sen, A. K., 1968, "A simpler stability criterion for a class of nonlinear systems," *IEEE Trans. Automat. Control*, AC-13, 451-452.

Shaw, L., D. Sarlat and Y. Thomas, 1978, "Synthesis of nonlinear controllers," *Preprints Seventh IFAC World Congress*, Helsinki, 3, 1737-1745.

Shibata, H. and S. Hata, 1971, "Weak stochastic stability for the Lur'e type nonlinear system," *IEEE Trans. Automat. Control*, AC-16, 498-499.

Singh, V. and M. R. Mukerjee, 1975, "A note on two counterexamples to Aizerman's conjecture," *IEEE Trans. Automat. Control*, AC-20, 179-180.

Singh, V., 1977, "Further remarks on 'On third-order systems and Aizerman's conjecture,' " *IEEE Trans. Automat. Control*, AC-22, 285.

Skoog, R. A., 1974, "Positivity conditions and instability criteria for feedback systems," *SIAM J. Control*, 12, 83-98.

Soliman, J. I. and H. Kwoh, 1970, "On the absolute stability of automatic control systems," *Proc. IEE*, 117, 2306-2310.

Sundareshan, M. K. and M. A. L. Thathachar, 1973, "Generalized factorizability conditions for stability multipliers," *IEEE Trans. Automat. Control*, AC-18, 183-184.

Sundareshan, M. K. and M. Vidyasagar, 1977, "L_2-stability of large-scale dynamical systems: Criteria via positive operator theory," *IEEE Trans. Automat. Control*, AC-22, 396-399.

Takeda, S. and A. R. Bergen, 1973, "Instability of feedback systems by orthogonal decomposition of L_2," *IEEE Trans. Automat. Control*, AC-18, 631-636.

Thathachar, M. A. L. and M. D. Srinath, 1967, "Some aspects of the Lur'e problem," *IEEE Trans. Automatic Control*, AC-12, 451-453.

Thathachar, M. A. L. and H. S. Ranganath, 1970, "Exponential boundedness of nonlinear and time-varying feedback systems," *IEEE Trans. Automat. Control*, AC-15, 277-278.

Thathachar, M. A. L., 1970, "Stability of systems with power-law nonlinearities," *Automatica*, 6, 721-730.

Thathachar, M. A. L. and M. K. Sundareshan, 1971, "A generalized stability multiplier," *Automatica*, 7, 111-112.

Tsai, S. C. and M. Loo, 1972, "A graphical synthesis technique for nonlinear control systems," *Int. J. Control*, 15, 705-716.

Tsypkin, Ya. Z., 1962, "On the stability in the large of nonlinear sampled-data systems," *Dokl. Akad. Nauk.*, 145, 52-55.

Tsypkin, Ya. Z., 1964, "A criterion for absolute stability of automatic pulse-systems with monotonic characteristics of the nonlinear element," *Sov. Phys. Dokl.*, 9, 263-266.

Tsypkin, Ya. Z., "Absolute stability of a class of nonlinear automatic sampled-data systems," *Automat. Remote Control*, 25, 918-923.

Tsypkin, Ya. Z., 1964, "Frequency criteria for the absolute stability of nonlinear sampled data systems," *Automat. Remote Control*, 25, 261-267.

Tsypkin, Ya. Z. and Popkov, Yu. S., 1973, *Theory of Nonlinear Sampled-Data Systems.* Moscow: Publishing House "Science."

Tsypkin, Ya. Z. 1974, *Relay Control Systems.* Moscow: Publishing House "Science."

Venkatesh, Y. V., 1970, "Noncausal multipliers for nonlinear system stability," *IEEE Trans. Automat. Control*, AC-15, 195-204.

Vidal, P., 1969, *Non-Linear Sampled Data Systems.* New York: Gordon and Breach.

Willems, J. L. and R. W. Brockett, 1965, "Remarks on the stability of nonlinear feedback systems," *IEEE Trans. Automat. Control*, AC-10, 104.

Willems, J. L., 1967, "Comments on a stability inequality for a class of nonlinear feedback systems," *IEEE Trans. Automat. Control*, AC-12, 223-224.

Willems, J. L., 1967, "Stability of a system with nonlinear nonautonomous feedback," *Electronics Letters*, 3, 360.

Willems, J. C. and M. Gruber, 1967, "Comments on 'A combined frequency-time domain stability criterion for autonomous continuous systems,' " *IEEE Trans. Automat. Control*, AC-12, 217-218.

Wu, M.-Y., 1972, "Stability criteria for a class of multiplicative time-varying nonlinear systems," *IEEE Trans. Automat. Control*, AC-17, 141-142.

Yakubovitch, V. A., 1960, "On nonlinear differential equations for control systems with a single regulator," Vestn. LGU, 2, 7.

Yacubovich, V. A., 1962, "Solution of certain matrix inequalities occurring in the theory of automatic controls," *Dokl. Acad. Nauk SSSR*, 143, 1304-1307.

Yakubovitch, V. A., 1963, "Absolute stability of nonlinear control systems in some critical cases, Part 1," *Avtom. i. Telemekh*, 24, 3.

Yakubovitch, V. A., 1963, "Frequency-type conditions for the absolute stability of control systems with a hysteresis nonlinearity," *Dokl. Akad. Nauk SSSR*, 149, 2.

Yakubovitch, V. A., 1963, "Absolute stability of nonlinear control systems in some critical cases, Part 2," *Avtom. i Telemekh*, 24, 6.

Yerugin, N. P., 1950, "On some questions of global stability of motion in the qualitative theory of differential equations," *Prikl. Matem. i Mekh.*, 14, 5.

Zames, G., 1968, "Stability of systems with sector nonlinearities: A comparison of various inequalities," *IEEE Trans. Automat. Control*, AC-13, 709-711.

3.6 Time-Varying Systems

Acker, A., 1975, "Stability criteria for time-varying systems in Hilbert space," *SIAM J. Control*, 13, 1156-1171.

Anderson, B. D. O. and J. B. Moore, 1968, "Structural stability of linear time-varying systems," *IEEE Trans. Automat. Control*, AC-13, 126-127.

Bongiorno, J. J., 1963, "An extension of the Nyquist-Barkhausen stability criterion to linear lumped-parameter systems with time-varying elements," *IEEE Trans. Automat. Control*, AC-8, 166-172.

Bongiorno, J. J., 1964, "Real-frequency stability criteria for linear time-varying systems," *Proc. IEEE*, 52, 832-841.

Davis, J. H., 1972, "Mean-square gain criteria for the stability and instability of time-varying systems," *IEEE Trans. Automat. Control*, AC-17, 214-219.

Desoer, C. A., 1969, "Slowly varying system $\mathring{x} = A(t)\,x$," *IEEE Trans. Automat. Control*, AC-14, 780-781.

Desoer, C. A., 1970, "Slowly varying discrete system," *Electronics Letters*, 6, 339 (see also errata 6, 424).

Freedman, M. and G. Zames, 1968, "Logarithmic variation criteria for the stability of systems with time-varying gains," *SIAM J. Control*, 6, 487-507.

Kalman, R. E., 1962, "On the stability of time-varying linear systems," *IRE Trans. Circuit Theory*, CT-9, 420-422.

Kwon, W. H. and A. E. Pearson, 1978, "On feedback stabilization of time-varying discrete linear systems," *IEEE Trans. Automat. Control*, AC-23, 479-481.

Noldus, E., 1975, "Instability criteria for time-varying nonlinear functional differential systems," *SIAM J. Control*, 13, 420-433.

Ramarajan, S. and K. L. P. Mishra, 1977, "Comments on 'L_2-stability of linear time-varying systems—Conditions involving noncausal multipliers,' " *IEEE Trans. Automat. Control*, AC-22, 285.

Ramarajan, S. and K. L. P. Mishra, 1977, "Miscellaneous criteria for L_2-stability of linear time-varying systems," *IEEE Trans. Automat. Control*, AC-22, 474-476.

Rosenbrock, H. H., 1963, "The stability of linear time-dependent control systems," *J. Electronics and Control*, 15, 73-80.

Sandberg, I. W., 1965, "A stability criterion for linear networks containing time-varying capacitors," *IEEE Trans. Circuit Theory*, CT-12, No. 1.

Skoog, R. A. and C. G. Y. Lau, 1972, "Instability of slowly varying systems," *IEEE Trans. Automat. Control*, AC-17, 86-92.

Sundareshan, M. K. and M. A. L. Thathachar, 1972, "L_2-stability of linear time-varying systems—Conditions involving noncausal multipliers," *IEEE Trans. Automat. Control*, AC-17, 504-509.

Sundareshan, M. K. and M. A. L. Thathachar, 1973, "Time-varying system stability—Interchangeability of the bounds on the logarithmic variation of gain," *IEEE Trans. Automat. Control*, AC-18, 405-407.

Sundareshan, M. K. and M. A. L. Thathachar, 1974, "L_2-stability of nonstationary feedback systems: Frequency-domain criteria," *IEEE Trans. Automat. Control*, AC-19, 217-224.

Sundareshan, M. K. and M. A. L. Thathachar, 1974, "Average variation L_2-stability criteria for time-varying feedback systems—a unified approach, *IEEE Trans. Automat. Control*, AC-19, 427-429.

Sundareshan, M. K. and M. A. L. Thathachar, 1975, "L_2-stability of a class of nonstationary feedback systems with dynamical nonlinear subsystems," *IEEE Trans. Automat. Control*, AC-20, 412-415.

Venkatesh, Y. V., 1969, "On the stability of a linear time-varying system," *IEEE Trans. Automat. Control*, AC-14, 426-427.

Venkatesh, Y. V., 1973, "On the stability of nonlinear time-varying systems," *IEEE Trans. Automat. Control*, AC-18, 67-68.

Willems, J. L., 1968, "Stability theorem for linear systems with a periodic element," *Electronics Letters*, 4, 56.

Willems, J. L., 1968, "Two stability criteria for linear systems with a periodic feedback element," *Electronics Letters*, 4, 55.

Willems, J. L., 1968, "Stability criteria for non-stationary feedback systems," *Int J. Control*, 7, 425-431.

Willems, J. L., 1970, "A general stability criterion for non-linear time-varying feedback systems," *Int. J. Control*, 11, 625-631.

Wu, M. Y., 1974, "A note on stability of linear time-varying systems," *IEEE Trans. Automat. Control*, AC-19, 162.

Wu, M.-Y., 1975, "Some new results in linear time-varying systems," *IEEE Trans. Automat. Control*, AC-20, 159–161.

3.7 Stochastic Systems

Blankenship, G. L., 1976, "Frequency domain stability criteria for stochastic nonlinear feedback systems," *SIAM J. Control*, 14, 1107–1123.

Kleinman, D. L. 1969, "On the stability of linear stochastic systems," *IEEE Trans. Automat. Control*, AC-14, 429–430.

Kleinman, D. L., 1969, "Optimal stationary control of linear system with control-dependent noise," *IEEE Trans. Automat. Control*, AC-14, 673–677.

Kozin, F., 1969, "A survey of stability of stochastic systems," *Automatica*, 5, 95–112.

Nakamizo, T., 1969, "A simpler mean-square stability criterion for a class of linear stochastic systems," *IEEE Trans. Automat. Control*, AC-14, 584–585.

Nevelson, M. B. and R. Z. Khas'minskii, 1966, "Stability of a linear system with random disturbances of its parameters," *Prikl. Math. Mekh.*, 30, 487.

Rabotnikov, I., 1964, "On the impossibility of stabilizing a system in the mean square by a random perturbation of its parameters," *Appl. Math. Mech.*, 28, 1131–1136.

Socha, L., 1975, "Frequency-domain criteria for stability of a class of nonlinear systems with random parameters," *IEEE Trans. Automat. Control*, AC-20, 284–287.

Willems, J. C. and G. L. Blankenship, 1971, "Frequency domain stability criteria for stochastic systems," *IEEE Trans. Automat. Control*, AC-16, 292–299.

Wonham, W. M., 1967, "Optimal stationary control of linear systems with state-dependent noise," *SIAM J. Control*, J. 486-500.

IV. MULTIVARIABLE SYSTEMS

4.0 General Background Material

Barnett, S. and C. Storey, 1970, *Matrix Methods in Stability Theory.* London: Nelson.

Barnett, S., 1971, *Matrices in Control Theory.* London: Van Nostrand Reinhold.

Bell, D. J. (Editor), 1973, *Recent Mathematical Developments in Control.* London: Academic Press.

Bellman, R., 1961, *Adaptive Control Processes: A Guided Tour.* Princeton, NJ: Princeton University Press.

Bliss, G. A., 1933, *Algebraic Functions.* Providence, RI: American Mathematical Society.

Brockett, R. W. 1970, *Finite Dimensional Linear Systems.* New York: Wiley.

Casti, J. L., 1977, *Dynamical Systems and their Applications: Linear Theory.* New York: Academic Press.

Chen, C.-T., 1975, *Analysis and Synthesis of Linear Control Systems.* New York: Holt, Rinehart and Winston.

Cruz, J. B., 1972, *Feedback Systems.* New York: McGraw-Hill.

Fisher, D. G. and D. E. Seborg, (Editors), 1976, *Multivariable Computer Control: A Case Study.* Amsterdam: North-Holland/American Elsevier.

Fossard, A. J., 1977, *Multivariable System Control.* Amsterdam: North-Holland.

Gregson, M. J., (Editor), 1978, *Recent Theoretical Developments in Control.* London: Academic Press.

Kalman, R. E., 1960, "On the general theory of control systems," *Proc. First IFAC Congress*, Moscow, 1, 481–492, Butterworth, London.

Kalman, R. E., 1965, "Irreducible realizations and the degree of a rational matrix," *SIAM J. Control*, 13, 520–544.

Kalman, R. E., P. L. Falb and M. A. Arbib, 1969, *Topics in Mathematical Systems Theory.* New York: McGraw-Hill.

Horowitz, I. and U. Shaked, 1975, "Superiority of transfer function over state-variable methods in linear time-invariant feedback system design," *IEEE Trans. Automat. Control*, AC-20, 84–97.

Lanczos, C., 1960, *The Variational Principles of Mechanics.* Toronto: University of Toronto Press.

Layton, J. M., 1976, *Multivariable Control Theory.* Stevenage, England: Peter Peregrinus Ltd.

MacFarlane, A. G. J., 1976, "Feedback," *Journ. Inst. Meas. and Control*, 449–462.

MacFarlane, A. G. J. and N. Karcanias, 1978, "Relationships between state-space and frequency-response concepts," *Preprints Seventh IFAC World Congress*, 3, 1771–1779.

Marcus, M. and H. Minc, *A Survey of Matrix Theory and Matrix Inequalities*, Boston: Allyn and Bacon.

Mcmillan, B., 1952, "Introduction to formal realizability theory," *Bell Syst. Tech. J.*, 31, 217–279, 541–600.

Merriam, C. W., 1974, *Automated Design of Control Systems.* New York: Gordon and Breach.

Mesarovic, M. D., 1960, *The Control of Multivariable Systems.* Cambridge, Mass: MIT Press.

Owens, D. H., 1978, *Feedback and Multivariable Systems.* Hitchin, England: Peter Peregrinus.

Popov, V. M., 1973, *Hyperstability of control systems.* Berlin: Springer-Verlag.

Rosenbrock, H. H., 1974, *Computer-Aided Control System Design.* London: Academic Press.

Saeks, R., 1973, *Resolution Space, Operators and Systems.* Heidelberg: Springer.

Sain, M. K., J. L. Peczkowski and J. L. Melsa, (Editors), 1978, *Alternatives for Linear Multivariable Control.* Chicago: National Engineering Consortium.

Willems, J. C., 1969, "Stability, instability, invertibility and causality," *SIAM J. Control*, 7 (4), 645–671.

Willems, J. C., 1971, *The Analysis of Feedback Systems.* Cambridge: Mass: MIT Press.

Wolovich, W. A., 1974, *Linear Multivariable Systems.* New York: Springer-Verlag.

Wonham, W. M. 1974, *Linear Multivariable Control: A Geometric Approach.* Berlin: Springer-Verlag.

Zadeh, L. A. and C. A. Desoer, 1963, *Linear System Theory: The State Space Approach.* New York: McGraw-Hill.

4.1 Early Work on Multivariable Problems

Bohn, E. V., 1960, "Stabilization of linear multivariable feedback control systems," *Trans. IRE Automat. Control*, AC-5, 321–327.

Bohn, E. V., 1962, "Design and synthesis methods for a class of multivariable feedback control systems based on single-variable methods," *Trans. AIEE*, 81, 109–116.

Chatterjee, H. K., 1960, "Multivariable process control," *Proc. First IFAC Congress*, Moscow, 2, 132–141.

Freeman, H., 1957, "A synthesis method for multipole control systems," *Trans. AIEE*, 76, 28–31.

Freeman, H., 1958, "Stability and physical realizability considerations in the synthesis of multipole control systems," *Trans. AIEE*, Part 2, 77, 1–15.

Golomb, M. and E. Usdin, 1952, "A theory of multidimensional servo systems," *J. Franklin Inst.* 253 (1), 28–57.

Kavanagh, R. J., 1957, "Noninteraction in linear multivariable systems," *Trans. AIEE*, 76, 95–100.

Kavanagh, R. J., 1957, "The application of matrix methods to multivariable control systems," *J. Franklin Inst.*, 262, 349–367.

Kavanagh, R. J., 1958, "Multivariable control system synthesis," *Trans. AIEE*, Part 2, 77, 425–429.

Kavanagh, R. J., 1961, "A note on optimum linear multivariable filters," *Proc. IEE*, 108C, 412–417.

Kavanagh, R. J., 1966, "The multivariable problem," *Progress in Control Engineering*, 3, 94–129.

Raymond, F. H., 1953, "Introduction a l'etude des asservissements multiples simultanes," *Bull. Soc. Franc. des Mecaniciens*, 7, 18–25.

4.2 Non-Interactive Control and Decoupling Theory

Bayoumi, M. M. and T. L. Duffield, 1977, "Output feedback decoupling and pole placement in linear time-invariant systems," *IEEE Trans. on Automat. Control*, AC-22, 142–143.

Boksenbom, A. S. and R. Hood, 1949, "General algebraic method applied to control analysis of complex engine types," National Advisory Committee for Aeronautics, *Report NCA-TR-980*, Washington, DC.

Cremer, M., 1971, "A precompensator of minimal order for decoupling a linear multivariable system," *Int. J. Control*, 14, 1089–1103.

Denham, M. J., 1973, "A necessary and sufficient condition for decoupling by output feedback," *IEEE Trans. on Automat. Control*, AC-18, 535–537.

Fabian, E., and W. M. Wonham, 1974, "Generic solvability of the decoupling problem," *SIAM J Control*, 12 (4).

Fabian, E. and W. M. Wonham, 1974,"Decoupling and disturbance rejection," *IEEE Trans. on Automat. Control*, AC-19, 399–401.
Fabian, E. and W. M. Wonham, 1975, "Decoupling and data sensitivity," *IEEE Trans. on Automat. Control*, AC-20, 338–344.
Falb, P. L. and W. A. Wolovich, 1967, "Decoupling in the design and synthesis of multivariable control systems," *IEEE Trans. Automat. Control*, AC-12, 651–669.
Gilbert, E. G., 1969, "The decoupling of multivariable systems by state feedback," *SIAM J. Control*, 7, 50–63.
Gilbert, E. G. and J. R. Pivnichny, 1969, "A computer program for the synthesis of decoupled multivariable feedback systems," *IEEE Trans. Automat. Control*, AC-14, 652–659.
Lecrique, M., M. Tessier, A. Rault and J. L. Testud, 1978, "Multivariable control of a steam generator: characteristics and results," *Preprints Seventh IFAC World Congress*, Helsinki, 1, 73–80.
Morse, A. S. and W. M. Wonham, 1970, "Decoupling and pole assignment by dynamic compensation," *SIAM J. Control*, 8, 317–337.
Morse, A. S. and W. M. Wonham, 1970, "Triangular decoupling of linear multivariable systems," *IEEE Trans. Automat. Control*, AC-15, 447–449.
Morse, A. S. and W. M. Wonham, 1971, "Status of non-interacting control," *IEEE Trans. on Automat. Control*, AC-16, 568–580.
Muft, I. H., 1969, "A note on the decoupling of multivariable systems," *IEEE Trans. Automat. Control*, AC-14, 415–416.
Power, H. M., 1977, "Simplification and extension of the Falb-Wolovich decoupling theory," *Int. J. Control*, 25, 805–818.
Rae, W. G., 1964, "Synthesis of noninteracting control systems," *Control*, 8, 245-247.
Rekasius, Z. V., 1965, "Decoupling of multivariable systems by means of state variable feedback," *Proc. Third Allerton Conf. on Circuit and System Th.*, University of Illinois, 439–447.
Sato, S. M. and P. V. Lopresti, 1971, "New results in multivariable decoupling theory," *Automatica*, 7, 499–508.
Shamash, Y. and J. Feinstein, 1976, "The decoupling of multivariable systems using matrix polynomial equations," *Int. J. Systems Sci*, 7, 759–768.
Silverman, L. M., 1970, "Decoupling with state feedback and precompensation," *IEEE Trans. Automat. Control*, AC-15, 487–489.
Silverman, L. M. and H. J. Payne, 1971, "Input-output structure of linear systems with application to the decoupling problem," *SIAM J. Control*, 9, 199–233.
Takamatsu, T., I. Hashimoto and Y. Nakai, 1978, "A geometric approach to multivariable control system design of a distillation column," *Preprints Seventh IFAC World Congress*, Helsinki, 1, 309–317.
Wang, S. H., 1970, "Design of precompensator for decoupling problem," *Electronics Letters*, 6, 739–741.
Wang, S. H. and E. J. Davison, 1975, "Design of decoupled control systems: a frequency domain approach," *Int. J. Control*, 21, 529–536.
Wolovich, W. A. 1975, "Output feedback decoupling," *IEEE Trans. Automat. Control*, AC-20, 148–151.
Wonham, W. M. and A. S. Morse, 1970, "Decoupling and pole assignment in linear multivariable systems: A geometric approach," *SIAM J. Control*, 8, 1–18.
Yuan, J. S-C., 1978, "Dynamic decoupling of a remote manipulator system," *IEEE Trans. Automat. Control*, AC-23, 713–717.

4.3 Inverse Nyquist Array Method

Ashon, S. I. and H. Nicholson, 1976, "Improvement of turbo-alternator response using the inverse Nyquist array method," *Int. J. Control*, 23, 657–672.
Cook, P., 1973, "Stability of linear constant multivariable systems," *Proc. IEE*, 120, 1557.
Cook, P. A., 1974, "Nyquist-plot methods of investigating multivariable feedback systems," *Proc. of the Third IFAC Symposium on Multivariable Technological Systems*, Manchester, Publ. by Inst. Meas and Control, London, Paper S-28.
Crossley, T. R., 1975, "Envelope curves to inverse Nyquist array diagrams," *Int. J. Control*, 22, 57–63.
Crossley, T. R., N. Munro and K. S. Henthorn, 1977, "Design of aircraft autostabilization systems using the inverse Nyquist array method," *Proc. Fourth IFAC Symposium on Multivariable Technological Systems*, Fredericton N. B., Canada, 625–631.
Hawkins, D. J., 1972, "Pseudodiagonalisation and the inverse-Nyquist-array method," *Proc. IEE*, 119, 337–342.
Hawkins, D. J. 1972, Graphical technique for the design of 2-variable control systems," *Proc. IEE*, 119, 1740–1742.
Hawkins, D. J., 1973, "Determination of stability regions with the inverse Nyquist array," *Proc. IEE*, 120, 1445–1448.
Hodge, S. S., 1971, "Design procedure relating open-and closed-loop diagonal dominance," *Proc. IEE*, 118, 927–930.
Hughes, F. M., 1977, "A simplified frequency-response design approach for power-station control," *Int. J. Control*, 25, 575–587.
Ibrahim, T. A. S. and N. Munro, 1975, "Design of sampled-data multivariable control systems using the inverse Nyquist array," *Int. J. Control*, 22, 297–311.
Leininger, G., 1977, "Diagonal dominance using function minimization algorithms," *Proc. 4th IFAC Symposium on Multivariable Technological Systems*, Fredericton N. B., Canada, 105–112.
Mcmorran, P. D., 1970, "Design of gas-turbine controller using inverse Nyquist method," *Proc. IEE*, 117, 2050–2056.
Mcmorran, P. D., 1970, "Extension of the inverse Nyquist method," *Electronics Letters*, 6, 800–801.
Mcmorran, P. D., 1971, "Parameter sensitivity and inverse Nyquist method," *Proc. IEE*, 118, 802–804.
Munro, N., 1972, "Design of controllers for open-loop unstable multivariable system using inverse Nyquist array," *Proc. IEE*, 119, 1377–1382.
Munro, N. and S. Novin-Hirbod, 1978, "Multivariable control of an engine/dynamometer test rig," *Preprints Seventh IFAC World Congress*, Helsinki, 1, 369–376.
Ostrowski, A. M., 1952, "Note on bounds for determinants with dominant principal diagonal," *Proc. Amer. Math. Soc.*, 3, 26–30.
Rosenbrock, H. H., 1969, "Design of multivariable control systems using the inverse Nyquist array," *Proc. IEE*, 116, 1929–1936.
Rosenbrock, H. H. and N. Munro, 1978, "The inverse Nyquist array method," *Alternatives for Linear Multivariable Control*, National Engineering Consortium, Chicago, 101–137.

4.4 Generalized Nyquist and Generalized Root-Locus Methods

Allwright, J. C., 1970, "Commutative controllers," *Electronics Letters*, 6, 276.
Barman, J. F. and J. Katzenelson, 1974, "A generalized Nyquist-type stability criterion for multivariable feedback systems," *Int. J. Control*, 20, 593–622.
Belletrutti, J. and A. G. J. MacFarlane, 1971, "Characteristic loci techniques in multivariable control system design," *Proc. IEE*, 118, 1291–1297.
Bohn, E. V., 1960, "Stabilization of linear multivariable feedback control systems," *IRE Trans.* AC-5, 321–327.
Bohn, E. V., 1962, "Design and synthesis methods for a class of multivariable feedback control systems based on single variable methods," *AIEE Trans.*, 81, part II, 109–115.
Bohn, E. V. and T. Kasvand, 1963, "Use of matrix transformations and system eigenvalues in the design of linear multivariable control systems," *Proc. IEE*, 110, 989–996.
Falb, P. L. and M. I. Freedman, 1969, "A generalized transform theory for causal operators," *SIAM J. Control*, 7, 452–471.
Falb, P. L., M. I. Freedman and G. Zames, 1969, "Input-output stability—A general viewpoint," *Proc. IFAC*, (Warsaw), §4.1.
Freedman, M. I., P. L. Falb and G. Zames, 1969, "A Hilbert space stability theory over locally compact Abelian groups," *SIAM J. Control*, 7, 479–495.
Kouvaritakis, B. and U. Shaked, 1976, "Asymptotic behaviour of root loci of linear multivariable systems," *Int. J. Control*, 23, 297–340.
Kouvaritakis, B. and J. Edmunds, 1977, "The characteristic frequency and characteristic gain design method for multivariable feedback systems," *Alternatives for Linear Multivariable Control*, National Engineering Consortium, Chicago, 229–246.
Kouvaritakis, B., 1978, "Gain margins and root locus asymptotic behaviour in multivariable design," *Int. J. Control*, 27, 705–729, 725–751.
Kouvaritakis, B., 1978, "The optimal root loci of linear multivariable systems," *Int. J. Control*, 28, 33–62.
Kouvaritakis, B., 1978, "Asymptotic multivariable root locus behaviour for non-proper systems," *Int. J. Control*, 28, 419–440.
Kwakernaak, H., 1976, "Asymptotic root loci of multivariable linear optimal regulators," *IEEE Trans. on Automat. Control*, AC-21, 378–382.
MacFarlane, A. G. J., 1970, "The return-difference and return-ratio matrices and their use in the analysis and design of multivariable feedback control systems," *Proc. IEE*, 117, 2037–2049.

MacFarlane, A. G. J. and J. J. Belletrutti, 1973, "The characteristic locus design method," *Automatica*, 9, 575–588.

MacFarlane, A. G. J. and B. Kouvaritakis, 1977, "A design technique for linear multivariable feedback systems," *Int. J. Control*, 25, 837–874.

MacFarlane, A. G. J. and I. Postlethwaite, 1977, "The generalized Nyquist stability criterion and multivariable root loci," *Int. J. Control*, 25, 81–127.

MacFarlane, A. G. J. and I. Postlethwaite, 1977, "Characteristic frequency functions and characteristic gain functions," *Int. J. Control*, 26, 265–278.

MacFarlane, A. G. J. and I. Postlethwaite, 1978, "Extended Principle of the Argument," *Int. J. Control*, 27, 49–55.

MacFarlane, A. G. J., B. Kouvaritakis and J. M. Edmunds, 1978, "Complex variable methods for multivariable feedback systems analysis and design," *Alternatives for Linear Multivariable Control*, National Engineering Consortium, Chicago, 189–228.

Nwokah, O., 1975, "Stability and the eigenvalues of G(s)," *Int. J. Control*, 22, 125–128.

Owens, D. H., 1977, "A note on series expansions for multivariable root-loci," *Int. J. Control*, 26, 549–557.

Owens, D. H., 1978, "Multivariable root loci and the inverse transfer-function matrix," *Int. J. Control*, 28, 345–351.

Owens, D. H., 1978, "Dynamic transformations and the calculation of multivariable root loci," *Int. J. Control*, 28, 333–343.

Postlethwaite, I., 1977, "The asymptotic behaviour, the angles of departure, and the angles of approach of the characteristic frequency loci," *Int. J. Control*, 25, 677–695.

Postlethwaite, I., 1977, "A generalized inverse Nyquist stability criterion," *Int. J. Control*, 26, 325–340.

Postlethwaite, I., 1978, "A note on the characteristic frequency loci of multivariable linear optimal regulators," *IEEE Trans. on Automat. Control*, AC-23, 757–760.

Ramani, N. and D. P. Atherton, 1975, "A note on the stabililty and eigenvalues of G(s)," *Int. J. Control*, 22, 701–704.

Retallack, D. G., 1970, "Extended root-locus technique for design of linear multivariable feedback systems," *Proc. IEE*, 117, 618–622.

Rosenbrock, H. H. and P. A. Cook, 1975, "Stability and the eigenvalues of G(s)," *Int. J. Control*, 21, 91–104.

Shaked, U., 1976, "The angles of departure and approach of the root loci in linear multivariable systems," *Int. J. Control*, 23, 445–457.

Shaked, U., 1978, "The asymptotic behaviour of the root loci of multivariable optimal regulators," *IEEE Trans. on Automat. Control*, AC-23, 425–430.

Vesty, P., 1975, "Geometric interpretation of complex vectors arising in the frequency-domain analysis of multivariable systems," *IEEE Trans. on Automat. Control*, AC-20, 157–158.

4.5 Sequential Return Difference Method

Chuang, S. C., 1974, "Design of linear multivariable systems by sequential return difference method," *Proc. IEE*, 121, 745–747.

Daly, K. C. and S. C. Chuang, 1976, "Design of multivariable digital control systems using the sequential return difference method," *Proc. IEE*, 123, 98–100.

Mayne, D. Q., 1974, "The effect of feedback on linear multivariable systems," *Automatica*, 10, 405–412.

Mayne, D. Q., 1973, "The design of linear multivariable systems, *Automatica*, 9, 201–207.

Owens, D. H., 1974, "Sequential design of linear multivariable systems retaining full output feedback," *Electronics Letters*, 10, 79–80.

4.6 Dyadic Decomposition Methods

Marshall, S. A. and D. H. Owens, 1976, "Feed-forward-feedback control of multivariable systems," *Int. J. Control*, 23, 693–701.

Owens, D. H., 1973, "Dyadic approximation method for multivariable-control systems analysis with a nuclear-reactor application," *Proc. IEE*, 120, 801–809.

Owens, D. H., 1973, "Multivariable-control-system design concepts in failure analysis of a class of nuclear-reactor spatial-control systems," *Proc. IEE*, 120, 119–125.

Owens, D. H., 1974, "Dyadic expansion for the analysis of linear multivariable systems," *Proc. IEE*, 121, 713–716.

Owens, D. H., 1974, "Dyadic modification to sequential technique for multivariable control system design," *Electronics Letters*, 10, 25–26.

Owens, D. H., 1975, "Dyadic approximation about a general frequency point," *Electronics Letters*, 11, 331–332.

Owens, D. H., 1975, "Dyadic expansion, characteristic loci and multivariable-control-systems design," *Proc. IEE*, 122, 315–320.

Owens, D. H., 1975, "First and second-order-like structures in linear multivariable-control-systems design," *Proc. IEE*, 122, 935–941.

Owens, D. H., 1975, "Compensation of multivariable 1st-order-type systems," *Electronics Letters*, 11, 511–512.

Owens, D. H., 1976, "Modal decoupling and dyadic transfer function matrices," *Int. J. Control*, 23, 63–65.

Owens, D. H., 1976, "Integrity of multivariable first-order-type systems," *Int. J. Control*, 23, 827–835.

Owens, D. H., 1976, "Cascade canonical form for linear multivariable systems," *Int. J. Control*, 23, 837–850.

4.7 Optimal Control and Optimal Filtering

Arcasoy, C. C., 1971, Return-difference-matrix properties for optimal stationary discrete Kalman filter," *Proc. IEE*, 118, 1831–1834.

Athans, M., 1966, "The status of optimal control theory and applications for deterministic systems," *IEEE Trans. on Automat. Control*, AC-11, 580–596.

Athans, M. and P. L. Falb, 1966, *Optimal Control*. New York: McGraw-Hill.

Athans, M., 1971, "The role and use of the stochastic Linear-Quadratic-Gaussian problem in control system design," *IEEE Trans. on Automat. Control*, AC-16, 529–551.

Barrett, J. F., 1977, "Construction of Wiener filters using the return-difference matrix," *Int. J. Control*, 26, 797–803.

Bar-Shalom, Y. and E. Tse, 1974, "Dual effect, certainty equivalence, and separation in stochastic control," *IEEE Trans. on Automat. Control*, AC-19, 494–500.

Bellman, R., 1954, "The theory of dynamic programming," *Bull. Amer. Math. Soc.*, 60, 503–516.

Bellman, R., 1956, "On the application of the theory of dynamic programming to the study of control processes," *Proc. Symp. on Nonlinear Circuit Analysis*, Polytechnic Inst. of Brooklyn Press, 199–213.

Bellman, R., 1957, *Dynamic Programming*. Princeton, NJ: Princeton University Press.

Boltyanskii, V., R. Gamkrelidze and L. S. Pontryagin, 1956, "On the theory of optimal processes, Reports of the Academy of Sciences of the USSR, 110 (1), 7-10. Translated in *Selected Papers on Mathematical Trends in Control Theory*, R. Bellman and R. Kalaba, Ed., New York: Dover, 1964.

Bryson, A. E. and Y.-C. Ho, 1969, *Applied Optimal Control*. Waltham, Mass: Blaisdell.

Bucy, R. S. and P. Joseph, 1968, *Filtering for Stochastic Processes with Applications to Guidance*. New York: Wiley-Interscience.

Chang, S. S. L., 1961, *Synthesis of Optimum Control Systems*. New York: McGraw-Hill.

Doyle, J. C., 1978, "Guaranteed margins for LQG regulators," *IEEE Trans. on Automat. Control*, AC-23, 756–757.

Fallside, F. and H. Seraji, 1970, "Design of optimal systems by a frequency-domain technique," *Proc. IEE*, 117, 2017–2024.

Fuller, A. T., 1962, "Bibliography of optimum nonlinear control of determinate and stochastic-definite systems," *J. Electronics Control*, 13, 589–611.

Gessing, R., 1978, "The generalized certainty equivalence principle," *Preprints Seventh IFAC World Congress*, Helsinki, 3, 2175–2182.

Harvey, C. H. and G. Stein, 1978, "Quadratic weights for asymptotic regulator properties," *IEEE Trans. on Automat. Control*, AC-23, 378–387.

Kalman, R. E. and R. W. Koepcke, 1958, "Optimal synthesis of linear sampling control systems using generalized performance indexes," *Trans. ASME*, 80, 1820.

Kalman, R. E., 1960, "Contributions to the theory of optimal control," *Bol. Soc. Mat. Mex.*, Second Series, 5, 102–119.

Kalman, R. E. and R. S. Bucy, 1961, "New results in linear filtering and prediction theory," *Trans. ASME J. Basic Engrg.*, 83D, 95–108.

Kalman, R. E., 1963, "The theory of optimal control and the calculus of variations," in R. Bellman ed. *Mathematical Optimization Techniques*, Berkeley: University of California Press.

Kalman, R. E., 1964, "When is a linear control system optimal?" *Trans. ASME Jnl. Basic Eng.*, Ser. D, 86, 51–60.

Kalman, R. E. and T. Englar, 1966, "ASP-The automatic synthesis program (Program C)," *NASA Contractor Report*, CR-475.

Kaminski, P. G., A. E. Bryson and S. F. Schmidt, 1971 "Discrete square root filtering; a survey of current techniques," *IEEE Trans. on Automat. Control*, AC-16, 727–735.

Lee, E. B. and L. Markus, 1967, *Foundations of Optimal Control Theory*. New York: Wiley.
MacFarlane, A. G. J., 1963, "An eigenvector solution of the optimal linear regulator problem," *J. Electronics Control*, 14, 643-654.
MacFarlane, A. G. J., 1971, "Return-difference matrix properties for optimal stationary Kalman-Bucy filter," *Proc. IEE*, 118, 373-376.
Mee, D. H., 1970, "Factorisation result for optimal discrete-time systems," *Electronics Letters*, 6, 233.
Mendel, J. M. and D. L. Gieseking, "Bibliography on the Linear-Quadratic-Gaussian problem," *IEEE Trans. on Automat. Control*, AC-16, 847-869.
Moylan, P. J., 1975, "On a frequency-domain condition in linear optimal control theory," *IEEE Trans. on Automat. Control*, AC-20, 806.
Paiewonsky, B., 1965, "Optimal control: a review of theory and practice," *AIAAJ*, 3, 1985-2006.
Pontryagin, L. S., V. G. Boltyanskii, R. V. Gamkrelidze and Ye. F. Mischensko, 1963, *The Mathematical Theory of Optimal Processes*. New York: Interscience.
Potter, J. E., 1966, "Matrix quadratic solution," *SIAM J. Appl. Math.*, 14, 496-501.
Rosenbrock, H. H. and P. D. Mcmorran, 1971, "Good, bad or optimal?" *IEEE Trans. on Automat. Control*, AC-16, 552-554.
Rynaski, R. G., 1966, "Optimal helicopter station keeping," *IEEE Trans. on Automat. Control*, AC-11, 346-355.
Safanov, M. G. and M. Athans, 1978, "Robustness and computational aspects of nonlinear stochastic estimators and regulators," *IEEE Trans. on Automat. Control*, AC-23, 717-725.
Sage, A. P. and C. C. White, 1977, *Optimum Systems Control*. Englewood Cliffs, NJ: Prentice-Hall.
Schmotzer, R. E. and G. L. Blankenship, 1978, "A simple proof of the separation theorem for linear stochastic systems with time delays," *IEEE Trans. on Automat. Control*, AC-23, 734-735.
Tam, T. J., 1971, "Extended separation theorem and exact analytical solution of stochastic control," *Automatica*, 7, 343-350.
Tyler, J. S. and F. B. Tuteur, 1966, "The use of a quadratic performance index to design multivariable control systems," *IEEE Trans. on Automat. Control*, AC-11, 84-92.
Whitbeck, R. F., 1968, "A frequency domain approach to linear optimal control," *Proc. Joint Aut. Cont. Conf.*, 726-737.
Witsenhausen, H. S., 1971, "Separation of estimation and control," *Proc. IEEE*, 59, 1557-1566.
Wong, P. K. and M. Athans, 1977, "Closed-loop structural stability for linear-quadratic optimal systems," *IEEE Trans. Automat. Control*, AC-22, 94-99.
Wong, P. K., G. Stein and M. Athans, 1978, "Structural reliability and robustness properties of optimal linear-quadratic multivariable regulators," *Preprints Seventh IFAC World Congress*, Helsinki, 3, 1797-1805.
Wonham, W. M., 1968, "On the separation theorem of stochastic control," *SIAM J. Control*, 6, 312-326.

4.8 Modal Control and Pole Shifting

Brasch, F. M. and J. B. Pearson, 1970, "Pole placement using dynamic compensators," *IEEE Trans. on Automat. Control*, AC-15(1), 34-43.
Davison, E. J. and W. M. Wonham, 1968, "On pole assignment in multivariable linear systems," *IEEE Trans. on Automat. Control*, AC-13, 747-748.
Davison, E. J. and H. W. Smith, 1971, "Pole assignment in linear time-invariant multivariable systems with constant disturbances," *Automatica*, 7, 489-498.
Davison, E. J. and R. Chatterjee, 1971, "A note on pole assignment for linear systems with incomplete state feedback," *IEEE Trans. on Automat. Control*, AC-16, 98.
Davison, E. J. and S. G. Chow, 1973, "An algorithm for the assignment of closed-loop poles using output feedback in large linear multivariable systems," *IEEE Trans. on Automat. Control*, AC-18, 74-75.
Davison, E. J. and S. H. Wang, 1975, "On pole assignment in linear multivariable feedback systems using output feedback," *IEEE Trans. on Automat. Control*, AC-20, 516-518.
Ellis, J. K. and G. W. T. White, 1965, "An introduction to modal analysis and control," *Control*, 9(82), 9(83), 9(84), 193-197, 252-266, 317-321.
Fallside, F. (Ed), 1977, *Control System Design by Pole-Zero Assignment*, London: Academic Press.
Gordon-Clark, M. R., 1964, "A novel approach to the control of dynamically unfavourable processes," *IEEE Trans. on Automat. Control*, AC-9, 411-419.
Heymann, M., 1968, "Pole assignment in multi-input linear systems," *IEEE Trans. on Automat. Control*, AC-13, 748-749.
Kimura, H., 1975, "Pole assignment by gain output feedback," *IEEE Trans. on Automat. Control*, AC-20, 509-516.
Kimura, H., 1977, "A furthur result on the problem of pole assignment by output feedback," *IEEE Trans. on Automat, Control*, AC-22, 458-462.
Mayne, D. Q. and P. Murdoch, 1970, "Modal control of linear time invarient systems," *Int. J. Control*, 11, 223-227.
Porter, B., 1969, *Synthesis of Dynamical Systems*. London: Nelson.
Porter, B. and T. R. Crossley, 1972, *Modal Control*. London: Taylor and Francis.
Power, H. M., 1971, "Pole-shifting techniques for multivariable feedback systems," *Proc. IEE*, 118, 387.
Retallack, D. G. and A. G. J. MacFarlane, 1970, Pole-shifting techniques for multivariable feedback systems," *Proc. IEE*, 117, 1037-1038.
Rosenbrock, H. H., 1962, "Distinctive problems of process control," *Chem. Engg. Progress*, 58, 43-50.
Shaw, L., 1971, "Pole placement: stability and sensitivity of dynamic compensators," *IEEE Trans. on Automat. Control*, AC-16, 210.
Simon, J. D. and S. K. Mitter, 1968, "A theory of modal control," *Inform. Control*, 13, 316-353.
Willems, J. C. and W. H. Hesselink, 1978, "Generic properties of the pole placement problem," *Preprints Seventh IFAC World Congress*, Helsinki, 3, 1725-1729.
Wonham, W. M., 1967, "On pole assignment in multi-input controllable linear systems," *IEEE Trans. on Automat. Control*, AC-12, 660-665.
Wonham, W. M. and A. S. Morse, 1970, "Decoupling and pole assignment in linear multivariable systems: a geometric approach," *SIAM J. Control*, 8, 1-18.
Wonham, W. M. and A. S. Morse, 1970, "Decoupling and pole assignment by dynamic compensation," *SIAM J. Control*, 8, 317-337.

4.9 Algebraic Theory

Barnett, S., 1974, "Some topics in algebraic systems theory: A survey," *Int. J. Control*, 19, 669-688.
Bose, N. K. and S. K. Mitra, 1978, "Generalized inverse of polynomial matrices," *IEEE Trans. on Automat. Control*, AC-23, 491-493.
Brunovsky, P., 1970, "A classification of linear controllable systems," *Kybernetica*, 3, 173-187.
Forney, G. D., Jr., 1975, "Minimal bases of rational vector spaces, with applications to multivariable linear systems," *SIAM J. Control*, 13, 493-520.
Gejji, R. R. and M. K. Sain, 1977, "Application of polynomial techniques to multivariable control of jet engines," *Preprints of Fourth IFAC Symposium on Multivariable Technological Systems*, Fredericton, N B, Canada.
Honnell, P. M., 1951, "The generalized transmission matrix stability criterion," *Trans. AIEE*, 70, 292-298.
Kalman, R. E., 1962, "Canonical structure of linear dynamical systems," *Proc. Nat. Acad. Sci.*, 48, 596-600.
Kalman, R. E., 1963, "Mathematical description of linear systems," *J. SIAM Control*, Ser A, 1, 152-192.
Kalman, R. E., 1965, "Algebraic structure of linear dynamical systems: 1 The module of Σ," *Proc. Nat. Acad. Sci.*, 54, 1503-1508.
Kalman, R. E., 1965, "Algebraic theory of linear systems," *Proc. Third Allerton Conf. on Circuit and System Theory*, 563-577.
Kalman, R. E., 1965, "Irreducible realizations and the degree of a rational matrix," *J. SIAM Control*, 13, 520-544;
Kalman, R. E., 1967, "Algebraic aspect of the theory of dynamical systems," in *Differential Equations and Dynamical Systems*. Ed. J. K. Hale and J. P. Lasalle. New York: Acad. Press.
Kalman, R. E., 1969, "Introduction to the Algebraic theory of linear dynamical systems," *Lecture Notes in Operations Research and Mathematical Economics*, Vol. 11. Berlin: Springer.
Kucera, V., 1978, "Polynomial equations in control system design," *Preprints Seventh IFAC World Congress*, Helsinki, 3, 1815-1822.
MacFarlane, A. G. J., 1968, "System matrices," *Proc. IEE*, 115, 749-754.
Peczkowski, J. L. and M. D. Sain, 1977, "Linear multivariable synthesis with transfer functions," *Proc. NEC International Forum on Alternatives for Multivariable Control*, Chicago.

Pernebo, L., 1978, "Algebraic control theory for linear multivariable systems," *Report No. LUTFD2/TFRT-1016/1-307*, Lund Institute of Technology, Lund.

Popov, V. M., 1972, "Invariant description of linear time-invariant controllable systems," *SIAM J. Control*, 10, 252–264.

Rosenbrock, H. H., 1966, "On the design of linear multivariable control systems," *Proc. Third IFAC Congress*, London, 1, 1–16.

Rosenbrock, H. H., 1970, *State Space and Multivariable Theory.* London: Nelson.

Rosenbrock, H. H., 1972, "The stability of multivariable systems," *IEEE Trans. on Automat. Control*, AC-17, 105–107.

Rosenbrock, H. H., 1973, "Bounds for transfer functions in multivariable systems," *IEEE Trans. on Automat. Control*, AC-18, 54–56.

Rutman, R. and Y. Shamash, 1978, "Matrix polynomial equations in control theory," *Preprints Seventh IFAC World Congress*, Helsinki, 2, 1135–1140.

Sain, M. K., 1975, "A free-modular algorithm for minimal design of linear multivariable systems," *Proc Sixth IFAC Congress*, Part 18, pp. 9.1.1–9.1.7.

Sain, M. K., 1976, "The growing algebraic presence in systems engineering: An introduction," *Proc. IEEE*, 64 (1), 96–111.

Wolovich, W. A., 1974, "Multivariable system synthesis with step disturbance rejection," *IEEE Trans. on Automat. Control*, AC-19, 127–130.

Wolovich, W. A., 1974, *Linear Multivariable Systems.* New York: Springer-Verlag.

4.10 Geometric Theory

Basile, G. and G. Marro, 1968, "Luoghi caratteristici delo spazio degli stati relativi al controllo dei sistemi lineari," *L'Ettrotechnica*, 55 (12). 1–7.

Basile, G. and G. Marro, 1969, "Controlled and conditioned invariant subspaces in linear system theory," *J. Opt. Th. and Applns.*, 3 (5), 306–315.

Basile, G. and G. Marro, 1969, "On the observability of linear time-invariant systems with unknown inputs," *J. Opt Th. and Appl.*, 3 (6), 410–415.

Basile, C. and G. Marro, 1970, "A state space approach to non-interacting controls," *Ricerche di Automatica*, 1, 68–77.

Bengtsson, G., 1973, "A theory for control of linear multivariable systems," *Report No 7341*, Lund Institute of Technology, Lund.

Bengtsson, G., 1977, "Feedback realizations in linear multivariable systems," *IEEE Trans. on Automat. Control*, AC-22, 576–585.

Wonham, W. M., 1970, "Dynamic observers: Geometric theory," *IEEE Trans. on Automat. Control*, AC-15 (2), 258–259.

Wonham, W. M. and A. S. Morse, 1970, "Decoupling and pole assignment in linear multivariable systems: a geometric approach," *SIAM J. Control*, 8, 1–18.

Wonham, W. M. and A. S. Morse, 1972, "Feedback invariants of linear multivariable systems," *Automatica*, 8, 93–100.

Wonham, W. M., 1973, "Tracking and regulation in linear multivariable systems," *SIAM J. Control*, 11, 424–437.

Wonham, W. M., 1974, *Linear Multivariable Control: A Geometric Approach.* Berlin: Springer.

Wonham, W. M. and J. B. Pearson, 1974, "Regulation and internal stabilization in linear multivariable systems," *SIAM J. Control*, 12, 5–18.

Wonham, W. M., 1978, "Geometric state-space theory in linear multivariable control," *Preprints Seventh IFAC World Congress*, Helsinki, 3, 1781–1788.

4.11 Internal Model Principle

Bengtsson, G., 1977, "Output regulation and internal models—A frequency domain approach," *Automatica*, 13, 333–345.

Conant, R. C., 1969, "The information transfer required in regulatory processes," *IEEE Trans. Sys. Sci. and Cyb.*, SSC-5, 334–338.

Conant, R. C. and W. R. Ashby, 1970, "Every good regulator of a system must be a good model of that system," *Int. J. Systems Sci.*, 1 (2), 89–97.

Francis, B. A., O. A. Sebakhy and W. M. Wonham, 1974, "Synthesis of Multivariable regulators: The internal model principle." *J. Appl. Maths. and Optimization*, 1 (1).

Francis, B. A. and W. M. Wonham, 1975, "The internal model principle for linear multivariable regulators," *J. Appl. Math. Optimiz.*, 2.

4.12 Multivariable Regulator and Multivariable Servomechanism Problems

Cheng, L. and J. B. Pearson, 1978, "Frequency domain synthesis of multivariable linear regulators," *IEEE Trans. on Automat. Control*, AC-23, 3–15.

Davison, E. J., 1975, "A generalization of the output control of linear multivariable systems with unmeasurable arbitrary disturbances," *IEEE Trans. on Automat. Control*, AC-20, 788–795.

Davison, E. J. and A. Goldenberg, 1975, "Robust control of a general servomechanism problem: The servocompensator," *Automatica*, 11 (5), 461–472.

Davison, E. J., 1976, "Multivariable tuning regulators: The feedforward and robust control of a general servomechanism problem," *IEEE Trans. on Automat. Control*, AC-21, 35–47.

Davison, E. J., 1976, "The robust decentralized control of a general servomechanism problem," *IEEE Trans. on Automat. Control*, AC-21, 14–24.

Davison, E. J., 1976, "Steady-state invertibility and feedforward control of linear time invariant systems," *IEEE Trans. on Automat. Control*, AC-21, 529–534.

Doyle, J. C., 1978, "Guaranteed margins for LQG regulators," *IEEE Trans. on Automat. Control*, AC-23 (4), 756–757.

Francis, B. A., 1975, "The linear multivariable regulator problem," *Electron. Res. Lab. Memo—ERL-M560*, Univ. of California, Berkeley.

Francis, B. A., 1977, "The multivariable servomechanism problem from the input-output viewpoint," *IEEE Trans. on Automat. Control*, AC-22, 322–328.

Fuller, A. T., 1976, "Feedback control systems with low frequency stochastic disturbances," *Int. J. Control*, 24, 165–207.

4.13 Zeros

Brockett, R. W., 1965, "Poles, zeros and feedback: State space interpretation," *IEEE Trans. on Automat. Control*, AC-10, 129–135.

Davison, E. J. and S. H. Wang, 1974, "Properties and calculation of transmission zeros of linear multivariable systems," *Automatica*, 10, 643–658.

Davison, E. J. and S. H. Wang, 1977, "Properties and calculation of transmission zeros of linear multivariable feedback systems," in *Control System Design by Pole-Zero Assignment*, F. Fallside (Ed.), London: Academic Press. 16–42.

Davison, E. J. and S. H. Wang, 1978, "An algorithm for the calculation of transmission zeros of the system (C,A,B,D,) using high gain output feedback," *IEEE Trans. on Automat. Control*, AC-23, 738–741.

Desoer, C. A. and J. D. Schulman, 1973, "Cancellations in multivariable continuous-time and discrete-time feedback systems treated by greatest common divisor extraction," *IEEE Trans. on Automat. Control*, AC-18, 401–402.

Desoer, C. A. and J. D. Schulman, 1974, "Zeros and poles of matrix transfer functions and their dynamical interpretation," *IEEE Trans. on Circuits and Systems*, CAS-21, 3–8.

Francis, B. A. and W. M. Wonham, 1975, "The role of transmission zeros in linear multivariable regulators," *Int. J. Control*, 22, 657–681.

Karcanias, N., 1978, "The use of Grassman products in the computation of the invariant zero polynomial of square linear proper systems," *Int. J. Control*, 28, 361–381.

Kontakos, T., 1973, Ph.D. Thesis, University of Manchester.

Kouvaritakis, B. and A. G. J. MacFarlane, 1976, "Geometric approach to analysis and synthesis of system zeros, Part 1: Square systems," *Int. J. Control*, 23, 149–166.

Kouvaritakis, B. and A. G. J. MacFarlane, 1976, "Geometric approach to analysis and synthesis of system zeros Part 2: Non-square systems," *Int. J. Control*, 23, 167–181.

Laub, A. J. and B. C. Moore, 1976, "Calculation of transmission zeros using QZ techniques," *Syst. Cont. Rept. No 7618*, Dept. of Elec. Eng., Univ. of Toronto.

MacFarlane, A. G. J. and N. Karcanias, 1976, "Poles and zeros of linear multivariable systems: A survey of the algebraic, geometric and complex-variable theory," *Int. J. Control*, 24, 33–74.

Owens, D. H., 1977, "Invariant zeros of multivariable systems: A geometric analysis," *Int. J. Control*, 26, 537–548.

Patel, R. V., 1978, "On transmission zeros and dynamic output feedback," *IEEE Trans. on Automat. Control*, AC-23, 741–742.

Rosenbrock, H. H. and A. Rowe, 1970, "Allocation of poles and zeros," *Proc. IEE*, 117, 1879-1886.

Rosenbrock, H. H., 1973, "The zeros of a system," *Int. J. Control*, 18, 297–299.

Rosenbrock, H. H., 1974, "Correction to the zeros of a system," *Int. J. Control*, 20, 525–527.

Shaked, U. and N. Karcanias, 1976, "The use of zeros and zero-directions in model reduction," *Int. J. Control*, 23, 113–135.

Simon, J. D. and S. K. Mitter, 1969, "Synthesis of transfer function matrices with invariant zeros," *IEEE Trans. on Automat. Control*, AC-14, 420–421.

Wolovich, W. A., 1977, "Multivariable system zeros," in *Control System Design by Pole-Zero Assignment*, F. Fallside, (Ed.) London: Academic Press. 226–236.

4.14 Analytical Design Techniques and Wiener-Hopf Approach

Krasovsky, A. A., 1971, "A new solution to the problem of a control system analytical design," *Automatica*, 7, 45–50.

Letov, A. M., 1960, "Analytic controller design I,II," *Avtomatika i Telemekhanika*, 21, 436–441 and 561–568.

Letov, A. M., 1960, "Analytic controller design III," *Avtomatika i Telemekhanika*, 21, 661–665.

Letov, A. M., "Analytical design of control systems IV," *Avtomatika i Telemekhanika*, 22, 283–290.

Newton, G. C., L. A. Gould and J. F. Kaiser, 1957, "Analytical design of linear feedback controls," New York: Wiley.

Weston, J. E. and J. J. Bongiorno, Jr., 1972, "Extension of analytical design techniques to multivariable feedback control systems," *IEEE Trans. on Automat. Control*, AC-17, 613–620.

Youla, D. C., J. J. Bongiorno, Jr. and C. N. Lu, 1974, "Single-loop feedback-stability action of linear multivariable dynamical plants," *Automatica*, 10, 159–173.

Youla, D. C., J. J. Bongiorno and H. A. Jabr, 1976, "Modern Wiener-Hopf design of optimal controllers Part I: The single-input-output case," *IEEE Trans. on Automat. Control*, AC-21, 3–13.

Youla, D. C., H. A. Jabr and J. J. Bongiorno, Jr., 1976, "Modern Weiner-Hopf design of optimal controllers Part II: The multivariable case," *IEEE Trans. on Automat. Control*, AC-21, 319–338.

4.15 Multivariable Circle Criteria

Cook, P. A., 1973, "Modified multivariable circle theorems," in *Recent Mathematical Developments in Control*, D. J. Bell, Ed., London: Academic Press. 367–372.

Cook, P. A., 1976, "Conditions for the absence of limit cycles," *IEEE Trans. on Automat. Control*, AC-21, 339–345.

Mees, A. I. and P. E. Rapp, 1977, "Stability criteria for multiple-loop nonlinear feedback systems," *Proc. Fourth IFAC Symposium in Multivariable Technological Systems*, Fredericton N B, Canada.

Rosenbrock, H. H., 1973, *Multivariable Circle Theorems in Recent Mathematical Developments on Control*. D. B. Bell, Ed., London: Academic Press.

Smith, R. A., 1976, "Multiple circle criterion for diagonally dominant transfer matrices," *Int. J. Control*, 24, 261–273.

4.16 Nonlinear Multivariable Systems

Blight, J. D. and N. H. McClamroch, 1975, "Graphical stability criteria for large-scale nonlinear multi loop systems," *Proc. Sixth IFAC Congress*, Boston, Part 1 D, Paper No 44.5.

Blight, J. D. and N. H. McClamroch, 1977, "Graphical stability criteria for nonlinear multiloop systems," *Automatica*, 13, 189–192.

Dewey, A. G., 1967, "Frequency domain stability criteria for non-linear multi-variable systems," *Int. J. Control*, 5, 77–84.

Gray, J. O. and P. M. Taylor, 1977, "Frequency response methods in the design of multivariable nonlinear feedback systems," *Proc. Fourth IFAC Symposium on Multivariable Technological Systems*, Fredericton, N B, Canada, 225–232.

McGee, R. W. and G. D. S. MacLellan, 1968, Stability of nonlinear multivariable control systems," *Proc. IEE*, 115, 590–591.

Mees, A. I. and P. E. Rapp, 1977, "Stability criteria for multiple-loop nonlinear feedback systems," *Proc. Fourth IFAC Symposium on Multivariable Technological Systems*, Fredericton N B, Canada, 183–188.

Porter, D. W. and A. N. Michel, 1974, "Input-output stability of time-varying nonlinear multiloop feedback systems," *IEEE Trans. on Automat. Control*, AC-19, 422–427.

Rae, W. G., 1970, "Stability criteria for control systems with many non-linear elements," *Automatica*, 6, 463–467.

Ramani, N. and D. P. Atherton, 1974, "Stability of nonlinear multivariable systems," *Paper S-10, Proc. Third IFAC Symposium on Multivariable Technological Systems*, Manchester.

Safanov, M. G. and M. Athans, 1978, "On stability theory," *Report No. ESL-P-816*, Electronic Systems Lab. M.I.T. Cambridge, Mass.

Shankar, S. and D. P. Atherton, 1977, "Graphical stability analysis of non-linear multivariable control systems," *Int. J. Control*, 25, 375–388.

4.17 Other Work on Multivariable Systems

Amara, R. C., 1959, "Application of matrix methods to the linear least squares synthesis of multivariable systems," *J. Franklin Inst.*, 268, 1–6.

Amara, R. C., 1959, "The linear least squares synthesis of multivariable control systems," *Trans. AIEE*, 78, 115–119.

Anderson, B. D. O. and D. G. Luenberger, 1967, "Design of multi-variable feedback systems," *Proc. IEE*, 114, 395–399.

Anderson, B. D. O. and J. B. Moore, 1969, "Linear system optimisation with a prescribed degree of stability," *Proc. IEE*, 116, 2083–2087.

Araki, M. and O. I. Nwokah, 1975, "Bounds for closed-loop transfer functions of multivariable systems," *IEEE Trans. on Automat. Control*, AC-20, 667–670.

Arbib, M. A., 1965, "A common framework for automata theory and control theory," *SIAM J. Control*, 3, 206–222.

Baumann, R., 1978, "Computer aided design and implementation of control algorithms," *Preprints Seventh IFAC World Congress*, Helsinki, 1, 649–655.

Bongiorno, J. J., Jr. and D. C. Youla, 1968, "On observers in multi-variable control systems," *Int. J. Control*, 8, 221–243.

Bongiorno, J. J., 1969, "Minimum sensitivity design of linear multi-variable feedback control systems by matrix spectral factorization," *IEEE Trans. on Automat. Control*, AC-14, 665–673.

Bradshaw, A. and B. Porter, 1978, "Design of linear multivariable discrete-time output-feedback regulators," *Int. J. Systems Sci*, 9, 857–863.

Bristol, E. H., 1966, "On a new measure of interaction for multivariable process control," *IEEE Trans. on Automat. Control*, AC-11, (1), 133–134.

Bristol, E. H., 1967, "A philosophy for single loop controllers in a multiloop world," *Proc. 8th Nat. Symp. on Instrumentation in the Chemical and Process Industries*, St. Louis, Mo., 4, 18–29.

Bristol, E. H., 1976, "Industrial needs and requirements for multi-variable control," *Chemical Process Control*, AIChE Symposium Series No. 159, 72, 88–98.

Brockett, R. W., and M. D. Mesarovic, 1962, "Synthesis of linear multi-variable systems," *Trans. AIEE*, 81, 216–221.

Brockett, R. W., 1966, "The status of stability theory for deterministic systems," *IEEE Trans. on Automat. Control*, AC-11, 596–606.

Callier, F. M. and C. A. Desoer, 1972, "Discrete-time convolution feed-back systems," *Int. J. Control*, 16, 567–575.

Callier, F. M. and C. A. Desoer, 1973, "Necessary and sufficient conditions for stability for n-input, n-output convolution feedback systems with a finite number of unstable poles," *IEEE Trans. on Automat. Control*, AC-18, 295–298.

Callier, F. M., 1975, "On the stability of convolution feedback systems with dynamical feedback," *Automatica*, 11, 85–91.

Callier, F. M. and C. A. Desoer, 1975, "A stability theorem concerning open-loop unstable convolution feedback systems with dynamical feedbacks," *Proc. Sixth IFAC Congress*, Boston, Part 1D, Paper No. 44.2.

Callier, F. M., W. S. Chan and C. A. Desoer, 1978, "Input-output stability of interconnected systems using decompositions: An improved formulation," *IEEE Trans. on Automat. Control*, AC-23, 150–162.

Chen, C-T, 1968, "Stability of linear multivariable feedback systems," *Proc. IEEE*, 56, 821–828.

Cook, P. A., 1978, "On some questions concerning controllability and observability indices," *Preprints Seventh IFAC World Congress*, Helsinki, 3, 1699–1705.

Cruz, J. B. and W. R. Perkins, 1964, "The role of sensitivity in the design of multivariable linear systems," *Proc. Nat. Electronics Conf.*, 20, 742–745.

Cruz, J. B., and W. R. Perkins, 1964, "A new approach to the sensitivity problem in multivariable feedback system design," *Trans. IEEE on Automat. Control*, AC-9, 216–223.

Damborg, M. J., and A. W. Naylor, 1973, "Stability structure for feedback systems having unstable open loops," *IEEE Trans. On Automat. Control*, AC-18, 318–319.

Davison, E. J., 1969, "A nonminimum phase index and its application to interacting multivariable control systems," *Automatica*, 5, 791–799.

Davison, E. J. and R. W. Goldberg, 1969, "A design technique for the incomplete state feedback problem in multivariable control systems" *Automatica*, 5, 335–346.

Davison, E. J. and S. G. Chow, 1977, "Perfect control in linear time-invariant multivariable systems: The control inequality principle," in *Control System Design by Pole-Zero Assignment.* F. Fallside, Ed., London: Academic Press. 1–15.

Denham, M. J., 1978, "A program package for computer aided design of control systems," *Preprints Seventh IFAC World Congress*, Helsinki, 1, 437–442.

Desoer, C. A. and M. Y. Wu, 1968, "Stability of multiple-loop feedback linear time-invariant systems," *J. Math. Anal. Appl.*, 23.

Desoer, C. A. and F. M. Callier, 1972, "Convolution feedback systems," *SIAM J. Contr.*, 10, 737–746.

Desoer, C. A., 1974, "Multivariable systems: Factorization of det[I + FG] as a product of measurable gains," *IEEE Trans. on Automat. Control*, AC-19, 606.

Desoer, C. A. and W. S. Chan, 1977, "Interconnected linear multivariable systems with delays: System properties and input-output stability," *IEEE Trans. on Automat. Control*, AC-22, 604–610.

Desoer, C. A., F. M. Callier and W. S. Chan, 1977, "Robustness of stability conditions for linear time-invariant feedback systems," *IEEE Trans. on Automat. Control*, AC-22, 586–590.

Ding, C. Y., F. M. Brash, Jr. and J. B. Pearson, 1970, "On multivariable linear systems," *IEEE Trans. on Automat. Control*, AC-15, 96.

Estrada, R. F., 1972, "On the stability of multiloop feedback systems," *IEEE Trans. on Automat. Control*, AC-17, 781–791.

Fallside, F., and H. Seraji, 1971, "Direct design procedure for multivariable feedback systems," *Proc. IEE*, 118, 797–801.

Foss, A. S., 1973, "Critique of chemical process control theory," *IEEE Trans. on Automat. Control*, AC-18, 646–652.

Francis, B. A., and K. Glover, 1978, "Bounded peaking in the optimal linear regulator with cheap control," *IEEE Trans. on Automat. Control*, AC-23, 608–617.

Freeman, E. A., 1973, "Stability of linear constant multivariable systems," *Proc. IEE*, 120, 379–384.

Freeman, E. A., 1974, "Relation between some criteria for the stability of constant linear multivariable systems," *Proc. IEE*, 121, 725–729.

Gilbert, E. G., 1963, "Controllability and observability in multivariable control systems," *J. SIAM Control Series A*, 1(2), 128–151.

Gilbert, E. G., 1969, "Controllability and observability in multivariable control systems," *J. SIAM Control*, 7, 50–63.

Horowitz, I., 1960, "Synthesis of linear, multivariable feedback control systems," *IRE Trans. on Automat. Control*, AC-5, 94–105.

Hsu, C. H. and C. T. Chen, 1968, "A proof of the stability of multivariable feedback systems," *Proc. IEEE*, 56, 2061–2062.

Isermann, R., 1978, "On advanced methods of process computer control for industrial processes," *Preprints Seventh IFAC World Congress*, Helsinki, 1, 411–421.

Jameson, A. and R. E. O'Malley, 1975, "Cheap control of the time-invariant regulator," *J. Math. and Optimiz.*, 1, 337–354.

Joseph, P. D. and J. Tou, 1961, "On linear control theory," *Trans. AIEE*, 80, 193–196.

Jury, E. I. and B. W. Lee, 1966, "A stability theory for multinonlinear control systems," *Proc. Third IFAC World Congress*, London, Session 28, Paper 28a.

Kalman, R. E. and J. E. Bertram, 1958, "General synthesis procedure for computer control of single and multiloop linear systems," *Trans. AIEE*, 77 Part III, 602–608.

Kalman, R. E., 1963, "Liapunov functions for the problem of Lur'e in automatic control," *Proc. NAS*, (USA), 49, 201–205.

Kalman, R. E., Y. C. Ho and K. S. Narendra, 1963, "Controllability of linear dynamical systems," *Contr. Diff. Eqns.*, 1, 189–213.

Kalman, R. E., 1966, "On the structural properties of linear, constant multivariable systems," *Proc. Third IFAC Congress*, London, 6A1–6A9.

Kinnen, E. and D. S. Liu, 1962, "Linear multivariable control system design with root loci," *Trans. AIEE*, 81 Part II, 41–44.

Kouvaritakis, B., 1976, "A geometric approach to the inversion of multivariable systems," *Int. J. Control*, 24, 609–626.

Krishnan, K. R. and S. Brzezowski, 1978, "Design of robust linear regulator with prescribed trajectory insensitivity to parameter variations," *IEEE Trans. on Automat. Control*, AC-23, 474–478.

Lasley, E. L. and A. N. Michel, 1976, "L_∞- and l_∞-stability of interconnected systems," *IEEE Trans. on Circuits and Systems*, CAS-23, 261–270.

Lasley, E. L. and A. N. Michel, 1976, "Input-output stability of interconnected systems," *IEEE Trans. on Automat. Control*, AC-21, 84–89.

Laub, A. J., 1978, "Linear multivariable control: Numerical considerations," *Report No. ESL-P-833*, Electronic Systems Lab., MIT, Cambridge, Mass.

Levy, S. and R. Sivan, 1966, "On the stability of a zero-output system," *IEEE Trans. on Automat. Control*, AC-11, 315–316.

Lindgren, A. G., 1966, "A note on the stability and design of interacting control systems," *IEEE Trans. on Automat. Control*, AC-11, 314–315.

Luenberger, D. G., 1964, "Observing the state of a linear system," *IEEE Trans. Military Electronics*, MIL-8, 74–80.

Luenberger, D. G., 1966, "Observers for multivariable systems," *IEEE Trans. on Automat. Control*, AC-11, 190–197.

Luenberger, D. G., 1967, "Canonical forms for linear multivariable systems," *IEEE Trans. on Automat. Control*, AC-12, 290–293.

Luenberger, D. G., 1971, "An introduction to observers," *IEEE Trans. on Automat. Control*, AC-16(6), 596–602.

MacFarlane, A. G. J., 1969, "Use of power and energy concepts in the analysis of multivariable feedback controllers," *Proc. IEE*, 116, 1449–1452.

MacFarlane, A. G. J. and N. Karcanias, 1978, "Relationships between state-space and frequency-response concepts," *Proc. Seventh IFAC World Congress, Preprints*, 3, 1771–1779.

McBride, L. E. and S. Narendra, 1963, "An expanded matrix representation for multivariable systems," *IEEE Trans. on Automat. Control*, AC-8, 202–210.

Morgan, B. S., Jr., 1966, "The synthesis of linear multivariable systems by state variable feedback," *IEEE Trans. on Automat. Control*, AC-9, 405–411.

Morgan, B. S., Jr., 1966, "Sensitivity analysis and synthesis of multivariable systems," *IEEE Trans. on Automat. Control*, AC-11, 506–512.

Moylan, P. J. and D. J. Hill, 1978, "Stability criteria for large-scale systems," *IEEE Trans. on Automat. Control*, AC-23, 143–149.

Myers, B. R., 1959, "A useful extension of the Nyquist criterion to stability analysis of multi-loop feedback amplifiers," *Proc. 4th Midwest Symposium on Circuit Theory*, Marquette University, Milwaukee, Wisconsin, 1–17.

Niederlinski, A., 1970, "Analysis and design of 2-variable interacting control systems using inverse polar plots," *Proc. IEE*, 117, 2056–2059.

Niederlinski, A., 1971, "A heuristic approach to the design of linear multivariable interacting control systems," *Automatica*, 7, 691–701.

Pearson, J. B. and C. Y. Ding, 1969, "Compensator design for multivariable linear systems," *IEEE Trans. on Automat. Control*, AC-14 130–134.

Pearson, J. B. and P. W. Staats, 1974, "Robust controllers for linear regulators," *IEEE Trans. on Automat. Control*, AC-19, 231–234.

Pearson, J. B., R. W. Shields and P. W. Staats, 1974, "Robust solutions to linear multivariable control problems," *IEEE Trans. on Automat. Control*, AC-19, 508–517.

Retallack, D. G., 1970, "Transfer-function matrix approach to observer design," *Proc. IEE*, 117, 1153–1155.

Rosenbrock, H. H., 1967, "On linear system theory," *Proc. IEE*, 114, 1353–1359.

Rosenbrock, H. H., 1971, "Progress in the design of multivariable control systems," *Trans. Inst. Meas. Cont.*, 4, 9–11.

Rutman, R. and Y. Shamash, 1975, "Design of multivariable systems via polynomial equations," *Int. J. Control*, 22, 729–737.

Safanov, M. G. and M. Athans, 1977, "Gain and phase margin for multiloop LQG regulators," *IEEE Trans. on Automat. Control*, AC-22, 173–179.

Sandberg, I. W., 1963, "On the theory of linear multiloop feedback systems," *Bell System Tech. J.*, 42, 355–382.

Silverman, L. M. 1969, "Inversion of multivariable linear systems," *IEEE Trans. on Automat. Control*, AC-14, 270–276.

Sivan, R., 1965, "On zeroing the output and maintaining it zero," *IEEE Trans. on Automat. Control*, AC-10, 193–194.

Tong, H., 1974, "Frequency-domain approach to the regulation of linear stochastic systems," *Automatica*, 10, 533–538.

Vidyasagar, M., 1972, "Input-output stability of a broad class of linear time-invariant multivariable feedback systems," *SIAM J. Control*, 10, 203–209.

Vidyasagar, M., 1975, "Coprime factorizations and stability of multivariable distributed feedback systems," *SIAM J. Control*, 13, 1144–1155.

Vidyasagar, M., 1975, "Simplified graphical stability criteria for distributed feedback systems," *IEEE Trans. on Automat. Control*, AC-20, 441–442.

Willis, B. H. and R. W. Brockett, 1965, "The frequency domain solution of regulator problems," *IEEE Trans. on Automat. Control*, AC-10, 262–267.

Wolovich, W. A., 1969, "A frequency domain approach to the design and analysis of linear multivariable systems," *NASA Tech. Rept., C104.*

Wolovich, W. A. and P. L. Falb, 1969, "On the structure of multivariable systems," *J. SIAM Control*, 7, 437–451.

Woon, S. K. and S. A. Marshall, 1975, "Design of multivariable control systems using reduced-order models," *Electronics Letters*, 11, 341–342.

Youla, D. C., 1963, "On the stability of linear systems," *IEEE Trans. on CT*, CT-10, 276–279.

Youla, D. C., J. J. Bongiorno, Jr. and C. N. Lu, 1974, "Single-loop feedback stabilization of linear multivariable dynamical plants," *Automatica*, 10, 159–173.

Young, K-K. D., P. V. Kokotovic and V. I. Utkin, 1977, "A singular perturbation analysis of high-gain feedback systems," *IEEE Trans. on Automat. Control*, AC-22, 931–938.

V. MULTIDIMENSIONAL SYSTEMS

5.0 General Background Material

Anderson, B. D. O. and E. I. Jury, 1973, "Stability test for two-dimensional recursive filters," *IEEE Trans. on AU*, AU-21, 366–372.

Anderson, B. D. O. and E. I. Jury, 1974, "Stability of multidimensional digital filters," *IEEE Trans. on Circuits and Systems*, CAS-21, 300–304.

Ansell, H. G., 1964, "On certain two-variable generalizations of circuit theory with applications to networks of transmission lines and lumped reactances," *IEEE Trans. on CT*, CT-11, 214–223.

Bickart, T., 1978, "Existence criterion for nonessential singularities of the second kind," *Proc. IEEE*, 66(8).

Bose, N. K., 1976, "A criterion to determine if two multivariable polynomials are relatively prime," *Proc. IEEE*, 60, 134–135.

Bose, N. K., 1976, "An algorithm for GCD extraction from two multivariable polynomials," *Proc. IEEE*, 64, 185–186.

Bose, N. K., (Ed.), 1977, *Special Issue on Multidimensional Systems, Proc. IEEE*, 65(6).

Bose, N. K., 1977, "Problems and progress in multidimensional systems theory," *Proc. IEEE*, 65(6), 824–840.

Davis, D. L., 1976, "A correct proof of Huang's theorem on stability," *IEEE Trans. on ASSP*, ASSP-24, 423–426.

Farmer, C. and J. B. Bednar, 1972, "Stability of spatial digital filters," *Mathematical Biosciences*, 14, 113–119.

Goodman, D., 1976, "An alternate proof of Huang's stability theorem," *IEEE Trans. on ASSP*, ASSP-24, 426–427.

Goodman, D., 1977, "Some stability properties of two-dimensional shift invariant digital filters," *IEEE Trans. on Circuits and Systems*, CAS-24, 201–208.

Huang, T. S., 1972, "Stability of two-dimensional and recursive filters," *IEEE Trans. AU*, AU-20, 158.

Jury, E. I., 1974, *Inners and Stability of Dynamic Systems.* New York: Wiley.

Jury, E. I., 1977, "Stability tests for one-, two- and multidimensional linear systems," *Proc. IEE*, 124, 1237–1240.

Jury, E. I., 1978, "Stability of multidimensional scalar and matrix polynomials," *Proc. IEEE*, 66(9), 1018–1047, 1978.

Justice, J. H. and J. L. Shanks, 1973, "Stability criterion for N-dimensional digital filters," *IEEE Trans. on Automat. Control*, AC-18, 284–286.

Humes, A. F. and E. I. Jury, 1977, "Stability test for two-dimensional linear multivariable digital filters," *Int. J. Control*, 26, 225–234.

Maria, G. A. and M. M. Fahmy, 1973, "On the stability of two-dimensional digital filters," *IEEE Trans. on AU*, AU-21, 470–472.

Murray, J., 1977, "Another proof and a sharpening of Huang's theorem," *IEEE Trans. on ASSP*, ASSP-25, 581–582.

Shanks, J. L., 1969, "Two-dimensional recursive filters," *SWIEECO Rec.*, 19E1–19E8.

Shanks, J. L., S. Treitel and J. H. Justice, 1972, "Stability and synthesis of two-dimensional recursive filters," *IEEE Trans. on AU*, AU-20, 115–128.

Siljak, D. D., 1975, "Stability criteria for two-variable polynomials," *IEEE Trans. on Circuits and Systems*, CAS-22, 185–189.

Siljak, D. D., 1975, "Stability criteria for multivariable polynomials," *Electronics Letters*, 11, 217–218.

Strintzis, M. G., 1977, "Tests of stability of multidimensional filters," *IEEE Trans. on Circuits and Systems*, CAS-24, 432–437.

5.1 Multidimensional Nyquist Theory

Decarlo, R., R. Saeks and J. Murray, 1977, "A Nyquist-like test for the stability of two-dimensional digital filters," *Proc. IEEE*, 65, 978–979.

Decarlo, R., R. Saeks and J. Murray, 1977, "Three graphical tests for the stability of multi-dimensional digital filters," *1977 IEEE Intl. Symp. on Circuits and Systems*, 665–669.

Decarlo, R. A., J. Murray and R. Saeks, 1977, "Multivariable Nyquist theory," *Int. J. Control*, 25, 657–675.

Humes, A. F. and E. I. Jury, 1977, "A graphical stability test of two-dimensional multi-input multi-output digital filters," *Proc. 11th Asilomar Conference on Circuits and Systems*, Monterey, Calif., 75–77.

Author Index

Subject Index

Editor's Biography

Alistair G. J. MacFarlane (SM'75) was born in Edinburgh, Scotland in 1931. He received the B.Sc. and D.Sc. degrees from the University of Glasgow in 1953 and 1968; the Ph.D. degree from the University of London in 1964; the M.Sc. degree from the University of Manchester in 1973; and the M.A. and Sc.D. degrees from the University of Cambridge in 1974 and 1979, respectively.

After graduating in electrical engineering from the University of Glasgow, he joined the Metropolitan-Vickers Electrical Company in Manchester in 1953 to complete his postgraduate training in the Radar and Servomechanisms Division. After some years working on a variety of feedback and signal-processing problems he became group leader of the Moving Target Indication and Receiver Laboratories of that company in 1956-58. He was then appointed Lecturer in Electrical Engineering in Queen Mary College, University of London, and was promoted to Reader in Electrical Engineering in 1965. In 1966 he moved to the University of Manchester Institute of Science and Technology as Reader in Control Engineering in the newly established Control Systems Centre, becoming Professor of Control Engineering in 1969. Following this he was elected to a Chair of Engineering in the University of Cambridge in 1974 and became Head of the Control and Management Systems Division of the Engineering Department at Cambridge. His research interests are in the fields of feedback theory, dynamical theory, and automatic control. For papers on these topics he was awarded the Institution Premium of the IEE in 1966, the IEE Control and Automation Division Premium in 1970 and the ICI Prize of the Institute of Measurement and Control in 1975.

Dr. MacFarlane is a Fellow of Selwyn College Cambridge, a Fellow of the IEE and of the Institute of Measurement and Control, a Vice-Chairman of the IFAC Theory Committee, and Editor of the *International Journal of Control*.